C000261532

Technical Topics Scrapbook
1990 - 94

Pat Hawker, G3VA

Diagrams drawn by
Derek Cole
Bob Ryan

Radio Society of Great Britain

Published by the Radio Society of Great Britain, Cranborne Road, Potters Bar, Herts EN6 3JE.

First published in book form 1999

ISBN 1 872309 51 8

Cover design: Bob Ryan
Production: Mike Dennison
Reproduction: JJ Typographics, Southend on Sea

Printed in Great Britain by Nuffield Press, Abingdon

Contents

Preface v

'Technical Topics' 1990   1

'Technical Topics' 1991   61

'Technical Topics' 1992 125

'Technical Topics' 1993 185

'Technical Topics' 1994 246

Notes on corrections 308

Index 309

Preface

This is the second quinquennial volume of the complete collected pages of the monthly *Technical Topics* column as originally published in *RadCom,* the journal of the Radio Society of Great Britain. It continues the policy of bringing together a varied collection of new and established circuit ideas, HF/VHF antennas, general hints and comments on running an amateur radio station on a modest budget. For new readers, *Technical Topics (TT)* is a column that I began in April 1958 and have continued to compile ever since. The popularity of this feature has continued for over four decades despite the changing face of amateur radio, a testament to the belief that despite the ready availability of complex factory-built equipment most radio amateurs, both old timers and newcomers, retain a real interest in understanding the technology which they use on the air, together with a wish to understand better just how and why the technology has developed and how we have arrived at the present state-of-the-art.

Technical Topics has always concentrated on providing in clearly understandable language a large number of circuits, hints and tips. The aim is to offer information that has real or potential practical value in everyday operation on the amateur-radio bands without recourse to a heavy lacing of mathematics, and is relevant and/or interesting to the majority of both professional and non-professional experimenters. Latest developments are intermingled with the occasional look back to ideas and technology used in the earlier days of this unique hobby. As noted in the earlier volume, although simplicity and KISS ('keep it simple, stupid') technology has been a prime aim, every effort is made to introduce amateurs to advances in the basic technologies of receivers, transmitters, simple wire antennas and the understanding of radio propagation.

The five years, 1990-94 inclusive, covered in this volume saw further significant advances in the use of semiconductors for power amplification from HF to microwaves, yet the role of RF power valves has continued to remain important: There is a requirement for both low-voltage 12V power supplies and high-voltage power units for valve equipment with voltage regulation, current limitation and switch-on and other protection. The emergence of tiny surface-mounted components has called for the development of methods of handling these tiny devices - no easy task, calling for 20/20 vision or good magnifying glasses and a dab hand with the soldering iron. In the important field of antennas, the appearance of computer-based modelling programs has given amateur and professional designers a most important new tool, permitting *if properly used* a means of assessing the likely performance of a design while it is still little more than a sketch on the back of an envelope.

The use of low-cost ceramic resonators to replace quartz crystals in filters and for both fixed and variable frequency oscillators has proved an important development for cash-strapped amateurs and those with a particular interest in the still home-built low-power rigs. Consideration is also given to the basic requirements of stable LC oscillators.

A revisit to the classic G2DAF linear amplifier of the 1960s also encouraged a number of readers to build this tried and tested design based on thermionic valves, while some other high-power linear amplifiers covered in this volume, stemmed like so many other good ideas from the Netherlands.

The 'mature' technology of storage batteries has been given a renewed push to meet the requirements of portable, cordless and hand-held equipment as well as for the operation of solid-state transceiver both in the shack and the field, and this is discussed in a number of items.

The continued interest in the role of radio amateurs during World War 2 is reflected in this volume with some further comments on the clandestine radios of Special Communications and the Special Operations Executive and the intercept receivers used by the Radio Security Service (with its many Voluntary and Specially-enlisted radio amateurs), with acknowledgement also of the important role of the London Poles who designed and built their own range of equipment. There is also a growing recognition of the mechanical excellence of many of the classic communications receivers of the 1930s and 1940s, such as the HRO, AR88 and the Super-Pro. as well as the continued value for home-construction of simple regenerative receivers and other forms of direct-conversion designs.

Readers have continued to contribute many useful and ingenious hints and tips aimed at overcoming the difficulties now often experienced in obtaining components for home construction that were once plentiful but are now no longer readily available.

It has always been assumed that most readers already have and use the more formal handbooks and no effort has been made, in general, to cover basic theory but rather to concentrate on new or little-understood concepts and techniques of proven or potential practical value - and to show ways in which good results can be achieved at low costs. *Technical Topics* remains dedicated to amateur radio experimentation.

In short, this volume once again reflects the policy that has been adhered to during over 40 years of *Technical Topics* as expressed in its very first appearance in April 1958: "We cannot promise that this new feature will solve all difficulties. All we can hope to do is to survey a few ideas from the technical press; a few hints and tips that have come to our notice, with perhaps an occasional comment thrown in for good measure." This policy has been maintained despite the many changes that have taken place in the pursuit of a hobby that remains interesting, exciting and unique as well as providing a sound introduction to radio-frequency engineering - yet capable of being pursued within restricted budgets by young and old.

As I wrote in a reflection on the passing of a similar column in the Dutch journal *Electron* written for 25 years by Dick Rollema, PA0SE: "Perhaps only a minority of readers fully appreciate that, behind the scenes, a regular monthly column generates and depends on copious correspondence and personal research. Columns come to take over one's life. While reading or listening one has constantly to be wondering 'Is this something for the column?'". To keep up a monthly feature without undue repetition, the columnist has to come to grips not only with the personal interests, idiosyncrasies and foibles of oneself, but also with those of readers and editors. I feel lucky in having been privileged in being able to write over so many years for a readership that seems to share so many of my own feelings towards the hobby that has dominated so many of my working and retirement years.

Grateful acknowledgement is made to all the many radio-amateurs, professional engineers and scientists worldwide and to the amateur-radio and professional engineering publications from which so much of the material was originally drawn. It is my policy always, wherever possible, to acknowledge fully the source of all abstracts and ideas and to credit the originators. Acknowledgement is also made to Mike Dennison, G3XDV, RSGB's Publications Manager, who conceived the idea of providing collected editions of *TT* and persuaded the Society to publish them, and to his editorial staff during the years 1990-94, including Marcia Brimson, 2E1DAY, Technical Editors Paul Lovell, G3YMP (1993) and Peter Dodd, G3LDO (1994), Derek Cole who prepared the many diagrams for *TT* until his retirement in 1994 and Bob Ryan, 2E1EKS, who then became the Society's Technical Illustrator. For their patience in dealing with a sometimes opinionated and fractious contributor, my profound thanks!

Pat Hawker, G3VA

London, February 1999

CONSTANT-CURRENT NICAD CHARGING

Nicad cells and batteries can last for one or two thousand charging cycles — but to do so need to be treated carefully without being subjected to overcharging, or other abuses. In recent months, much information has been included in *TT* on the various charging constraints and the advisability of using constant-current systems; also reducing the charging rate if the attempt is to be made to keep the battery fully-charged by means of continuous trickle-charging. But it is some years since *TT* included practical advice on how to make a constant-current charger using either a FET or an adjustable three-terminal IC regulator such as the LM317 (*TT*, March 1982, pp229-230). It seems time to return to this subject.

But, first, some more general comments on the charging of nicad batteries as recommended in Part 4 of the series by Anton Wilson (*International Broadcast Engineer (IBE)*, May 1989, p4): "The electric power must first be converted to chemical potential energy which is what a battery actually stores... it is this initial conversion step that is largely responsible for the aberrant behaviour so often observed from nicad batteries... the effective capacity of a battery can be significantly reduced depending on conditions during charge ('reduced charge acceptance')... a 4Ah battery may be capable of accepting only 2Ah but is then fully charged and not capable of storing additional energy.

"Two of the dominant factors affecting charge acceptance are temperature and charge rate. Cell type, formulation and construction will also influence these factors. In general, charge acceptance is maximum at room temperature (16° to 26°C) and begins to diminish above and below this range. The effective capacity of a nicad can be reduced by 30% when charged at 45°C. At 55°C capacity can be halved. The effect of cold temperatures is somewhat different. Below 0°C the nature of the charging reaction within the cell begins to change and, depending on the charge rate, the electro-chemical reaction can produce hydrogen gas instead of storing energy. Not only will the battery not accept a normal charge but, more importantly, the hydrogen gas can create a catastrophic explosion causing injury to the operator as well as destroying equipment."

The *IBE* article is concerned primarily with the larger nicad batteries (eg 4Ah) currently used to operate broadcast video equipment: "most of the new high energy cell designs have been formulated to achieve maximum charge acceptance with fast charge currents that are approximately equal to the capacity rating of the battery. This translates to charging for between 45 and 90 minutes." Nicad cells used in the professional video industry are of the sealed cylindrical type which includes an internal over-charge protection mechanism.

They stand a very much faster charging rate than is suitable for the usual range of nicad batteries where a 'one-tenth' (0.1C) rate for up to 14 hours for fully discharged cells is the usual preferred rate. If you really need to keep cells fully charged over extended periods of intermittent use, the trickle rate should not be more than 20% (one-fifth) of the normal charging rate: see **Table 2**.

Because of the near-constant voltage discharge-curve, it is often difficult to be sure of the state of charge of a partially discharged battery, leading to uncertainty as to how long it is safe to charge the battery at the 0.1C rate. It is this factor that has led to the belief that cells/batteries should be completely discharged before recharging for 14 hours at the 0.1C rate, despite the fact that deliberately fully discharging a nicad battery may shorten its life (see *TT*, May 1988, p349). I remain uncertain what is the best answer to this problem.

But to turn to the question of practical constant-current chargers. A simple charger suitable for charging a nicad battery at its specific 0.1C rate was described by David Potter, W2GZD in *QST* (October 1981, pp34-35): see **Fig 10**. A more sophisticated unit, incorporating a timer and 0.1C and 0.02C rates for various types of cells as in Table 2 has appeared as a constructional project by Peter Phillips in *Electronics Australia*, July 1989, pp80-86: **Fig 11**. The timer automatically switches from charge to trickle-charge after periods of 44 minutes, 1.5, 2.9, 5.8 or 11.7 hours. If 14-hour charging is needed, select 11.7 hours and then when this is timed-out switch to either 1.5 hours or 2.9 hours and re-start the charger. Two LM317 current regulators are used, IC1 sets the trickle charge rate; IC2 the main charge current,

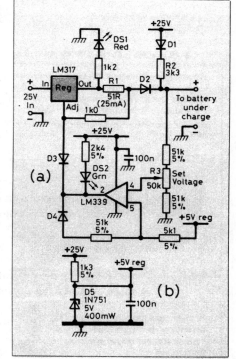

Fig 10. Constant-current charger for nicad batteries with automatic shut-down feature as described in *QST* in 1981. R3 is adjusted to provide the maximum desired battery voltage. R1 determines the maximum current (value shown for 25mA). The capacitors are disc ceramic, D1-D4 are 1A, 50PRV silicon rectifiers. DS1/DS2 are LEDs. R3 is a linear-taper, wire-wound control. (b) can be set for automatic shut-down at a fixed voltage (not really suitable for nicad cells).

each with switchable resistors for the currents shown in Table 2. During the main charge, IC1 is in effect by-passed by the action of TR1. A TO220 heat-sink needs to be fitted to IC2. R8 and R9 each need two resistors to give the required values of 24 and 20 ohms respectively.

Type	Capacity	Charging Current	Trickle-charging Current
9V battery	100mAh	10mA	2mA
AAA cells	180mAh	18mA	3.5mA
AA cells	500mAh	50mA	10mA
AA cells	600mAh	60mA	12mA
C & D cells	1.2Ah	120mA	24mA

Table 2 — Nicad charging and trickle charging currents catered for in the *Electronics Australia* design.

THE KNOBBLY RF CHOKE

George Southgate, VK5QG/G3LXO writes: "For a linear amplifier I wound up an anode RF choke as specified in 'The Classic — a grounded-grid 813 linear amplifier' by C F Atkins, G3HCV in *RadCom*, April 1971: 'A ⅞-in former is wound with four sections of 34swg enamelled copper wire, the bottom section is 145 turns, followed by two sections of 30 turns each and a top section of 15 turns. The top winding is spaced ³⁄₁₆-in from its neighbour and the others are spaced ⅛-in apart.' I found this choke very good for the HF bands but with the aid of a GDO found some nasty resonances between 30 and 150MHz. Australian TV works between 60 and 200MHz so I was concerned at this finding. Changing the geometry of the choke made little difference. I then tried threading about two dozen Radiospares ferrite beads on the 20swg wire I was using, and wound up the choke again, producing a 'knobbly choke' which has good properties on HF and which irons out a lot of problems in VHF. If the first try doesn't give the desired results, unwind, re-scatter the beads, and try again!"

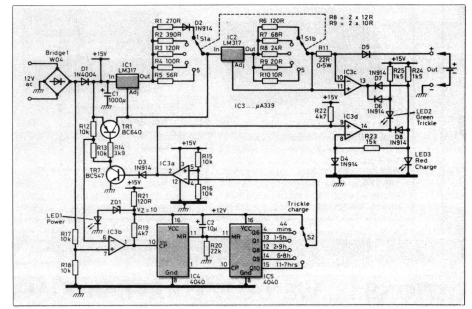

Fig 11. Flexible nicad charger with constant-current regulation for both charge and trickle charge rates on a variety of nicad cells (see Table 2).

KEEPING ANTENNA - SUPPORTS HEALTHY

For the past 30 years I have depended on some overhanging branches of a large sycamore tree in my neighbour's garden (plus my roof) to support my various HF wire antennas. Occasionally, the wires have come tumbling down, usually due to the abrasive effect of the branches moving in strong winds. But, to be honest, I have never thought over much about the health of the tree: judging by the number of unwanted shoots that spring up in my neglected garden, it seems to be in the prime of life. As you may gather, gardening and horticulture have never been my strong point.

Such a confession would probably horrify Doug Brede, W3AS — a former Associate Professor of Horticulture at Oklahoma State University. In 'The care and feeding of an amateur's favourite antenna support — the Tree' (*QST*, September 1989, pp26-28, 40), W3AS advises: "If trees are part of your antenna system take a good look at them. Are you keeping them healthy?"

His article does include a good deal of practical advice that I cannot recall ever having seen before in an amateur radio periodical. For example, I had never realised that the traditional practice of tree 'topping' is now greatly deplored as "a crime against nature," many other hints similarly emphasise that trees are alive and can be mortally wounded:

(1) Attaching ropes or wires to trees can sometimes lead to major problems for the tree. Wrapping a rope around a limb or trunk and leaving it unattended will suffocate the tree and cause a distortion of growth or the death of the limb.

(2) Most amateurs install tree-mounted antennas by throwing a line over a branch crotch. This should be used only as a temporary installation because abrasion of the rope and tree results.

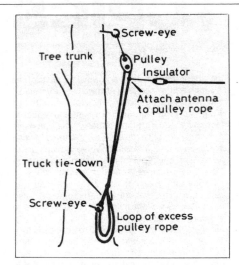

Fig 3. W3AS's recommended method of supporting an antenna from a tree that you want to remain healthy.

Over time, girdling may occur leading to the loss of one or more of the branches.

(3) The best way to secure a wire to a tree is with an eyescrew mounted into the wood. As the tree grows and expands however, the eyescrew will become embedded and must be removed and replaced.

(4) For heavy antenna loads, an eyebolt passed through the trunk or limb will support more weight than an eyescrew. Allow about ½-inch of play between the bolt and trunk or limb. Don't tighten the bolt completely, this allows for tree growth.

By using an installation with a pulley (**Fig 3**) raising and lowering the antenna for repairs (or

changing) can be done without the need to climb the tree. Use an expandable lorry tie-down to apply tension to the antenna. A weight swinging from a tree can be hazardous.

Drilling a hole through a tree causes much less trauma to the tree than wrapping something (tightly) around it. Much of the core of a tree is dead tissue. . . although there will be some wounding of the tree at the site of the bolt or screw, this will be far less than results from wrapping a wire around the trunk. Wire wrapped in hose is just as injurious to the tree as bare wire.

W3AS also gives advice on getting the wire up the tree. For those 'temporary' installations, apart from the now time-honoured use of a bow and arrow, he mentions such alternatives as slingbats, attaching a string to a golf ball and whacking it with a sand wedge, and simply throwing a rope over a branch crotch and tieing off the loose end.

On scaling trees, he stresses that a fall from a 40-ft tree is as dangerous as a fall from a 40-ft tower: "Wear a tower-climbing belt for all tree climbs. Commercial arborists also lob a rope over a tree crotch just above the height at which they will be working. They tie the rope to their safety belt. The loose end of the rope can be held by a helper on the ground. Be sure to use good quality rope that is heavy enough to support your weight. Before use, inspect the rope for wear. Arborists prefer to use hemp rope rather than nylon, because it stretches less. Always have a helper available to fetch tools or summon help in an emergency. Be sure they wear a hard-hat; tools or branches dropped from even a moderate height can be dangerous."

Or, as Les Moxon, G6XN also once suggested consider procuring the help of a professional arborist (or his student assistant) who can usually do the job in a couple of hours.

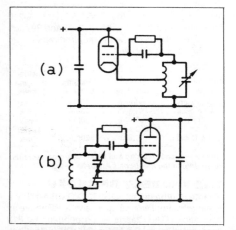

Fig 4. (a) One form of the classic Hartley oscillator with tapped inductor. (b) Equivalent form of the classic Colpitts oscillator with 'tapped' (split) capacitance.

HARTLEY OSCILLATORS: VALVE & Q-GATE FET

The two most familiar types of tunable oscillators are those based on the traditional Colpitts or Hartley arrangements using positive feedback by means of series capacitors or tapped inductor (**Fig 4**). The stability of such oscillators depends to a significant degree on the regulation of the HT and filament/heater voltages/currents. In the early 1930s, a useful variation was introduced by using screen-grid (tetrode) or pentode valves in which the output tank circuit was coupled through the electron-stream by using, in effect, the screen-grid as the 'anode' of the oscillator and taking the output from an anode circuit preferably tuned to the second harmonic of the grid circuit. A Colpitts

form of electron-coupled-oscillator (ECO) was described by J B Dow (*Proc IRE*, 1931) **Fig 5(a)** but for amateur radio the most usual form of ECO was based on the Hartley configuration: **Fig 5(b)** with a large C/L ratio, and the tap near the earthy end of the coil, good frequency stability, even with a keyed oscillator, could be achieved.

It was, however, not always appreciated that one of the advantages of the ECO was its lower susceptibility to supply voltage variations in the days before the use of voltage-regulator tubes became common practice. With a tetrode/pentode ECO, an increase in anode volts with constant screen-grid voltage results in an increase in frequency whereas an increase of screen-grid voltage with the anode voltage unchanged results in a decrease in frequency. There is thus a specific anode/screen voltage ratio where a variation of a common supply results in very little change in frequency. In other respects, the requirements for good frequency stability remain much the same as for the basic Hartley or Colpitts circuits.

Some time ago Dick Rollema, PA0SE, kindly sent me a copy of a single-valve 'frequency-doubling ECO transmitter' which was one of a series of 'standard apparatus' for radio-amateurs developed by DASD (the pre-war German national society, forerunner of DARC). It was described in DASD's journal *CQ* Nr 3/1937 and later reprinted in the Dutch magazine *Radio-Expres*: **Fig 6**.

This provided an RF output to the antenna of about 15W on 3.5MHz reducing to about 5W on 28MHz with a T8/T9 note using an HT supply of 450/500V and a German RS289spez pentode (12W anode dissipation) with the suppressor grid brought out to a separate base-pin permitting it to be used in this design as a tetrode with connected electrodes. Drift was reduced to about 1.5kHz (after 30 minutes) by an early use of temperature

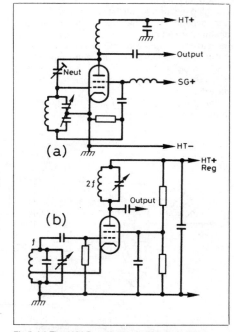

Fig 5. (a) The 1931 Dow electron-coupled-oscillator (ECO) based on the Colpitts configuration. (b) The more usual form of frequency-doubling ECO based on the Hartley form of oscillator as used by many amateurs throughout the valve era from about 1936 when the VFO began to replace crystal-control.

compensation by replacing C3 with two ceramic capacitors having negative temperature coefficients (not bad for 1937!).

In 1943/44, Dutch amateurs/professionals in the Zeeland province of Holland adopted this

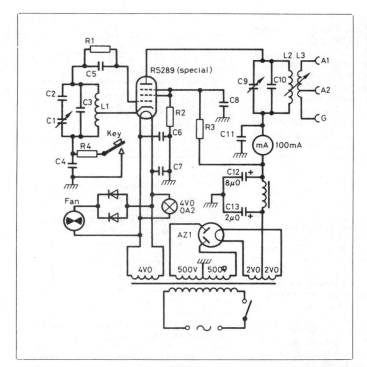

Fig 6. The DASD one-valve ECO transmitter of 1937 based on the frequency doubling ECO. A modified form of this transmitter was used by some Dutch amateurs for the 1944 clandestine Dutch Inland Radio Service on about 2.7MHz.

German design as the basis of a single-valve transmitter for use in the clandestine Dutch Internal Radio Service on about 2.7MHz (other groups mostly used a Luxor medical diathermy power oscillator modified in the Philips factory to form a variable frequency transmitter).

TT, June 1987 provided details of an up-dated version of the wartime Whaddon Mark VII/B three-valve transmitter-receiver (often known as the 'Paraset') built by S Pauwe of Mijdrecht, Holland. PA0SE reports that another reconstructed Paraset was built by William Oorschot, PA0WFO and successfully operated on 3.5 and 7MHz using FT243 crystals and he even had contacts on 14MHz using a 7MHz crystal. This encouraged PA0WFO to modify his reconstructed Paraset by replacing the crystal with a tuned circuit in the form of a Hartley ECO. PA0SE writes: "To avoid problems with heating PA0WFO put the tuned circuit in a separate metal box, connected to the remaining part of the transmitter by a piece of 'stereo cable'. He also increased the fixed capacitance in the oscillator tuned circuit to about 1000pF. It turned out to be essential to use an oscillator coil of generous dimensions with large size wire. Obviously a lot of current circulates in the 1.75MHz tuned circuit; his first small coil ran hot resulting in unacceptable drift. But as now modified it runs so stable that the signal stays within the 500Hz passband of the crystal filter in his receiver. He made many contacts on 3.5MHz without any of the stations worked noticing anything unusual about the signal from this one-valve-transmitter using a VT501 valve (similar to the original 6V6 used in the Paraset). The only drawback was that the keying has to be rather 'hard'. Any effort to 'soften' it by increasing the time-constants in the keying circuit immediately resulted in noticeable chirp. Tuning the anode tank circuit pulls the frequency somewhat, but not more than a few hundred Hertz. This frequency-doubling ECO must be about the ultimate in simplicity for a VFO-controlled transmitter — not easy to achieve with semiconductors".

I recall that some of my wartime colleagues built a simple VFO to use with a Whaddon MkIII (6V6-807) transmitter and then brought wrath down on their shoulders by sending in plain language: "Have VFO can tune up or down". Personally, I used a frequency-doubling Hartley ECO on the amateur bands for 25 years and still have one that is occasionally brought into use.

My excuse (though I don't believe one is needed) for recalling valve-type oscillators arises from a letter received from George Southgate, VK5QG, who was G3LXO from 1958 to 1968 before emigrating to Australia. He has developed a tunable oscillator which is virtually a (Class A?) solid-state version of the Hartley oscillator of Fig 1(a). VK5QG writes: "What makes me put pen to paper is an interesting FET oscillator that I have developed recently. I call it a QGate oscillator to match the suffix of my callsign. I have not seen it before in print although I expect your readers will tell me I have rediscovered the wheel, as there is not a lot that comes up new in this world today. The QGate oscillator is a Hartley oscillator as used in the ECO version but with a few unusual characteristics.

"It came about while building a solidstate

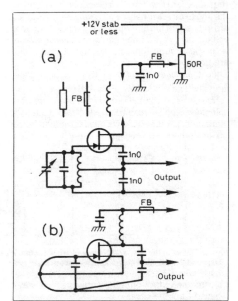

Fig 7. The QGate solid-state FET version of the Hartley oscillator developed by VK5QG with no gate coupling capacitor or gate-leak resistor. (b) a 300MHz version using 'hairpin' inductance.

receiver with a couple of 10.7MHz 8-pole crystal filters in the IF strip and MC1350 chips. I got all this part working using a signal generator as a local oscillator and then had to think seriously about an in-built tunable oscillator which needed to tune from 24.7MHz to 25.05MHz to provide coverage of the 14MHz band. I soon discovered that to give good stability one needs high-C and hence low-L. None of the conventional oscillators I tried wanted to work in this way, ie only about 0.15μH and 270pF. I tried a conventional Hartley with a gate capacitor/resistor but couldn't push it up much above 15MHz with this high C/L ratio so I started making the coupling capacitor between the gate and tuned circuit larger but this did not seem to improve matters much. So, as a last resort, I tried the effect of removing both the coupling capacitor and the associated gate-leak resistor in order to keep the damping on the tuned circuit to a minimum. Much to my surprise, this worked very well with all sorts of L/C ratios, including very high C/L ratios, albeit with reduced output.

"The circuit arrangement shown in **Fig 7(a)** produces a very clean sine-wave output with amplitudes of 5 to 10mV rms, throughout the range of a few tens of kHz to over 300MHz. In its lash-up form, I found my 25MHz oscillator drifts about 120Hz in the first minute from switch-on and then with room temperature changes over a range of ±15Hz or so, taking as much as 15 minutes to move about 10Hz or so! I have taken the usual VFO precautions including a mixture of silver-mica and polystyrene capacitors across the tuned circuit to provide temperature compensation, although probably, with care, these drift and stability figures could be further improved. A useful feature is the reduction in component count to a bare minimum, with the minimum loading of the tuned circuit when used with the very high gate-source impedance of a junction FET. I have tried this circuit using a MOSFET device but it seems more difficult to get going. There is the disadvantage of the tapped coil though I have not found this a problem.

"Other features include: (1) It will oscillate with very low voltage, 2-3V usually being sufficient: hence the 50-ohm potentiometer; (2) it will tolerate being loaded with less than 10-ohms at the output, yet still oscillate although the output drops considerably. The output impedance of the arrangement shown in Fig 4(a) appears to be in the order of 50-100ohms; and (3) the frequency changes little when the load changes, a feature found in few other oscillators! A 50MHz oscillator was found to move only 210Hz when loaded down from 50ohms to 8ohms.

"I have used 2N3819 junction-FETs but these need between about 7-15mA to go into oscillation, depending on the spread of characteristics. The MPF102 seems a better choice, needing only 3 to 4mA. I also tried a 2N5459 and this needed about 10mA. Note that it is always necessary to include the capacitor to ground after the standard blocking capacitor in order to complete the RF circuit. The drain load can be a resistor of a few hundred ohms, a small RF choke or even just a ferrite bead on the transistor lead. I find that it is useful to start off with the tap at the centre of the coil, then adjusting it towards the earthy end to suit individual circumstances. With its low-impedance output this oscillator drives into the base of a bipolar transistor buffer/amplifier with ease.

"The 300MHz QGate oscillator I made up had a hairpin loop about one inch long and was tuned with 5pF: **Fig 7(b)**. I suspect that this type of oscillator could be pushed up towards the UHF region by using either coax lines or cavities but I do not have the necessary test gear to try this. Could this be the elusive class A oscillator that people have been searching for in the past?"

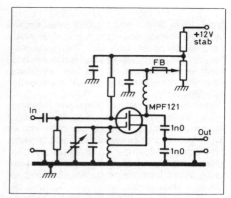

Fig 8. Dual-gate MOSFET frequency-changer tried by VK5QG but note that the QGate oscillator seems to work better (more readily) with junction-FET devices.

VK5QG also tried this form of oscillator in a dual-gate MOSFET mixer arrangement using an MPF121 device: **Fig 8**. The mixer works well but difficulties were experienced with the oscillator section which tended to squeg. There was also a need to adjust the tapping point on the coil to achieve a good sine wave output, though this is greater than with the single-gate JFETs, around 20mV RMS: it might, however, form the basis of a 28MHz direct-conversion receiver, and VK5QG intends to try this when time permits.

SECONDARY BATTERIES: POINTERS & PROGRESS

The subject of how to obtain long active lifetimes from rechargeable batteries continues to attract the attention of many amateurs. One thing is clear: batteries are not the deceptively simple components that they may appear; used wisely and all will be well; used unwisely and costs will shoot up and reliability shoot down.

Dr Roy Hill, GM0IJF, writes: "Experience taught me, years ago, that solid-state chemistry is one of the most difficult branches of chemistry. Why was I ever daft enough to do research in this subject? Any chemical systems involving solids (so we can include electrochemical systems, and electro-chemical cells in particular) present special difficulties: it is easy enough to say what should, by theory, happen — but how fast? That's another matter. However, one thing seems to be certain: the faster you make a process go, the more finely divided and reactive the product will be; so that the reverse process, when you try it, will go faster and easier. (There are good thermodynamic reasons for this). Ni-cad cells are an object lesson, as has so often been described in *TT*. If they are charged fairly slowly, say at 0.1C and then discharged slowly or left lying about unused, they rapidly deteriorate. Sometimes, even, crystals grow so large that they short-circuit the electrodes.

"The moral is: if we want a cell to have a good high-current discharge performance we should charge it fast. And I think this is true also of lead-acid batteries. This is why I did not much like G4LSA's battery charger controller (*TT*, October 1939, p39). When I tried it, it tends to give proportional control, and so charges slowly much of the time. The arrangement (**Fig 10**) I use simply switches the charger on when the voltage falls to 12.1V (say) and off when it gets to about 14.2V. The charging rate is always at 4A or more."

Ron Wilson, G3DSV, also commenting further on the G4LSA controllers to which he drew attention in the October *TT* writes: I have recently purchased a new rig and it must be more sensitive than the old one since I have noticed a small amount of hash at the point where the controller cuts off the charge. A complete cure is effect with the arrangement shown in **Fig 11**. The capacitor to the earth line is essential since for obvious

RF VOLTMETERS FOR TRANSMITTER TUNING

I have never been able to shake off the traditional belief that what really matters is feeding amps of RF into the antenna, even though nowadays most amateurs, with solid-state transceivers with broadband output networks, would never dream of operating their transmitters without an SWR meter. With an end-fed 'long-wire' (40m) antenna and an old 813 power-amplifier with pi-network and ATU, I still use the tip given me many years ago by Roy Wilkins, G2ALM of using simultaneously both current (shunted torch bulb) and voltage (neon bulb) indicators.

Gerald Stancey, G3MCK, in his browsing through old issues of *QST* came across an article 'RF Voltmeters — a lower-cost alternative to the thermocouple ammeter' by George Grammer, W1DF (the then Technical Editor) published in September 1952. This included circuit diagrams of RF voltmeters for use as HF transmitter output indicators for both unbalanced and balanced lines. G3MCK points out that with the current increased interest in open-wire feeders the balanced arrangement, the only circuit ever noted for balanced lines, could still be of interest.

W1DF introduced his designs as follows: "There is no really satisfactory substitute for an RF indicator in a transmitter. Adjusting by plate loading only approximates the proper tuning conditions for maximum output and sometimes, especially with tetrodes, the approximation is not as close as could be desired."

Fig 9 shows circuits for (a) unbalanced and (b) balanced lines. The germanium crystal-diode (eg 1N34) has a peak inverse rating of only about 50V so it is necessary to reduce the applied voltage by using a potential divider; the resistors also help to minimise the harmonics generated by the diode which otherwise might be a source of TVI.

Of the balanced arrangement, W1DF wrote: "The voltmeter has a definite advantage over ammeters here. For one thing only one instrument is required. More important, the circuit shown will prevent parallel (common-mode) voltages on the line from operating the meter, a condition that cannot easily be overcome when ammeters are used. The only RF voltage acting on the (crystal) diode is that developed across R2, which is proportional to the voltage difference across the (transmission) line. Parallel components, assuming the line to be reasonably well balanced to ground, are in phase in the line wires and cannot develop a voltage across R2. They could act between each wire and ground through the crystal-diode, but are prevented from doing so by the RF chokes. Thus the meter reads only the actual voltage applied to the line by the transmitter."

W1DF notes that the values of R1, R2, R3 depend on the impedance of the line. R1 + R2 or

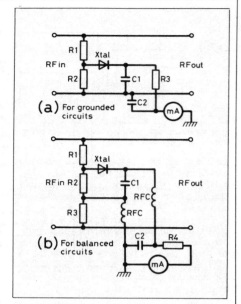

Fig 9. The 1952 W1DF RF voltmeter circuits used for tuning transmitters to deliver maximum power into transmission lines. R1/R2 and R1/R2/R3 are voltage dividers used to reduce voltage applied to germanium 'crystal diodes' of the period. C1 and C2 are RF bypass capacitors, typically 0.005μF. See text for component ratings etc.

R1 + R2 + R3 (where R3 has the same value as R1) should total at least 100 times the impedance at that point on the line. A *matched* 300-ohm line calls for R1 and R3 to be about 15,000-ohms. The value of R2 depends on meter sensitivity (1mA fsd in W1DF's units) and transmitter power (about $\frac{1}{25}$th of the total if R4 is 10,000-ohms).

For 600-ohm matched lines values of R1, R3 should be doubled with R2 remaining as before.

For voltage-fed open-wire resonant lines, where the impedance could be several thousand ohms, problems can arise partly because resistor values would need to be very high (and of suitable voltage rating) and partly because they will have shunt capacitance which can affect the calculations. For tuned lines, however, W1DF provides a simpler solution: measure the RF voltage across the unbalanced coax line between transmitter and ATU at the point where it goes into the ATU: "When the coax line is properly matched, voltmeter indications at this point mean every bit as much as across the open-wire line itself."

For the unbalanced circuit, the power rating of R1 needs to be about $\frac{1}{100}$th of the RF in the line (1W for every 100W RF output). In the balanced circuit, power is shared by R1 and R3 and can be about 1W rating for 200W RF output.

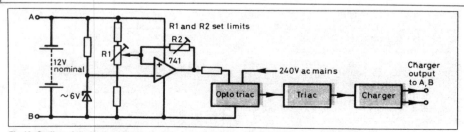

Fig 10. Outline of the lead-acid battery-charger controller used by GM0IJF to ensure that the battery is always charged at the optimum charging rate of about 4A or more.

reasons the output of battery chargers is always isolated from the case."

Recently, due to a prior commitment, I was unable to attend an IEE discussion meeting on 'Advances in secondary batteries' but I did obtain a brief abstract from which the following notes are culled:

Dr M L Whitehead (ERA Technology) stressed that the lead-acid battery, in response to the current need for lightweight, low-maintenance power sources, has been progressing at an accelerating rate: "The quantum leap in the

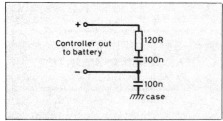

Fig 11. Hash suppression fitted by G3DSV to his charger-controller (see *TT* October).

technology has been the development and commercial exploitation of sealed lead-acid technology. Achieving the 'impossible' is having far-reaching implications for both the battery manufacturer and the user."

On nickel-cadmium batteries, Dr R N Thomas (SAFT UK) notes that advances have been made in high temperature performance, fast charging and energy density including the potential of nickel metal hydride and lithium alternatives to offer even higher density and a less environmentally-damaging (green) product.

Dr R M Dill (AERE) reminds us that the Harwell Laboratory of AEA Technology has been engaged in research on advanced batteries for more than 15 years, with progress being made in nickel/hydrogen cells for use in satellites; sodium/metal chloride batteries for traction applications; and, most relevant to *TT* readers, solid-state lithium/polymer batteries for consumer and other applications.

Finally in this section a nicad tip from George Southgate, VK5QG/G3LXO. He writes: "Having a few nicad C-type cells that had grown crystals internally and developed short-circuits, I gave them the well-known 'big-C zap' treatment (discharging a large value electrolytic capacitor through the cell) to blow them clear. This worked fine, but they soon short-circuited again if left on the shelf for any length of time. I drilled a very small hole, No 60 drill, into the vent hole under the metal top-hat cap and injected about 0.5cc of distilled water into them, resealing with a plug of silicon rubber solution. Then I made what I thought was my big mistake. I accidentally charged one of them at normal rate (0.1C) for 14 hours but with reverse polarity. Not wanting to

admit defeat and throw the cell away, I discharged it at a rate of a few mA for a time; the charge only held for about 30 minutes and was then down to zero again. I then charged it for 14 hours at normal rate with the correct polarity. To my surprise, the cell now seems as good as new, back to full capacity and showing no tendency to grow short-circuiting crystals if left for a time in storage. In view of the success of this treatment, I have since repeated the process deliberately for other cells suffering from short-circuits. It seems to work every time. Good things sometimes come from accidents — long live serendipity!"

HEALTH HAZARDS: TOUGHER GUIDELINES

A *TT* item in August 1985 'Radiation and leukaemia risks' drew attention to a letter from Dr Samuel Milham in *The Lancet* (April 6, 1985) reporting his study of the 'cause of death' as recorded on the death certificates of 1691 amateurs whose names had been listed in *QST* 'Silent Keys' columns between 1971 and 1983 and who had lived in California or Washington State. Dr Milham had found that 24 deaths were ascribed to leukaemias (a form of blood cancer) as compared with an expected 12.6 from statistical averages. Although clearly the increased risk (11 out of 1700) was small it was statistically significant and raised new doubts about the possibility that long-term exposure to non-ionizing radiation at levels found in some American amateur stations might have microbiological effects.

This was and remains a matter of controversy. As noted in *TT* at the time, the possibility of an increased risk of some leukaemias among 'electrical workers' had also been postulated by a New Zealand study, although this had suggested that the link was more likely to be due to exposure to metal and flux fumes during soldering and substances such as polychlorinated biphenyls (PCBs) than to non-ionizing radiation.

Similarly, a recent 675-page American book *Biological Effects and Health Implications of Radiofrequency Radiation* by Sol Michaelson and James Clin (Plenum Press) makes no reference to Dr Milman's work and on page 626 states: "Microwave-induced cancer has not been reported or suspected in medical surveillance examinations of microwave workers or service personnel (Sil-

verman 1979, 1980). Two cohort epidemiological studies (Robinette and Silverman, 1977; Robinette *et al*, 1980; Lilienfeld *et al*, 1978) that looked into the question systematically did not show an excess of any form of cancer that could be interpreted as microwave related (Silverman 1979, 1980, 1985)."

However, a well-researched article 'Is Amateur Radio Hazardous to our Health?' by Ivan A Shulman MD, WC2S (*QST* October, 1989) notes that Dr Milman later increased his research base to 2485 amateur-deaths (2083 in California). This further study revealed no significant difference in cancer deaths from the population at large but showed a disproportion within this category of certain rare forms of cancer such as multiple myeloma and non-Hodgkin's lymphomas; the death rates from all leukaemias were only slightly, and not statistically significant, increased except for acute myelogenous leukaemia which was found to be significant. On the other hand, deaths due to cancer of the pancreas and lung, and to all respiratory, circulatory diseases and to accidents were less in amateurs as a group than in the total population. From this study, Dr Milham concluded: "Amateur Radio licensees in California and Washington State do have a higher death rate due to acute myelogenous leukaemia, multiple myeloma and possibly other specific types of lymphoma". He believes that exposure to magnetic or electrical fields, either as a consequence of work or hobby, should be considered significant enough to support further research into both the epidemiology of and the biologic mechanisms involved. He recognizes that studies based on death certificate data alone are subject to limitations and errors.

One of the expert medical researchers in this field is the Australian W Ross Adey, K6UI (formerly VK3 and VK5) who supports the view that further research is needed into the microbiological effects (if any) of magnetic and electro-magnetic fields, and who read through the *QST* article. WC2S draws up a set of guidelines that he feels would cover all potential or suspected hazards affecting radio amateurs. These guidelines are more restrictive than any that I have seen previously (several of them breached in operating G3VA!) and are geared to the higher American legal-limits of power. However, they are worthy of study:

(1) Do not stand or sit close to your power supplies or linear amplifiers while operating, even when they are in stand-by mode.

(2) Stay at least 24-in away from any power transformer, electrical fans or other source of high-level 60Hz magnetic fields while in operation.

(3) Do not tune up or operate a high-power linear amplifier while the shields or covers are off.

(4) Run your transmission lines away from where you or other people sit in or near your shack.

(5) Properly terminated coaxial transmission feed lines should be used in preference to open-wire or end-fed antenna installations which come directly into the transmitter, as the RF radiated from a co-axial feed line is much lower.

(6) Use common sense about placing all antennas well away from yourself and others, especially for VHF, UHF and particularly microwave applications. No one should be in the near field of an antenna.

(7) No person should be near any transmitting antenna while it is operating. This is especially true for all mobile or ground mounted vertical antennas. The use of indoor transmitting antennas which are close to people in a house or apartment should be reconsidered.

(8) Use the minimal power needed to make a QSO, especially if the antenna is less than 35ft above the ground.

(9) Handheld radios should be used on the lowest power setting needed to carry out communications.

ANTENNA ELEVATION DRIVE

The growing use of microwave dish antennas for TV-reception from geostationary satellites, satellite-communications, Earth-Moon-Earth (EME 'moon-bounce') etc has brought about a requirement to be able to change the elevation of an antenna from the operating position.

Stuart Jones, GW3XYW provides details **(Fig 12)** of the arrangement he has used successfully for two antennas: a 22ft-diameter EME dish and a 6ft (1.8m) TVRO dish. He writes: "Separate potentiometer units are used for position indicators with either a computer or moving coil meter. If the constructor is doubtful about good water-proofing it might be safer to use a 110V or lower-voltage motor in conjunction with a suitable isolating transformer."

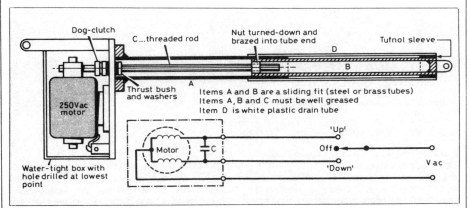

Fig 12. Antenna elevation drive as used by GW3XYW for large and medium-sized microwave dish antennas.

(10) Handhelds should be kept as far from the head as possible when operating. The use of a separate microphone or similar device is recommended.

(11) Transmissions using a handheld radio should be kept as short as possible.

(12) Power density measurements should be made before running more than 25W in a VHF mobile installation, particularly if the antenna is rear-deck mounted and passengers may ride in the back seat. The safest mobile antenna location is in the centre of the metal roof.

(13) The development of an accurate inexpensive power-density meter would be of major benefit to the Amateur Radio community so that RF power-density measurements could be taken in all radio installations. Because of the current high-cost of such devices, groups of amateurs or clubs may wish to purchase one and share in its use.

(14) Soldering should only be done in a well ventilated area. A small fan should be used to blow away toxic fumes.

(15) When using toxic chemicals, such as when etching printed-circuit boards or repairing fibreglass, wear gloves and goggles, use proper tools, and avoid contact with any of the chemicals. If accidentally contaminated, wash off the compounds immediately with copious quantities of water. Again, the importance of always working in a well ventilated area with personal protective covering cannot be overemphasised.

(16) Hazardous chemicals, such as those in the PCBs class, are used in some capacitors and dummy loads. Use extreme care in handling these materials and consult with the appropriate local authorities to determine the proper means of disposing of these chemicals in an environmentally responsible way.

A worrying aspect of the WC2S survey is that he suggests there is a growing body of opinion that not all handheld transceivers with less than the usually accepted figure of 7W RF output are safe if held near the operator's head, and that more stringent guidelines may be introduced in this area.

I would, however, emphasise that even if one accepts that low-level, non-ionizing radiation may prove to have microbiological effects, the risks must be very small indeed compared with some other natural hazards, including most probably the radon gas that leaks into many homes and which has been found to account for nearly one-half of the average UK exposure to ionizing radiation (accounting for a UK average of 1.2 millisieverts and, in some parts of Cornwall, up to 20 millisieverts per annum).

POT-POURRI

The peak of solar cycle N22 is now being predicted for February 1990 and may be of similar magnitude as the record cycle 19 which peaked about 33 years ago. During 1989 two giant solar flares of unprecedented magnitude occurred, one in February and the other at the end of October. The February event even set off the safety cut-outs in the electricity supply grid in Quebec, Canada, triggering a black-out over most of the province.

TT January 1989, Fig 4, page 38, reproduced the circuit diagram of the Moorabin Mark IV 20A PSU. I note that Doug Friend, VK4AIZ (Amateur Radio, January 1989) raises the question of susceptibility to local RF fields that has also been encountered with other PSU designs. He wrote: "I found the design (I don't think it was my PCB design or wiring layout) susceptible to RF energy, notably HF. The cure of the problem has been to place a 4.7µF 25V tag tantalum electrolytic capacitor between pin 3 of the 723 and earth, with short leads right at the IC pin itself."

LINEARS AND DISTORTERS

John Clarke, TK5FF/G8KA has been following the *TT* items about linears and distortion. He writes: "One advantage of sticking to two 3-500z valves is that with our ordinary 100W black boxes it is virtually impossible to overdrive them. Of course any idiot can overdrive his black box by turning up the microphone gain. If he uses a speech processor or an RF processor all he has to do is to watch his ALC limits on the meter of his (say) Trio. The KW1000 uses 572B valves but these have jumped up in price, are hard to drive, but can run on much higher voltages than most people believe: 2400V with slight colour. My homebrew and my factory Viewstar using the Eimac valves give almost identical performance. One novel excitement was when the anode blocking capacitor of the Viewstar blew up with a sound like a rifle shot and accompanying lightning. The capacitor was a Centralab 1000pF (5000V wkg)! As my friend Marv W6FR pointed out one needs to think not merely about the voltage but also the RF current flowing through anode blocking capacitors. He sent me four 250pF capacitors rated for 30kV working. These are installed and give an added feeling of safety!

FEEDBACK:

The component marked 'meter' in the circuit diagram of I1ARZ's IC tuning controller for loop antennas (*TT*, November 1989, Fig 3, page 37) should have been marked 'motor'. In the text, the minimum motor voltage should have read 3-4v. □

MORE ON SWITCHING-FET RF AMPLIFIERS

Two recent *TT* items — 'Using fast-switching power FETs as RF amplifiers' (July 1989, correction September) and '50-watts RF from low-cost FET at 7MHz' (December 1989) — have underlined the feasibility of using switching- or audio-type power FETs, such as HEXFET packages, as HF power amplifiers working at useful power levels without undue circuit complications. This month it will be shown that switching-type FETs are capable of providing substantially more power output than the 12.5 watts-per-device suggested by Doug DeMaw, W1FB in the July item which was based on his *QST* article of April 1989 (feedback May).

Wes Hayward, W7ZOI and Jeff Damm, WA7MLH in the 'Technical Correspondence' column of *QST*, November 1989 point out that W1FB encountered two major problems in using switching-type HEXFETs: (1) considerable difficulty in obtaining

reliable stability; and (2) the need to use a 24V supply in order to achieve reasonable output. They believe that both these problems can be overcome: "Our experience with HEXFET amplifiers is much more optimistic than that reported by Doug DeMaw. Stability is ensured if low-resistance, non-inductive terminations are used. Useful output power is available from amplifiers with '12V' (13.5v) power supplies if a higher device quiescent current is used."

They outline two FET amplifiers: (1) an amplifier based on the IRF511 device (as used by W1FB) providing 8W CW or SSB PEP between 3.5–14MHz from a 13.5V supply; and (2) a high-power

amplifier which can provide up to 50W for 14MHz CW from a 24-28V supply using a IRF530 device with a drive power of 1.5W.

W7ZOI and WA7MLH write: "Our experience with medium-power amplifiers using inexpensive FETs is very encouraging. They are generally easier to use and tame than bipolar transceivers at similar power levels. Stability is ensured by a low-impedance gate-drive design without excess inductance in series with the gate. Amplifier performance is improved when higher-voltage power supplies are used, but practical results are still possible with 12V supplies."

Fig 1 shows the circuit diagram of their 8W amplifier as used for a portable 3.5/7MHz SSB transmitter. A broadband 2:1-turns-ratio bifilar-wound transformer at the output is followed by a low-pass-filter. Quiescent bias current is about 100mA and it should be noted that no ferrite-bead inductance is used. A similar amplifier with a 50-

HIGH-POWER 'FRINEAR' LINEAR (3 x PL519)

TT, June 1989, p35, Figs 9-10 (correction September p41-42, Fig 4) included a linear amplifier designed by Frits Geerligs, PA0FRI using a single PL519 (or PL509) and providing an HF output of about 100W. PA0FRI has now sent along details of a basically similar but higher power amplifier using three PL519 valves capable of providing a full legal output of about 400W of speech-processed SSB (about 800W PEP input) with forced-air cooling.

The PSU uses voltage-quadrupling to avoid the need for a high-voltage power transformer but for safety includes a high-power 1:1 isolating transformer; this arrangement provides roughly 1250V under no-load conditions and an average of some 350mA at 1150V in processed-speech SSB or CW modes.

It must be stressed that such a high-power

amplifier requires the application of good engineering practices to ensure good stability and good linearity on the higher frequency bands — and care in construction to achieve reliability and safety. While the annotated circuit diagram **(Fig 3)** provides the necessary basic information, care must be taken to use suitably rated components, adequate fan cooling, etc. Remember always that this is a high-power amplifier with potentially lethal voltages.

PA0FRI writes: "The 10-ohm cathode resistor providing RF negative feedback usefully reduces IMD products, further aided by the 22-ohm variable resistor which can absorb excess drive power. On the 7-28MHz bands it is essential to tune-out the input-capacitance of the paralleled PL519s with the input coils in order to obtain a low SWR and sufficient drive-power (7-10W across 50-ohms). The output network uses smaller com-

ponents and values than those commonly specified for the 3.5/7MHz bands, but has proved quite adequate as regards efficiency, linearity and harmonic-suppression. The design incorporates an unconventional automatic protection system that is designed to prevent overdriving or instability: should such a condition occur one of the four 1N4148 diodes in the screen-grid circuit will 'blow' and the amplifier cease to function. I have modified the old-style one-valve (PCF200) transmit-receive switch by incorporating a four-diode bridge circuit to provide additional isolation in the transmit mode; the negative bias increases the non-conducting state of the diodes, creating an additional blocking pad between input and output of the amplifier.

"On-air reports received using this amplifier are proving encouraging and two-tone tests show a correct envelope pattern."

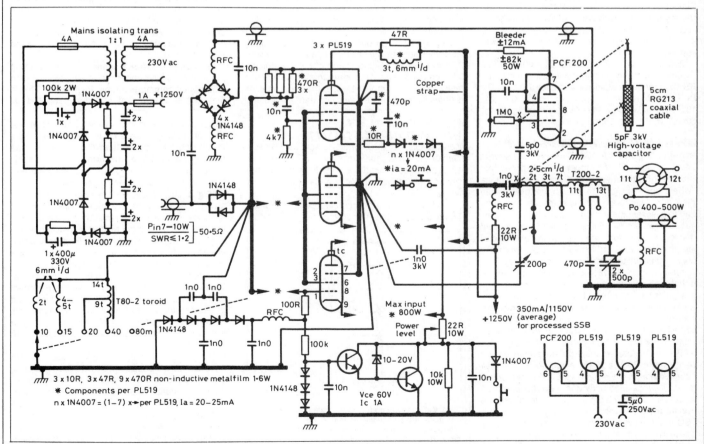

Fig 3. PA0FRI's 400W-output QSK (break-in) 'Frinear' amplifier using three PL519s capable of handling speech-processed waveforms.

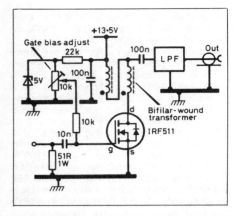

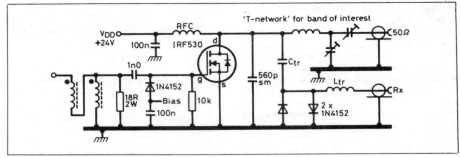

Fig 1. FET power amplifier based on IRF511 switching-type HEXFET providing about 8W CW or SSB PEP between 3.5/14MHz from 13.5V supply.

Fig 2. 50W 14MHz FET power amplifier based on low-cost IRF530 using 24-28V supply with 1.5W drive.

ohm output termination functions with a 1W output SSB driver when biased to only 25mA.

Fig 2 is their higher-power amplifier using a larger, more robust FET, type IRF530 which, in the USA, costs less than $3 new in mail-order catalogues (about £3 + VAT in UK). In this case, a 2:1-turns-ratio step-down transformer provides a low-impedance drive input circuit. An LCC T-network is used for output and matching. Both the input and output networks are roughly similar to those commonly used for similar-power bipolar amplifiers: "Part of the bias is derived from RF drive. When RF drive is removed, the drain current drops to a very low level. The internally-generated noise also drops making this circuit especially useful for QSK (break-in) CW operation (an optional T-R switch for break-in operation is shown in Fig 2 with the reactance of Ltr and Ctr each about 500-ohms).

They conclude: "The IRF530 amplifier is capable of reliable high power from a 24-28V power supply. We have measured an RF output as high as 50 watts at 14MHz with a drive power of 1.5W. Similar output power is available on 3.5W when the amplifier is driven with nothing more than a crystal oscillator. Lower, but useful, output is available from this circuit with a 12V power supply."

Outline characteristics (at 25°C) for the IRF530 (N channel enhancement) device as given in the RS Components catalogue are: case TO220(AB): P_T 75W; R_{DS}(max) 0.18-ohm; I_f(max) 10A; V_{DG} 100V; V_{DS} 100V; $V_{GS(TH)}$max 4V; I_{DSS}(max) I_{GSS}(max) 500nA; tr, tf (max) 150nS.

BLINKING MAINS SUPPLIES

In presenting a 250VA DC/AC inverter for use with 24V batteries (*TT*, November 1989), I noted that this design stemmed from Papua New Guinea "where apparently there are frequent electricity blackouts." Generally, one assumes that in urban and to a lesser extent rural areas of the UK, mains supplies are pretty reliable even if, during the past decade, the London area has had its full share of lengthy blackouts. I still keep a few candles and a crystal set available as "emergency standby.'

John Roscoe, G4QK, has found some unanticipated problems can follow in the wake of a supply outage even although his contingency plans worked smoothly enough when a part of Bridgwater was blacked out recently, apparently due to a cable fault: his Honda generator, resting between visits to Andorra, soon restored lighting etc.

"But" he writes, "when we got our supply back it was a mere 210V and remained so for over 24 hours. Although this breaches the statutory requirements, the local Electricity Board was not prepared to adjust the tap-changers on the local service transformer. The result was that my DRAE 24A PSU was most unhappy but, on the other hand, my Yaesu switched-mode supply coped happily and seems capable of working down to 195V on its higher tapping."

G4QK notes that the chief difference between the two PSUs is that one regulates on the secondary, the other on the primary. He wonders whether "there is any reason why PSUs of conventional, rather than switched-mode type, could not be regulated on the primary without producing ghastly waveforms."

Paradoxically, at an IEE meeting on 'Interference aspects of consumer power electronics and supply systems' it was pointed out that when a number of high-power switch-mode PSUs are used, the load comprises short-duration, high peak-currents and this can result in distorted AC waveforms being supplied to other users in the area; the short-duration pulses near the instants of peak supply voltage tends to slice-off (clip) the peaks of what should be a near sine waveform. In systems feeding numbers of industrial SMPS the pulses are additive and heavy current waveform distortion can result. Apparently this is proving quite a problem; just as at one time when large numbers of TV sets with half-wave rectification were in operation, there tended to be a pronounced DC component on the AC supplies — a problem that no longer exists with the general use of bridge rectifiers.

At the meeting various aspects of EMC problems as they relate to the mains suplies were raised: "Connection or disconnection of energy storage elements (eg capacitors, inductors) to an electric network leads, in most cases, to the generation of signals with a high-frequency content, which can cause interference... modern techniques for the conditioning of power signals using semiconductor devices can lead to the generation of significant distortion and harmonics." A point often overlooked is that brute force RFI filters should include 'lossy' components; otherwise the unwanted RF signals will not be dissipated but will reappear at some other point from which they may be radiated. This, of course, is the rationale behind the absorptive form of low-pass TVI filter where the unwanted harmonics are separated from the fundamental by means of a cross-over network and then dissipated in a resistor; curiously the absorptive filter has never become widely used.

Peter Kendall (Electricity Council) listed some of the disturbances that can affect electricity supplies: steady voltage changes; voltage fluctuations (these for example can result in large current fluctuations in rectifier float charging of batteries even from relatively small input voltage changes); voltage dips typically caused by the clearance of system faults (these can disturb the operation of electronic equipment not designed to resist such dips); transients (spikes) which can reach several kilovolts and may destory semiconductors or alternatively may appear as a spurious signal in equipment leading to temporary disturbances to its operation.

Reverting to G4QK's comments, he raises a point of possible concern to those involved with emergency communications, Raynet etc. This is that in the absence of electricity supplies *all*

KELVIN-VARLEY HELI-POT SUBSTITUTE

Don Nappin, G3MLS, when he saw Jim Rowe's 'Substitute for a multi-turn pot' (*TT*, November 1989, p36), recognised once again the truth of the saying that there is nothing new under the sun. He writes:

"That excellent 19th-century scientist William Thomson (Lord Kelvin) in conjunction with Varley,

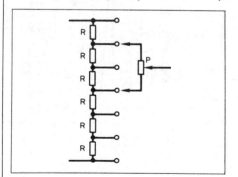

Fig 4. Kelvin-Varley classic configuration used as 'heli-pot' multi-turn potentiometer. With a chain of six similar resistors (R) and potentiometer P this provides five steps. With P = 2R there would be no overlaps. With P = 3R there would be 20% total overlap.

solved the same problem which in his case was that of making a decade potentiometer — the measuring kind rather than the component we now normally mean by the term, though the same principles apply — in a rather more elegant way than Jim Rowe, using fewer resistors.

"Fig 4 shows the Kelvin-Varley principle. A chain of equal resistors of value 'R' are connected in series, with one more resistor than the number of steps required, is connected to a switch which allows a potentiometer of value 'P' to be shunted across any *two* resistors in the chain. ('P' may be a conventional potentiometer as shown or a further decade or set of decades as in the original Kelvin-Varley arrangement.) Now if the value of P is equal to 2R it will be evident that an exact stepped potentiometer is produced, with no overlaps. This is, in effect, the conventional Thomson-Varley or Kelvin-Varley potentiometer of constant input resistance.

"To achieve overlap between steps it is not necessary to introduce Jim Rowe's R/10 resistors, merely to increase the value of P. If, say, P=3R, then the parallel value of P and the two chain-resistors is 1.2R, thus giving approximately 20% total overlap (in practice slightly less since the total chain resistance is increased). The economy in resistors is evident and there is no requirement for a high-value pot."

modern petrol pumps cease functioning; the older pumps could be cranked by hand if necessary, but such models have long vanished in most, if not all, parts of the country.

FRANKLIN AND BUTLER TWO-DEVICE OSCILLATORS

One of the most prolific British pioneers of radio communication was undoubtedly Charles S Franklin, born in Walthamstow, London in 1879, youngest of a family of 13. He trained under a famous teacher, Sylvanus Thompson, and then in 1899 joined the Wireless Telegraph & Signal Co Ltd, the original radio company set up by Marconi with whom he became associated virtually throughout his working career. From assembling 'wireless receivers' from wooden boards, coherers, relays etc he soon departed to South Africa, pioneering military uses of radio during the Boer War. He became a sea-going radio operator/engineer and accompanied Marconi as his operator on the voyage of the *Philadelphia* in 1902 to settle the raging controversy that surrounded the reception of the 'S' signals from Poldhu in 1901 at Signal Hill, Newfoundland. It was during this voyage that Franklin became the first to notice the difference in the range of radio waves at night.

Along with Henry Round, Franklin soon became one of Marconi's most valued engineers. He was inventor of the variable capacitor (1902), ganged tuning (1907), variable coupling (1907) and then in 1913 became the first to patent the use of positive feedback ('reaction' or 'regeneration') as a means of enormously improving the sensitivity of valve receivers (British Patent Specification No 13,636 of June 12th, 1913: see **Fig 5**) a discovery he had made independently of Edwin H Armstrong in the USA who is often credited with discovering regeneration on the basis of his notarized statement of January 31, 1913 (unknown to Franklin).

In 1916, during the first World War, Franklin joined Marconi in Italy and began to experiment in the use of 'short waves' recognizing that it would be possible to beam transmissions far more effectively on short waves than on the very long wavelengths then in use. After the war this work continued in England, with the Marconi company competing with radio amateurs in pioneering long-distance communications on HF. Franklin set up an HF station on the Poldhu site for a series of experimental transmissions in 1923-24 which led to the offer by the Marconi Company to build the Empire Beam System. Franklin was responsible for both the HF transmitters and the directional antennas and also developed the first coaxial transmission lines.

As though 'reaction' (Q-multiplication) and coaxial feeders were insufficient, Franklin also developed a tunable HF oscillator akin to the Eccles-Jordan astable (multivibrator) using two valves: **Fig 6**. As noted in *TT*, November 1977, November 1977, in presenting a solidstate form of Franklin oscillator developed by BRS36760, any tunable oscillator consists in essence of two parts: a tuned circuit of high Q and a 'maintaining' amplifier to replenish the losses in the tuned circuit. A basic advantage of the Franklin oscillator is that the maintaining circuit need be only very loosely coupled to, and impose very light loading on, the resonant circuit; another practical advantage is the single two-terminal coil which has one end at RF earth, with no capacitive or inductive divider (as in the Hartley or Colpitts circuits and most of their variants) that is frequency conscious. Because of the loose coupling those changes affecting the maintaining amplifier, whether valve or solidstate, can be arranged to have only very limited effect on the frequency. Despite its many advantages, the Franklin oscillator remains virtually unknown to the bulk of American amateurs.

In the original Franklin valve circuits the two

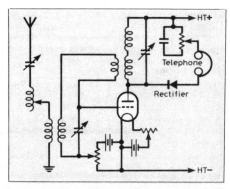

Fig 5. C S Franklin's original regenerative receiver as patented in 1913. Franklin had no knowledge of the similar work being done in the USA by Armstrong and he was the first to point out the effect of positive feedback in reducing the damping and sharpening the tuning (Q-multiplication). His work may or may not have preceded that of Armstrong. As Franklin's circuit was patented only in the UK priority was never tested in the Courts.

coupling capacitors were of the order of only 1pF, although later circuits, for no good reason, often specified 5 or even 10pF, significantly increasing the coupling to the tuned circuit. It is important to remember that the stability of a Franklin oscillator depends upon the quality of the LC tank circuit and the looseness of the coupling to it. With FET low-voltage devices, having greater input-capacitance and often less gain than valves, it does appear that the value of the coupling capacitors may have to be increased to about 10pF to sustain oscillation, although in 1977 BRS36760 successfully used 5pF.

The latest revival of the Franklin oscillator is by Robert Armstrong, VE3RF ('An inexpensive VFO for the Yaesu FT-102', *Ham Radio*, November 1989). He writes: "I started looking for a suitable circuit. My ideal was preferably without coil taps, and certainly without parallel capacitors too big to be air-spaced ... I wasn't having much luck until I came across the circuit for the Franklin oscillator in the *RSGGB Handbook* ... as an external 5.0-5.5MHz VFO for my FT.102, it doesn't require any modifications to the transceiver or cost a small fortune ... it uses the transceiver's digital frequency readout, works on either or both transmit and receive, and drifts so little you'll need a frequency standard to measure it." While his unit is designed specifically for use with an FT-102 using a darlington emitter-follower to step down the

3.5MHz 45W CW TRANSMITTER FOR LESS THAN $20

The W7ZOI-WA7MLH letter drew attention to a four-year-old design by Robert G Cutler of Tektronix (amateur call not given) in the 'Design Ideas' section of *EDN* (November 28, 1985, p280) which presents a crystal-controlled CW transmitter with an output power of about 45W (from 24V supply) using just two power MOSFETs. In its basic simplicity, this design is strongly reminiscent of the once popular arrangement for CW valve transmitters such as the 6V6-807 CO-PA designs. Including a low-cost 3.5795MHz NTSC colour-TV crystal, it is claimed that the component parts cost less than $20 in the USA thus helping to overcome the myth that the 'cost of entry' to HF operation is necessarily measured in hundreds or thousands of pounds. The transmitter consists simply of a keyed crystal power-oscillator/driver (Pierce oscillator), high-efficiency switching-mode (Class D) power amplifier and an output matching network matching into 50-ohm cable: **Fig 11**.

Circuit notes given in *EDN* are as follows: "In the oscillator section, an inexpensive colour-burst TV crystal determines output frequency. In addition the 700- to 1200-pF input capacitance C_{iss} of MOSFET TR2 constitutes an essential part of the oscillator's feedback — the oscillator won't operate without TR2. TR1 retains enough gain for oscillation while driving amplifier TR2 in a 50%-duty-cycle (approximate) switching mode.

"The output stage achieves 84% efficiency rather than the 50% you'd expect with a class-C amplifier. When TR2 turns off, current through inductor L3 causes the drain voltage to rise well above the 24V supply (the 100V zener diode ZD1 limits this voltage excursion) and remains high for part of the conduction cycle as well. The high drain voltage allows the FET to deliver a given amount of power with less internal dissipation and hence with greater efficiency than if the drain voltage remained constant.

"The output impedance-matching network is based on TR2's drain impedance R_o, which is twice the DC value as a result of the 50% duty cycle: $R_o = V_{CC}^2/2P_o = 24^2/(2 \times 45) = 6.4$ ohms."

Note: Unlike the NTSC colour-burst crystal frequency which is inside the 3.5MHz band, a 4.43MHz PAL crystal could not be used. Use a 100V zener diode with a 100V-rated TR2. A zener diode would not be required with MTP8N18 or similar high-voltage component. Adjust the drive for minimum oscillation delay on keying.

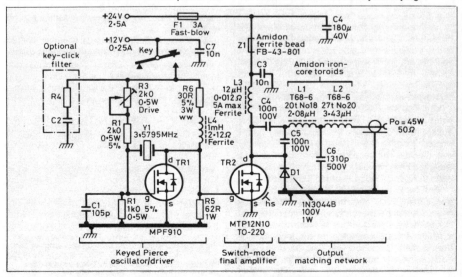

Fig 11. The '20' 3.5MHz CW transmitter providing some 45W output using MOSFET power oscillator and high-efficiency MOSFET power amplifier. Switching-mode amplifier unsuitable for SSB.

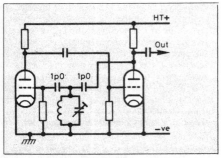

Fig 6. The basic Franklin two-valve oscillator.

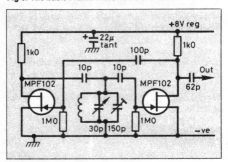

Fig 7. Solidstate Franklin oscillator as used (with buffer amplifier etc) by VE3RF.

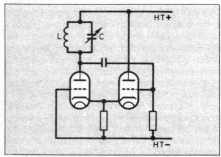

Fig 8. The basic Butler cathode-coupled oscillator (LC circuit can be shunt-fed as in Fig 9).

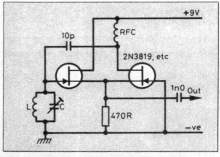

Fig 9. A solid-state source-coupled FET oscillator.

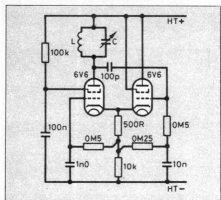

Fig 10. The original 'practical' cathode-coupled oscillator as described by Butler in 1944.

impedance from about 1KO (1.3Vp-p) to the 200mV p-p at 50-ohms required for the FT-102, with a lowpass filter similar to the one used by Yaesu for the internal VFO, other arrangements could be for other rigs, etc — but it seems a good idea to use an emitter- or source-follower as a buffer to reduce load variations on the oscillator. **Fig 7** shows the oscillator stage of his VFO. VE3RF used a military-surplus 6.8μH coil, 30pF (3 x 10pF) FM-broadcast tuning gang with a 150pF air-spaced, screwdriver-adjusted trimmer to set the tuning range. He recommended the 10pF coupling capacitors should be high grade, preferably silver-mica units although he feels ceramic disc would probably do (my suggestion would be to try 5pF as starters). It would probably be wise to avoid using electronic tuning diodes in such an application.

A later derivative of the Franklin circuit is the Butler cathode-coupled oscillator **(Fig 8)** first described by the late Frederick Butler (RAF/GCHQ) in *Wireless Engineer* (November 1944). He then summarised the advantages of his oscillator as:

(1) Alteration of frequency range can be made by inductance changes, using a single pole switch. No reaction windings or tapped coils are employed.

(2) The high input-impedance of the cathode-follower valve (source-follower FET) imposes light loading on the tuned circuit.

(3) Unity gain in this stage provides ample driving voltage to ensure reliable oscillation (from AF) up to very high frequencies, even when using tuned circuits of low Q value.

(4) The series (anode) circuit can be replaced by its shunt-fed equivalent (as in **Fig 9**). In either case one side of the tuned circuit is earthed as regards RF potential.

(5) Triode or pentode valves may be used ...

His 1944 article included a practical circuit based on two 6V6 valves (possibly not the optimum choice unless appreciable output is required): **Fig 10**. With the tuned circuit directly connected to one of the active devices, one may be losing one of the good points of the original Franklin arrangement — but either can provide excellent tunable oscilators and both seem well-suited for use with FET solidstate devices rather than valves.

Provided due care is taken in design and construction, such oscillators should prove adequate for most HF purposes. For those cases where continuous tuning is needed with drift-free stability of just a few Hz, Klaus Spaargaren, PAoKSB has developed a new form of his 'huff & puff' locked oscillator using a variable crystal oscillator (VXO) as the reference 'timing' oscillator, 'pulled' over just a few kHz but able to stabilise with a sample-and-hold IC an LC oscillator tuning continuously over a range of say 500kHz. This seems a most ingenious arrangement but is fairly complex and will need to appear in 'instalments' over several months.

MESNY — A FRENCH PIONEER

H R Mesny, GJ3LFJ, noted with interest the references (*TT*, June 1989, p33 and November 1989, p38) to the 1920s push-pull oscillator of his namesake "(R) Mesny." In the June *TT*, I mentioned that neither G8FEQ nor I had traced anything further of his work, though in my case I had forgotten that in *TT*, January 1977 I included a diagram of the Chireix-Mesny HF beam antenna that was developed in France as an early alternative to the original Marconi-Franklin beam arrays made up of large numbers of 'uniform' vertical dipoles. At that time I noted: "In the Chireix-Mesny array the ½λ dipoles are disposed in the form of saw-teeth, rather like a series of 2λ quad elements. This has the advantage over the Franklin

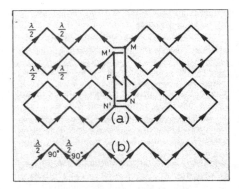

Fig 12(a). Large Chireix-Mesny array of half-wave dipoles arranged in saw-tooth configuration and providing vertically-polarized signals with broadside directivity. Might have application as fixed beam on VHF/UHF.
(b). Simplified Chireix-Mesny array which can be end-fed: such 'zig-zag' arrays have been used at VHF/UHF for TV broadcasting.

array that each dipole element may be driven directly by the one preceding it. **Fig 12(a)** shows a large Chireix-Mesny array which would require vast space for HF but might be well worth investigating for VHF or UHF. From the point of view of the radiated field, such a sawtooth network is equivalent to an array of parallel dipoles. **Fig 12(b)** forms the basis of the 'zig-zag' antennas used at VHF/UHF for television broadcasting."

GJ3LFJ traced a reference to the Chireix-Mesny beam in *The Radio Engineers Handbook* by Henney. He recalls that some years ago the late Max Tourniquet de Brandt, F5HJ mentioned that Mesny was still well remembered and respected in France for the work he did as an engineer in the French Army. He was responsible, with others, for introducing radio communication in the French forces before and during the First World War.

I can now add a further reference. Elizabeth Antebi, in her massive *The Electronic Epoch* (Van Nostrand Reinhold, 1982) in discussing the parallel development of radar in many countries writes: "In France, Henri Gutton and Pierret began to experiment with (very) short waves; and Maurice Ponté, who had been working with Gutton, Sylvain Berline and Hugon at the CSF Laboratory, since 1930, began his work on the magnetron. In 1931, Mesny and David, technical consultants for the French Military Signals Department, noted that a disturbance was created in communications whenever an aircraft passed through the zone between the transmitting and receiving stations. At the beginning of 1934, the first equipment using returning radio wave echoes to locate a moving obstacle was produced ..."

Without detracting from the value of the break-through made by J T Randall and H A H Boot in demonstrating the first high-power 10cm cavity magnetron at Birmingham University in early 1940, and the important role of the French team, we should also be proud of the part played in this work by Eric Megaw, MBE, DSc, GI6MU/G6MU, a former RSGB Council Member and contributor to the old *T&R Bulletin*. He worked on magnetrons at the GEC Research Laboratories in the 1930s, liaised with Henri Gutton and was the man chiefly responsible for turning the experimental Bir-mingham magnetron (which worked directly on its vacuum pump) into a production device. He had an E1188 cavity magnetron designed and made in collaboration with Birmingham working by 16 May 1940 producing 500W CW or pulse at 10cm. Previously, in collaboration with HM Signal School, he had been able to obtain 1.5kW pulse output from a segmented magnetron at 37cm. A most notable British professional scientist who was also a keen amateur.

USING LOW-VOLTAGE-DROP IC REGULATORS

It is generally agreed that the weakest link in the hand-held transceiver chain is the battery, whether disposable dry batteries with their high running costs or rechargeable nicad batteries with their problems of high self-discharge and rapid deterioration unless correctly used and with a suitable charger. Although the nicad battery should last for several thousand charge-discharge cycles this is not often achieved in practice without incurring the so-called 'memory effects' that limit its usefulness.

An article 'An adaptor for powering hand-held rigs from 12V sources' by Mitchell Lee, KB6FPW of National Semiconductor (*QST*, November 1989, pp17-21) suggests that lead-acid power sources, including car battery vehicle electrics or 12V gelled-electrolyte batteries, are more versatile than the original batteries for hand-held units, when used with a suitable adaptor. Gelled batteries are available with capacities from about 1Ah (size of a very large nicad battery) to 40Ah (small-car battery size). Units of up to about 2.5Ah are of a size and weight that make them suitable for an effective battery belt for portable operation. Since leclanché, nicad and lead-acid batteries all have different on-load voltages and different discharge curves, it will usually be necessary to use a voltage regulator when powering a hand-held transceiver from an external power source.

While conventional NPN adjustable IC regulators such as the LM317 can be used to provide, for example, 10.8V at up to 1A they require external protection if used in conjunction with a vehicle source to cope with the high transient voltages and also need at least a 1.7V input-to-output voltage differential to maintain output regulation. KB6FPW draws attention to the advantages offered by the new low-dropout LM2941T IC regulator, based on a series-PNP pass-device and with freedom from some of the delicacy problems associated with the usual NPN regulators such as the LM317. With the LM2941T the drop-out point is simply the saturation voltage of the PNP pass device, viz only 270mV at a load current of 0.5A. Additionally no extra headroom is required to operate the error amplifier and voltage reference since these sub-circuits are powered from the full input voltage and not from the input/output differential. Furthermore there is no need to use a series blocking diode and, better still, PNP pass devices can withstand 60V transients, eliminating the virtually mandatory for an external, power-consuming, transient-suppression network. **Fig 13** shows a regulator based on the LM2941T with adjustable voltage output suitable for powering a handheld transceiver from a car or sealed lead-acid battery.

KB6FPW's five-page article provides a detailed explanation of the advantages of and application notes for the LM2941T, together with basic information on IC voltage regulators used for battery adaptors. Tables 1 and 2 have been extracted from his article. **Table 1** indicates the value of R2 in Fig 1 used to adjust the output voltage based on the type and number of the cells to be replaced. **Table 2** gives a summary of the basic features of NPN and PNP IC regulators. He also emphasises that lead-acid batteries have a built-in charge indicator in their open-circuit (unloaded) voltage; a facility that is not available with nicad batteries where the voltage discharge curve remains nearly flat over much of the discharge (the reason why it is difficult to use a voltage-operated controller for nicad charging). He also notes that: "Open-circuit voltage is directly affected by the specific gravity of the battery's electrolyte, which in turn varies with battery type. Signalling batteries designed for standby service typically have lower electrolyte specific gravities than deep-discharge batteries, resulting in slightly lower output voltages for the signalling types. For exact output voltage figures for your battery, check the manufacturer's specification sheet."

No of cells NiCd (1.2V)	Leclanche (1.5V each)	Total voltage	R2 (without trimmer)	R2 (with trimmer)	R3
5	4	6.0	3K74	3K3	2R2
6		7.2	4K64	4K3	1RO
	5	7.5	4K87	4K3	1RO
7		8.4	5K62	5K1	OR47
	6	9.0	6KO4	5K6	OR33
8		9.6	6K49	6K2	OR22
9		10.8	7K5	6K8	OR1

Table 1. Values for R2 based on type and number of cells to be replaced. R1 is 1KO, 1% tolerance, metal film, 0.5W.

Characteristics	NPN (LM317T)	PNP (LM2941T)
Short-circuit current limit	Yes	Yes
Thermal shutdown	Yes	Yes
Over-voltage shutdown	No	Yes
Reverse-battery protection	No	Yes
Dropout at: 50mA	1.6V	60mV
500mA	1.8V	270mV
1A	2.0V	500mV
Maximum input voltage	40V	60V

Table 2. NPN and PNP regulators: features compared

PROTECTING POWER TETRODES

An article by Mark Mandelkern, KN5S (*QST*, November 1989) on 'Protecting power tetrodes' in amplifiers using conventional screen supplies includes some general advice that seems worth drawing attention to: "For tetrodes, screen current is the best indicator of resonance and loading conditions. Don't try to tune for a plate-current dip. Resonate tetrodes by tuning for maximum screen current. In a stable, grid-driven tetrode amplifier, resonance and peak output are indicated by a peak in screen current. Adjust the loading until this screen-current peak is the value that yields maximum RF output. After you find the settings for maximum output, increase the loading so that the output at resonance is 5-10% less than the maximum available. (That last step produces a narrower signal!) . . . I suspect that some of the bad press that tetrodes have received is simply due to overdrive and improper tuning. Dave Meachan, W6EMD said it best in a *QST* article ('Understanding tetrode screen current' *QST*, July 1961, pp26-29): 'Never tune a tetrode for maximum output.'" □

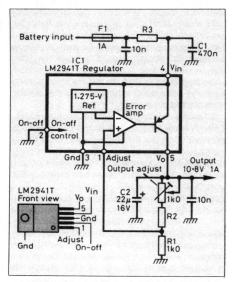

Fig 13. LM2941T PNP regulator for hand-held units etc. Output voltage is set by R1 and R2. R3 (2W wirewound) is optional but provides RF filtering and helps to dissipate some power with high input voltages. The 1KO trimmer is optional but permits fine adjustment of voltage output. Do not decrease value of C2 below 22µF or there may be instability. R1, R2, 1% metal-film resistors. R3, 5% wire-wound rectangular resistors. For values see Table 1.

TIP FOR ICOM IC-2A OWNERS

A useful tip and warning for IC-2A owners comes from David Barneveld, VK4BGB (*Amateur Radio*, June 1989, p19):

"For those who own an IC-2A handheld and its companion fast charger, the BC-30, one does not have to be told of the convenience of slipping the whole unit, complete with battery pack, into the charger and commencing a recharge cycle.

"But beware! Having not removed the battery pack from my transceiver for some months, I was intrigued that when I went to replace it with another pack, I could barely slide it more than 3mm without it binding in some place. My attempts at gentle persuasion failed to get it to budge.

"The cause of the problem turned out to be that one of the screws in the bottom of the transceiver proper had worked its way out, and was catching on the battery pack as it was moved across. As one cannot get the back off, how do you screw back the screw?

"The answer is that the two screws on the back must first be removed and then, ever-so-gently, the case is prised apart just enough to allow the battery pack to be lifted clear of the runners. After removal, check the tightness of all the other screws in the bottom plate. Don't let it happen to you!"

BATTERY POWER SYSTEM

Arrie Wessels, ZS6UY in 'Amateur Radio Station Power Supply System' (*Radio-ZS*, January 1989, pp16-17) provides details of a constant-voltage charger used with a lead-acid vehicle battery to supply power for his equipment. His introduction sets out the reasons why this approach has gained so many adherents. He writes:

"The price of amateur radio equipment is constantly rising and today it is not unusual to have equipment worth several thousands of 'rands' in the radio shack. Most of the modern solidstate equipment is 13.8V working and particularly the linear amplifiers and HF transceivers draw considerable currents during transmit. Typical radio shack requirements would be around 35A during transmit, dropping to a few amps during receive, assuming a number of peripheral equipment is also switched on.

"This equipment, unfortunately, is extremely sensitive to any over-voltage. An over-voltage of a few microseconds can destroy your expensive investment. It is false economy to connect a 'cheap' power supply to your equipment. Unfortunately, most commercial power supplies for amateur equipment I have seen have inadequate protection, if any, against over-voltage surges. Also most of these power supplies, despite the name tag, are barely rated for more than 10A continuous output. I have seen very expensive amateur equipment totally destroyed by these power supplies. Just listen on your local repeater and hear the sorry tales and very expensive repair bills!

"There are commercial power supplies available that will safeguard your equipment. Unfortunately, these are beyond the means of most amateurs. To design and build a safe power supply capable of handling in excess of 35A continuous is very complex... The best solution to the radio shack power supply problem is the lead acid battery route... A car or truck battery kept on float 24 hours per day with a properly designed and adjusted charger will last many years with virtually no attention. My battery is already ten years old, only needs water once in three years and, at the last capacity check, was still 95% good! It stands on the carpeted shack floor, which remains in good shape. Acid leakage in brand-name low-maintenance or sealed batteries is not a problem. Stick to brand names, spend a few extra rand and get the semi-transparent nylon case type of battery..."

He describes in detail the building of a charger (**Fig 1**) providing some 5A output which is simple to build ("No circuit boards etc needed. Components need only be wired point-to-point") but advises strongly against using lower-rated components and attempting to build it too small ("I have yet to see a radio shack that does not have plenty of room under the table").

He advises constructors to make sure the transformer can carry the current for 24hr/day by testing it with a lamp load and checking that its temperature does not exceed 55°C (hot to touch but not hot enough to burn your fingers): "Make the heat sink as large as your box can accommodate and ensure that it is exposed to enough natural airflow to keep the temperature below 60°C after five hours on full load. Avoid using fans; apart from cost and noise, they affect long-term reliability. For safety, a thermal cut-out (70°C) is fitted to the heat-sink with the transformer thermally coupled to the heat sink (alternatively fit a separate cut-out to the transformer). Both the mains and output wires should be threaded through toroids or ferrite-rod filters to prevent RF from entering the unit. Observe extra care with the pins of the LM338K voltage regulator since a short-circuit will result in 0V output or, if connected to the battery, spectacular results (*This could be prevented by using suitably rated diodes to prevent current flowing back from the battery into the charger — G3VA*). If charging a new battery, set output voltage to 14.40V until charging current drops below 500mA and then reduce the output to 13.80V and check that the battery stabilises at this point, drawing approximately 100mA. If the battery becomes fully discharged, an unattended charger will restore full charge after approximately one week (14.40V may be used if full capacity is required within 24 hours but never, never exceed 14.40V and immediately reduce voltage once current drops to 500mA since otherwise the battery life may be severely curtailed). It is very important to set the float-charge voltage to exactly 13.80V since if the voltage is even fractionally lower, sulphation will set in with time and battery capacity permanently lost. If voltage is set higher, gassing will take place, water consumption will increase, active material will be shed off the plates with permanent loss of capacity. Use a reliable, high quality meter for this adjustment."

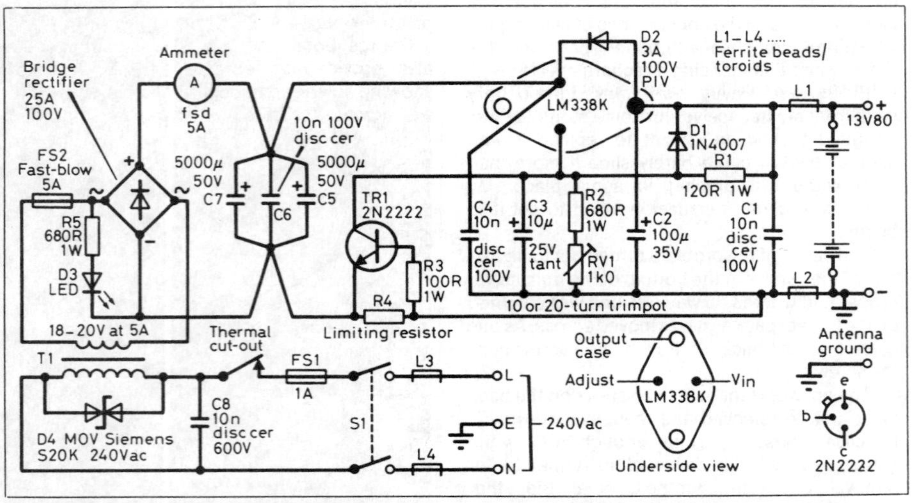

SIMPLIFIED FREQUENCY MODULATION

Geoff Bagley, G3FHL recently came across an interesting voltage-tuned oscillator, used to generate FM, from the valve era but which he feels might provide a useful means of frequency-modulating (or providing a VCO) using an FET oscillator with greater freedom from phase-noise than the conventional use of a varactor. This was 'Simplified Frequency Modulation' by G S Bruck (*ProcIRE* (USA), Vol 34, p458, 1946) as shown in **Fig 2**. L1-C1 form the main oscillator tuned-circuit of a grounded-anode Hartley oscillator. The cathodes are tapped into the coil for feedback. The second tuned circuit, L2-C2, is coupled inductively to L1-C1 so as to form a 90° phase-shifter. The quadrature voltages at the ends of L2 are both added or subtracted to that at the top of L1 (the centre-tap).

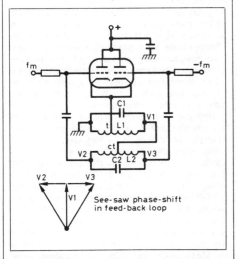

Fig 2. Simplified frequency modulation (Bruck, 1946) which should be adaptable for FETs and give lower phase-noise than using a varactor.

Thus the feedback in the oscillator is vector-modulated to produce a variable phase shift within the feedback loop of the oscillator. The vector diagram, suggests G3FHL, is probably similar to that in a Foster-Seeley FM discriminator. The voltages used to swing the frequency are applied in push-pull to the two grid-leak resistors.

BATTERY DEVELOPMENTS

The January *TT* (pp35-36) included a brief summary of the significant progress currently being made in the field of rechargeable (secondary) batteries, including what Dr M L Whitehead described as 'The quantum leap in (lead-acid) technology' with particular reference to the development and commercial exploitation in recent years of sealed lead-acid technology. I also included a mention by Dr R M Dill of the progress being made with lithium/polymer batteries for consumer and other applications.

Two reports in *New Scientist* (6 January 1990, p36) underline how such developments will affect portable operation of radio equipment — and the operation of 12V or 24V gear from home locations. In 'Rechargeable battery unlocks the power of polymers', Chris Vaughan states: "Scientists in California claim to have developed a rechargeable battery that provides more power, stores more energy and has a longer shelf life than any other. The key to the device is a new type of positive electrode, made of a plastic polymer, and layers of

Fig 1. ZS6UY's constant-voltage charger for lead-acid vehicle batteries designed to be left on float-charge. R4 is current limiting resistor (eg two 0.3-ohm 5W resistors in parallel but adjust to keep temperature rise within the limits set by the thermal cut-out).

a gel and lithium. The result, say the inventors, is a solidstate battery that weighs about half as much as others of the same power."

This is thus a practical implementation of the solidstate lithium/polymer battery mentioned in the January *TT*. The American work stems from Lutgard De Jonghe and Steven Visco (Lawrence Berkeley Laboratory). They believe that such batteries would be relatively easy and inexpensive to make with current technology and should reach the market in some two to four years time. Rechargeable batteries would be suitable for many different applications, from the sustained micro-power demands of a watch to the medium power of portable transceivers or video camcorders etc, with the battery at room temperature. At raised temperatures, larger lithium/polymer batteries could be used for such applications as electric vehicles (at 80°C producing an average of about 160–180Wh/kg). Even at room temperature they should give about twice the power/weight characteristics of nicad batteries.

It is claimed that this is the first polymer battery that releases the energy stored in the polymer's disulphide bonds: "When the bonds are broken, energy is released in the form of electrical current and the polymer becomes a salt — a process known as depolymerisation. When the current is reversed, the disulphide bonds form again and the battery is recharged." Each unit of the polymer can consist of any of a number of different molecules, from a simple chain of sulphur-carbon bonds to complicated ring structures, with polymers containing fluorine or nitrogen providing the most power. The Lawrence Berkeley Laboratory prototype has a ring-structure polymer containing nitrogen and sulphur, a thiadiazole ring (SRS in **Fig 3**).

Possibly the role of rechargeable nicad batteries is under more immediate attack from compact sealed lead-acid batteries. Some years ago, Chloride Power Ltd introduced the 'Chloride Cyclon' range for portable or emergency operation with a claimed life of up to about eight years. In this range, the cells are cylindrical with thin, wound electrodes made of high purity lead. Instantaneous discharges up to 100A and sustained discharges of 30A are possible with a 2.5Ah cell of this type. The batteries retain their charge over long periods (up to three years at room temperature) although it is worth remembering that the self-discharge increases rapidly at high temperatures. **Fig 4** shows typical discharge curves of Cyclon and nicad batteries.

The manufacturers state that the optimum charging option is float-charged by a constant-potential charger carefully adjusted to give between 2.30–2.40V per cell, with a full recharge in under 20 hours (A 16-hr recharge at 2.45V per cell should give a cycle life of 200-250 cycles for 100% complete discharges but added life expectancy with 2.30V).

This type of cell is already finding application in areas previously using nicad cells. For example, the latest Apple-Macintosh portable computer uses cylindrical lead-acid batteries providing 12 hours operation per charge.

The second item in the *New Scientist* reports the development by the American firm LDI of Scotts Valley, California of a flat-shaped, lead-acid battery which doubles the energy per unit rate and provides a more-constant discharge voltage characteristic by reducing the thickness of its plates from 0.25cm to 0.05cm — it thus appears to be a flat form of the type of wound thin-plates of the Cyclon type of lead-acid battery. It is also claimed to have improved heavy-current discharge over periods of less than 2 hours. The performance of a lead-acid battery with such thin plates is claimed to match that of a nicad battery of the same weight at discharge times of 1.5 to 2

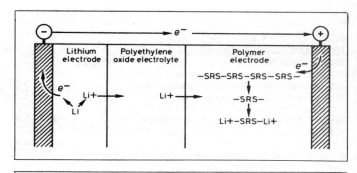

Fig 3. Solidstate lithium/polymer rechargeable cell as developed at Lawrence Berkeley Laboratory. The polymer's disulphide bonds (S-S) release energy as they break.

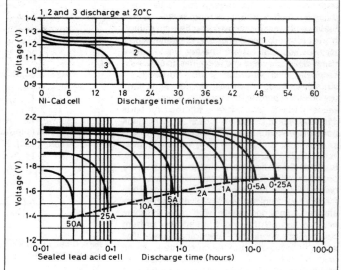

Fig 4. Nicad (a) and Cyclon sealed lead-acid cells (b) under various discharge conditions.

hours, is cheaper and takes up about half the volume.

The LDI batteries, of various voltage and discharge ratings, are in cases measuring about 0.9cm thick, 22cm long and 10cm wide with two outer negative lead plates, and a middle positive electrode of lead dioxide, with the electrolyte (sulphuric acid) absorbed in a fibreglass separator. The position of the plates is stated to be critical with a steel plating acting as a spring pressing down on the assembly to achieve even pressure over the entire surface area.

Frank Harris, G4IEY has drawn attention to an article by Hidekazu Sato of the Furukawa Battery Company 'Development of sealed type lead-acid battery for solar power system' (*The Battery Man*, November 1989, pp14-15, 20, 22-23). This shows how the cost of solar power systems for remote areas has come down to the stage where the cost of the necessary storage battery has become a significant part of the total cost. In about ten years, solar panels have fallen in cost from about

US$35.2/W(peak) to about $6/W. Furukawa supply several ranges of lead-acid batteries for such applications: for example PS-TL shallow discharge batteries in the range 50-2600Ah, CS-L deep discharge types for 130-2000Ah, both capable of 10-year-life; and, more recently, 12CT and 12CTE sealed 'maintenance free' units, 40-200Ah with expected life of 5 years.

MORE ON Q-GATE FET OSCILLATORS

First, I must apologise for the error that crept into Fig 7(a) of the January *TT* showing the QGate FET version of the Hartley oscillator. Fortunately, comparison with Figs 7(b) and Fig 8 indicated the correct connections in the source circuit, but in case anyone is still in doubt, the corrected diagram appears in **Fig 5(a)**.

George Southgate, VK5QG (ex-G3LXO) has also provided an up-date on this oscillator, showing how an additional bipolar buffer amplifier will increase the RF output and enable the circuit

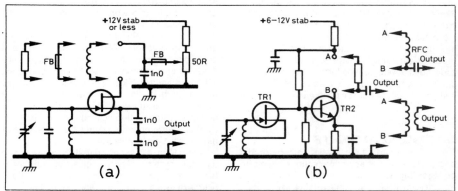

Fig 5. The QGate FET oscillator. (a) Corrected basic diagram. (b) With added bipolar buffer amplifier.

KISS CONSTANT-CURRENT NICAD CHARGER

Mike Brooker, G0IBL, a former seagoing radio officer who has now swallowed an anchor, was not impressed by the complex 'constant-current' IC-regulator chargers shown in the January *TT*. He writes: "Whatever has happened to simplicity (KISS)?". And then adds his tried and tested KISS solution:

"As an R/O for many years, I would often get complaints from the Deck Officers that their Storno VHF hand-held transceivers were not recharging. This was usually due to the (salt-laden) sea-air causing corrosion in the charger-units which were promptly consigned to a watery-grave. I would then knock together the simple form of constant-current charger which I have used for over 25 years and which has given stirling service in a variety of forms; it has proved to be virtually foolproof. Even if a fault does occur, it will not break the bank to throw the faulty unit into the waste-bin and replace it with another! All parts can usually be found in any junk store — be it junk box or junk room.

"This simple charger **(Fig 6)** has been used successfully in all climates, from tropical to arctic. In all that time, I have never (touch wood) had any problems with nicad batteries; I even have some old DEAC cells that have taken more charges than the Bank of England yet still give good service after an occasional shave with an electrolytic razor to zap off the odd whiskers. My present charger, as always, is a 'temporary' lash-up that would fit in a match box. Such chargers can be used with virtually any 12-15V PSU (even an el-cheapo 'battery eliminator' unit). Just connect the mA range of a multimeter, adjust the potentiometer to the required charging current, set an alarm timer (eg wrist-watch with alarm) and rest assured that most nicads will then happily recharge.

"This (PNP) charger uses a very old TF78 audio transistor (similar to the old AD149/AD169 types) but virtually any transistor capable of easily handling the required charging current will do. If in doubt, use a heat sink. The LED lights only when charging (unless Re comes adrift). As shown, it copes with charging currents of 3 to 150mA (some variation likely with different devices

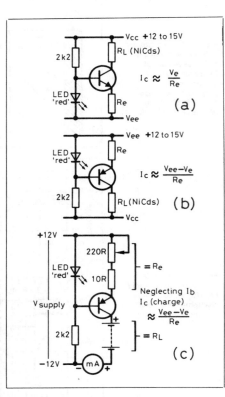

Fig 6. G0IBL's simplified constant-current nicad charging technique.

and LEDs which tend to have different voltage drops). I usually use an input of about 12V for, say, four type AA cells, and about 15V for a PP3-equivalent nicad battery. But it does not matter if the potentiometer is set to the correct charging current and if you check that the LED glows. Once the current-adjustment has been set, the multimeter can be removed. This circuit is by no means original, just an application of basic transistor theory. One final thought, this arrangement would be suitable for mobile operators drawing their supply from the car battery."

to run from a conventional 6-12V stabilised power source: **(Fig 5(b))**. He writes: "If one uses a resistive collector load for TR2, it is necessary to beware of mode jumping producing various weird output waveforms as the collector voltage is varied; so adjust for a pure sinewave output. This problem doesn't seem to arise with chokes or toroidal transformers used as the collector load. This circuit has the advantage that it adds some badly needed gain to the oscillator, producing about 50mV RMS across 50ohms, and also allows the circuit to be run from a higher rail voltage in the more conventional range of 6 to 12V. I have not included component values in these circuits in order to encourage others to think about this aspect and develop things further. In practice, the circuit seems to tolerate a wide range of values and no difficulty should be encountered in getting it to work."

SPEAKING IN DIGITS

One of the important areas where amateur radio and professional telecommunications seems to be following diverging paths is that of the digital transmission of speech. While we stick to analogue speech waveforms, the professionals seem to be

moving ever more rapidly towards encoded digital systems both for 'line' (now increasingly optical fibre) and for 'radio' systems. Pulse-code-modulation (PCM) or one of its many derivatives can provide better communications efficiency at low signal-to-noise ratios than non-coded analogue systems, such as SSB, AM or FM. The drawbacks of added complexity and wider bandwidths are being overcome by the development of very large-scale integrated circuits (VSLI) with many thousands of transistor functions on the same chip and by the development of various forms of bit-rate-reduction and such modulation techniques as 'tamed frequency modulation' (TFM) that was developed over a decade ago by Philips engineers to permit a 16Kbit/s speech channel to be well-contained within a standard 25kHz VHF channel. This does not mean that digital systems are free of all problems; transmissions can be degraded by multipath (propagation delays) resulting in inter-symbol interference in exactly the same way as digital data communications.

Before long, it is expected that the entire public telephone system will be all-digital, from subscriber to subscriber, and even now many conversations over urban-junction lines and trunk lines are carried in digits. The international plans allocate a

hierarchy of digital bit-rates from a basic 64Kbit/s single channel to 140Mbit/s for multiplexed speech and/or video channels. With optical fibres bit rates up to about 560Mbit/s are already practical, while systems capable of Gbit/s are being developed. Optical fibres rather than satellite communications are now regarded as the way telecommunications is developing.

However, 64Kbit/s for a single speech radio channel is regarded as excessive and some very ingenious and complex algorithms for carrying speech at lower bit rates are being developed. A recent IEE colloquium on 'Speech coding' (reported in *Electronics World & Wireless World*, January 1990) showed that a lot of work is going on in British universities in this arcane field, based on the differing requirements in speech quality: broadcast quality (7kHz baseband, SNR better than 35dB; 'toll' (trunk telephone) quality, 200-3400kHz, SNR better than 35dB); and 'communications' quality in which the prime requirement is intelligibility rather than voice fidelity.

It has been shown possible to achieve 'toll' quality with a bit rate of 9.6Kbit/s with efforts to extend this down to 4.8Kbit/s without serious loss of quality. The public aeronautical satellite telephone service (now in experimental use) has the speech coded at 9.6Kbit/s although signalling information increases this to 10.368Kbit/s and the addition of forward error correction (FEC) raises this to 20.736Kbit/s. A new coding strategy, being developed at the University of Southampton, with a 7.5Kbit/s coder and embedded error-correction, is claimed to provide a robust overall transmission rate of 11.4Kbit/s at an economic cost that would be applicable to mobile radio. I imagine that with TFM a transmission rate of 11.4Kbits could be accommodated in a 15kHz VHF channel and would thus be a feasible system for amateur experimentation. Sooner or later, I suspect that we shall need to follow the professionals into speaking in digits. Furthermore, there is work at the University of Liverpool on a form of digital quantizer (line spectral pair) which is claimed to work satisfactorily with a bit error rate of 1 in 40, and thus more robust to channel errors than conventionally error-protected digital transmission systems.

On the more-immediately relevant topic of HF packet data transmission problems (see *TT*, October 1989, p38), H E Dempsey (Threshold Communications Systems, PO Box 188, Brampton, Ontario, L6V 2LI, Canada) has suggested that a solution to the problems of HF digital communications under adverse propagation conditions might be found in the use of the 'Parker Code' developed in the 1960s by B D Parker while he was with the Decca Radar Company (British Patent No 860,830 etc), later implemented by Dollman Electronics Canada Ltd. Mr Dempsey wrote: "It seems to me that it is time for the amateur radio fraternity ... to rescue the UK technological community from the wilful blindness of its Telecommunications Establishment. Those who wish to make the best of HF digital communications under adverse propagation conditions should consider the use of the Parker Code. A Parker Communications Club might get things going". The claimed advantages include detection of multiple bit errors with only four bits overhead; self-clocking with bit rate equal to the symbol rate; elimination of intersymbol errors from multipath delays of less than a symbol dwell time; and it can use classic FEC and be adaptive with ARQ.

I have described the Parker Code system in more detail for *EW & WW* but hope to return to this subject later in *TT*. On paper it sounds an attractive system though I remain uncertain whether it would be excessively complex to implement on the amateur bands: with microcomputers I would not think this to be the case.

UNDERSTANDING THOSE RADIATION HAZARDS

The inclusion of the severely restrictive guidelines on health hazards drawn up by WC2S originally published in *QST* and in the January *TT* (p36) has stirred up some thoughts on the social problems that could confront amateur activity in the 1990s. It is less a question of the possible health risks — which at most would seem to be minimal — but how they are perceived by neighbours and families.

As G3IJL puts it: "As people become aware of the possibility of non-ionizing radiation health hazards, no matter how tiny, we face the possibility that our neighbours will declare transmitting antennas a health hazard to their families. Will amateur activity come to be confined to rural dwellers with no near neighbours, with the rest of us forced into silence? In London, it is virtually impossible to avoid strong 50Hz magnetic fields; for example, when travelling on or waiting for tube trains or on intercity electric trains with 25kV lines above our heads. Is this more or less hazardous than 400W PEP to a 28MHz beam antenna at, say, 20ft?"

Clearly, much depends on the advice that may be given in future official guidelines. The current UK 22-page guidelines — NRPB-GS11 'Guidance as to Restrictions on Exposures to Time Varying Electromagnetic Fields and the 1988 Recommendations of the International Non-Ionizing Radiation Committee' — published by the National Radiological Protection Board (HMSO, May 1989, £4) confine themselves primarily to protection against the proven thermal effects from the absorption of electromagnetic energy and protection against the possibilities of electric shock and burn. The basic guidelines in NRPB-GS11 do not differ greatly from the American ANSI recommendations which have been described on various occasions in *TT*. These do not seriously affect normal amateur operation except when closer than usual to transmitting antennas (except perhaps for grounded monopole type vertical antennas where recommended limits may be exceeded within a few feet of the base).

NRPB agrees with the conclusions of the international committee (INIRC) that "there is at present insufficient biological and epidemiological data to make a health risk assessment or even to determine whether there is a potential hazard to health with regard to athermal (non-heating) effects of electromagnetic fields." Such, then, is the current official view. But it does imply that if more convincing evidence is uncovered then the guidelines may need to be changed again, and become more restrictive.

In 'Fatal Distraction, or, Is Amateur Radio a Health Hazard' Morris Odell, VK3DOC (*Amateur Radio* (VK), September 1989, pp34-35) provides a further survey of the present evidence, based partly on material supplied to WIA by Ross Adey, K6UI who, as noted in the January *TT*, is a prominent research scientist in the biomedical field.

VK3DOC notes that the current concern is not with 'acute' effects such as headaches or even personality changes but in long-term effects, possibly leading to cancer-type diseases. The difficulty is that no simple experiment can definitely settle the matter. Epidemiological studies which look at people exposed to suspected dangers and statistically compare their rates of disease and death with that of the general population are neither as simple nor as certain as they might seem. We all die eventually of something, what is important to society is if it were found that persons exposed to EM fields died significantly younger on average to those not exposed; but, so far as one can see, none of the present studies indicate this — indeed amateurs seem to be *less* vulnerable to

MORE ON FITTING COAXIAL PLUGS

The publication in *TT* (September 1989, p40) of the Antiference advice on fitting coaxial cable to their standard TVP2 plug brought in a number of letters emphasising the advantages of the alternative method of teasing out the braid, rather than twisting it into a tail (see *TT*, December 1989, Fig 6, p37). Several readers, including Alec Hodgekinson, ZS6BMU/G3LLJ and John Harris (chairman, Stratford upon Avon & District Radio Society) recalled that the preferred method stems from the recommendations of Belling-Lee in the days when the company was a major supplier of TV antennas. B-L were also firm advocates of soldering the centre conductor.

John Harris has provided a copy of the B-L instruction sheet covering loading instructions for their standard coaxial plug (type L734/P). This was as follows(see **Fig 7**):

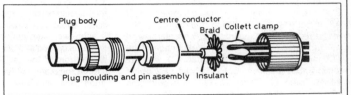

Fig 7. The preferred Belling-Lee method of fitting standard co-axial plugs to the cable.

Trim feeder by removing 1-in outer cover, ¾-in of braid and ⅞-in of insulant. Slide clamping nut and collet on to feeder and spray the braid. Push centre conductor through plug pin as far as possible and bend sharply for soldering. Solder and trim. Slide collet up to splayed ends of braid and trim braid flush with plug moulding, using knife against collet. Push assembly home into plug so that collet enters it. Screw nut firmly to grip feeder. The plug pin must be firm.

In the case of feeder larger than 0.261-in diameter over cover, the hole in the collet clamp encircles braid only. Avoid scoring centre conductor and braid when removing insulant. Solder the conductor with a 'quick' iron to avoid melting the cable and plug insulant. Trim loose ends to avoid short circuiting. Ensure that the claws of the collet are the correct way round so as to grip the outer sheaf. Avoid twisting cable when re-assembling plug, as this tends to break the conductor.

many common diseases and accidents than the population at large.

Carcinogenic influences may be as initiators or promotors. Asbestos dust and ionising radiation are known initiators. Promotors act on tissue that has previously been initiated or undergone pre-malignant change, speeding up progression to cancerous growth. Tobacco smoke is thought to have a mixed action as both initiator and promotor.

Some test tube studies have shown an effect of RF fields on the function of lymphocytes (the cells of the immune system) but this is very difficult to test in the living body; moreover the rare cancers noted in the Milham studies etc are not the same as those that appear in other deficiencies of the immune system such as Aids. There is, as noted before in *TT*, some evidence that RF exposure may act as a very weak promotor of some rare leukaemias. But similarly, there is the possibility that such carcinogenic effects stem from solder fumes, solvents and other chemicals used in design, manufacture, repair or installation of electronic equipment.

This does not mean that we should not be concerned to read in WC2S's *QST* article that 800MHz handhelds with modest RF outputs of 1.0 and 1.8W have been found to result in the

presence of a 'hot-spot' in the eye of the user with a ½λ dipole antenna and in the frontal portion of the brain while using a ⅝λ antenna. VK3DOC, however, concludes: "The chance of an amateur dying as a result of amateur radio is miniscule — enjoy the pleasures of our magnificent hobby without worrying whether it will kill you!"

3-in-1 ANTENNA TUNER & AF METER

A couple of ideas borrowed from the November 1989 issue of *73 Amateur Radio*:

'Three-in-One Antenna Tuner — Matches virtually any random wire!' by J Frank Brumbaugh, KB4ZGC, shows how three standard matching networks can be combined in a simple switched antenna tuner: **Fig 8**. Network A matches random wire antennas presenting a relative high (voltage fed) impedance. Network B copes with low-impedance wires (eg 0.25λ). Network C is a standard T-configuration suitable for matching to coaxial feeders, twin lead or single wires over a reasonably wide impedance range: "If you can't get below 2:1 SWR try a different network but do not change switch S1 with RF applied." For use up to about 50W, the 100pF or 365pF capacitors can be of the broadcast

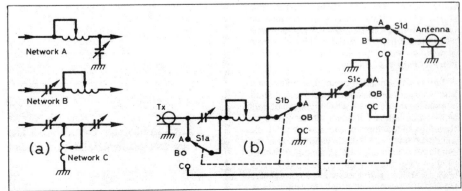

Fig 8. Three-in-one ATU.

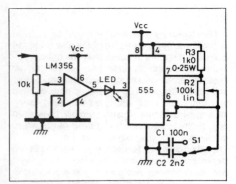

Fig 9. Low-cost audio-frequency meter.

receiver type and the switch a standard wafer switch. Inductance can be a tapped coil, coil wound on a T-106-2 toroid or a surplus rotary inductor.

'Bargain Audio Frequency Meter ($10)' by William Lazure, KB5CTH, shows a simple form of AF meter **(Fig 9)** in which the signal to be measured is nulled against a 555 oscillator with null indicated by the dimming or extinction of the LED when the frequencies match. C1 with R2 covers about 60Hz to 3kHz; C2 with R2 about 2.5kHz to about 130kHz. R2 (which should be a trim-pot) must be linear and it is necessary to calibrate it against known AF signals. The LM356 provides a gain of about 20 with pins 1 and 8 open. Almost any type of LED should prove suitable and should glow when the two signals do not match in frequency. If no null try and adjust the input potentiometer.

CARE AND FEEDING OF BATTERIES

TT has already included advice (hopefully not too contradictory) on the maintenance and recharging of both nicad and lead-acid batteries but this is a topic that continues to attract interest, with additional information still emerging. This month we quote from a number of sources, including: 'Lead-acid batteries, myths and fables' Parts 1 & 2, by Arrie Wessel, ZS6UY, *Radio-ZS*, January & February 1984; 'Rechargeable power supplies, Part 5: Nicad battery life' by Anton Wilson (*International Broadcast Engineer*, September 1989, pp60 & 62); and correspondence from John Brown, G3EUR.

First some common advice on chargers:

For nicads: Preferably always use constant-current chargers, taking care not to overcharge even at 0.1C. Trickle charging rate should not be above 0.02C.

For lead-acid batteries: Preferably always use constant-voltage units (eg 13.7± 0.1V for '12V' batteries, 2.3V for cells). Maximum charging current should not exceed about 0.2C but for vehicle batteries 4-5A is a typical figure. With a correctly-set constant-voltage charger there should be little damage if the charger is left continuously connected. Where the charger or PSU is capable of providing more than about 0.2C, some form of current limiting is advisable.

Batteries designed for portable applications, whether nicad or sealed lead-acid types, should be treated with care. It is wise to choose batteries with strong outside cases as opposed to soft coverings so that the entire shock of a fall or blow will not be transmitted directly to the inside of the cells. Short-circuits of the plates may be caused by their being forced together as a result of a physical shock or, with nicads, more normally by the growth of crystals that penetrate the separator (whiskers). Nicad crystals can often be successfully

zapped, but it is safer to use a high-value electrolytic capacitor for this purpose than to use a high-current PSU/charger which may burn a larger hole in the separator. Another cause of internal short-circuits in high-energy nicads is separator break-down caused by high temperatures, due either to overcharging or being left inside a vehicle in the hot sun. Keep all batteries in a cool place, but note that nicad cells should not be charged in very low temperatures.

A lead-acid battery should preferably be kept fully charged, just below the stage of gassing. A battery should be called upon to do as little work as possible. Preferably it should not be expected to act as a large-value smoothing capacitor to eliminate supply ripple since the cumulative fractional charge/discharges will eventually result in premature battery failure due to ageing.

Battery temperature during charging (or sustained heavy-current discharges) should not be allowed to rise more than 10°C above ambient.

'Dryfit'-type small sealed lead-acid batteries have a very low rate of self-discharge while stored; they should not be stored in a completely discharged state. Avoid excessive deep discharges.

With 'wet' lead-acid batteries, the 'dead' plate material is shed and settles as sediment/sludge at the bottom of the cell (if excessive it may short-circuit the plates). A 'dry' (sealed) battery cannot shed this dead material, so much greater care should be taken in their treatment. A good rule is to leave the battery continuously on its correct (constant-voltage) charger; when discharged bring it up to full charge as soon as possible.

For professional high-energy nicad systems, as used in broadcast video, Anton Wilson points out that those spending £400 or more on a complete nicad battery system feel it should last for ever. But asking how long a nicad will last is like asking a doctor in a maternity ward the age to which a particular baby will live. Batteries, he stresses, are

prone to 'diseases' that affect the life of a system as well as 'coronaries' that can kill them almost instantly. Taking 80% charge-acceptance as an 'end-of-life' point, a nicad battery may tolerate as many as 10,000 charge/discharge cycles or as few as 250. With high-energy cells and fast-charging, he puts the average life-expectancy as around 400-500 cycles with 300 to over 800 typical: "Only under the most adverse conditions should a nicad deliver fewer than 250 cycles. Conversely a nicad would require divine intervention to exceed 1000 deep discharge cycles."

He adds that: "Over-discharging a battery invites a short-circuit since the cells no longer pack sufficient punch to vaporise internal short-circuits (whiskers) as they develop." This self-correcting phenomenon cannot take place if the cell is discharged almost fully, so it is good practice to avoid over-discharging a nicad battery. It is advisable to change to a fresh battery at the first indication of depletion and to recharge batteries as soon as possible after use. Batteries should be stored charged and because of their high self-discharge rate, receive an additional slow charge the night preceding re-use.

G3EUR found that with a 45Ah Delco sealed car battery connected across a stabilised 13.8V PSU as the supply for a 100W SSB rig, the charging current, after a long transmission, can zoom up to 20A or so, then falling quickly to a low level. He feels convinced that punching such heavy currents into batteries can quickly knock the stuffing out of the plates; making it advisable to provide at least a degree of current-limiting with any PSU/charger capable of supplying more than about 5-8A continuously (depending on the capacity of the battery). Although batteries may be either 'shallow discharge' or 'deep discharge' types, both should be capable of providing their rated Ah capacity if used under the conditions specified by the makers.

STEERABLE 7MHz DX ANTENNA

Tony Preedy, G3LNP notes that anybody who still has an unguyed 18-metre tower supporting an HF rotary beam (and a garden that can accommodate a circular radius of some 4.6m) still standing after the winter's persistent gales can easily provide themselves with an effective steerable 7MHz DX antenna: see **Figs 1 and 2.**

He writes: 'A figure-of-eight horizontal radiation pattern with a theoretical gain of about 5.5dB over a quarter-wave (monopole) radiator is achieved by driving two vertical wires in antiphase. The central metal tower does not greatly influence the radiation pattern since the net current induced from the two wires is theoretically zero. Similarly the horizontal feed sections are dimensioned such that they have no net radiation perpendicular

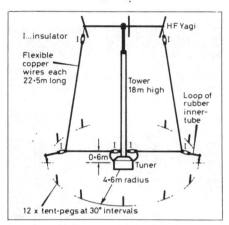

Fig 1. Construction details of G3LNP's steerable 7MHz DX antenna providing roughly 5dB bi-directional (figure-of-eight) gain and good low-angle characteristics with some 30dB rejection of signals from the sides.

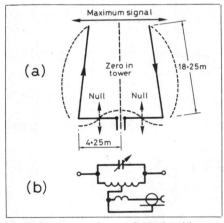

Fig 2(a) Dimensions and current distribution of the G3LNP antenna for optimum directional performance. (b) Tuner as built in waterproof plastic carton. Coil 26 turns, 16 swg, 5cm diameter, 15cm long. Link 3 turns insulated wire. High-voltage 50pF variable capacitor.

to their axis. Radiation is therefore only end-fire and at low angles of elevation.

'The method of driving the wires in antiphase by using a balanced ATU as shown eliminates any need for a counterpoise or ground radials. The tuner, assembled in a plastic ice-cream carton, was adjusted for minimum VSWR at the centre of the band only.

'Construction is straightforward, as illustrated, but unfortunately rotating the beam is a three-stage operation which involves first unhooking the ground attachments, rotating the HF Yagi and then re-attaching the wires to the appropriate pair of tent pegs.

"Performance has been impressive in spite of poor local ground conductivity. DX stations were typically 3 'S-points' stronger compared with a horizontal dipole; Western European stations about 5 'S-points' weaker; side rejection at least 30dB."

A GERMAN CHIREIX-MESNY UHF ANTENNA

Walter Farrar, G3ESP who, in the immediate post-war period, had the interesting task of evaluating and compiling detailed reports on German military radio equipment, writes: "I spotted your *TT*, February 1990 reference to the Chireix-Mesny array of half-wave dipoles and your comment that such an array might have application as a fixed beam on VHF/UHF.

"Well, Hitler's army had a portable station called the SEG2T (Sender-Emphaenger-Geraet 2T), alternatively designated DMG2T (Dezimeter-Geraet 2T) which worked on about 60cm (500MHz) using such an antenna, but with only two squares instead of the four illustrated in *TT* in each element. The transmitter output was 40-60 milliwatts on speech or MCW (A2A), using an Acorn-type valve (DS310) as power oscillator. The receiver was a super-regen.

"The electronics were in a case 340 by 210 by 210mm. The PSU case (same size) was fastened below it and held a 2V accumulator and two 180V (tapped) dry batteries. Together these weighed 26kg and were mounted on a tripod weighing 7.7kg. The station was completed by an accessories and spares case weighing 13kg. In transit, the radio and battery box went on the soldier's back, the tripod was shoulder-slung like a rifle and the spares box was carried by hand. With a total weight of some 47kg it represented a staggering load for any soldier!

"My notes state: 'Radiation from the aerial is highly directional. Therefore equipment must be adjusted for optimum working. There must be no intervening objects between the two stations.'

SOLDERING TO IRON & STEEL

For those prepared to handle (carefully) chemicals which are hazardous to touch and breathe, Roger Del Nero, WA2HNQ (QST August 1989, p39) reports successfully soldering to stainless steel, iron, cast-iron, brass, copper and other metals by using homemade acidic soldering flux. This he made from the following ingredients: 37g of zinc choloride, 23g of glacial acetic acid and 40g of hydrochloric acid. He points out that these quantities make a considerable amount of flux and can be scaled down in proportion as required. Acidic flux should not be used for normal wiring of components to printed circuit boards etc. The zinc chloride can be made by dissolving zinc in hydrochloride acid until the solution is saturated; the remaining ingredients are then added carefully. AK7M, the editor of QST's Hinks & Kinks adds a warning that readers unsure of their ability to handle dangerous chemicals should purchase ready-to-use zinc-chloride instead of attempting to blend their own. He notes that preformulated acidic fluxes are hazardous and should be used carefully.

Incidentally solder, with its lead content, should not be used where there is any risk of particles being ingested. A very graphic example of its

danger can be found in the recent final solving of the mystery that for long surrounded the loss of the 129 crewmen and officers of Sir John Franklin's 1845-48 expedition in search of a north-west passage around the northern coast of Canada. Some years ago analysis of recovered bones suggested that these contained toxic levels of lead that adversely affected the health, judgement and ultimate survival of the members of the expedition. It has recently been reported (Nature, 25 January 1990) that further investigations has shown that it is virtually certain that food preserved in soldered tins was the source of the high lead levels.

THE NEI CLANDESTINE TRANSMITTERS AND RECEIVERS

Dick Rollema, PA0SE (*Electron,* February 1990) describes a series of 'NEI' (Netherlands East Indies) transmitters and receivers developed in Australia from 1943-45 by the Netherlands Forces Intelligence Service for clandestine operations in and around the Netherlands East Indies (now Indonesia etc). He gives the circuit diagram of the four-valve "straight" (1-v-2) receiver (NEI-II and NEI-III) which used four 6J7-G glass-octal valves (use of a single type of valve much eases the spares situation). The NEI-II receiver covered 3-6, 6-12 and 12-30MHz in three, switched wavebands with the 6.3V, 0.3A heaters wired in series-parallel, drawing a hefty 0.6A from the 12V 25Ah lead-acid battery in its wooden container box. The 30-watt NEI-II transmitter used the popular 6V6G crystal oscillator and 807 power amplifier combination. The later 50W NEI-III set was powered from 12V with the aid of a rotary converter and comprised a 6G6G CO/6G6G doubler/tripler/807 PA. With crystals between 4-5MHz, the output could be from 4-15MHz. The receiver for the NEI-III was basically similar to the NEI-II but covered 2-17MHz in four bands.

I suspect that the equipments were primarily intended for ship-borne operations, possibly akin to those mounted by the British SBS (Special Boat Service) and the 'private navies' of SIS/SOE. I recall one Special Communications operator who claimed that, when he was invited to go on a short trip round the harbour in one of the converted French fishing boats based in the Helston Estuary in Cornwall, he found that he had been 'shanghaied' for an operational trip to Brittany to pick up agents and mail! The MI-6 'private navy' carried Mark III (6V6-807) transmitters and the ubiquitous HRO receivers to keep in touch with Whaddon.

LINEAR UHF TRANSCEIVER WITH CARTESIAN-LOOP FEEDBACK

Some ten years ago I first mentioned in *TT* the work of Dr V Petrovic at Bath (later Bristol) University in developing what he originally termed a polar-loop feedback technique that enables a high-efficiency Class C HF power amplifier to function as a highly-linear amplifier.

TT (June 1985) was able to report on this project in some detail, including spectrum analysis curves, of the remarkable results Dr Petrovic had been able to achieve using this special form of negative feedback (now usually termed cartesian feedback). He had shown that the technique could reduce the near-in spurious noise and unwanted carrier to around -60dB compared to the 25-30dB down on peak tones of a two-tone test for typical (good) amateur equipment and around 40dB for high-grade professional communications equipment.

That *TT* report was based on a paper by V Petrovic and A H Brown in *IEE Conference Publication No 245,* 1985, pp81-85. This describes in outline a 1.6 to 30MHz, 100W PEP transmitter in which the feedback reduces the third-order products by a massive 37dB, resulting in products on two-tone test 67dB below the tones and with image sidebands suppressed by 68dB. It was noted that the paper claimed that the correct use of cartesian feedback not only improves the spectral purity but also results in: (1) lower output noise, achieved by reducing the overall gain of the transmitter; (2) improved efficiency, obtained by operating the solid-state PA with reduced bias and using an unregulated power supply; and (3) simplified design of the PA, since neither its linearity nor frequency response needs to be exceptionally good.

I wrote then: "Basically, this cartesian loop transmitter employs phasing-type SSB generation (Weaver third-method) to which the modulation information obtained by synchronous demodulation of a sample of the output signal is fed back in quadrature form. In other words, audio signals at 90° to each other are recovered and used as negative feedback. Since the bandwidth of the AF signals is much narrower than with RF negative feedback, as used on some SSB transmitter, much larger amounts of feedback can be applied.

"The problem of obtaining AF signals over the range 300 to 3000Hz in accurate quadrature by means of phase-shift networks is well known and has been the reason why relatively few phasing-type SSB transmitters are used, particularly where they need to operate over a wide temperature range. The vast majority of amateurs continue to use filter-type SSB generation despite the attractions of third-method and polyphase networks. The novel feature of this latest transmitter is to use a combination of third-method SSB generation with filter-type demodulation to supply the quadrature feedback, using 10.7MHz SSB crystal filters."

With so many advantages, it may seem surprising that this feedback technique has not rapidly established a role in both professional and amateur communications but there are clearly problems not mentioned in the published papers. I seem to recall that Plessey were involved in the Bristol work but am not sure whether any commercial product has yet appeared. However the 5th International Conference on Mobile Radio & Personal Communications at Coventry, December 1989 included a paper "Direct Conversion Linear Transceiver Design" by A Bateman, D Haines and R Wilkinson of Bristol University (*IEE Conference Publication No 315*, pp53-56) in which Cartesian feedback is used in a low-power 900MHz transceiver of high-linearity: **Fig 3**. In this paper, the authors conclude: "The application of Cartesian feedback for transmitter linearisation (**Fig 4**) coupled with recent advances in A/D (analogue-to-digital) converter technology are undoubtedly the two most significant factors which have made the implemention of a universal (linear) low-cost transceiver architecture possible. The performance of a Cartesian-linearised transmitter is impressive, with markedly better linearity achieved even with a Class C power stage than with a conventional well-designed Class A configuration. With the PA stage designed using efficient Class C modules, the added benefits of smaller heat sink and low cost (standard FM modules can be used) come for free. Transmitters have been designed at VHF and UHF (900MHz) with no difficulty, and with standard 'off the shelf' components, giving the performance indicated in the paper. Linearisation of Class C devices at 1.7GHz is currently underway at Bristol."

This transmitter and receiver system is based on the Weaver *'third method'* system together with a direct-conversion receiver with audio digital-signal-processing to provide what amounts to a flexible reconfigurable radio capable of operating with both analogue and digital signal formats

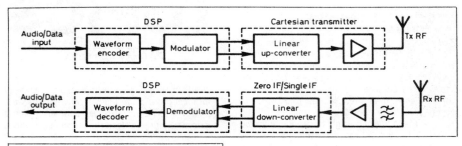

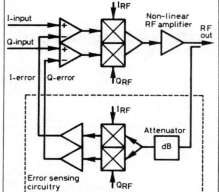

Fig 3. The linear transceiver architecture proposed by the Bristol University team.

Fig 4. Cartesian feedback transmitter linearisation outline.

Fig 5. Direct-conversion receiver configurations suitable for use with post-detector digital-signal-processing (DSP) filtering. (a) Zero-IF system. (b) Single-IF (Super-DC-gainer) system.

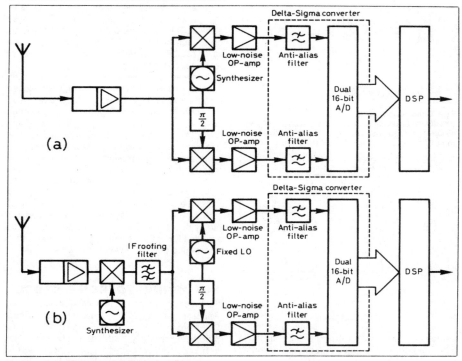

regardless of their amplitude and phase characteristics. In practice, the design of the receiver section is claimed to have proved more difficult than the transmitter, requiring wide dynamic range and good sensitivity. In practice, the Bristol receiver uses the *'super-DC-gainer'* technique described in *TT* August 1987, pp581-2) in which a superhet-type frequency-changer section is placed in front of a fixed-tuned DC receiver to give a 'single-IF' rather than a *"zero-IF"* configuration: **Fig 5**. The major breakthrough in favour of direct-conversion (or either type) is given as the current availability of wide-dynamic-range A/D converter ICs: "Devices with 18-bit resolution can be obtained allowing digitalisation of both I & Q channels in a single device which also incorporates anti-alias filtering. Provided the front-end circuitry of the receiver can be made sufficiently linear, adjacent channel selectivity in excess of 80dB can be achieved using digital filtering techniques

alone…We are not far from the ultimate goal of single-chip transmitter and receiver realisation of a linear transceiver, with several companies pursuing design programmes in this area."

Clearly, this provides yet another example of where and how professional communications is tending to diverge away from the type of standard practices used in amateur equipment. Perhaps this item may encourage somebody to look into the possibility of adapting Cartesian feedback and digital signal processing to a practical design. However it may not be easy. The Bristol team writes: "The transmitter and receiver system is based on the Weaver frequency-translation technique (ie the 1956 paper "Third Method of generation and detection of SSB, *Proc IRE*, December 1956, but with many practical designs in past issues of *Rad Com*). This method was chosen for the property that the image products fall in the user's own channel, thus greatly reducing the gain and phase-matching requirements of the quadrature processing paths. The transmitter design includes RF amplifier linearisation by means of Cartesian closed-loop feedback. Problems that have plagued this method in the past have been largely solved…virtually any modulation format can be handled using this technique with no requirement for constant envelope." I have yet to come across a fully-described practical circuit for a Cartesian loop PA (using either analogue or digital techniques) at HF, VHF or UHF — nor any account of what have been "the problems that have plagued this method."

BEWARE OF COSTLY DUST

The drilling of chassis and panels and similar workshop operations can produce metallic and graphite or carbonized dust particles that can subsequently result in equipment faults. Even ordinary building dust is recognised as producing major problems when installing mechanical/electronic equipment such as videotape or audio recorders etc in brand new studio complexes.

Geoff Brown, GJ4ICO contributes an example of *expensive dust* although in his case the problem was overcome inexpensively. He writes: "Last year my company was involved in over-hauling a French 100MHz (Band II) power amplifier which had been used in a local FM radio station. This had a 3CX800A7 ceramic triode as now found in some amateur linears. When the amplifier, complete with its power supply, was fired up it provided full RF output but, every so often, there would be a small 'click' or 'arcing' noise, followed by loss of power and anode meter fluctuations. The user had noted the same symptoms on the fault-report card.

"The power supply was checked but proved faultless and attention turned to the amplifier. Each component in the anode section was carefully inspected — EHT connector, EHT leadthrough, EHT chokes etc — without result. A new (£325) 3CX800A7 was fitted and the problem disappeared.

"However, I was not satisfied to leave it at that. I sat down with the valve in my hand and tried to puzzle out why it should have apparently developed such an intermittent fault. Finally, close inspection of the ceramic section with a magnifying glass revealed all.

"A very fine hairline of dust, virtually invisible to the naked eye, was laying between the anode and grid pins! The ceramic was thoroughly cleaned with alcohol, the valve replaced and the amplifier fired up. The intermittent fault had completely disappeared. It was an illuminating experience that could have proved expensive. It suggests that no matter how much air-filtering is used, dust can still get to and form tracks on ceramic (and possibly other) valves. Since then, similar faults have been traced in amplifiers fitting the widely used 4CX250B tetrodes."

I feel tempted to misquote Lewis Carroll:
The Walrus and the Carpenter
Were standing close I trust
They wept like anything to see
Those tiny tracks of dust
"If these were only cleared away
The rig would not be bust!"

BOOSTING THE QRP RIG

Wes Hayward, W7ZOI in a two-part constructional article on a complete 14MHz QRP SSB/CW transceiver (*QST*, December 1989/January 1990) aptly expresses his feelings about the changes that have largely changed the shape of Amateur Radio: "It's hard to justify the construction of a complete SSB/CW HF transceiver in this 'modern' era of readily available commercial equipment. The popular, multiband MF/HF transceivers offer excellent performance, often at a reasonable cost. Still I feel a twinge of guilt when I use them. They

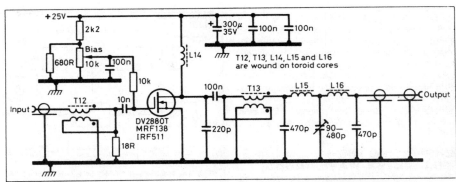

Fig 6. W7ZOI's FET linear amplifier designed to boost the 1-watt output of his 14MHz QRP SSB/CW transceiver to about 10 watts. The compact transceiver is presented as a home-construction project in *QST* December 1989/January 1990.

offer nothing of the feeling of exploration that I've grown to expect from Amateur Radio."

His new project provides a compact transceiver with a 1-watt output and a higher standard of performance than usually expected from QRP rigs. It has a superhet receiver with SBL-1 double-balanced mixer and a second one as product detector; a 9MHz crystal filter and 8998.5kHz crystal-controlled BFO.

With apologies to the stalwarts of the G-QRP Club, my personal feeling is that 1W output on 14MHz is pitching things a bit too low for pleasant two-way contacts. However, W7ZOI provides details of a suitable external FET power amplifier that gives about 10 watts linear RF output for CW or SSB. This uses an arrangement basically similar to the amplifier described by WA7MLH and him in the November *QST* and reproduced in the February *TT* (Fig 1 p31) but including adjustable bias circuitry etc: **Fig 6**. Such an amplifier could be used with any QRP rig providing about 1-watt drive.

The M/A Com DV288OT power FET used by W7ZOI is no longer available but can be replaced without other alterations by the similar Motorola MRF138 or the switching-type IRF511 Hexfet. Details of the wound components include: T12 broadband transformer, 7 bifiliar turns No 22 enamel on FT-50-43 ferrite toroidal core (observe phasing); T13 similar but 11 bifiliar turns No 18 enamel on FT-82-60 core; L14 50 turns No 26 on T68-2 powdered-iron toroidal core. L15, L19 both 19 turns No 20 on T-50-6 powdered-iron toroidal core.

Del Arthur, G0DLN is someone else who feels that the typical 1-3-watt solidstate QRP rigs for 3.5MHz can be a little frustrating, with contacts too often lost due to fading or QRM. He points out that a possible solution is to convert, at virtually no cost, a discarded domestic valve radio (jumble sale or even the local council rubbish tip) into a Class A linear RF amplifier.

He writes: "The secret is simple. Pull out all the valves except the audio output (and rectifier if this is a valve). The AF stage is likely to be an EL84 or similar self-biased for Class A operation. Disconnect the HT line to the earlier stages. Replace the AF output transformer with a home-made tank coil tuned with the fitted variable capacitor. Replace existing AF bypass capacitors with RF types taken from the early stages (virtually everything you need should be found on the receiver chassis). The only bought component should usually be a 50-ohm carbon resistor to go between grid and earth of the EL84 stage with the output from the QRP transmitter connected to the grid. This passive-grid configuration is simple, reliable and stable. The advantage of Class A operation is that less drive is needed than for Class AB or C and the output signal is clean (relatively harmonic free). My conversion provides 10 watts RF output on 3.5MHz with 3 watts input. Anode 350V (many domestic receivers have a 250V HT line), Screen

300V, grid bias –8V with the original 150-ohm cathode resistor. Although used only for CW, I have two-tone tested it and the scope display is near perfect. I would not recommend attempting to drive such an amplifier directly from a VFO since with passive-grid appreciable drive is required while if a tuned grid circuit were introduced there would be stability problems etc. To those familiar only with solid-state equipment, remember that even a domestic radio receiver with 250 to 350V HT will give a nasty bite if provoked, so take care."

MICROMINIATURE FUEL CELLS

For many years, there has been keen interest in developing more practical forms of fuel cells as a replacement for conventional forms of primary or secondary 'storage' batteries. In a fuel cell the substances that react chemically at the electrodes in the cell are stored partially or wholly outside the reaction cell; when these substances are exhausted, the current stops until more 'fuel' is added. A fuel cell is thus more akin to, say, a petrol generator in being run on 'fuel' stored outside and fed in as required. Dry batteries, accumulators and fuel cells, however, all depend on the same basic laws of electrochemistry with the chemical energy directly converted into electrical energy without significant energy-loss in the form of heat. Theoretically, electricity can be generated by electro-chemical devices at efficiencies exceeding 70%, as compared to around 30% for a thermal power station using coal, oil or nuclear fuel and only about 15% for an internal combustion engine.

The first laboratory-model electric fuel cell was made by Sir William Grove some 150 years ago but it has never proved easy to develop practical fuel cells that can operate efficiently at low temperatures (ie ambient room temperatures). Much development work has been directed at developing relatively powerful fuel cells for such applications as electric vehicles but with relatively little success.

Now, however, C K Dyer of Bell Communications Research has described (*Nature*, 8 February 1990) a new form of solid-state fuel cell based on the oxygen-hydrogen reaction in which the reactive cell can be less than a micrometre across. Although the current output of a single cell is a matter of microamperes, its simple design and small size may make it suitable for use in series arrays of many cells as a means of powering microchips, and as a small, lightweight fuel cell that could be manufactured cheaply.

In an accompanying commentary on this development, Thomas Mallouk writes: "Conventional fuel cells use the combustion of hydrogen or methane to generate small voltages. To do this, they are constructed in the manner of an electrochemical battery, with the oxidation of hydrogen at one electrode releasing electrons and reduction of oxygen at the other mopping them up. The unexpected novelty of Dyer's cell is that it develops an unusually large voltage in *mixtures* of hydrogen and oxygen (voltages about 0.5-1V, currents 500 to 20μA respectively).

"Regardless of the precise mechanism involved (apparently still uncertain), the facility with which the phenomena can be reproduced with a variety of different membrane materials should lead to rapid duplication of these results and eventually to a broad range of applications from low-cost, small, lightweight fuel cells as replacements for high-use batteries to new applications in information processing which was the original objective of this work."

EXPLOITING THE MILLIMETRE-WAVE BANDS

Amateurs normally think in terms of how to extend the range of their transmissions. Paradoxically, for military and telecommunications systems, the desire these days is often to *limit* the range, either to reduce the likelihood of interception or to reduce the distance at which the same frequency-channel can be re-used without the risk of interference. This combined with the ever increasing congestion on much of the VHF and UHF bands is leading to a growing interest in exploiting the still wide open spaces above 30GHz (EHF).

For over a year, BTRL have been testing at Saxmundham a mm-wave system working at 29GHz as a means of distributing multiple video channels as an alternative to the more expensive laying of broadband cables and last year it was confirmed that MVDS (microwave video distribution systems) will be licensed to use a band just above 40GHz with an expected service area of about 2-4km diameter. The prospect of domestic use of such frequencies is encouraging the development of low-cost MMIC devices, including the use of HEMT (high-electron-mobility transistors) devices that should give a receiver noise factor of under 7dB.

There is also much military and professional communications interest in using frequencies close to 60GHz where there is a very sharp peak of severe attenuation due to oxygen absorption even in the absence of rain attenuation which is also very severe at such frequencies: see **Fig 7**.

Peter Fry, G3TZV draws attention to an article in the August 1989 issue of *MSN* (Microwave Systems News) which describes how Hughes Aircraft have developed a "EHF applique millimetre-wave 'strap-on' radio". This enables vehicles with a conventional 30-88MHz VHF radio to use it, when required, on mm-frequencies between 53.469 and 53.715GHz: **Fig 8**. It uses a special circulator switch assembly that allows a single EHF mixer to perform both up-

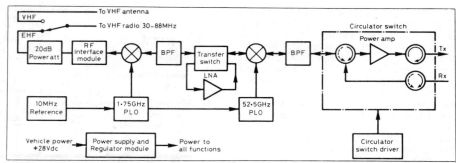

Fig 8. The Hughes VHF-to-EHF transverter designed as a 'strap-on' unit for use with standard US military VHF vehicle radios.

and down-conversion. Hughes have also been developing a new UHF bicone antenna with a view to its use for a dual-band (UHF/EHF) concept. The EHF range is limited to a few miles line-of-sight.

It may be worth a reminder that our UK amateur licences already include *primary* frequency allocations at 47, 75.4, 142 and 250GHz!

PREFERRED CW-COPYING TONES

TT (December 1989, p38) included some notes on the interesting 'Project Frequency Band' experiments carried out by members of the G-QRP Club to determine the optimum audio-frequency beat note for the reception of CW. As noted then, this emphasised that receiver designers should take fully into account the characteristics of human hearing. These are not necessarily the same for different operators but in general it was found that the lower frequencies of around 450Hz seemed preferable to the oft-recommended 750-850Hz.

Angus Taylor, G8PG has now passed along the results of a follow-up experiment carried out by G-QRP council member Tony Tuite, an experienced ex-RAF operator, with the help of a panel of ten operators, all aged 50 years or more. (As we grow older we lose the ability to hear the higher end of the audio spectrum: whereas a youth can often hear tones above 15kHz, this gradually reduces to around 8-10kHz, although this is perhaps not relevant to this particular experiment.)

In this project, the ten participants were asked to state their preferred usual BFO frequency and then to set up a receiver to this frequency and copy some morse at 18-20wpm. The actual audio frequency was then measured with an oscilloscope. The results were as follows:

Six out of the ten gave their preferred frequency as about 750Hz. In each case the actual frequency proved to be close to 500Hz.

Three gave 600-700Hz but found to be about 475Hz.

One (who had received musical training) gave 500Hz and set his BFO to within 50Hz of this figure.

Test material was then transmitted at 25wpm. Those of the operators who could copy at this speed, tended to adjust the BFO to give a tone of about 600Hz (ie some 100Hz higher than for the slower speed).

G8PG comments: "So far all our work points to frequencies in the range 450-600Hz as being the most acceptable, with many operators unconsciously adopting them. The impact on AF filter design and BFO crystal selection is obvious."

It is perhaps worth noting that at one time, operators with most designs of communication receiver were able, having adjustable BFO controls, to select their own preferred tone without worrying whether this accorded with their own 'guestimates'. But with sharp AF filters and crystal-controlled BFOs, combined with narrow-band IF crystal filters it is clearly important that designers/constructors of factory/home receivers/transceivers should be aware of that 450-600Hz preference.

TAKING OUT D/F

The average age of Australian amateurs has been recently put at 51 years, and there seems no reason to suppose that such a figure would differ greatly in the UK. This means that most of us have lived through (though not necessarily as licensed amateurs) a period of enormous technical change and development — but not always in the basic fundamentals of radio communication, for which the entire period of 1895 to 1945 was immensely important.

I have to confess a personal interest in the specialised topic of wartime 'clandestine' portable radio transmitter-receivers which has a habit of spilling over into *TT*. In this I am not alone. For instance, Rudolf Staritz, DL3CS has put much effort into tracing information on the many different such equipments developed not only for the German Abwehr (military intelligence) service but also in the UK, USA, USSR, Norway, Denmark and Finland etc. Another is Hugh Muller, KA7LXY who was surprised to read (*TT*, January) that the clandestine Dutch Inland Radio Service (originally organised by Jan Thijssen ('Lange Jan') in anticipation of a rapid liberation of occupied Holland) operated on frequencies between 2.7 to 3.0MHz. He felt (unfortunately correctly) that this must have been "a near perfect wavelength for the enemy D/F services (Funkabwehr etc)" and needed "a good long antenna to look for" making traffic on such frequencies "a near suicide mission". Unhappily, as I have mentioned before in *TT*, this was all too true with many groups wiped out by the D/F rigs described in the book by Fritz Trenkle "Die deutschen funkpeil-und-Horch-Verfahren bis 1945", roughly translated as "German D/F and listening services up to 1945," published by AEG-Telefunken in 1982 (once again my sincere thanks to Dr Ing Hans L Rath, DLK6KG for sending me copies of this series of publications).

It is clear from this book that some at least of the mobile and portable HF D/F equipments developed for the Funkabwehr did not operate below 2.9 or 3.0MHz, a fact possibly known to the Dutch engineers. For example, the well-built, miniaturised 'suitcase' D/F equipment, type Kofferpeiler Fu H P B ku3, which could be 'worn' under outer clothing and had a miniature 'wrist-watch' indicator, covered only 2.9 to 15MHz. Unfortunately, the Funkabwehr also used some twelve "Storch" army co-operation aircraft with D/F receivers (R30) that covered 192 to 25,000kHz, and had fixed D/F stations that covered the complete MF/HF bands.

But the two operators of the Dutch Inland Service that survived from August 1944 until the end of the war in Holland in May 1945 — Jan Zandbergen, PAoZY and Jack Verhagen running the very active G11 station in and around Alkmaar, including a long spell with their station located in the nuns' bathroom of the St Elisabeth Hospital — did succeed in striking back at the D/F threat in a remarkable way. During December 1944, they observed increasing activity, in the district, of German D/F vehicles and decided to try and discover where these were based. They set out on

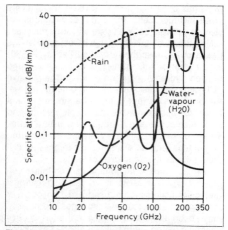

Fig 7. Attenuation of millimetric-waves by atmospheric gases and rain (medium rate). Oxygen (O_2) has a particularly sharp peak at about 60GHz, cutting signal intensity by 95% for each kilometre. Note that the effect of the various attenuations is cumulative. While rain/water-vapour attenuation varies in different climates, the Oxygen attenuation applies world-wide.

bicycles, with a bag of potatoes on the carrier of one as though collecting food from the farms — an all-too-common sight in that dreadful 'hunger-winter' during which some 15,000 civilians died of hunger. They found the D/F base at a farm at Dirkshorn, some 15km north of Alkmaar, spotting several loop antennas on the roof, covered by camouflage netting. On 30 December 1944 they transmitted the following cipher message: "Radio service threatened by newly erected German radio bearing station. Position as follows. Moving in southerly direction from the village Dirskhorn along the road leading to Oudkarspel some 550 yards along this road in meadow about 35 yards east of the road. Recognisable by two low redbrick buildings flat black roofs on which 10 circular direction finding aerials. No anti-aircraft guns."

On 6 January 1945, the RAF destroyed the farm! Later, a second German D/F base was "taken out" at Castle Marquette near Heemskerk, 15km south of Alkmaar. (Information received from PA0ZY and Dick Rollema PA0SE.) I have to admit that the December message was sent by the Alkmaar station a few days before I became actively involved with the Dutch service, although soon afterwards I had many contacts with the redoubtable Jack Verhagen, an ex-marine operator of outstanding ability who sent many messages for RvV/OD/BS even after G11 was told to discontinue the link with Eindhoven following the loss of many stations between December and February.

KA7LXY points to another category of portable HF equipment developed during the second world war: the beach-landing equipments. He gives the US Navy models as TBX to TBX-7 which used a single-valve transmitter (837) covering 2-5MHz with 500V HT from either a rotary convertor or hand-cranked generator, in a waterproofed aluminium case that (theoretically) could be floated to shore, opened and used. The TBX range were primarily for landing operations in the Pacific and as a lifeboat radio. A final model, TBX-8, which did not enter service until late 1945, used a two-stage 3A4 — 2E22 (miniature 807) transmitter with relay break-in switching.

The single-valve transmitter was AM/CW and VFO or crystal-controlled (two internal switchable crystals). KA7LXY points to an unusual feature: the power oscillator remained running and was controlled by putting a high negative voltage on the suppressor grid; keying the transmitter 'on' reduced the negative bias so that anode current flowed providing an RF output of about 25W CW or about 3W AM speech. Modulation was also achieved by controlling the suppressor bias: suppressor-grid modulation of power amplifiers was quite popular pre-war in the UK amateur transmitters and was also a feature of the RAF T1154 transmitters in conjunction with the PT15 pentode PA.

VHF/UHF ground/air/ship phone transmitters for clandestine operations included SOE's S-phone and the later OSS Joan-Eleanor (J-E) equipment with its airborne wire-recorder and an American military FM equipment on about 30MHz used by MI-6. These have all been mentioned before in *TT*. I wonder, however, if any reader could supply details of the 'Ascension' equipment developed by MI-6 for the 1944 joint US/UK/French 'Sussex' operation during which the HF CW links depended on the French QRP battery-operated MkXXI transmitter-receivers? According to Anthony Cave-Brown in his biography of Sir Stewart Menzies "The Secret Servant", some 20 Ascension equipments were to be installed for Sussex in Mosquito aircraft and flown nightly over France to receive reports from the French agents by means of 'a recording device' (wire recorder?) installed in the tail of the aircraft. As someone who went to Normandy in support of the Sussex HF operations, I would be interested to find out more about

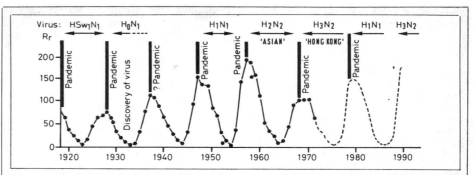

Fig 9. The yearly means of daily sunspot relative numbers compared with dates of influenza pandemics, as published in *Nature* in connection with the letter from Sir Fred Hoyle and Professor Wickramasinghe. The record up to 1971 is based on the earlier material collated by Hope-Simpson; the dashed curve has been added to show the situation betweenn 1971-89.

SUNSPOT FLU?

Sunspots have been blamed and/or praised for many things other than high MUFs. Now Sir Fred Hoyle and Professor N C Wickramasinghe have described (*Nature*, 25 January 1990) further evidence in support of the belief, first expressed by R E Hope-Simpson in 1978, that there is a remarkable coincidence between large-scale, world-wide outbreaks (pandemics) of influenza and peaks of the sunspot-cycle. **Fig 9** shows the more recent 'coincidences'. They conclude: 'It is tempting to connect the recent (November/December 1989) flu epidemic in Britain with the maximum or imminent maximum of (Cycle 22) solar activity. Although the new wave of flu and flu-like illness has not yet assumed pandemic proportions, the chances of this happening within a single complete cycle of terrestrial seasons must be reckoned to be high... we note that electrical fields associated with intense solar winds can rapidly drive charged particles of the size of viruses down through the exposed upper atmosphere into the shelter of the lower atmosphere... this could define one possible causal link between influenza pandemics and solar activity." Sir Fred Hoyle for a number of years has been suggesting that microbiological material exists in space and could have been the origins of Life on Earth. It has long been recognised that the outbreak of 'Spanish flu' in 1919 caused more deaths than the first world war — but the idea that such outbreaks might be due to solar activity is a new concept to me!

'Ascension', for which presumably a miniature portable equipment must have been developed for the agents on the ground.

FEEDBACK AND POT-POURRI

Geoff Perkins, G3VIJ spotted an unfortunate error that crept into the circuit diagram of PA0FRI's high-power 'Frinear' linear amplifier (*TT*, February, p30, Fig 3). The diagram wrongly shows the positive screen voltage connected through a 100-ohm resistor to the control grid of the lowest PL519 (pin 1). In fact, the 100-ohm resistor should have been connected to pin 3 (screen grid) and the line common to the three screen-grid pins. Apologies to readers and to PA0FRI.

John Roscoe, G4QK adds a postscript-correction to his warning (*TT*, February) that modern petrol-pumps, if deprived of mains electricity, will fail to deliver. He subsequently made enquiries from the large retail chain that controls the petrol station attached to his local supermarket and received the following reassuring reply: "In the event of a power failure, the store's emergency generator will service the main store but not the petrol station. However, our petrol pumps are able to be manually operated and we would expect business to continue although at a much slower pace... we would expect any requests for petrol by the emergency services to be given priority. Cash transactions are always acceptable."

The increasing interest in 'wireless before transistors' is reflected in the number of specialised publications and newsletters now available in the UK. These manage to maintain high standards and to dig out much information on the equipment and practices of yesteryear (not all of which were crude or primitive). A number of such publications come my way and I take this opportunity of congratulating their editors and bringing these publications to the notice of *TT* readers who may not be aware of their existence:

Vintage Wireless (quarterly bulletin of the British Vintage Wireless Society) edited by Bob Hawes. An occasional extended *Supplement* has recently been introduced. The Society's Membership Secretary is Gerald Wells who runs the fascinating Vintage Wireless Museum in West Dulwich, south London.

Radio Bygones (bimonthly) the relatively new 'glossy' magazine complete with full-colour cover illustrations edited by Geoff Arnold, G3GSR, former editor of *Practical Wireless*. Covers communications as well as domestic radios.

The Radiophile (bimonthly) edited by Chas E Miller concentrates on domestic valve radios and is now emerging in printed rather than duplicated form.

Morsum Magnificat (quarterly) edited by Tony Smith, G4FAI as the "magazine for morse-telegraphy". Due to other commitments, G4FAI, who founded the UK edition several years ago (MM originated in Holland in 1983), is anxious to hand over editorship this year.

OT News (quarterly old Timers' News) publication of the UK Radio Amateur Old Timers' Association, edited by Dennis Lisney, G3MNO.

As a follow-up to G3MLS's explanation of the 'Kelvin-Varley heli-pot substitute' (*TT*, February, p31), Nev Kirk, G3JDK relates how walking into his local junk shop recently, he found a most elegant 'Kelvin-Varley Divider'. It was in pristine condition, beautifully made in 1978 by Electro Scientific Industries of Portland, Oregon. Some 9-in tall overall, about 3-in diameter, the adjustment is with the aid of three concentric aluminium dials, each slightly less in diameter, at the top, graduated and engraved with black lettering. Purchased for an "unbelievable 50p", G3JDK is not quite sure what he will do with it, but in the meantime "it makes a wonderful shack ornament."

J P Bell, G4LSA mentions that since the circuit diagram of his battery-charger controller appeared in *TT* (October 1989, pp38-39, Fig 6) he has received a number of enquiries asking where a BT151 thyristor (SCR) can be obtained. His came ex-equipment but he points out that any modern thyristor will do provided that it is rated about 5A and 100V.   □

TOPICS

PAT HAWKER G3VA

TAMING THE STATION COMPUTER

I must confess that I have never felt any great desire to install a computer as part of G3VA — but equally I recognise that by now this is a minority view regarded by the majority in much the same way as my personal preference for brass keys and copying morse with a ball-point pen! For it is clear that the marriage of radio-communications and computers has been consummated in many amateur radio shacks — although not always without a few lovers' tiffs and tears in the process.

A useful eight-page article "Amateur Radio and Computers" by Wolfram Wagner ZS6KE (**Radio-ZS**, August 1988) was aimed at smoothing the way to happier marriages: "In our hobby very few technical innovations have gained ground as rapidly as the 'microcomputer' — the properties of these fascinating devices have cast a spell on an increasing number of radio amateurs" — as ZS6KE puts it. He outlines the differences between the 8-bit home computers (from the simple ZX80, ZX81 to the rather more complex BBC, Acorn, Commodore etc) which usually have some built-in programming, mostly in a reasonably standard version of BASIC and the 16-bit or 32-bit personal computers (IBM PC or PC-compatibles by other makers). The PC family have all the units and features of the home computers coupled with a general and more universal user level. (**Fig I**) ZS6KE believes that the 'general' nature of the PC makes it a very powerful tool for the amateur but considers that it does require a certain amount of experience before a user becomes fully accustomed to just what can be done with it. In practice, the more complex versions of 8-bit home computers can perform many but not all of the functions that the 16-bit and 32-bit PCs provide.

Much of his article is concerned with the many ways in which either the "stand-alone PC" or the "PC connected to your station" can be used on a variety of tasks and the necessary interfaces. Such material is rather outside the scope of *TT* but what does seem worth quoting at some length is his section "Considerations in the shack" (including RFI suppression hints). He writes: "The most restrictive property for the use of any digital

electronics in a radio amateur's shack is the intense RFI these devices generate. This interference ranges from VLF right up to microwaves, and above as digital electronics uses higher and higher switching speeds. For this reason it is important to ensure that the device you acquire has some commerical guarantee: FCC number, FTZ number, BS 6527 etc. (In the UK, there is still no legal requirement that computers must meet BS 6527 EMC standard.)

"Such specifications indicate the radiation limits the unit is *supposed* to satisfy. In spite of this certificate, you will find most units still radiate more than the acceptable amount of noise and you have no other option but to use all your skill (or that of your friends or acquaintances) in suppressing the noise to an acceptable level. The following are some of the ways this can be tackled:
(1) Provide a fully graded (BS/VDE/SABS etc) power-line suppressor (RFI filter) in the power cable of the computer.
(2) Ensure that external units (printers, display screens, plotters) are also suppressed by a similar power-line suppressor.
(3) Be very careful that the ground (or earth) on the different units do *not* form "earth loops" via the signal cables.
(4) Try to place *all* the equipment in the shack on a common ground-plane (steel shelving, steel desk or copper foil) which is grounded to *one common ground* (your station earth if you have one).
(5) In severe cases it may be necessary to suppress any power lines to your radio equipment (see (1)). This may also get rid of any TVI or telephone interference in your system.
(6) You may also attempt to place ferrite ring suppressors on the coaxial cable feeder to your station and in some instances even up at the junction to the antenna to choke any RFI that travels up your feeder.

Fig 1. Basic structure of a microcomputer installation. ROM Read Only Memory. RAM Random Access Memory. CPU Central Processing Unit. Mass Storage Memory (external).

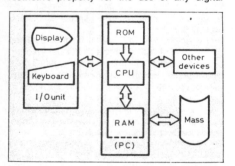

Fig 2. ZS6KE's suggested EMC measures to reduce RFI problems arising from digital equipment forming part of an amateur station.

"The easiest manner to find the source of the interference is to disconnect each unit in your shack until the interference vanishes. From personal experience I can say that display screens can be the cause of some very irritating interference. This can be suppressed by literally wrapping the case of the unit in foil (make sure that you **don't cover ventilation holes**). The more adventurous may place this screening inside the cabinet by glueing it to the inside of the cover with contact adhesive. "In homemade digital circuitry it is important to ensure that the board is constructed along the lines of good VHF/UHF designs using ground planes and plenty of decoupling capacitors on power lines. **Fig 2** shows some measures that may be necessary (not guaranteed!) to suppress RFI from your computer."

RSI, "KEYBOARD CRAMP" AND "BRASS ARM"

The past few years have seen growing concern in commerce, journalism and the Information Technology (IT) industry with an obscure and still controversial medical condition affecting some keyboard/VDU operators — the fact that cases have occurred in the computerised newsrooms of newspapers and broadcasters has ensured that this condition has been widely reported by the media. Commonly called RSI (repetitive strain injury) or "occupational overuse injury" or, by the medical profession, "upper limb disorders", it does appear to be the re-emergence of what many years ago was known as "telegraphist's cramp" or, more colloquially as "brass arm" that in the 1920s affected a small minority of professional line and radio telegraphists using up and down brass keys and a smaller number of teleprinter keyboard operators. In spite of the evidence that accumulated over many years of this medical problem, many doctors still refuse to accept that RSI really exists — but firms are being forced to take the condition more seriously since the award in an out of court settlement of £45,000 to a bank employee who spent much of her time using a computer keyboard under strain inducing conditions.

Telegraphist's cramp was no joke — in severe cases experienced operators lost completely the ability to manipulate a morse key and, in its final stage, "telegraph operation becomes a matter for dread and the emotional repercussion may be such that the touch, sight or even memory of a telegraph instrument and its working may induce intense apprehension, tachycardia, tremors, hyperidrosis or loss of emotional control" — to quote from a long, unpublished, monograph written in the late 1930s by Colonel H V Prynne, CBE, DSO, FRCS a retired Chief Medical Officer of the GPO, a typescript of which I recently unearthed in the Post Office Archives, London.

I recall from the 1940s a former marine Radio Officer then working as a civilian for Special Communications who was suffering from "brass arm" to the extent that he could only be allocated listening watches for clandestine stations that were no longer expected to come up on schedule. It had become virtually impossible for him to send readable morse and he had become what was then known as a "bundle of nerves". Although there seems little evidence of amateurs using morse keys or keyboards being affected by brass arm, it could well account for why some former CW enthusiasts decide to abandon the key for the microphone.

Recently, *The Independent on Sunday* (25 February 1990) devoted a whole page to RSI and a new document being issued by the Health and Safety Executive: "Work Related Upper Limb Disorders: A Guide to Prevention." This reflects advice from ergonomists, medical experts and representatives from trade unions and employers' bodies. It is suggested that the problem primarily

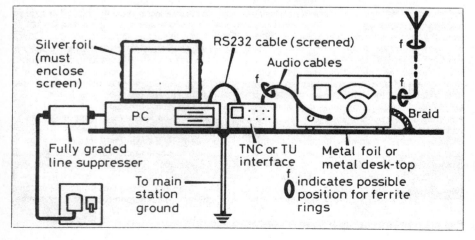

SIMPLE RS-232C TO KEYING-LINE INTERFACE

John Swancara, WA6LOD in *QST* (February 1990) reports the use of a cheap and quick computer-to-keying line interface as follows: "While experimenting with my Tandy 1000 home computer and some ham code generation programs, I learned that the computer's RS-232C DTR line switched from +14 to -14V when the programs executed the code. In about one hour, with a few radio shack parts, I built the interface shown in **Fig 3**. It works great and easily keys my transceiver. I now send perfect CW!

"When the Tandy 1000's +14/-14V DTR signal switches to -14V the optocoupler's LED turns on the output transistor, pulling the circuit's output line low. If you need a circuit that goes low on positive excursions of the input line, just reverse the 1N914 diode and the connections to pins 1 and 2 of the optocoupler. If keying your rig involves switching a higher voltage than the optocoupler can handle, you can control a DC relay with the optocoupler and key the rig with the relay."

If you prefer an all-solid-state solution rather than using electromechanical relays, an article in the same February issue of *QST* describes "Simple Control-Signal Level Converters" on pages 24-27.

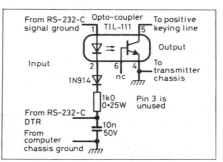

Fig 3. WA6LOD's RS-232-C-to-keying-line interface requires only four components on a piece of scrap copper-clad circuit board.

affects people who do relatively monotonous, repetitive work while in a fixed position: the risk factors appear to be bad working posture, high frequency of hand movements couple often with a degree of forceful exertion and poorly organised work processes.

Col Prynne suggested that "Telegraphists Cramp is a disease of the central nervous system, and is the result of a weakening or breakdown of the cerebral controlling mechanism in consequence of strain upon a given set of muscles, characterised by visible spasm of hand or arm during the manipulation of a telegraph instrument and by the impairment of the power of making the required co-ordinated movements. Before any cramp or spasm is apparent there may be a stage characterised by subjective symptoms only, where the operator feels pain or discomfort in the operating hand or arm." A feeling of stiffness or loss of control "as if the muscles would not do what was required of them" or undue apprehension was sometimes the first symptom.

In the 1920s, the GPO employed some 20,000 male and female land-line telegraphists sending and receiving telegrams at working speeds of around 25wpm. Col Prynne investigated some 313 cases that appeared in the years 1921-30 and considered an additional 147 cases that had been reported between 1905-1920. Of the 313 new cases, some 168 responded to treatment directed at re-establishing the confidence of the operator — often after a period of complete rest from telegraphy. He estimated that about 2 per cent of GPO telegraphists were affected at some time (many within two years of qualifying). He sought information from other countries. Several, including the USA (where brass keys were not commonly used), reported only negligible numbers of cases, but Norway replied that over 5 per cent of their operators suffered manipulative difficulties in the form of 'telegraphists' cramp'. With the phasing out of hand-Morse and the introduction of teleprinters, the number of cases in the GPO dropped dramatically but did not disappear entirely. The GPO authorities, however, (as apparent from correspondence in the archives) were anxious that if Col Prynne found a publisher for his monograph, all references to teleprinter-operator's cramp should be deleted!

Col Prynne clearly recognised that the condition could be produced by either physical or psychological causes. Yet it is only recently that modern RSI is not being written off as psychosomatic. This all adds up to an inducement for amateurs to ensure that their operating "environment" provides comfortable, relaxed operating conditions — and

perhaps a reason to avoid over-intense extended periods of strain-inducing operating such as can arise in some contests. Such advice applies not only to CW and keyboard systems but even with hand-held microphones — at least one sufferer from RPI claims that she cannot pick up a fork or hold a telephone instrument without pain. Nor does one have to be a "senior citizen" to be affected by upper limb disorders — remember that the GPO found that many of their young telegraphists could be affected within the first two years of qualifying.

BALANCED ATU FEEDS OPEN-WIRE LINES

TT has frequently pointed out that the radiating element of a doublet or dipole antenna fed by an open-wire transmission line does not itself have to be of resonant length in order to radiate efficiently — always provided that the complete antenna system is brought into resonance by being correctly matched to the transmitter. The high SWR that can exist happily on open-wire, low-loss feeders (though *not* between the ATU and the transmitter) is demonstrable proof that very little of the energy reflected back down such a feeder (so setting up the SWR) is lost but subsequently is radiated from the element. With an effective ATU and open-wire feeder a 132ft centre-fed dipole does not (contrary to the still

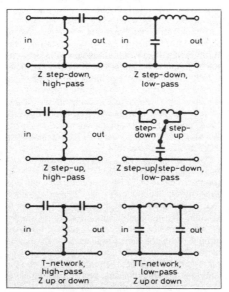

Fig 4. Basic unbalanced RF matching networks.

often held belief) radiate significantly more power on 3.5MHz than would say a similar dipole with an 80ft top fed with the same transmitter output power. Equally important is that such an 80ft dipole, with suitable ATU, can radiate very effectively on any frequency from about 1.8-30MHz (or higher), although the horizontal and vertical radiation patterns will differ.

Richard L Measures, AG6K in "A **Balanced** Balanced Antenna Tuner" (*QST*, February 1990, pp28-32) points out: "Now that we have nine amateur radio bands below 30MHz (not all harmonically related) an open-wire line, centre-fed-wire antenna system looks even more attractive than it did when such antennas first came into popular use in the 1930s when we had only five bands (all harmonically related) below 30MHz, viz 1.75, 3.5, 7, 14 and 28MHz). Taking advantage of this versatile system requires a box that will interface the 50ohms unbalanced output of today's transceivers to the highly variable impedance (Z) of the balanced feed points of such multiband antennas."

He considers, however, that most of the contemporary "matches everything, balanced or unbalanced" antenna tuners produce only a semi-balanced output when used with a balanced load. This, he suggests, can result in a less than wonderful situation: "Antenna tuners are like shovels. It takes more than one kind of shovel to perform a variety of jobs effectively ... no single antenna tuner circuit can do every antenna-matching job extremely well. A balanced-load tuner should be designed — from the ground up — for the job it is intended to perform." He describes an ATU specifically designed for feeding open wire, ladder-type, transmission lines on a variety of frequency bands, stressing that this arrangement **(Fig 5)** cannot (or at least should not) be regarded as suitable for unbalanced loads such as a coaxial cable or for end-fed Marconi or Hertz antennas.

His tuner depends on a choke balun made from a length of coaxial cable wound on a plastic-pipe former. With a 3·5in diameter pipe, about 30ft of 50ohm cable should form an effective balun at frequencies between 1.8-30MHz. If 1.8MHz is not

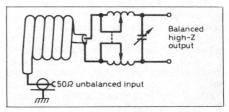

Fig 5. AG6K's carefully balanced ATU for feeding multiband wire-doublet antenna via open-wire feeders. The ATU is capable of feeding a wide range of reactive impedances but not intended for use with unbalanced feeders or end-fed antennas. Physical and electrical symmetry and balance should be maintained.

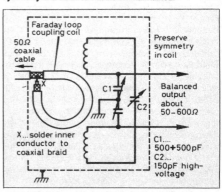

Fig 6. Low-cost balanced ATU which in the past has proved useful for feeding 300-ohm or 600-ohm matched balanced feeders on 14/21MHz with pi-network and Faraday-loop coupling coil.

required about 18ft of cable should suffice. The ends are fastened to the pipe using nylon cable ties. Solid dielectric cable is best for this application. Layout and components should be arranged to maintain good RF balance; good symmetry is important on the higher frequency band. Unless you have two identical roller-coaster inductors in your junk box, such a tuner will be quite costly to implement with new components although costs can be reduced if you can find a source of surplus-MoD components etc. The variable inductors need to be driven in synchronism by one tuning shaft. A less flexible but lower cost unit could be made using tapped inductors with switched selection of the taps. An even cheaper arrangement which has been used at G3VA for feeding 300ohm folded dipoles on both 14 and 21MHz with a single split coil and pi-network is shown in **Fig 6**. This uses a Faraday loop type of balun which also helps reduce harmonic output.

MORE ON FET POWER AMPLIFIERS

Recent *TT* items on the use of low-cost audio and switching FETs as amplifiers capable of providing up to about 50 watts of RF output (eg *TT* February 1990, December 1989) have prompted Tim Walford, G3PCJ to report on the results achieved in the past two years with two such amplifiers: one using IRF510 devices from 12V supplies; his preferred second method using VN88AFD devices from a 35V supply. He writes: "My first experiments were with the IRF510 because it was/is the fastest of this family of devices having low 'on' drain-source resistance (Rds(on)) and thus suitable for use from 12V supplies. With four of these devices in a parallel push-pull arrangement **(Fig 7)** I have obtained 50W pep on 3.5MHz with 1 watt of drive using a 12V supply. Parallel operation is possible with these devices and they are relatively destruction-proof! I do however recommend that the DC bias is arranged always to be applied **after** the antenna relay has connected the load; this is the purpose of the large value capacitors on the gate/bias line. Broadband operation is possible using untuned toroidal transformers.

"This amplifier is suitable for 1.8 or 3.5MHz but not for 7MHz or higher-frequency bands. The layout is not too critical and the capacitor between the drains helps dramatically to improve the waveshape of the output. The gate bias voltage is adjusted to provide the best compromise between maximum output and minimum distortion (typically about 1A for all four devices). If the drain capacitor is omitted some (although much reduced) RF output is possible at 7MHz; it was this limitation that led me to use the VN88 series of devices in the amplifier shown in **Fig 8**; this is my current design for use up to 30MHz. The VN88 devices have a much higher Rds(on) than the IRF510 and need a higher supply voltage. Both these types of devices are relatively inexpensive (about £1.20 per device) and I feel that it is unnecessary to incorporate any form of ALC in these amplifiers, provided that the output load is tuned up at low power or with a bridge that restricts the range of impedances presented to the amplifier. Good heat-sinking is very important since the FETs operate near to the limit of their power ratings. I have mounted both versions in tobacco tins with the heatsink on the outside; the tins form an excellent ground plane. The VN88 design dissipates rather more power than the IRF510 due to the device's higher Rds(on). The better heatflow properties of the VN88AFD in the T0220 package is to be preferred to the more commonly available VN88AF (all four VN88AFs blew on one occasion and were replaced by VN88AFDs).

"The VN88 amplifier is very similiar to the IRF510 design except for the supply voltage and

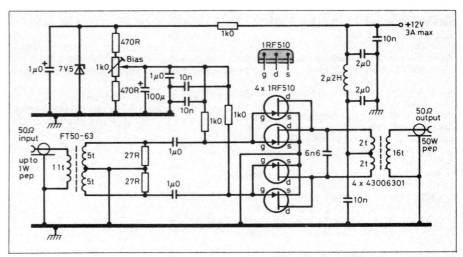

Fig 7. G3PCJ's broadband RF amplifier capable of providing 50-watts PEP output on 1.8/3.6MHz from a 12V supply. It uses four IRF510 devices in a parallel-pushpull configuration. Bias control set for about 1A (total) standing current.

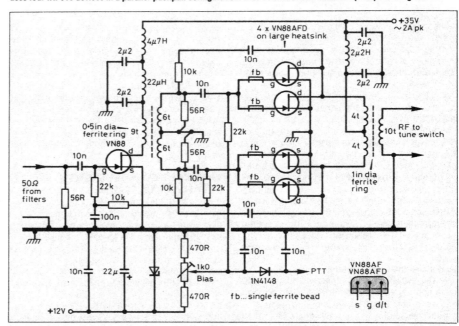

Fig 8. G3PCJ's "Mk II" FET amplifier capable of use to 30MHz. It provides about 50W PEP output from four VN88AF or (preferred) VN88AFD devices from 35V supply. Bias adjusted for a standing current of about 0.75A (total).

output transformer. Because the drain voltage of the VN88, when 'on', is about 10V, a supply of up to about 40V may be used while still keeping within the rated 80V Vds limit. Since, in my case, I crammed boths stages into one tin, stability was more critical than would otherwise have been the case; I found some negative feedback was required — but other constructors might find it possible to omit the 10k resistor/10nF capacitor between gate and drain. In this design, the diode to the PTT line kills the DC bias as soon as the switch is released, thus reducing the chance of damage when the antenna relay opens (I use a PTT switch between +12V and relays to earth.)

"Both amplifiers have been extensively used, but I now favour the VN88AFD design owing to its greater bandwidth. These devices will work to even higher frequencies than 30MHz provided that a low gate-driving-impedance is used to counter the high gate-input-capacitance. Incidentally, I do not believe that a highly-regulated supply is required since the devices must not be allowed to 'bottom' since this causes RF clipping, harmonics, splatter etc. Any residual ripple from a simple bridge-rectifier/smoothing-capacitor PSU is rejected by the RF output "transformer."

Tim Walford, G3PCJ recognises that these

notes may be a little cryptic to those without a very great deal of previous experience of building FET amplifiers. He is more than willing to assist in suggesting sources of components, etc (Telephone Long Sutton (045824)n 224 or (with SEA) Upton Bridge Farm, Long Sutton, Langport, Somerset).

POT-POURRI

Ray Hill, GM0IJF apologises that the outline of his battery-charger (*TT*, January 1990, Fig 9) could have proved misleading since with the polarities shown it would switch 'on' instead of 'off' when the battery voltage rises. He has sent a full circuit diagram (**Fig 9**) of his charger which has served him well for a considerable time: "In **Fig 9** the 33K resistors at the inputs of the 741 op-amp allow me to put the reference zener-diode *and* the feedback on to the non-inverting input of the 741. The 33k resistors and the 22µF capacitors were originally put in to get rid of picked-up noise, which seemed rather bad in my case."

NTT, the Japanese telephone company, has stopped using lithium rechargeable batteries in mobile radiotelephones after an accident which injured a user, following a short-circuited battery. Firms in this field are expected to stick to nickel-

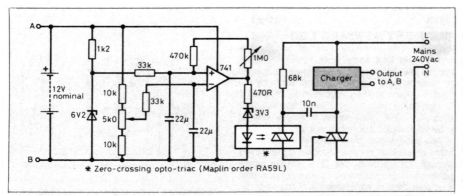

Fig 9. Circuit details (with corrections) of GM0IJF's lead-acid battery charger controller (see January *TT*, p35).

cadmium rechargeables in the near future — Noted in *ABU Technical Review* (January 1990).

A *QST* article points out that when using a vacuum-variable-capacitor it is important to realize that the maximum RF-voltage rating at 30MHz is usually only 60 per cent of the rating for DC or 60Hz AC peak-voltage rating. Thus a 5kV DC/60Hz rating is roughly equivalent to a 3kV peak RF rating. Used or surplus vacuum capacitors need to be checked before use since they may have developed an air leak that renders them useless.

G3KSU is concerned that amateurs should be at least extremely circumspect in considering promotional material and advertisements for an American "automatic antenna matcher" (priced at almost $500 for a 150W rating) which, in effect, seems to be based on using a dummy load to bring the transmitter SWR down with only a small proportion of the power diverted into a non-resonant short antenna. Remember the old tag "let the buyer beware" and study the explanations carefully.

BOUNCING BEAUTIFUL RF SINE WAVES

The long-term future of amateur radio clearly depends on arousing and maintaining the interest of young people in the art and craft of radio communication — something that at present we seem to be failing to do. We need, perhaps, to think more carefully about just why the hobby (or specific parts of it) has been able to retain the interest of so many of us for so many years. In *QST*, Eric Nichols, KL7AJ puts forward an individualistic view that may not be so far off the beam:

"Just about my entire career, as a broadcast engineer and active amateur, has been devoted to the generation of RF energy. I can think of little else I'd rather do. And yet I have discovered that most of the people who do what I do are at least a generation older than I am . . . Good RF engineers are almost impossible to find. Industry is wondering where the next crop of technicians and engineers will come from.

"Why has this discipline of radio — at one time the very heart of electronic technology — come to the point where people consider it an arcane science? I have been forced to consider what first attracted me to radio during my formative years. I liked radio because it was *aesthetically* appealing. I was not nearly as impressed by the capabilities of radio as by the very nature of radio. Radio is great, not because of what it does, but because of what it is. Nobody buys an original Da Vinci painting to cover a hole in the wall. By the same token there are other means of communication that are more efficient than bouncing signals off the ionosphere; but the very fact that we can bounce signals off the ionosphere makes it worth the effort. "Maxwell's equations appeal to the body, soul and spirit. Sine waves are veritable works of art. Antenna radiation patterns are beautiful. "It is incumbent upon radio initiates to convey the mystique and aesthetic

aspects of our hobby to newcomers. To fail to do so is to doom our hobby and the radio profession to the status of a lost art."

It is apposite to recall that "PP" Eckersley, (G)200, the first Chief Engineer of the BBC (1923-29) and a Vice-President of the RSGB, once admitted that his attachment to "wireless" as a schoolboy from 1906 onwards was, at least initially, an emotional one; brought about by his delight in the then colourful artefacts — the bright green coils, the black ebonite panels, the brass switches and morse keys, the crackle of the spark coils. This was rather than the deeper scientific interest of his brother T L Eckersley who became an outstanding research physicist and unravelled many of the mysteries of HF propagation.

LOW-POWER 12V-TO-30V DC/DC CONVERTER

By using a 555 IC "chopper" working at about 100kHz and a voltage multiplying diode rectifier arrangement, it is possible to build a simple converter **(Fig 10)** providing a stabilized 30V DC output at about 30-40mA when powered from a 12V car battery. This design comes from the February 1990 issue of *Electronics Australia* as a means of powering an *EA* 144MHz 1-watt transmitter (November 1989) from a single 12V source. (In this equipment the 30V line is required only for the LM351/LM308 audio amplifier, the RF circuits being fed directly from 12V or, in the case of the VXO, from a regulated 5V.) It is stated that the arrangement of **Fig 10** can deliver up to about 13mA from an 11V supply, increasing to 28mA at 12V and 43mA at 13V.

The solid-state inverter and/or switched mode PSU is today the accepted method of powering equipment from a variety of sources — AC mains, low-voltage DC — to provide almost any required output voltages and powers. In this respect, solidstate technology has taken over completely from former mechanical conversion techniques that today have lapsed into history, but were in

common use up to the mid-1950s. For car radio receivers and low-power "suitcase" transmitter-receivers, the 6V and 12V "vibrator units" provided chopper frequencies of around 100Hz and could in fact be surprisingly efficient (up to 90 per cent or so conversion efficiency). Unfortunately vibrators suffered from limited lifespan, mainly because the contact points tended to become pitted and to stick — a problem that could sometimes be overcome by subjecting them to a sharp tap on switch-on. Repair was sometimes possible by filing the points and adjusting the spring tension and gap, but such measures usually afforded only temporary relief.

It is worth remembering that for all equipment operating at low input voltages, the main on/off switch has to carry a relatively high current, and any resistance introduced by dirt or oxidation, or caused by arcing, can drastically reduce the efficiency of the unit. This applies to solid state inverters as well as those relying on mechanical devices such as vibrators. Where powers of from about 30-watts upwards were needed for portable or mobile transmitters, the usual solution was a rotary conversion machine. This could be a rotary transformer (ie dynamotor) with a single armature, wound with two separate windings, each connected to a commutator at either end, and excited by a common field system. Any DC ratio could be obtained with a suitable ratio of turns in the windings, but overall efficiencies were lower than for vibrators, often delivering from 50 to 500 watts with overall efficiencies ranging from about 50 to 60 per cent.

Whereas a rotary transformer (dynamotor) is a DC to DC device, a rotary converter converts DC to AC and vice versa. It has a single armature winding, from which tappings are connected to slip-rings at the AC end of the machine and to a commutator at the DC end. The AC/DC transformation ratio is fixed by the number of phases and is equal to root-2 for a single phase machine. The motor generator was perhaps the most versatile of the rotary converting machines, and may still be used for high power installations. It consists of a motor driving a separate generator on a common shaft: it is possible to design machines for any voltage ratio, DC to AC, AC to DC, or to change AC from one frequency and voltage to another frequency and voltage, at virtually any power.

DR PAUL EISLER — "MR PCB"

It has been said that every industry has its visionaries, but that ideas, like wine, must be given time to mature. True enough, but unfortunately one result is that many of the great inventors and innovators never receive the public recognition they deserve for their pioneering work. One such is Dr Paul Eisler who in 1943 was the first person to patent the now almost universal form of printed circuit board — an idea he had pursued for years

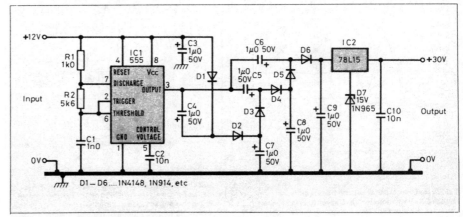

Fig 10. Low-power 12V-to-30V DC/DC converter using 555 IC "chopper".

but which remained little used for more than a decade — despite the efforts of John Sargroove in the immediate post war period to advocate the use of printed wiring for simple, low cost radio receivers for developing countries. Walter Frolic, G0CAO draws attention to Paul Eisler's recently published *My Life with the Printed Circuit* (Associated University Presses, London 1989, 170pp, hard covers £13.95).

Austrian born Paul Eisler came to England in 1936 at the age of 29 years becoming, after the Anschluss in effect, a Jewish refugee. Even while working in Austria, he had become convinced that it should be possible to replace wiring in radio receivers with printed circuits, but like so many other inventors, could not get commercial backing for his ideas. In the UK, he joined Oscar Deutsch's Odeon Theatres as an "ideas man" but in 1940 was, for a time, interned as an enemy alien. When released he set to work on printed circuits in an attic flat. To demonstrate the principles he built a first printed circuit radio receiver which still exists, but was also convinced that PCBs could find application for military applications. The Americans took up the PCB as the basis for the first truly microminiature (Tinkertoy) device, an anti-aircraft proximity fuse that in 1944 enabled many hundreds of V1 "flying bombs" to be shot down before reaching London. With the coming of peace, Paul Eisler tried to interest the mass consumer product industry. It was not until about the mid-1950s that PCBs eventually took off. Even then the path of the inventor was not smooth. Boardroom clashes and quarrels with Government ministries led to resignations. Eisher, at 82, is still an active inventor, with more than hundred patents to his credit.

EXTRA DIODES PROVIDE IMPROVED VOLTAGE-DOUBLER

Dick Rollema, PA0SE in his "Reflecties door PA0. SE11 column (*Electron*, p122) draws attention to an improved voltage doubling circuit that ofers better regulation and less pronounced ripple to the more conventional cascode-type voltage doubler (*TT*, November 1989). This was originally described by the Swiss engineer TH Gisper in *Elektronica* 89/22. With this arrangement, the full voltage

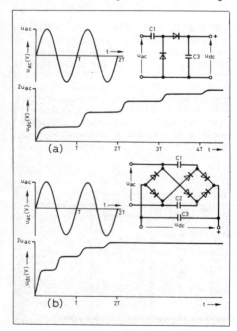

Fig 11. (a) Conventional cascode-type (common terminal) voltage-doubler. (b) Improved arrangement using extra diodes in a bridge-type (symmetrical) arranged as originally described by a Swiss engineer.

CURRENT SENSING LED

Indicator lamps, whether filament or LED, are widely used to indicate when voltage is being applied to an appliance; but very few are arranged to sense whether current is being drawn by the load. A contribution by R Love in the "Circuit & Design Ideas" column of *Electronics Australia* (February 1990, p68) shows a simple way of providing an LED current sensor: **Fig 13**.

Operation is straightforward. When current is being drawn from the device socket, current flows through the silicon diodes, D1 to D3 during the positive half-cycles of the AC mains input, providing a voltage drop of approximately 0.7V per diode. With the three diodes in series this results in a pulsed DC voltage of about 2.1V across the LED through a 10ohm resistor to limit the current through the LED to about 40mA peak on positive cycles half cycles. The fourth diode, D4, shunts the LED during negative half cycles, protecting it from damage while at the same time providing a further current path for the appliance.

Sensitivity of the circuit is determined by the

output is built up over a single 50Hz cycle instead of the two cycles of the conventional cascade voltage doubler: sea **Fig 11(b)**. With an input of 240Vac, the unloaded peak DC output is approximately 675V. Regulation is governed by the value of the electrolytic capacitors, although the values can in practice be lower than for the conventional doubler.

D/F GROUND-WAVE HF SIGNALS

In the April *TT* brief mention was made of the mobile D/F vehicles used by the German Funkabwehr in their attempts to trace clandestine transmitters that operated during 1940-45 in virtually all of the occupied countries of Europe.

In Germany, the Telefunken Company was encouraged to develop a relatively high performance, battery operated direction finder, type P57N. This was in production from 1935 until

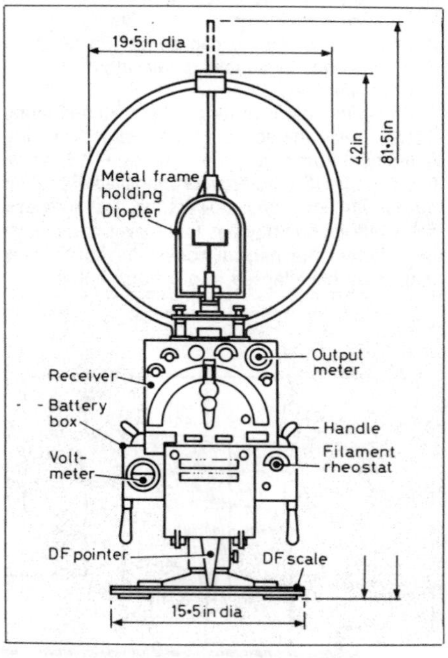

Fig 12. The Telefunken P57N "portable" HF direction-finder as produced from 1935 to 1942. This equipment was widely used in wooden-sided 'delivery' vans by the Funkabwehr in their pursuit of the wartime clandestine radios in occupied countries.

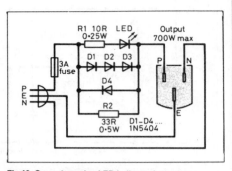

Fig 13. Current-sensing LED indicator for mains-powered appliances.

value of R2 which also "prevents operation due to RFI suppressor capacitors or transformer primary windings in some loads." Since the circuit operates at the AC mains potential, all components should be totally enclosed in a suitable, insulated box, to ensure that no contact can be made by the user with mains potentials.

1942. Although described as "portable", the complete unit, when packed in a special box and with canvas cases for the tripod used in the open air, weighed what must have been a back breaking 192lb (87kg)! The P57N **(Fig 12)** had a six-valve battery superhet receiver with three interchangeable coil-assemblies covering 3-6, 6-12 and 10-20MHz. Mounted above the receiver was a 50cm diameter loop and an auxiliary (sense) rod antenna that extended a further one metre above the top of the loop. When set up in the open air, the bearing scale was orientated optically using a "diopter" sighting device similar in principle to those used on prismatic compasses.

For Funkabwehr operations the P57N was installed in a wooden framed van and could be used stationary or on the move. It was intended for use on ground wave signals at distances up to 30km from the transmitter, giving reasonably accurate bearings when well sited, but was subject to errors when used in towns. The P57N was described in *Wireless Direction Finding* by Major R Keen who was later responsible for engineering the D/F network established by the Radio Security Service (MI8c). Even in 1938, he showed a clear understanding of the difficulty of quickly locating clandestine transmitters, when he wrote: "The response of a closed-loop D/F in a city street to the radiation from a horizontal aerial on a 100ft high building some streets away is likely to display 'aeroplane effect' in its most virulent form with excessive errors. (Aeroplane effect is experienced where an abnormally polarized wave is radiated from the trailing aerial of an aeroplane; when arriving at a D/F station with an angle of incidence less than 90° can produce errors which vary from 0° to 90° depending on the degree of polarization.) The only method of locating such an aerial — after its approximate position has been found by long-range bearing using a D/F that is not susceptible to polarization error — is by averaging of a very large number of bearings using a portaable loop. "In the final stages of such a search, the D/F may be made up in suitcase form and taken to the roofs of buildings or to any point from which it seems likely that a bearing can be obtained... Ground-ray D/F in city streets may also be affected by poor signal-to-noise ratio in certain areas, due to the attenuation of the signal in its passage over and through the semi-conducting masses in its path. SNR is, on the other hand, maintained at a high level and for greater distances over the sea, or well clear of the earth's surface."

FLEXIBLE CW AUDIO FILTER

Albert Roehm, W2OBJ in '75Hz-wide audio filter' (*Ham Radio*, January 1990) presents a simply-constructed CW filter with several novel features: **Fig 1**. In brief, the 741 is wired as a dual feedback bandpass amplifier with a Q of 10 and a gain of 4. With this Q only one rather than the several stages of most op-amp active filters is used but with an arrangement to counter 'ringing'. The result is a sharper and improved shape factor, according to W2OBJ. R1 adjusts the centre frequency to match the receiver offset (typically 700-800Hz) and can be pre-set unless your rig has BFO adjustment. The second stage is a comparator (one section of an LM339) whose output is low if the signal applied to pin 5 is lower than the bias on pin 4. The flat top of the passband guards against ringing because pin 2 remains at a constant high level. R2 varies the bias (threshold) level of the comparator, determining the bandwidth. A second section of the LM339 is used to adjust the comparator's bias. Its input is connected to the first op-amp to sense the same audio signal and threshold setting (points X and Y). The output switches an LED to indicate threshold setting; the LED follows the incoming code signals which may, or may not, help you read the code. R3 provides a volume control, with R4 providing any required blend of unfiltered to fully-filtered audio.

IMPLEMENTING VEROBOARD LAYOUTS

Chris Budd, G0LOJ has found the following procedure a useful way of designing Veroboard layouts from circuit diagrams. He writes: The system consists of producing a grid of black lines on a large sheet of white paper (preferably A3-size paper) to mimic the pattern of tracks and holes on the Veroboard in such a way that each hole corresponds to the centre of a square cell of the pattern, and then following this procedure:

(1) Place the sheet 'pattern side down' on top of a sheet of white paper of the same size. Unless the paper chosen is unusually thick, it will be possible to see the pattern through the paper.

(2) Mark the component positions, the necessary track breaks and the necessary wire links in pencil on the **blank** side of the sheet using a mixture of conventional circuit-diagram symbols and outlines of the shapes of components. I have found it useful to:

(a) Mark track breaks faintly (in case they have to be erased later) in pencil.

(b) 'Temporarily-isolate' each device as it is added to the drawing with a set of track breaks which can be erased later if necessary. This trick makes it much easier to keep track of what is supposed to be connected to what.

(c) Number the pins of each IC as it is added to the drawing.

(3) When all the devices, track breaks and link wires have been marked, place the sheet on a wooden surface and use a sharp instrument to pierce the paper at the centre of each track break.

(4) Turn the sheet over and mark each track break (now identified by a small hole in the paper) in pencil on the pattern.

(5) Cut the Veroboard to size, and make the necessary track breaks on the Veroboard on the basis of the markings on the patterned side of the drawing.

(6) Now turn the drawing over (ie patterned side down) and place it against a light surface so that the pattern of tracks, the positions of the devices and the positions of the wire links can all be seen at once. Assembly is then straightforward.

The necessary patterned sheets of A3 paper may easily be produced using a ruler, an ink pen and a photocopier. Though the idea is very simple, I have found it extremely effective and a great saver of both Veroboard and temper!'

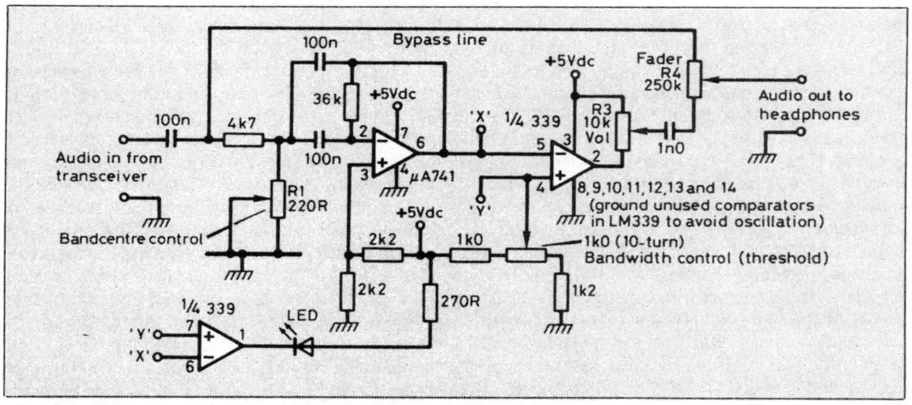

THE MECHANICS OF STABLE OSCILLATORS

S M Dyke, G3ROZ comments on the continued difficulty of implementing a KISS approach when it usually ends up with having to make a band-switched VFO stable enough above 20MHz to permit satisfactory SSB operation: 'Anybody who thinks *that* is simple either hasn't tried or has a guardian angel smiling down on him. With the temperature variations found in a garden-shed shack it is very difficult; for mobile operation near-impossible. I have tried often with varying degrees of non-success!

As *TT* has noted before, a major problem with any LC oscillator, no matter how loosely the resonant circuit is coupled to the amplifying device(s), be it valve or solidstate, is the temperature-coefficient of the tank circuit components, particularly the coil. 'Pol' Parrott, G3HAL noting the February *TT* comments on the original Franklin master oscillator (as used for many years in the Marconi range of 'SWAB' high-power HF transmitters) points out that their high stability depended as much on the mechanics as on the electrics. As described and illustrated in the classic '*Short Wave Wireless Communication*' book by Ladner and Stoner, the Franklin master oscillator was built around an elaborate arrangement designed to provide self-compensation of the resonant circuit against temperature variations. Few people would attempt to implement such an arrangement today (with the ready availability of ceramic capacitors having a variety of temperature coefficients both positive and negative). Briefly it depended on the selection of materials used in the coil former/mounting so that as the coil warmed up (increasing its inductance) an end plate moved away from a second plate reducing the capacitance. In the late 1920s and 1930s a number of temperature-compensated inductors were developed; see, for example, chapter 9 of '*Theory and design of valve oscillators*' by Dr H A Thomas (Chapman & Hall, 1939), a book which also gave detailed information on the mechanical properties of dielectric materials used as coil formers etc. The Marconi Franklin oscillators were used in transmitters that had to meet an overall stability of better than ±1 in 25,000 from which, as G3HAL points out, we may infer that the stability of the Franklin oscillator with its mechanical tuned circuit was better than this.

G3ROZ decided to investigate how Rowley Shears, G8KW and his firm KW Electronics succeeded in making reasonably stable VFOs in the valve era — despite being a firm that eschewed high-cost 'one-off' components and systems. He looked inside his KW Atlanta VFO and found that the formers appeared to be cut-down electric fire elements! He writes: 'You have to hand it to KW Electronics. What a perfect off-the-shelf former for a high-stability VFO. Oh, they had been cut down to nearer 'coil former' lengths and were likely to have been made specially as coil formers for KW but, none the less, they looked as though they had come straight from the Belling Lee

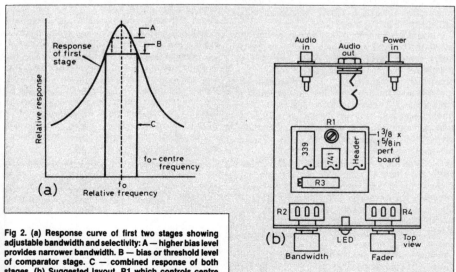

Fig 1. Circuit diagram of W2OBJ's narrow-band audio filter (*Ham Radio*)

Fig 2. (a) Response curve of first two stages showing adjustable bandwidth and selectivity: A — higher bias level provides narrower bandwidth. B — bias or threshold level of comparator stage. C — combined response of both stages. (b) Suggested layout. R1 which controls centre frequency should be a panel control if you have an adjustable BFO.

factory! Mind you, the firm had still worked hard to achieve good stability. One trimmer had five different temperature compensation capacitors across it! But the 'Belling Fire' former is a tip worth noting. Try the car boot sales!'

24MHz DUAL-LOOP HALF-SIZE CHIREIX-MESNY

In view of recent items on the classic Chireix-Mesny antenna (*TT*, February and April) with its arrays of half-wave dipoles arranged in squares (each square 2-λ perimeter), I was interested to note in 'Ham Radio Techniques' by Bill Orr, W6SAI (*Ham Radio*, January 1990) a 24MHz antenna described as a 'dual quad-loop antenna' but which could equally well be considered as a half-size Chireix-Mesny array using ¼-λ rather than ½-λ sides: **Fig 3**. Such a design would be effective also on even harmonic bands, eg a 24.9MHz double-loop would probably work well on 50MHz.

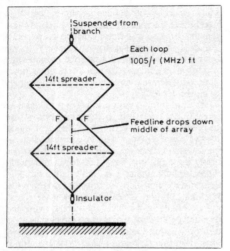

Fig 3. K4BLT's dual-loop 24.9MHz antenna. This is in effect a half-size Chireix-Mesny array on 24.9MHz and should work as a full-size array on 50MHz.

W6SAI writes: 'A single vertical quad-loop makes an effective antenna. It has the radiation pattern of a dipole and provides an additional gain of approximately 1.2dB. The quad loop has a very broadband response and a feedpoint impedance of about 120 ohms. Place two of these loops in phase and feed them at the common point, and you have Jeff O'Connell's K4BLT dual-quad loop antenna. Jeff's antenna is cut for the 12-metre (24.9MHz) band. It's suspended from a branch of a pine tree. Two oak spreaders, 1¼-in square and 14ft long form the diamonds. The pattern is bidirectional and the gain is estimated to be about 3.5dBd. Polarisation is horizontal.

'The antenna is fed at the centre with a coaxial line. The feedpoint impedance is very close to 50 ohms. The line is wound into an RF choke at the feedpoint. The choke consists of four turns of coaxial 5-in in diameter. This helps keep RF off the outer shield. Bring the line down the middle of the array, as shown.'

MORE FET AMPLIFIER HINTS

Roberto Craighero, I1ARZ was interested to see in *TT* (February 1990, p30) the IRF511 8-watt and IRF530 50-watt FET power amplifiers stemming from Wes Hayward, W7ZOI and Jeff Damm, WA7MLH as originally published in the 'Technical Correspondence' column of *QST*, November 1989. Additionally W7ZOI also used the IRF511 in the 10-watt add-on booster for his 1 watt SSB/CW transceiver, as noted in the April *TT*. I1ARZ wrote to Wes Hayward seeking some constructional information on the IRF511 amplifiers. In reply,

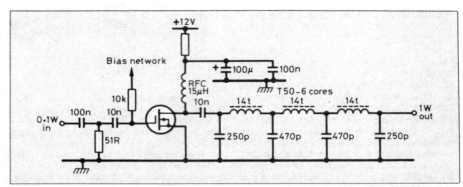

Fig 4. The 1-watt output stage of W7ZOI's compact 14MHz transceiver using IRF511 FET. Corrected by W7ZOI from a diagram in November 1989 *QST*.

W7ZOI provided some helpful ideas which I1ARZ feels may be of interests to others now keen on exploiting these relatively low-cost devices. W7ZOI wrote:

'The FET amplifiers are very simple and not especially critical. Jeff and I always use PCB material for our circuits. However, the boards are rarely etched. Instead, the board is used merely as a low inductance ground. An IRF511 is mounted on a small heat sink which is then fastened to the board with insulated hardware. The source lead is soldered directly to the board, maintaining a short lead length. Lead lengths are kept short elsewhere, but are not as critical as the source lead. We usually build using "ugly" methods, as described in an article that my son and I wrote and published in *QST* in August, 1981.'

W7ZOI's 1981 'ugly' concept, as noted in *TT* May 1982, is based on the use of 'old-fashioned' point-to-point wiring rather than the use of etched PCBs. He confessed that 'The one place where I find etched boards to be worthwhile is for circuits containing many digital integrated circuits which are terribly boring to build without a PCB. Even there I have used "ugly" methods for many digital projects. The DIP IC devices are placed on a ground plane, like a dead beetle with legs pointing upward. Some pins are bent to hit the ground foil and soldered. Others are soldered to bypass capacitors. The combination then fixes the "pills" in place, providing support for the rest of the circuitry. About half of the frequency synthesiser I use in my present (1982) receiver is built this way.' For many 'one-off' and prototype experimental projects etched PCBs are an unnecessary complication and make it more difficult to introduce changes and modifications. This, of course, is not to deny the usefulness of PCBs to constructors wishing to duplicate exactly published designs rather than to evolve their own.

But to continue with W7ZOI's reply to I1ARZ: 'While the "ugly" methods work well, perforated board should **never** be used in RF applications unless it is the only thing available. Scrap circuit board material is preferred. The ferrite core is not too critical in the amplifiers that Jeff and I have built, for we are not operating at high power. The transformers are easy to build if you are only transforming down to 12 ohms from a nominal 50 ohms. We usually use the Amidon FT-37-43 core, or something similar.

'Note that there was a mistake in the November 1989, *QST* article. The correct transformer winding is shown in Fig 1, *TT* February 1990 for the 8 watt amplifier. The December 1989/January 1990 *QST* articles on the SSB transceiver had the basic box running 1 watt output with an IRF511 with an external amplifier delivering about 10 watts. There was a missing resistor in the 1 watt RF power amplifier in that rig. The correct circuit is shown in **Fig 4**. It should be possible to get 1.5 watts (as desired by I1ARZ) from this amplifier if you increase the standing current from the 25mA I

used to perhaps 35 or 40mA, and if you use a slightly modified output network. The output filter I used presents 50 ohms to the drain. Design a double pi network that, instead, presents about 30 or 40 ohms to the drain. No output transformer is needed in such a low power amplifier. My amplifier peaks at about 250 to 300mA, although the average current is lower. The IRF511 is really very easy to use and I'm sure you will have no trouble.'

20W PUSH-PULL FET LINEAR FOR 50MHz

In *TT* (May 1990) it was noted that the Siliconix VN88AF and VN88AFD power FETS are capable of giving useful output above 30MHz despite the high input capacitance of such devices. With a push-pull pair of VN88AF devices, V P Hill, GW4HDF obtains a useful 20 watts output from a 30V supply line when driven by a 500mW output transverter. He writes:

'After completing the transverter, it was necessary to build an amplifier to boost the linear RF output. The prime requirement was to achieve lowest possible cost without excessively compromising performance. Consideration was given to the popular combination of 2N6080 driver and 2N6082 power amplifier, as used in a number of well-known 50MHz designs. However the combined cost of these two bipolar devices would have been over £30. My choice fell on the VN88AF VMOS FET which is capable of switching 2A in five nanoseconds with a maximum dissipation of 15 watts, readily available at around £2 per device. As noted in the May *TT*, for a maximum power output and efficiency, a supply line of 30V is required,

SWITCH-TRICK

There are quite a few applications where it is essential to switch one circuit 'on' before another. **Fig 5** shows one way of doing this: whichever double-pole switch is closed first, circuit A-A will be completed before circuit B-B since B-B requires both switches to be closed. Similarly, whichever switch is turned 'off' first, circuit B-B will be broken first. The idea comes from an item in the Russian magazine *Radio* (2/90) although, with a Russian text in the Cyrillic alphabet, I have no idea what application the writer had in mind for this switching arrangement.

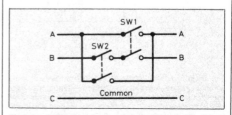

Fig 5. A switching arrangement that ensures A-A is always "on" before B-B and "off" after B-B.

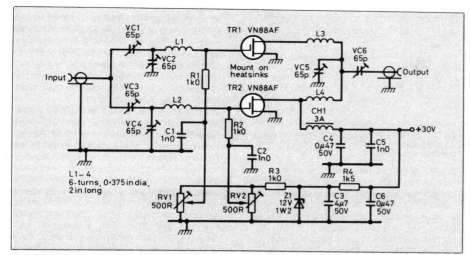

Fig 6. GW4HDF's 20-watt push-pull VN88AF FET linear for 50MHz

although the devices will work at 12V with substantially reduced output. The circuit I used was evolved from information supplied by Siliconix: **Fig 6**.

'The amplifier was built on a piece of double-sided copper-clad board measuring 5in by 3.5in. Both sides are used as a groundplane and must be shorted together in as many places as possible. Insulated posts were used as component lead supports. Layout is left to the individual constructor, but as in any VHF project lead lengths should be kept as short as possible.

'For alignment, a dummy load is connected via a power meter to the output socket and a 30V supply connected. VR1 and VR2 are adjusted for 100mA quiescent current per FET. Drive is applied to the input socket and VC1 to VC6 adjusted for maximum output. Drive is then increased until the power meter measures 15 watts, VC1 to VC6 are again adjusted for maximum output, with the current now of the order of 1A. If a spectrum analyser is available, VC1 to VC6 should be adjusted for lowest intermodulation distortion (IMD) at maximum output.

'This amplifier design has been in service at GW4HDF for about a year without any problems being experienced. Reports over the air have been good, and no adverse comments received. But, as with any amplifier, the output signal can only be as good as the signal put in. Care must be taken to avoid overdriving the amplifier; this is easily done since only about 500mW of drive is required for full output. A 144MHz version has been designed and constructed using similar VN88AF devices. In this case, neither efficiency nor gain is as high as for the 50MHz amplifier; however 10 watts output has been obtained with an input of 2 watts.'

D-I-Y GRAY-LINE GLOBES

In *TT* (August 1989, p36), Colin Horrabin, G3SBI drew attention to the value of Columbus Verlag 'planet earth' globes in enabling an amateur to determine the times and dates during which "gray-line" (dawn-dusk, dawn-dawn and dusk-dusk) propagation paths are likely to open between the UK and specific parts of the world — paths of particular importance to those seeking DX contacts on the lower-frequency MF/HF bands. Unfortunately, 'Planet Earth' globes, although available in the UK, are not exactly cheap — with the 13.5-in diameter model priced at some £130.

John Cronk, G3MEO, finding that there are some very reasonably priced internally-illuminated plastic globes sold by, for example, W H Smith and Woolworths, felt it should be possible to fit a shield in such a way as to cast the correct night-time shadow and so form the basis of a d-i-y gray-line globe.

He writes: 'Initially, I hoped to fit the shield inside the globe. In practice I was not able to install a suitable mechanism through the lamp hole. But having started this train of thought, I realised a very simple alternative by which the gray-line throughout the year can be visualised, as well as some other useful amateur-radio data. It is simply a suitably marked-out cardboard disc on which the base of the globe is positioned. The principle can be used with any globe provided it has the tilted (23°) type of mount. 'Construction: A pointer mark is required on the base in line with the support arm, eg the direction to which the North Pole tilts. This is used to set the date. The cardboard disc, which has a second disc glued concentrically as a centring guide, should be marked out in months, weeks and even days (forget leap year!). Start by marking the summer and winter solstice (June 21 and December 22) and the vernal and autumn equinox (March 21 and September 22). These marks will be at right angles to each other. Then fill in the rest of the dates with January to December running anti-clockwise: see **Fig 7**.

'Next, calibrate the globe around the equator in GMT. Start with 1200 on the Greenwich meridian,

Fig 7. How GW3MEO lays out his rotatable disc for the D-I-Y gray-line globe.

1100 to the right (Africa) and 2400 on the International Date Line. These times can be marked with the aid of suitably prepared labels, and it is also useful to mark these labels so that the international time differences can be read off: ie 1300 (-1), 1400 (-2) etc to 2400 (+12) etc. I found some suitable printed labels by cutting up a small map from an old pocket diary. Incidentally, the longitude lines on my globe were 10° apart but the hourly marks must be positioned 15° apart. As a final check on the geometry, when the date pointer is set to June 21, the North Pole should be enjoying 24 hours of daylight.

'*Operation:* The disc is placed with the summer solstice line (June 21) facing the viewer whose eye should also be at the centre height of the globe. The base pointer is set to the appropriate date and the time mark (GMT) should face the viewer. Dusk will be in line with their vernal equinox and dawn the autumn equinox. A ruler placed vertically at these points initially may help but it is quite easy to visualise the illuminated area of the earth. The disc can also be calibrated with the meteorite showers that the earth passes through during its annual journey round the sun and a graphical indication of their relative intensity (rate), names and other data. Fig 7 is based on a copy of my Mark II disc. Perhaps someone with artwork and printing facilities could prepare and run off some copies.

'The foregoing comments take longer to explain than to carry out. While D-I-Y gray-line globes may not be as precise or as visually attractive as "Planet Earth" globes they will do the job quite well. I realise that as well as the gray-line globes there are a computer program and a clock-driven wall map on the market, but they cost much more than the above scheme and I doubt if they can be run forwards and backwards as easily.'

MORE ON GELL CELLS

Dave Lunn, G3LSL, with reference to the item in the March *TT* ('Battery power system' p30), supports ZS6UY's advocacy of float-charged car batteries in the shack as a sound approach to powering either HF or VHF equipment, adding: 'One useful tip, which avoids any risk of a leaking battery case causing damage to carpets or floor-boards is to stand the battery in a plastic bucket.

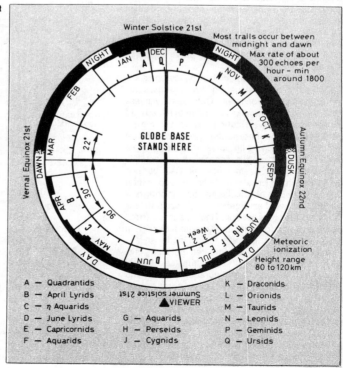

A — Quadrantids	G — Aquarids	K — Draconids
B — April Lyrids	H — Perseids	L — Orionids
C — η Aquarids	J — Cygnids	M — Taurids
D — June Lyrids		N — Leonids
E — Capricornids		P — Geminids
F — Aquarids		Q — Ursids

DIRTY DC CHARGING OF DISPOSABLE BATTERIES

M Clift, G3UNV draws attention to a recent write-up on a new battery-charger being marketed by Wellgood Electronics that is claimed 'to put new life into disposable dry zinc-carbon and manganese-alkaline batteries, allowing them to be re-used several times.' Although the magazine suggests this is a 'new invention' with the charger using 'a carefully-controlled DC current, modulated by a special wave to avoid conditions which lead to either evolution of gas or enhanced zinc electrode corrosion' one cannot help feeling, as G3UNV points out, the basic principle may well reflect the 'dirty-DC' type of charging, as advocated for zinc-carbon (Leclanché) dry batteries as long ago as October 1955 (*Wireless World*). This article noted that dirty-DC charging originated in the Netherlands. Joe Cropper, G3BY, brought the idea to the notice of *TT* readers in the 1960s (subsequently included in *ART*) when he reported that he had found the system very effective in reactivating the lantern-type cycle batteries, that he used on the old 'Low power Field Day' contests, up to five times using a very simple mains-charger with no filter capacitors, half-wave rectification and a resistor (200-250-ohms) wired across the diode: **Fig 8**. But, as far as I am aware, the item on the Wellgood charger is the first to point out that this approach also applies to high-energy manganese-alkaline cells.

In *ART*, I coupled the notes on dirty-DC charging with some advice from the US National

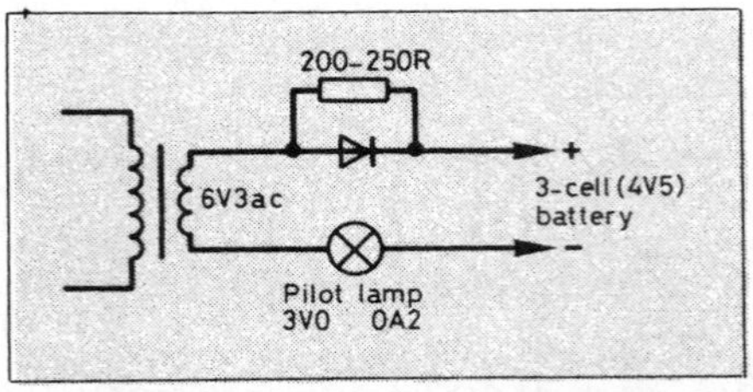

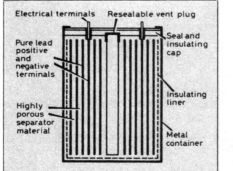

Fig 8. Simple "dirty-DC" charger for reactivating Leclanche-type dry batteries. Values shown for 4.5V three-cell lantern-type battery.

Bureau of Standards which noted that, even without a dirty-DC waveform it is usually possible to recharge carbon-zinc batteries (this was issued before alkaline batteries had become established) in some circumstances, provided that care was taken to avoid the risk of explosion of sealed cells:

(1) The operating voltage on discharge should not be below 1.0V per cell when the battery is removed from service for charging.

(2) The battery should be placed on charge very soon after removal from service.

(3) The ampere-hours of recharge should be 120-180 per cent of discharge.

(4) Charging rate should be low enough to distribute recharge.

(5) Cells must be used soon after charging as the recharged cells have poor shelf life.

NBS added: 'In general, recharging of dry cells may be economically feasible only when quantities

of dry cells are used under controlled conditions with a system of exchange of used cells for new ones already in practice, and with equipment available to provide DC for charging. Recharging of cells which are not specifically designed for charging can be dangerous since excessive amounts of gassing from too high current may cause a tightly sealed cell to explode.'

While in the long-term, rechargeable nicad or lead-acid cells are the most economical way of powering hand-held transceivers and similar equipments, the high cost of nicad battery packs mean that dry cells are often used; where this is the case the possibility of getting perhaps five or more charge cycles must make dirty-DC charging very attractive: similarly for many of the portable HF 'short-wave broadcast' portable receivers and 'scanners' which can sink a lot of current. Running costs of over 20p/hr are common for such receivers. The sales departments of battery makers tend to dismiss as 'impossible' the idea that you can recharge dry batteries — but they would wouldn't they?

The Wellgood recharging unit is designed so that popular sizes of cylindrical dry cells can be inserted between spring clips. It is stated that 'the technique will apparently not work with poorly-made batteries, or with those that have been fully discharged over a long period. Voltage characteristics of recharged dry batteries differ from those of the original cells, and internal resistance can actually be reduced after about five cycles.'

Most of the standard-sized car batteries of around 50Ah capacity will fit snugly inside the rectangular plastic buckets on sale in any hardware shop.

The March *TT* also discussed briefly the cylindrical 'Cyclon' rechargeable Gel-type sealed lead-acid cells with thin pure lead grids coated with lead-oxides and separated by an absorbent, fibreglass mat: **Fig 9**. This type of cell/battery, made by Gates Energy Products Inc in the USA, is marketed in the UK under various brand names including Chloride, RS etc. Such cells form the basis of a six page article by W Max Adams, W5PFG 'Briefly Speaking: Gel Cell Batteries' (*CQ*, February 1990) based in part on information from Gates. This form of sealed lead-oxide cell provides a nominal 2V (disconnect load when this drops to 1.6V) and are available in the UK with capacities (based on ten hour discharge rate) of 2.5Ah (dimensions 61mm high by 35.5mm diameter) 5Ah (46mm by 72.5mm dia) and 25Ah (158mm by 67.4mm dia). Typical discharge curve shown in **Fig 10**.

W5PFG provides information on typical constant-voltage chargers, including fast chargers for returning a discharged cell to full capacity in less than four hours. He makes the point that lead acid batteries can enable a station to remain on the air, at least for a short time, during a power cut or in an emergency, enabling an operator to report into a regular net or keep a scheduled contact. He writes: 'A $5.00 fleamarket Gell Cell bargain battery is only a trivial investment to keep several thousand dollars of whistles and bells tooting and ringing in case of emergency! Six D-size 5Ah Gell Cells provide over one hour of intermittent transmit/receive power for both my Kenwood 7950 (7Ah load) and 144MHz repeater (6.5Ah load).'

It should always be remembered that Gell Cells, like other high-energy cells, are capable of delivering dangerous short duration currents and care must be taken to prevent direct short circuits which can result in excessive cell heat, burns, fire or explosions. Although 'sealed', Gell Cell batteries should be operated in a well-ventilated environment. Do not wear metal rings or metal watch straps etc when working on powered equipment (short circuits can result in serious burns to the wearer).

As with nicad batteries, there can be problems with Gell Cell batteries brought about by relatively small differences in the capacity of the individual series connected cells: discharging a cell completely, to zero volts, can cause polarity reversal; this can usually be overcome by making several complete, normal charge/discharge cycles.

When more than four cells or batteries are operated in parallel, steering diodes and individual fuse protection should be provided. The arrangement shown in **Fig 11** is advocated by W5PFG who writes: 'The charge diode and fuse prevents shorted cells from shunting and accepting all the charge current; the discharge diode prevents shorted cells from discharging other parallel-connected cells. The fuse rating is selected by $I(F) = 2I(C)max/X(B)$ where $I(F)$ is the individual fuse current rating in amperes; $I(C)$ is maximum charge current in amperes; and $X(B)$ is the number of parallel-connected cells.

'When a number of cells are charged in series, use a C/500 maximum trickle rate where C is the capacity of the cell (battery) in ampere-hours. Since the same current flows in all the series-connected cells, trickle charging tends to balance the charge of each cell. For standby power applications, Gell Cells should be maintained at 2.35V (±0.05V) with float (trickle) charge. Rates

Fig 9. Typical construction of a Gel Cell.

Fig 10. Typical discharge curve of a Gel Cell.

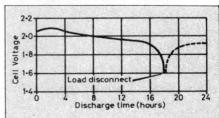

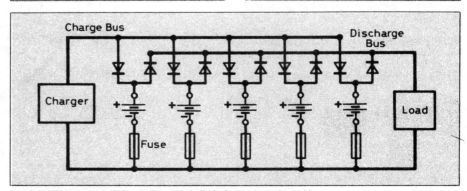

Fig 11. Multi-battery parallel operation with individual steering diodes and fuses.

above 2.4V per cell should be avoided in order to prevent excessive plate corrosion. An overcharge rate of 0.001C is sufficient to maintain a 2.35V charge, after a high charge rate is complete.'

OZONE NO-GO-ZONE

Not so many years ago one could still find among the electronic devices on the consumer market a number of 'ozone generators', reflecting the idea that ozone was associated with the bracing atmosphere of the seaside where a similar odour to ozone is produced by rotting seaweed: ozone, O_3, is an unstable form of oxygen in which the molecule contains three rather than two atoms. It is generated during high-voltage electrical discharges, for example during thunderstorms. But, far from being beneficial to health, ozone is now recognised as a toxic gas. Exposure for two hours to concentrations as low as 1.5 parts per million may result in coughs and excess production of sputum; while 30 minutes in 50ppm can even be fatal!

New Scientist (7 April 1990, p26) draws attention to the fact that desktop laser-printers and xerographic copying machines both produce ozone since both rely on high-voltages to make the toner stick temporarily to a print drum before its transfer to paper. While such machines usually have filters containing activated carbon to break down the ozone, few users seem to be aware that in time these filters tend to become less efficient, especially if they become clogged with dust. Few instruction books warn of the need to use machines in areas where there is adequate ventilation or the need to replace clogged filters. Apparently the Health & Safety Executive is taking further steps to make this problem known to office-workers and to encourage makers to give more information on replacing filters.

This matter could be of concern to those radio-amateurs who use a laser-printer in a relatively small and possibly poorly ventilated shack. If you smell that 'seaside' atmosphere watch out!

HERE & THERE

J G Wroe, G4IUJ writes: 'If there is anybody else out there still grinding or etching crystals they may be interested in the method I use to calibrate them. I removed the 4.194304MHz (2^{22} Hz) crystal from a quartz clock and wired the crystal of unknown frequency in its place. This made the clock run at the wrong speed. By allowing the clock to run for about 24 hours and comparing clock-elapsed-time with real-elapsed-time, the frequency of the crystal can be calculated: Crystal frequency (Hz) = elapsed time on clock multiplied by 2^{22} divided by elapsed real time.'

P Harrad, G8UN was not impressed by the reaction of the local BT field engineer to his complaint that after having his old dial-type, carbon-microphone telephone replaced by a push-button 'Tribune' plug-in instrument, he found that every time he transmitted on 3.5MHz the new telephone rang unless he reduced power to under about 10 watts. The BT engineer brought his investigation to a singularly unsatisfactory conclusion by claiming: 'It's your equipment that's at fault — it wants suppressing'. G8UN then solved the problem by simply removing the telephone plug while transmitting. More recently he wired a telephone extension socket in his kitchen (a run of about 14m) and then discovered that, even without the extension phone being plugged in, the original problem vanished. He wonders whether the extra wiring could be acting as some sort of a stub? Nothing else has been changed. My own guess is that the leads may be acting as a bypass capacitor. □

25-AMP POWERMATE PSU (35-AMP PEAK)

Recent *TT* items have tended to emphasise the attractions of powering 12V transceivers from float-charged lead-acid vehicle batteries which can form an economical source of the high peak currents involved in SSB operation. However, with say a 100-150W transmitter and a maximum charge rate of about 4-5A, it is difficult to maintain over extended periods anything like a constant voltage supply with a high transmit duty-cycle or with FSK/CW type modes. Then even with a plastic bucket (as suggested by G3LSL in the June *TT*) there may well be objections to having a spillable acid electrolyte in the domestic environment.

There thus remains a demand for heavy current mains PSUs. With the tendency for higher-power barefoot black-boxes these need to be able to deliver up to 25A continuously and relatively droop-free peaks of around 35A. This represents a pretty tough specification for a home-built PSU and is essentially a more costly approach (unless you have suitable components on hand) than a vehicle battery. A deceptively simple-looking French design by FC1JEK in *TT*, October 1989 promised 20A maximum using components that may not be readily available in the UK.

Mark Cheeseman in *Electronics Australia* (January 1990) presents a new project in the magazine's series of 'Powermate' units; the highest power to date: this is the 'Powermate 25' capable of providing 25A continuous with maximum peaks up to 35A: **Fig 1.** It is protected by both foldback current limiting and an over-voltage crowbar circuit working with a re-settable contact breaker 'fuse'. He points out that modern practice is for amateur-radio transceivers to be designed for 13.8V operation with an external PSU which can then be used to power several rigs simultaneously provided that not more than one transmitter is operating at the same time (the receiver sections take relatively little power). While most professional computer installations use heavy-current switching-mode power units, these tend to have a rather 'noisy' output, requiring considerable filtering to reduce the noise to an acceptable level when used to power a sensitive receiver. For home constructors another problem is that it is not easy to obtain suitable high-frequency transformers which 'are

TECHNICAL TOPICS

PAT HAWKER G3VA

difficult (read expensive) to source in small quantities.'

Another technique is to use a switching regulator-type supply with a conventional 50Hz transformer, rectifier, filter and using switching techniques to convert the unregulated DC supply to the desired voltage: 'This still has the problem of output noise and the more one tries to reduce this noise, the more the efficiency tends to suffer' — to quote Mark Cheeseman.

For these reasons, the Powermate 25 design follows similar lines to the lower current PSUs in the Powermate series except that it uses two mains transformers and two bridge rectifiers in parallel to reduce the problems and stresses that would be involved with single heavy-current components. By using two identical transformers and bridge rectifiers the load is shared equally between them.

Like the other Powermate units, it is based around the LMC723 regulator chip which provides a temperature-compensated voltage reference, error amplifier and current limiting circuitry in a single package. However, the PSU has quite a long chain of command between the 723 and the six 2N3055 pass transistors. The 723 controls directly TR9, a BD681 darlington-type device which in turn controls the base current of TR8 (MJE2955). Resistors R2/R15/R16 ensure that their respective transistors turn off when they are supposed to, as the drive supplied by the stage preceding each of these transistors is capable only of providing current to turn the next transistor 'on', not 'off'. Resistors R9-R14 effectively sum the individual voltage drops across the current equalising resistors to ensure that the current-limiting is not compromised by the failure of a single pass transistor. IC2 serves to increase the sensitivity of the current limiting device in the 723 connected to pin 2. ZD1 provides a reference voltage for the voltage-limiting crow-bar arrangement provided by TR1, TR10 and associated resistors RV2/R22/R23. A 32A contact-breaker (GEC 'Super switch' or equivalent) is opened by the crow-bar; if this

happens the CB can be reset unless there is a fault condition. A short-circuit across the output should cause the output to drop to about 5A protecting the pass-transistors/transformers/bridge rectifiers. Those connecting leads required to carry up to 35A should be of substantial gauge to prevent voltage drops from mounting up.

Electronics Australia presents the Powermate 25 as a complete constructional project with a kit available from Dick Smith Electronics priced at $(A)249 without a cabinet or $(A)450 total, compared with commercial units costing around $(A)700. Among the component specifications listed are a 120mm cooling fan; six 0.1ohm 5W resistors (R3-R8); three 500ohm ten-turn trimpots; four 135mm lengths of 25 by 25mm angle aluminium — one of these is to mount each of the transistor heat sinks vertically; a thyristor (SCR) NO29 RH05 (25A), Radiospares 261-520 or equivalent. Incidentally it would seem that *EA* now reaches the UK by bulk air-mail since copies now turn up around the beginning of the month of issue. But *Ham Radio* has reverted to sea mail.

COMPUTER-SIMULATED ANTENNAS

TT has referred on a number of occasions to the important development during the past decade of effective computer-software based on the so-called Numerical Electromagnetic Code (NEC) using the very sophisticated mathematical 'Method of Moments' procedure originally formulated, although not as a computer program, by R P Hartington in 1968. As I have stressed elsewhere (for example *Electronics World + Wireless World*, November 1989, pp1119-20): 'NEC has opened a new era in antenna analysis and design that is quickly overtaking the costly, time-consuming and not always reliable use of model antenna ranges, permitting the paper design of practical antennas systems, determining and modifying the directivity, gain, input impedance and radiation patterns.

'The original NEC software, developed in the USA, required the use of a mainframe computer and was thus of limited appeal to field engineers. However about 1982, the US Naval Postgraduate School in California wrote a simpler MININEC program for use with readily available personal computers.' **Fig 2.**

Successive programs have been aimed at making the programs more user-friendly, although this has usually meant accepting rather more constraints and limitations on the problems that can be tackled. One of the professionals who have been particularly active in showing how MININEC can be used by the more technically-minded amateurs and students to tackle practical problems has been Dr Brian Austin, G0GSF/ZS6BKW of Liverpool University. He has shown convincingly that, properly used, MININEC computer programs can successfully 'model' many of our basic antennas including inductively-loaded short-monopoles, capacitive end-loaded wires, simple forms of Yagi-Uda antennas based on wire elements, linear travelling-wave antennas, corner reflectors, including questions arising from the interaction of antennas with metal supporting masts. He concluded a professional paper presented at ICAP89 as follows: "MININEC can be used with confidence to model a variety of antenna configurations given its constraints in terms of the number of wires and segments available."

G0GSF has also published a long paper on the value of these programs in teaching students to understand the basic principles of antenna design and analysis: 'A simulation exercise in antenna analysis using MININEC' *(Int. J. Elect. Enging. Educ.,* Manchester University Press, 1989, pp355-366). This shows how students can achieve reliable and meaningful results using MININEC

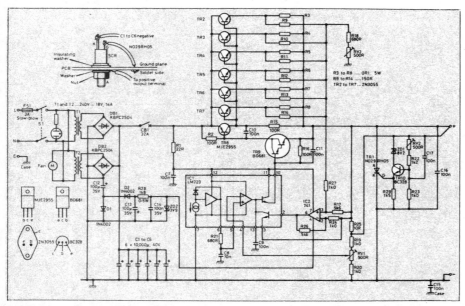

Fig 1. Circuit diagram of the 13.8V, 25A (35A peak) 'Powermate 25' power supply unit which shares the load between twin transformers and bridge rectifiers. Also shown is the suggested mounting detail for the thyristor (SCR) used as an over-voltage crowbar. As it conducts only briefly until the 32A contact-breaker (CB) opens, it can be mounted directly on the PCB. Internal or external conductors required to carry up to 35A must be suitable for this purpose.

(Electronics Australia)

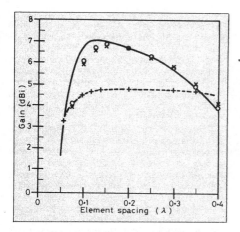

Fig 2. As part of his work on the validation of MININEC computer antenna simulation, Dr Brian Austin, G0GSF plotted the effect on forward gain of the reflector-to-radiator spacing of a two-element Yagi antenna. This diagram shows the results using MININEC (rings), the MININEC version developed by D M Pozar (crosses) and the curves based on the work by J L Lawson, W2PV (solid line) and the 1977 study by Peter Viezbicke (plus signs). The NBS study based on the use of 400MHz model antennas is clearly the odd man out giving excessively low maximum gain — a fact that was deduced many years ago by Les Moxon, G6XN from the original 1930s study by Dr George Brown (RCA) on close-spaced Yagi arrays (see *TT* January and April 1978). The MININEC and W2PV curves correspond very closely with classic theory. If the 7dB maximum gain seems high for two elements remember to subtract 2.1dB to give the answer in dBd (reference to a dipole).

software on a personal computer: 'Whereas a computer-based simulation exercise is not a substitute for full-scale measurements, the ability to model or simulate complex antennas is becoming particularly important to both student and researcher alike. Problems which were previously intractable or for which no closed-form analytical solutions existed can now be solved by iterative or other numerical techniques on the computer.'

It should perhaps be stressed that the use of MININEC software is not something that one would recommend to the average amateur experimenter who would be happier following published designs or the ideas and techniques described by Les Moxon, G6XN in *HF Antennas for all Locations* (RSGB, 1982).

Another well-known amateur who has become a firm believer in the value of MININEC programs to professional and advanced-amateur designers is Dr Ian White, G3SEK: see 'MININEC antenna modelling on a PC' *EW+WW* (December 1989, pp1214-1216). In this article he drew attention to 'an enhanced, user-friendly version of MININEC 3 is available for $80 and is the best buy for general use — details Brian Beezley, K6STI, 507½ Taylor Street, Vista, California 92084, USA.' But although convinced of the value of such software *if properly used*, G3SEK is alarmed to find that some firms have begun making claims for the performance of their antennas that appear to be based on misapplication of MININEC procedures.

Dr White writes: "One of the exhibitors at the recent RSGB National Convention advertised a compact HF beam with a gain of no less than 11dBd, with MININEC computer analysis used to prove it! I think this calls for some comment.

"The gains of HF antennas have always been notoriously difficult to measure, so it is a good thing that computer programs such as MININEC are now readily available to anyone who takes antenna design seriously. Used with care, these programs can provide gain and pattern predictions which are more accurate than any amateur measurements. The MN program (a further development of MININEC by Brian Beezley, K6STI) also makes it easy to predict the performances of antennas over 'real' ground. But take care in interpreting the results . . . !

"*TT* and other commentators have gone to great pains to inform readers about inflated claims for the gains of beam antennas. For example, a VHF antenna with a gain of about 11dBd would require a boom length of almost one wavelength. Conventionally, VHF beams are measured or modelled in a free-space and gains in dBd are referenced to a half-wave dipole likewise in free space. Yet one exhibitor at the Convention/Exhibition was showing MN predictions to verify a claimed gain of 11dBd for a compact HF beam with a boom length of only 0.3λ. Is this the antenna breakthrough we've all been waiting for? Sorry, no. The answer is that the HF beam was being modelled over ground. Unless

the ground conductivity is very poor indeed, *any* horizontally-polarised antenna picks up an additional 6dB of ground-reflection gain at its most favoured wave angle, compared with the same antenna in free space. In these terms, even a half-wave dipole has a gain of 6dBd!

"I would stress that this is not the fault of the antenna modelling program; MININEC programs are intended for skilled users who can take such results in their stride, and will mentally knock 6dB off all predicted gains over ground. But it seems that the apparently high gains shown on the computer printouts have brought a gleam to the eyes of the marketing man, and thus created a new fashion for what can only be regarded as artificially inflated gain figures.

"In all probability the HF beam being advertised at the NEC Convention is a good antenna, having benefited from computer-aided design. Certainly the predicted patterns looked good, and that means a lot in an HF beam array. Subtracting 6dB from the claimed gain to give the conventional free-space gain relative to a real comparison dipole brings the probable gain to about 5dB — quite respectable for a compact beam but nothing spectacularly out of the ordinary."

ARMY LOW-PROFILE LOOP ANTENNA

Quite a few compact transmitting (magnetic) loop antennas can be heard these days on the amateur bands putting out respectable signals for their small size. This approach has also been taken up recently by the Royal Signals in the form of a dismantable, rectangular loop designed and manufactured by British Aerospace (Dynamics) Ltd at Filton, Bristol.

At an IEE Colloquium, David Griffiths and Alan Baker of BAe described how this loop has been designed to provide both high-angle, near vertical incident skywave (NVIS) and effective ground-wave propagation for two-way communications between mobile sites (vehicles, helicopters etc) at ranges up to 300km (with minimum or no 'skip zone') on frequencies between 1.5 and 12MHz. Traditionally, military tactical HF communications have depended on 3-4m vertical whips which give good ground wave signals up to about 30km but very little NVIS radiation. This has meant that for ranges over about 30km it has usually been necessary to erect a low horizontal dipole; for the lower night-time frequencies resonant half-wave dipoles need a large site; short non-resonant dipoles can be used but require more complex matching units that often need considerable operator experience to achieve good results. Again, dipoles cannot be fitted to mobile platforms. A transmitting loop can overcome these problems provided that careful attention is given to the fundamental problem of the extremely low radiation resistance of any compact loop.

In their colloquium paper 'A low profile loop

antenna for communications using NVIS', the authors outline the basic considerations and component selection necessary to reduce loss-resistances to a minimum; describe a capacitive-type (automatic) tuning/matching network; and the result of trials of a 2m x 1m (rectangular) loop and tuner unit fitted to a Land Rover and coupled to a standard 50W HF transceiver. The tests with this loop showed once again that it is virtually impossible to design a single loop that is effective over more than about an octave range of frequencies (eg 7/10/14MHz amateur bands). This has led to the design of a loop formed from lengths of 1¼in diameter aluminium tubes) with slide-fit joints that can be assembled either as a 2m x 1m rectangular loop usable from 2 to 10MHz (but with low-efficiency below about 5MHz) or a bigger 'night-frequency' loop (3m x 2m) for use between about 1.5 to 5MHz: see Fig 3.

Calculated values of the voltages across and currents through the tuner network capacitors (Fig 4) underline the demanding specification that must be met by these components. With 200W input to the 2m x 1m at 2MHz the peak voltage across the series capacitor (120pF) will be about 3.8kV while the shunt capacitor (1300pF) has to carry an RF current of 62 amps! With this type of all-weather loop, gas filled or vacuum capacitors become virtually essential for professional applications.

While I am not convinced that amateurs would be wise to take the British Aerospace approach (the I1ARZ approach in the February 1989 *Rad Com* seems more suitable), it is nevertheless interesting to study the results of the trials etc. With the original 2m x 1m loop, trials during the day showed that the loop achieved much the same performance as existing tactical antenna systems. However, adequate night-time performance was not achievable because of the need to use low frequencies to facilitate ionospheric reflection of NVIS waves.

It was concluded that: "the gain could be improved only by increasing the size of the loop, at the expense of mobility. Discussion with typical

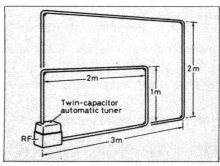

Fig 3. The British Aerospace 1.5 — 12MHz transmitting loop antenna using 1¼in diameter aluminium tubing that can be fitted together to form 2m x 1m or 3m x 2m loops etc.

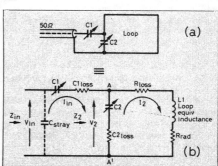

Fig 4. (a) Practical matching/tuning unit with series and shunt capacitors used as the basis of the automatic tuning unit. (b) Equivalent circuit emphasising the importance of using low-loss components.

THE 'COUNTERPOISE' REVISITED

For many years the word counterpoise virtually vanished from the vocabularies of amateur radio antenna designers. The once-popular technique of using a single or multiple wire in lieu of a direct earth (ground) connection to bring a Marconi-type (non-resonant) wire antenna into resonance largely disappeared from both amateur and professional practice except in the form of the radials of elevated ground-plane antennas. Radials, in fact, like counterpoises convert a monopole form of antenna to dipole form, though this is not always recognised by users.

One exception to the disappearance of counterpoises is the W3EDP 84ft wire with its 17ft counterpoise (6ft on 14MHz) which seems to have been undergoing something of a revival since the *TT* references to it as the 'ageless W3EDP' in January and April, 1985: **Fig 5**. Last year, Byron Goodman, W1DX (ex-W6CAL, -W1JPE) brought to my attention the very first description of the 'W3EDP' as 'An unorthodox antenna' by Yardley Beers, W0JF (but then W3AWH) in *QST*, March 1936, pp32-33. This describes how H J Siegel (then W3EDP) had used over 1,000ft of wire in experimenting with various standard antennas. Finally he hung a 100ft roll of wire to his mast and carefully tabulated the results he achieved on 7MHz using this as an end-fed wire antenna: 'Four feet of wire was then cut off and this process repeated several times. When all his tabulations were complete, a length of 84ft seemed to stand out as best ... Not liking entirely the idea of an end-fed single wire antenna, W3EDP set about to find a counterpoise for the best results with his 84ft antenna. Going through a pruning process similar to that with the antenna itself produced a counterpoise length of 17ft as the one working best in combination with the antenna. This combination seemed to work excellently on 160, 80, 40 and 10m, but on 20m a counterpoise length of 6½ft seemed to outshine all others. (Note there was no 15m band in the 1930s).

My own feeling and practice is not to regard 84ft as a 'magic' length but rather to use virtually any long length of end-fed wire and then to find a counterpoise length that results in most current RF current flowing into the antenna when the whole system is brought into resonance with the aid of an antenna tuner. I continue to be surprised at the difference in current on some bands between a counterpoise and the shortest direct earth connection possible from my upstairs 'shack'.

Undoubtedly, the 'end-fed' Marconi antenna with counterpoise remains a useful multiband antenna for those locations where it is inconvenient to erect a centre-fed dipole with open-wire feeders (with the dipole section not necessarily resonant). This may often be the case when operating from a temporary or upstairs shack where it is usually impossible to provide a true low-impedance earth connection. Even if the 'earth' is an excellent low-resistance connection from buried rods, an 11ft lead from this represents

Fig 5 (below). The 'unorthodox' multiband antenna that emerged from the experiments by W3EDP in 1936: an 84ft end-fed antenna with 17ft or (on 14MHz) 6½ft counterpoise. Fig 6 (right). The simple antenna systems that were suggested for use with the Polish 'clandestine' receiver-transmitter type AP5 which covered 2 to 16MHz. Connections A and P for the 6L6 transmitter are shown in Fig 9.

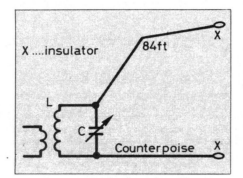

a quarter-wavelength at 21MHz so that from the transmitter ATU end it 'looks' like a top-fed (high-impedance) monopole — quite the opposite to what is required. A much better way of delivering current into the antenna will often be to insulate the 11ft wire from true earth and use it as a single-wire counterpoise. A quarter-wave counterpoise also has the effect of removing 'hot spots' from the transmitter chassis.

Recently, Keith Edwards, G3XUO mentioned to me that he had found a suggestion of using a counterpoise antenna in the instruction sheet relating to the wartime Polish clandestine radio type AP5 (see below): he has a model in good working order. Although the text of this leaflet is in Polish, it includes three diagrams of suitable wire antenna systems for use between 2 to 16MHz: **Fig 6**. He had tried out the counterpoise arrangement with his AP5 (about 7-8 watts output) and had been surprised at how effective it proved on the amateur bands.

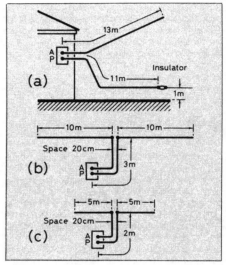

COPYING WEAK CW SIGNALS

Recent items (*TT*, April 1990, p32 and *TT*, December 1989, p38) on the work by the G-QRP Club in investigating preferred audio tones for CW, resulting in finding 450-500Hz as optimum for most operators, have encouraged Ron Taylor, G3AVQ to add some further thoughts that emphasise his belief that audio filtering should be based also on low-pass rather than narrow bandpass filters. He writes:

"The best article that I have ever come across giving the reasons for the use of a low (around 400Hz) rather than a high beat-note was 'Tunable audio filter for weak-signal communications' by Ken Holladay, K6HCP (*Ham Radio*, November 1975, pp28-34) in which he argues that most amateurs who have worked with weak CW signals have found they prefer a lower pitch as signals get weaker ... another reason is that, if there is interference, the lower-frequency signal is easier to detect due to the greater percentage differences in frequency of the wanted and most unwanted signals. He also is strongly against the use of very narrow bandwidth filters: "The human ear-brain copies signals by comparing signal against signal or signal against noise. If a narrow bandpass filter, say 200Hz wide, is used in the receiver it excludes other signals as well as some of the noise. This is fine for strong signals but causes problems with weak ones because too much bandwidth-restriction limits the amount of noise the ear has to compare with the signal. Very sharp filters also have a tendency to 'ring' making signal-to-noise comparison difficult, if not impossible, with very weak CW signals. In addition they are usually tuned to a

fixed frequency so that an operator cannot optimise the frequency and bandwidth of the filter to complement his own hearing. Since the human ear is already (without a filter) capable of a 50Hz bandwidth, very narrow filters are not the best for weak CW detection except for eliminating interference." This does not apply to non-human decoding systems where a narrow filter increases the signal-to-noise ratio, as well as rejecting interference.

Certainly, as far as I am concerned, G3AVQ and K6HCP are preaching to the converted. Many years ago, probably in the 1950s, an article appeared in *QST* (by George Grammer, W1DF?) that argued very strongly in favour of low-pass audio filtering for CW reception; from time to time I have followed his advice with satisfactory results when using receivers which do not provide sufficient IF selectivity. The *QST* article pointed out that a simple low-pass filter can be formed by using a simple pi-network using (at high impedance)

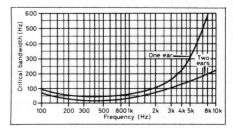

Fig 7. Critical bandwidth of the human ear(s) as a function of frequency as shown by K6HCP in *Ham Radio*, November 1975.

---

users indicated this was acceptable and a larger loop 3m by 2m was devised." The new system, with a gain improvement of about 5dB at low frequencies, was tested exhaustively and showed a performance comparable to earlier tactical antennas "with the added attraction that loop elements of various sizes can readily be constructed to maximise directivity (gain) at frequencies between 1.5 and 12MHz which readily covers the NVIS frequency range. Measurements have also been made of ground-wave radiation comparing the results with traditional 4m whip elements. These have again showed comparable performance."

A final conclusion is that "the use of gas filled variable capacitors in the matching unit will permit high-power transmitters to be used in any weather conditions. The work on loop impedance fluctuations with changes of local environment has shown that the introduction of pre-determined positions for the capacitors to provide a 'silent-tune' capability is not feasible."

I cannot help feeling that the use of slide-fit aluminium tubes is almost bound to introduce much loss-resistance after a time; nor would amateurs often strive to achieve maximum NVIS radiation. At the meeting, the authors discounted any possibility of a radiation hazard to the users, even when very close to the loop. Personally I would not want to sit very close for long to a vehicle loop when powered from 50 to 200W of RF! Nevertheless this loop does prove once again that small loops can radiate well provided always that the resistive losses do not greatly exceed the radiation resistance.

the winding of an audio choke or interstage (valve) audio transformer as the inductive element.

In his 1975 article, K6HCP noted some earlier tests carried out by W2IMU using a 3kHz bandwidth receiver and a signal generator. These tests showed that when a CW signal is adjusted to the same audio level as the noise (zero dB signal-to-noise ratio) the signal was 100% readable: "The input signal was then reduced to 3dB steps. Copy became more difficult but callsigns could still be accurately identified at 9 to 12dB *below* the noise level. Although the *presence* of signals 20dB below the noise could still be detected, they could not be copied. The reason why these weak signals can be copied below the noise level is that the ear-brain filter has narrowed its bandwidth to about 50Hz. **Fig 7** shows the frequency response of the experienced human ear versus its bandwidth: this also shows that 1,000Hz is *not* the optimum tone at which to copy weak CW signals even if the sensitivity of the ear is maximum at around 1,000Hz."

It is perhaps worth mentioning that modern theories of human hearing indicate that it is not possible to distinguish between two tones only 50Hz apart: see *TT*, June 1989.

A POLISH CLANDESTINE RADIO

The wartime need to establish secret radio links with the occupied countries of Europe played an historically important role in the development and miniaturisation of entirely new forms of HF/VHF/UHF communications equipment including portable 'suitcase sets' capable of providing reliable CW links for often relatively inexperienced operators over hundreds of miles and suitable for operation from mains supplies or (with vibrator units) from 6V car batteries.

TT, over the years, has provided circuit details of a number of the equipments developed at Whaddon, near Bletchley for British Intelligence; at The Frythe, Welwyn for SOE; at Berlin-Stahnsdorf for the Abwehr's 'Geheimen Funkmeldedienst' (Secret Radio Reporting Service); the 'Telephone Directory' lightweight AC/DC set designed by Duus Hansen, OZ7DU for the Danish underground; and has outlined the improvised sets used by the Dutch Inland Radio Service.

However, I have long been acutely aware that I have failed to give due credit to the excellent series of compact transmitter-receivers developed and produced at the Polish Radio Centre Workshops at Stanmore, north-west London between 1942-45, with the Polish engineer Tadeusz Heftman as the chief designer of the agent radios.

This is not the time or place in which to pay full credit to the wartime work of the Polish intelligence and resistance (home army) radio operations. It is still seldom recognised that the Poles played a key role in the early clandestine links not only with Poland but also with both the occupied and non-occupied zones of France, with French North Africa (where their French radio-operator Joseph Briatte at Station Rygor in Algiers played a particularly important role in the months leading to the 'Torch' landings in November 1942), with Belgium, and with the Balkans. But, in view of the reference in this month's item on counterpoise antennas, I take the opportunity of including the circuit diagram of the single-6L6 transmitter section used in the Polish 'A' (later 'AP') models A-1 to AP-6. These were all HF transmitter/receiver/PSU equipments in a single metal container (11 by 8.5 by 4 inches) with a close-down lid and weighing from 10 to about 13lbs: **Fig 8.** Models varied in the receiver and wave ranges. Receivers were two or three-valve 'super-gainer' type superhets with a regenerative detector (6K8/6SC7 or 6K8/6SJ7/6SC7). Transmitters with a single metal 6L6 covered either 2 to 8MHz or 2 to 16MHz according

to model. Rectifier 5Z4, with provision for either mains or vibrator operation.

The AP series (and the higher power BP series with 829 double-tetrode power-amplifier) quickly gained the reputation (in 1942-43) as the best available sets of this general type and numbers were acquired by the British, French and Yugoslav agencies involved in covert radio operations and the Poles encouraged to increase production. For a single AP model the nominal 'price' was £71 but I discovered from the records at the Polish Institute and Sikorski Museum in London that in July/August 1942 the Poles supplied SOE with 20 A-1 and two B-1 equipments for a total of £1132 17s. In the summer of 1943, they provided the French D.SR/SM intelligence organisation which worked for General Giraud rather than General de Gaulle with five AP and five BP equipments for use for secret links between Algiers and metropolitan France. AP models were also supplied to British intelligence.

Tadeusz Heftman was one of the post-war founders of British Communications Corporation (BCC) at Wembley, a firm which has specialised in military communications equipment in the post-war period and is now part of the Racal group of companies (Tadeusz Heftman still lives in England). The Polish engineering team at Stanmore, including Heftman, Mieczyslaw Makowski and others, developed the A(P) series; the B(P) series with a higher-power transmitter and superhet receiver in a similar metal box to the A-series but with a separate PSU, the B1, B2 and B3 models covered 2-8MHz but the longer range BP4 covered 4-16MHz with a 6K8/6SK7/6SQ7/6SC7 receiver and 6V6/829 transmitter providing some 30W RF output; the high-power AR11 transmitter with four 807s in parallel push-pull and with 866A mercury vapour rectifiers in the PSU; and the 'pocket' battery-operated OP3 miniature receiver (1R5/1T4/1T4/1S5/1T4) and associated NP3 (push-pull 1J6) and NP3A (single 3A5) transmitters working from 67.5V and 1.5V layer batteries.

Although the AP series had no conventional meters it was well furnished with miniature neons and a pilot bulb antenna current meter that made it reasonably simple to adjust. I recall trying-out, on the air, one of the AP models in Holland in late 1944 and being much impressed with this equipment although finding the receiver suffered pretty badly from 'image' during night-time conditions, a problem that did not occur with the 'straight' regenerative receivers in most Whaddon agent sets.

In 1945, in the final months of the war, the Poles developed the prototype of what would have been the smallest transmitter-receiver of all — the AP-7 using miniature valves and the whole not much larger than a 20-pack of cigarettes; I believe there was also a BP-5 model, but do not think either of

these equipments ever went into production.

After the war, I remembered the 'super-gainer' technique used in the Polish receivers and for many years used this approach, rather than a BFO/diode detector, in a superhet built around the Tobe Model H coil pack and triple-tuned IF transformers (it still works!).

NEW TECHNOLOGY AND MOBILE/PERSONAL RADIO

At the 5th International Conference on Mobile Radio and Personal Communications last December, Dr Peter Saul, G8EUX and M Jacob of Plessey Research, Caswell in a paper 'The potential for new technology in mobile/portable radio' (*IEE Conference Publication No 315,* pp99-102) suggested that the near future will see a sharp move away in this area from the classic combination of frequency modulation and superhet receivers (both stemming from the work of that most inventive American engineer Howard Armstrong): "The next decade or so will see many changes, so that by the year 2000, very few radios will conform to the principles set out by the many pioneers; instead, the designers of today will hardly be able to recognise and understand fully their progeny."

While personally I suspect that the rate of change may not be quite that fast (or as radical as they have proved to be for the Plessey Company), there are undoubtedly major changes in the pipeline, including the increasing use of digital signal processing (DSP); digital speech with digital modulation; direct frequency synthesis even at UHF; spreading use of gallium arsenide (GaAs) IC and discrete devices at high frequencies; and the use of direct-conversion rather than superhet receivers in order to facilitate the development of complete receivers on a chip.

In their paper, the authors described the advantages offered by new silicon, GaAs and interconnection technology in radio communication systems: "The radio of the future will go from the antenna to a DSP system by the shortest possible route, at the lowest cost and consuming the lowest power." They note that the time delay from

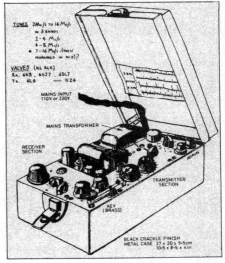

Fig 8. Drawing of G3XUO's Polish AP-5 wartime transmitter-receiver designed and built at the Polish Radio Centre Workshops, Stanmore, Middlesex (Illustration based on a drawing by G3XUO's son, David Edwards).

Fig 9. The single-valve transmitter section of the Polish AP5. Basically similar transmitters (some omitting the 8-16MHz band) were used in Polish models A-1, A-2, AP-3, AP-4, AP-5 and AP-6.

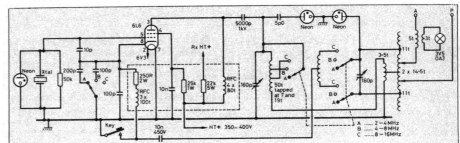

research to production for an advanced semiconductor technology is about five years .... In the main, a semiconductor process has a life of about five years from early availability to peak production, with a further five at the peak and a decline which may last a little longer .... for successful products in the mid-90s, today's research processes are likely to be a good choice.

In silicon bipolar technology, they suggest, the choice is now between analogue processes featuring high-voltage operation and many component options but limited speed, or the newer, very fast digital processes, such as the Plessey Process HE, a one micron geometry process with 24GHz cutoff frequency (Ft) and VLSI capability — already demonstrated in digital form at over 10GHz in a prescaler and in more complex form in a direct frequency synthesiser (DFS) with a clock frequency of 2GHz: "DFS devices (**Fig 10**) are likely to become very important in radio design, since they offer an almost entirely digital solution to frequency synthesis. The DFS itself needs no lock loop, and

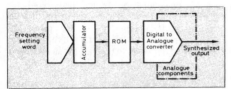

Fig 10. Basic arrangement of a direct frequency synthesiser (DFS).

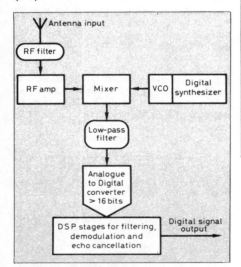

Fig 11. Arrangement of a direct-conversion receiver front-end with digital signal processing.

essentially no analogue components with the exception of a digital to analogue converter ... extremely fast frequency hopping is possible, with very close channel spacing, two mutually incompatible requirements for a phase-locked-loop synthesiser.

"After discussing the various options for receiver front-ends, including direct-conversion (**Fig 11**), the authors conclude: "It is possible now to integrate almost all of a high performance radio receiver onto a single chip; future systems may even include all the filters on the chip too. More importantly, it is possible to build these receivers at very low cost in very large volume, provided that the market size justifies it; this will be the case in cellular and cordless phones, and possibly other new areas of personal communications, not necessarily in telephony. All the above comments could have referred equally to digital transmissions, indeed this is the route intended for most future services, even where the intelligence conveyed is speech. The limitations are more likely to be in the concept than the realisation."

MORE ON CHIREIX-MESNY/ ZIG-ZAG ANTENNAS

Antennas seem to follow a cyclic pattern of interest: forgotten, hardly mentioned for years and then a period of sharply mounting interest. In the February *TT*, I included diagrams of the Chireix-Mesny array of half-wave dipoles (developed by French engineers in the 1920s) and the associated simplified zig-zag form: my first mention of this basic but seldom mentioned array technique since 1977. This encouraged G3ESP to recall (*TT,* April) how a relatively compact 500MHz Chireix-Mesny array had been used by the Germans in the second world war. Next, came the May issue of *Television* (IPC) with an article 'An experimental Band IV (470-585MHz) zig-zag aerial' described by Percy Lamb: **Fig 12.**

This describes his experience with what he calls a 'double zig-zag' but what is in effect a classic Chireix-Mesny array mounted in front of a mesh reflector and providing a horizontally-polarised, broad-band receiving antenna with a measured gain of about 14dBi. The gain comes from the narrow vertical radiation pattern, akin to that of stacked dipoles. Directivity is thus sharp in the vertical plane but broad in the horizontal plane. Although designed for Band IV, sensitivity and gain is maintained well up into Band V. Percy Lamb concludes: "The performance could probably have been improved by using ⅜in aluminium strip instead of the ⅛in solid rod. The reflector's efficiency would probably have been enhanced by using ½in spacing instead of the 1in mesh. In addition a more precise matching to the feeder cable would appear to be desirable. Even without these refinements however the zig-zag configuration offers interesting possibilities when a wideband design with low horizontal directivity is to be combined with high directivity in the vertical plane." For UHF television reception the sharp vertical radiation pattern should reduce 'aircraft flutter,' a useful feature for viewers living close to air lanes.

VALVE LINEAR OPERATING CONDITIONS

Bob Bastow, G3BAC writes: "A number of circuits have appeared recently in *TT* and elsewhere using several paralleled valves of the PL519 type operated with high voltage, low current in the interests of better linearity. It seems worth reminding readers that unfortunately this mode requires high load impedances such that anode and stray capacitances make it virtually impossible to achieve correct LC values for the higher frequency (HF) bands. Operation with anode voltages of the order of 600V, although a bit more demanding on the current supply capability of the PSU, does enable correct LC values to be used on 28, 24 and 21MHz bands. The extra capacitance required on 7 and 3.5MHz can be made up by switching in parallel high-voltage mica capacitors."

IN BRIEF

The item 'Exploiting the millimetre bands' (*TT,* April 1990, p22) reported the current interest among those involved in professional and military communications in the still wide open spaces above 30GHz and coupled this with the existence of a number of exclusive amateur bands in this part of the spectrum. Now comes news that one of the first systems to be marketed in the UK and meeting the DTI conditions for virtually unregulated local systems has been announced by Microwave Modules Ltd, the Liverpool firm well-known in the amateur radio and specialist communications field. This is the 'Microlink 60' designed to provide a millimetre-wave radio link for closed-circuit

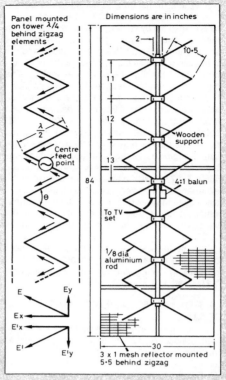

Fig 12. (a) Principles of the zig-zag antenna array. RF power fed to mid point produces horizontally polarised radiation from a vertically mounted panel since the vertical vectors cancel while the horizontal vectors add. (b) The experimental Band IV 'double zig-zag' (ie Chireix-Mesny TV receiving antenna with reflecting screen as described by Percy Lamb in Television (May 1990).

Clearly, if such an array is mounted horizontally rather than vertically, the result would be low directivity in the vertical plane and high horizontal directivity, with vertical polarisation.

television (CCTV) security systems over distances of up to 1km. It works in the 54-55GHz band and it is claimed that over this distance, it transmits clear colour TV pictures and two-way audio plus telemetry control signals without suffering the loss of quality experienced in rain, fog and snow with infra-red systems. It is expected that it will receive DTI type approval to MPT1415.

Bruce Sutherland, G3IES (336 Charlton Road, Bristol BS10 6JZ, telephone 0272-500742) has become sole UK agent for the 'Power Search & Store Module type PS-90' and 'Search & Store Module SS-45' which provide Tandy PRO-2004 and PRO-2005 scanning receivers with the facility to store frequencies automatically while in the search mode — a facility normally found only on high-cost scanning and surveillance receivers (eg the £950 Icom-7000). The PS-90 has two modes of operation, the simple mode of the SS-45 where the frequencies found during a search are stored in the ten monitor memories; and a more complex mode where the frequencies are stored directly in the scanner's main memory. Users can set a limit on how many searched frequencies (up to 255) will be stored. Users of scanner receivers should be aware of the dangers of breaching the terms of the Wireless Telegraphy Acts and the Interception of Communications Act which make it a criminal offence for any person *intentionally* to intercept a communication in the course of its transmission by means of a public telecommunications system. This does not, of course, apply to stations in the amateur or broadcast bands other than telecommunications services in shared bands. □

APPLICATION SPECIFIC INTEGRATED CIRCUITS (ASICs)

Integrated circuits began to revolutionise communications and electronics equipment some thirty years ago. It was in *TT* (January 1967) that I included my first detailed note on these devices under the heading 'The potential of microelectronics', with the comment: "A major upheaval in equipment practice is building up more rapidly than most of us suspected, and is unquestionably going to affect our gear in the very near future. Those with their ears to the electronics ground will probably have already surmised that the opening sentence refers to the approaching era of low-cost integrated circuits (ICs). Over the past few years, we have referred from time to time to the progress of micro-electronics devices ... but this had usually been accompanied by the proviso that such devices, though interesting, were still some way from entering the day-to-day practice of Amateur Radio."

What changed my mind in 1967 was the receipt from Mike Barlow, ex-G3CVO (who had long departed our shores for Canadian television engineering) of a Fairchild 'Micrologic' plastic encapsulated μL914, a simple dual-gate device incorporating just four small-signal silicon transistors and six resistors, and selling in North America for about one dollar. Mike Barlow had commented: "This is fantastic — just last year ICs were $4 and up, and in 1960 they were $100 per device."

The years since 1967 have seen further fantastic progress, particularly in the number of active devices squeezed on to a single chip — from the IC to LSI (large scale integration) to VSLI (very large scale integration) with hundreds and thousands of active devices on a single chip. There has been the introduction of low-cost integrated op-amps suitable for analogue as well as digital applications; the introduction of power-saving ICs based on CMOS rather than bipolar technology; ICs for consumer electronics providing virtually complete receivers, requiring just a few external discrete components; most recently the growing use of tiny surface-mounted components; etc, etc. One form of IC which has been assuming increasing importance in the professional field over about the last five years or so, but which has not previously been discussed in *TT* or *RadCom* is the ASIC — the Application Specific Integrated Circuit.

ASICs already amount to around 20% or so of the total IC market and have come to represent a reassertion of the importance of the equipment design engineer vis-à-vis the component manufacturer. Instead of standard 'chips' designed by a few IC experts and then produced in enormous volume, we are now seeing the growing influence of LSI and VSLI chips intended for just one specific application, designed in part by systems engineers with the help of CAD (computer aided design) even though their knowledge of semiconductor fabrication technology may be rudimentary; the devices are then manufactured for their own use in relatively small numbers. What has made this metamorphosis possible is primarily the increased availability to professional design engineers of CAD techniques applied to LSI chip design and layout.

Admittedly, the VSLI chips increasingly in use in modern consumer electronics such as television receivers are designed for specific applications — for example as teletext, MAC (multiplex analogue component), NICAM 728 digital stereo (Near Instantaneous Companding and Audio Multiplexing at a bit rate of 728 kilobits per second) decoders and the decryption chips for subscription television channels — but these complex ICs have been developed by semiconductor manufacturers for volume production and are not generally regarded as ASICs. Custom or semi-custom ASICs are thus

chips specifically designed: (a) to perform reliably a complex function that cannot conveniently and/or effectively be implemented with just one or two standard IC devices; (b) to help reduce the volume, weight and/or power consumption of equipment by integrating a large number of logic functions on a single chip.

Readers may feel with some justification that ASIC technology is not one that can be applied to home-construction or even small batch production for the Amateur Radio market. However the fully 'customized' cell-based device is not the only form of ASIC: also important are the large 'gate arrays' which are personalised only in the final processing steps. It is with some forms of gate arrays that useful opportunities are already arising for their use in home-constructed equipment.

What were termed 'uncommitted logic arrays' were introduced by Ferranti almost twenty years ago. These ULA devices consist of a regular array of unconnected logic elements with pads for external connections **(Fig 1)**; the internal connections are made by later diffusion processes usually by the semiconductor firm. Applicable to the do-it-yourself ASIC approach are various families of programmable logic arrays (PLAs) using PROM or EPROM technology. 'Standard' user-programmable devices such as conventional ROMs and microprocessors are not usually regarded as 'customized' ASIC devices. PLA devices suitable for digital circuitry comprise a regular array of transistors/gates and a fixed number of bonding pads, each with an I/O buffer. They are relatively inefficient in terms of the number of gates in a given chip area, but even so may include more than enough functions for complex units. In such arrays, the internal 'elements' each comprise a number of transistors, with the interconnection defining the final function of each element: see, for example, **Fig 2**. CMOS technology is generally used and there is an expanding number of families of programmable devices becoming available from a number of semiconductor firms, including the 'erasable programmable logic device' (EPLD) which, as Colin Horrabin, G3SBI shows this month, offers most interesting possibilities for amateur radio equipment. He stresses: "In my opinion these EPLD chips are the most important hardware development since the microprocessor;

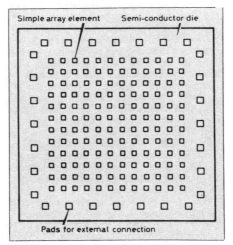

Fig 1. Basic array structure of an uncommitted logic array. The principle remains the same in the programmable arrays (source *Electronics Engineer's Reference Book*).

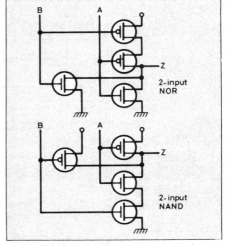

Fig 2. Example of how a basic cell element can be interconnected as a 2-input NOR gate or as a 2-input NAND gate (Source as Fig 1).

they can replace a large number of conventional logic chips, and are extremely versatile."

While CAD facilities to assist in designing the logic arrangements may not be available to 'non-professional' amateurs it is clear, from G3SBI's pioneering work in this field, that EPLDs for specific applications can be developed by those knowledgeable in this approach and then devices programmed in the small numbers that would never justify the introduction of a mass-produced conventional IC device. It also seems likely that the ASIC approach will appeal to firms making amateur radio equipment, as we have seen with surface-mounted devices.

AN EPLD IAMBIC KEYER

Colin Horrabin, G3SBI (71 Duckworth Grove, Padgate, Warrington, WA2 0QU, Tel 0925 825383) writes: "This note describes an iambic keyer integrated circuit that is similar to the Curtis keyer chip, but uses a programmable device and is capable of being used in a 'coherent CW' (CCW) system or as an ordinary iambic keyer. Eight speeds may be selected by a BCD-coded switch using a master clock of 750Hz or 1kHz. The master clock can be crystal-derived for CCW or use a simple CMOS oscillator for normal keyer use. In this latter case, a gate output pin from the chip automatically starts the oscillator when the paddles are in operation. An iambic-mode pin determines if an extra dot after dash, or dash after dot occurs when the paddles are released: 0V for normal iambic operation; +5V for the extra dot or dash.

"The IC in which the design is programmed is an EPLD from Altera, type EP610, although direct equivalents are now available from a number of manufacturers. This device contains sixteen logic cells, each of which has a register that may be programmed to be D, T, JK or RS flip-flop, while the input to each cell is a programmable AND OR array. Another feature is 'non-turbo mode' which gives lower power consumption at low clock speeds; about 15μA at 5V and 750Hz clock, making it ideal for battery powered applications, although care must be taken not to exceed 5V.

"The easiest way of designing circuits with the device is to run a program called APLUS on an IBM PC. With this software, logic diagrams can be drawn on screen with the aid of a mouse. The software minimises the logic and, with the addition of a programing card, programs the completed design into the chip. If the design does not work correctly the chip can be UV erased and used again with the modified design. In my opinion these chips are the most important hardware development since the microprocessor; they can

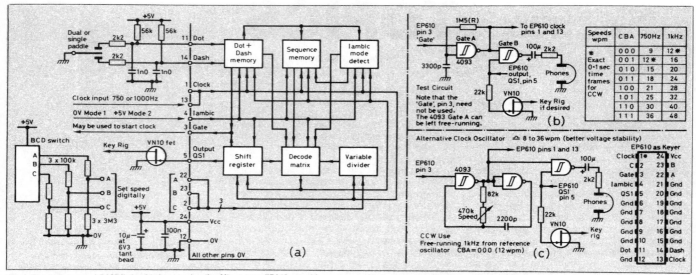

Fig 3. Block diagram of G3SBI's iambic keyer using the Altera, type EP610 erasable programmable logic device (EPLD) together with test circuit, variable clock oscillator etc.

replace large numbers of conventional logic chips and are extremely versatile.

"A block diagram of the keyer chip is shown in **Fig 3**. An external clock source is required which may be 1kHz derived from a crystal for CCW operation or the simple arrangement shown using a CMOS 4093 device. Basic operation is as follows: the output morse code from the EP510 chip is from a shift register which is only updated when the variable divider that sets the speed in relation to the master clock counts down to one. Information from the dot and dash paddles, together with the shift register contents, determines the next state of the shift register output. In other words, if dot plus space, or dash plus space, or alternate dot dash sequences are generated. The important difference between this chip and the Curtis chip is the use of a digital divider to control morse code speed, an essential feature for CCW operation where long-term mark/space transitions must be accurate to better than one part in a million.

"To test the device, a simple test circuit using a 4093 may be used: **Fig 3 (b)**. Operation is as follows: Gate A is used as a simple clock source with the keyer output gate starting the oscillator, the frequency of which is set to 750Hz by adjusting the value of R, the output of this gate going to the keyer clock pins. The keyer-chip's morse code output QS1 is connected to gate B input 1, and the clock oscillator to input 2. The output from this gate can be connected to a resistor and capacitor in series with a pair of headphones to monitor the generated code. A connection to the BCD-coded speed control pins of CBA = 001 gives 12wpm morse with a 750Hz clock and 36wpm with CBA = 111. If it is desired to key the rig a VN10 FET can be driven from QS1 for normal polarity or, alternatively, a reed relay for universal use. It is not necessary to use digital speed control: the R in the clock oscillator can be made variable, **(Fig 3 c)**, in which case CBA is set to 000 (all 0V). When used in a normal CCW scheme with a 1kHz clock, CBA = 000.

"It is also possible to develop the basic circuit to provide the heart of a memory keyer. A prototype has been made using a 24-cell EPLD with three additional chips; this performs as a 16-memory keyer with 1kbits per message; latent power is 20µA and about 0.5mA when operating. With the next larger EPLD array, just the EPLD and memory would have been required."

G3SBI mentions that should anyone wish to purchase the basic EPLD keyer programmed into an Altera EP610 he could supply this for a cost of £8.50.

BATTERY ACID AND SAFETY

In my late teens, I was once unwise enough to store an unused 2V (lead-acid) accumulator on top of a wardrobe. For reasons unknown, it tipped over, some of the acid electrolyte leaked out and dripped on to an elder brother's jacket; the results were disastrous. I escaped the consequences (the brother concerned was away spending four years as a prisoner-of-war) but the incident taught me that battery acid is pretty nasty stuff.

I was reminded of that event by notes on 'safety' in the third of the three-part articles by George L Thurston, W4MLE 'Practical Battery-Back-Up Power for Amateur Radio Stations' (*QST*, May 1990 with Parts 1 and 2 in March and April issues). The safety notes include the warning: 'Heavy-duty lead-acid cells are potentially very dangerous. Each cell contains fairly strong sulphuric acid, which can cause injury when in contact with the skin and blindness when in contact with the eyes. Handle the cells with great caution and respect.'

W4MLE recommends: "Whenever you handle these (large) cells, installing or moving them, wear liquid-proof safety goggles and acid.resistant rubber (or plastic) gloves. Keep a garden hose handy, with water turned on. Keep a supply of sodium bicarbonate (also known as bicarbonate of soda, or baking soda) at hand to neutralize acid that may get on your skin. Have another person standing by to help if something goes wrong. If any electrolyte makes contact with your skin or clothing, safety experts recommend taking the following measures *immediately*. Hose down the affected part of your body. While you are under the hose, quickly remove and discard any clothing splashed with acid. If you get acid on your skin, flood the spill with water *immediately*, rinse thoroughly for several minutes, then dust the affected area with sodium bicarbonate. If any electrolyte splashes into your eye(s), *immediately* flush your eyes with water for at least fifteen minutes, including under the eyelids. Speed in starting the flushing is *critical*. While your eyes are being flushed, *call medical help*. A 911 call (the American equivalent of a 999 call) is appropriate.

W4MLE continues: "Flushing with large quantities of water is also the proper treatment for electrolyte spills on skin. Elderly people and young children's skin is especially vulnerable to acid, but 6-molar electrolyte causes itching and stinging even in healthy young adults within a few seconds of contact. (Broken or irritated skin reacts quicker, and more strongly.) If the electrolyte is flushed away with water and neutralized with baking soda, chances of serious injury are minor.

"The polycarbonate-plastic cases of back-up batteries and cells are extremely strong and acid-resistant, but they must be treated with respect. A 300Ah float cell weighs about 85 pounds. If you drop it and its case cracks, you have a very dangerous mess on your hands (or feet)! Dust and gunk of various kinds tend to accumulate on the cases and must be cleaned off periodically. The best cleaner is a damp cloth or paper towel. But if acid is spilled on the outside of the case, it should be neutralized so it won't damage other materials or injure skin that comes into contact with it. Battery manufacturers recommend a dilute solution of baking soda. This extremely mild alkali neutralizes the acid *without damaging the plastic*. (Baking soda fizzes because it reacts with the acid to produce sodium sulphate and carbon dioxide gas.) Do not use stronger alkalis, such as lye (sodium hydroxide) or ammonia (ammonium hydroxide) on back-up batteries. These chemicals damage the cases, causing cracking that may lead to leaks. Also, do not use organic solvents such as alcohol or carbon tetrachloride."

W4MLE also lists a number of steps to be taken when disposing of unusable cells, considered by environmental agencies to be hazardous materials. He lists the procedures recommended by safety experts including the neutralization of the electrolyte by carefully adding small quantities of slaked lime (hardware and garden-supply stores) to emptied out acid in a plastic bucket, but warns that the chemical reaction results in a great deal of heat and lime should not just be dumped into the liquid. Like the electrolyte, slaked lime is highly caustic and should not be touched or its dust breathed in.

He concludes his three-part article by stressing that "Back-up power for Amateur Radio stations is useful, and need not be expensive. Heavy-duty batteries *intended for float service* are available to do this job well."

MORE VOLTAGE-DOUBLER CIRCUITS

Practical applications of voltage-doubling and voltage-multiplication diode rectifiers have been featured in a number of *TT* items over the past year: July, October, November 1989; May 1990. This topic is of considerable interest these days when high-voltage mains transformers, unless recycled from old equipment, are increasingly rare (ie expensive) and now that improved linearity or higher efficiency can be achieved with FET or bipolar solidstate power amplifiers by using 24-28V or higher voltage supplies.

John Brown, G3EUR who has already made notable contributions on this topic has been prompted by the appearance in the May *TT* of the

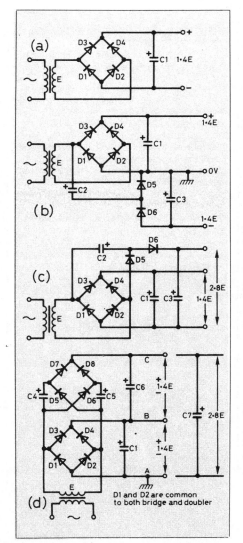

Fig 4. Voltage doubler configurations based on full-wave bridge rectifiers. (a) Conventional bridge rectifier. (b) Arrangement producing positive and negative outputs of ±1.4Edc from Eac input. (c) Arrangement producing 2.8Edc and 1.4Edc outputs. (c) Practical arrangement with eight diodes used by G3EUR to provide power for a B-2 transmitter-receiver without the requirement for a centre-tapped mains transformer secondary and with no requirement for 600V or so electrolytic capacitors.

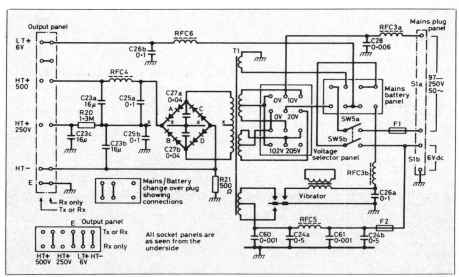

Fig 5. The original 1943 B-2 power supply unit designed by G3EUR and suitable for AC mains from 97 to 250V or 6V DC vehicle batteries. This used centre-tapped windings on the mains transformer.

full-wave voltage-doubler ('Extra diodes provide improved voltage-doubler' page 32) to delve back into one of his laboratory notebooks which provides further consideration of this approach which he used to power a Type 3 Mk 2 (B-2) suitcase transmitter/receiver. He writes: "Starting with **Fig 4 (a)**, and the need to get a negative supply for a small CRT, I hung a half-wave rectifier D5 and D6 on to a standard bridge rectifier (D1-D4) as shown in **Fig 4 (b)**. The small DC current in the transformer core did not bias the core unduly and all was well. Later I used the same trick to get a positive supply (**Fig 4 (c)**) also for a CRT).

"Doing this again but in a full-wave configuration as in **Fig 4 (d)** gave me a supply to feed a B-2 transmitter, using much larger capacitors. Note that, since the transformer secondary is symmetrically loaded, no DC bias current results and a toroid transformer can be used without the risk of saturation. Since it is possible to earth any of the points A, B or C one can get positive or negative supply lines as required. This is essentially the same as the circuit shown in the May *TT*, but with two extra diodes (D3, D4). This gives a centre tap to the supply which is most convenient when using both a transmitter and receiver and avoids

the need for 500V or 600V-working electrolytics, which are increasingly rare these days.

"One assumes that the arrangement shown in the May *TT* and in PA0SE's column in the March 1990 *Electron* was intended for use with a mains transformer but, of course, the bridge can be connected directly to an AC supply, although in this case the output is then *very* live to earth and must be treated with great respect. "In **Fig 4**, since these circuits work at all voltages, I have shown the outputs in terms of E, the RMS voltage of the supply; the capacitors all work at 1.4E, except C7 which, if used, must be 2.8E plus some margin for safety in each case. Naturally, at 12V RMS and an output of an order of 1A or so, the capacitors need to be of the order of 470-2200μF and the voltage drops of the silicon or germanium diodes must be taken into account. With E equal to 200-300V RMS, the voltage drops in the silicon diodes can be ignored and capacitor values of 10-47μF apply.

"I do not favour use of very large capacitors to get low ripple in the output, since this means large current-spikes in the AC supply. I consider it better to design for a ripple of 2 to 5% and use a choke/capacitor filter in the DC line(s) unless an electronic voltage regulator is used with enough 'head-room' to accommodate the ripple as well as the variation of DC voltage due to regulation and variation of the mains supply."

As a matter of interest, I have added the circuit diagram **(Fig 5)** of the flexible PSU originally developed by G3EUR for the B-2 in 1943, providing 500V and 250V HT from a conventional bridge rectifier and centre-tapped transformer, intended for use on AC mains from 97-250V RMS or, by means of the vibrator unit, from 6V DC car batteries.

In those days, one depended on the less-efficient copper-oxide or selenium rectifiers. Even selenium units, developed originally in Germany, were in short supply, although STC through its ITT connections was able to begin manufacturing selenium rectifier disks in the UK in 1939. The story is told in *Power of Speech — A History of Standard Telephones and Cables, 1883-1983* by Peter Young (George Allen & Unwin, 1983). He tells how, in the early 1930s, the associated STC company Kolster-Brandes (Brimar) began to import selenium rectifiers from an ITT associate company in Nuremberg, mainly for use in battery chargers. In the summer of 1939, probably in view of the possibility of war, STC engineers began to acquire production equipment and know-how from Germany to establish their own production: "One thing the Germans did not supply was the formula

for the mysterious ingredient 319. When supplies of this were cut off after 3 September, 1939, its content was ascertained from a French associate company." Production of disks was expanded from half a million in 1939 to twenty-three million in 1944 mainly for use in Service equipment. Selenium rectifiers could work in appreciably higher ambient temperatures than copper-oxide rectifiers which needed much larger cooling fins when rectifying more than a few milliamps.

Incidentally, there are still quite a few B-2 equipments in use on the amateur bands. In connection with the Duxford Radio Society of the Imperial War Museum, John Brown, G3EUR has formed a users' group of amateurs interested in the B-2 suitcase set with its own newsletter. If interested, write to "B2-UG" at the Duxford Radio Society, Duxford Airfield, Cambridge, CB2 4QR.

THOSE NOISY RFI-GENERATING COMPUTERS

The May *TT* item 'Taming the station computer' discussed a number of steps that can be taken that help to allow microcomputers to form an integral part of amateur stations without reception being disrupted by RFI stemming from the computer and its peripherals. Equally or perhaps more common are problems arising from digital equipment, including computers, operated anywhere near the receiver, often belonging to a neighbour or nearby commercial establishment. Computer-generated RFI is increasingly a problem even for relatively strong-signal broadcast reception, let alone for weak-signal reception of distant amateur stations.

In the UK, there are still no legally-enforcable limits on spurious radiation from Information Technology (IT) equipment — and even when, under the EC EMC Directive, legislation is implemented, this is most unlikely to be retrospective, applying only to new equipment and installations. The Radio Investigation Service (RIS), when notified by (preferably a group of) broadcast listeners/viewers, will often do its best to 'persuade' owners of clearly offending equipment to do their best voluntarily to reduce RFI. In this connection remember that you and your neighbours can notify the RIS of sources of interference to broadcasting without incurring the £21 charge for a personal visit.

Even in the USA where, since January 1981, there have been FCC regulations imposing radiation limits on microcomputers, the more powerful 'business' Class A machines are permitted to generate significantly more RFI than the cheaper

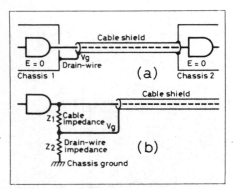

Fig 6. As explained in *TT* (April 1988) a screened cable can still radiate RF noise/signals if the cable-boot connection includes an appreciable 'pig-tail' connection (drain-wire). The inductance of the drain-wire can cause much of the RF noise to appear on the outside of the shield. This applies to minimizing both unwanted noise radiation and unwanted signal/noise leakage into shielded enclosures. (b) Shows the equivalent circuit.

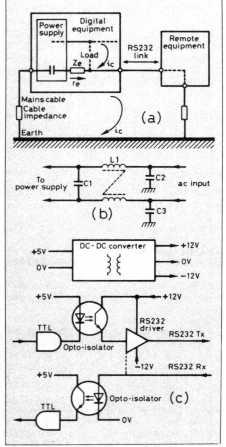

Fig 7. Tips on reducing RFI from computers as described in *TT* (August and April 1988). (a) Circulating common-mode currents in mains cables and interfacing links between digital equipment results in RF signals being injected into the mains supply or radiating directly. (b) Typical mains filter to reduce noise from power rectifiers and switch-mode PSUs etc being injected into AC power leads. An alternative form of filter is to wind the power cable around a suitable ferrite bead. NU1N considers the best method of isolating signals coupled through the power lines is to use a combination of RF line filters and transient suppressors. (c) Method of isolating an RS232 interface by means of an opto-isolator and 1W DC-DC converter chip.

domestic Class B machines. Class A includes many of the PC-compatible machines based on the Intel 80386 devices; quite a few such machines are now commonly used in the domestic or amateur-radio environment. A four-page article 'Understanding computer-generated RFI — some

remedies for this malady' by Bryan P Bergeron, NU1N (*Ham Radio*, March 1990) makes it all too clear that the problems of RFI will not end when the UK finally gets round to IT-RFI legislation.

NU1N is concerned primarily with suggesting how to minimise radiation from microcomputers under the amateur's control. He describes how RFI is generated not only in the microcomputer and its associated switched-mode power supply, but also by peripherals including: the mouse; trackballs; light pen; tablets; touch screens; joysticks; modems; printers; RF modulators; and local area networks (LANs). His advice on RFI suppression follows well-trodden paths but extends well beyond the measures suggested by ZS6KE (May *TT*). To summarize his main points:

a) An FCC Class B rated machine is difficult enough to tame — think twice before opting for a machine with an FCC Class A rating.

b) Do not remove shielding in computers or peripherals to prevent heat build up. Open metallized plastic enclosures carefully to avoid chipping off or wearing away the conductive paint. Metal shielding is now increasingly restricted to the power supply.

c) Use shielded cables wherever possible and add snap-on ferrite inductors to peripheral cables, especially if they are not shielded. Do not forget to add a snap-on inductor to the telephone cable where it exits your modem. See also **Fig 6.**

d) Judicious use of RF bypass capacitors with resistive touch pads, mechanical mice and joysticks is often worthwhile.

e) If possible isolate your receiver from the computer by using separate power sockets (preferably not directly connected on a ring mains circuit — G3VA): "If all the power sources in your shack are controlled by a single circuit breaker, try adding two good surge protectors — one for your communications gear and one for the computer equipment. A simple protector with MOVs won't do. The best method of isolating signals coupled through the power line uses a combination of RF line filters and transient suppressors." See also **Fig 7.**

f) A good earth is essential: "It's surprising how many hams who have six foot ground rods connected by heavy coaxial braid to their gear fail to ground their computer equipment" (Note that special precautions should be taken in using 'real earths' in houses with electricity supplies using protective multiple earthing, PME — see for example the article by Peter Chadwick, G3RZP, in the June 1987 issue of *RadCom*. In any case there should be no direct connection between mains earth and real earth — G3VA).

g) Minimize cable lengths; where possible use an internal modem, move your micro and peripherals as far from your receiver as possible. Running an external disk drive cable parallel and adjacent to the antenna is asking for trouble.

h) Minimize the entry points of RFI into your receiver. If you have an external loudspeaker cable with more than a few inches of cable, use a low-pass filter and shielding to prevent the cable acting as an antenna.

i) If you develop your own software, try and minimize the reading and writing of data to disk. Try to avoid using software that requires frequent operation of the disk drive: "The stepper motors and associated drive circuitry are extremely noisy in the RF spectrum."

NU1N urges that amateurs should think of their computer system in the same way as communications gear with peripheral cables, telephone connections and power cables acting as the antenna system.

HERE AND THERE

A famous name in both amateur and professional antenna engineering, Dr John D Kraus, W8XK has

FEEDING AN 80-metre DELTA LOOP ON 1.8MHz

The 1-λ delta loop has become a very popular HF antenna and provides a useful multiband loop, particularly if fed with open-wire line. In practice it is seldom possible to erect such a system with a 1-λ loop on 1.8MHz as this would require something like a 500ft loop perimeter. Even a 3.5MHz 1-λ loop (268ft) needs a fair space and high supports. Roy C Koeppe, K6XK in *QST*'s 'Hinks & Kinks' (April 1990) indicates a satisfactory way of feeding an 80 metre loop on 1.8MHz, an approach that could also be adopted for scaled down loops to permit operation on a lower band: **Fig 8.** K6XK writes: "C1 tunes the antenna to act as a three-quarter-wave resonator and allows the SWR at the feed point to be no more than 1.1 across the 160 metre band."

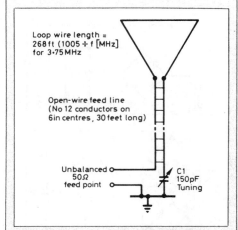

Fig 8. K6XK's arrangement for feeding an 80 metre delta loop antenna on 160 metres.

been awarded the 1990 IEEE Heinrich Hertz Medal (gold medal, bronze replica, certificate and $10,000). He became a radio amateur at 14, gained a physics PhD at 23 and "trained himself to design experimental apparatus which is elegant in its simplicity". He was responsible for the helical antenna, corner reflector, and the original close-spaced bi-directional W8XK family of antennas. He was also one of the pioneers of radio-astronomy and designed and built the giant 'Big Ears' radio telescope for Ohio State University, of which he is Emeritus Professor of Electrical Engineering & Astronomy and Director of the Radio Observatory.

Another 14 year old amateur, Todd Kramer, N4WOR seems set to follow in the footsteps of W8XK. He recently made the first known amateur radio contact (31 December 1989) using an antenna made from one of the new 'high-temperature' (liquid nitrogen coolant) superconductors: a 1-2-3- yttrium-barium-copper dipole made by ICI Inc with a handheld Repco SYN2100 transceiver. He made a 12 minute contact with KN4BC via a 70cm repeater.

G E Cripps, G3DWW has found an excellent source of VFO components. He writes: "If you can acquire an ex-WD passive preselector unit known as an Acceptor Unit ZA54916, this contains a number of suitable ceramic formers plus a beautiful four-gang variable capacitor with slow-motion drive, and all housed in a very well screened cabinet. These seem to appear at rallies etc. Mine was a bargain at around £20. I guess the coils alone cost more than that."

A problem with long-wire and voltage-fed antennas, unless one end is brought into the shack (increasing the risk of TVI/RFI) is that the ATU is remote from the operator. Dick Rollema, in his 'Reflecties door PA0SE'. *Electron* June 1990 summaries an article by DL2NI (*cq-DL* April 1990)

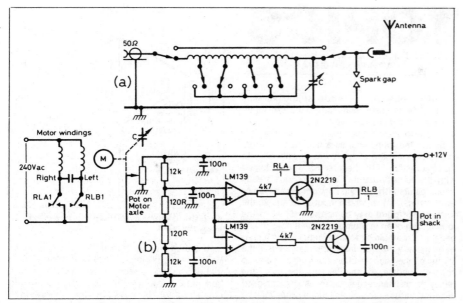

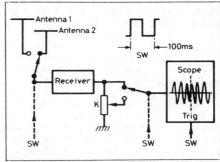

Fig 11. G3IBY's normal method of measurement. ANT 1 reference antenna. ANT 2 Antenna under test or second dipole. Antenna height 40ft, spacing 30ft, horizontal polarization. Receiver SSB mode linearised by backing off RF gain to disable AGC. Adjust K until signal levels on the two sides of the screen of the 'scope are, on average, equal (signals normally SSB speech). Then with K_A value of K with antenna under test and K_B value of K with second dipole in place of test antenna with location correction factor. The measured test antenna gain, G_A = 20 log (K_B/K_A).

Fig 9. (a) L-network ATU for voltage fed multiband long-wire antennas etc. Remote switching of the inductance can be implemented with relays. (b) DL2NI's electronic remote-tuning system with operator potentiometer tuning control. Full component/motor details not available from PA0SE's digest of a *cq-DL* article by DL2NI.

on a 1.8MHz to 10MHz long-wire antenna that uses a relay switched L-network ATU with remote tuning of the capacitor as shown in **Fig 9 (a)**. PA0SE does not provide any details of the reversible motor, relays etc but the principle seems to be that the electronic controller causes the tuning shaft potentiometer to move to the same relative setting as the potentiometer tuning control in the shack: **Fig 9 (b)**.

MEASURING ANTENNA GAIN

The considerable difficulty of obtaining realistic and reasonably accurate measurements of the far-field forward gain of HF/VHF antennas without (and sometimes with) the use of a good professional standard model antenna range is well known. This is one reason for the current interest in the increasing use of the NEC 'Method of Moments' computer approach. But neither model ranges nor computer simulations provide the actual gain of a full-size, installed antenna, and whether it really gives your signals the boost promised by the manufacturer's sales department. A major problem with trying to measure gain by comparing signals received on the array with those on a reference dipole is the rapid fading of HF and 50MHz signals.

Dr TH Wilmshurst, G3IBY has developed a useful method of measuring the forward gain of various types of 50MHz beam antennas. He feels that not only should the results be of interest, but

so also the method of measurement, which is not beyond the means of any technically minded amateur or SWL. He writes: "**Fig 10** shows the results of a series of forward-gain measurements made on some of the more popular 50MHz beam antennas. The method of measurement was, for the most part, as in **Fig 11**, although there was a small degree of evolution during the series. The antenna gain measurement figure (GA) is in dBd. This means that the figure represents the increase in received signal strength when the station is received first on the dipole and then the dipole is replaced by the test antenna. In practice, useful measurements cannot be made in this way, because by the time the change of antennas has been made the station being received may have closed down or, even if he is still there, fading will have changed the signal strength. These problems can be avoided by using two antennas with rapid switching between them. Fading can be surprisingly rapid and requires very rapid switching of the order of a 100 milliseconds switching period.

"There is a range and bearing-dependent difference between the two antenna locations which, if not corrected for, gives a further spread of about 3dB for each histogram, making the comparisons less accurate. The difference is measured and compensated for by including a simple dipole in the series of antennas put in the 'test' position. It is clear that many measurements have to be taken to obtain a good enough distribution to be able to

make a meaningful comparison. Thanks are due to many local and semi-local stations in the Southampton area who gave me carrier bursts, whistles, 'aahs' etc in attempts to improve accuracy. It ultimately became clear that the only realistic way of obtaining an adequate number of measurements was to have a system that would operate on a station transmitting normal speech, not necessarily in contact with me. The arrangement of **Fig 11** fulfils this requirement well. The method is to tune in to the station, point-up the two antennas and adjust K till the mean signal amplitudes seen on the two sides of the 'scope face are the same. This usually takes at least one 'over'.

"The received stations were mostly within a range of 100 miles and all were via tropo. There were no sporadic E or other propagation-mode signals. The location is a fairly good one but by no means giving antenna test-range conditions. The results shown in **Fig 10** indicate that, for the most part, the published gain values recorded on antenna ranges do give quite a good indication of the performance that can be expected in normal use.

"It would be interesting to have some results from sporadic-E, auroral, TEP (trans-equatorial propagation) and other propagation modes, also for some of the larger antenna types now in use, and for other bands. It should be noticed that this is a 'receive-only' test and could be carried out by a technically-minded SWL. The reciprocal performance of antennas means that forward gain will be similar on transmit as on receive."

ELIMINATING WOODPECKER INTERFERENCE?

Despite the virtual ending of the 'Cold War', there seems little immediate prospect of any sudden disappearance of the interference from Russian 'over-the-horizon' (OTH) radars, although in recent years this has been rather less intrusive than when it started back in the 1970s. An interesting but non-technical item has, however, appeared in the May 1990 issue of *The JARL News* which provides notes on 'Highlights of Amateur Radio activity in Japan'. This is as follows: "Kokusai Denshin Denwa Co Ltd (international telephone and telegram corporation) recently developed an equipment which almost completely eliminates 'woodpecker' interfering with short wave radio communication.

"The noise is thus called because it resembles the rhythmic tapping sound the woodpecker makes when it taps the tree trunks. Previously only a noiseblanking method was used but now this equipment enables clearer conversation. For the time-being, however, it is being used for short wave radios of ship telephones but utilization for amateur radio is also under consideration." □

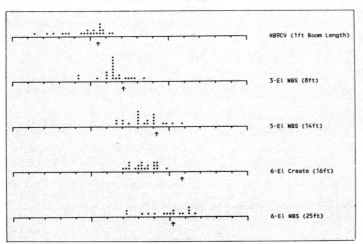

Fig 10. Some of G3IBY's 50MHz antenna gain measurement histograms. X-scale: range 0 to 15dBd. Histogram resolution 0.2dB. Arrows indicate gains as published in *RSGB VHF/UHF Manual* (HB9CV array), *ARRL Handbook* (NBS arrays), manufacturer's literature (Create).

HB9CV (1ft Boom Length)

3-El NBS (8ft)

5-El NBS (14ft)

6-El Create (16ft)

6-El NBS (25ft)

TOPICS

PAT HAWKER G3VA

HORIZONTAL LOOP ANTENNAS (REAL AND WITH MININEC)

Although the 1λ wire loop antenna (square or triangular (delta)) has long been established both as a single-element antenna or, with a parasitic reflector loop, as the respected two-element quad beam, it is usual practice to have the loop in the vertical plane, providing either horizontally or vertically polarized signals according to how it is fed. A loop antenna mounted in the horizontal plane is still something of a rarity despite having been discovered by serendipity (the happy accident) over 20 years ago by the late Peter Pennell, G2PL, who for many years was a prominent DXer.

A *TT* item in July 1968 (later included in many editions of *ART*) described how, during some severe gales, he took the precaution of lowering his three-band quad, mounted on a tilt-over mast, so that the quad elements were in effect firing straight upwards, with the reflector loop touching the ground in places. *TT* continued: "Under these conditions, he found the performance of the aerial to be superior to that of a resonated vertical on all three bands (typically receiving S9 from VK on 14, S7 from W6 on 21 and 28MHz). The feeder SWR was little different from that in the usual vertical position . . . the 28MHz driven element was about 7ft above ground and that of the 14MHz element about 12ft . . . Tests at G2PL suggest that the angle of radiation compares with a dipole a half-wave above ground, and he feels it would be a simple matter to erect such a system using four (short) vertical posts." Personally, I would not expect a low, horizontal loop to have much low-angle radiation, although entirely suitable for NVIS (near vertical incident skywave) short-range working.

A few years later (June 1972 *TT* and digested in later editions of *ART*) S M de Wet, ZS6AKA, reported on a series of "experiments with multiband loop aerials" including loops 1λ and ⅔λ (with stub matching), rectangular and triangular loops in both vertical and horizontal planes and with the horizontal loops at heights of about 35-40ft: **Fig 1**. He pointed out (as G6XN had done earlier) that a 1λ loop (unlike a ½λ dipole or ½λ loop) provides a low-impedance (resistive) feed-point not only at *f* but at all harmonics of *f*. His 1λ (3.5MHz) loop had an input impedance of about 100Ω at 3.5MHz, rising to roughly 200Ω at 28MHz, with intermediate impedances at 7, 14 and 21MHz.

General observations made at the time by ZS6AKA seem worth recalling: "(1) the loop tuned much more broadly than a dipole; (2) the voltages along the loop were much lower than a dipole; (3) although the loop requires a minimum of three supports, the extra support was usually easy to find in practice — the best results were obtained with the loop horizontal, but it did not greatly affect results with the loop horizontally slanted or even vertical; (4) when the input is balanced, the furthest mid-point may be earthed; (5) when the loop is fashioned in rhombic shape it does in fact become a rhombic directional aerial at the higher frequencies with a low input impedance; (6) if the shape of the loop is changed from circular to square, triangle, rectangle and the like, the radiation resistance decreases as the enclosed area decreases — this means that a shape may be found which has an input impedance of approximately 50Ω; and (7) there are many shapes and mounting configurations which remain to be explored."

ZS6AKA noted that on lower frequencies the loop (as with a low dipole) provides omnidirectional radiation, but breaks up into a series of lobes at higher frequencies.

That was back in 1972. Coming up to date, Doug DeMaw, W1FB, provides 'A closer look at horizontal loop antennas' (*QST* May 1990, pp28, 29, 35) providing E- and H-plane radiation pattern diagrams for a large multiband loop antenna, computer-generated by Harold Johnson, W4ZCB, using an IBM computer with MININEC software (see July *TT*). W1FB's loop **(Fig 2)** is in the form of a square with 132ft 2¾in sides at a height of 50ft, and the radiation patterns are at 1.9, 3.84, 7.16, 14.2, 21.2 and 28.5MHz; **Fig 3**. If moved up a band, the patterns should hold approximately correct for a scaled-down loop with 66ft sides at a height of 25ft. The patterns resemble those noted by ZS6AKA.

With this large multiband loop, W1FB found that "the system produces 14, 21 and 28MHz performance that is on par with, and sometimes better

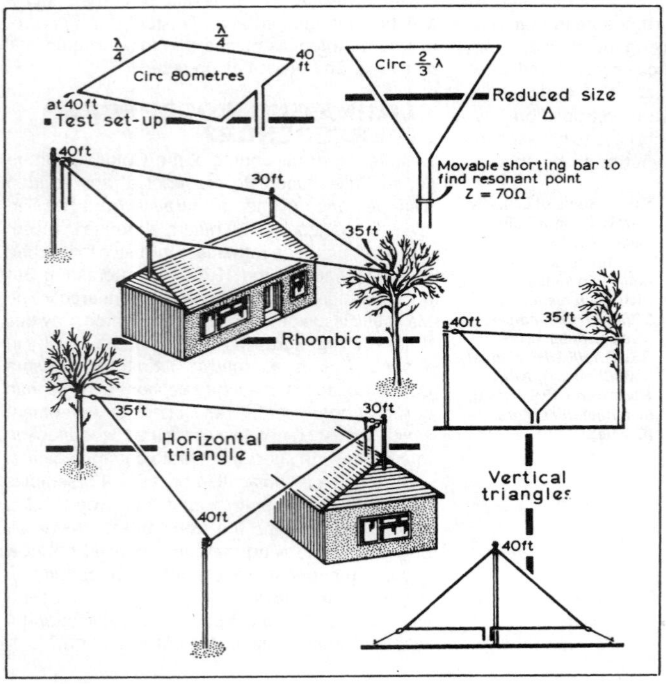

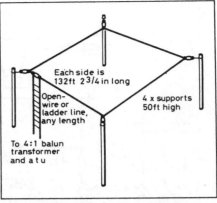

Fig 2. The 1.9MHz/multiband horizontal loop at 50ft as used by W1FB.

than, that of my commercial triband Yagi at 55ft." He concludes his article as follows: "The point is that, if you have space for one, you can use a horizontal loop as a multiband antenna. You need not tailor it for 160m. A 75 or 40m full-wave loop will usually fit into a city lot. The higher you erect it above ground, the better its performance will be. But, don't give up the notion of a loop if you can't get it high above ground. Height extends the useful working distance of a loop, but many loops at low heights still permit good DX results at the higher end of the HF spectrum. The improvement in noise rejection during receive may be sufficiently rewarding to justify putting up a large piece of wire, especially if you live in a noisy neighbourhood.

"One word of caution: Wire that has thick polyvinyl insulation (such as No 14 (American) electrical wire) causes the antenna resonance to be somewhat lower than the formula dictates. Apparently the propagation factor of the wire, when used in a closed loop, causes this phenomenon."

GETTING THE BEST FROM THE NE602

TT, January and April 1989, provided a good deal of information on some of the many ways that the Signetics/Philips NE602 IC can be put to good use in amateur radio projects while, at the same time, pointing out that it was never intended to provide a state-of-the-art front-end receiver mixer. The NE602 chip includes a double-balanced mixer, associated bipolar oscillator and integral buffering. The mixer is *not* intended for the front-end of VHF receivers, but the oscillator section can be connected as an LC or crystal oscillator up to about 200MHz. The device was used in K2BLA's low-cost spectrum analyser featured over several months in *TT* during 1988.

QST's 'Technical Correspondence' column (May 1990) includes an interesting letter from Bob Zavrel, W7SX which notes that some amateurs have complained of inferior performance of the NE602, explains the way to use the device correctly, and discloses that Signetics are about to introduce an NE602A device identical in function and pin-out to the NE602 but providing an additional 4 to 5dB of dynamic range and a somewhat better noise figure — and will be a drop-in replacement for most existing NE602 designs.

W7SX, however, remains enthusiastic about the current NE602. He is convinced that most reports of 'inferior performance' are due either to unreasonable expectations or improper use. He explains that the device was originally intended to be used as the second-mixer in double-conversion VHF 'cellular radio' double-superhets. When used as a first mixer at HF, the device can provide a two-tone dynamic range of up to 85dB but this figure is

Fig 1. Some of the loop antennas tested by ZS6AKA in the early 1970s. No unbalanced line currents were detected with either twin or coaxial feeder despite the absence of a balun transformer.

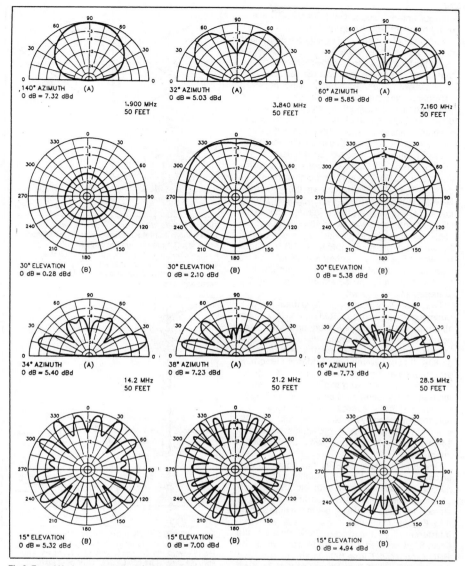

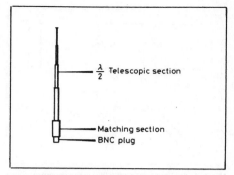

Fig 5. The AEA 'Hot Rod' λ/2 end-fed dipole antenna for 144MHz as reviewed by ZS6GM.

Fig 3. E- and H-plane radiation patterns for the loop of Fig 2 derived by W4ZCB using MININEC computer-simulation for 1.9, 3.84, 7.16, 14.2, 21.2 and 28.5MHz.

greatly diminished if a pre-amplifier is placed ahead of the mixer (with a noise figure of about 5 to 6dB pre-amplification should usually be unnecessary on HF). The oscillator can be configured as a traditional LC or VFO circuit, fundamental or overtone crystal oscillator, or even as a VCO (voltage-controlled oscillator). However the 602 is *not* a good choice as a VHF first mixer (6dB NF, 60-70dB dynamic range) because of its unacceptable noise performance and diminishing intermodulation performance at higher frequencies. When the 602 is used as a second mixer, the total gain of the preceding stages should not exceed about +10dB. The 602 requires only 2.5mA from a single 5V or (preferably) 6V DC supply.

W7SX stresses: "Because of its very high performance/power ratio, the 602 is an ideal choice for portable, HF direct-conversion and superhet receiver designs. The device will not provide the equivalent performance of a factory-built high-performance receiver with a 100dB dynamic range. It will, however, offer outstanding performance (80dB-plus dynamic range) when you consider its simplicity, power requirements, size and cost."

For pin-out, device and circuit information see *TT*, January and April 1989. The NE602 is stocked by some UK suppliers although not always easy to locate. The NE602A is still something to look forward to!

SMALL-SIGNAL DIODE-BRIDGE DETECTOR

Bruno Fagnini (Siemens-Albic AG) in *RF Design* (March 1990) describes a novel 200MHz detector for weak signals: **Fig 4**. Conventionally, a diode detector requires the amplitude of the input signal to be relatively high because of the need to exceed the forward voltage of the diodes. He concludes his article: "A simple detector for RF signals of small amplitude has been presented. It has been shown that a high output voltage can be obtained for further processing even when the RF signal has a small amplitude. Without amplifying the incoming signal, this high output is possible

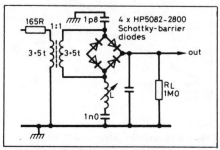

Fig 4. 200MHz diode-bridge detector suitable for small signals and using a resonant circuit to produce a resonance peak before detection.

because a resonant circuit has been introduced in the detector which produces a resonance peak before rectifying the signal. By selecting the appropriate components, ie diodes, transformer and inductor, the circuit operates in the very large frequency range from a few MHz to beyond 1GHz. Components specified for use at around 200MHz include: transformer 1:1, 3t each winding with 0.13 diameter wire; core Siemens B62152-AB-X30. The adjustable inductor (L) 99nH with Neosid core 99-048-96, 2¼ turns, 0.4mm diameter wire.

END-FED DIPOLE FOR HANDHELDS

The short ¼λ helically-wound 'rubber duck' is a most convenient antenna for hand-helds (provided that the power radiated close to the user's eyes is kept low) since such units are not usually expected to make contacts over difficult paths. However, it is not a particularly efficient type of antenna. One reason for this is that the 'ground plane' is dependent to a large extent on the capacitance of the hand-held transceiver to earth via the 'lossy' body of the user. An antenna that does not depend on an 'earth' connection should prove both more efficient and more consistent.

In *Radio-ZS* (February 1990), Chris Turner, ZS6GM, reviews favourably the AEA 'Hot Rod' 144MHz half-wave antenna: **Fig 5**. In tests with ZS6BTD via the local repeater, he reports achieving a very clear improvement in performance compared with a 'rubber ducky'. Laboratory tests showed that the feed impedance varied only over the range 40-65Ω compared with the 45-350Ω of a rubber duck helical where the feed impedance depended on how close the transceiver was to the body. He concludes: "It is my opinion that AEA has succeeded in overcoming the matching problems associated with end feeding a ½λ monopole. The result is a highly efficient portable antenna which performs well under laboratory conditions and in the field. If it were not for the 1m length I would have no hesitation in using this antenna permanently. For anyone who uses a handheld and needs to communicate from an area of poor signal strength, this antenna is certainly the answer."

Unfortunately for home constructors, it is not clear from this review of a commercial product what type of matching section AEA have included to transform the '50Ω' transceiver output to the 1000-1500Ω of an end-fed rod dipole. I recall that some multi-element UHF TV receiving antennas have been marketed with end-fed elements.

THE 8JK REVISITED AND THE NEW BRD-ZAPPER

The major breakthrough in the design of amateur rotary beams came in 1937 from Professor John D Kraus, W8JK (my apologies for giving him last month the callsign W8XK, that of the old Pittsburgh HF broadcast station, later KDKA). Both his work on the first close-spaced 'flat-top' bidirectional driven arrays (often implemented as fixed beams),

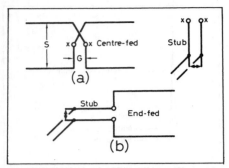

Fig 6. Basic single-section W8JK flat-top antennas. In 1981 Dr Kraus pointed out that the centre-fed arrangement with a typical spacing, S, of about λ/8 on the lowest frequency used, L can range from less than λ/2 to more than 1.5λ, permitting its use over a continuous frequency range of 3:1. With L equal to 7.3m (centre gap G forms part of the measurement) and S equal to 2.6m, the bidirectional gains are: 14MHz 5.7dBi; 21MHz 6.7dBi; 28MHz 7.7dBi; 50MHz 8.2dBi. Values for 18 and 24MHz bands can be interpolated. The end-fed version should provide roughly similar results if correctly tuned.

and that of Walter Van Roberts, W3CHO, shortly afterwards on the first close-spaced, two-element Yagi-Uda unidirectional parasitic array, were based on recognizing the significance of the work of Dr George Brown (RCA) on vertical monopole arrays for medium-wave broadcasting. Until then it had always been assumed that a Yagi parasitic reflector should be ¼λ behind the driven element, requiring a boom length, at least on 14MHz, that virtually ruled out flat-topped arrays, although a few amateurs had built Yagi rotary beams based on vertical elements spaced ¼λ apart.

By the time that UK amateur operation was closed down on 1 September 1939, knowledge of the family of 8JK bidirectional arrays and close-spaced Yagi arrays had crossed the Atlantic (see for example brief references in the first edition of the RSGB's *The Amateur Radio Handbook* (1938) but were still rare. It was not until the early post-war period that the three-element Yagi array began to establish itself worldwide. Due to their unidirectional properties, Yagi arrays became, and remain, far more popular than the 8JK driven bidirectional arrays, although these have some important advantages, including multiband operation with a single set of two elements: **Fig 6.**

In *QST* October 1981 (see *TT*, November 1982) Dr Kraus restated the very real attractions of the centre-fed design when it comes to multiband use, showing that a compact single-array with 7.3m elements can cover 14, 18, 21, 24, 28 and 50MHz bands. Among the plus points he listed in 1981 were: (1) continuous frequency span of more than 3 to 1 (with suitable matching/tuning arrangements); (2) no traps or loading coils; (3) no critical dimensions, as the entire antenna and feed system can be resonated; (4) it can be used horizontally or vertically for optimum radiation angle; (5) it is ideal for finding round-the-world (long path) openings; (6) it has theoretically zero radiation off the ends of the elements; (7) it can be fed with low-loss, inexpensive twin line (or very-low-loss cut-away 300Ω line or open-wire line); and (8) a compact array can cover many bands including the non-harmonically related bands. Minus points are that the bidirectional pattern does not give protection against continental European signals when the array is pointed towards North America; the forward gain is lower than with a good monoband Yagi array; and the low radiation resistance does not make it a good system to install indoors in the presence of metal structures etc (but in practice some amateurs have found the 8JK most satisfactory as a fixed indoor array). The end-fed form is particularly easy to install in, for example, a roof space or as an

outdoor antenna supported from a mast or tree using two light wooden spreaders.

For those who require unidirectional patterns, it is possible to convert the 8JK into this form by using the fact, shown in Dr Brown's classic paper, that when two driven elements are fed 135° out-of-phase with equal amplitudes of RF power, a cardioid radiation pattern results, giving forward gain and a deep rejection null in the reverse direction. Exploitation of this principle has led to such antennas as the ZL-Special, the HB9CV and G8PO antennas as described in *TT*, October 1981.

The ZL-Special was so named and described in print by Fred Judd, G2BCX, (*Shortwave Magazine* July 1950, pp337-9) where he commented on its origins: "Data on the aerial came to the writer from New Zealand, hence the name ZL-Special. Little is known of its origin save that it was designed in the USA just prior to the war, for commercial purposes. (This is probably a reference to the work of Dr Brown on MP broadcast antennas – G3VA). Since the war it has been modified and developed for amateur use by W5LHI, W0GZR and ZL3MH. Further tests and measurements made by the writer may be of interest."

The 'G8PO Special', as described by J E Ironmonger, G8PO, in the *RSGB Bulletin* (November 1947), provides a 'reversible' unidirectional fixed beam, originally developed as a result of a 'mistake' in cutting feeder lengths when erecting an 8JK. It uses two feeders of different length, ie arranged so that either feeder can be ⅛λ longer than the other by having two sockets into which the transmitter feed-line is connected: see **Fig 7.**

The same basic approach is also used in the antenna developed by Rudolf Baumgartner, HB9CV, which in recent years has become a popular 144MHz portable antenna, with unidirectional characteristics.

Now Rod Newkirk, W9BRD, has come up with an antenna that combines the relatively little-used 8JK end-fed arrangement with the 135° out-of-phase approach. This has been implemented as an indoor 21MHz fixed wire-beam pushing signals into Europe from the Chicago area with less interference from the western States than with the basic 88JK end-fed array (**Fig 8**) from which the 'BRD Zapper' (*QST* June 1990, pp28-29: 'The 'BRD Zapper: A Quick, Cheap and Easy "ZL Special" Antenna') was developed with the same basic dimensions.

Instead of feeding the elements 180° out of phase, they are driven 135° out of phase by feeding the stub λ/16 from the stub's shorted end so that the feed path to one element is ⅛λ (45°) longer or shorter than the other, which, after the stub's 180° phase reversal, produces the required

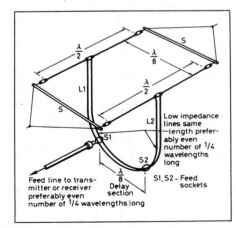

Fig 7. G8PO reversible unidirectional 14MHz array as described in 1947. Direction depends on whether transmitter feed is connected at S1 or S2. Note the delay line section is twisted once to provide the 135° out-of-phase drive.

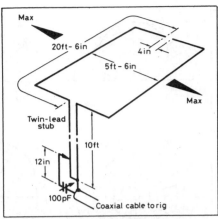

Fig 8. W9BRD's W8JK gamma-fed wire beam for 21MHz made to fit the dimensions of the bedroom it occupies. Dimensions are not critical for the elements but they should be close to λ/2 (total each), with the stub about λ/4 or multiples. Phasing point is fairly critical and should be selected as described.

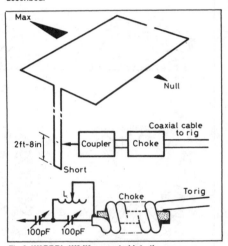

Fig 9. W9BRD's W8JK converted into the unidirectional 'BRD Zapper. L consists of 10 turns of No 16 wire, 1.5in dia, space-wound. Broadcast-type variable capacitors can be used at powers up to about 100W. Adjust inductor tap for lowest SWR. Coaxial choke made of 30 turns of RG-58 cable wound on a ferrite rod.

(180-45 = 135°) phase shift. W9BRD points out: "You can find the proper feed point on the stub by 'sniffing' signals of known origin along *one side* of the stub with the insulated centre conductor of some coax hooked to a receiver. (Start looking for this point by measuring λ/16 up from the bottom.) Directivity is reversed by selecting the opposite side of the twin-lead stub... Pattern distortion through incidental radiation and pickup must be minimized. The coupler must be built in the most compact form possible, mounted right at the stub, and isolated to keep the feed line from distorting the pattern. Such isolation is done at W9BRD via a home-brew coaxial choke made of 30 turns of the antenna's RG58 feed line wound on a ferrite rod just before the matching network: see **Fig 9(b)**. The single wire run from matching network to antenna had better be no more than an inch or two. Here, I'm borrowing on the single-wire-feed theme by Windom. Since any circuitry above the choke will be hot with RF a bulky matching unit will not do... System Q is lower with wider spacings but gain is maximum with the elements spaced ⅛λ."

SOLAR CYCLES AND PROPAGATION

It now seems evident that Solar Cycle 22, which began in September 1986, passed through its high

EASY-TO-BUILD 144/28MHz CONVERTER

Mike Parkin, G0JMI, had need to help another amateur to listen to his GB2CW slow morse transmissions. He had tried to build a 144MHz to 28MHz converter from a kit but had not been able to make it work satisfactorily. This encouraged G0JMI to develop an easy-to-build converter which in practice took him about four hours to build from start to finish (including preparing the PCB) at a cost of less than £10 using all the bits (including the crystal, Dalon pen and etching solution) acquired at the Longleat and Mercury Radio Rallies.

The converter worked reasonably well when connected to G0JMI's five-element Yagi antenna, with GB3VHF only about 3 or 4dB down on his factory-made Microwave Modules converter. G6JOI also tested it on a three-element 50MHz Yagi, receiving G0JMI's signal as 5/9 over a 30-mile path. G0JMI writes:

"I have tried to keep to a KISS approach. The converter **(Fig 10)** was built on double-sided copper-clad fibre-glass board, etched after drawing on the circuit layout with a Dalon marking pen, as shown. The passive components are attached to the top of the board, onto the PCB copper tracks directly, and the transistors mounted under it (ie screened from the inductors etc) with their leads passing through counter-sunk holes to maintain the insulation. The BFY90 transistors used have a fourth leg that is the screen terminal; this is soldered directly to the copper screen. The FET is soldered into position on top of the PCB (the opposite side to the bipolar BFY90s). Components mounted on the top of the board are soldered to the bottom of the board by passing the component's leg through suitably drilled holes (see PCB layout diagram **Fig 11**). The board was mounted in an aluminium box with BNC connectors used to attach the coaxial cables."

G6JOI is now finding the converter very useful when listening to the GB2CW morse practice transmissions.

breakers that had been designed to protect the networks from power surges induced by geomagnetic storms, following the experience of Sweden where the electricity grid was lost for several days during the high solar-activity of 1958. Whether, in future, the depletion of the protective ozone layer may increase the number of high-energy and UV particles reaching ground level to hazardous levels at sunspot maxima remains to be seen.

Mike Parkin, G0JMI, has, since February 1988, been keeping his own regular weekly observations of the Sun in the hope of being able to gain an indication of when events, such as aurora, may be likely to result in interesting 50MHz propagation.

He writes: "The observations have been made using a 60mm refractor telescope that I set up in the back garden to observe the Sun by means of projection on to a sheet of white paper. (Need I repeat the warning *never* to look at the Sun through binoculars or a telescope! - G3VA) The image formed is about 8cm in size and any solar activity, in the form of sunspot groups or other similar activity, shows up fairly well.

"After making a drawing of what has been observed I calculate the sunspot count by using the British Astronomical Association's recommended formula: Spot Count = K (10g + N) where K is approximately equal to 3.5 (for my case), g is equal to the number of sunspot groups seen, and N is the total number of spots counted overall. Thus, if I observe two groups of spots with each group containing three spots each, then the count for that observation would be 91. I use a K value of 3.5 that has been derived from examination of the solar data given on GB2RS each week.

"Bearing in mind the interest that Solar Cycle 22 has generated, I feel the bar chart of **Fig 12** may be of interest to *TT* readers; it shows clearly the rapid rise and fall (?) of Cycle 22. Each bar represents the total count observed for the particular month – it is of interest to look at the March 1989 bar – this was the month of the largest aurora since 1937 and was visually seen and photographed from my back garden in Alton, Hampshire. The results show a dip in the count that month (following the major geomagnetic storm of February 1989 — G3VA)."

Many of us find the terms used by the professional radiophysicists in discussing the ionosphere pretty esoteric, with the result that the whole subject is often dismissed as an arcane branch of science despite the important effects on radio communication. I was therefore interested to find a long, *readable*, review paper "Ionospheric effects on modern electronic systems" by Dr John M Goodman (US Naval Research Laboratory) and Dr Jules Aarons (Boston University Center for Space Research) in *Proc IEEE*, March 1990, pp512-528. This surveys ionospheric effects from ELF to earth-space (transionospheric paths) propagation at SHF, listing no less than 95, mostly recent, reference sources.

It seems worth digesting briefly some points from the paper which notes that "The HF band is

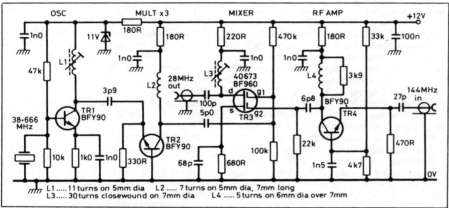

Fig 10. G0JMI's 'simple-to-build' 144MHz to 28MHz converter.

L1 ..... 11 turns on 5mm dia   L2 ..... 7 turns on 5mm dia, 7mm long
L3 ..... 30 turns closewound on 7mm dia   L4 ..... 5 turns on 6mm dia over 7mm

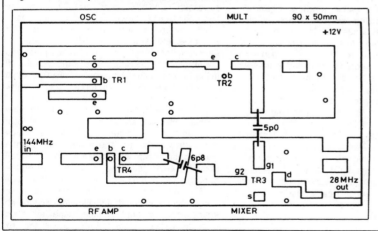

Fig 11. PCB layout of the G0JMI converter.

maximum last autumn, 10 years after the peak of Cycle 21 in 1979, showing once again that the '11-year cycle' is an average, not an absolute, period. Having begun listening on HF in my early teens in 1935, this marks my sixth peak, a fact that brings home to one how quickly the years pass! I am glad to say that my log last year shows reasonably good use of the exceptional DX conditions on some at least of the higher HF bands.

Not only does Cycle 22 appear to have produced the highest sunspot numbers since the all-time record peak of 1957/58 (supporting the belief that solar activity has been, on average, rising steadily over the past 400 years) but also, as a consequence, the second half of 1989 proved to be the most prolific period of high-energy cosmic-ray/particle

production by the Sun since continuous monitoring of cosmic-ray activity reaching the Earth by neutron detectors was begun in 1957. A major burst of activity (solar flare) was recorded by the team at the Canadian University of Calgary on 29 September 1989. Only particles of very high energy (about a billion electron volts) reach ground level because of interactions with the Earth's magnetosphere and atmosphere. The levels experienced in the final months of 1989 were such that there was a potential hazard to passengers in aircraft flying at heights of 10-15km as well as to spacecraft. A magnetic storm in February 1989 attracted media interest by causing a major blackout of electricity supplies in Quebec Province, despite the use of resistive circuit

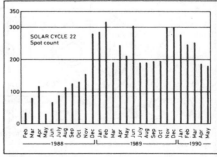

Fig 12. G0JMI's bar chart of his observations of the Sun during Solar Cycle 22 from February 1988 to May 1990.

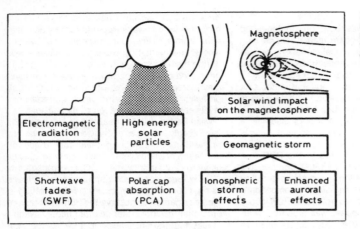

Fig 13. Effects on the ionosphere that are directly related to solar flares and related activity on the Sun.

by far the most sensitive to ionospheric effects. Indeed, HF radio waves experience some form of almost every conceivable propagation mode, including groundwave, line-of-sight and earth-space modes, reflected modes, refracted modes, ducted modes, chordal (earth-detached) modes, and scatter modes. The major ionospheric layers possess characteristic plasma frequencies that lie within the HF band, and as a result, ionospheric interaction is most pronounced... One of the major problem areas that arise in connection with HF performance is the variability in coverage and reliability for a fixed transmitter site and a specified frequency...

"Included among the quasi-global disturbance phenomena that may impact long-haul HF systems are: Sudden Frequency Deviation (SFD) and Short Wave Fades (SWF), both of which occur within seconds of the appearance of an X-ray flare on the solar surface. These events are important only on the sunlit portion of the ionosphere and the effects are diminished as the ionospheric distance from the sub-solar point increases. Less immediate but near-term phenomena associated with energetic solar protons are also encountered. PCAs (Polar Cap Absorption) are perhaps the most catastrophic events in connection with HF radio propagation in the high-latitude zone, with attenuation over skywave circuits in excess of 100dB sometimes encountered. These absorption conditions may last from hours to days. Fortunately, they are rare events not typically encountered at solar minimum and observed about once a month at solar maximum.

"Probably the most interesting phenomenon to be encountered at HF is the ionospheric storm **(Fig 13)** which gives rise to a hierarchy of effects at midlatitudes... it may be devastating since it may limit ionosopheric support in the normally-propagating higher frequencies, causing a non-absortive 'blackout' of HF trunks in the affected area."

The following is a summary of ionospheric disturbances affecting HF propagation based on a table in the *Proc IEEE* paper:

Sudden ionospheric disturbances (SID): has the effect, in the sunlit hemisphere, of strong D-layer absorption (HF blackouts) and F-region effects which start approximately simultaneously and last about a half-hour. Around solar maximum occur about twice a week; at solar minimum about twice a year. Probable cause is enhanced solar X-ray and EUV flux from solar flare.

Polar cap absorption (PCA): results in intense signal absorption in magnetic polar regions, starting a few hours after a flare and lasting one to several days. Occurs about once a month around solar maximum. Does not occur during solar minimum. Probable cause solar protons 1-100MeV.

Magnetic storm: affects F-region causing an *increase* of f_oF2 (ie higher MUF) during first day, then depressed f_oF2 (ie lower MUF), possibly lasting for days with strong daily variations. About 26 per year at solar maximum, 22 per year at solar minimum. Probable cause is interaction of solar low-energy plasma (solar wind) with Earth's magnetic field, causing energetic electron precipitation, auroral effects, heating and TID generation.

Auroral absorption (AA): produces enhanced absorption along the auroral oval (located in high latitudes) in areas hundred to thousand kilometres in extent. This is a complex phenomena lasting from hours to days. Essentially omnipresent, probably caused by precipitation of electrons with energies a few tens of keV within an oval region equatorward of the polar cap.

Travelling ionospheric disturbances (TIDs): these cause changes of f_oF2 with corresponding changes of MUF, sometimes periodic. Typically the periods are from tens of minutes to hours. Essentially omni-present with larger scales enhanced during magnetic storms. Probable cause is atmospheric waves.

144MHz 'MEF' SNIFFER (DF) ANTENNA

The April *TT* noted the development by 1943 of the German Funkabwehr 'Guerteipeiler' (Stomach direction-finder), a miniaturised seven-valve, 3-20MHz (with plug-in coils) receiver carried in a form of satchel across the stomach under outer clothing and with a loop antenna around the neck of the user. This equipment was used by the ORPO (police) DF teams when closing in on an urban clandestine transmitter. Such equipments, including those developed in the UK and USA, became known as 'sniffers' and were intended only for use in the final stages of a 'foxhunt'.

Today, although most amateur DF contests in the UK are still run on 1.8MHz with its reliable groundwave propagation, in many other countries the amateur 'foxhunts' usually take place on 144MHz, often without the use of motorised transport. In *Radio-ZS* (February 1990), John Williscroft, ZS6EF, describes his novel MEF (Miniature Electromagnetic-coupled Foxhunting) antenna constructed on a 420 by 150mm single-sided glass-laminate PCB and used with a well-screened receiver. It was designed to complement his handheld 'DEF' DF receiver (described in *Radio-ZS* March 1990) to which it is mechanically attached to form a gun-shaped assembly. His DEF receiver is specifically designed as a sniffer with high immunity to strong, local RF breakthrough, but the antenna could be used with other 144MHz receivers/transceivers if sufficiently well-screened. The loops are formed from the PCB copper but it is possible to substitute the tracking with copper wire (not less than 2.5mm diameter) on a non-conductive piece of laminate etc.

The antenna is in effect a miniature tuned loop (similar in concept and coupling to the I1ARZ transmitting loop) as the 'driven' element, plus an in-line parasitic loop as a reflector tuned 1.5MHz below the fox frequency. Dimensions shown in **Fig 14** are stated to be fairly critical, particularly the dimension between the loops which ZS6EF suggests should be checked carefully. The quality and type of the two tuning capacitors are important. Small amounts of inductance in the capacitor affect the field pattern at the ends of the inductor; the capacitors must have small metal parts and preferably be of the variable dielectric type shown in Fig 14 with a capacitance of 1-10pF (air-spaced trimmers have too much inductance; beehive capacitors are not recommended).

After completing assembly and connecting the coaxial cable, test and align the antenna at least 1m away from any metal structures; this can be done with a GDO. Tune the driven element to the fox frequency with an insulated trimming tool. Place the GDO coil close to the element on the opposite side of the loop to the capacitor. A deep dip should be obtained with the GDO 40mm or so away from the element; a shallow dip may be an indication of an unsatisfactory capacitor. Next tune the parasitic loop 1.5MHz below the fox frequency. When the coaxial cable is plugged into the receiver (which *must* be well enough shielded so that local signals do not break through when no antenna is connected), very carefully peak the tuning of the loops for maximum signal with the antenna pointed straight at the test transmitter.

Finally, it is suggested that the antenna board is covered with Solarfilm or similar covering to protect it from water, humidity changes and accidental knocks. In use the antenna detects the polarisation and direction (including whether above or below your position) of the fox transmitter (always optimise reception first for polarisation). Unfortunately there are few commercial 144MHz receivers with sufficient immunity to local signals that can prevent signal breakthrough when very close to the transmitter, and a special-purpose receiver can give better results. □

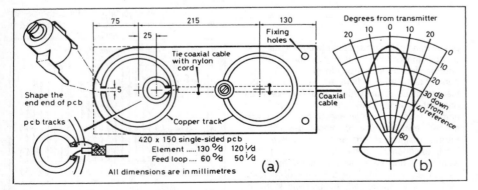

Fig 14. (a) The 144MHz 'MEF' DF antenna as used by ZS6EF. Place the coaxial cable on the non-copper side of the board. (b) Pattern measured using 200mW test transmitter and 60dB attenuator in series with receiver. The level of the S-meter was adjusted back to the same value for each 5° of rotation.

TOPICS

PAT HAWKER G3VA

OPERATORS YES - BUT BASICALLY A TECHNICAL HOBBY?

WHEN *HAM RADIO* BEGAN publication in 1968 under the editorship of Jim Fisk, W1DTY, it rapidly showed itself to be a near-ideal source of useful technical information and ideas for all experimentally-minded amateurs. It introduced many ways of improving receivers, transmitters, antennas and simple test equipment for HF, VHF and microwaves; not only constructional articles but also useful guidance on applied theory, propagation etc.

It established itself as the only amateur radio periodical of standing that concentrated entirely on the technical and scientific side of the hobby, devoting no space to contests, awards, band reports, social events etc. During its 22 years of publication, *HAM RADIO* articles have been the source of innumerable items in *Technical Topics* - with Jim Fisk (until his death in 1981) and then Rich Rosen always happy to see digests of *HAM RADIO* articles appearing on this side of the Atlantic.

Thus the closure of *HAM RADIO* following the June 1990 issue is a matter of deep personal regret but also, I feel, a sad reflection on the changing role of our hobby - from a basically technical and scientific hobby recognized as such in influential, regulatory circles moving increasingly in the direction of a purely fun hobby for appliance operators, with little interest in the technology unless this arises from their professional work.

Dick Ross, K2MGA, publisher of *CQ* (which has taken over unexpired subscriptions and which will in future feature articles by some of the regular *HAM RADIO* contributors without adopting its technical-only approach) puts it thus: "The true ham technician - the person who actually dug into the innards of a radio and made it work, the person who experimented with novel antenna designs and new modes of communications in amateur radio, was becoming a smaller and smaller minority . . . The technicians among us no longer provide the numbers needed to support a monthly magazine of the calibre of *HAM RADIO*. Those who question that statement need only examine the contents of *QST* over the past few years as it relentlessly moves further away from its traditional role as a technical journal, in response to the changing needs of its readers . . . Let's get on with the world as it is, not as we'd like it to be." Similarly *CQ's* editor, Alan Dorhoffer, K2EEK writes: "Today's amateurs are operator orientated and somewhat less technically geared . . . in a shrinking technological society. Amateurs like things to remain the same forever. Things change, people change and most certainly the hobby has changed . . . It may not be what everyone likes or wants, but this is reality."

Personally I find these opinions, while realistic, deeply depressing. I have always believed that the operator of a radio station (whether or not it is composed entirely out of commercially-manufactured equipment) can be - should be - keenly interested in the technology. Contests, awards, DX-peditions, QSL cards etc were intended to act as spurs to developing better, more reliable, more portable/transportable low-cost equipment and enabling us to understand better the capabilities of the radio spectrum. Yes, Amateur Radio is an interesting fun hobby - but it is (or was) also basically a technical and scientific hobby held in high regard in professional and regulatory circles, serving as a valuable form of self-training and contributing to the art of radio communication.

[Reassuring news is that preliminary results of the RadCom Readers Survey indicate that more technical articles (but simpler ones) are what is wanted by RSGB members - Ed]

In this connection, I have been dismayed this year to find the Science Reference and Information Service Library off Chancery Lane, part of the British Library, and formerly the Patents Office Library, on which I have always depended in the preparation of *TT*, has closed its files on virtually all the overseas and some UK Amateur Radio and hobby-radio periodicals. For many years it has provided open-access to *QST*, *HAM RADIO*, *73 Magazine*, *Amateur Radio (Australia)*, *Short-Wave Magazine*, *Radio-REF* and at various periods *CQ*, *Electron* (VERON), *VHF Communications*, *QRV* (Germany) all of which have now been discontinued at the Library - possibly also *Radio-ZS* although some 1990 issues are still appearing.

Earlier this year, when this change of policy was becoming evident, I wrote to the Head of Technical Services at this famous library, stressing that many of these journals were of interest to professional communications engineers as well as to hobbyists. In reply, EJ Copley wrote:

" The Library is in a difficult position in that it is seriously under funded and simply does not have enough money to maintain the subscriptions to all its periodicals. Cancellations have been, and continue to be, inevitable; we very much regret that it is impossible to effect them without depriving one or other group of users of the titles they have grown used to finding here. I am impressed by your arguments in favour of the amateur radio periodicals and would like to reinstate them, but cannot - we cancelled them last year as an economy, and since then our financial position has deteriorated still further. The best I can say, and I am sorry it does not sound very promising, is that if things do improve we will be glad to think again."

So it would seem that Government parsimony will have to be blamed if *Technical Topics* ranges less widely in future! A few years ago the idea of the British Library not taking such world-famous technical periodicals as *QST* would have been unthinkable! Sic transit gloria . . .

KN5S'S LOW-DRIVE, HIGH POWER LINEAR

IT HAS BEEN STRESSED before that the design and construction of a really high-power linear amplifier calls for considerable technical expertise and care in view of the high-voltage involved, coupled with the high-cost and vulnerability of modern valves and transistors capable of delivering large amounts of RF power. There is still much to be said for adopting the valve rather than an all-solid-state approach.

In *CQ* (July 1990), Mark Mandelkern, KN5S (a number of whose *QST* articles have previously been noted in *TT*) describes a powerful 4CX1000A tetrode amplifier **(Fig 1)**. It is capable of delivering 1.5kW output throughout the range 1.8 to 50MHz with only 30W drive, almost all of which is absorbed in the 50 ohm grid resistor eliminating the need to match the input circuit or provide neutralization. In Class AB1, drive is only required to overcome circuit losses, usually under a watt.

Clearly this American amplifier is designed for the US legal limit, runs well above the UK legal limit and would not be cheap to construct.

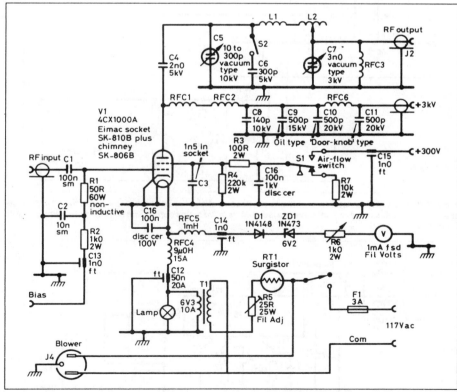

Fig 1. The RF deck of KN5S's 1.5kW linear amplifier. This diagram is included in *Technical Topics* only to show the basic approach adopted to obtain optimum life of the valve and general reliability. Construction would require reference to the detailed articles in *CQ* and *QST* to include the bias and screen protection circuits incorporated in the power and switching sections. The feedback capacitors indicate the boundaries of the shielded grid compartments.

Nevertheless the design features are of general interest even for amplifiers intended to be run at considerably lower power. The July article is not complete in itself. KN5S uses a 3kV HT supply from a previous project and does not cover the 300V screen supply which needs to incorporate adequate protection circuitry. Similarly, blower cool-down delay circuitry, low-pass TVI filter and sequencing control for the antenna relay and amplifier have been covered in *HAM RADIO*, November 1987, page 17. The classic pi-network output circuit uses two vacuum-capacitors and a roller inductor.

A point worth noting is the care taken by KN5S to lengthen the life of his high-cost tetrode by reducing and monitoring the heater voltage. This topic was addressed earlier in *Technical Topics* (June 1982) under the heading "Use and abuse of valves". Then it was noted that good filament management is particularly important with high-power directly-heated valves having thoriated tungsten filaments. However, it is not unimportant even with indirectly-heated valves with oxide-coated cathodes, where the heater voltage should be kept within at least 5% of the nominal value as measured directly at the valve socket. KN5S claims that, in his experience, for 6.0V nominal 5.7 to 5.8V have proved optimum with a three minute warm-up period achieved by using a thermal delay relay in the bias circuit. He warns that failure to observe this warm-up time may destroy the valve. An air-flow sensor switch disconnects the screen voltage should the blower fail to keep the cooling air flowing correctly.

A Surgistor (GC25-933-S) is in the primary of the filament transformer to reduce in-rush current at switch-on. The AC heater voltage is diode rectified (lifting the DC voltage above ACrms) and monitored with an "expanded scale voltmeter" based on using a 1mA FSD meter in conjunction with a 6.2V zener diode (1N473), reading approximately 5 to 6V (ACrms) with the heater sampling line connected directly to the valve socket with its own feedthrough capacitor. KN5S mentions that zener diodes behave rather strangely at low currents: "It may be necessary to try diodes of different ratings from different manufactures. I obtained linearity from only 5.4 to 6.0V, which is more than adequate - for those who demand precision, an op-amp expanded scale metering circuit might be easier." The meter scale does not need detailed calibration since its purpose is to show whether heater voltage is above or below the chosen datum point. The voltage can then be corrected by means of a 25 ohm, 25W wirewound adjustable resistor (R5) in the primary of the heater transformer (this rating is for 117V AC mains, for 240V mains the value may need to be increased).

KN5S continues: "RT1, an in-rush current limiter, provides gradual heater warm-up. Using a 6.3V, 10A transformer for a 6V, 9A tube lets you adjust the heater voltage by varying R5.

It also allows for some drop in RT1 . . . The required three minute warm-up period is provided by a thermal delay relay in the bias using a normally open three minute Amperite no 6N0180 tube. The bias control and delay tube are located on the RF deck, while the circuit forms part of the control panel . . ."

KN5S provides a detailed tuning-up procedure emphasising the precautions needed with high-gain tetrode amplifiers of this class. For example, he warns that tuning up key-down with low drive should be avoided as it can produce over 100mA negative screen current. Instead, use a pulsed driving signal, for example using dits from a keyer at 60WPM and full drive level, always using a monitor scope.

Although many precautions need to be taken, in practice if this is done such an amplifier can give very reliable service. KN5S reports that his has given reliable service for 19 years under very strenuous contest operating conditions.

ACID SPILLS CAN BE COSTLY

IN THE AUGUST TT, in introducing an item on safety precautions to reduce hazards when handling lead-acid batteries, I recalled how I had once accidentally damaged beyond repair a jacket when an old 2V accumulator tipped over undetected. An even more costly experience recently befell Brian Davies, G3OYU. This underlines the need to be ready to apply remedial measures in double-quick time. He writes:

"Part of my business is setting up public address systems. Many events do not have access to mains power so batteries are normally used. I use tractor batteries of about 95Ah capacity. I was transporting two of these in my E-registered Saab 9000i and one rolled over when taking a corner somewhat fast! I heard the noise and stopped immediately. By the time I had climbed out of the car, walked round to the back and opened the boot, a quantity of battery acid had spilled out onto the floor of the boot and seeped under the back seat.

"I rushed home, not more than 15 minutes drive, removed the boot floor and flushed out everywhere with a strong solution of sodium

HEATER VOLTAGE REGULATION

IN THE KN5S AMPLIFIER, the heater voltage is monitored with the aid of the expanded-scale voltmeter and then adjusted manually to cope with the appreciable voltage variations that can occur on mains supplies - particularly if your house is well away from the HV line-transformer and subject to wide variations in the load when, for example, a large number of domestic ovens are switched on.

In 'Reflecties door PA0SE' (*Electron*, August 1990), Dick Rollema includes details of a stabiliser used by Leo Duursma, PA0LMD to stabilise the AC heater supply to a 4CX250 amplifier requiring 6A at 6V (or a little under) (**Fig 2**). This automatically adjusts the AC supply voltage across the primary of the heater transformer which has its secondary rated at 7V to compensate for voltage reduced by the action of the stabiliser. Note that the electronics of the stabiliser are not isolated from the mains supply so suitable precautions should be taken to avoid potential hazards. It would appear that such a stabiliser would be suitable for use also with amplifier valves requiring a stabilised heater-voltage at up to about 10A.

PA0LMD also draws attention to an adjustable PSU (**Fig 3**) using the SGS L396 IC regulator. The DC output is adjustable from 5.1 to 15V with a maximum current of 4A (but note minimum load must exceed 100mA). The ripple voltage is less than 20mV. This could be useful for heater/filament supplies with suitably-rated valves or as a general-purpose PSU.

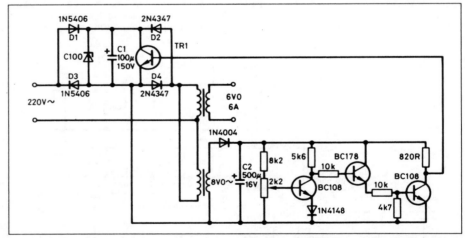

Fig 2. PA0LMD's AC regulator for stabilising the heater voltage applied to valves such as the 4CX250. Note that the electronics of the regulator are not isolated from the mains supply and suitable precautions should be taken.

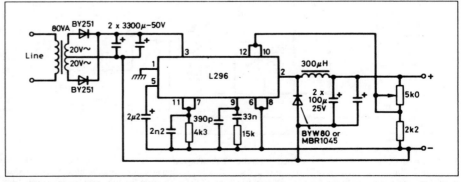

Fig 3. Variable DC PSU using L296 IC regulator. Output adjustable between 5.1 and 15V with maximum current 4A, minimum load 100mA.

bicarbonate in order to neutralize the acid. This it did well, but not quickly enough. Much of the boot floor had soaked up enough acid to make a replacement necessary as the man-made fibre covering the plywood had dissolved! The metal-work beneath the boot floor and the spare wheel were saved, but the carpet under the back seat was not. It too was made of man-made fibre and had dissolved.

"A couple of hours later I stood back to assess the damage, rather more than I had expected. The local Saab agent quoted me for the replacement parts, a new boot floor plus rear carpet and labour for fitting. Nearly £600!

"The point I want to make is that if acid is spilt, neutralizing it rapidly is critical: sodium bicarbonate is cheap, easy to obtain and effective. Have some available when the unthinkable may happen and acid is spilt."

THE BI-SQUARE ARRAY REAPPEARS

RECENT *TECHNICAL TOPICS* ITEMS have described various forms of antennas using closed loops. But there is another approach in which the loop is open rather than closed, formed from two full-wave sections bent to form a square with an insulator at the top junction, voltage-fed at the base with (600 ohm) open-wire or (450 ohm) ladder line **(Fig 4)**. C Drayton Cooper, N4LBJ (*HAM RADIO*, May 1990) shows that this old favourite, dropped from most recent handbooks, known as a bi-square array, "works wonders on the new 17m band".

Such an antenna is usually hung from a single, high support to give vertical polarization. With a suitable ATU providing balanced output to the transmission line, the whole system can be resonated on several bands. N4LBJ finds his 18MHz bi-square works quite well also on 14 and 21MHz, though gain and directivity will differ somewhat to that on its design frequency. Because current flow reverses at the half-wave points, elements A and A' are in phase: similarly B and B' are in phase. The antenna thus operates as four collinear elements in phase yielding about 4 to 5dBd gain on its design frequency with broadside directivity. It was originally derived in this form as a variant of the once-popular Lazy-H fixed array (I once had a Lazy-H on 28MHz and was delighted with the results). N4LBJ hung his bi-square with two 53ft lengths of wire for a full wavelength at 18.1MHz from a 65ft self-supporting metal tower. Although in the past such antennas generally used wooden (non-conductive) masts, he did not find any obviously detrimental effects. Amateurs without such high supports could probably accommodate a bi-square cut for 28 or 50MHz.

There can be little doubt that the greater use now being made of the 18 and 24MHz "WARC" bands is leading to a revival of interest in antennas capable of working over more than a single band - for example the W8JK and 'BRD Zapper described last month. Another article in *HAM RADIO* (May 1990) by Robert Wilson KL7ISA covers "Non-resonant delta and V-beam Antennas" including a design optimized for 14MHz that can be contained in an area 104ft by 93ft or so **(Fig 5)**. He also introduces the concept of a tie wire between the ends of the V wires, including the terminating resistor (he forms a single 800 ohm non-inductive resistor by paralleling fifty 39K, 2W carbon resistors soldered between two parallel copper wires). This will cope with an average output power of some 200W since half the power will be radiated before reaching the resistor. SSB only can be used at slightly higher powers but excessive average power will quickly

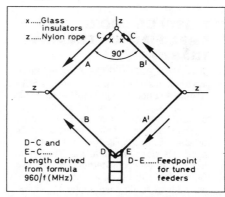

Fig 4. 18MHz bi-square array used by N4LBJ capable of reasonable performance on 14 and 28MHz bands. N4LBJ considers it performs best when feedpoint is about a quarter to a half wavelength above ground but adequate performance possible at lower heights, down to about 3 to 5ft above ground. Note that since the array is voltage fed, care should be taken with medium or high power that this does not represent a hazard to people or animals.

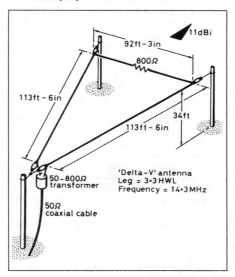

Fig 5. KL7ISA's broadband Delta-V antenna optimised for 14MHz band. Requires a triangular (pie-shaped) area 104ft by 93ft base.

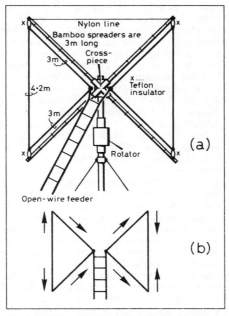

Fig 6. Multi-band V-dipole for 14, 18, 21, 24 and 28MHz bands as used by PA3BNT.

result in a permanent change to the value of the resistors.

A low-cost form of multiband V-dipole which can be used with open-wire feeder and suitable ATU on 14, 18, 21, 24 and 30MHz stems from Maarten v.d. Velde, PA3BNT and appears in 'Reflecties door PA0SE' (*Electron*, August 1990) **(Fig 6)**. This broad band wire dipole uses a framework made from four 3m bamboo spreaders with a centre cross-piece. It could be used as a fixed or rotary antenna.

IS IT REALLY ANCIENT MODULATION?

THERE HAS BEEN RECENT correspondence in both *Practical Wireless* and American journals seeking to encourage more use of low power AM on some of the less crowded bands such as 1.8 and 28MHz or on VHF where it requires less spectrum than FM/NBFM transmissions. Over the years, this view has been echoed several times in *Technical Topics* and there is still quite a bit of AM in use, for example on 28MHz using low cost converted CB AM transceivers re-crystalled for the band.

There is still much to be said in favour of "old fashioned" double sideband with carrier amplitude modulation. With high-level (anode or anode/screen) modulation of a power amplifier (calling for an audio power about half that of the DC input power to a Class C amplifier) it is much easier to achieve near "broadcast quality" transmissions suitable for reception on any HF broadcast-type receiver, without being limited by the use of narrow SSB filters and the need for accurate carrier re-insertion. There is no such thing as good quality SSB with amateur HF transceivers, at least by broadcast standards.

AM lost popularity for a number of reasons: spectrum conservancy and reduction of heterodynes on crowded HF bands (not that all SSB transmissions keep within a 3kHz bandwidth!); a belief that much more effective use of power resulted from eliminating the carrier and one sideband; lower cost by eliminating the need for a high power audio amplifier/modulator, etc. On VHF, AM lingered longer but finally lost out to FM in spite of its better "punch" mainly on grounds of cost, greater tendency to cause EMC problems and the fact that RF bipolar power transistors were not really suitable for coping with the high peaks on the collectors (double the voltage bus). However voltage limitations are much less serious with power FETs than with the usual bipolars. AM and FM share the advantage over SSB that the power amplifier need not be linear, permitting the use of more efficient Class C or D stages (note that any further stage after AM modulation must of course be linear). It is easier to apply quite severe speech processing and clipping to an AM signal than to SSB.

For radio broadcasting, there are now various forms of high-efficiency AM systems, some depending on novel use of digital techniques and some developed from the old carrier-controlled forms of transmission originally developed in the 1930s.

While we would not recommend the use of AM on the main HF bands, it should be remembered that there is probably no easier piece of equipment to build and get going satisfactorily than a 1.8MHz AM rig, based on either still available valves or FET solid state. The main practical disadvantage is the low level of daylight activity on the band, often limited to the occasional local net at weekends.

In the heyday of AM, some amateurs were proud of achieving "near broadcast quality" speech, significantly better than the "communi-

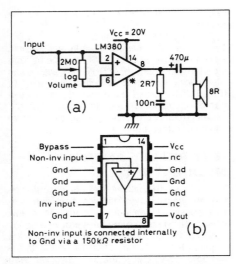

Fig 7. For applications requiring less gain than the TBA820M, use of the LM380 audio output IC would be a suitable alternative. (b) Pin-out diagram for LM380.

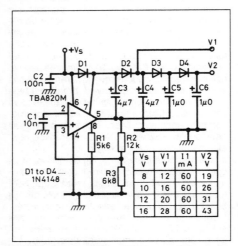

Fig 10. A 1.5W DC/DC converter (f about 40kHz) using TBA820M. Additional filtering and screening may be advisable where RFI may be a problem.

Vs V	V1 V	I1 mA	V2 V
8	12	60	19
10	16	60	26
12	20	60	31
16	28	60	43

A USEFUL AUDIO AMPLIFIER IC - THE SGS TBA820M

BOB ANDERSON, G4AEV draws attention to - and sings the praises of - the SGS TBA82OM audio power amplifier IC. In his case he has used this device successfully to repair an old but trusty FT101 transceiver when its original (and now unobtainable) Sanyo STK-401 audio module failed. He considers that the TBA82OM provides an ideal replacement for the audio devices found in that generation of HF transceivers, listing its advantages as follows:

(1)   It requires only a single supply rail (upper limit 16V) and delivers over 1W audio output from a 9V DC rail.

(2)   Unlike many of the alternative available audio power ICs, the device is happy feeding an earthed load, eg headphones.

(3)   It requires only 8 - 10 external resistors and capacitors (many of which were already on the PCB of his FT101 Mk 1).

(4)   It is cheap (only about 53p from Radiospares (RS) part number 30 2-491), and seems to work first time with no trace of instability.

(5)   With a 33 ohm resistor used for RF it gives some 45dB gain, into an 8 ohm load.

For applications requiring less gain, the basically similar LM380 would be a suitable alternative (maximum fixed loop gain of about 34dB).

The information shown in **Figs 7-10** is taken from RS data sheets 2927, covering the LM380, TBA82OM; dual (stereo) amplifiers TDA2004; and the high quality monolithic audio amplifier TDA2030 capable of providing some 21W output into a 4 ohm load. **Fig 10** shows the use of the TBA82OM as a 1.5W DC/DC converter. When used with a voltage doubler rectifier this can provide up to 30V output from a 12V supply.

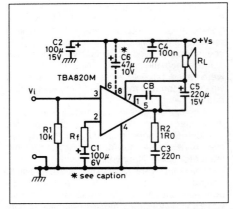

Fig 8. Using the TBA82OM with load connected to the supply voltage. Capacitor C6 must be used when high ripple rejection is required.

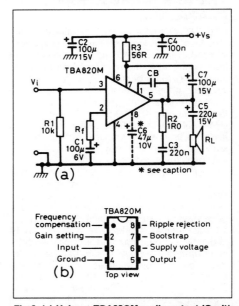

Fig 9. (a) Using a TBA82OM audio output IC with load connected to ground. Capacitor C6 must be used when high ripple rejection is required.

---

cations quality" speech heard today, restricted and processed to a bandwidth of 300 to 3000Hz. I was recently reminded of good quality amateur AM transmissions, extending back to the 1930s, in reviewing for another journal a new book *Broadcast Sound Technology* by Michael Talbot-Smith, for many years Training Manager in Audio at the BBC Engineering Training Centre, published by Butterworths (Library classification 621.3893, ISBN 0-408-05442-5). This book provides an unusually clear, understandable and readable explanation as an introductory text on the whole field of acoustics and modern audio technology at a practical level - studio acoustics, microphones, loudspeakers and virtually the gamut of modern audio technology without going into subjects too deeply or mathematically. A book well worth seeking out and borrowing from your local library even if this means asking them to obtain one for you from a central library.

A lot of sound common sense without the excesses of much writing on hi-fi!

SOLAR FLARES - PROBLEMS TO COME?

TT NOTED LAST MONTH the problems that can arise from the magnetic storms and high-energy particle radiation associated with the intense solar flares of February and October 1989. A recent 30 minute edition of the BBC's "Science Now" (Radio 4) magazine programme at the beginning of August was devoted entirely to solar activity and some of its lesser known aspects, including the question of ozone depletion and the much more controversial question of the "Greenhouse Effect" on global climate, as well as the better known effects on radiocommunications, electricity power distribution, communications and weather satellites, space flight etc.

Peter Evans interviewed a number of leading American radiophysicists on "the natural firework display we call a solar flare" with Joe Allen making the point that "solar flares seem to peak a year or so after the sunspot peak. We think that the current cycle is probably going to be the second largest that has ever occurred in terms of sunspot numbers and we think the smoothed maximum will have been February 1990. There's no question but that the higher flare activity in 1989 is very much related to the rise towards the maximum in solar activity. However, we've noted over the last three previous solar cycles that the flares seem to peak a year to a year and a half later . . . satellite problems track the occurrence of major magnetic storms more than they do the sunspot number . . . I find a 2 to 3 and a half year lag of the greatest level of magnetic activity after the peak in the sunspot cycle. So these two observations, for what they're worth, suggest that we have several years of potentially extreme active conditions from the Sun ahead of us."

A particularly important result of solar flares is the permanent reduction in the power output of the large solar arrays used to provide electrical power for satellites. This is especially true of the usual silicon photovoltaic diodes. There would be less degradation with gallium arsenide or indium phosphide cells although these are considerably more difficult to manufacture. Cells are damaged by the high-energy particles radiated from the Sun. To counter this, satellites intended to be parked in geostationary orbits for ten years (eg weather satellites. DBS satellites, communication satellites etc) are provided with arrays which initially can generate more power than necessary, calculated on the anticipated degradation spread over ten years. However, the BBC programme pointed out that during the severe proton event of October 1989, the effect on the power panels in *six days* was the equivalent of the calculated degradation averaged over *five years*! In other words it swallowed up half of the total reserve power built into the satellites. As one speaker put it: "It was extremely alarming to see five years of ageing in almost as many days." Apparently NASA and satellite designers have traditionally used a major proton event of August 1972 as a reference in the planning of space missions since this was the most intense event that had been recorded in space. In practice, the August 1972 event was equalled in August 1989 and was exceeded for several days during October 1989. Back to the drawing board!

High intensity particles also cause problems to on-board computers and satellite electronics. A high energy proton particle or ion from a solar flare leaves a path of ionisation through the satellite causing a "single event upset". Typically, the faults can be overcome by ground control: "The operators are alert, they reload the software, reconfigure the satellite and they keep going, although if they miss the upset the satellite can be lost: "In the large events last year, satellites had these upsets ninety to a couple of hundred times a day at the peak of the events."

Astronauts in Space Shuttle missions (which have tended to coincide with several larger flares) have reported seeing flashes caused by the response of the optic nerve to charged particles; in October 1989 they retired to an interior compartment. They discovered that for this level of event the shielding was not really adequate; even though, at the relatively low Shuttle orbital height, high-energy particles are less of a problem than at geostationary altitudes, during interplanetary flight or, for example, on the surface of the moon. Even at the heights reached by supersonic aircraft (such as Concorde) radiation levels during intense flares may reach 100 to 1000 times background level, with dose levels the equivalent of several chest X-rays during a normal flight. During a very large solar flare, as much energy may be radiated in a few hours from a tiny area of the surface as is radiated from the entire Sun in a second.

The Sun is, in effect, a superhot ball of gas with a nuclear bomb at its core, radiating heat and light, with the outer layers of gas forever being churned over while the whole body inside and out shows a complex pattern of rotations - a natural dynamo over 1 million km in diameter, ringing like a bell with sound waves being bounced around and affecting the geometry of the whole body, with not one but several cycles inseparable from the complicated tangle of magnetic fields that thread across the whole surface.

RADIO UNDER PRESSURE

TT (eg JANUARY 1986, pp37-38) has previously noted how secret radio receivers were built and used under extremely difficult conditions in German and Japanese prisoner of war camps. Among the pre-war amateurs know to have built and concealed such receivers were Ernest "Shack" Shackleton, G6SN, Tom Douglas, G3BA, and Herb Dixon, ZL2BO - but there appears to have been others who were not necessarily radio amateurs.

An obituary in *The Daily Telegraph* (July 18, 1990, brought to my notice by Ray Herbert, G2KU,) of a wartime RAF sergeant wireless-operator/air-gunner, John Bristow, reveals how he built sets at three camps: Stalag Luft I, III and VI, after escaping by parachute when his plane was shot down on August 13, 1940. This was during a disastrous daylight bombing raid on a Luftwaffe base at Aalborg, Denmark, when eleven out of 12 Bristol Blenheim light bombers failed to return. John Bristow was initially sheltered by a Danish doctor but insisted on giving himself up when he learned that his host would be shot if he was discovered.

In the camps, his sources of components were limited, often involving considerable ingenuity or risk. He once stole material from the camp commandant's office telephone while others distracted the attention of the office staff; capacitors were fashioned from Red Cross parcel tins, with the plates separated by the India paper from a bible. Crushed razor blades were made into magnets which, with adapted tooth-powder tins, were fashioned into earphones. He persuaded some guards to supply components in undercover black market trading deals and smuggled a receiver from Stalag I to Stalag III hidden in a concertina which could still, after a fashion, be played.

In 1944 he is reported to have built a transmitter (although there seems no evidence that this, or any other PoW camp transmitter, such as the one believed to have been built by G6SN, was ever used to effect secret two-way communication from a camp). In need of a power valve, one was located in an audio amplifier supplied by the Swedish YMCA for the camp theatre. To cover the theft, the theatre was set on fire with a small time bomb. According to *The Daily Telegraph*, he left on the turntable a record of 'I don't want to set the world on fire, I just want to start a flame in your heart.' Son of a London electrical engineer, after the war he returned to the family business but continued to devise gadgets. Two of his secret radio sets - one concealed in a wind-up gramophone, the other in a mess tin - are reported as being on display at the Hendon RAF Museum.

In these days of microminiaturization we tend to forget how big, bulky, fragile - and out of date - most pre-war (and even some post-war) military radio equipment could be, built to be carried by reluctant mules [or camels, see *RadCom* August 90, p9 - Ed]. A long, fascinating article published last year, 'A Polish Odyssey' by Lt Col C A Henn-Collins, GU5ZC (*The Journal of The Royal Signals Institution*, Summer 1989), describes, with a wealth of detail, how, as a young lieutenant shortly before the outbreak of the war in September 1939, he was put in command of a detachment of Royal Signals intended to provide a radio link from the newly appointed British Military Mission, under General Carton de Wiart VC, in Poland back to the War Office, and to supplement the existing Foreign Office HF link. After several changes of plan, the detachment, with crates and crates of equipment, finally left Victoria Station on August 25, with the Army insisting that the party should travel to Poland via Alexandria, Egypt, by train to the south of France, by boat to Egypt and thence via Greece to Romania. Over five tons of equipment in 80 boxes - much of it destined to be deliberately burned in a remote corner of Poland!

As a result by the time the unit actually reached Poland the country had been virtually over-run. However, when the crates were unpacked it was quickly apparent that the Army/RAF equipment was unsuitable: "The SEE (Army Signals Experiments Establishment) receiver was too noisy and unselective to copy the signal well enough for traffic handling. So in disgust I had someone throw it in the river." Christopher Henn-Collins admits to wishing that he could have had the chance to bring along some of his amateur equipment - a feeling that was confirmed later when, after coming out of Poland, he stayed on in Bucharest helping out with the civilian FO radio links using an HRO and Comet Super Pro receiver. He built his own transmitter to establish a link with Cairo, grinding crystals with valve grinding paste scrounged from the Minister's chauffeur. These were much more effective than the military monstrosities. Later when he finally

got back to Alex he was promptly arrested by the police as a deserter!

HERE AND THERE

IN THE AUGUST *Technical Topics* I suggested wrongly that, even with conventional house wiring, a mains earth should not be directly connected to real earth. What I had meant to say was that mains *neutral* should never be connected to real earth (or to mains earth). With protective multiple earthing a real earth should be spaced at least two metres from anything connected to a mains earth, owing to the possibility of a serious hazard arising under fault conditions (see "The Killing Ground - Earth Your Station Safely" *RadCom* June 1987, pp 404-5). Second, in my review of *British Intelligence in the Second World War Vol IV* (August, p38) I twice referred to the BP decrypts of the SD (RSHA) hand coded traffic as Isosoles. This should have been Isosicle. Apologies.

David Newark, AK7M in *QST* (July 1990) reports that one of his PSUs emitted a noise that sounded like line noise on an AM radio. Thinking this might indicate a power transformer or somesuch, he used a cardboard tube to locate exactly where the noise was coming from. He was puzzled to find the source was the bridge rectifier components, more specifically the disc-ceramic by-pass capacitors. He recalled a 1984 *QST* tip that the ceramic dielectrics of some capacitors can exhibit piezoelectric properties, generating electricity when vibrated. Recognizing that piezoelectric effects often work both ways, he realized that his 0.01 µF, 1kV disc capacitors were acting as miniature piezo-electric loudspeakers, emitting line noise transients as acoustical noise.

He suggests that if your PSU, when plugged into the mains, emits rather more ticking or buzzing than usual, this may not indicate a component fault, but a noisy, transient prone AC supply mains.

Following the final release of the controversial US Environmental Protection Agency (EPA) report that suggests that there is sufficient evidence to demonstrate a "significant" link between some rare forms of cancer and exposure to extremely low frequency (eg 50 or 60 Hz) electromagnetic fields near electricity power lines, a Bill is being introduced in the US Congress proposing a $34m federal research programme into the effects of electromagnetic radiation and the setting up of an "Electric and Magnetic Fields Research Advisory Committee" composed of representatives from Government, industry and environmental organisations. *Nature* (16 August 1990) reports this under the heading "Electromagnetic risk - All Aboard The Bandwagon."

Brian Hayes, G3JBU calls attention to the "Powerbank Portable Power System" a 12V rechargeable cordless powersource weighing 3.5kg in a distinctive carrying case for use with domestic appliances, fluorescent tent lights etc with a 60Wh capacity. G3JBU is pleased with the service he obtains with one of these units although it is more expensive than a conventional lead/acid battery which he regards as dangerous to use indoors. The leaflet he sent along gives no information on the type of cells used in the "Powerbank" - personally I suspect these are the new generation of maintenance free "sealed" lead-acid batteries described in recent *Technical Topics* items (eg June 1990). The Powerbank units are available from some of the larger d-i-y stores and certainly appear to be a convenient and safe source of portable power for camping, caravanning and boating - or for use with low power transceivers etc. ❏

SIMPLE 3.5MHz SSB/CW SUPERHET RECEIVER

ALBERT EINSTEIN is credited with believing that "everything should be made as simple as possible, but not simpler." This need not conflict with the view that "there is no better way than constructing a receiver - even a comparatively simple one - for finding out infinitely more about receivers than you can ever learn purely from reading theory" (or using a factory-built set without ever having dabbled, no matter how briefly, with a D-i-Y receiver project).

In *TT* (January 1989) I wrote: "In so often advocating a KISS approach to amateur radio generally and home-constructed equipment in particular, I am acutely aware of the paradox presented by the increasing availability of medium, large and very-large scale integrated circuits (MSI, LSI, VSLI). These often provide extremely complex circuitry yet represent to the constructor relatively simple devices requiring a minimum of external passive components."

This view was expressed with specific reference to an article "Simple receivers from complex ICs" by Bill Parrott, W6VEH which dealt with the Signetics/Philips NE602-series of ICs. These with their double-balanced mixer, built-in oscillator and buffer devices could be used, inter-alia, in the construction of simple, reasonable-performance direct-conversion and superhet HF receivers, including single-band receivers forming part of compact, low-power transceivers. As described, for example, in "An NE602-based QRP transceiver for 20-meter CW" by Rick Lit-

TECHNICAL TOPICS

PAT HAWKER G3VA

tlefield, K1BQT, *Ham Radio*, January 1989 and briefly noted in *TT*, April 1989, using three NE602 devices.

As reported in *TT*, September 1990, pp30-31, some amateurs have expected too much from the NE602 when used as a front-end device; it does have a strong signal performance appreciably worse than that now offered in some high-cost factory receivers and transceivers with their claimed 100dB-plus dynamic ranges. Yet (*vide* W7SX): "Because of its very high performance/power ratio, the 602 is an ideal choice for portable, MF direct-conversion and superhet receiver designs . . . . it offers outstanding performance (80dB-plus dynamic range) when you consider its simplicity, power requirements, size and cost." The dynamic range will be further extended when the drop-in replacement NE602A becomes available but that should not deter us from using the current device, which I note was advertised in the September issue by The Chip Shop, priced £2.84.

One of those who have been attracted by the facilities offered by this device is Mike Grierson, G3TSO. His attention was first attracted by its use in the simple spectrum analyser unit for which Al Heltrik, K2LBA won an RF Design

Award; *RF Design*, January 1988, *TT* April 1988 with subsequent notes in *TT* July, August, September, November 1988 and with the NE602 retained by Roger Blackwell, G4PMK, for his improved design fully described in *RadCom*, November 1989.

G3TSO writes: "I have experimented with the NE602 as a receiver mixer and whilst many may scorn its performance, it is exceedingly useful in the construction of simple receivers giving very satisfactory results. When combined with the Plessey SL6700 it is possible to make a very simple superhet receiver, far simpler and superior in performance to many of the direct-conversion receivers which appear so popular, especially amongst the kit constructors. The addition of a suitable audio IC makes possible a three-chip receiver capable of about 1 µV sensitivity and able to drive a loudspeaker.

"**Fig 1** shows the circuit of a simple 3.5MHz receiver which draws very little current, the audio IC could be changed to a 6V type for battery operation. In my case the receiver forms the receive side of a miniature transceiver using a second NE602 as the transmit mixer, with the VFO contained in the receive NE602 buffered by an external FET and fed to the transmit NE602 via pin 7.

"The major limitation of this design is the 455KHz IF, making image responses a problem at higher frequencies; however, it is perfectly satisfactory for 3.5 or 1.8MHz. The use of a relatively cheap 2.4KHz ceramic filter gives good sideband performance and excellent (communications) quality if used on transmit. The receiver

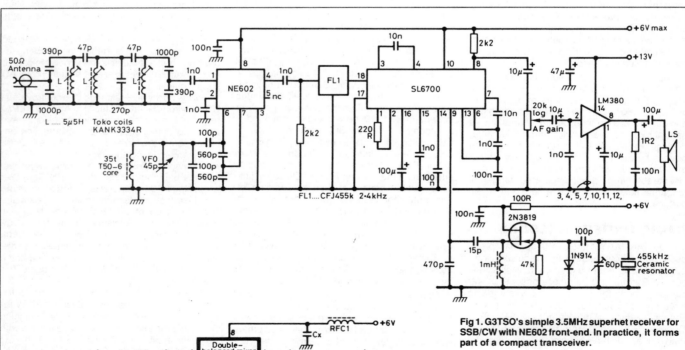

Fig 1. G3TSO's simple 3.5MHz superhet receiver for SSB/CW with NE602 front-end. In practice, it forms part of a compact transceiver.

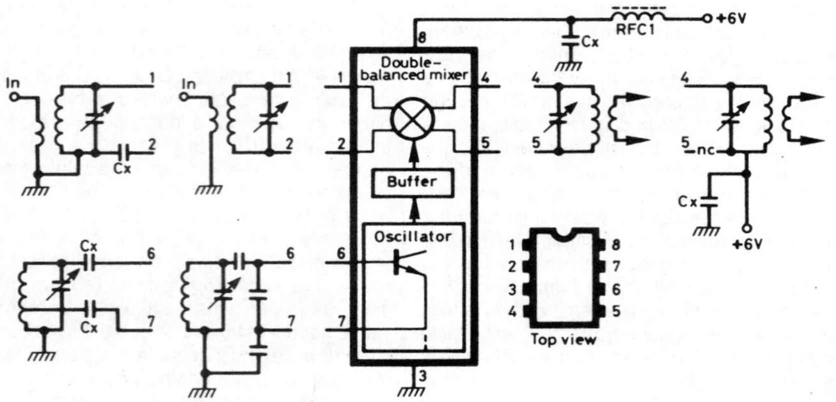

Fig 2. Typical configurations of the NE602N as described in *TT*, January 1989. Balanced circuits are to be preferred but may be more difficult to implement. Cx blocking capacitor 0.001 to 0.1µF depending on frequency. RFC1 (ferrite heads of RF choke) recommended at higher frequencies. Supply voltage should not exceed 6V (2.5mA). Noise figure about 5dB. Mixer gain 20dB. Third-order intercept -15dB (do not use an RF pre-amplifier stage). Input and output impedances both 2 x 1.5kΩ. Typical 28MHz direct-conversion receiver using NE602 appears as Fig 2 in *TT*, January 1989. Future drop-in replacement type NE602A will have an extra 5dB or so of dynamic range.

has RF derived AGC, and AM output is available from the SL6700 if required (see Plessey Application Notes). The input RF filter is broadband using three Toko inductors and polystyrene capacitors. A ceramic resonator is used for the 455kHz carrier-insertion/BFO oscillator.

Others have found that although the simple 'kit' DC receivers are surprisingly effective they do suffer from serious disadvantages including the absence of suppression of the unwanted sideband on SSB channels and the corresponding 'audio image' on CW. This does not mean that direct-conversion is inherently inferior to the superhet approach since a phasing-type demodulator can be used, but this does involve considerable additional complexity. Phasing-type SSB demodulators capable of good sideband suppression over the full audio bandwidth (eg 300-4000Hz), with its performance maintained over a wide range of temperatures, are not constructor-friendly circuits, although a number of practical circuits have been described in *TT* and elsewhere: see for example the use of several op-amps as all-pass phase delay elements in *TT*, September 1988.

Surprisingly little attention has been given in the past to the considerable simplifications possible when the accurate quadrature (90°) phase difference needs to be maintained only over the relatively small audio bandwidth involved in CW reception. Tim Walford, G3PCJ has been developing a direct-conversion CW phasing receiver as part of a 7MHz CW transceiver. Although not as yet at a stage to go public he has measured a 54:1 (35dB voltage) suppression over the whole of a restricted audio bandwidth of 750 +/- 300 Hz using a phasing-type arrangement based on two NE602 ICs with relatively simple lead/lag networks, involving about two extra chips and one transistor compared to the usual form of DC receiver.

Incidentally, Tim Walford, G3PCJ has put together a kit (price £35) for the Mk II power-FET amplifier, using four VN88AFD devices capable of giving up to about 50W PEP output up to 30MHz. This amplifier attracted a number of enquiries and the availability of a kit should ease the problem of acquiring the components. His address is Upton Bridge Farm, Long Sutton, Langport, Somerset TA10 9NJ; telephone Long Sutton (045 824) 1224.

MORE ON STABLE OSCILLATORS

DR MIKE KING, G3MY, was interested in VK5QG's Q-Gate FET oscillator (*TT*, January and March 1990) as some years before he had developed a basically similar oscillator for use in a remote VFO in a mobile SSB transceiver that he built at the time. He writes: "In my version (**Fig 3**) there is a low-value resistor between source and the coil tap and this enables the oscillator to be run at normal drain voltage. With 9V on the drain, output at the source is about 4V pk, more than adequate to feed a conventional two-stage feedback buffer amplifier. I have since used this arrangement in a number of my QRP transceivers. The output of the buffer amplifier is quite sufficient to drive a heat-sinked VN10KM VMOS to 2.5 - 2W output on various bands from 3.5 to 14MHz."

On the general topic of stable, variable frequency LC oscillators, it has been emphasised many times in *TT* that no matter what form of oscillator is used, the final limit to stability is the tank circuit. In the June *TT*, S M Dyke, G3ROZ, commented on the difficulty of constructing LC oscillators really suitable for SSB reception above 20MHz: "With the temperature variations found

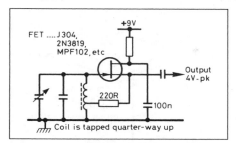

Fig 3. G3MY's version of the Q-Gate FET variable oscillator developed many years ago is suitable for use from 9V supply. Coil wound on T37-6 toroid core in G3MY's portable QRP transceiver.

in a garden-shed shack it is very difficult; for mobile operation near impossible." It was then pointed out that much depended on the selection of materials used as coil formers and their mounting. It was pointed out that KW Electronics had made effective use of formers fashioned from Belling-Lee electronic-fire element material.

One of the most detailed accounts that I have come across of precautions taken in developing accurately stabilised band-switched oscillators for use at the temperatures involved in hermetically-sealed, valve-type communications receivers dates back to an article by JA Knight of AT & E (Bridgnorth) Ltd. This described the development of the Services HF Receiver, type R210 (which still turns up as a useful `surplus' receiver), and was published in the *ATE/BICC* journal of the early 1960s. The R210 is a single-conversion superhet (IF 460kHz) covering 2-16MHz in seven bands, enclosed in a hermetically sealed (dry air) robust aluminium alloy diecast panel and case. Although not designed for SSB reception, great care was clearly taken in stabilising the local oscillator, based on a CV850/6AK5/EF95 pentode valve. The R210 calls for a local oscillator covering roughly 2.5 to 16.5MHz, in its seven bands.

J A Knight wrote: "Development then turned to a stable free-running oscillator. Investigation into the temperature coefficient of various variable capacitors showed that one commercially available type gave a small and consistent positive drift with increase in temperature of approximately 5 to 10 parts per million. It is interesting to note that this is a straight-line capacitance unit with the rotor plates forming a true semicircle about the driving shaft. There is no unbalanced overhang of the plates and no bonding strip, which in some capacitors is of dissimilar materials. The capacitor is all brass with a simple ball race at each end, and it has the added advantage of being quite small . . . . by splitting the frequency coverage into seven bands it was possible to use a reasonable amount of parallel capacitance in addition to the trimmers and switch `strays'. Providing this capacitance has a consistent temperature coefficient it adds to the stability, by swamping valve and other capacitances.

"To obtain consistent results all the compensating capacitors had to be in one unit of say -30ppm/°C. This gave better results than a large mica capacitor of +5 to +50ppm shunted with a small capacitance of large negative temperature coefficient, say -750ppm.

"This receiver uses -150+/-20 ppm/°C capacitors to compensate the three low-frequency coils. The four high-frequency coils have in addition -30+/-20ppm/°C capacitors. On the HF band, which in practice appeared to be the least difficult to compensate, the parallel capacitor is 180pF.

"The third important factor is the oscillator coil

itself. Not only had it to be a stable inductance, but a number of coils had to fit neatly round the waveband switch, with trimmers in accessible positions. The coil-formers required tags to support rigidly both the wires of its own turns and those to the switch. The capacitance trimmer also had to be supported.

"In many receivers the RF coils are designed to screw on a metal dividing screen, with their tags passing through it. Since it is quite unnecessary to screen the coil from its own switching circuit this only adds to the stray capacitance. Any movement of the wires near to this screen will cause extra uncontrolled drift.

"The coil-former has an extended base, which carries both the tags and capacitance trimmer. Two tapped holes in the side of this base mount it so that the axis of the coil is parallel to the screen. The capacitance trimmer mounts through a hole in the base, and solders into a raised earth tag underneath . . . . seven of these formers are mounted round an Oak type of switch with short and rigid connections . . . .

"The coil-former is moulded in Nylon-loaded Bakelite, and has the anchor ring that has been incorporated in coil-formers made at Bridgnorth for the past ten years. This consists of a washer punched in high-grade Bakelite sheet, with a projecting key that locates in a slot moulded into the former. By passing wire through holes in this ring it is possible to secure it at any point on the former and obtain a good winding tension with no fear of it slipping when stoved for drying and varnishing. The four holes in this ring are always in line with the tags moulded in the former so that the wires go directly from the tapping point over the ring to the tags. This keeps the coupling and stray capacitance consistent. A thin version of the ring is used for tapping to the middle of a coil, and another (normal) one for terminating it . . . . Bands 6 and 7 are threaded at 16 turns per inch and have a positive temperature coefficient of 12 ppm/°C. Bands 4 and 5 at 32 tpi and have a positive temperature coefficient of 26 ppm/°C. Bands 1, 2 and 3 have a plain former with a positive temperature coefficient of 55 pm/°C. All coils are adjusted with a 6mm threaded dust-core. They have concentric-type trimmers. The antenna, mixer and oscillator sections are each mounted on a common metal pressing, which also forms the valve platform. The individual sections are wired before being fitted with gang mounting bracket and screens. The three right-angle cross braces make the unit into a very rigid box section . . . ."

Most high-performance communications receivers of that era used double-conversion, often with a crystal-controlled HF oscillator and with the second oscillator spanning only a small range of frequencies without band-switching. With the precautions taken in the R210, it was claimed that "the frequency drift compares favourably with that of crystal-controlled oscillators. The specially selected variable tuning capacitor and the sealing of the receiver with dry air also contribute to a thermal drift of less than 0.002% per °C."

While few home-constructors would expect to undertake a similar degree of development work, it does show that switched-oscillators can provide excellent stability at least up to 16MHz and cope with a wide range of temperatures. But clearly great care is needed.

SQUARE AND DELTA LOOP ANTENNAS

TT SEPTEMBER described some of the useful, multiband properties of closed square loop antennas with sides of 0.25λ mounted in horizontal or vertical plane. It seems worth adding some follow-up comments applicable to HF, VHF and UHF designs.

A basically similar antenna to that described by W1FB (*TT*, September Fig 2) is discussed in 'The full-wave 80-metre loop antenna - revisited' by Paul D Carr, N4PC in *CQ*, August 1990. He uses a 272ft perimeter ('almost square') horizontal loop suspended at about 50ft from pine trees. He concludes: "There are only three antennas for any amateur - the one you had, the one you have presently, and the one you plan to build. This antenna has helped to postpone the one I plan to build."

N4PC reminds us that the virtues of horizontal loops were described by Dave Fisher, W0MHS in 'The Loop Skywire', *QST*, November 1985, an article sub-headed 'Looking for an all-band HF antenna that is easy to construct, costs nearly nothing and works great DX? Try this one!'. W0MHS suggested that: "There is one wire antenna that performs exceptionally well on the HF bands, but relatively few amateurs know about it or use it . . . . what one user has described as the 'best kept secret in the amateur circle' . . . . Since 1957, I have used this antenna (**Fig 4**) in many locations with great success every time." He dismisses the idea, held by some, that the horizontal loop is basically a high-angle radiator. In fact, the vertical angle of radiation, like that of other horizontally polarized antennas, depends on the height of the loop and even a 25ft high loop should prove effective as a DX antenna above 14MHz. It is worth looking at the vertical radiation patterns shown in the September *TT*, Fig 3.

W0MHS used a co-axial cable rather than open-wire transmission line, providing some useful constructional hints and showing also how the antenna could be used effectively on the 1.8MHz band as a top-loaded vertical antenna: **Fig 5**.

Dr Mike King, G3MY is another advocate of closed loops. He writes: "Over the years I have used nothing but closed loops on the HF bands, having a great liking for the low-Q characteristics of this type of antenna. This interest started in 1963 while on holiday in Cornwall. I was using an end-fed 3/4 wave antenna tuned against a 1/4 wave counterpoise and realised that the end of the bent wire and of the counterpoise were in phase, so I decided to see what would happen if I joined the ends together. I will say only that on my return home that triangular loop went up, supported by two trees and the house. It stayed up for more than twenty years.

"More recently, I developed what I call the HOVER loop which I described in *Sprat* (issue Nr 54, Spring 1988). I hope that **Fig 6** makes the format and feed method clear. Suffice to say that it has been used effectively on all bands from 1.8MHz to 28MHz and has given me 85 countries in 6 continents using QRP (3W or less).

"Hover" comes from HOrizontal/VERtical, and the *Sprat* description makes its operation a little clearer:

The HOVER loop is basically a full-wave wire loop antenna cut to the usual loop formula L = 1005/f where f is the frequency in MHz and L the length in ft. The physical form is an inverted V with the apex at 60ft. Each leg of the V is about 60ft long with an apex angle of about 110°. The rest of the length comprises a low horizontal V at some 12 to 15ft above the ground. The feedpoint is at the apex of the inverted V. The feeder comprises two equal lengths of low-loss UHF TV coax cable, giving a screened balanced 150Ω feedpoint. Measurements have shown that the loop has a feedpoint resistance of about 110

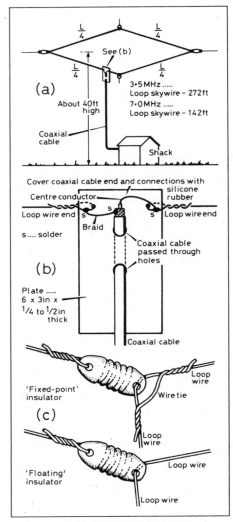

Fig 4. The W0MHS "Loop Skywire" horizontal loop antenna as described in *QST*, November 1985.

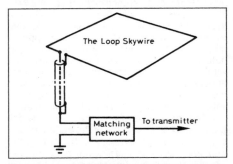

Fig 5. Feed arrangement for the loop as a top-loaded vertical antenna on lower frequency band.

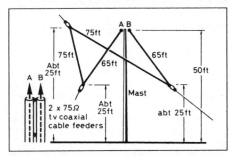

Fig 6. G3MY's 'HOVER' loop effective on 1.8 to 28MHz. Two equal lengths of 75Ω coaxial cable provide a 150Ω balanced screened feed to the apex (A-B) of the inverted-V section of the loop. Use a balun at the ATU, or an ATU with balanced output.

ohms on 3.5MHz, rising to around 220-250Ω on 28MHz. If a valve-type power amplifier is used, the two feeders can be brought into a simple 1:1 balun on the back of the transceiver, and the pi-network will then match it satisfactorily. When using a solid-state PA, I use a small QRP Z-match to tune out the reactance on higher frequency bands.

On 1.8MHz it is possible to use the antenna in one of two modes: (1) As a 'fat' quarter-wave against earth with the two feeders in parallel to give a 37.5-ohm feeder; or (2) The lines can be tuned at the bottom end to give a voltage feed to the two free ends of a half-wave antenna. Although this puts a high SWR on the line, the losses do not seem excessive.

Large single-turn resonate loop antennas mounted in the vertical plane have a long history. Some interesting work was reported in the 1930s by L S Palmer and D Taylor (University College, Hull) in *Proc IRE*, January 1934, pp93-114. They noted that:

"When a frame or loop aerial is tuned, the current produced in it by a passing wireless wave will be increased many hundred-fold compared with the current produced in an untuned frame of the same dimensions. With wavelengths which are long in comparison with the dimensions of the frame, the only other method of increasing the current is to increase the area of the frame. If the length of the wave is of the same order as the dimensions of the frame then it is found that the current, even in a tuned frame may be still further increased by many hundredfold not by increasing the area of the frame, but by critically adjusting the ratio of the frame dimensions to the wavelength. In a previous communication this process was described (Palmer & Moneyball, *Proc IRE*, August 1932, pp1345-67) and a theory outlined which accounted for the experimental values of the critical ratios of frame-height/wave-length (H/λ) and frame-width/wavelength (W/λ) for which the received current became abnormally large."

In effect, this adjustment resulted in the two vertical wires being in phase resulting in a directive antenna in the plane of the frame. The 1934 paper extended the work to transmitting loop antennas, using a VHF transmitter on about 5-6 metres with an adjustable framework that allowed rectangular loops of differing aspect ratios to be investigated. To quote again from the paper:

"For the particular case of radiation along the earth's surface in the plane of the frame, both of the (above) equations are satisfied simultaneously only by a frame of dimensions H = 0.40λ and W = 1.0λ and for no other dimensions (less than 1λ) will the radiation be as great for the same applied electromotive force. If the transmitting frame receivers reflected waves from the ground there will be another set of critical dimensions, namely H = W = 0.47λ for which the radiation (or re-radiation in this case) will be a maximum."

RUSTY-BOLT/PASSIVE INTERMODULATION PRODUCTS

ARE YOU BOTHERED by PIMPs? Don't get me wrong, as music-hall comedian Max Miller might have said. I am referring, of course, to passive intermodulation products (PIMPs) generated by non-linear materials and metallic contacts, commonly termed the 'rusty-bolt' effect. This subject was dealt with at some length in *TT*, May 1989, page 33 'Rusty-bolt TVI' and page 35 'Tracing rusty-bolt and diode interference'. The second of these items included details of an RF sniffer used by W6BUY to trace a difficult case of TVI which ultimately proved to be caused by overlapping lengths of wire mesh buried between the plaster and the boards in his house walls. Fortunately, only rarely is TVI caused by harmonics generated in such non-linear external junctions, not necessarily connected directly to the transmitter or antenna system. But, as noted then, this problem is much more common and more important for professional mobile base stations or other multi-transmitter installations where a single mast may support the antennas of half-a-dozen transmitters liable to be operating at the same time; in such circumstances rusty-bolt rectification can result in even two transmitters generating literally hundreds of intermodulation products any of which can seriously affect reception of incoming signals.

Bob Anderson, G4AEV draws attention to a recent ten-page article 'Passive intermodulation interference in communication systems' by Pak-Leng Lui (The University, Canterbury) in the IEE's *Electronic & Communication Engineering Journal*, June 1990, pp109-118. This deals exhaustively with this topic, including references to a large number of previous investigations.

This paper is introduced as follows: "In multi-frequency communications environments, such as land mobile radio sites, satellite earth stations, ships and surveillance aircraft, passive intermodulation products (PIMP) generated by nonlinear materials and metallic contacts can cause serious radio interference. This problem is well known and a wide range of coaxial cables, connectors and materials have been investigated. This paper gives an overview of passive intermodulation interference in communication systems. It describes briefly the theory of intermodulation, types of passive non-linearities, mechanisms responsible for the generation of PIMP, guide-lines for minimising PIMP generation and techniques for locating PIMP sources. Previous investigations of PIMP are summarised and the design of PIMP measurement systems is discussed. An example of PIMP measurement is also included."

It would be foolish to attempt to summarise in a few words this very detailed paper. It does, however, note that there are three main areas where intermodulation can occur: in transmitter output stages due to the non-linearity of power amplifier circuits; in the receiver input stages, due to the non-linearity of the mixer and RF circuits; and in nonlinear materials and nonlinear metallic contacts, such as corroded and/or loose contacts in coaxial cables, waveguides, connectors, multi-couplers, wire fences, tower and mast assemblies.

Suggested guide-lines for minimising PIMP generation include:

● nonlinear materials should not be used in or near the current paths, If for some reason they have to be there, they should be coated with linear materials.

● keep the current densities low in the conduction paths by using larger conductors or having bigger contact areas between metals.

● minimise metallic contacts, especially loose contacts and rotating joints. If these cannot be avoided, then provide insulators or alternative current paths at the contacts or joints. Also minimise the exposure of loose contacts, rough surface and sharp edges to radiated signals.

● keep thermal variations to a minimum as the expansion and contraction of metals and materials can create nonlinear contacts.

● use bonded joints if possible, but make sure that these joints are good and have no nonlinear

BAND-SWITCHED DIP METER

Doug DeMaw, W1FB (*QST*, July 1990, pp18-20) describes 'An experimental band-switching dip meter'. This has a cable-plus-probe designed to make resonance testing and wave-meter measurements less awkward than with the usual technique of holding the dipper coil close to the circuit concerned. Band-Switching eliminates the need for a set of plug-in coils which tend often to be missing when wanted. The range of the unit shown in **Fig 7** is about 2 - 20MHz, but W1FB points out that with two extra switch positions this could be extended to cover 1.8MHz and up to 30MHz. He also recommends the use of a

shorting-type band-switch rather than as shown. Similarly, UHF JFETs such as the 2N4416 could be used instead of the two dual-gate MOSFETs with their gates tied together. The design is presented "purely as an experimental gadget" based on W7ZOI-type 'ugly construction' (components glued to board). It includes provision for attaching a frequency counter to provide more accurate readings than the direct calibration of the slow-motion tuning dial.

R1, shown as 8.2K, needs to be selected to limit the meter sensitivity and to prevent the pointer hitting the peg when the sensitivity control (R2) is turned up. This value may need to be increased if a 12V supply is used or a more sensitive meter fitted.

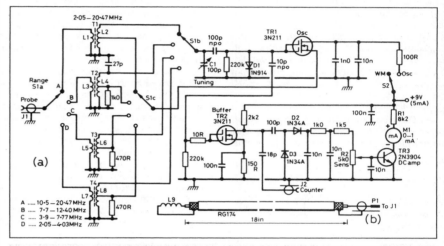

Fig 7. W1FB's experimental band-switched dip meter with probe (b). Fixed capacitors are disc ceramic. C1 10-100pF air variable. L1 2t, No26 enam. over earthy end of L2 21t, No26 enam (1.8µH) on T-50-6 toroid with tap 5t from earthy end. L3 2t No26 enam over earthy end of L4 28t No26 enam (2.8µH) on T-50-6 toroid with tap 5t from earthy end. L5 4t No26 enam over earthy end of L6 49t No26 enam (16µH) on T-68-2 toroid with tap at 12t from earthy end. L7 3t No22 over earthy end of L8 36t enam (90µH) on FT-82-61 toroid with tap 8t from earthy end. L9 (probe) 8t No22 bare or enam wire spaced one wire diameter between turns 3/8-in ID. Coil can be close-spaced if enamelled wire is used. TR1, TR2, 3N211 or 40763 or JFET (see text). R2 linear-taper 5K carbon-composition. S1 three-pole, four-position ceramic rotary two-wafer switch. S2 SPST toggle switch.

materials, cracks, contamination or corrosion.

● avoid having tuning screws or moving parts in the current paths. Keep all joints and contacts clean and tight, and if possible keep them free from vibration.

● cable length, in general, should be minimised and the use of quality and low PIMP cables is essential.

● minimise the use of nonlinear components, such as lumped dummy loads, circulators, isolators and some semiconductor devices.

● achieve good isolation between the high-power transmit signals and the low level receive signals by filtering and physical separation

● frequency planning should take account of the higher-order products as they can be potential interference signals in some communication systems.

In addition to these general guide-lines, P L Lui stresses the need for careful planning, good workmanship, stringent quality control and a high standard of maintenance.

It will be appreciated that few amateur radio installations, with a single transmitter and single receiver used sequentially, would need to adopt fully such stringent guide-lines in normal circumstances, but they form a useful check list when problems are encountered.

On the other hand, PIMP problems may read-

ily affect the operation of repeaters, particularly those located on shared masts where it is important not to add to the problems that may already exist, affecting reception of both amateur and professional users; in this case the guidelines may need to be studied carefully and rigorously observed, especially those relating to co-axial cables and their connectors.

Recently, D A R Naylor, G3GHI (4 Cullesden Road, Kenley, Surrey, CR8 5LR) queried whether there is any available information on the benefits (or disadvantages) of the different finishes available for N connectors, plugs and sockets etc. While I imagine that he was thinking mainly of the weather aging effects on signal losses, incoming and outgoing, I suspect that the different characteristics would affect also the generation of PIMPs. P L Lui provides a large number of references to previous papers reporting studies of PIMP interference as it relates to components and materials, including coaxial cables and connectors. On cables, he notes that RG-58C/U is a good choice among many types of coaxial cables because of its linearity, light weight and low cost: "However, if cost is not an important factor, then the double-screened, silver-plated RG-214U may be considered. Silver-plated steel cables should not be used because the nonlinear hysteresis effects in steel can generate a significant level of PIMP." ❑

CAPACITIVE FILTERING & THE EMC DIRECTIVE

BACK IN THE 1930s, the ripple (smoothing) filters (**Fig 1**) in the PSUs of both transmitters and receivers generally consisted of a reservoir capacitor having a value of only about 4 or 8μF, an iron-cored smoothing choke (in receivers this was often the energising coil of a moving coil loudspeaker before improved permanent-magnet speakers were developed) and a further capacitor, again usually not more than about 8μF. Alternatively, for better regulation in transmitters, with a varying load, a choke input filter was used in which there was no reservoir capacitor in front of the choke (or special swinging choke).

Later, with improved electrolytic capacitors and the low-voltage, high currents of solid-state equipment, the filter is often just a single very high-value capacitor, although additional ripple-reduction may be provided by a voltage regulator. Unfortunately, as noted below, the use of a large capacitor means that power is drawn from the mains supply as a series of short-duration high value peaks of current: **Fig 2**. This has the unfortunate effect of distorting the wave-form of the AC supplies sometimes sufficiently to affect the operation of other equipment in the area.

A *TT* item last February (p31) noted the concern of the electricity industry at the large number of switch-mode PSUs (or indeed any other

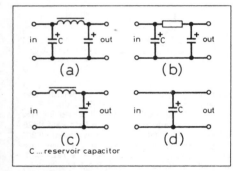

Fig 1. Basic PSU ripple filters. (a) As commonly used for many years for valve receivers/transmitters. The reservoir capacitor was usually not more than 4 to 8μF. (b) Lower cost filter with resistor replacing the LF smoothing choke introducing power loss and reduced DC voltage output. (c) Choke-input filter provides better DC regulation on varying loads but with lower peak output voltage. (d) Typical modern capacitive-only filter using very high-value electrolytic reservoir capacitor which, for 12V supplies, may be 10,000μF or more resulting in short-duration high-current peaks being drawn from mains supply.

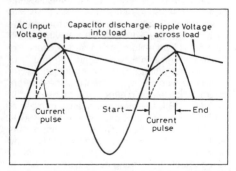

Fig 2. Approximate wave-forms with half-wave rectification and a capacitor-input ripple filter. Current is drawn from the mains supply only during the periods when the positive peaks of the 50Hz AC cycle exceeds the stored DC voltage in the reservoir capacitor. With full wave rectification there will be similar (but slightly less pronounced) input current pulses at 100Hz.

TECHNICAL TOPICS

PAT HAWKER G3VA

form of PSU using capacitive filtering) now in use, all taking short duration peaks of current and resulting in distorted AC wave-forms being supplied to all other users in the area.

Sid Dunn, G0BIF has drawn attention to a long letter in *IEE News* (23 August 1990) from M Burchell of Saffron Walden, who points out that: "As a result of various changes being enacted in EEC legislation and international EMC standards, virtually all forms of capacitive smoothing in mains-derived power supplies is being outlawed in the next few years. This means a design change of varying magnitude will be required by nearly every piece of electronic or electrical equipment (including battery chargers) to reduce the 'peakiness' of the line current waveform to new lower limits.

"Ever since the introduction of the modern low-series-resistance aluminium electrolytic capacitor in the 1960s, with its ability to carry high levels of ripple current without overheating and premature failure, the capacitively smoothed power supply has supplanted the previously inductively smoothed power supply due to its low cost and efficiency.

"It has always been accepted that, because this form of rectification and smoothing creates non-sinusoidal current pulses in the supply line, with their attendant series of harmonic currents, some degree of voltage distortion is inevitable. A simple analysis shows that these currents occur at the odd harmonic frequencies and, in particular, the lower-frequency harmonic currents, which are in phase with the fundamental current, cause flattening of the voltage-waveform peaks. The third harmonic current, in fact, approached the magnitude of the fundamental current and is known to cause problems in three-phase installations of single-phase equipment, where the third-harmonic currents are in phase with each other in the neutral line and can create a neutral current which is larger than the line current."

M Burchall suggests that as a result of decisions taken recently in the international standardisation committees of the BSI and the IBC, this situation will be changed dramatically and that the final result of the changes is that the design of nearly every piece of 240V AC equipment in the UK using capacitive smoothing will have to be modified to meet the new EC Directive which comes into force January 1992. "For very low power equipment the requirement can be met with a small series inductor, but this becomes increasingly bulky and impractical, particularly in direct offline switched-mode power supplies, where there isn't sufficient room for such an inductor."

It is by no means clear from the letter in *IEE News* the extent to which amateur radio equipment will be affected (only home-built amateur equipment is outside the scope of the EC EMC Directive).

M Burchall notes that "one of the main culprits is the vast installed base of TV sets which cause considerable voltage distortion at all levels of the supply distribution system, particularly in the evenings". As noted before in *TT*, the EMC Directive will not be retrospective but applies to all products (other than home-built amateur radio equipment) marketed after January 1992, no matter when they were first put on the market. It does appear that IEC555-2 is being revised to apply more stringent limits to all equipment us-

ing capacitive filtering in both linear and direct offline switched-mode power supplies and battery chargers. It thus seems likely that it will require changes to new equipment designs and, as G0BIF points out, will become a matter of great interest and concern to RSGB members.

OFF-CENTRE-FED MULTI-BAND DIPOLES

THE ORIGINAL SINGLE-WIRE transmission line 'Windom' dipole, originally developed at Ohio State University (but named after Loren Windom, W8GZ, who described it in *QST* back in 1929) was, like a conventional centre-fed half-wave dipole, intended to be a single-band antenna, **Fig 3 (a)**. It was the late Jim MacIntosh, VS1AA (later GM3IAA), who found that a one-third-wave tapping point (ie one-sixth-wave from its centre point) can match well on several harmonically related bands. This tapping point gives a resistive feed impedance of roughly 300 ohms. The VS1AA was described in the *T&R Bulletin*, November 1936 although often described as a 'Windom' antenna: **Fig 3 (b)**.

As Les Moxon, G6XN, has pointed out, any single-wire transmission line, even when correctly matched, radiates some RF energy which will affect the radiation patterns. This does not, however, imply that a Windom or VS1AA, if correctly set up, is not capable of giving excellent results.

The dislike of single-wire feeder radiation, with its increased possibility of RFI problems, led in the late 1940s to the use of 300 ohm balanced line as a non-radiating feeder to a VS1AA/Windom 'one-third' tapped element: **Fig 3 (c)**. This antenna was described in *QST* and the *Radio*

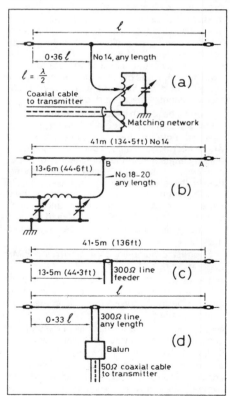

Fig 3 Basic off-centre-fed dipoles. (a) The original 'Windom' half-wave dipole as developed at Ohio State University over 60 years ago. (b) The multiband VS1AA introduced the concept of 'one-third' tap for multiband operation. (c) The twin-feeder (300 ohm) version became popular in the late 1940s. (d) Later still, a 6:1 balun was introduced to permit the use of 50 ohm coaxial feeder for direct connection to the transmitter.

Amateurs Handbook and was subsequently included in an early *TT* (July 1958 and all editions of *ART*). With a 136ft top, fed 44ft from one end, this could be used on 3.5, 7, 14 and 28MHz from an ATU providing balanced output. It could also be modified to include 21MHz by adding two shorted-quarter-wave stubs at 76ft and 38ft from the feed point. Later the use of a balun was introduced: **Fig 3 (d)**.

As noted by Tom Sorbie, GM3MXN, in *Sprat*, Autumn 1990, a modified form of the four-band off-centre-fed dipole was described by DJ2KT in QRV (December 1971) and has since become widely used, particularly in Germany, under the name 'FD4 Windom'. This substituted 75Ω or 50Ω coaxial cable for the balanced 300Ω line but with a 4:1 or 6:1 balun at the one third feedpoint. This means that it can be used on modern transceivers with 50Ω unbalanced sockets without an ATU on 3.5, 7, 14 and 28MHz. **Fig 4** shows the FD4 antenna used for QRP operating by GM3MXN, who is well satisfied with the results, and also his ferrite-rod balun based on a well-known G6XN design (see for example 'Balanced to unbalanced transformers' by Dr Ian White, G3SEK, *RadCom*, December 1989, pp39-42). GM3MXN simply used twin-coloured grey and black wire wound together six turns on a scrap ferrite rod. He finds that his FD4 provides also an acceptable match on 18 and 24MHz but for 10.1 and 21MHz he needs an ATU.

A year after the appearance of the FD4, F Spillner, DJ2KY (*QRV*, August 1972) showed how the multi-wire dipole technique enables the 21MHz band to be used without an ATU by adding two wires to the basic FD4, 4.5m and 2.52m long (*TT*, October 1972 and *ART*): **Fig 5**.

More recently, as described in an Appendix to a detailed discussion of Windom-type antennas 'The off-centre-fed dipole revisited: a broadband, multiband antenna' by Dr John Belrose, VE2CV, and Peter Bouliane, VE3KLO (*QST*, August 1990, pp28-32) - Hubert Scholle, DJ7SH and Rolf Steins, DL1BBC (*CQ-DL*, September 1983) have shown that a 'double Windom' based on the FD4 can be extended to cover all eight HF bands without an ATU, or, if the space is available, expanded to cover also 1.8MHz. **Fig 6 (a)** shows the eight-band design while **Fig 6 (b)** gives SWR measurements made by DJ7SH and DL1BBC indicating very low SWR on all bands except possibly 7MHz. However, the 7MHz figures are perfectly acceptable unless your solid-state rig starts cutting back power output at about 1.5:1 SWR. The longer nine-band version is shown in **Fig 7**.

LASER-PRINTER OZONE

THE JUNE TT ITEM on the potentially harmful effects of using xerographic copying machines or laser-printers, both of which produce a significant amount of ozone, in poorly ventilated areas or without adequate maintenance, has resulted in comments that confirm that toxic levels can build up in some circumstances.

Moreover, both Dennis Lisney, G3MNO, and Dirk Koopman, G1TLH, point out that safe threshold levels are likely to be exceeded before you notice the smell of ozone. G1TLH believes that since the level of ozone builds up gradually while the machine is in use, the user is most unlikely to detect it by smelling, except possibly when first opening the door and entering the room - the same problem applies also to the hydrogen-sulphide (H_2S) fumes from batteries. He mentions the laser printers and xerographic copying machines often use the same basic EHT-generating mechanisms so that comments applying to copiers apply equally to most laser printers.

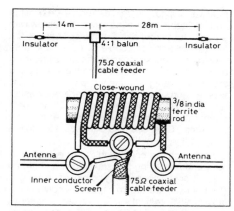

Fig 4. Since the 1970s, the four-band 'FD4 Windom' has been popular, particularly in Germany, with the balun up at the feed point. Shown also the simple 4:1 balun used by GM3MXN for low-power operation. The FD4 does not match on 21MHz (*Sprat*).

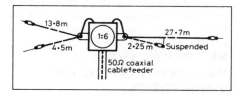

Fig 5. DJ2KY's five-band version of the FD4 introduced the concept of the double-Windom. Note 300 ohm line could be used without a balun.

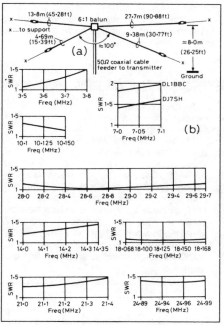

Fig 6. (a) The eight-band "double-Windom" with (b) SWR measurements made by DJ7SH and DL1BBC.

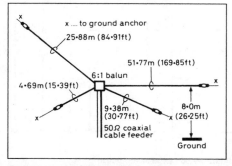

Fig 7. The extended nine-band version covering all bands from 1.8MHz to 28MHz.

G3MNO recalls that he was once concerned professionally in a lengthy investigation of the problems arising from the use of a copier in a small print room by a lady who liked to keep warm and never opened the large windows despite the room being over-provided with radiators (the problems arose during winter). A chemist taking her some documents to copy noted and queried the level of ozone with G3MNO who was then in charge of accommodation at a large research establishment. G3MNO sought out the environmental chemist with whom he proceeded to measure ozone levels in the room. The very first test showed levels above the safe threshold, subsequent tests showed that the levels built up over the working week and reached a maximum on the Friday evening. G3MNO felt it would be wrong simply to fit extractor fans and let the operator sit between the machine and the fan; he sought to overcome the problem at source. The makers (Rank Xerox) were most co-operative; his own office-machine people far less so; attempting to prove that their own tests failed to detect any ozone at all!

In the outcome, the lady operator (who had suffered respiratory problems although it could never be proved that the ozone was to blame) was moved to another job and replaced by a young man who shut off one radiator, always kept one small window open and used the small extractor fan that G3MNO had reluctantly fitted. All subsequent tests even when attempting to simulate the original conditions, failed to show any above threshold levels. He felt the problem had arisen because of (a) the operator keeping her room hot and dry with windows shut tight; and (b) possibly a small defect in the machine which had been cleared with routine maintenance. It was a matter of concern that although ozone is unstable, it appeared to build up over the week.

G3MNO believes that there is something of an *Achilles heel* in the environmental specification for copying machines since the assumption seems to be that normal open-window ventilation is provided by the building rules; but this cannot be enforced on the operator. Finally, in the course of looking into ozone problems, he found references to the fact that safe levels can even be exceeded in the open air in thunderstorm conditions. As noted in the June *TT* exposure for two hours to concentrations as low as 1.5 parts per million may result in coughs and excess production of sputum.

WINDING COILS ON PVC

LOADING COILS FOR USE in antennas requires a good deal of care if high efficiencies are to be achieved, particularly with short vertical antennas with top capacitive loading above a top loading coil. It is all too easy to lose more power in the coil than is gained by the loading. A four-page article "Loading coils for 160 metre antennas' by Charles J Michaels, W7XC (QST, April 1990) is based on his detailed study of loading coils and their placement in connection with 1.8MHz antennas up to about 60ft in height. He provides a lot of practical information on loading coil losses, skin effect, proximity effect, distributed capacitance and the effects of varying the coil length, diameter and wire size as well as consideration of materials suitable for use as coil formers of 2, 4 and 6 inch diameter.

He found that some readily available PVC tubing, tested by noting whether it heats up in a microwave oven (with the minimum load of a cup of water), remained no warmer than the air exhausting from the oven magnetron compartment and could be considered as satisfactory low-cost formers. (Some PVC tubes have fillers that make them unsuitable). Without attempting to summarise the whole of W7XC's very detailed article, it seems worth quoting his novel method of winding a very light coil on PVC formers, as this could have application for other purposes including the winding of ATU coils etc.

W7XC writes: "I have a novel means of winding a tight coil on PVC. Drill the form at the winding-end points and install brass machine screws with brass nuts and lock washers. Put the screw heads inside the form. Secure the far end of the wire to a wall, fence or vice. Bend the near end of the wire around a screw on the coil form, in a tight U shape, over a brass flat washer. Do not cross the wire and leave a generous pigtail. Secure the U with another brass flat washer, lock washer and nut. Tuck the pigtail inside the form. Check for clearance between the flat washers and the first turn. If necessary, add an extra nut to be sure the flat washers will not short to the first turn. Keeping the wire tensioned, turn the form as you walk towards the anchored end. When the required number of turns are on the form, wrap the wire around the other screw just enough to keep it from slipping off. Cut the wire, leaving a generous pigtail.

"Place the wound form in the freezer for a couple of hours. The coefficient of expansion/contraction of the PVC exceeds that of copper, so the winding will be looser that in was at room temperature. Working quickly so as not to allow the PVC form to come up to ambient temperature, work the loose turns towards the loosely secured end of the coil, adjusting the space reasonably uniformly. The heat from your hands will warm the copper and help it expand. Do not try to finish this process in one pass. The PVC

may warm up too much. Take up the slack at the end and again secure the wire to the screw with a partial turn around it. Put the coil back in the freezer for another couple of hours and then repeat the process, spacing the turns uniformly and taking up more slack. Bend the wire around the screw in a tight U-shaped loop over a brass washer, and secure it with another brass washer and nut. When the form comes up to room temperature, it will take a screwdriver to move the turns. They seem to squeeze up so tightly I suspect they dent the PVC.

"Although the coil is tight, after extremes of temperature cycling (if installed on an antenna) the soft-drawn copper may no longer be as tight. (Do not use hard-drawn copper, its conductivity is only 95% that of the soft-drawn variety.) I suggest a coat of Q-Dope (an American registered trademark) to ensure preservation of the spacing. The Q Dope can be purchased or can be made by dissolving polystyrene shavings in carbon tetra-chloride. Be careful - "carbon tet" is a suspected carcinogen that affects the liver and kidneys when inhaled or absorbed through the skin!"

VHF PARASITICS AND OVERDRIVE CAN INJURE YOUR TUBES

IN THE SEPTEMBER *QST*, Richard L Measures, AG6K, presents Part 1 of a two-part article on 'Parasitics Revisited' warning of the damage that can be caused to high-cost RF power valves by VHF parasitic oscillations or by overdriving linear amplifiers. Parasitics, he warns, can "boil gold, destroy amplifier tubes and blow meter

movements out of their cases." In Part 1, he describes and illustrates some of the damage inflicted on high-power amplifier valves.

Parasitic oscillation is not confined to home-built rigs; amateur linears and even professional broadcast transmitters are not immune. I note from an *IBA Newslink* a variant of Robert Burns' 'To a mouse', by Dave Walker, who, until his retirement, was based at the IBA transmitter site at Durris, near Aberdeen. I can't vouch for the accuracy of the dialect:

Wee sleekit 4CX250
Oh what a panic's in they breastie
Don't go into self-osc sae hasty
Wi parasitics
I wad be laith tae hae tae 'neut' ye
Wi electrolytics

I would hesitate to use an electrolytic capacitor to neutralize a 4CX250 but one has to concede a degree of poetic licence!

TT has previously (August 1986, p571) noted AG6K's concern with the fact that even though the popular high-power zero-bias, grounded-grid amplifier has zero phase shift and theoretically provides an unconditionally stable amplifier not requiring neutralization, this does not mean that such amplifiers are always free of VHF parasitic oscillations which, if undetected, can shorten the life of high-cost RF power valves.

A detection problem exists in that HF amplifiers may operate, apparently reasonably well, for several years without the user becoming aware of the intermittent presence of VHF parasitic oscillations, although possibly noting occasional flash-over of the tank capacitor or the overheating of parasitic-suppressor resistors.

555 WINDOW-DETECTOR CONTROLS BATTERY CHARGER

A SIMPLE 'FOUR-COMPONENT' window detector, based on the ubiquitous 555 IC timer, to form a controller in conjunction with a low-cost charger for lead-acid batteries has been described by Phil Hine in *Electronics Australia* (September 1990). He uses it to switch the charger on when the load pulls the battery voltage down to about 12V, and off again when it rises to about 15V, although the limits are adjustable. In this case, the load comprises a couple of 60W automatically-controlled garden lights for which he uses a 4A car-battery charger with the controller, believing that it is better repeatedly to cycle a battery than to float it continuously.

Fig 8 (a) explains the action of the 555 detector with the circuit arrangement of the unit shown in **Fig 8 (b)**. He writes:

"A portion of the input voltage is compared to the reference voltage V_z across the zener diode. If V2, set by RV2, is less than half V_z, the 555 flipflop is set - resulting in a Hi output capable of sourcing 200mA (for the relay). This will be maintained until V1, set by RV1, exceeds V_z. V_z should be less than the upper voltage to be detected. I used a 5V zener diode as that was what I had available. RV1 and RV2 can be any value from 10K to 100K with ten-turn trimpots best for fine adjustment.

"I used the window detector to drive a 12V relay which in turn switches 240V mains to a cheap commercial 4A automotive battery charger as in Fig 7 (b). If the battery is next to the charger then the output of the charger will be well filtered by the battery, but in my case the battery is some distance away connected by about 0.25Ω of cable, hence the need for the 4700μF capacitor across the output of the charger. Without this filtering, the pulsing waveform out of the charger would set and reset the window detector at 100Hz. The 33V zener diode and the two fuses form a belt and braces approach to 240V safety, and are only for my peace of mind."

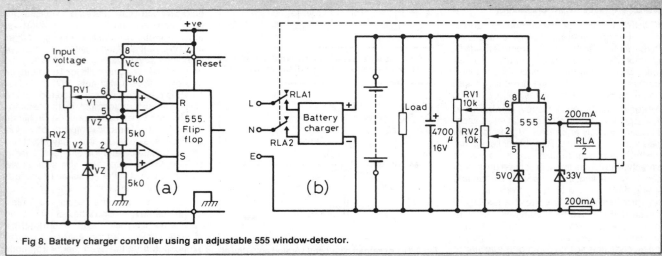

Fig 8. Battery charger controller using an adjustable 555 window-detector.

VHF parasitics result from resonances brought about by the unwanted but unavoidable reactances in leads, grid wires and components: **Fig 9** from *TT*, August 1986 shows (for a grounded-cathode amplifier) the difference between what we would like the amplifier to be and (b) the many stray inductances and capacitances that exist and can cause VHF parasitics.

One must not be too paranoiac about amplifier instabilities. Bill Orr, W6SAI, has pointed out (*TT*, December 1986, p854) that: "Generally speaking the cathode-driven amplifier is a docile beast when triode valves are used and shielding is adequate. Amplifier instability at the operating frequency can often be cured by careful attention to feedback paths external to the amplifier (proper by-passing of primary power leads) and by ensuring that the exciter and amplifier are operating at the same earth potential. An extra-short, heavy earth strap between exciter and amplifier will often cure an unstable amplifier . . . . Parasitics, when they occur, are usually mild and commonly above the self-neutralizing frequency of the valve . . . . A sure fire cure is to load the circuit at the parasitic frequency until the amplifier refuses to oscillate. The valve lead common to all parasitic circuits is the anode; this is where parasitic suppression should take place. A simple resistor-inductor circuit will do the job but winding too many turns around the resistor will cause it to overheat, too few and the parasitic will not be suppressed."

AG6K might disagree about the "mildness" of VHF parasitics, although he stresses that valve damage can be caused in other ways.

He writes: "If the gold plating on the grid wires of an amplifier valve is missing in places, a VHF parasitic was the most likely culprit. If a VHF parasitic has occurred, it's also common to find that some of the cathode coating has been dislodged. This leaves dark patches on the cathode surface. But if the grid's gold plating is completely intact, and the cathode coating has been damaged, a parasitic oscillation was *not* the reason for the failure. Instead the valve was destroyed by *cathode overdrive* . . . . A common misconception among radio amateurs is that it's okay to overdrive an oxide-cathode valve as long as the grid current is held to a safe level. I don't know how this idea got started but this notion is a thick slice of some very expensive bologna . . . . overdrive abuses a frangible oxide cathode"

AG6K notes that with a directly-heated filament-type cathode (eg 3-500z) the tungsten-dicarbide coating is bonded into the tungsten/thorium-oxide-alloy filament wire and cannot be dislodged by cathode overdrive (but can be wasted away by excessive filament voltage). However, in indirectly-heated valves, the cathode comprises a nickel cylinder coated with a mixture of barium-oxide and strontium-oxide. At the recommended drive level, the nickel-to-oxide bond is strong enough to keep the oxide coating in place. Overdriving pushes anode current beyond rated maximum and may be sufficient to dislodge the coating no matter what the grid current happens to be. He illustrates this with a *kaputt* 8873 valve (one of two from a Henry Radio 2K Ultra linear). Although the manual warns against exceeding 75 watts drive, it had been driven with over 95 watts - a $810 mistake!

He believes also that there is a common misconception that a valve will amplify linearly as long as its grid current is controlled by heavy loading. He writes: "Although heavy loading reduces grid current and usually improves linearity, *it does not linearize the amplifier if the valve is overdriven*. A valve cannot be made to operate linearly when it is severely overdriven

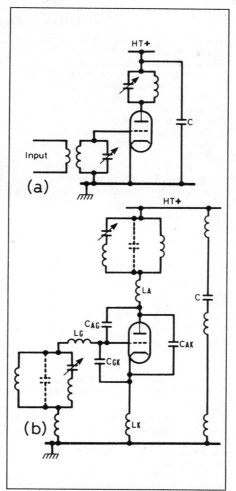

Fig 9. (a) Basic RF grounded-cathode amplifier which also forms a tuned-plate, tuned-grid oscillator unless the two tuned circuits are effectively isolated and not coupled inductively or capacitively so as to result in positive feedback. (b) The problem is made complex by the presence of stray capacitances at VHF resulting in VHF parasitic oscillation. This is how the circuit of (a) appears at very high frequencies.

because its cathode emission *saturates* - fails to increase with further increases in drive - causing flat-topping and on SSB causing *splatter*."

On the question of valve damage resulting from VHF parasitics, he writes: "Excessive grid current is the principal reason for failure in valves subjected to intermittent VHF parasitic oscillation. Often, however, the large anode-current pulse, which is fed by the energy stored in the HT-supply filter capacitor(s), damages other components. The pulse can create a powerful magnetic field that can pull a 3-500z's hot, thoriated-tungsten filament wires off centre, sometimes causing a filament-to-grid short-circuit; it may also damage the current-metering circuit and zener cathode-bias diode . . . . The damage typically inflicted on ceramic-metal valves by VHF parasitic oscillation can be spectacular. Such valves have indirectly-heated oxide-coated cathodes, high gain and gold-plated grids (to reduce secondary emission) . . . . VHF energy is capable of heating the gold-plating while leaving (due to *skin effect*) the grid cage relatively cool . . . . the gold can be heated to evaporation and the resulting hot gold-cloud condenses into tiny droplets some of which may land on the cathode, poisoning it, and reducing cathode emission . . . ; Migrating gold can also find a new home inside the ceramic anode

insulator and may cause flashover between the anode and adjacent grounded-grid ring."

These extracts from the four pages of Part 1 of AG6K's article show the need for care in using modern high-cost RF power valves (which can cost hundreds of pounds/dollars when bought new) in operating both factory-made and home-built high-power linear amplifiers.

HERE AND THERE

MIKE KING, G3MY MENTIONS that on 50MHz he uses a grounded-grid power amplifier developed over the past three years and now duplicated by a number of the local amateurs. This uses a single TV-line-output valve with adequate forced air cooling. Various types have been used with little difference in efficiency, and all the constructors have commented on the unequivocal stability. Power gain is 10 to 12dB depending on the anode voltage, physical design and layout. Efficiency usually proves to be around 50 to 55%. Valves used have included 6JB6, 6MJ6, 6KD6, 6LF6, 20LF6 (G3MY's preferred type), PL509 and PL519. All have given good results. An experimental version, so far only bench tested, using Laminar flow forced air cooling and 1200V on the anode of a 20LF6, gives some 140W PEP output without wilting.

Del Arthur, G0DLN notes that many amateurs struggle to receive CW through an SSB filter, since Narrow CW filters tend to be classed as expensive optional extras. This situation can be much improved by the use of an outboard audio filter which plugs in between rig and phones. He writes: "Most of these use a PP3 or similar battery which always seems to expire when needed. Spurred on by a recent *TT* item, I decided to knock up a passive filter as an experiment. In my junk box I found a small 1H toroid choke only about 3cm in diameter. When connected in series with an 0.15µF capacitor and the earpieces of a cheap pair of low-impedance headphones the results were quite remarkable. It provides a sharp resonance peak around 500Hz with higher and lower frequencies severely attenuated. The beauty of this arrangement is that the two small components can actually be fitted inside the earpiece cover, together with a miniature toggle switch, thus doing away with extra boxes and cables between rig and phones.

"There is some attenuation of the wanted signal but this is overcome by slightly turning up the volume control. In **Fig 10** the resistor R is to equalise the volume when switching the filter out, and its value needs to be slightly more than the DC resistance of the choke. More by luck than judgement I now have a KISS-type CW filter which is selective enough to wipe out some kinds of quite heavy QRM completely, as well as reducing some kinds of atmospheric static and receiver noise."

G0DLN proved his point by sending along a tape cassette recording of the effect of switching the filter in and out under conditions of severe interference. Certainly, the filter improves reception of the wanted signal.

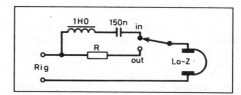

Fig 10. G0DLN fits a simple passive audio filter inside the cover of one earpiece of his low-impedance headphones to improve CW reception on a transceiver fitted with an SSB filter.

Bill Guest, G4IYB following up the *TT* item on Telegraphists Cramp/Glass Arm/Brass Arm/RSI/Upper Limb Disorders etc (May 1990, pp28-29) has found in the 1921 edition of T E Herbert's *Telegraphy* (4th edition reprint, Addendum p995) an interesting note relating to the Vibroplex key and the then current thinking on telegraphist's cramp: "The Vibroplex: This device is in extensive use in America to prevent telegraphist's cramp by relieving the operator of the work of forming the separate dots . . . . (description of the operation of a Vibroplex `bug' key) . . . . It is contended that the device permits faster sending with less fatigue to the operator, and that the strain on the receiving operator may be reduced by taking the message on a typewriter. In this way it is claimed that higher output is secured and the possibility of telegraphist's cramp is reduced. Whether these claims can, any or all of them, be substantiated in practice remains to be determined, since the experiments in progress are not yet conclusive. It is, however, true that when the device was tried some twenty years ago (presumably about 1900) it was, at that time, condemned by most practical telegraphists in this country.

"Telegraphist's cramp is neither very rare nor is it extensive, and there is some reason to think that in many cases where it does occur the prime cause lies in bad teaching and the consequent development of unnatural, jerky methods of sending. The replacement by properly adjusted double-current (brass) keys for single-current type keys on all busy circuits should tend to reduce the risk of cramp, even where the art of rhythmical sending has either never been acquired or has been impaired due to some obscure physical condition of the operator."

This note certainly reflects the long-held belief of British professional telegraphists of the merits of the up-and-down straight brass key that lasted for at least half-a-century - and the anti-bug' feeling of the authorities. As someone who still uses a Post Office type double current key (and other straight keys), this is not an argument that I would want to enter into. But the modern electronic keyer, when correctly operated, does give extremely good morse with apparently little or no risk of incurring glass arm!

TT has referred from time to time to the difficulties and dangers (as well as the equipment involved) in clandestine radio operations during the second world war from enemy-occupied territory. But radio was only one of several forms of communication used by the Intelligence Services. Lt Col CJ Walters in *The Journal of the Royal Signals Institution* recalls that homing pigeons brought back to the UK useful information from the inhabitants of the occupied countries of Western Europe.

Birds were dropped from aircraft in cardboard containers with message holders, message pads, a little food for the bird, instructions in the local language on the type of information needed, and even a pencil. From April 1941 to September 1944 some 16,554 birds were dropped of which 1,722 or just over 10% returned. The high casualty rate is ascribed to enemy counter-measures which paralled those directed at radio agents, and included big rewards to anyone handing in a pigeon and the death penalty for any civilian caught with one. Other problems included the shortage of experienced, fully-trained pigeons and the seasonal bad weather. One suspects also that at least some of the missing 14,832 birds ended up as pigeon pie - at least nobody was tempted to try and eat a suitcase radio, although there is a story of one radio-agent who found himself in France without a radio but carrying the overnight suitcase of the conduct-

UHF CO-AXIAL CERAMIC RESONATORS

Leon Heller, G1HSM draws attention to an article in *Siemens Advance* which describes the use of their range of co-axial ceramic resonators between 300 and 1500MHz.

This notes that resonators of high-permittivity, temperature-stable ceramic are finding increasing application at frequencies up to 30GHz. For mobile radio there is an increasing demand for small resonators with good RF characteristics for use above 400MHz.

Co-axial ceramic resonators as now marketed by Siemens are claimed to be an attractively-priced solution for stabilising fre-

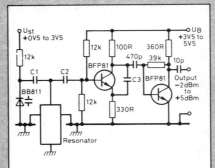

Fig 11. UHF voltage-controlled oscillator stabilised with a Siemens co-axial ceramic resonator.

quencies in voltage-controlled oscillators for small, portable mobile radios.

Fig 11 shows a regenerative broad-band amplifier that begins to oscillate when an electronically tuneable resonator is connected to the input gate: "Because of the design and the influence of lead and stray capacitances, the oscillator frequency (fo) is some 10% lower than the resonance frequency (f) of the unloaded co-axial resonator. The oscillator output is buffered and amplified in the second transistor stage, which has an output impedance of about 50Ω. This circuit can be used for oscillator applications between 300 and 1500MHz. The required frequency is obtained by using an appropriate resonator and fitting suitable coupling capacitors C1, C2 and C3.

Such resonators can also be used for frequency stabilisation in IC oscillators. To achieve the optimum oscillator response, the resonator should be soldered to the PCB on both sides of the outer cylinder jacket and along its entire length. This results in good earthing as well as excellent mechanical strength. Further improvement can be achieved with the cylindrical form of resonator (which has an additional nickel barrier to produce good solderability even under difficult conditions) by recessing it in a slot on the board. Besides giving the shortest possible connection between the inner conductor and the circuit, this also reduces installation height.

ing officer who had seen him off from the Tempsford aerodrome!

Jim Glanville, G3TZG, noting my recent comment that I found opaque the Cyrillic alphabet of the Russian magazine *Radio* sent along a copy of his "Russian Morse for the Amateur and Commercial Operator" published in 1988 and still available price £3.50 post free. This is a short ten page duplicated-style booklet, but it does provide a useful guide to copying and transmitting to Russian Amateurs in the Cyrillic Morse alphabet after learning a few extra Morse symbols and becoming accustomed to the Latin equivalent of the 33 letters. G3TZG provides a guide to common phrases including, for example, abbreviations and phrases which occur in Russian CW satellite working and Russian marine operations, etc. His address is 3 Seneschal Road, Coventry. CV3 5LF if you are interested. But remember that not all operators in the various Soviet Republics use Russian as their

mother tongue. Some now get a little touchy if you insist on using Russian abbreviations these days! All Russian amateurs have to understand International Morse and the standard abbreviations. But I have long found such abbreviations as SPB (spasibo - thanks) ZA (for) QSO and DSW (Do svidanya - goodbye) goes down well.

I still feel that in order to avoid introducing errors into *Technical Topics*, it is better to mix Imperial weights and measures with metric rather than to strive after pedantic consistency - hardly, I admit, a scientific approach, but personally I still think in feet and inches. A recent letter in *Nature* from Ernest L Asten, who runs a hardware store in San Francisco, notes that the USA alone obdurately clings to the old British patchwork of systems that are often not what they say they are. He points out that in a 100 year old house, 2 x 4 timber really was 2in by 4in; in a 50 year old house usually 1⅝ by 3⅝ in; and in a deflated modern house 1½ by 3½ inches!

"Half-inch" galvanised pipe isn't half an inch anywhere: the inside diameter is about ⅝ in and outside diameter about ¹³/₁₆ in. Nails are measured in "pennies" with the symbol d as in £sd - so a 4d nail is 1½ in long. 6d is 2 in, 8d is 3 in so it should be perfectly obvious that a 3½ in nail will be, that's right, 16d. Concrete comes by the cubic yard, timber by the board foot, shingles by the square, yarn by the skein, but a sack of cement is always 94 pounds. "It's a Jim Dandy system and any country that would give it up for something as straightforward as metric has no sense of humour." □

Gerald Stancey, G3MCK provides a method of securing small batteries, such as the PP3, inside equipment that is much cheaper than buying battery holders: **Fig 12**. He writes "Cut a piece of PCB or paxolin about 2 ¾ by ⅞ inches and drill two 4BA clearance holes in it. Secure the battery to this strip by wrapping Sellotape round them. Bolt the combination inside the equipment".

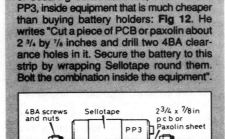

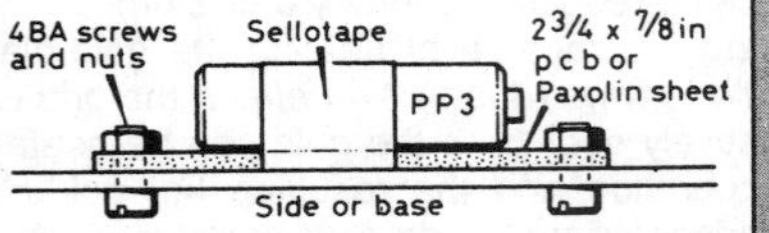

Fig 12. G3MCK's low-cost "battery holder"

HOME-BREW END-FED ANTENNAS FOR HANDHELDS

TT, SEPTEMBER 1990 p31, DREW attention to a South African review of the AEA 'Hot Rod' 144MHz, end-fed, half-wave antenna which plugs into hand-held transceivers in place of the usual short helically-wound 'rubber-duck' antenna. ZS6GM reported a very noticeable improvement in performance, although his review gave no information on the matching section used by AEA to permit end feeding from the transceiver socket (it has been pointed out to me that some CB antennas are end-fed dipoles).

The item has resulted in useful comment from Hans-Joachim Brandt, DJ1ZB, who sent along a copy of a 1985 article he wrote for the German magazine *Funk* describing a home-brew half-wave 144MHz dipole that gave markedly superior results to rubber-duck antennas. He writes:

"In the February 1985 issue of *Funk* I presented a concept for home-brewing a 144MHz end-fed half-wave antenna with an LC matching section in a small plastic box, a telescopic antenna of rather random length (80cm to 133cm) and a flange BNC plug (or similar): **Fig 1**. The trimmers were 7pF air-dielectric made by Tronser. Starting values for the coil are 5 turns, inner diameter 5mm, total length 8mm. The coil may be varied if the setting of capacitor C2 is at an extreme end (when the section is being aligned using a VHF SWR meter). The plastic box is superior to a metal box in two aspects: it is easier to isolate the telescopic antenna; and there is no difference in tuning with the box open or closed.

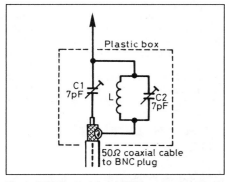

Fig 1. DJ1ZB's end-fed 144MHz antenna using a telescopic rod (80cm to 133cm) with matching network enclosed in plastic box (57mm x 28mm x 28mm). When the box is fitted with a flange-type BNC plug the antenna can be plugged directly into a hand-held transceiver or mounted separately and connected to the transceiver by length of 50Ω low-loss cable.

"Simple comparisons between a rubber duck and this telescopic antenna were conducted from the flat roof of a city building in Munich. With the rubber duck and 2.5W, the Austrian repeaters OE2XSL and OE7XKI could just be opened, but the German repeater DB0XF north of Munich could not be opened. With the telescopic antenna, all three repeaters could be opened easily with the low power option of 0.3W of this hand-held, indicating an improvement of at least (10log 2.5/0.3) equal to 9dB.

"Other comparisons were done as follows: An aluminium plate 20cm by 20cm was placed

TECHNICAL TOPICS

PAT HAWKER G3VA

as a ground-plane on the roof of a car having a sliding opening in the roof, with the test antenna mounted on this. The feeder cable was routed into the interior of the car to the handheld receiver via a variable step attenuator. Either a fixed S-meter reading or the closing of the squelch was used as the input voltage reference. With each antenna, the attenuator was adjusted so that this condition was met. With a telescopic length of 90cm an improvement over the rubber-duck of 7 - 11dB was noted; with a length of 116cm the improvement was 11 to 15dB.

"Another type of matching section for this type of antenna employs a parallel resonant circuit, with a tap on the coil for the 50 ohm input (as often used on HF for voltage-fed antennas - G3VA). Such an antenna is being marketed in Germany by Bensch. This saves the use of a second high-grade trimmer but I would guess that the matching transformation cannot be as accurate as when using two continuously variable trimmers. I am also using this type of matching section for an 'under the roof' fixed vertical antenna for local FM working. In this case two quarter-wave radials are used as a counterpoise (see *Sprat*, Autumn 1981 'QRP via repeaters')."

DJ1ZB also mentions that his matching section arrangement with the two trimmers appears in the latest edition (11th edition) of *Antennenbuch* by K Rothammel, Y21BK, the most popular antenna book in the German language. Y21BK died a few years ago, but his widow hopes to recruit a group of competent antenna specialists to continue to update this most useful book. A copy of the first edition (1961) is still in use at G3VA, the many illustrations and tables overcoming the language barrier!

Rubber-duck antennas can, of course, be replaced by home-made quarter-wave systems without the use of matching networks. J M Osborne, G3HMO, writes: "I recently acquired a dual-band handheld (IC24FT) with the usual rubber-duck antenna. I had decided to use this for mobile operation during my summer holiday but two days before leaving had got only as far as reading the literature on mobile antennas. The shortage of time forced an empirical, but in the event entirely satisfactory, KISS solution.

"I extracted a telescopic antenna from a scrap transistor radio and fixed it to a piece of plastic channelling. An odd length of coaxial cable (about 2m long) with a BNC connector was also secured to the plastic, the inner being connected to the telescopic rod and the outer to a screw through the plastic channelling. The whole was fixed with insulating tape to the integral roof rack (Passat estate) so as to earth the coax outer to the roof rack via the screw. The lead was brought through a rear door to the handheld on a front seat through an SWR/power meter. The telescopic rod length was then adjusted for best compromise SWR on both 70cm and 2m bands (about 1.3:1 SWR on both). This proved to be with about a 54cm extension of the rod (roughly

quarter-wave on 2m and 3/4-wave on 70cm). No coils were used for loading or matching and the antenna connected to the handheld via the meter or direct.

"My excuse for bringing this simple system to your attention is that the results were most satisfactory. From South Devon, I worked stations from Dorset to Cornwall (and in France) via a Brittany repeater on 144MHz during a lift, and routinely simplex as well as many other repeaters en route. On 70cm, results were equally good; during my return trip, I raised G0AKN (Twickenham) via the Farnham (UHF) repeater to give my ETA while on a high spot on Salisbury Plain (about 36 miles from the repeater). The handheld was producing about 5 watts on the power meter when running off the cigar lighter 12V supply.

"Once the optimum setting had been ascertained, the segments of the antenna were taped to fix the length. Mechanical performance was (unexpectedly) good. Once the contraption was dislodged by a branch in a Devon lane, but a spare reel of tape quickly restored it. Three months later the system still functions normally."

HF/VHF SCATTER COMMUNICATIONS

WHILE WE NORMALLY THINK OF radio signals being propagated to long distances by being reflected (refracted) from conductive surfaces (ionised layers or ground/sea surfaces), they can also be propagated by the scattering which occurs when radio signals pass through the layer or are reflected from the ground. Scattering normally implies only very weak signals, but since the effect occurs with signals passing *through* ionised layers it is not limited to frequencies below the MUF.

It is worth recalling that one of the pioneers of VHF scatter communications, shortly after the end of the second world war, was the same Dr E C S Megaw (G6MU) who, as noted previously in *TT*, played an important role in the 1940 development of the cavity magnetron, was a former Council member of the Society and several times described his microwave experiments in the *T&R Bulletin* [another note for newer members; this was the fore-runner of the RSGB Bulletin - Ed] in the 1930s. In the USA, the prime movers were H G Booker and W E Gordon, whose studies led to a major investigation of scatter propagation on a frequency just below 50MHz in conjunction with the US Bureau of Standards, Collins Radio and a large number of American amateurs. These studies showed that with very high-power transmitters using frequencies well above the MUF, weak signals could be received consistently far beyond the horizon due to incoherent scattering caused by random fluctuations in the refractive index in the troposphere or the lower ionosphere (primarily the E-layer). This work led directly to the development for commercial and military communications of troposcatter (and some ionospheric-scatter) systems, often using enormous 'billboard' antennas and multiple-diversity systems, although relatively low power systems can be used for narrow-band communications in conjunction with high-gain antennas.

A survey of the various forms of scatter

propagation of interest to radio amateurs by Mike Bosch, ZS2FM appears in the September 1990 issue of *Radio-ZS*. The following is a brief digest of some of the points made by ZS2FM plus some additional information.

Tropospheric forward scatter: Communication up to about 700 miles is theoretically possible on the VHF/UHF bands (a few hundred miles is more practical) by the reception of energy scattered in the troposphere, although at VHF this is usually not the sole propagation-mode involved. It requires high-power transmitters or very high-gain antennas and sensitive receivers of much the same order as those required for the Earth-Moon-Earth (moonbounce) path. VHF troposcatter on the 144MHz band was observed on amateur signals in South Africa in 1982. Troposcatter signals are weak, with very slow and deep fading in a cycle lasting up to 15 minutes, with the signals likely occasionally to dip below noise. Troposcatter can be present when band conditions are too flat for conventional tropo propagation.

Ionospheric forward scatter: Since the lower ionosphere is permanently turbulent, some degree of forward scattering is present at all times as indicated by the 1951 US investigations on 50MHz. System ranges up to more than 1200km are possible using frequencies between about 25 and 100MHz.

Signals are subject to rapid fading with some diurnal and seasonal variation. The need for very high power (eg 50kW or so) rules out amateur use of this mode, but ZS2FM points out that European Band I TV stations can sometimes be received in South Africa by scattering from the F2 layer, some hours before the VHF TV band (Band I) opens for normal ionospheric propagation in the sunspot maximum period.

Backscatter: Signals are scattered when returning to the surface of the Earth (particularly the sea) after first hop reflection from the ionosphere. This occurs at HF/VHF whenever a path is open for F2-layer propagation. Backscatter signals are often receivable on ordinary transceivers, antennas etc. The signals are weak but readable and largely free from fading, over distances up to 5000km when listening on bands close to the MUF. It is, for example, often by this mode of propagation that UK amateurs located well beyond ground-wave range, can be heard in the UK while they are working long distances on bands between 14 to 50MHz. Frequently noticed, for example, when the stations concerned are in contact with South American stations.

Meteor scatter: Well-known mode of VHF propagation as a result of bouncing signals off the short-lived plasma trails left by incoming meteors, with amateurs making effective use of the longer-lasting trails during the main meteor shower periods. Commercial/military meteor-burst systems, however, also exploit the very short-lived underdense trails of the micrometeors that occur in large numbers throughout the year, using a continuous probe signal to trigger off high-speed, computer-controlled duplex bursts of data. Among the commercial systems is one developed in South Africa by Salbu(Pty) Ltd under the direction of Dave Larson, ZS6DN. Transmitter powers of the commercial systems tend to be about 400W, with 4-5ele Yagi arrays.

Rain scatter: Forward scattering of microwave and millimetre-wave energy by heavy rain showers can provide a practical, if only intermittently available, mode for amateurs at 10GHz and above, for contacts well beyond the horizon or across hills, etc.

SIMPLE HEATER-VOLTAGE STABILISER

STAN BROWN, G4LU, NOTED the arrangements for heater voltage stabilisation suggested by PA0LMD (*TT*, October 1990, p29) including the use of a PSU with an L296 IC regulator providing adjustable-voltage DC output. He uses, and has found more than adequate for his pair of 2C39s in a 23cm power amplifier, the simple arrangement shown in **Fig 2** running at just over 5VDC output.

He writes: "The circuit is simplicity itself

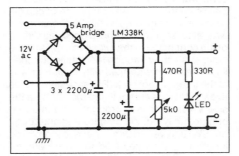

Fig 2. G4LU uses this stabilised DC supply to power the heaters of two 2C39 valves in a 23cm power amplifier, running at just over 5VDC output.

and the large-value capacitor across the adjusting resistor provides a slow rise characteristic. The LM338K needs a finned heatsink, which is augmented by being mounted on the aluminium bracket for fixing to the case."

G4LU also notes that RS are now offering the LM396K IC regulator which is rated at 10A and incorporates internal current limiting.

1.8MHZ HELICAL VERTICAL DIPOLE

NOT MANY OF US COULD contemplate putting up a vertical resonate half-wave dipole for 1.8MHz since, if unloaded, it would call for at least a 250ft mast. However with a helically wound element (normal mode) the total height can be brought down to well under 20ft, though of course at the cost of lower radiation efficiency and more critical tuning.

In the Australian magazine *Amateur Radio* (October 1990), N Chivers, VK2YO described experiments with such an antenna, using wire wound on two 2m fibreglass rods (wooden curtain rod could be used): **Fig 3**. Each rod has a PL259 coaxial plug at one end which screws into a coax 'Tee' piece so that the lower rod hangs vertically under the higher rod, and is mechanically rigid. The top rod is fitted with a hook to hang it from a convenient support which could be a rope stretched between two points.

VK2YO describes construction as follows: "Wind enough wire onto one of the rods at the opposite end to the PL259 plug so that when it is coupled to a GDO it shows self resonance at about 3.6MHz. This took 132m of 26SWG enamelled wire scrounged from an old power transformer primary. The wire is close-wound over 1.2m of rod, then the winding is tapered to connect with the PL259 connector at the other end. Repeat this process for the other rod. The wire on the upper rod is connected to the centre pin of the PL259 plug, while that on the lower rod connects to the outer collar of its PL259 plug.

"With the two rods assembled with the inter-connecting coax 'Tee' and supported horizontally on three chair backs, a socket with one turn was screwed on to the plug section of the tee connector. A GDO coupled to this loop dipped at 1.79MHz but when the antenna was raised vertically with the lower rod about 1m above ground, the resonant frequency went up to 1.86MHz. Squashing up the turns a bit lowered this to about 1.83MHz a popular frequency in Australia. The turns were then fixed with a coating of araldite.

"When coupled directly to a TS680S transceiver with 50Ω coax, results on reception were satisfactory but on transmit the VSWR was high and the built-in protection circuit reduced the power output."

With an impedance bridge, the antenna was found to null broadly about 20Ω at 1.86MHz indicating the need for some form of impedance matching. VK2YO put together the arrangement shown in Fig 3, winding 100 turns of 18SWG wire, tapped every 5 turns onto a piece of orange 20mm diameter electrical conduit, with a wide-spaced 20-150pF variable capacitor of second world war vintage.

This combination tunes from about 1.75 to 1.95MHz. By trial and error, moving the taps up and down the coil and adjusting the capacitor, a low VSWR could be achieved. The interconnecting cable between antenna and tuner should be kept as short as possible to minimise radiation from the outer skin of the coax-cable braid (unbalanced feed to balanced antenna). VK2YO adds: "Do not connect the transceiver to the tuner or the tuner to the load (antenna) via a coax switch, since the braid side will be common to all connected antennas and connected to earth for lightning protection. This antenna floats above ground and is independent of ground. If the station transceiver is separately RF grounded, then the tuned circuit should be fed by a link coupling wound over the centre of the tapped coil with a series capacitor (eg 10-100pF ceramic-based mica capacitor) in one leg of the link winding of about 20 turns 18 SWG."

VK2YO finds this modest 1.8MHz vertically-polarised antenna works as well as or better than his end-fed wire about 80m long, usually one S-point up on transmit.

THE LAZY MAN'S MULTIBANDER

GEORGE CRIPPS, , G3DWW, WRITES: "For some time I have obtained very good results from a 66ft inverted-L antenna used as a quarter-wave on 3.5MHz and fed directly from 50Ω coaxial cable. The need then arose for operation on 7MHz in daylight and 3.5MHz at night. A second 33ft length of wire was then strung under the first spaced from it with plastic insulators of the type used for open-

wire line (about 6in). This worked well. It was then realised that the 33ft wire would also provide a low-impedance feed-point on 21MHz as a three-quarter-wave antenna. Later still a 16ft 6in wire was hung vertically downwards from the horizontal wire to form the arrangement shown in **Fig 4**. The final result performs well on 3.5, 7, 14 and 21MHz with a low SWR on each band and permitting direct feed from the 50Ω cable. The vertical portion of the antenna is at the bottom of my garden, about 48ft from the house and away from the zone of domestic electrical interference noises."

While clearly G3DWW is satisfied with his multibander, it needs perhaps to be said that the low SWR (if really low) does not necessarily imply high-efficiency. His diagram does not indicate a direct earth connection at the antenna end of the coax cable (which I would expect to see) so presumably there is an RF earth provided at the transceiver end of the feeder. Since one would expect the feed-point impedance of a quarter-wave wire to be only about 19-20Ω resistive, it is possible that the 'earth' is contributing extra RF resistance to achieve a match somewhere near~unity and that considerable RF current is flowing back down the outer braid of the cable (unless perhaps G3DWW buries the cable in its

passage down the garden, in which case one would expect an SWR of at least 2:1). Such an SWR would be perfectly satisfactory from a radiation-efficiency point of view but might cause the transceiver to reduce power. A unity SWR might be more worrying since it would suggest power wastage. As W2DU pointed out many years ago: "A low SWR is *not* evidence that an antenna system is working efficiently. On the contrary, a lower than normal SWR over a significant bandwidth is reason to suspect that a dipole or vertical antenna is being affected by resistance losses. These may arise from poor connections, poor earthing systems, lossy cable or other causes."

STABLE INDUCTANCES

RECENT *TT* ITEMS (eg 'More on stable oscillators', November 1990, p29) have underlined the importance of good coils when attempting to achieve a stable free-running LC VFO. The lower and more consistent the temperature coefficient of the tank coil, the easier it is to provide effective compensation by means of negative coefficient capacitors. Even with the Nylon-loaded Bakelite formers and special techniques used in the R210 receiver, the coils were stated to have positive temperature coefficients of 12, 26, and 55ppm/°C with, as usually the case, the larger values of inductance having the greater temperature coefficients.

It is interesting to compare the R210 figures with data given in the book *Theory and Design of Valve Oscillators* by H A Thomas (first published 1939) for the performance of high-grade oscillator coils, including some using skeleton formers, complete formers (solid keramot) and a silica tube former with tinned copper wire wound in grooves while hot and allowed to contract. Such a silica 8-turn (2.65in dia) coil with an inductance of 4.4μH had a cyclic positive temperature coefficient of only 7ppm/°C, compared with 32, 19, 34, 36 and 38ppm/°C for the coils wound on keramot and skeleton mycalex formers.

Dr Thomas commented: "Examination of the results shows that the temperature coefficient of any of the coils consisting of wire wound on a skeleton former is of the order of twice the temperature coefficient of expansion of the metal . . . . for coils employing a complete insulating former it appears that the temperature coefficient likely to be obtained is greater than the temperature coefficient of the metal but less than that of the former. For the silica-former coil, the wire was wound on the former while under tension and at a temperature of 80°C. The wire was soldered to end clamps and then allowed to cool. This ensured that the wire was permanently under tension within the elastic limit . . . . it is clear that this method of construction gives partial compensation, since the temperature coefficient of inductance is less than half that of the copper itself, but it is clear also that an imperfect contact exists between the wire and the former which produces changes in configuration on temperature change. This view is confirmed by L Rohde (1934) who gives values of +43, +41, +42 and +45ppm/°C for four coils in which copper wire was wound on a cylindrical ceramic former having an expansion coefficient of 7.8 x 10⁻⁶ per °C. In these cases

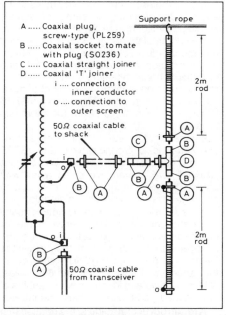

A ..... Coaxial plug, screw-type (PL259)
B ..... Coaxial socket to mate with plug (SO236)
C ..... Coaxial straight joiner
D ..... Coaxial 'T' joiner
i .... connection to inner conductor
o .... connection to outer screen

50Ω coaxial cable to shack

50Ω coaxial cable from transceiver

Support rope

2m rod

2m rod

Fig 3. VK2YO's 1.8MHz helical-type vertical antenna can be suspended from a height of less than 20ft and operates independently of an RF earth connection.

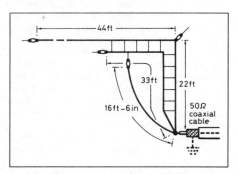

44ft

33ft

22ft

16ft-6in

50Ω coaxial cable

Fig 4. G3DWW's 'Lazy Man's Multibander' antenna for 3.5/7/14/21MHz.

with no special tensioning of the wire, non-cyclic behaviour was also observed."

Dr Thomas notes that the logical development of this principle is to deposit the conductor on the former to ensure perfect adhesion, with the Germans developing such a technique in the 1930s: "but at present the inductance coefficient cannot be reduced below 8ppm/°C due to the mechanical properties of the former material." The good stability of German military equipment in the second world war presumably drew on this technique.

For amateur radio equipment, it seems to me, there is one further important factor encountered in practice: the use of paxolin formers and other materials that absorb significant amounts of moisture from the air (ie hygroscopic materials). This can result in enhanced, non-consistent rates of drift particularly where equipment is left switched-off for relatively long periods in dampish, unheated shacks. Back in the 1950s, an effective dodge was to fit a low-consumption (5 or 7 watts) light bulb close to the coil-pack which could then be left running between operating periods. A problem with hygroscopic formers is the difference between the temperature coefficient of a coil when completely dried out and when there is absorbed moisture. This makes it virtually impossible to compensate such inductors effectively. In the case of the R210 receiver, it was noted that this was enclosed in a hermetically sealed (dry air) aluminium-alloy diecast panel and case.

It can, of course, be argued that with the improved frequency synthesizers, having much less phase-noise, now available in factory-built equipment, the need for high-stability LC VFOs has diminished. True enough, but there is surely still a role for *low-cost* home-built designs capable of medium/high performance. It is in the tradition of the hobby to devise ways of equalling or bettering commercial designs at a fraction of the cost.

NVIS, SKYBEAMS AND NEW HF BEACONS

SEVERAL RECENT *TT* ITEMS have referred to the use for military HF communications of near vertical-incidence skywave (NVIS) propagation where the requirement is an antenna system with a high rather than a low vertical radiation pattern. When an antenna of this type is used on frequencies significantly below the long-distance MUF, the usual 'skip zone' vanishes permitting effective communication over any distance up to about 500 miles or so.

Amateurs, on the other hand, usually seek low-angle radiation to optimise long-distance operation, pleased rather than concerned that their 14 to 30MHz signals skip over nearby countries. But there are exceptions. For example, Stuart Kind, G4AYP in Harrogate, Yorkshire is particularly interested in the French language and seeks good, clear daytime contacts with French stations at distances between roughly 300 miles (Northern France) and 800 miles (Southern France). At this stage in the sunspot cycle, he finds 7MHz range often too short at around noon and with too much QRM when the path lengthens. He is thinking of buying a 14MHz Yagi array, mounting it low, possibly devising a method of

controlling the vertical angle or even leaving it pointing vertically upwards.

He queries whether this would in practice have the required result of giving more reliable 14MHz contacts with France. My answer would be yes, provided that at the time the MUF towards the south was reaching 20 to 30MHz, as can often be expected at this phase of the sunspot cycle. However, before investing in a costly array, I would be inclined to try a very low horizontal dipole at a height of about 10ft above good ground, remembering that the feed-point impedance of a very low dipole is significantly lower than at normal height and may require matching if your rig baulks at SWRs of more than about 1.5 to one, or 2:1 to one.

I recall that the use of upwardly-shooting 'skybeams' and high-angle arrays was well covered in a two-part article by Paul Sollom, G3BGL, ex-VS7PS, in the *RSGB Bulletin [for newer members, this was the fore-runner of RadCom - Ed]* back in July, August 1952. This resulted from extensive investigations he carried out between 1947-51 at VS7PS while located on the premises of the Government HF broadcasting station, about 17 miles north of Colombo, Ceylon (now Sri Lanka) in order to devise an antenna system for the broadcast station that would give good signals throughout the island. This stretched some 200 miles to the north, 140 miles to the south with minimum wastage of signals coming down in the sea or in Southern India. In the course of this work, G3BGL developed a number of fixed skybeams providing high-angle radiation that covered the island in one or multiple hops, including an 8-element array mounted horizontally at a height of quarter-wave above ground: **Fig 5** and a VS7PS 'howitzer' a high-angle beam for short-skip broadcasting (**Fig 6**).

One result of the strong high-angle signals and virtual lack of ground-wave on the VS7PS or the broadcast transmissions was that an RAF HF D/F station five miles away was unable to take bearings on either station although receiving very strong signals.

In his article, G3BGL also provided a useful chart showing the optimum wave-angle for one-hop transmission by reflection from the F2 layer, based on its average height over the UK of about 185 miles: **Fig 7**. This shows that, for ranges of between 300 to 800 miles, G4AYP should aim ideally at wave-angles of between 20° to 50° rather than straight up.

A rough but useful guide to the relationship between the MUFs for different distances was given many years ago in *QST*: see **Table 1**. This shows, for example, that when a band is just open to stations more than 2500 miles away, the critical frequency (at which signals going straight up will be reflected back to Earth, ie skip of 0 miles) will be about 2.9 times lower, while the MUF for 750 miles would be approximately half the frequency (remembering always that the MUF towards the south is likely to be considerably higher than along East-West paths). Similarly, if you are receiving strong 14MHz signals from stations about 1000 miles away, the 21MHz band should be open for DX (ie stations more than 2500 miles away) in the same general direction.

For all those interested in 14MHz band conditions, the world-wide system of auto-

matic amateur-radio beacons with stepped reduction of power that has operated for many years on 14,100kHz has proved a most valuable guide to real-time conditions. So much so, that it appears to have inspired CCIR Study Group 6 to plan an even more ambitious network of beacons, spaced throughout the HF spectrum in order to improve the data base of HF propagation, with a view to making better use of the HF broadcast bands.

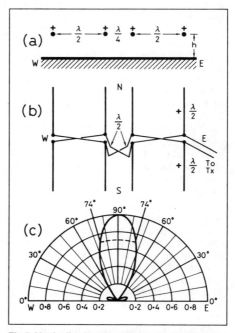

Fig 5. Vertically shooting 'skybeam' developed by G3BGL/VS7PS in the late 1940s with element spacing arranged to minimise side lobes. (a) side elevation; (b) plan view; (c) vertical radiation pattern with 'h' 0.125-lambda. Centre section must be 0.5-lambda so that the elements are all in phase. The gain with h 0.125-lambda is about 12.5dB with reference to a free-space dipole.

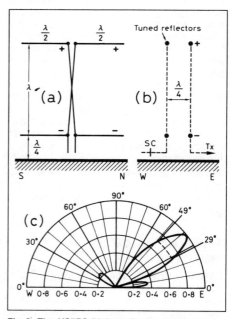

Fig 6. The VS7PS high-angle 'howitzer' antenna designed for a broadcast service from Sri Lanka to southern India, 300 to 700 miles range but covering most of India by multi-hop transmission. Gain (including ground reflection gain) about 13dB over a free-space dipole.

It has taken much longer than anticipated to obtain the necessary co-operation and to set up the system. Originally it had been hoped that up to 15 beacons would each operate on five co-ordinated, time-shared frequencies as on 14,100kHz. This is now most unlikely, and fewer beacons, each with their own set of frequencies, now seem to be the best that can be hoped for. However, the first beacon, of particular interest to UK amateurs, is now operating, transmitting the CW identification AUS1MLB and located near Melbourne, Australia with a 1kW transmitter and omni-directional, vertically-polarised antenna. It has been received in Germany on four of the five frequencies and should provide an excellent real-time guide to G-VK paths on 7, 10, 14, 18 and 21MHz.

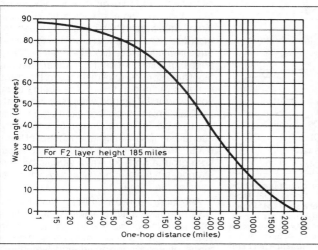

Fig 7. Vertical wave angle for distances up to 2500 mile hops assuming an average UK F2 layer height of 185 miles as given by G3BGL in 1952. In practice optimum wave angle will vary as the reflecting layer height changes. Ionospheric layer heights are roughly: E-layer 60-85 miles (100-140km); F1 layer 90-150 miles (150-250km); F2-layer (day) 150-300 miles (150-500km); F2 layer (night) 190-250 miles (300-400km).

AUS1MLB operates continuously to a fixed time schedule; each transmission lasts approximately four minutes, the signal format being a series of 12 second sequences, with the transmitter then changing to the next frequency. The times/frequencies of this beacon are: (1) 5470.845kHz (centre) at 00, 20 and 40 minutes past each hour; (2) 7870.845kHz at 04 24 44; (3) 10,407.845kHz at 08, 28, 48; (4) 14,407.845kHz at 12, 32, 52; and (5) 20,945.845kHz at 16, 36, 56 minutes past each hour.

A beacon transmitter in Scandinavia is expected shortly (possibly before these notes are published) but frequencies have not yet been announced.

The Study 6 format has been designed to permit a number of measurements to be made automatically on receivers using a specified form of active antenna. However

First hop distance (miles) versus Frequency factors where "1" represents the MUF for that distance					
0	1	0.8	0.7	0.6	0.4	0.35
500	1.2	1	0.8	0.7	0.5	0.4
750	1.5	1.3	1	0.8	0.6	0.5
1000	1.8	1.5	1.2	1	0.8	0.6
1500	2.3	2.0	1.5	1.3	1	0.8
2500	2.9	2.4	1.9	1.6	1.2	1

Table 1 - MUF frequency factors for various distances

the Morse identification and steady tone should provide amateurs with a ready means of assessing path conditions. The 12 second sequence comprises 1S of 100bit/s FSK (850Hz shift); CW identification (about 3S); 1.2Kbit/s sequences (about 0.75S); 4S of FSK reversals; steady tone for at least 3S. Final sequence may be cut short to permit change of frequency.

IMPROVING IMAGE REJECTION - A 1940 TECHNIQUE

WHEN, IN THE 1920s, Howard Armstrong persuaded RCA to develop his 'supersonic heterodyne' receiver for broadcast reception, the IF was often (for about ten years) 110kHz or thereabouts, only later moving to the 'standard' frequencies of 455kHz (American) and 465 or-470kHz (European) in order to reduce the amount of (high-cost) pre-mixer selectivity needed to keep 'image' rejection to an acceptable level for MF/LF reception. Image is the reception of 'spurious' signals spaced twice the IF away from the wanted frequency on the 'other side' of the local oscillator frequency. It is probably the most serious of all the various spurious responses to which superhets are prone.

With a receiver having only one signal-frequency resonate circuit in front of the mixer, often with its Q damped by the coupling to the antenna, image rejection is often poor even on MF (the higher Q ferrite rod antenna notwithstanding). When such a receiver is used on HF, where the tuned circuit becomes relatively less selective (percentage difference between image and signal frequencies reduces progressively as frequencies increase), transmissions on the image frequency may be received almost as strongly as when the receiver is tuned to the frequency of the transmitter. With 455kHz there is the particular problem on 14MHz that the image frequency falls in the 19m broadcast band with its enormously strong signals, at least when the oscillator is tuned (as commonly the case) on the high side of the signal frequency.

Designers of the early (valved) communications receivers stayed with 455kHz but tackled the problem of image rejection by adding more pre-mixer selectivity. The HRO had three pre-mixer tuned circuits requiring four ganged capacitors to tune also the local oscillator: even so, image rejection on the 28MHz band was only about 30dB or so. With less costly models, often having only one tuned RF stage, many amateurs improved image rejection by using an active or passive preselector with two or more tuned circuits in front of their receivers - a still valid arrangement (provided gain is kept low) with modern receivers in order to prevent overloading by strong out-of-band signals.

It was soon appreciated that image rejection on HF could be improved at less cost simply by raising the IF to say 1600kHz or (later) 9MHz, though for some time it remained difficult to manufacture really good bandpass crystal filters at HF, while the once-popular mechanical filters have always remained limited to below about 500kHz. For VHF/FM broadcast receivers, the standard IF has long been 10.7MHz. Some modern communications receivers have a VHF first IF with up-conversion mixing.

However, for home construction of simple, low-cost superhet receivers such as the interesting 3.5MHz design reported by G3TSO in the November 1990 *TT*, using a NE602/SL6700 combination with a ceramic IF filter, there is still much to be said in favour of using a 455kHz IF, at least for 1.8 or 3.5MHz receivers. G3TSO noted that with the three-coil bandpass RF filter he used, image rejection was perfectly satisfactory on these bands, although he felt image response could be a problem at higher frequencies.

Lorin Knight, G2DXK, brings to attention a relatively simple but now largely forgotten technique used to improve image rejection in the Murphy Radio A92 'Stationmaster' receiver of 1940. This set provided, apart from MW/LW, bandspread reception of the 13M, 16M, 19M, 25M, 31M, 40/49M HF broadcast bands. It was developed as a successor to the 1939 A76 as the fourth of a series of Murphy Short-wave Specials (A36, A52, A76, A92) recently described by G2DXK in *Radio Bygones*. The February-March 1990 issue contains details of the novel image rejection circuit used in the A92. This utilised the same electrical principles found in a quartz crystal with its dual series-resonate and parallel-resonate frequencies, though whereas in a crystal these are separated by a matter of Hertz, in the LC circuit of the A92 the two frequencies are made to be 2 x 465kHz apart.

G2DXK considers that this technique, now seemingly forgotten, could possibly be adapted for simple modern amateur receivers having tuned signal-frequency tuned circuits. To quote directly from his *Radio Bygones* description:

"The basic circuit is shown in **Fig 8(a)**. f1 is the series-resonant frequency of L and Cb; thus at this frequency the impedance between frequency-changer grid and earth is very low. At higher frequencies, the combination of Cb and L looks like an inductance, and this inductance forms a parallel-resonant circuit with Ca at f2. Consequently at this frequency the impedance between grid and earth is high. Because the A92 had its oscillator on the lower side of the signal, the designers were able to arrange that f2 corresponded to the signal frequency and f1 to the image frequency.

"They were able to obtain the required bandspreading by placing a small variable capacitance in parallel with L. Variation of this capacitance caused f1 and f2 to move up and down together, the spacing between them conveniently staying fairly constant throughout the capacitance swing.

"The capacitance Ca was provided entirely by circuit strays, in particular the anode ca-

pacitance of the RF amplifier valve and the grid capacitance of the frequency-changer valve. The value of Cb was chosen so that, with L adjusted for maximum gain at the signal frequency, the frequency of minimum gain was a little higher than the image frequency of the various capacitance (fixed and stray) had their nominal values. The actual circuit used in the A92 is shown in **Fig 8(b)**, the starred values are those used for the 19m band."

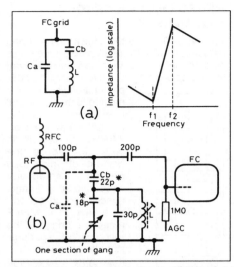

Fig 8. Ingenious image rejection circuit used in the 1940 Murphy 'Stationmaster' (Model A92) table model broadcast receiver, one of a series of Murphy models providing bandspread tuning on the HF broadcast bands. The technique might prove useful for simple superhet models with 455kHz IF. (a) Basic circuit providing series-resonance at f1 and parallel resonance at f2 (b) A92 intervalve circuit. *(G2DXK, Radio Bygones)*

HERE AND THERE

MORE YEARS AGO THAN I care to remember, I had a CW contact with G6CL, callsign of John Clarricoats who for so long was Secretary-Editor of the RSGB. But it was not Clarry at the key but his teenage son Peter who had qualified as an operator of his father's station. Peter Clarricoats never took out his own licence - he was too busy becoming one of the world's leading experts on ferrites and microwaves and becoming a professor at Queen Mary and Westfield College, London. This year he has been elected a Fellow of the Royal Society (FRS), the world's oldest continuously-operating learned society, founded in 1662. No more than 40 Fellows are elected in any one year, and engineers are in a small minority since the Society covers all fields of science. One of the few radio amateurs who have ever been elected FRS was Sir Martin Ryle, G3CY, the Astronomer-Royal. The recent work of Professor Clarricoats has included important development work on reconfigurable reflector antennas for space satellites. Although other forms of space-deployable reflectors exist, his team has developed the novel idea of changing in space the shape of a mesh reflector as an alternative to the phased array concept.

Electronic smog has long covered urban areas, generated by a myriad of domestic appliances, vehicle ignition, lifts etc. Fortunately for amateurs, the smog tends to be

most dense at LF/MF, thinning out at higher frequencies, nevertheless the difference between the background noise levels between the towns and the countryside can make a lot of difference when it comes to hearing the weaker DX.

This difference is well illustrated and quantified by considering the signal levels accepted in the USA as being required to achieve a satisfactory signal-to-noise ratio on medium-wave AM broadcast transmissions: Urban areas 25mV/m (88dBµ); residential areas 5mV/m (74dBµ); and rural areas 0.5mV/m (54dBµ) where 0dBu equals 1mV/m. Apart from the electronic smog, the figures reflect also the problem of receiving signals in and among buildings with reinforced concrete. Incidentally, since coverage is deemed to depend on the range of good ground-wave signals, the night-time service-area of a medium-wave transmitter tends to be much less than its day-time service area due to interference from sky-wave signals. Even in the absence of interference from other stations, night time service-area distance from a transmitter is defined in the USA as being to the point where the ground-wave/sky-wave ratio is 10dB. This implies that night-time service area, even in the absence of co-channel interference, is virtually independent of transmitter power, since as power is increased both ground and sky wave signals become stronger but the ground-wave/sky-wave ratio remains the same.

Although the recent interim report of the US Environmental Protection Agency stated that there is sufficient evidence to demonstrate a 'significant' link between some rare forms of cancer (eg childhood lymphoma, leukaemia and brain cancers) and exposure to extremely low frequency (eg 50 or 60Hz) electromagnetic fields near electricity power lines (*TT* October, p32) not everyone is convinced that a casual link has been demonstrated. In a letter to *Nature* (4 October), James R Jachem of the Radiation Sciences Division of the US Air Force School of Aerospace Medicine points out that other recent studies (eg that by Savitz and Feingold) found that the incidence of childhood cancer was associated with traffic density, with odds ratios *greater* than those reported for EMF and cancer. He notes that one potential consequence of living close to traffic routes is a high level of benzene, a well-established cause of leukaemia. He quotes R A Cartwright as saying: "Our present scientific knowledge points at the very best to a minute risk of EMF verging on the point of non-existence".

THOSE LOOP RADIATION PATTERNS

THE SEPTEMBER *TT* ITEM 'Horizontal loop antennas (real and with MININEC)' included as Fig 3 elevation and azimuth-plane radiation patterns of a multiband 1.9MHz (4 x 132ft) horizontal square loop antenna at a height of 50ft. These patterns were generated by W4ZCB using an IBM computer with MININEC-variant software and used by Doug DeMaw, W1FB, in 'A closer look at horizontal loop antennas' (*QST*, May 1990). Unfortunately, they show how easy it is to use valid computer-software to come up with incorrect results.

James W Healy, NJ2L (a staff member of ARRL), in *QST*, September 1990, with the assistance of KI6WX, VE2CV and W7EL shows that the patterns and gains in the May article were wrong. This was due to an axis-of-symmetry discrepancy. It is apparent that the patterns reproduced in the September *TT* were based on an incorrect axis, brought about by the fact that the MININEC variant used by W4ZCB assumes an axis shown by the line CD in **Fig 1**, whereas the axis of the corner-fed antenna described by W1FB is in fact A-B.

Fig 2 shows KI6WX's NEC3-generated patterns which differ substantially from those shown in September. NJ2L writes:

"The elevation angles at which the azimuth-plane patterns in the May *QST* (September *TT*) were plotted (30° at and below 7MHz, 15° at the higher frequencies) were probably chosen because those were the signal-arrival angles of most interest to the author. The patterns of Fig 2 are shown at the same elevation angles, not at the elevation-plane gain peaks.

"The gains shown in Fig 2 are in decibels relative to an isotropic source (dBi) in free space whereas the earlier patterns show gains relative to a half-wave dipole in free space. Comparing antennas to that of a dipole in free space can be misleading.

MININEC says that the gain of a half-wave dipole in free space is 2.14dBi (OdBd) but at 50 feet above average ground, NEC3 shows that the gain of that same dipole is 6.26dBi (4.12dBd). How can a dipole have 4.12dB gain over a dipole? Easy - the reference antenna is in free space, but the dipole over ground is subject to ground reflections that increase its gain (in this case) by 4.12dB. The same 1.9MHz dipole antenna 50ft above average ground has a whopping 10.4dBi gain at 28MHz - only 4dB less than the 1.9MHz loop's gain at 28MHz. In general, it's less potentially confusing to compare antenna gains to that of an isotropic source in free space".

TOPICS

PAT HAWKER G3VA

It may be recalled that in the July *TT*, G3SEK drew attention to what he felt to be a potentially misleading use of ground reflection gain in MININEC diagrams/leaflets associated with a recently introduced compact HF beam with 11dBd claimed gain. It seems only fair to mention that I subsequently received (indignant) letters from the designers of that antenna who pointed out, *inter alia*, that the

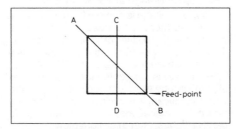

Fig 1: Top view of the horizontal loop described in QST, May and *TT*, September. Line AB represents the true axis of symmetry. CD is the axis that was incorrectly used in calculating the patterns published at the time.

promotional literature made it clear that the gain was stated to be over real ground and was not a promotional gimmick (or words to that effect). True enough, but it does show the

need for amateurs to be aware of the differences between an isotropic reference, a dipole reference, free space and above real ground. As G3SEK made clear in his letter, no criticism of the actual antenna was intended but he was surely right to draw attention to this important distinction in the way antennas may be described.

Ground gain has been well understood for many years by professional antenna engineers but this is not necessarily the case for many amateurs. It can be substantial. To quote data from the *HF Communications Data Book* published by Rockwell International (Collins Radio), the maximum gains of theoretical lossless elementary antennas, together with the direction of maximum gain, are as follows:

● Short dipole in free space: 1.76dBi in plane perpendicular to axis.
● Half-wave dipole in free space: 2.15dBi in plane perpendicular to axis.
● Vertical short monopole over perfect ground: 4.76dBi on horizon.
● Vertical quarter-wave monopole over perfect ground: 5.15dBi on horizon.
● Horizontal half-wave dipoles:
(a) Infinitesimal height above perfect ground: 9.1dBi straight up.
(b) Quarter-wave above perfect ground: 7.4dBi straight up.
(c) Half-wave above perfect ground: 8.2dBi in plane perpendicular to axis 30 deg above horizontal.
(d) Sixth-tenths-wave above perfect ground: 9.2dBi in plane perpendicular to axis 24.6 deg above horizontal.
● Vertical half-wave dipole, half-wave (to centre of antenna) above perfect ground: 8.2dBi on horizon.

In practice, unfortunately, no antennas are lossless (particularly monopoles) nor, except at sea, will the ground be even nearly perfect!

Reverting to the question of the performance of horizontal loop antennas, after the September *TT*, I received letters from Gus Taylor, G8PG, and Roy Hill, GM0IJF, both of whom have for some time been very pleased with the results achieved with multiband horizontal loops at very modest heights.

G8PG has used a rectangular loop (**Fig 3**), about 20ft high, for about six years, feeding it with only about 3 watts of RF with which, on CW, he has worked more than 100 countries, including to his surprise spanning the Atlantic on 3.5MHz and all continents except Oceania on 7MHz. His loop is non-resonant, lower and smaller than those usually recommended. He writes: "I believe that to get the best out of these loops one should make it as big (and as high) as local conditions allow, and feed it via

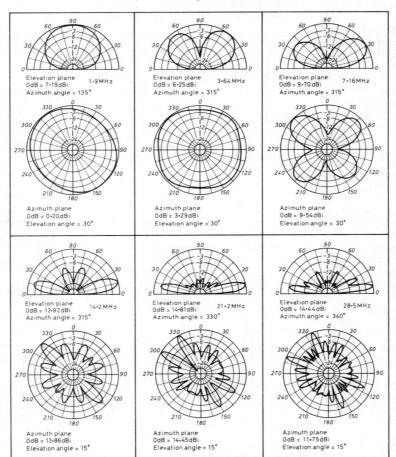

Fig 2: Recalculated radiation patterns of the large horizontal loop antenna using the correct axis of symmetry in conjunction with NEC3 software.

tuned, open-wire line by means of a suitable coupler such as the Z-match with balanced output shown in Fig 12.77 of the fifth edition of the *Radio Communication Handbook*. He wrote up his antenna in *Short-Wave Magazine* (February 1985) and mentions that other QRP enthusiasts have been very satisfied with the results achieved using various horizontal and (smaller) vertical loops. Recently he has been testing an indoor 8ft-square version about 17ft high, with good results on all bands from 10.1MHz upwards and short-skip contacts on 7MHz. He hopes to enlarge on this indoor version in *Sprat*.

GM0IJF has been similarly pleasantly surprised with the DX performance of large loops only 4, 6 or 8m high, one of which was around the eaves of his bungalow. He feeds the loop with 300Ω slotted ribbon feeder with a Z-match coupler. Unlike the majority of such loops, he feeds in the middle of one span rather than at the corner.

POOR MAN'S VARIAC

I RECALL WAY BACK IN the late 1940s, when there were occasional voltage reductions on the electricity supply mains, that somebody published in the *RSGB Bulletin* a simple dodge for increasing or decreasing the line voltage for the station equipment. This used a spare heater transformer with its secondary in series with the load to buck or boost the voltage, depending on the sense of connection. A rather more elaborate form of this idea appears in *Electronics Australia* (September 1990, p109) by someone who uses the pseudonym 'Dr Henry Choke'. He writes:

"When testing electronic equipment, it is sometimes necessary to observe the effects of high or low mains voltage. The arrangement shown in **Fig 4** allows the mains to be increased or reduced by 30V in steps of about 8V. The secondary of the transformer is inserted in series with the load to buck or boost the voltage, depending on polarity. It uses the popular ARLEC 6672 (Australian trade part number) transformer which has a multi-tapped 30V/1A secondary; this means that the load should be limited to about 250W.

"It could also be used with a soldering iron, to give a 'standby' mode when not in use and a 'high power' mode for heavy jobs. It is better to have a clockwise rotation of the switch to increase the output voltage, but if you find the switch works backwards, just reverse the connections to the primary. Finding a suitable switch is the only problem. Light wafer switches are not good enough for the voltages and currents involved, and the switch should be non-shorting.

"The same principle can be used for lots of power control applications as a poor man's Variac, and there will be none of the RFI problems associated with phase control circuits. The voltage boost and depression, and number of steps, depend on the transformer used (ie number of tappings or separate secondary windings). Two such circuits could be cascaded to provide coarse and fine control."

SIMPLE LOGIC PROBE

A SIMPLE LOGIC PROBE, operating from a 6V AC source (eg an old valve heater trans-

former) has been described by Glen Harris in the 'Circuit & Design Ideas' feature of *Electronics Australia* (October 1990, p107) **Fig 5**. It is designed to cope with logic circuits working between 3V and 6V and to display Hi(1), Lo(0) and pulse states of the circuit under investigation with the complete unit conveniently fitting into one of the fatter ball-point pen bodies.

Glen Harris writes: "When the probe is brought Hi, D2 conducts, turning the BC548 transistor on and lighting the red side of the tricolour LED. A Lo lets D1 conduct and turns the BC558 light on, lighting the LED. A pulse turns on each LED alternately, at the frequency of the input signal. This makes the LED appear orange at about 10Hz or more.

"Supply voltage is derived from a full-wave rectifier so there is no need to worry about which lead is positive or which is negative. The only bias needed on the transistors is a 47K resistor on the base of the BC558 . . . . When power is connected the LED will glow slightly orange from leakage current, brightening significantly above about 6V. The Hi, Lo and pulse indications, however, are significantly brighter than this slight glow."

VARIABLE CERAMIC-RESONATOR OSCILLATORS

LC OSCILLATORS, NO matter which circuit arrangement is adopted, require most careful design, construction and choice of high-quality components to achieve stable (drift-free) operation and pure T9X output waveform. Crystal oscillators, on the other hand, can virtually be thrown together yet still give en-

tirely satisfactory results over a reasonable temperature range. The variable crystal oscillator (VXO) represents a useful compromise between a fixed-frequency crystal oscillator and a fully-tunable LC oscillator. Unfortunately most crystals can be 'pulled' over only a very small frequency range, usually not more than one part in a thousand even with inductive as well as capacitive loading, ie not more than 7kHz at 7MHz and often considerably less, before significant degradation of the crystal stability and tone begins to appear. A bank of spaced crystals can overcome this problem, but this has never been a low-cost solution and in practice has been

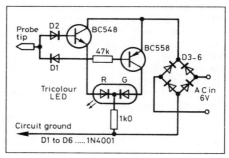

Fig 5: Simple logic probe.

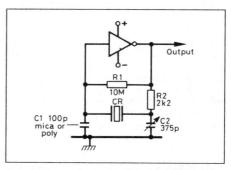

Fig 6: G3BBD finds that up to 70kHz shift by the use of variable capacitance can be obtained from a 3.58MHz ceramic resonator oscillator using resonators costing less than 60p. This gives good frequency stability provided that the temperature remains reasonably constant.

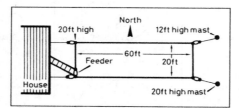

Fig 3: G8PG's horizontal loop antenna as described in *Short-Wave Magazine*, February 1985.

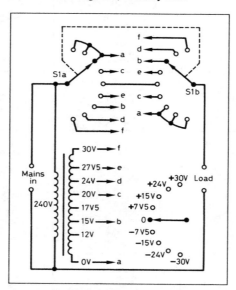

Fig 4: The poor man's Variac using a multi-tap low-voltage transformer to buck or boost the mains supply voltage.

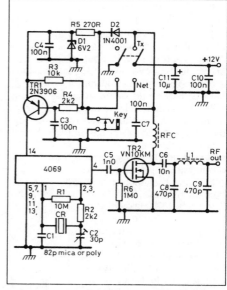

Fig 7: Ceramic resonator controlled 1W QRP transmitter/driver covering about 3.52 to 3.59MHz with single 3.58MHz resonator.

AN EFFECTIVE SUPER-GAINER

WHEN TONY LANGTON, GM4HTU, decided to build a 7MHz receiver, he opted to give the 'super-gainer' technique (superhet mixer in front of high-gain regenerative direct-conversion receiver) a try - and found this a most effective approach. He based the DC section of the receiver on the 'blooper' circuit adopted by Des Vance, GI3XZM, (*TT* October 1987, pp748-9) which used an FET as an infinite impedance detector in conjunction with a bipolar Q-Multiplier.

GM4HTU writes: "The GI3XZM design seemed well thought out and inspired confidence. I used a Denco coil as a fixed tuned 1700kHz 'IF' and preceded it with a simple 40673 dual-gate mixer with a band-pass front end for 7MHz and a VFO tuning 8.7 to 8.8MHz. The audio amplifier provides about 50dB gain and rolls off at about 3kHz.

"Results are very impressive: there is only a slight warm-up drift and SSB is easily copied. An eight-pole Butterworth filter (not shown in **Fig 8**) provides stunning selectivity for telegraphy reception (coincidentally, this is also based on an Irish design, stemming from the University of Belfast).

"Separating the detector from the feedback circuit, as suggested by GI3XZM, proved a masterful idea; it really does give very smooth regeneration control. Initially, I used a 10-turn trimpot for the 'reaction' control but later replaced it with an ordinary pot since, once it had been set to 'just oscillating', it has never been adjusted; it could be replaced by an internal preset. Even when I later added a 10.1MHz option, shifting the VFO to cover 8.4 to 8.45MHz, no adjustment was needed. It is a far cry from

the old two-handed tuning of the straight regenerative ('blooper') receivers with which I started listening many years ago. The super-gainer technique isolates the detector from whatever the front-end is doing very effectively. Another possible reason is the gain control which is a 36dB switched attenuator between the antenna and the band-pass input filters.

"It is as easy to operate as any DC receiver and performs better than any I have ever built. It appears to be immune to hum, microphony and Radio Moscow. It also has a good 'presence': one feels right in among the signals and not isolated by high-technology.

"Thanks, Des, for a really good circuit. I am now working on a transmitter to go with the receiver".

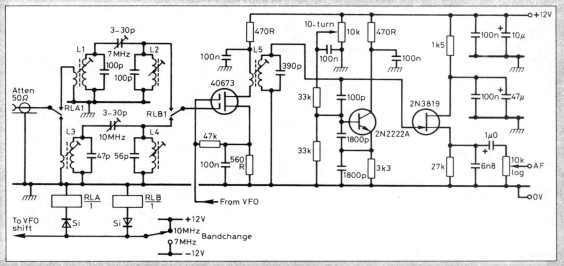

Fig 8: Heart of GM4HTU's super-gainer receiver for 7 and 10.1MHz showing the bandpass RF input filters, mixer and GI3XZM-type regenerative detector which operates on the fixed IF of 1700kHz. The VFO (not shown) covers 8.7 to 8.8MHz and is shifted to 8.4 to 8.45MHz for 10.1MHz. For CW reception an eight-pole Butterworth audio filter (not shown) is used. L1, L3 Toko KANK3334R 5.5µH. L2,L4 Toko 4.8µH; L5 Denco Red 3 adjusted to 1700kHz.

rejected in favour of the PLL frequency synthesizer despite its more 'noisy' output.

There is, however, another possibility emerging, as John Townend, G3BBD has found. This uses a low-cost ceramic resonator instead of a more costly quartz resonator. Ceramic resonators can be 'swung' over a much wider frequency range than quartz crystals; there is the snag, however, that the temperature co-efficient of ceramic resonators is considerably greater than that of a 'zero-temperature-coefficient' AT-cut crystal. But let G3BBD describe his experiences with ceramic resonator oscillators, sparked off by a *TT* item summarising some of the results achieved by Al Helfrick, K2LBA (*Ham Radio*, June 1985, pp 18-26) using ceramic resonators as mechanically and varactor tuned oscillators on 10 and 14MHz.

G3BBD writes: "Noting the *TT* (December 1985) item on the use of ceramic resonators in oscillator circuits, my interest was aroused by the inclusion in the *Radio Spares* (RS) catalogue of a number of ceramic resonators and, in particular, one having a frequency of

3.58MHz costing a mere 54p (RS part number 656-170).

"Experiments with this resonator in an oscillator circuit using one hex-inverter section of a CMOS 4069 IC showed that it produced a frequency-stable output provided that there was little change in the ambient temperature. The wide frequency change that could be achieved compared with a quartz crystal was confirmed. With the circuit-arrangement of **Fig 6** some 70kHz shift could be obtained with the 375pF variable capacitor. It was also found that the oscillator could be keyed by breaking the supply to the device and this produced a very acceptable keyed waveform without chirp provided that the supply voltage did not exceed 7 volts.

"A simple QRP (1W) driver/amplifier transmitter was then constructed (**Fig 7**) using the oscillator. This provided a frequency coverage from 3.522MHz to 3.590MHz - a most useful section of the 3.5MHz CW band. Because the oscillator is keyed, full break-in operation is provided.

"For this QRP transmitter, a second sec-

tion of the 4069 IC was used as a buffer stage driving a VN10K VMOS device providing an output of a little over a watt. This would be more than adequate to drive one of the VMOS or HEXFET amplifiers described in recent issues of *TT* should an output of, say, 10W or so be required. Construction is extremely simple and, provided care is taken to ensure a reasonably constant temperature around the oscillator, temperature drift is minimal. In practice it was found to be less than 200Hz during the course of a 30-minute QSO.

"A number of further developments would seem possible. Firstly, the use of the two remaining 4069 hex inverters to act as an audio side-tone oscillator. The variable oscillator could be used also for a direct conversion receiver turning the transmitter into a transceiver. Although I have not tried it, a 4.00MHz ceramic resonator (RS part number 656-186) could be used as the variable frequency oscillator for a superhet receiver having an IF of 455kHz (possibly in conjunction with an NE602 mixer-oscillator - G3VA) which would cover most of the frequency range of the transmitter. A 455kHz ceramic resonator could be used for the BFO. These devices are available from Cirkit at only one-fifth the price of a crystal.

"Further uses of ceramic resonators were considered. For example **Fig 9** shows an arrangement that provides a 1750Hz tone burst signal for a 'home-brew' 144MHz FM transmitter. Again, the 3.58MHz resonator is used with the oscillator output fed to a CMOS 4020 binary divider IC. The divide-by-two output on pin 15 provides a stable 1750Hz output, the oscillator being set to 3.584MHz. The remainder of the circuit uses a 555 timer IC which acts as a monostable, providing a high output on pin 3 which is sufficient to power the oscillator. The 555 is triggered when the PTT switch is closed and the duration of the burst is controlled by the 1MΩ preset resistor.

"To sum up. I am most impressed by these

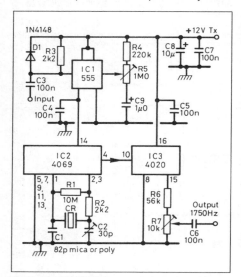

Fig 9: Use of 3.58MHz ceramic resonator oscillator (tuned to 3.584MHz) to provide 1750Hz tone burst signal for a 144MHz transmitter as used by G3BBD.

ceramic resonator devices. Used in oscillator circuits, they provide a good compromise between a crystal VXO and an LC variable oscillator without some of the difficulties experienced with the more complex LC circuits. The frequencies readily available are limited, but mixing techniques using conventional crystal oscillators should enable the wide frequency swing of the ceramic resonator to be achieved at any required frequency".

HEAVY-CURRENT 28V PSU

A NUMBER OF heavy-current (up to about 30A) 13.8V power supply units have been described in *TT*. However it has long been evident that for high-power linear amplifiers there are considerable advantages (including improved linearity) in using RF power devices (bipolar or FET) designed for higher voltage supplies such as the 24-28V commonly used for professional aeronautical equipment etc. A 28V PSU intended for use with high power linear amplifiers (eg 300W PEP output) has been described by Brian Jones, VK2BRD in *Amateur Radio* (VK) December 1990, pp15-16: **Fig 11**. (May I take this opportunity of thanking Bill Roper, VK3ARZ, General Manager & Secretary, Wireless Institute of Australia, for arranging to send me airmail copies

AURAL PCB TRACK-TRACER

IT IS SELDOM EASY to trace the track layout of a printed circuit board for which no layout details are available, particularly in the case of double-sided boards. An ohmmeter or continuity tester, although useful, can pose the problem of trying to keep an eye on the display while holding both probes on the tracks. A tester needs to differentiate between the low resistance of a continuous track and the forward voltage drop across a semiconductor junction in order to eliminate false indications. It is, of course, also necessary to ensure that the active devices on the board are not subject to damaging voltages or currents from the tester.

A simple PCB track-tester, with aural rather than visual indication of continuity, has been described by Brian Weller, ZS2AB (*Radio-ZS*, March 1990, p11): **Fig 10**. This uses a 311 IC comparator with a reference voltage value of only about 0.2V established at pin 3 by the forward voltage drop of a *germanium* diode, while the other input on pin 2 is clamped at 0.6V by a silicon diode (1N4148). The 0.2V is below the forward voltage drop across the silicon semiconductor junctions of the board components and thus eliminates false indications from the junctions found on most PCBs.

Aural indication of continuity is provided by a piezo bleeper of the type with a built-in driver circuit; these bleep when DC is applied across their terminals. The 5K6 resistor limits current through the probes to about 1mA when these are short-circuited. Since the unit has low current

consumption, power can be derived from, for example, four 1.5V penlight cells. There is no need to worry about the polarity of the probes when using the tester.

As long as the test-probes are not short-circuited through a track or low resistance, the voltage at pin 2 of the 311 IC is higher than at pin 3 and the output is 'high' so that the bleeper remains silent. As soon as the voltage at pin 2 drops below the 0.2V reference at pin 3, the 311 output switches to 'low' and the bleeper sounds.

ZS2AB found that his original unit would sound when the probes were across resistances of less than 300 ohms and could provide a false indication of track continuity. To reduce this, a 150 ohm resistor was added as shown in Fig 10. This overcomes the problem unless the on-board resistor has a value of less than about 100 ohms; such low-value resistors are uncommon on most PCBs. He describes track-tracing with the aid of this little unit as 'magic' and believes that it is likely to prove useful for other applications.

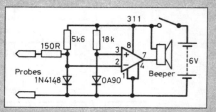

Fig 10: ZS2AB's simple PCB track-tester provides aural indication when the probes are short-circuited leaving eyes free for the probes.

of the excellent WIA journal *Amateur Radio* - a much appreciated gesture!)

The VK2BRD PSU features good regulation based on the use of four LM338 IC regulators, plus also survivability from accidental overloads. As VK2BRD puts it: "Good regulation is essential to prevent distortion in a high-power linear amplifier. Other factors

taken into account in this design are controlled dissipation by all components to reduce the energy wasted at both low and high load currents. Component types used were chosen for their characteristics and reliability. "The hefty power transformer should be rated at about 1kW, with a heavy current secondary delivering 32V RMS (42/1.414 + 2V). An

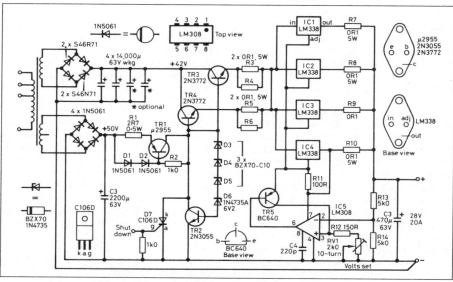

Fig 11: VK2BRD's heavy-current (over 30A) 28V power supply unit.

auxiliary supply requires a 37V RMS winding which can be on the same or a separate transformer; continuous load on this winding is only about 100mA.

The main rectifier uses four stud-mounted diodes (400V PIV, 40A) in two complementary pairs, mounted on two 76mm lengths of Philips 35D heatsinks, mounted vertically and insulated from each other and from earth, with insulated (mica) spacers. The 'normal' pair on one heatsink, providing positive output; the 'reverse' pair on the other heatsink providing negative output. Since up to 20W needs to be dissipated on each heatsink, VK2BRD warns against using four-terminal bridge rectifier assemblies as they may be unable to dissipate sufficient power and are likely to fail in this application.

Main filter capacitors should have low equivalent series resistance (ESR) and be rated for high ripple current in order to reduce the power dissipated by the series-pass devices. Similar care should be taken with wiring and layout: "Wiring technique and component placement are important around the rectifier area. A minimum of 4mm hook-up wire should be used and wire lengths kept as short as practicable. Capacitors should be mounted near the main rectifier but not so close as to heat them. Wiring should go from the transformer to the rectifier; from the rectifier to the filter capacitors; and then from the capacitors to the regulator components. The series-pass pre-regulator uses a 'zener diode' network comprising D3, D4, D5, D6 and TR2. This network dissipates most power at minimum PSU loading. The current source comprises R1, R2, D1, D2 and TR1, the voltage drop across R1 being held constant by the voltage across D1 and D2 and the beta of TR1. Both TR1 and TR2 are mounted on 76mm lengths of Philips 35D heatsink. All TO3 devices in this design mounted on heatsinks need to be insulated from them using high-quality mica washers with 'copious quantities of thermal paste applied'. The TO3 devices should have TO3 transistor insulator caps fitted to minimise voltage hazards. TR3 and TR4 series-pass transistors are heat-sinked with the IC regulators, using two 200mm lengths of Philips 55D heatsink (mounted vertically): TR3, IC1 and IC2 on one heatsink; TR4, IC3 and IC4 on the other. Load current sharing resistors are used with TR3, TR4 and the four IC regulators.

To prevent the IC load-sharing resistors from degrading the output voltage regulation, an LM308 op-amp (IC5) is used to monitor the output voltage and feeds a modified control voltage to the IC regulator 'adjust' pins via TR5. Output current is limited by the input-to-output voltage differential across the regulators. All wires carrying the heavy current lines should comprise short lengths of 4mm wire. Other wiring can use 0.5mm insulated wire.

HARRIS CATHODE-FOLLOWER (SOURCE-FOLLOWER) OSCILLATORS

IN THE STILL important world of analogue electronics, much basic solid state circuitry can be traced back to the valve era. Developments are often optimisied solid-state versions of circuits pioneered in the heydey of valves. For much of that period, there was

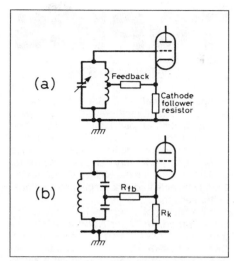

Fig 12: Two basic forms of the Harris cathode-follower stable LC oscillator.

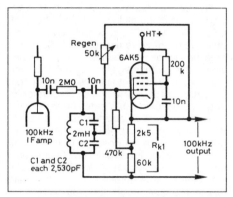

Fig 13: The simplified 100kHz Q-Multiplier described by H E Harris in *Electronics* (April 1951) using regenerative cathode-follower stage to provide variable selectivity.

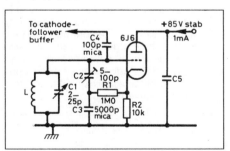

Fig 14: A Harris cathode-follower oscillator used for a 3.5MHz VFO by R Ropes and adopted also by PA0VGR. The Ropes design used both sections of the 6J6 dual-triode with 150V (regulated) HT (anode current 1.2mA) covering 3.5 to 4MHz (approximately 90% rotation of the 25pF tuning capacitor) with L 21μH (24 turns No 22, enamelled copper wire closewound on 1.25" diameter former).

intense interest in improving the characteristics of tunable LC oscillators: Hartley, Colpitts, Franklin, ECO, Gouriet-Clapp, Seiler, Vackar oscillators all had their enthusiastic followers - and all have since appeared in solid-state guise.

My interest in one largely forgotten form of oscillator, first described by H E Harris in 1951, was aroused by the Dutch journal *Electron* (December 1990) which reprinted from its February 1958 issue an article by J J van Gelderen, PA0VGR describing a form of Harris VFO, using a 6J6 valve.

The *Electron* item led me to *Radio & TV News*, June 1957 'A high-stability oscillator circuit' by Robert J Ropes; this in turn referred me to J K Clapp's 'Frequency stable LC oscillators' (*Proc IRE*, Aug 54) providing a detailed survey of a number of LC oscillators and to the original presentation of the cathode-follower family of oscillators by H E Harris in connection with an article on a 'Simplified Q Multiplier' (*Electronics*, May 51,).

In the Harris oscillators (**Fig 12**) use is made of the fact that while a cathode-follower has less than unity voltage gain, it has power gain, good phase regulation and presents a very high impedance at its grid. With a valve having a low grid-cathode capacitance this means that full advantage can be taken of the high-Q LC tank circuit with good isolation between the i/p and o/p circuits. In other words, stability is largely determined by the LC tuned circuit.

In effect, a portion of the cathode-follower output is stepped up by passive components and fed back to the grid of the valve to provide the positive feedback necessary to sustain oscillation. In the original application as a (regenerative) Q-Multiplier, it gave controllable selectivity of a very high order with excellent stability: **Fig 13**. The later applications, developed by Ropes and PA0VGR, showed that the basic Harris ideas could usefully be applied to HF VFOs for amateur radio, providing a stable output that can remain constant over wide variations of the LC ratio, a characteristic that cannot be achieved with the conventional high-C Colpitts oscillator.

R J Ropes dubbed his version a 'Class A Colpitts' (more precisely Class AB) but pointing out that it differs radically from the conventional Colpitts oscillator: "Since the oscillator operates in Class AB, no grid current flows during any part of the oscillatory cycle, there is no 'grid-leak' capacitor and no grid-bias voltage is produced by grid-current flow, as is the usual case in a Class C oscillator."

He also noted that: "As pointed out by Clapp, the frequency coefficient of an oscillator is independent of the LC ratio *if* the operation of the circuit is *linear*, that is Class A, AB or B. Since Class A operation of an oscillator is, for all practical purposes, impractical, Class AB or B operation must be used to give the necessary linearity of oscillation."

As with other Colpitts, Hartley, ECO type oscillators, maximum stability is obtained when the capacitive divider or inductive tapping is as close as possible to the earthy-side of the tank circuit while still providing the necessary feedback. With capacitive tapping, this implies making the lower capacitor of higher value than the capacitor connected to the grid. It should be noted that R1 (**Fig 14**) provides the positive feedback and is not intended to pass DC in the manner of a grid leak. For Q-multipliers, the degree of positive feedback and hence the onset of oscillation can be controlled by making this resistor variable. Active devices should have reasonably high gain and low input capacitance. Ropes used a 6J6 twin-triode with both sections in parallel. PA0VGR's circuit shows only a single section of the 6J6.

There seems no reason why Harris-type oscillators should not work well with FET source-followers provided that the input-capacitance of the device is reasonably small.

TOPICS

PAT HAWKER G3VA

SIMPLE HF SUPERHET USING THE MC3362 CHIP

RECENTLY, IT HAS BEEN emphasised in *TT* that the availability of complex IC devices at relatively low-cost has made it as easy to build a superhet receiver as the usual form of direct-conversion receiver. This is particularly so for the increasingly popular QRP HF transceivers with about 1 to 5W RF output.

For example, in *TT* (April 1989) some details were given of a 14MHz 'QRP-20' (5W) CW transceiver described by Rick Lillefield, K1BQT (*Ham Radio*, January 1989) based on the use of three NE602 double-balanced mixer/buffer/oscillator devices. K1BQT has since described a 21MHz version updated by a number of refinements (*CQ*, September 1990). In practice, the 21MHz band should prove more rewarding for QRP operation than among the high-power crowd on 14MHz. In this version, the receiver section is a superhet using NE602 front-end with the VFO tuning 5000 to 5150kHz, a four-crystal ladder filter using low-cost 16MHz series-resonant computer crystals, MC1350P IF amplifier, NE602 product detector with a further 16MHz crystal-controlled oscillator, AF filter and LM386 output with several discrete active devices providing additional facilities. A third NE602 with 16MHz crystal is used as mixer/oscillator to convert the 5MHz VFO to provide 21MHz tunable frequency input into the transmitter section.

An even simpler approach is adopted by Gary A Breed, K9AY, for 'A portable QRP CW transceiver' (*QST*, Part 1 - receiver section, December 1990). This 14MHz 5W transceiver has a superhet receiver based on a single Motorola MC3362 IC as its heart, from RF input to low-level AF.

The 24-pin Motorola device (**Fig 1**) is designed to provide all the functions of a dual-conversion VHF/FM superhet requiring no other active devices except an audio power amplifier. It has two oscillator/mixer sections with buffers, a six-stage limiting (IF) amplifier, quadrature (FM) detector, signal strength indicator output (RSSI) and a comparator for data reception. In K9AY's design the limiting IF amplifier section and the quadrature FM detector are not used; however, K9AY points out that it would be possible to use the IF section as a low-level audio amplifier or as a second IF (up to about 500kHz) in a double-conversion arrangement; the quadrature detector section could then be used as a product detector.

Clearly, an operator requiring an HF receiver of really high performance could not expect to achieve this with a chip intended for less demanding VHF applications, neither in terms of dynamic range nor oscillator stability over a wide range of temperatures. K9AY reports: "I breadboarded a few designs with this chip to determine how it performs at HF for CW and SSB. Performance is good, and I was amazed at the simplicity of the external RF circuitry requirements."

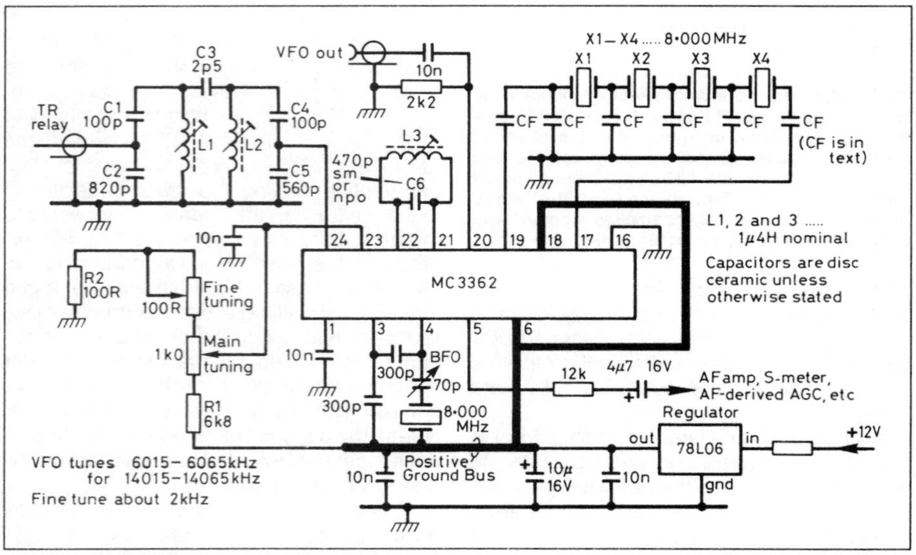

He gives the performance of the receiver (**Fig 2**) as: very high sensitivity (minimum discernible signal about -123dBm); measured third-order IMD dynamic range about 70dB which, he points out, is "not exceptional" but good for such a simple receiver. (The limited strong-signal performance suggests that it would be wise to provide a simple variable-attenuator, eg **Fig 3** at the input to the receiver - G3VA).

The 8.000MHz four-crystal Cohn ladder filter is designed to provide a 400Hz (-3dB) bandwidth for CW reception with the CF capacitors each 300pF (for 600-800Hz bandwidth, about 220pF should be used). The 400Hz filter provides about -30dB selectivity at 1325Hz but the audio-image sideband rejection is a little under -40dB since, with an 8MHz IF, the isolation of the chip and filter circuits is insufficient to permit better performance. (It might be worth considering the use of a ladder filter based on low-cost PAL colour-TV crystals at 4.63MHz, adjusting the tuning range of the variable oscillator accordingly - G3VA).

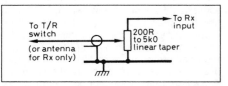

Fig 3: Simplest form of RF input attenuator that can improve handling of strong signals in receivers of restricted strong-signal performance.

K9AY considers that the only real weakness in performance for its intended application (as a compact portable transceiver for use in mountain-climbing etc) is temperature stability that can affect outdoor use, resulting in dial calibration being possibly off by a few kHz in extremely cold or hot situations. He points out that short-term stability is good both indoors and outdoors, with the receiver holding within a few tens of Hertz for hours on end in a shack environment.

CABLE ELBOWS - A WORD OF WARNING

AROUND THE NEW YEAR, BBC News reported the delivery of a Christmas card posted in India that had taken 45 years to reach its UK destination. It thus seemed quite a coincidence when, a couple of days later, a QSL card arrived from Doug Allerston, G5PQ, for a 7MHz CW contact made 52 years before on 21 December 1938 for which no cards had previously been exchanged! It duly checked out with an entry in my first log book.

But the main purpose of G5PQ writing to me was to draw attention to the defects of some impressive-looking 90° co-axial elbow connectors that had seemed a very good buy at a local rally for about 49p each. He writes:

"Unfortunately, they provide an illustration of 'You get what you pay for'. At first, I found them very convenient for bringing some thick (0.5-in) co-axial cable to my TS520 and home-built linear amplifier only a few inches from the shack wall. But increasingly I found that when I released the T/R switch on the microphone, the incoming signal seemed much weaker than originally. Eventually, I set up a signal generator to give a steady S9 on the

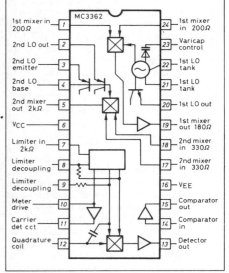

Fig 1: The MC3662 chip showing pin-out and basic functions.

Fig 2: How K9AY uses the MC3662 as the complete front-end of the 14MHz superhet receiver section of his 5W QRP transceiver.

meter and flicked the T/R switch a good few times. About 70% of the times, the meter showed a reading of only S5. My reaction was to suspect the back-contacts on one or both of the antenna relays. So out they came from the TS520 and the linear and received a good spraying, etc.

"Result - no improvement. I began to suspect a fault in the front-end of my ten-year-old TS520 transceiver but, fortunately before starting to work on it, I checked for continuity and short-circuits in all the co-axial links. To my surprise, one indicated a varying resistance of up to 320Ω! I traced the fault to one of the elbows although the reason did not become clear until I sawed away the outer shield and revealed a horrible little black metal spring wire which had been carrying up to 400W RF between the plug and socket portions, gripped only by the wire spring turns. I had fondly imagined there would have been a solid conductor between plug and socket!

"Another of these elbows, still in my spares box, proved to have open circuit. The elbows are well finished outside, little better than junk inside! Apart from open circuits and varying DC resistance, such wire-spring connections seem virtually bound in time to form harmonic-generating diodes and generate 'rusty-joint' interference."

One can see the problem of manufacturing elbows with solid 90° connections, and G5PQ wonders if the elbows advertised by some reputable component firms, at two or three times the price he paid at the rally, have secure conductors between the plug and socket sections, or only similar horrible little springs. There seems no way of finding out without sawing them open. As G5PQ puts it: *Caveat Emptor* - let the buyer beware!

WEATHER-RESISTANT WIRE ARRAYS

AGAIN THIS WINTER, MOST PARTS of the UK have suffered from frequent high winds and gales that have not proved kind to HF antennas. Some tips for achieving longer life for wire-type arrays such as quads, VK2ABQ or G3LBQ antennas have been given by Paul T Atkins, K2OZ, with editorial additions in *QST*, (November 1989, p39). K2OZ has succeeded in keeping his quad antenna up and working for about 25 years, following modifications when it began to deteriorate after about 10 years - no mean feat! He writes:

"Sad experience has been my teacher. My first quad required periodic patching because of ice and wind-related flexing. Typically element wire breakage occurred at the element corners where they are supported by the spreaders. Adding a two-wire strengthener, as in **Fig 4(a)**, at each corner solved this problem. Teflon insulated wire is a better choice than stranded bare wire for the elements which suffer from oxidation (elements turning green). The spreaders were tied together (**Fig 4(b)**) with 50-pound monofilament (nylon) fishing line which deteriorates in sunlight from UV radiation and was replaced by more durable cord (Editorial note: Nylon cord, especially that treated to improve UV resistance, is much better than monofilament fishing line for outdoor use; *Dacron* cord is even better. Because it deteriorates rapidly in

UV light, avoid using polypropylene lines in sunlit locations - *QST*).

"My quad used tapped-coil inductive reflector tuning. I replaced the Miniductor coils with home-made, 1" ID coils wound with No 12 tinned bus wire (winding each coil on a 1" dia temporary form then removing it from the form and slipping it into position on its respective quad insulator). In the belief that tapped coils, whether unused turns are left open or short-circuited, introduce loss, I tuned the quad reflectors by adjusting the coil turn spacing as necessary. Following these modifications, I have not had to repair my quad for almost 15 years."

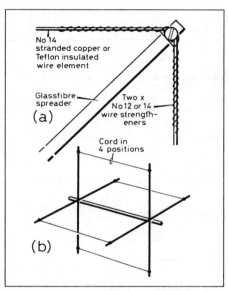

Fig 4: K2OZ's survivable quad modifications, applicable also to other wire-element arrays.

Some additional information is given in the *QST* caption. This points out that Teflon-insulated No 14 stranded copper wire is a better choice than bare stranded copper but care is needed not to nick the wire strands when removing its insulation for soldering (if possible use a thermal stripper). Each corner strengthener consists of two pieces of No 12 or 14 bus wire some 14 to 16" long. After cleaning the element wire until it is bright and solderable, twist on one strengthener wire *in the other direction*. Using resin-cored solder and a soldering iron hot enough to heat the work thoroughly, solder the three wires together. Complete the job by cleaning the joint to remove whatever resin remains. The finished strengthener can be wrapped with tape as required.

BATTERIES AND SAFETY TOPICS

JANUARY *TT* DREW ATTENTION to the explosive nature of the mixture of hydrogen and oxygen surrounding a battery gassing while on charge. This item reminded Brian Kendal, G3GDU, of an incident that shows the danger of disconnecting a charger or a heavy load from a battery still under charge. He writes:

"Some years ago, I used an old car battery to provide a 12V supply from my workshop. The charger was always kept in circuit in a vain attempt to keep the battery in reasonable condition and delivering in the region of 12V. At one period I had been working in the workshop for several days and, consequently, the battery was well up and gassing freely.

"I was working on a piece of gear which took about 10A. Due to laziness, I did not switch off before disconnecting the load from the battery. This, inevitably, caused a spark which ignited the hydrogen-oxygen mixture and caused a minor explosion. Although, fortunately, I was not injured, the force was sufficient to split the side out of the battery".

As noted in the January *TT*, it is essential to avoid doing anything that could spark off an explosion where there is any possibility of an explosive mixture that has not been dispersed by waiting or by fanning with a magazine etc. Otherwise, it could be as risky as looking for a gas leak with a candle!

Ron Wilson, G3DSV, recalling his service days in WW2 as a Royal Navy radio mechanic, adds a final comment on battery acid: "I often visited the EM (electrical-mechanical) workshop. Over the battery charging bench was a very large sign: *Do wot u oughta, add acid to water.*"

WA8MCQ and *QST*'s *Hints & Kinks* editor warns of the danger of close-up soldering without the use of safety goggles. WA8MCQ, while unsoldering a connection, was struck on his lower eyelid by a small piece of hot solder - it could as easily have struck his eye. Hardware and discount stores sell inexpensive plastic safety goggles, it is pointed out.

NATTY FRONT PANELS

KUNIO MITSUMA, KA3RRF, IN *Hints & Kinks* (*QST*, December 1990) provides a method of producing handsome front panels that he learned as a youngster in Tokyo. He writes:

"A nice-looking front panel reflects the quality of the project inside the box. Here is a simple way of making an attractive front panel that has a matt-finish silver hairline design. If your project already has an aluminium front panel, great. If not, cut an aluminium plate the same size as the box's front panel and attach it to the box. Before beginning, make all necessary holes and cuts in the front panel(s). Then proceed as follows:

Step 1: Wrap fine sandpaper around a piece of wood and sand the aluminium panel in one direction until fine hairlines begin to appear. If the panel is coated with paint, be patient and do this *until the paint comes off* and the hairlines appear.

Step 2: Thoroughly clean the panel surface. Now spray the panel with clear *lacquer* paint. The purpose of this is to make the surface of the panel smooth for applying dry rub-on lettering. Wait until the lacquer dries completely, then apply the lettering.

Step 3: Spray the panel with clear *enamel* paint. (**Important:** Use a different type of paint than you used in Step 2. Otherwise this coat may mix with that paint, causing the lettering to float around in a sea of clear paint!). Spray a few coats until the paint completely covers the lettering.

Step 4: Heat the front panel from *behind* the

25W (1.8 - 7MHZ) PUSH-PULL MOSFET LINEAR

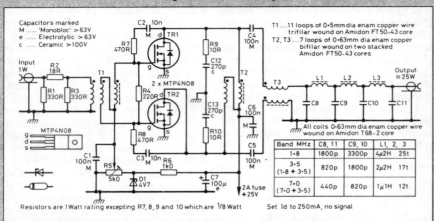

Fig 5: The VK3XU push-pull MOSFET linear amplifier providing about 25W RF output up to 7MHz with about 1W drive and 25V, 2A power supply.

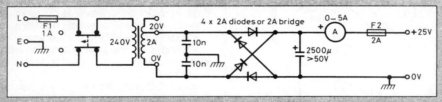

Fig 6: VK3XU's suggested power supply for the 25W MOSFET amplifier.

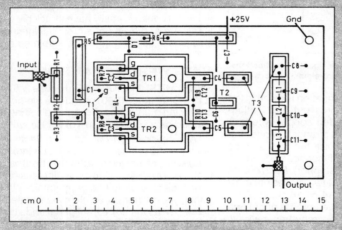

Fig 7: Component and PCB layout for the 25W MOSFET amplifier using double-sided PCB with the other side forming continuous ground-plane (reproduced half actual size).

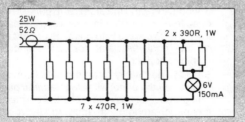

Fig 8: Suggested dummy load for the MOSFET amplifier using ordinary 1W carbon or metal-film resistors. Capable of dissipating 25W at 50% duty cycle in short bursts. Dissipation can be increased by immersion of resistors in a benign clear oil (see text). Such a dummy load suitable for other transmitters of roughly similar output power.

DREW DIAMOND, VK3XU, IN THE Australian *Amateur Radio* (January 1991, pp7-10) describes in detail the construction of a broadband linear push-pull amplifier based on low-cost switching MOSFETs normally used for switching-mode PSUs suitable for boosting the output from a QRP rig: **Figs 5-7**. It uses a pair of Motorola MTP4N08 (80V/4A) devices, available in Australia for under A$1 each. These devices have the same pin-out as the better known IRF510 and IRF511 devices. Since the 510 has lower input and output capacitances for the same voltage and current rating as the MTP4NO8, direct substitution of a pair of IRF510 devices should yield significantly more RF output above about 7MHz, when used with suitable LPF output filters.

VK3XU lists performance with MTP4N08 devices as: frequency range 1.8 to 7MHz (usable with reduced output to 14MHz); output power nominally 25W, typically 30W PEP or CW; input drive power nominally 1W; power gain about 14dB, input SWR less than 1.2:1; two-tone IMD products in the order of -35dB. Harmonic output -50dB (depends on LPF); output protection - will withstand any load SWR, including short and open-circuit at full drive without damage; supply 25V at up to 2A (reduced output at 13.8V).

The amplifier with a symmetrical layout is built on a double-sided circuit board with the unetched side providing a continuous 'ground-plane' under the active component area as an aid to circuit stability. No holes are required for component leads, but rather these are soldered directly onto the copper pads 'VHF-fashion'.

The MOSFETs must each be fitted with a heatsink such as type 6030. The bias zener diode (D1) 4.7V/400mW, should be positioned against one of the heatsinks to provide a degree of thermal tracking. A small blob of heatsink compound may be applied to assist heat-transfer.

The dummy load suggested by VK3XU (**Fig 8**) should take 25W at 50% duty cycle in short bursts, but he suggests that it would be a good plan to house the load and lamp inside a glass jar with a suitable connector fitted to the screw top lid. To increase dissipation, the jar could be filled with some benign clear oil such as paraffin or peanut oil, leaving an air gap for expansion. During on-air operation, input drive must be kept low enough to give linear operation (quiescent no-signal current Idq about 200mA) as over-driving may cause splatter on SSB or clicks on CW. In operation, the I_{dc} may gradually rise to about 300mA but should drop back to about 200mA during receive periods.

painted side until it is almost too hot to touch. You can do this over a gas stove, but be careful to keep the painted side from making direct contact with the flames. Remove the panel from the heat source and *immediately* spray on another coat of clear enamel from some distance away (1ft or more) so that the paint particles land on the panel spread widely

apart. As the panel cools, the paint particles will shrink, giving a matt finish on the panel."

Another tip from *Hints & Kinks* by H L Van Ness, W7MPW: "Finishing washers, commonly available in hardware stores, make professional looking LED mounts. Two dabs of hot glue between the back of the LED and the panel hold the assembly in place."

50.1MHZ YAGI DIMENSIONS

RON FISHER, VK3OM, AND Ron Cook, VK3AFW, in their *Random Radiators* column (*Amateur Radio* VK, October 1990) provide a useful table to facilitate the construction of DL6WU-type optimised Yagi antennas compiled by VK3AUU: **Table 1** (overleaf).

144MHZ SNIFFER DF RECEIVER/FIELD-STRENGTH METER

THE SEPTEMBER 1990 *TT* PROVIDED a description of a compact twin-loop 144MHz MEF (Miniature Electromagnetic-coupled Foxhunting) antenna developed by John Williscroft, ZS6EF, as an integral part of a hand-held direction-finding 'sniffer' system capable of being used to uncover well-hidden transmitters in 'fox-hunting' contests. At least one copy of this antenna was built and used successfully by a member of the Southgate Amateur Radio Club in conjunction with a professional receiver having an attenuator to reduce the signal fed to the screened receiver when closing in on the transmitter. The September item, however, stressed that ZS6EF considered that most factory-built, amateur-type 144MHz receivers/transceivers were insufficiently well screened to prevent direct breakthrough of signals when very close to the 'fox' and that he had built a special DEF sniffer receiver described in the March 1990 issue of *Radio-ZS*.

It is only recently that I have been able to see a copy of this article ('The DEF Receiver - The Sniffer that makes a Difference' by John Williscroft, ZS6EF). His 'Direction-finding Equipment for Foxhunting' proves to be a simple non-regenerative 'straight' receiver comprising a dual-gate FET input stage, interstage tuned RF bandpass filter, germanium diode detector and LM301N IC DC amplifier: **Fig 10**. The DEF is, in fact, de-

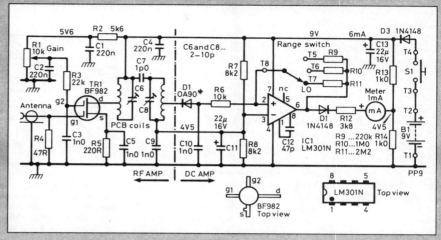

Fig 10: Circuit diagram of ZS6EF's 144MHz well-screened 'sniffer' receiver used with the MEF miniature twin-loop antenna described in *TT*, September 1990.

rived from experience with a field strength meter described in the *ARRL Handbook* and such a system could be used as a sensitive field strength meter.

The gain of the BF982 input stage is controlled by R1 and arranged so that its 'gain' can be reduced below unity then forming an input attenuator, while also allowing maximum gain for the PCB layout. ZS6EF stresses that the layout of the PCB is critical to avoid breakthrough and oscil-

lation at maximum gain. The gain of the DC amplifier is kept as low as practicable during operation with a range switch provided to reduce its gain as the operator approaches the fox. No speaker/phone socket is provided (presumably to eliminate the risk of pick-up on the leads etc) with the output indicator taking the form of a 1mA FSD meter. The three-page *Radio-ZS* article includes PCB layout and constructional details.

This provides a selection of element lengths and spacings related to the diameter of tubular (non-tapering) elements. For intermediate diameters it should be possible to find dimensions by interpolation.

Fig 9 shows the suggested matching arrangements for the driven folded-dipole element with the two rods spaced about 75mm apart. The balun transformer is based on an electrical half-wave length of coaxial cable, typically about 1976mm long for 50.1MHz. If the elements pass through a metal boom they should be lengthened by two-thirds of the diameter of the boom.

As a nine-element array, the power gain should be about 11dBd, considerably more than most of the arrays used on 50MHz. Even with four directors, it should provide up to about 8dBd gain, but the matching may suffer and some adjustment in the optimum spacing of the first director is likely to be required.

NEW TECHNOLOGY AND THE SPECTRUM

Experimenting with new modes of communication represents a valuable and important part of experimental Amateur Radio. Since 1945, amateurs have led the way towards widespread use of fully-suppressed HF SSB, slow-scan and wideband image transmission, later HF facsimile, AMTOR RTTY and facsimile, most recently Packet Radio on HF, VHF and microsatellites. It cannot be long before use will be made of digital speech modes although here the trail so far has been blazed by the professionals as they prepare

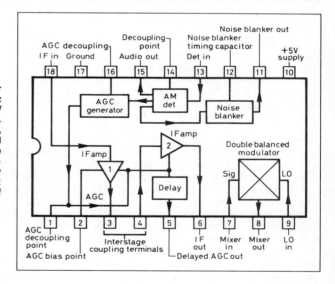

Fig 9: Matching system for DL6WU-type Yagi. For 50.1MHz the dimensions of elements/spacings are given in Table 1. For the driven folded dipole, the elements can be spaced 75mm apart. The balun is made from an electrical half-wavelength of cable (typically 1976mm at 50.1MHz but dependent on velocity factor of the cable).

TABLE 1 - 50.1MHz Yagi Design Data

Element lengths are for constant diameter tubing. Both incremental and progressive spacing dimensions are given.

Element	Spacing Incremental	Spacing Progressive	Element lengths			
			6mm	9mm	12mm	16mm
Reflector	0	0	3002	2980	2964	2949
Radiator	1436	1436	2920	2880	2851	2823
1st Dir	449	1885	2774	2741	2716	2689
2nd Dir	1077	2962	2753	2718	2692	2664
3rd Dir	1287	4249	2733	2697	2669	2640
4th Dir	1496	5745	2715	2677	2649	2618
5th Dir	1675	7420	2698	2659	2630	2598
6th Dir	1795	9215	2682	2642	2612	2580
7th Dir	1884	11099	2667	2627	2596	2562

dimensions in mm

A 50MHZ PL519 AMPLIFIER

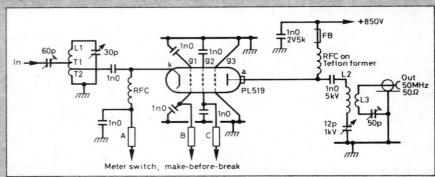

Fig 11: Skeleton circuit of G3SYC's 50MHz amplifier using a single PL519 valve. L1 6 turns 0.5-in ID (18SWG). L2 9 turns, 0.75-in ID (rectangular section strip one-eighth by one-sixteenth-in from old transformer). L3 1.5 turns around middle of L2 but well spaced from it (18SWG). A, B, C are current shunts for meter (A anode plus screen current; B grid current; C screen current).

BRIAN BOOTH, G3SYC, NOTED the brief reference *TT*, (December 1990, p33) to the use by G3MY of various types of TV line-output (deflection) valves on 50MHz. While circuit details of PL519 HF amplifiers have been given in *TT* over the past few years, G3SYC has found that a rather different approach may be needed on 50MHz to overcome the problems posed by the relatively high input and output capacitances of these valves which were designed primarily for operation at 15,625Hz (625-line) or 15,750Hz (525-line).

G3SYC writes: "I have built the power amplifier shown in **Fig11** and drive it with 2W from a Yaesu FT690/11 transceiver. Even without optimising the series-tuned PA tank circuit, I obtain an unconditionally stable gain of 12dB (ie output over 30W), although an initial attempt using a conventional pi-network tank circuit failed to produce much output. However, G3MY has used pi-network tank circuits successfully on 50MHz possibly with a layout having less stray capacitance.

"It was possible to obtain an excellent input SWR with the circuit arrangement of Fig 11 (many published circuits are vague about this detail). The valve base was built into a brass sub-chassis as shown in **Fig 12**. This is spaced from the main chassis and all earth returns are made to this including the PA tuning capacitor. For simplicity, two grid and two screen-grid decoupling capacitors

are shown; in practice four 0.001μF capacitors were used in each case. A *strong* air draught was provided within the PA box by a boxer fan.

"The cathode of the PL519 requires a few volts of negative bias provided by a string of IN1004 diodes. The number of diodes required varied with individual PL519 valves quite widely and should be determined by experiment to provide 25-30mA standing current."

Those with cherished memories of the excellent components once available from Eddystone may be interested to learn that G3SYC's PA tuning capacitor is an Ed-

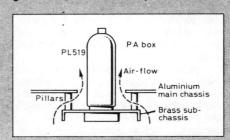

Fig 12: Details of brass subchassis showing air cooling path.

dystone type (Catalogue No 589) bought by him in his 'teens but never previously used.

---

for 'personal' communications networks such as CT2 and DECT cordless telephones. Amateurs will be able to take advantage of the complex VSLI devices now becoming available for CT2. Plessey Semiconductors have recently published a new 293-page *Personal Communications IC Handbook* covering many new devices for small hand-held transceivers and pagers in the 450MHz and 900MHz region of the spectrum, including devices for 'third-method' SSB direct-conversion demodulation of FSK data signals (SL6639/SL6638) at 1200bit/s in the 200MHz region to be released shortly.

But, unfortunately, a problem arises when equipment for modes mutually incompatible with the operation of basic analogue-speech and CW modes is marketed, and then taken up by large numbers of amateurs interested primarily in operating, with little interest in further developing the technology. They begin to demand and expect 'exclusive' allocations even within already crowded and much-used bands and/or operate with the new, non-compatible modes without checking that their transmissions are unlikely to interfere with other users (including those where the skip zone precludes their being heard directly). Some Packet, facsimile and SSTV operators on HF seem to be following the practice of commercial/military RTTY stations in shared bands of suddenly landing on occupied channels, often transmitting 'idling' signals over long periods, or demanding that users of other modes should QSY.

Les Moxon, G6XN, for example, questions

recent IARU decisions, apparently taken without democratic endorsement by the bulk of amateurs, to allocate an admittedly small slice of the 14MHz band for the 'exclusive' use of SSTV (although many SSTV stations still continue to operate throughout the SSB portions of the band). The answer would seem to be that no matter what mode you use, there remains a need to show an understanding of the needs and rights of all users. Make QRL? calls before using a channel, listening carefully for any answering request to QSY. We simply cannot afford to engage in mode wars on our bands and must find ways of encouraging the experimental development of new technology, including digital modes, without spoiling the bands for others.

HERE & THERE

Tim Wright, G1BCR (and commercial-testing G9BZW) has uncovered a form of wideband VHF noise that could be regarded as an active rather than a passive form of 'rusty bolt' (parasitic diode) interference - and one that may be more common than has previously been recognised. When he experienced severe noise, apparently originating locally, on all channels of a two-way mobile telephone receiver, he was able with the aid of an RF probe and RF attenuator to pinpoint the

source as one of the wire elements of the rear window heater. When, with the aid of a razor blade, this particular wire was cut out of circuit, the noise stopped. G1BCR deduced that what had happened was that due to oxidation, a microwave diode had formed in the wire, reverse biased by the heater supply and so forming a diode noise generator. Subsequently, other cases of similar broadband noise in mobile radios have been treated and cured in the same way. It seems clear that the way some particular forms of window heaters on laminated glass are manufactured can quite commonly lead to the creation of diode noise generators, with the window heater wires acting as a noise antenna. Other makes of vehicle seem immune to this problem.

Derek Austin, G4BLX, recently had cause to investigate and solve a problem with his 18-year-old Heathkit SB220 linear amplifier. Both panel meters were sticking or responding very sluggishly. It seemed unlikely that both meters had acquired dirt or other foreign bodies at the same time. In fact, he simply loosened the front pivot screws of both meters by turning them a couple of degrees anticlockwise. This released the meter movements after which they worked correctly. He also noticed that the antenna-change-over relay coil on the SB220 did not have any back-EMF diode across the coil, resulting in an unwanted spark across his transceiver's remote PTT relay contacts. Simply adding a 1N4001 diode across the relay coil reduced the spark considerably. Two tips that may be of use to other owners of large HF amplifiers.

ANALYSING GROUND-PLANE AND SLEEVE ANTENNAS

TT, NOVEMBER 1987, pp836-837 included an item 'The groundplane dissected' that referred to the computer (NEC) study by Melvin Weiner of a "Monopole element at the centre of a circular ground plane whose radius is small or comparable to a wavelength" (*IEE Trans on Ant & Prop*, May 1987). This indicated the vertical radiation patterns of quarter-wave elements with varying forms of circular (radial) ground planes, introducing the novel concept of a GPA with a ground-plane of zero-extent.

The zero-extent concept was followed-up by Dr Brian Austin, G0GSF, who ran it to earth (no pun intended) in the book *Monopole Elements on Circular Ground Planes* by M M Weiner *et al* (Artech House, 1987). This resulted in *TT* (March 1988) reproducing a diagram of the Weiner form of zero-extent GPA, showing the use of lossy ferrite toroids (beads) around the coaxial feeder cable, providing a choke against the flow of outer-braid current. This description, unfortunately, left unanswered the question of the return current, and I received no further comments on this potentially interesting form of antenna until recently Peter Chadwick, G3RZP, mentioned the Artech book as a source of reference.

The GPA, particularly for VHF, remains of considerable interest not only to radio amateurs (for whom it provides one of the most popular simple antennas on HF) but also for professional users. This interest is reflected in 'Sleevve Antenna with Ground Wires' by Mitsuo Taguchi *et al* (*IEEE Trans Ant & Prop*, January 1991, pp 1-7). This presents a detailed mathematical and experimental analysis of a sleeve antenna, a monopole antenna with ground wires (ie the GPA with wire radials) and a sleeve antenna with ground wires.

Among the information presented in this paper is some useful information on the input impedance of a GPA with the radials at different sloping angles (**Fig 1**). The authors note that the input impedance depends on the length of the ground wires (radials) and their inclination, making it easy to match the antenna to a 50Ω feeder by adjusting these parameters, adding: "Since the input resistance of this antenna with inclined ground wires decreases considerably for some feeder lengths, the mismatch of impedance with the feeder and degradation of radiation characteristics arise."

The sleeve antenna is much less popular with amateurs than the GPA although long featured in the handbooks. It normally consists of a monopole with a quarter-wave extension surrounding the feeder cable; the idea of adding radials to the sleeve, as described in the IEEE paper, is new to me, but it is concluded that a sleeve antenna with ground wires combines the advantages of both a sleeve antenna and a Brown GPA: "The input impedance of the sleeve antenna with ground wires can be easily changed by adjusting the length, inclination angle, and position of the ground wires. The directivity is not sensitive to these parameters when the lengths of the ground wires are less than 0.2λ.

"The input impedance is 50Ω and the actual gain is about 2.1dBi when the length of the sleeve is 0.2λ, the length and inclination angle of the ground wires are 0.1λ and 0°, and the distance of the ground wires from the feed point is 0.025λ. The current induced on the feeder of the sleeve antenna can be reduced at the design frequency of the *sperrtopf*."

The experimental UHF (340MHz) model antennas used by the Japanese authors include a 'quarter-wave *sperrtopf*', to suppress or reduce the RF current feeding back down the outer braid of the coaxial feeder cable. This appears to be some form of tuned, coaxial stub forming, in effect, an RF choke on the outer braid. Unfortunately, no details of the construction of such a *sperrtopf* is given in

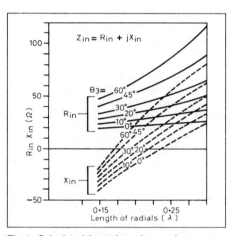

Fig 1: Calculated input impedance of a quarter-wave ground-wave type antenna with varying lengths of radials for different downward inclinations.

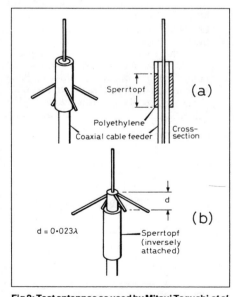

Fig 2: Test antennas as used by Mitsui Taguchi *et al*. (a) Sleeve antenna with ground wires (radials). (b) Monopole with ground wires (i.e. GPA). the *sperrtopf* appears to be a form of coaxial stub arranged to suppress RF currents on the outer-braid of the coaxial cable feeders.

the paper, but the reader is given a reference to the Japanese-published book *VHF Antennas* by H Uchida and Y Mushiake, Tokyo 1955, p192. Of the sleeve antenna without ground wires, it is considered difficult to match this antenna to a 50Ω feeder, so that it "is usually constructed with a matching circuit such as a coaxial impedance transformer." **Fig 2** shows details of the 340MHz test antennas.

Of the quarter-wave monopole with ground wires in the horizontal direction, it is concluded that the input resistance is near 20Ω even if the length of the ground wires is increased up to 0.3λ: "It increases as the ground wires are inclined below horizontal and their lengths are increased. The input reactance varies towards inductive as the lengths of the ground wires are increased.

The so-called Brown antenna (ie the ground-plane antenna as originally described in the 1930s by Dr George Brown of RCA - G3VA), which is a monopole antenna with quarter-wavelength horizontal ground wires, has a directive gain of 1.61dBi. The gain increases slightly as the ground wires are inclined in the downward direction. When the angle of inclination is 60°, the gain increases to 2.11dBi, which is about the same gain as a half-wave dipole.

The antenna can be matched with a 50Ω feeder if the ground wires are about 0.17λ long and are directed 60° downwards. The gain is then improved by about 0.5dB compared with the horizontally directed quarter-wavelength ground wires. However, the current induced on the surface of the feeder is not small compared with the current on the antenna. Without a *sperrtopf*, the input resistance seems to depend on the length of the feeder, and is smaller than the value calculated by neglecting the effect of feeder if the ground wires are inclined downwards. This creates an impedance mismatch and results in performance degradation." I wonder if any reader can provide fuller details of the (clearly useful) *sperrtopf*?

IF-DERIVED AGC WITH PLESSEY ICS

JAN-MARTIN NOEDING, LA8AK, has in the past not used the well-known Plessey 600/1600 series of integrated-circuit device because of his dislike of AF-derived AGC. He believeves that Plessey adopted this system because of the excessive broadband noise produced at the IF-output when, for example, three SL612 (1612) devices are connected in series. This noise tends to 'overload' a normal AGC circuit. G8LRH referred to this effect in *DUBUS* (1983) in connection with the ICOM IC402 transceiver, and SM6HYG encountered the problem when using three SL612 devices in series.

He cured the broadband noise problem in one of his receivers by fitting an extra crystal filter in front of the last IF stage - an excellent solution that has been advocated several times in *TT* in reference to the Drake R4C receiver (see August, October 1984, July 1986 etc). Professional communications receivers often tackle the problem of broadband noise produced in the IF chain by using a 'roofing filter' early in the chain and the placing the main SSB/CW filters further down the chain.

LA8AK comments: "I suspect that the same problem of IF broadband noise found in the Drake R4C receiver exists also in the ICOM IC735 and IC740, and possibly many other receivers, since friends with these transceivers tell me there is a background noise which does not disappear even when the incoming signals are strong. But I wonder why such problems are apparently seldom, if ever, mentioned in the equipment reviews in the amateur-radio periodicals? Too often, they appear to be trying to help the manufacturers sell their equipment rather than helping the discerning amateur decide which equipment to buy". [An accusation which cannot be directed at RadCom's top reviewer, Peter Hart, G3SJX - Ed]

LA8AK has since written further on the problem that manufacturers tend to persist in retaining circuit techniques that can result in less-than-ideal and even mediocre performance in successive models extending over a number of years. I hope to digest his comments another month.

But to return to the topic of IF-derived AGC and an arrangement that, even though an SL621 is fed from a DC signal, control is directly detected from the IF signal. Old-time valve designers may recall that a double-diode valve was commonly used to provide separate audio envelope detection of AM signals and IF detection in order to provide delayed-AGC. In contrast, the usual SL621 AGC device is controlled only from the product-detected audio signal.

LA8AK writes: "Recently, I needed a simple circuit to use with my FT-902 transceiver to give an indication of the signal-to-noise ratio. The circuit functions of the SL620/621 were studied and it seemed worth trying another approach to using this AGC-generator device. My circuit is shown in **Fig 3**. Results seem fairly good, about what might be expected from a circuit with AGC control on only one stage.

"To obtain a higher output voltage swing and additional gain, an extra transistor buffer amplifier is used. I am puzzled why nobody else seems to have thought about using a similar arrangement since it enables the SL621 to be used for AM, FM and CW/SSB, which I feel is an important consideration. Instead of using this negative-going envelope-detector, the AGC-generator may be connected to some positive detector circuit, with the current mirror-connected to the input of the SL621 (SL1621) in which case the input (pin 1) stays at about +1.05 to 1.1V for varying RF input levels."

LOW-RESISTANCE EARTHING

IN COMMENTING ON THE 'lazy man's multibander' HF antenna contributed by George Cripps, G3DWW, (TT, January 1991), I expressed surprise at the absence, in the diagram he sent along, of an earthing point at the antenna end of the coaxial feeder cable. In this type of quarter-wave inverted-L type of antenna, the real earth provides the missing quarter-wave section. I also emphasised that the loss-resistance of such an earth not only reduced radiation efficiency but could also result in a misleadingly low VSWR on the feeder.

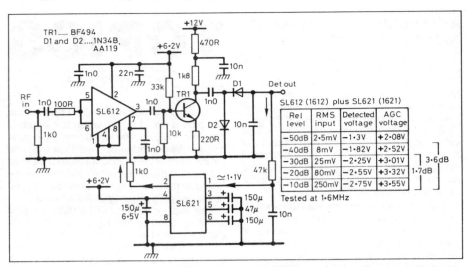

Fig 3: LA8AK's method of obtaining IF-derived AGC with Plessey SL600/SL1600-series of receiver ICs.

Rel level	RMS input	Detected voltage	AGC voltage	
–50dB	2·5mV	–1·3V	+2·08V	
–40dB	8mV	–1·82V	+2·52V	
–30dB	25mV	–2·25V	+3·01V	} 3·6dB
–20dB	80mV	–2·55V	+3·32V	
–10dB	250mV	–2·75V	+3·55V	} 1·7dB

Tested at 1·6MHz

KEYING A QRP TRANSMITTER

THE NUMBER OF PUBLISHED designs for compact QRP CW transceivers, with outputs ranging from about one to ten watts, has increased recently with TT featuring some of the basic circuitry for both receiver and transmitter sections. It is also possible to use such rigs to provide the drive for higher power amplifiers such as those based on low-cost switching FETs. However, an essential feature of such equipment is to provide the necessary control circuits needed to provide shaped keying waveforms, sidetone and transmit/receive (T/R) switching. TT has included (March 1991) the superhet receiver section of the 14MHz 5W transceiver described by Gary Breed, K9AY in his two-part article in QST, December 1990 and January 1991. The transmitter section in Part 2 uses an NE602 to convert the common VFO to signal frequency, followed by an LM6321 as buffer amplifier, 2N3866 as driver and the popular MRF475 bipolar transistor as power amplifier. His control circuits (**Fig 4**) are built on the transmitter board, providing sidetone, shaped keying of the LM6321 and 2N3866 and the T/R switch. Such control circuits could find other applications in this general class of equipment.

K9AY describes the functions as follows: "T/R switching is done by keying a 2N3906 transistor (TR4) which drives an RC network through a blocking diode. The rapidly charged RC network turns on TR5, pulling in the T/R relay. The discharge time of the RC network is controlled by a trimmer pot (DELAY) that can be set for the desired hold-in time. The relay is a small DIP-outline DPDT unit. One set of contacts switches the antenna and the other feeds power to the NE602 (transmitter) and the receiver-muting circuit.

"Keying begins with two sections of a CD4001 CMOS quad NOR gate (IC3). Its 12V output drives a TIP110 Darlington-pair power transistor (TR3) that switches DC to the LM6321 buffer and 2N3866 driver stages. A series-R, shunt-C network to ground from the keying transistor's base shapes the keyed waveform . . . . . . The sidetone is generated in IC3A and IC3B which form a keyed square-wave oscillator. The component values shown yield a roughly 800Hz note with a 12V supply which assists in zero-beating incoming signals. Some variation in pitch occurs with different CD4001s and changing supply voltage. The oscillator's high output level is attenuated by a 470K resistor in series with the 5K SIDETONE LEVEL control."

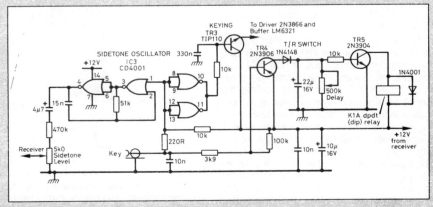

Fig 4: Control circuits of K9AY's QRP transceiver providing sidetone, shaped keying waveform and T/R switch.

In the follow-up letter, G3DWW agreed with my comments but added that in fact he does have a good RF earth connection at the antenna end of the feeder, though he omitted this in his diagram. His earth comprises a spike about 2ft from the end of the coaxial cable, paralleled to three 4ft earth spikes at the end of 20ft radials buried about 2in under his lawn. One radial runs directly under the horizontal run of the antenna.

Even so, he has measured the DC earth resistance as roughly 20Ω, which he assumes could be limiting the radiation efficiency to roughly 50% - a quite reasonable and practical figure for such a simple multi-band antenna. This assumes that the RF loss resistance is the same as the DC resistance, an assumption that is probably pessimistic in view of the presence of the radials; in practice the efficiency may be appreciably higher than he suggests. Incidentally, it is yet another indication that the use of elevated quarter-wave-resonated radials (possibly much reduced in size by the use of inductive loading as suggested by G6XN, or by the adaption of DL1VU's 'sardine tin opener' folding technique as a counterpoise rather than a top-loading system; see G4LQI's *Eurotek* column in the February *RadCom*, p45) is likely to prove superior to the use of earth spikes alone. It may, however, still be advisable to earth the system to reduce damage from nearby lightning strikes.

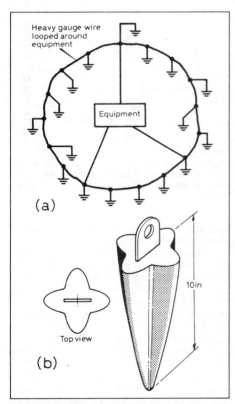

Fig 5: Surface-wire-ground (SWG) system as used by US Army. The SWG wire is looped around the equipment and earthed at 15 to 18 points, using the 10in ground stakes of cruciform shape with connecting bolt at top as shown in (b).

In practice, a DC earth resistance of 25Ω probably represents a better than average figure for amateur radio earthing in typical residential areas. A useful item on 'improved grounding techniques' appears in the new column by Bill Orr, W6SAI 'Radio Fundamentals; things to learn, projects to build and gear to use' which started in *CQ*, December 1990, p85. This is based on an article in the American military-communications magazine *Signal* (March 1988), brought to W6SAI's notice by George Riddle, W6FMZ.

Signal reported earth measurements made by the US Army Materials Systems Analysis Activity outfit in various parts of the USA. They found that measurements using a single 6ft earth rod (of the type used by the US military for over 50 years) ranged from 13Ω in moist soil at Fort Story, Virginia, to over 7000Ω at Fort Lewis, Washington. The US military regards 10Ω as the upper limit of acceptability, presumably requiring the use of multiple earth rods for virtually all installations.

The W6SAI item continues: "Continued testing on various grounding schemes led to the surface-wire-ground (SWG) technique. The early SWG consisted of a number of 6in-long stakes used to secure a 100ft-long, 1/8in dia, cable to the earth in a straight line. In the final design, the wire length is reduced to 70ft, the wire being grounded along its length by 15 stakes, each 10in long. The wire is looped around the equipment, and three heavy connecting wires ground the equipment to the SWG as in **Fig 5**.

"The short ground stake is a tapered, star-shaped design (**Fig 5(b)**) that provides enhanced soil contact and can easily be inserted into or removed from the ground.

"The SWG has been tested against a conventional 6ft ground rod in a number of locations in the continental United States, Alaska and Germany. In all cases, the SWG offered improved performance, with values ranging from 2:1 to 10:1 better than the ground rod."

144MHZ HAND DOPPLER DIRECTION-FINDER

UK AMATEURS SEEM TO have rather lagged behind those of some other countries in developing direction-finding equipment for VHF rather than for 1.8MHz "ground-wave" signals. *TT* (September 1990, p34) included details of a compact highly directional "miniature electromagnetic-coupled foxing (MEF) antenna, intended to be implemented as a gun-type hand-held system for use with a 'straight' field-strength-type receiver (*TT*, March 1991) as a 144MHz 'sniffer' system developed by John Williscroft, ZS6EF, and originally described in *Radio-ZS* (February & March, 1990).

More recently, ZS6EF has described (*Radio-ZS*, combined November/December 1990 issue) a very different form of 'ultimate 144MHz direction-finder' for which he claims the following advantages: (1) simple to build; (2) high accuracy; (3) works with any 144MHz receiver/transceiver; (4) does not need attenuators; and (5) takes you right to the transmitter.

He believes that "this piece of equipment is very close to the ideal direction-finding tool." It works with any FM hand-held receiver (factory-built or home-made) or transceiver (provided this is not used in the transmit mode with the doppler D/F antenna) without requiring an S-meter or any connections to be made inside the receiver. It can be used at night without lights and without adjustment of controls. ZS6EF considers that it is the most accurate VHF D/F equipment he has yet seen and also the most simple to build: **Fig 6**.

Unlike the more usual form of direction-finding based on swinging a directional antenna for minimum or maximum signal strength, his system represents a hand-portable adaption of the doppler D/F system which depends on the slight difference in path lengths from a hidden transmitter to two similar antennas connected to a receiver via an electronic change-over switch: **Fig 7**.

The switch connects each antenna to the receiver in turn at a rate of about 500Hz. Provided the whole system is balanced with equal feeder paths, when the path lengths are the same, **Fig 8(a)**, the signals from each antenna will be identical in frequency and phase. But only a very small swing of the doppler antenna structure, **Fig 8(b)**, will result in the signals presented to the receiver input being delayed and advanced at the switching rate. In effect, the receiver then 'sees' a frequency (phase) modulated signal and emits a 500Hz audio tone, which vanishes when the path lengths are identical. ZS6EF points out that the null point is very accurately defined, although as with a 1.8MHz loop without a sense antenna, the bearing does not indicate whether the transmitter is in front or behind the observer. However, the user need take only a few steps to the right or left, again find the null resulting in a heading a little to the left or right of the first heading, from which the direction as well as the bearing can be deduced.

How far it is necessary to walk sideways to establish a 'base line' depends on the distance from the transmitter, but ZS6EF suggests this need not be more than about 12 or 15 metres even if the transmitter is up to 40km distant, though this seems to me incredible with such a simple hand-held antenna and I wonder if this was a misprint for 4km. If the receiver tone is not a clean one but appears to contain a wobble or a high tone superimposed on the switched tone, this is an indication of multipath reflections, it will usually be possible to overcome this (except possibly in urban areas) by moving a short distance to a new position.

The electronic switch together with two broadband FET pre-amplifiers are built on a small piece of double-sided PCB (**Fig 9**) and fitted inside a standard electric-wiring junction box, taking care that the whole system is balanced. Mark/space ratio of the switch is adjusted by R3 (20K trimpot) preferably using an oscilloscope but quite possible by using a local transmitter.

While the antenna elements could be full-size half-wave dipoles, this would result in a rather bulky unit. ZS6EF shortens his element lengths from 1000mm to about 450mm by spiral winding the elements on 6mm dowel, making it easier to run through bushes or store the antenna in a car boot, as well as providing a convenient form of balun transformer.

The structure is made using two 20mm-diameter conduit T-pieces with inspection covers; one 20mm round junction box with an outlet each side and one on the bottom in the

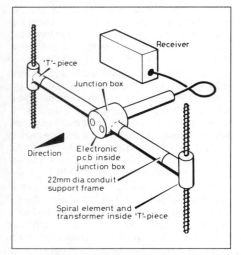

Fig 6: ZS6EF's hand-held 144MHz doppler direction finder.

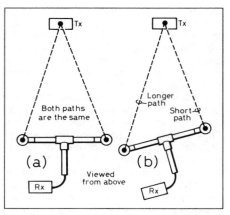

Fig 8: Principles of the doppler D/F. (a) Equal path lengths to the transmitter produce no 500Hz tone in the FM receiver, providing an accurate 'null'. (b) When the path lengths differ, even only slightly, the receiver 'sees' a phase-modulated signal and produces 500Hz tone.

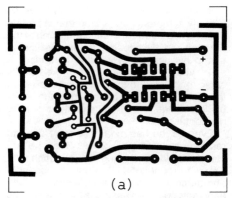

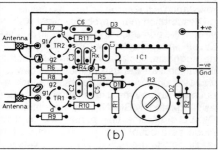

Fig 9: (a) Solder side of the PCB looking from the top. This is produced on double-sided board leaving the component side as a ground plane. Solder all ground pins on both sides of the board. The coaxial feeder cable is connected to component side (b).

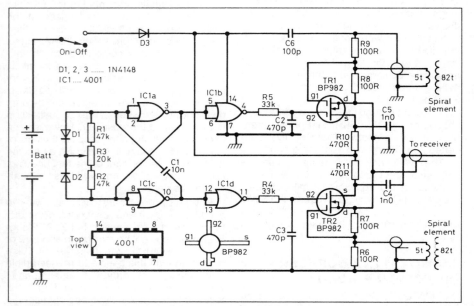

Fig 7: The 500Hz electronic switch and FET pre-amplifiers contained within the junction box of the doppler D/F.

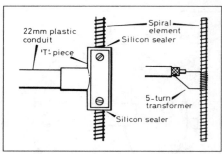

Fig 10 Constructional details of the spirally-wound antenna elements and coupling transformers (which must be wound over the electrical centre of the dipole elements).

middle; one round junction box to be used as a lid; three pieces of 20mm conduit tube each 300mm long; two lengths of 6mm dowel 450mm long; 1.5m of 50-ohm 6mm coaxial cable; a BNC coax connector; two 5mm by 40mm brass machine screws; four metres of 0.8 or 1.1mm copper wire for the antenna elements; one double-sided PCB; plus the electronic components.

The two elements are made by winding 82 turns of 0.8 or 1.1mm wire onto a 6mm wooden dowel 450mm long evenly spaced. Larger dowel will not resonate correctly as the ratio of interturn capacitance and the inductance must be correct. Elements must be balanced, the spiral construction allowing a transformer to be easily wound around the centre. The transformer consists of 5 turns around the exact centre of the element: **Fig 10**. Exact tuning of the elements to the required frequency is necessary to optimise the efficiency of the spiral elements. This can be accomplished by taking a grid dip meter exactly in the physical centre of the element and adjusting the turns until the element is on

145.5MHz (or the required frequency). Antenna elements will cover the whole 144MHz band if dipped at the centre of the band. Cover the elements with varnish once the complete unit has been tested and found satisfactory.

WIDEBAND AMPLIFIERS AND A WARTIME NFD

ONE MURKY AFTERNOON in mid-November 1941, I arrived at Hanslope Park where the 'special intercept station' of Special Communication Unit No 3 then comprised half-a-dozen HRO receivers in the corn bins of a small granary, plus a few nondescript random length wire antennas (plus one low quarter-mile or so long Beverage antenna pointing towards Norway). I had been unwillingly plucked out of 'Box 25 Discrimination', to which I had been originally assigned, on the grounds that I had been one of the first of the new VI special enlistments unwise enough to have passed the 'A' (25WPM) Morse reception test on entry. Hence, it was deemed that I should face the discomforts of the 'country

farmyard', as the Park was known, rather than live in billets in Barnet.

The granary soon gave way to the Lodge. Meanwhile, the large receiving station (demolished only a few years ago) was still being built. It finally became operational in May 1942, furnished with a magnificent set of rhombic antennas (8 - 16MHz), vee beams (4 - 8MHz) plus a set of drooping wire antennas suspended from catenary wires on four poles placed around the building. Each of the rhombic/vee-beam antennas, which together covered all points of the compass, was fed into a unique-design of wide-band amplifier, each with ten outlets that each could be patched into any of the 66 HRO receivers. The amplifiers and patching sockets were all assembled in the centre of the building in a metal structure that many years later was destined to be condemned to destruction on the grounds that it resembled a French street pissoir.

The antenna farm was largely the creation of Robin Addie, G8LT, as a member of Major Keen's SCU3 Engineering Section, aided by 'Digger' Buick, G3XJ, and his riggers. The wide-band amplifiers were the pride and joy of Dud Charman, G6CJ, who obtained leave of absence from his professional work at EMI to design and build the initial models at the Park, assisted by Jimmy Mathews, G6LL. It should be remembered that at the time only very limited experience had been gained in the design of highly-linear wideband amplifiers for radio engineering, although G6CJ had been involved in pre-war pioneering work on the distribution of TV signals over cable. The WBAs he developed used 807 transmitting valves as small-signal amplifiers to achieve the required linearity and isolation between the receivers. The HRO had a particularly strong HF local oscillator voltage that leaked out via its antenna terminals and could cause interference problems when a number of receivers were operated in close proximity.

G6CJ's WBAs proved extremely successful, so much so that I believe that the Canadian Professor Bayly, who had been brought secretly to the UK to advise on radio communications and cryptology, tried to persuade Dud to join him in North America after the war.

G6CJ, in describing his work on the WBAs in *OT News*, No 20, January 1991, writes: "With the filter amplifiers the maximum gain-bandwidth is determined by the input and output capacitances of the valves. About 15pF for the input and 3pF for the output. The filters incorporate such capacitances in the shunt elements and enabled an impedance transformation to get a little extra gain. A gain of about 10dB per stage could be achieved from Long Wave to about 15MHz in the amplifiers developed for the TV distribution system. An ordinary receiving valve could cope with the input from a large antenna over this band, but a power valve was needed to feed a large number of outlets without interaction or cross modulation products.

"The popular 807 did this job very well . . . Within the specified two months, the design work was done for three octave-band amplifiers and construction well under way . . . . They even improved the signal-to-noise ratio of the HRO receivers (the use of maximum possible impedance at the grid of the first stage meant that the stages had *optimum noise factor* although that phrase was yet to be invented) . . . . The whole system was screened and no complaint was ever heard about interference between the receivers (provided they were connected to the beam antennas through the WBAs, see below - G3VA), or about (spurious) signals that 'weren't there' . . . . In 40 years of radio engineering this was the job which gave me the most satisfaction".

What G6CJ may not have appreciated was that each operator was given key switches that connected one of the drooping wire antennas to his receiver directly. But let Gerry Openshaw, G2BTO, take up the story. He was another of the 100-plus pre-war amateur Voluntary Interceptors who spent many months at the 'country farmyard'. He later departed for the buried metal tanks, of the Special Communications network of Alcock-type HF D/F stations to which the special intercept stations passed the signals of the Geheimen Funkmeldedienstes (Secret Radio Reporting Service) of the German Abwehr. A fuller description of his wartime experiences with SCU3 'Wartime NFD' appeared

in *OT News*, No:15, October 1989. He writes: "Some 100 pre-war radio amateurs, plus Post Office and ex-marine radio officers, took over the first SCU purpose-built intercept station (in May 1942) and brought it to life. Each operating position contained two HRO communication receivers, with a control panel enabling different antennas to be switched in, receiver outputs parallelled or divided one to the left and the other to the right earpiece. It could also be fed througgh to the D/F network linked by land lines to stations as far apart as Thurso in the far north of Scotland, St Erth near Penzance in Cornwall, Belfast, and Wymondham in Norfolk.

"For less demanding use, each set had its own 'long wire' antenna which comprised some 30-ft of wire or so passing through window ducts and then slanting upwards at about 45° to the supporting wires slung between the poles, thus comprising many antennas in close proximity, producing an interference problem that we soon learned to turn to our advantage.

"The local oscillator in the HRO radiates well when the set is directly connected to an antenna. By using the selector switch on the bay's control panel as a Morse key it was soon found that operators on the same shift

could 'work' one another late at night when the Abwehr operators were safely asleep. It was 'real DX' to make contact with one of the operators at the opposite end of the station, 'locals' were the neighbouring bays. One HRO provided the 'transmitter', tuned to 455kHz below the frequency to which the 'receiver' HRO was tuned; then call TEST (UK amateurs were forbidden to call CQ from about 1925 until the resumption of activities in 1946). At around 0300-hours, with few 'skeds' and the higher frequencies 'dead', the 28MHz band would spring to life. In June 1942, one genius, realizing that in peacetime he would be at NFD, called Test NFD, and soon others joined in with their own callsigns or, if not pre-war amateurs, taking on the role of the DX stations. I well remember working a 'W6' and, then, the shift over, finding a home-made QSL card on the pillow of my bunk!"

G2BTO does not mention one cruel but possibly justified practical joke played on one bumptious young operator whose many excesses included boasting that he could copy anything the German or Italian operators could send. Keyed tone from a Morse key on the 'concentrator' console, (normally used to communicate with the D/F network) could be fed into the operators' headphones.

VFO TEMPERATURE COMPENSATION WITH THERMISTORS

JOHN BEECH, G8SEQ, in a note also prepared for *Sprat*, describes a practical way he hit upon a couple of years ago to compensate for temperature drift of free-running oscillators. This is based on the use of an NTC thermistor (resistor showing a steep reduction in ohmic value with increasing current/temperature) rather than the usual NP0 ceramic capacitors (or, if you are lucky enough to have one, the rather expensive Oxley Tempatrimmer, nominal capacity 6.5pF with temperature coefficient variable from + to - 2000 parts per million, or the less costly Oxley Thermo Trimmer with a nominal capacitance of 2.5pF with temperature coefficient variable from + to - 1000ppm).

G8SEQ shows that for varicap (electronic tuning diode) tuned VFOs, an NTC thermistor can be arranged to overcome either positive or negative frequency drift by controlling the voltage applied to the diode (Fig 11). For oscillators not tuned by varicaps, it is still possible to use the technique by fitting one across the tuned circuit. He writes: "As the temperature increases, the resistance of R_c decreases, thus reducing the voltage at point A. This causes the varicap to increase its capacitance, thus reducing the frequency of the tuned circuit and correcting *positive drift* (ie where the oscillator drifts higher in frequency with increasing temperature).

"To correct negative drift, the thermistor and preset should be connected in series with the top half of the potentiometer forming the main tuning control. the action is then reversed.

"The preset resistor is used to adjust the amount of effect that the thermistor has on the tuned circuit. If the correct thermistor is chosen, the drift can actually

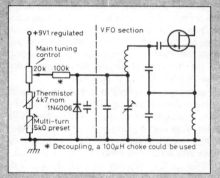

Fig 11: G8SEQ's temperature compensated VFO using an NTC thermistor to adjust the voltage across the electronic tuning diode.

be reversed within the range of the preset resistor; ideally the turnover point should be about the mid-range point of the multi-turn preset.

"I used a Spectrol ten-turn pot and a disc-type thermistor (Farnell KED 4721C7) to compensate an 8.3MHz VFO which was tripled and then doubled to 50MHz. Originally this drifted at the rate of about 100Hz per second at the output frequency with an almost imperceptible temperature increase. After compensation the frequency only changed by about 30Hz in a five minute period."

G8SEQ wonders whether this is a genuinely new idea. He has never seen it described in print and such an application is not mentioned in the Mullard (Philips) Technical Handbook 3, Part 1f, dealing with thermistor applications. He would be interested to discover if he can claim originality or whether he has only re-invented a wheel already used in TV tuners or somesuch!

Late one night, the operator in the bay next to the victim pretended to tune into a priority service and then claimed that the CW was too fast for him to copy. He passed over his headphones to the unsuspecting victim, with other participants standing by either to take their turn at sending the spurious 'traffic' or to snatch each message from the hapless victim as soon as it was complete, ostensibly to rush it to the teleprinter room for transmission to Bletchley Park, but in reality to fall about laughing as the concentrator 'station' continued for several hours to bat out a long series of messages. The victim was so bemused that he did not even twig what was going on when finally the QTCs lapsed into plain language such as 'Roses are red . . . . etc". I never learned when the penny finally dropped.

RF AFFECTS TEST METERS, ELECTRONIC REGULATORS ETC

RECENTLY, I DECIDED to check the dynamic regulation of the external 300V PSU that powers the buffer/frequency-multiplier stages of my ancient Labgear LG300 CW transmitter with the aid of a conventional (analogue/Russian-made) multi-testmeter. To my surprise, when I pressed the Morse-key, the volts dropped steadily downwards virtually to zero volts - yet the transmitter showed its normal PA current and usual RF output. It took time for the penny to drop. I use an end-fed 'long-wire' antenna with the ATU located a few feet away from the transmitter with the result that there is a good deal of RF floating around (though not, I hope, sufficient to constitute a serious health hazard).

Eventually, I realised that the meter leads were picking up enough RF to affect greatly the measurements made on a fairly sensitive meter. This was quickly confirmed by repeating the measurements while running the transmitter into a dummy load (electric light bulb, suitable for CW but not for SSB because of the large difference in resistance between cold and hot filaments). This showed the PSU regulation was reasonable for the application.

At the time, I felt this was an unusual problem unlikely to affect many others. However, in QST's Hints & Kinks (January 1991, p36), Charles P Baker, W2KTF, draws attention to this problem. On his 144MHz mobile transceiver, the nominal 12V reading dropped by nearly a volt when he keyed the transmitter on. Convinced that this was not actually happening, he by-passed his multimeter for RF and it then indicated the correct 12V when the transmitter was on or off.

W2KTF writes: "A multimeter can give strangely erroneous readings in the presence of an RF field, or when ultrasonic audio energy is present in the DC or low-audio circuit under test. This effect can be especially severe when the meter test leads pick-up RF energy. Modern multimeters include protective diodes across the terminals of their meter movements. This arrangement can allow rectification even when the meter rectifier is disabled (as when the meter selector switch is set to a DC voltage or current range). Indication of an abnormal voltage change, such as (false) evidence of poor voltage

regulation in a well-regulated supply, is one possible result of this. If the multimeter includes a protective solid-state circuit-breaker 'RF in the meter' may cause the breaker to false.

"A by-pass capacitor - a component that allows RF to pass while blocking DC - across the multimeter's test-lead terminals is an almost certain cure for these problems. Try 0.01µF at HF, or 0.001µF at VHF (be sure the working voltage of the capacitor is greater than the voltage expected in the circuit under test). Repositioning the multimeter test leads may also help where direct RF pick-up is a problem."

David Newkirk, WJ1Z, the Hints & Kinks editor, adds: "The high-gain sensing circuitry in electronically regulated power supplies may also be RF sensitive, so if you measure unexpectedly weird shifts in regulated-supply output with transmitter keying, your voltmeter may not be at fault. Trying a meter of different design (or a passive voltage/current indicator, such as a lamp or LED, capable of indicating relative level shifts) can help you determine whether the fault lies in the instrument or the circuit under test."

As mentioned above, the traditional electric light bulb can no longer be considered a satisfactory form of low-cost dummy load except for ancient transmitters. However Lorin Knight, G2DXK, has discovered a practical, if unusual, low-cost substitute for a high-power 50Ω dummy load in the form of an old Morphy Richard electric iron discarded from its usual domestic chores.

He writes: "All I had to do was replace the three-pin plug with a PL259 plug, taking the brown wire to the centre pin and the blue and green/yellow wires to the body of the plug. On test, the measured VSWR proved to be: 3.7MHz - 1.3:1; 7.1MHz - 1.8:1; 14.2MHz - 1.1:1; 21.2MHz - 2.3:1; 29MHz - 1.0:1. Not quite as good as a Heathkit 'Cantenna' but a lot cheaper!

"It is advisable to turn the knob on the iron to 'hot' in order to prevent the thermostat cutting out when the iron starts to get warm - however it takes a continuous two or three hundred watts of RF to make the iron really hot." But watch out if you're caught dashing away with a smoothing iron that has not been discarded, if I can be excused what these days might be construed as a sexist remark.

TIPS & TOPICS

Prevention of Corrosion in Antennas

Contact between copper and aluminium, for example in an antenna, can result in corrosion and, therefore, a poor electrical connection. According to Karel Barton (Protection against atmospheric corrosion, published by John Wiley, 1976), "contact between copper and aluminium should be avoided at all costs!". However, the author goes on to say that stainless steel causes no trouble. I suggest that a stainless steel washer between the copper cable and the aluminium of an antenna element may well reduce the likelihood of corrosion, especially if used with a stainless steel bolt. It is wise to add other precautions such as the application of grease, lanolin (my favourite) or RTV silicone rubber. If RTV silicone rubber, use the type that does

not give off acetic acid (vinegar-type) fumes. - Dick Biddulph, G8DPS.

100W UHF Power FET

Although there are state-of-the-art bipolar power transistors capable of providing 200W output per device up to about 850MHz, it has proved extremely difficult to develop such high power VMOS FETs for frequencies above about 100MHz. However, Hitachi have introduced a 2SK1640 device which can deliver 100W up to 860MHz with a drain power efficiency of the order of 48%, and a typical gain of 8dB (compared with 5-6dB for UHF power bipolars). The 2SK1640 is being marketed for UHF TV broadcasting and professional communications, rather than amateur-radio budgets. Nevertheless, it is interesting to note that the device is based on a proprietary lateral, rather than a VMOS-type vertical, structure of the drain substrate and thus represents a development which may come to influence lower-cost device. It is claimed by Hitachi that lateral structures have inherently superior high frequency characteristics and that the simple source grounding is particularly useful in common-source push-pull configurations.

Feedback

Some errors crept into recent TT items: In Fig 7 (February), C2 for the ceramic resonator oscillator of the QRP transmitter should have been a 375pF variable capacitor (as in Fig 6) and not a 30pF trimmer in order to achieve the pulling range 3.52 to 3.59MHz. The text and caption to Fig 11 (February) suggested that VK2BRD's heavy-current 28V PSU could deliver over 30A but a more realistic continuous load would be the 20A shown on the diagram.

TT, January, p34, wrongly showed a field strength of 0dBu as equal to 1mV/m instead of the correct 1µV/m.

Apologies also to those readers who have submitted interesting but still unpublished items over recent months. Pressure on space (and time) frequently makes it necessary to delay preparing material, particularly longer items with a number of drawings that would lose value by drastic pruning. Also, over the past year, our long-suffering Editor has been forced to hold over or omit quite a few items prepared for publication. Quarts and pint bottles.

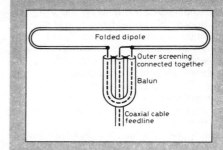

ERRATUM

IN THE MARCH issue of Technical Topics (page 32) we inadvertently gave the wrong diagram for Fig 9. We apologise for this and show the correct diagram below.

SAD STORY OF AN ELECTRONIC HOBBYIST

AS RADIO AMATEURS WE are still, if only on a much reduced scale, survivors of the golden age of electronic do-it-yourself. It *is* still possible to experience the satisfaction of making a unique piece of equipment or trying out your own antenna ideas, even if most gear now comes from the factory in black boxes. Other electronic hobbyists, who were once avid constructors, are less fortunate. Robert W Lucky in the *Reflections* column of *IEEE Spectrum* (July 1990, p6) tells a sad story of lost glory:

"Electronics used to be fun. Maybe it still is, but sometimes I have doubts. When I was a youngster, I discovered *Boy's First Book of Radio*. Each chapter told how to build an ever more complicated radio, starting with a crystal set and ending with a superhet . . . . I found that miracles could be wrested from vacuum tubes. All you had to do was to wire them up in endlessly possible configurations, and you could pull voices out of the ether . . . .

"Transistors came along, but no matter, they were just like little tubes, and by wiring them together with resistors and capacitors, you could do neat little things. I concentrated on kits. See my great hi-fi system? Built it myself, saved a bundle, and if anything ever goes wrong I can fix it . . . .

"Then something changed. Integrated circuits came along, and all those transistors and resistors got scrunched into little chips. Worse yet, all the wires were in there, too, with the external wires etched onto a printed-circuit board . . . . They still sold kits, but now all you did was stuff the parts onto the board and solder the connections . . . . I began to wonder why I was doing this.

"Just about the time most of the fun had gone, personal computers came along . . . . The microprocessor was a fantastic engine, but it was only a single chip. Lots of other stuff had to be designed and wired, and hardly any software existed. I was more proud of my home-designed computer than any of those hi-fi kits.

"Now my third-generation (factory-built) computer is humming quietly while I write this on one of those ubiquitous word processors. There is still something wrong with the computer, but I haven't the chance of the proverbial snowball of fixing it myself . . . . The VSLI chips have only cryptic markings. There is no circuit diagram for this clone without a brand name. Nothing is socketed.

"I never see ads for kits anymore. It costs more to package a kit than to build the finished product . . . . When you see PC boards go through the factory, you realize why it makes no sense to wire or solder things yourself. Ever try to buy the parts? Forget it. They cost a lot more than the finished and tested board. If something goes wrong, buy a new board.

"Software seemed the salvation of the hobbyist. Everyone could do his own thing. I wrote operating systems, compilers, editors . . . . it was more fun, it was educational.

"The golden age ended. I looked around for some program to write. Anything I could think of had already been packaged and worked far better than one I could write. There was no excuse for building either hardware or soft-

ware. I went to a computer flea market that has been a source of experimental junk . . . . I found myself looking at 500 stands all selling the same two dozen commercial products. What was I doing there?

"I hear that enrollment in electronic engineering has been dropping steadily. I'm looking at my keep-your-hands-off clone, do you think there is any connection?"

[Though the point is taken, this pessimistic view is not entirely supported by the number of ads in RadCom *for kits - see page 24 Ed]*

END FEEDING A WINDOM AND RELATED TOPICS

LES MOXON, G6XN, IN *TT*, February 1989, pp111-112, introduced the radical concept of end-feeding a Windom-type antenna by inserting a specific capacitive reactance a given length along a resonant wire element, preferably keeping reasonably short the length of the single-wire feeder connected to the end of the antenna: **Fig 1**.

He has now provided an up-date on this concept, including showing a means of end-feeding the element from co-axial cable with counterpoise, showing also the potential of this approach for other antennas, including arrays.

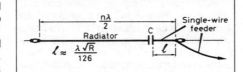

Fig 1: G6XN's end-fed Windom antenna with single-wire feeder as described in *TT*, February 1989). λ is wavelength in feet. R is radiation resistance (referred to a current loop). A value of 500Ω is assumed for the impedance of the single-wire feeder. Reactance of capacitor C is $1/\lambda C$ approximately equal to $70\lambda/l$. Values found in practice:

At 7MHz, l = 12ft for n = 2 (C = 27pF).

At 29MHz, 1 = 2ft for n = 1 (C variable and not measured but estimated to be about 5pF).

Principle of operation: From a point of maximum RF voltage on the antenna, one moves a short distance outwards to find an impedance (from a Smith Chart) equal to R + jx, where R matches the single wire feeder, X being tuned by the capacitor. Since l is short and current in it small, its virtual removal from the radiator has negligible effect on field strength.

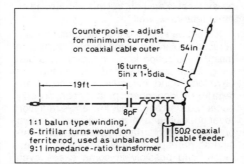

Fig 2: The G6XN Windom with 'zero-length' single wire feeder arranged for end-feeding from coaxial cable feeder with short resonant counterpoise.

G6XN writes: "As described in February 1989, the end-fed Windom has the same defects as the ordinary Windom, ie radiation from the feeder and losses in the ground return path, but nevertheless derives interest from the defects of *other* forms of end-fed antennas (despite their convenience at typical sites). Suppose, however, that we shorten the single-wire feeder so that the matching unit (complete with the artificial ground) gets dragged up towards the antenna followed by the 50Ω-ohm line connecting it to the transmitter (akin to the FD4 form of Windom described in the December *TT* - G3VA).

"Let's go all the way. We now have an antenna end-fed with a co-axial cable feeder as in **Fig 2**. The single-wire line, shrunk to zero length, cannot radiate. My work on ground planes provides proof that the antenna current will return directly to the counterpoise (except at very low heights) instead of via the ground. (Nor should the co-axial cable radiate unlike the situation with an off-centre-fed antenna - G3VA).

"Incidentally we can do anything we like with the antenna proper, subject to the conditions outlined in February 1989, without any change to the (matching) transformer since its impedance ratio is given by Z_o(wire)/Z_o(cable), ie about 11:1 with R not involved. We can shorten the antenna by loading its further half capacitively or inductively, it can be any number of half-waves (minus a little bit) long, or you could replace it with one of the 'inverted ground planes' (resonant T-antennas) described on many occasions in *TT* and *Amateur Radio Techniques*.

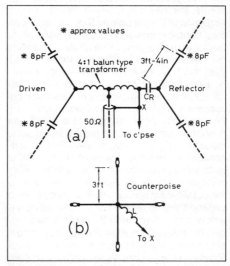

Fig 3: (a) Single-pole-mounted, switchable four-quadrant directional 21MHz array modified for end-fed Windom-type feed. CR tunes reflector by resonating with the single-wire feeders (which in the reflector case are "inductive connections to ground" so the inductance has to be removed.

(b) Counterpoise details. Four radials (each 3ft long) are used for reasons of symmetry. L is 8 turns, 2.75-in diameter, 6-in long, wound over fishing rod extension.

"Different again, and possibly much more important, is the *nearly* zero-length version which can be used to push points of high RF voltage away from places where they are causing problems such as inside the shack, or on switch contacts. This opens the way to what I believe to be a major breakthrough in the design of directionally switched arrays based on vertical dipoles (eg Fig 162, p333 of *Amateur Radio Techniques*; 7th edition out-of-print, or Fig 13.9b of my book *HF Antennas for all Locations*). These arrays, in which four dipoles are held up by a single pole, have attracted a lot of interest in spite of the difficulty of switching them remotely. One or two people have succeeded in this, but hitherto it has not been easy. By inserting capacitors at 0.075λ from the bottom ends of the dipoles they can become 'single-wire, end-fed' elements in pairs as in **Fig 3(a)** which shows some details of a 21MHz array I have just completed. This achieves four-quadrant directional switching by means of a pair of 'ordinary' double-pole reversing relays. Thin wire elements are used (20SWG) held up by a 17ft fishing rod with its base 4ft off the ground.

"Earlier experiments, at 14MHz, disclosed an important new aspect of this type of array: the very wide bandwidth which results from the use of two widely-spaced wires in parallel. Hitherto, this characteristic had been masked by the very *narrow* bandwidth of the Zepp-type feed, especially when using the (essential) G6CJ balancing stub. The change in SWR over a 2% band was barely detectable, and in one case the null depth exceeded 30dB over more than 100kHz without retuning. Less useful was the discovery of a small horizontally-polarised *low-angle* mode associated with *low* antenna heights. If one considers the top and bottom halves of the antenna separately, there is a small horizontal component resulting from the phase-difference between reflector and driven elements; this has a figure-of-8 pattern at right angles to the main beam. The 'top' and 'bottom' contributions should cancel each other out, but if the height and the angle of radiation are low enough the 'bottom' is less effective than the 'top' so cancellation is incomplete.

"Unfortunately at my present QTH, because of sandy soil and lots of trees, vertical antennas are very poor low-angle radiators (though quite useful at medium angles). The upshot of this was that in tests with VK5MS, towards the end of a path-opening, the horizontal mode actually took over! These 14MHz tests were discontinued when a faulty relay coincided with realisation of the need for a less cluttered environment. Not being able to expand the environment, I am contracting the antenna by changing to 21MHz instead!

"The result does little for popular beliefs about vertically-polarized antennas. On the other hand, in a good location they can give consistently good DX results with very modest structures *which do not need planning consent*!"

In a postscript to his report, G6XN adds some further relevant information: "I have found it impossible to design broadband (several octave) transformers for 550-600Ω impedance despite the ease of doing so for 200Ω. The trouble is self-capacitance, but for monoband operation all one needs to do is partly withdraw the core from the winding so that a GDO indicates resonance (with the transformer isolated) or if everything else is correct one can tune it for minimum SWR when *in situ*.

"Earlier references to this type of array have pointed out that the four wires of the

beam can be arranged in either a 2- or 3-element configuration, but 3-elements can no longer be recommended as one loses the broadband feature, and there is an overcoupling problem with 2-elements which is cured by the new feed system (another plus). Attempts to apply this to the 3-element case proved a dismal failure in line with experience with a 3-element Claw antenna, emphasising the general problem of having 'too many variables', whereas *given a proper understanding* of the principles, optimisation is easy with two elements. One has to concede an advantage of 1.5-2dB (half an average S-point) to three elements but only if one has a long boom and can get it up equally high! (NB 'trapped tribanders' are a different case)."

MORE ON OFF-CENTRE-FED (WINDOM) ANTENNAS

FURTHER TO THE ABOVE, G6XN writes to clear up a potentially misleading comment that I made in the discussion about the family of off-centre-fed (Windom/VS1AA) antennas in *TT*, December 1990. He points out that "far from being non-radiating, the two-wire (300Ω) feeder, especially as shown in Fig 3(d) of the December issue, can be quite efficient as a radiator of vertically-polarised signals, which may well account for its apparent success."

The reason is that, for a twin-wire feeder line to be non-radiating, the voltages and current need to be balanced throughout its length, a condition that does not apply when the feedpoint to a dipole element is not balanced about its centre.

G6XN writes: "Using my 'square-counting' method (see 'Radiation from a conductor' *HF Antennas for all locations*, p9). I have calculated that for a feeder length of one half-wave, total radiation from the antenna will have identical vertical and horizontal components. This, admittedly, ignores any change in impedance (Z) at the feed-point, which could change the balance between vertical/horizontal components, but seems unlikely in practice to make much difference."

To explain his conclusions, G6XN has sketched the current distribution starting from each end of the dipole element where current is zero: **Fig 4**. He writes: "There is (current) balance at the feedpoint, but below this (in the feeder) the maximum current in the right-hand wire nearly coincides with minimum in the other. For the arrangement of December's Fig 3(d) a likely consequence, apart from radiation from the 300Ω line, could be lots of current on the outer of the braid of the co-axial cable section, but this will depend on other factors as well."

It must be stressed that the radiation of a vertically-polarized component, resulting in mixed-polarization is not necessarily a bad thing, as users of inverted-L type antennas have long found. Indeed it can be an advantage for HF ionospheric propagation, not only because of the potentially low-angle radiation (over good ground) of the vertical component but also in reducing fading (polarization diversity) so perhaps we should not worry overmuch (and possibly in some cases even welcome) the radiation from the feeder in this form of Windom-type antenna.

In fact, Bill Wright, G0FAH reports finding a

66ft (half-size) version of the Fig 3(d) type of multiband Windom/VS1AA a useful antenna that can be arranged to be used, without an ATU, on 21MHz as well as on 7, 14 and 28MHz simply by using a resonant length of 300Ω ribbon feeder and then swapping on 21MHz a different ratio balun transformer.

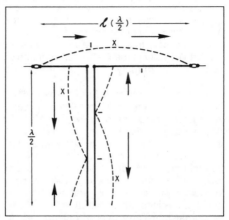

Fig 4: Using his 'square-counting' procedure (760 squares for both horizontal and vertical portions) G6XN considers that with the one-third off-centre-fed Windom/VS1AA of the dimensions shown, vertically-polarized radiation from the 300Ω twin-wire feeder would be about equal to that from the horizontal element.

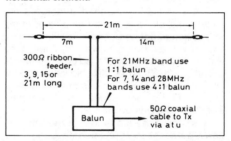

Fig 5: G0FAH's multi-band Windom/VS1AA antenna which on 21MHz uses the 300Ω ladder feeder as a quarter-wave impedance transformer to provide a match to the coaxial cable with a 1:1 balun, but is used on 7, 14 and 28MHz with a step-down balun. Without an ATU it should be possible to obtain a VSWR of 2:1 or better on each of the four bands, although a simple non-critical tuner (eg T or L network) can be used to adjust the VSWR to unity. Adjusting the feeder length a few centimetres may be required for optimum match on 21MHz. Best results were obtained using toroid-type coax baluns as described in *RadCom* March 1982, using two TVI ferrite rings taped together and then wound with RG58 cable. G0FAH advises coating the ribbon feeder with car polish to waterproof it since this reduces VSWR changes in wet weather.

G0FAH writes: "I have, like many experimenters, tried all manner of bits of wire in the search for that elusive 'all-band' antenna, but feel we need to consider just what we mean by 'all-band'. Given that most of what we call 'wire antennas' (ie ignoring quad-type and VK2ABQ-type arrays) are non-rotatable and, for the lower HF frequencies well under a half-wave above ground, we seldom have much control over where signals from it will be directed. 'Gain' is only worthwhile if it happens to be directed towards the distant station which we wish to contact. We do, however, have some control over how well the antenna system matches our transmitters and make it easier to do away with the need for an ATU - or at least not have to put up with critical ATU adjustments in order to meet the requirements of fussy black-boxes as well as operating convenience.

"Thus virtually all multiband wire antennas concentrate more on attempting to achieve a good 50Ω match on as many bands as possible, taking 'pot-luck' on the question of radiation lobes. My version of the Windom is no different in this respect. It presents a good match on four bands, and with the use of a wide-range ATU could be made to function on at least some of the other HF bands.

"As shown in **Fig 5**, it is a 'half-size' Windom of the December Fig 3(d) type, fed one-third from the end with balanced 300Ω slotted feeder. With a 4:1 balun this can be transformed to 75Ω unbalanced co-axial cable, providing a reasonable match on 7, 14 and 28MHz regardless of the length of the 300Ω line.

"On 21MHz the 'top' is three half-waves long and the feedpoint is at the junction of two of these half-waves, in other words a high-impedance point which can be transformed down to a low-impedance by making the feeder an odd number of electrical quarter-wavelengths. With slotted ribbon feeder having a velocity factor of about 0.85 this means the feeder can be 3, 9, 15 or 21m long, using a 1:1 balun on 21MHz.

"I put up this antenna using 9m of feeder and measured 2:1 or less VSWR on each band, swapping baluns when changing to the 21MHz band. A simple L-network ATU was used to get spot-on matching without restricting the good bandwidth. A useful solution to the multiband problem, although as a true experimenter since superseded with a bi-directional Lazy-H 21MHz antenna giving some 5.5dB gain towards the USA (though also to Italy)."

DANGER HIGH VOLTAGES

IN THESE DAYS OF 12V solid-state rigs, there exists the problem that many of the present generation of radio amateurs have never worked with valve equipment having a DC HT rail of anywhere from about 250V up to possibly 2kV, or even 3kV for the full-legal-limit-plus linear amplifiers, and with 240V AC mains and the transformed-up AC voltages all within the 'works'. It is rightly the practice in most articles describing valve amplifiers to draw readers' attention to the risks involved when working on or adjusting such equipment when not fully enclosed.

Since the most serious risks arise from current (of even a few mA) flowing near the heart and causing fibrillation, it has traditionally been the practice to advise those working on high-voltage equipment to keep one hand in their pocket and not to wear headphones or personal jewellery such as rings (equally important with 12V vehicle battery supplies since a short-circuit of such a battery through a ring or metal watch strap etc can cause very serious burns). As ancient doggerel lore puts it: "Volts jolts, mils kills". High RF voltages, which will be present in an ATU, tuned feeder, antenna etc even if the rig is only fed from 12V or nicad batteries, can produce painful skin burns from quite low power transmitters.

So prudence and safety precautions are always in order, particularly if other people (or pets) have access to any 'live' parts of an installation. But, nevertheless, it would surely

WIDE-TUNING-RANGE VXCO

THE ITEM 'Variable ceramic-resonator oscillators' in the February *TT* showed that it is possible to shift frequency by up to about 70kHz with a 375pF variable capacitor and a 3.58MHz low-cost resonator. But, as noted then, such an oscillator, although capable of giving a good, clean and stable output, will not have the same low temperature-coefficient that can be expected from an AT-cut quartz crystal with a suitable zero-temperature-coefficient turn-over point.

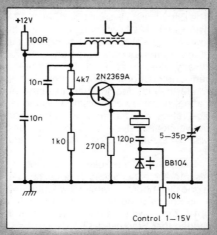

Fig 6: Series-resonant voltage-controlled crystal oscillator. Two similar oscillators are used by G3MEV at 20MHz and 21.4MHz.

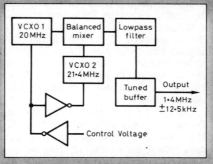

Fig 7: Block diagram of G3MEV's heterodyne VXCO providing an output at 1.4MHz +/- 12.5KHz.

Crystals, which are designed to work into a specific capacitance loading (usually about 30pF), oscillate at a frequency

that can be pulled only a modest amount by means of a variable capacitance; mechanical or electronic tuning diode. This can be extended by adding inductance, but even so this tends to degrade the signal after a few kHz. In the March *Radio Communication*, PA0KSB showed how, by using a VXO as a timing reference for a huff and puff type stabiliser, it is possible to achieve a highly stable oscillator working over several hundred kHz; but this is undoubtedly a rather complex approach.

Chris Cory, G3MEV, has devised a much simpler 'heterodyne' VCXO which, in his prototype model, achieves a required frequency swing of 25kHz (1.4MHz +/- 12.5kHz). He writes: "There are many occasions when an oscillator is required having the conflicting requirements of crystal stability and VFO tuneability. My solution has none of the disadvantages of synthesizers or VFOs, providing a wide-tuning-range voltage-controlled-crystal-oscillator (VCXO):

"The basic concept is an old one, using two high-frequency oscillators mixed together, to produce a much lower output frequency. For my particular application, one crystal frequency is nominally 20MHz and the other 21.4MHz, producing a required frequency of 1.4MHz.

"**Fig 6** shows the standard series-resonant circuit configuration used for both oscillators. This permitted pulling either crystal by 12.5kHz with a variable 3-35pF capacitance. By simultaneously pulling the two crystals in opposite directions, a range of more than 25kHz can easily be realised. Pulling is achieved by using varicap diodes (BB104), driven from opposing polarity voltage sources. A pair of 741 op-amps provide the required swings of 1-15V and 15-1V, with the advantage of keeping the varicap control line at low driving impedance. A block outline of the complete arrangement is shown in **Fig 7**.

"A suitable differential capacitor might do the job equally well, but bear in mind that stray capacitance is the biggest enemy of crystal-pulling. I have not attempted to explore an ultimate design and it is quite possible that the tuning range could be extended by a significant factor."

be a sad day if amateurs came to believe that all high-voltage equipment is 'too hot to handle'. Most of us who grew up in the valve era have known the painful experience of getting a finger or hand across 350V, 500V or even 750V DC. I can vouch for the fact that the experience, particularly if your skin is at all damp, leaves one extremely shaken and most reluctant to repeat the experience. *[Me too - Ed]*

But I cannot help feeling that one author in *Practical Wireless* (April 1991), in describing his reconstructed version of a 1953 *PW* design of a transmitter-receiver using a 6V6GT valve as a crystal power-oscillator, and 6K7GT/6SJ7/6V6GT 'straight' 1-V-1 (one RF stage/regenerative detector/one AF stage)

receiver, with both transmitter and receiver powered from a 250V HT line, goes rather over the top, in respect of a rig giving an RF output of only about 3-4W. He states: "A potentially hazardous problem is that **VERY HIGH VOLTAGES** (sic) are present in the unit. Under certain conditions RF voltages of up to 1000V peak-to-peak may be present."

Not much to argue with that, but then he goes on to write: "This level of voltage and frequency can 'jump' *several centimetres* (my italics) to 'earthed' fingers and knuckles. This is a particular hazard if you are wearing a ring. I'm speaking from experience, and I know this type of RF burn can take many months to heal."

Yes, very unwise to wear a ring, but can

anybody seriously believe that 1000V p-p from a 3-5W transmitter can really 'jump' several centimetres? This is in an equipment with a pi-network tank circuit having a receiver-type 350pF variable capacitor with plates less than one millimetre apart?

An old rule-of-thumb figure given in Reference Data for Radio Engineers suggests that (at sea level) it takes about 30kV (up to 300MHz) to break down a spark gap of 1cm. Even with a needle gap 1kV would 'jump' less than 1mm and much less than that between smooth or rounded surfaces! If one accepted the author's statements at their face value, the variable capacitors for high-power linears would need to be truly gigantic!

Don't get me wrong though, his 3.5MHz simple valve rig makes an interesting project for anyone wishing to try their hand at valve equipment similar to what many of us once cut our teeth on. Though old-timers may smile at the apparent surprise of author or editor in finding that "valves still produce good results on 3.5MHz". It would be even more surprising if they didn't! More relevant though is the difficulty these days for those without well-stocked junk boxes is finding high-voltage components and high-value variable capacitors.

THE MYSTERY OF THE DAH50

AN OBITUARY IN Nature (21 February) following the death on 30 January of John Bardeen who, late in 1947 at the Bell Labs, with W Brattain, discovered and named the transistor (he was twice the recipient of the Nobel prize for physics as he was also the 'B' of the BCS theory of superconductivity) commented: "It is impossible to overstate the importance of the transistor and the semiconductor physics which flowed from it. The developments far overshadow both nuclear fusion and fission and have unquestionably had the largest economic and social impact of any idea in modern physics."

It may seem oddly perverse that so many remain fascinated by the history and lingering applications of the pre-transistor thermionic valve with its wasteful filament or heater and the high voltages applied to the anode. I can offer no theory why this should be so - but there is plenty of evidence that, like the enthusiasm for steam trains, it exists.

Not all valves were designed to run from high voltages, at least for small-signal applications. In the late 1950s both Mullard (Philips) and Brimar marketed multi-electrode valves that could run directly from 12V car batteries. They were used in a number of 'hybrid' car-radio receivers with an early power transistor (usually OC16) as audio output stage. The Mullard series included ECH83, EBF83 with 6.3V heaters that could be wired in series-parallel and served as frequency changers, IF amplifiers, AF amplifiers etc. The Brimar range included the 12AC6, 12AD6, 12AE6 with 12V heaters. By combining these low-voltage valves with a transistor output stage, there was no requirement for vibrators or any other form of DC-DC inverter. The reducing cost of transistors, however, soon made 'hybrid' designs unnecessary, and I cannot recall anybody using these low-voltage valves for amateur radio, although some conventional valves would oscillate or provide voltage-amplification with an HT of around 15V.

Recently Dr Tom Going, in connection with his interest in the history of radio, has raised a question about an earlier low-voltage valve - the Philips diode-heptode type DAH50 with 1.4V 25mA twin filaments: Who was it intended for? Who used it?

He has discovered that this diode-heptode "with space-charge grid" was included in a 1943 wartime Philips (Dutch-language) data book, appearing also as "obsolete" in Vol III of the English-language Philips Industries Data & Circuits of Receiver and Amplifier Valves (1st supplement, 1949). Yet he cannot trace anyone who remembers this valve or knows whether it was ever used in portable receivers, or ever got beyond prototype development stage. It was not a 'miniature' like the later D-series valves.

The space-charge grid apparently allowed the valve to operate effectively with an HT rail of just 15V and it is claimed that it performed satisfactorily up to 50MHz. The data book includes details of a two-valve receiver covering the medium-waveband (200 - 600 metres) for headphone use with the filaments (one diode not used) consuming 75mA at 1.4V, and HT consumption 6mA at 15V. The circuit diagram (Fig 8) shows a 'reflex' arrangement with the first heptode used for both RF and AF amplification and with regeneration applied to the RF amplifier giving a sensitivity such that a 30μV input signal could give satisfactory reception, enabling the listener to receive a large number of broadcast stations even when only a few yards of wire was used as an antenna.

With broadcast receivers largely impounded in Holland during the German occupation, such receivers would have been extremely useful for clandestine listening, broadcast or HF CW or even for two-way working, if supplies were ever smuggled out of the Philips Eindhoven factories. Valves and components were smuggled out of Philips by the Underground but I have never seen any reference to the use of the DAH50 in this, or indeed any other connection. If anybody knows anything about this valve, I would be happy to pass the information to Dr Going.

Tom Going has also pointed out that in TT, September 1989, in describing the interesting history of the classic EF50 that played an important part in wartime radar receivers, I inadvertently misinterpreted two successive paragraphs of M Cosgrove's paper "The Contribution of Pye to Television History" with the result that I wrongly stated that the EF50 valves were made in the UK by up to 14,000 'out-workers' in local villagers and individual homes to minimise possible disruption from air raids. Re-reading Cosgrove's paper it is clear that it was Pye equipment that was assembled by out-workers. Production of the EF50 in the UK was, in fact, begun by Mullard at Mitcham and subsequently also at Blackburn, both large plants and decidedly not 'home-brew'.

HERE AND THERE

NEVILLE PAUL, G3AUB, has been quite surprised to hear the Australian HF beacon AUS1MLB (see TT, January) on all five frequencies quite regularly morning and after-

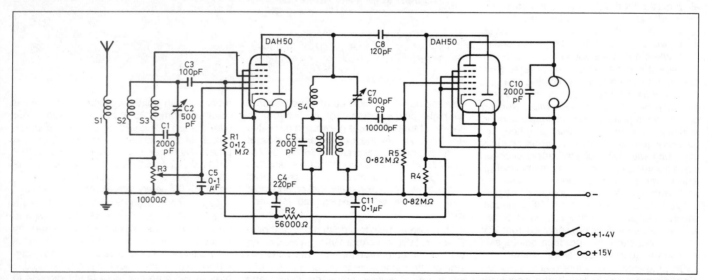

Fig 8: Circuit diagram of the reflex-type, two DAH50 medium-wave battery receiver with 15V HT. The first DAH50 is used for both RF (regenerative) and AF amplification, with the diode of the second DAH50 forming the demodulator as shown in Philips application data book. The DAH50, unlike the later D-series valves, was not a 'miniature' valve and had an octal-type base.

AN UP-GRADE FOR THE SIMPLE SUPERHET

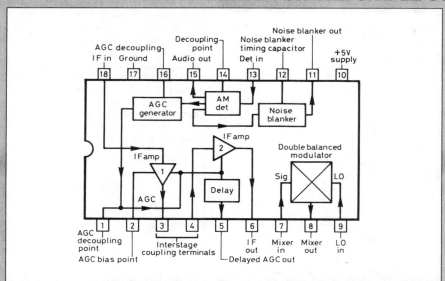

Fig 9: Block diagram of the Plessey SL6700 subsystem IC used as the heart of both the G3TSO simple superhet and the high dynamic range 3.5MHz receiver designed by G3RZP and described by W1FB in *QST* (April 1981).

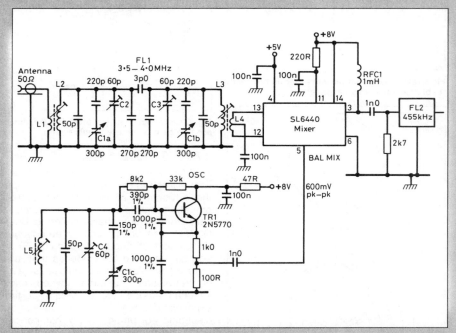

Fig 10: Circuit diagram of the front-end of the high-dynamic range receiver which was based around the then new Plessey complex ICs type SL6440 (doubly-balanced mixer) and SL6700 subsystem IC.

THE LOW-COST, simple-to-build 3.5MHz SSB/CW superhet receiver outlined by G3TSO (*TT*, November 1990, pp28-29 with feedback correction in the January issue) uses a Signetics/Philips NE602 IC frequency-converter with in-built local oscillator and buffer stage as front-end, with a band-pass RF fixed-tuned input filter. While there is no doubt that such an arrangement can provide a most useful simple receiver/transceiver, the dynamic range will inevitably be less than that of the latest generation of factory-built receivers/transceivers, although capable of superior results to the usual simple direct-conversion receivers.

One of the key components of the G3TSO design is the Plessey SL6700 subsystem IC which includes two IF amplifiers, a double-balanced modulator (as product detector), noise blanker, AM detector and AGC generator: **Fig 9**.

The G3TSO design reminded Peter Chadwick, G3RZP of a receiver that, with Doug De Maw, W1FB, was developed and described in *QST* ('Receiving with Plessey ICs' April 1981) almost a decade ago. It also used the then new SL6700, but featured a high dynamic-range front-end based on the SL6440 doubly-balanced mixer with separate 2N5770 bipolar transistor as the local oscillator, and a ganged-tuned 3.5 to 4.0MHz RF input filter. This resulted in a rather more complex and higher-cost arrangement than the G3TSO design, the complete receiver using four ICs and three bipolar transistors. Like the G3TSO design, a 455kHz ceramic SSB filter was followed by the SL6700, in this case with an external 455kHz IF transformer coupling between the two IF amplifiers. A second 455kHz transformer, rather than a ceramic resonator, was used for BFO.

Fig 10 shows the G3RZP/W1FB front-end capable of much higher dynamic range performance than the NE602/bandpass RF filter approach. W1FB reported that he was able to copy an RST569 CW signal only 5kHz away from the ARRL's 1kW W1AW station about 'two blocks' (about a quarter-mile) distant. Substitution of this front-end in the G3TSO design should result in a high-performance 3.5MHz receiver.

noon. His antenna is an untuned 250ft wire about 35ft above ground running East/West, but he finds the 14.4MHz transmission often "impossible" due to a very strong multitone transmission. He points out that there appears to be a keyer fault with the result that the 'dash' of the 'U' in the callsign is not transmitted so that it appears AI S1MLB.

Ian Hamilton, GM3CSM, was stirred by the *TT* (March) item about G5PQ's unfortunate experience with 90° coaxial elbow connectors to check his own stock of PL259 adaptors and was relieved they all showed continuity of 0.1Ω or better, even after mistreating them by dropping them about 2m onto the floor. His bear the legend "M359 CQA49192" and have

given many years of trouble-free use, although he has found that the pins do require wiping now and then with Electrolube or similar cleaning solvent/lubricator. Before putting them in service, he cleans the threads of both male and female ends with some Electrolube on a stiff brush.

He also considers it pays to check that the mating serrations are actually in mesh by backing off the locking ring about half a turn, then turning the plug/socket adaptor body by hand. If it moves it is not 'in mesh' (seated) and when it does it will be possible to screw the locking ring tighter and then the body will not move! A final check with a ohmmeter results in peace of mind, since he is not

prepared to attack any of his stock with a hacksaw! John W Rhind draws attention to an item in *IEE News* concerning the colour coding of protective earths (PE) and functional earths (FE) such as those used for telecommunications and radio communication equipment. This notes that the provision of FEs is discussed in BS6701, Part 1, 1990 *Installation of apparatus intended for connection to certain telecommunication systems, Part 1: General recommendations.* This recommends that FE wires and cables should be coloured cream so that installers do not mistake an FE for a PE as described in the *IEE Wiring Regulations (15th edition).* A new 16th edition of the Wiring Regulations is due soon.

VHF D/F LOOP WITH INTEGRAL SENSING

TT HAS RECENTLY carried (September 1990, March & April 1991) a series of items on 144MHz direction-finding and it may seem that this was enough for the time being. However, an article "Precision direction finding antennas" by Son and Tho Le-Ngoc (Memorial University, Newfoundland and Concordic University, Montreal) in *IEEE Trans on Consumer Electronics*, November 1990, pp918-921, captured the interest of both Peter Chadwick, G3RZP, and myself. This describes a novel VHF D/F antenna that combines a half-wave loop (**Fig 1**) with an integral quarter-wave monopole (sensing) antenna to provide a cardioid reception pattern with a single sharp null and so avoiding the usual sense ambiguity (**Fig 1(b)**) of a conventional loop.

Apparently, such antennas have been marketed in Canada for several years for such applications as wildlife and animal tracking, aircraft emergencies etc. It is pointed out that a complete VHF D/F antenna weighing less than half a pound can be constructed from materials costing less than $10.

In essence, the antenna shown in **Fig 2** comprises a half-wave loop antenna with a quarter-wave shield acting as the sensing antenna. The shield also acts as a quarter-wave stub to match the antenna. The authors write: "The antenna is simply made by using a piece of 50Ω coaxial cable. By trimming off the shield, the return loss of 18 to 20dB can be achieved. The forward pattern is very broad although the front-to-back ratio is excellent with deep nulls in the rear hemisphere. As the operating frequency is increased the patterns tend to become broader, but they retain their good front-to-back ratio and deep nulls in the rear hemisphere."

Construction and testing is described as follows:

(1) Cut coaxial cable to a desired length. Mark the loop length, ie a half wavelength, and lightly cut the shielding braid off, but not the insulation.
(2) Push the shielding braid out to one end until a quarter wavelength is exposed.
(3) The shielding braid is cut and soldered to the inner conductor as in Fig 2.
(4) Put a connector to the other end of the coaxial cable, and the antenna is now ready for the return loss test.
(5) The antenna can be easily tuned by trimming the shielding braid.
(6) After having achieved the return loss test, the loop support and the handle may be made by using plastic tubing as **Fig 3**.

Some points arise from the earlier items on VHF direction-finders. First an apology for not realising that the *Radio-ZS* diagram of the PCB for the hand-held Doppler switch had been wrongly reproduced and should have been the mirror-image of that shown with the ground-plane on the component-side. (No excuses since Derek Cole, who redrew the diagram, queried it but I advised him to keep it the same as in the South African journal!) I understand that corrected PCB's are now available from Badger Boards. Also the FETs are BF982 not BP982.

Clive Mott-Gotobed, G4ODM, has constructed two of the DEF Sniffer receivers (*TT*,

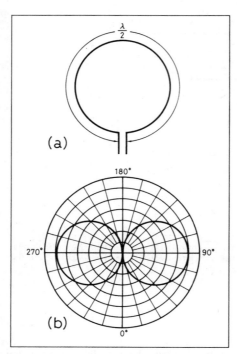

Fig 1: (a) Conventional half-wave loop antenna with (b) bidirectional radiation pattern.

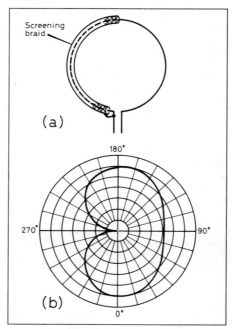

Fig 2: (a) The Canadian "precision D/F antenna" with (b) single deep null.

March 1991) using the additional information in the original *Radio-ZS* journal "with great success", plus some enhancements to improve sensitivity etc. On the other hand, he cannot achieve a sensible reception pattern from his attempt to construct the earlier MEF antenna. I am aware that at least one successful copy has been made in the UK but cannot recall the constructor's name/callsign. I feel certain that G4ODM ('Cherry Trees', 17

Reading Road, Chineham, Basingstoke, Hants RG24 0LN) would be glad to exchange notes with anyone who has made the antenna work as described, but has not yet tackled the sniffer receiver. G4ODM is Chairman of the Basingstoke ARC, a club that holds 144MHz foxhunts although they specifically exclude the use of Doppler equipment, primarily to stop the taking of bearings on the move. Personally I feel that this should not rule out the use of the hand-held type of Doppler equipment described by ZS6EF (*TT*, April) although G4ODM does point out some disadvantages in this approach.

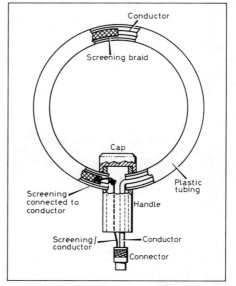

Fig 3: Construction of the precision D/F antenna assembled in protective plastic tubing.

SAFE SOLDERING

AS LONG AGO AS November 1979, a *TT* item 'Allergic to soldering?' drew attention to the advisability of carrying out soldering operations only in well-ventilated areas. This item came about when Dr Gerard Bulger, G3WIP, sent along a copy of an editorial in *The Lancet* (25 August 1979, pp397-8). The editorial reviewed the evidence that fumes given off by solder-fluxes could cause a form of troublesome asthma ('woodworker's asthma') among about 20-25% of those exposed to flux fumes in factories assembling electronic equipment. Many non-corrosive fluxes, including some cored solders, contain colophony which is the solid material remaining after turpentine has been distilled off pine resin (hence the connection with woodworking). I recall that, following publication of this item, one firm marketing cored solder pointed out that they had eliminated the problem of colophony, but I doubt whether this was done universally. I have no evidence that many amateurs now open their windows wider while soldering. Perhaps the full-length, detailed article 'Making soldering safer' by Bryan P Bergerone, MD, NU1N (*QST*, March 1991) will jolt more of us into taking sensible precautions. In his introductory note, he writes:

"Soldering is the centuries-old process of bonding metals through the use of a relatively low-melting-point metal, commonly a lead-tin amalgam, that *alloys* (binds) with the surfaces to be joined.

"The potential hazards associated with

soldering, aside from the obvious risk of thermal burns, arise from:-

(1) improper hygiene after contact with the lead and other metals in solder;

(2) inhalation of the smoke and fumes associated with soldering;

(3) inhalation of the thermal-breakdown products of wiring and component insulation; and

(4) direct contact with, as well as inhalation of fumes from, solvents used to remove the residue from soldered connections."

NU1N reviews two of the more common medical manifestations associated with soldering, namely asthma and, to a lesser extent, lead poisoning. Persistent asthma (ie not 'woodworker's asthma') induces attacks of shortness of breath, often accompanied by coughing and wheezing. It is due to an inherited, abnormally elevated sensitivity of the air passages to certain substances that results in a generally reversible partial obstruction. About 1% of the population has asthma.

Non-corrosive organic fluxes, as used for electronic soldering, commonly contain colophony, a pine resin with an active ingredient, abietic acid, NU1N points out, adding: "Reaction to solder-flux fumes can be immediate and pronounced. In a factory in England, 20% of workers exposed to solder flux fumes developed wheezing and breathlessness. (S Burge *et al* 'Occupational Asthma in an Electronics Factory' Thorax 34 (1979) pp13-18)".

NU1N also discusses the problem of lead poisoning as well as fumes from the heating of wire and component insulation: "Heating insulated wires during soldering releases toxic fumes. PVC begins to break down at 176°F (80°C) releasing hydrogen chloride, benzene, toluene and other irritants. Toluene di-isoryanate, an established asthmatic agent, has been shown to be generated from soldering polyurethane-coated wires. Fumes from soldering Teflon-insulated wires may also cause polymer fume fever." Remember that if you can smell soldering fumes, you're certainly breathing them. However, NU1N stresses that soldering safely is simple: "Any tool or product, if used improperly, is potentially dangerous. By observing simple precautions you can keep soldering a safe and enjoyable part of the amateur radio experience."

● Properly ventilate your work area - so that you or those around cannot smell fumes from your soldering. Preferably ensure a flow of air between two windows. Using a fan may expose others to an unreasonably high level of 'secondary soldering' fumes.

● Wash your hands after soldering and before handling food and smoking materials.

● Minimise direct contact with flux and flux solvents.

A few final points: For the amateur using a relatively low-temperature soldering iron, the main threat of lead poisoning lies not in inhaling lead vapours, but in handling solder. If the ventilation has to be poor, it may be advisable to use a cartridge-based respiratory system, which functions and looks much like a military gas mask (a simple dust mask is not suitable).

If you suffer from asthma, other than flux-induced symptoms, a respirator fitted with suitable cartridge that can absorb solder fumes, should be regarded as *mandatory*.

[see page 39 of last month's RadCom for more soldering safety points - Ed]

AGC - STILL A DIFFICULT TECHNIQUE

AS SOMEONE INTERESTED primarily in CW operation using headphones, I have never been convinced of any essential need for AGC in HF receivers, believing strongly that no AGC is better than poor AGC, and depending on audio-limiting by back-to-back diodes to protect my ears. It gives one a sense of being in control of the receiver when occasionally making manual adjustment to RF-gain controls! However, I recognise that most operators, even on CW, would regard this approach as a cop out - and would not today contemplate using a receiver that does not provide AGC for SSB and CW.

Unfortunately, there is far more to achieving really satisfactory AGC for these modes than many of those who produce 'black boxes' seem to appreciate even now, some 60 years after the original appearance of 'AVC' in broadcast receivers, and more than 50 years since the Germans showed how, by using switched time-constants and by reducing the leakage of the BFO signals into the IF stages, it is possible to provide quite effective AGC for CW and SSB.

In *TT* (April) LA8AK described a circuit for obtaining IF-derived rather than AF-derived AGC with the Plessey SL621 IC. This encouraged Peter Chadwick, G3RZP, to explain the background to this device, designed over 20 years ago. He writes:

"The original SL600 series was designed for use in a military radio in which an SL623 AM detector/RF-derived AGC/product detector operated in parallel with the SL621 AF-derived AGC. This meant that the RF-derived AGC was in action all the time, although the levels were arranged so that the AF-derived AGC 'took over' with rising output. When the level of the AF-derived AGC voltage fell, such as when the frequency of a single tone was low, the RF-derived AGC took over. The original multiple time-constant AF-derived AGC system (as opposed to W1DX's 'hang-

AGC' circuit) first saw the light of day in the Marconi Marine 'Pennant' channelised HF marine SSB receiver.

"The Pennant was a valved design of the early 1960's using, if I remember correctly, three E88CC twin-triode valves in the AGC circuit. Although I doubt if the IC designers were aware of the Pennant design, the SL621 is extremely close to being a solid-state version of the Pennant system. The Pennant also used a ring-bridge mixer with germanium diodes and achieved what, for its day, was a very good IMD performance.

"AF-derived AGC systems on their own (**Fig 4**) tend to suffer from a lot of faults. This is partly caused by the fact that as the input audio frequency drops, the response time must fall, while at frequencies below 10Hz, the phase shift in the AGC loop can lead to instability. Again, the lower input frequencies tend not to get well filtered, so some rectified AF gets on the AGC line, modulates the gain of the IF, and so increases the in-channel IMD. This was not so much a problem with valves, since the dB change per volt was so much less.

"However, putting RF-derived AGC in parallel gets round most of the problems. Probably much of the 'flak' that the SL621 has attracted can be traced to the simplified low-cost approach (originally exemplified by Brian Comer, G3ZVC - now KF6C - in not using the SL623 in parallel) being copied into areas where it is not the best approach. Incidentally, some of the much older applications information from Plessey showed the SL623 fed from a tuned circuit, thus reducing the amount of wideband noise hitting the AM and AGC detectors, as well as the product detector.

"One of the difficulties in using narrow filters at the back end of the IF chain (as in the 'roofing filter' approach) is the result of hitting the filters with a large amount of noise: this showed up in the case of the SL6700 where using a ceramic two-pole AM filter produced a very faint (but annoying) whistle down in the noise at the output, whereas a tuned circuit did not, since it did not 'ring'.

"In a simple SSB receiver operating linearly through to AF, the use of an AF low-pass-

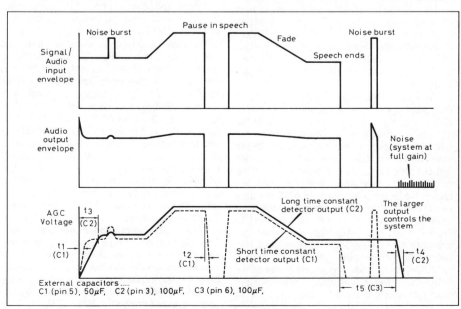

Fig 4: Dynamic response of an AF-derived AGC system controlled by an SL621C.

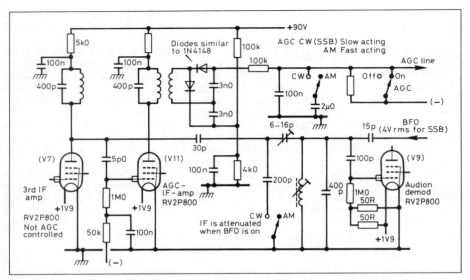

Fig 5: AGC/demodulator circuits of the German receiver type KW.E.a designed in 1939 with (a) two AGC time-constants; (b) IF signal to detector attenuated in CW position to achieve same audio level; and (c) 'modern' type use of diode AGC detector circuits. Unlike other communication receivers of this era the AGC function can be used for CW with the BFO switched on. German valve code RV2P800 indicates a 2V pentode amplifier valve with an amplification factor of 800. This receiver is considered by LA8AK as an excellent example of the designers really understanding the principles of receiver design - something he does not always find in modern receivers.

filter gets rid of the excess noise - a technique that was used very successfully with an LC filter in the KW2000CAT channelised HF transceiver.

"AGC systems often appear to be afterthoughts, whereas in reality they can be very difficult to design! Fast AGC systems with narrow IF filters can get really interesting because of the delay introduced in the filters, and some very fast AGC circuits used in certain Electronic Warfare applications end up using very complex and dedicated circuitry usable only in that specific equipment."

These notes from G3RZP should clear up some of the misconceptions about the SL620-21/SL1620/21 device, although I note that the useful notes on these devices in the Plessey *Radio Communications Handbook* (1977) make no mention of having an RF-derived AGC system in parallel with them. Nevertheless, as G3RZP points out:

"It's strange to realise in these days of new ICs every few minutes, that the SL600-series was designed in the mid-1960s. The SL521 logarithmic amplifier IC was designed about 1964 yet is still being designed into new equipments today, which must be some sort of record!"

Jan Martin Noeding, LA8AK is convinced that many of the currently available receivers exhibit strange faults that elude some of the reviews. He believes that some of the manufacturers, including Yaesu, tend to design new models adapted from earlier models without checking out fully the behaviour of the circuitry in the field rather than the test laboratory. He refers particularly to AGC circuitry which can continue to be used in successive models for many years without ascribing to the rules for good AGC as laid down, for example, by Professor U L Rohde, DJ2LR in various books and publications.

LA8AK writes: "My argument is that some firms have never understood the principal (and yet important) rules for how a good AGC system should operate and have not tried to understand that DC gain is not enough. Usually

they apply too high brute DC-gain, such that the AGC detector switches between on-and-off instead of performing like a linear element. DJ2LR considers that it is good practice to have a limiter function in the IF to limit, at 6dB above maximum normal IF level, although tests by LA7MI on his R-4C did not yield any significant results."

LA8AK describes how he modified a Collins 51-S valve receiver removing AGC from the final IF amplifier and providing a relay-switched reduction of the time-constant when receiving AM signals. But he considers that the "finest receiver I have used" is the German military receiver type KW.E.a (Kurzwellen Emfaenger Anton) designed in 1939. This has a 250.9kHz IF with LC filters having the selectivity variable in seven steps (with 250kHz BFO) and a further eighth step (same filter selectivity as the seventh step but with the BFO at 251.8kHz). The image rejection at 10MHz is specified as about 78dB despite the low IF. This is achieved by having either four or five (selectable) tuned pre-mixer stages.

He was surprised to discover that this vintage receiver has two AGC time constants, 'slow' for CW and 'fast' for AM. For CW (and for SSB) an IF-attenuator equalizes the audio for AM and CW, an arrangement which also reduces the BFO feedback to the AGC stage facilitating the use of AGC on CW (**Fig 5**) - a feature seldom, if ever, found in other receivers designed much before about 1960. LA8AK also comments favourably on the 'audion' demodulator used in the KW.E.a and a number of other German receivers which, in effect, was not subject to the poor, low-signal-performance of the usual AM diode envelope detector. He writes:

"The audion demodulator seems to have a fine 'capture' effect on the signal so that one can still hear (AM) broadcast stations in poor conditions when a conventional envelope detector has too little signal. The effect can be compared with modern PLL-AM demodulators (as experienced by SM6HYG).

"About ten years ago I was told that the

meteorological station at Tromsoe used these German receivers for many years but in 1960 replaced them with professional Collins receivers which worked extremely well as long as propagation conditions were reasonable but proved virtually useless during the severe magnetic storms experienced at this high latitude. The operators were forced to dig out and re-install the discarded German receivers. Some amateurs have criticised the KW.E.a for being so large and heavy (a criticism often levelled at the AR88 - G3VA) without appreciating that this receiver was never intended to be used in the field but only in fixed installations."

On the other hand, LA8AK still finds much to criticise in many relatively modern transceiver designs, including such models as the FT-7/FT-901/FT-902/FT-747 and other models of which he has had personal experience. He has been able to overcome, with relatively simple modifications, some of the problems such as keyclicks, RF-processor deficiencies etc and to make some improvement in the audio-quality of the FT-747 by removing from the circuit the 10nF 'chip' capacitor across the audio signal and similarly by changing C511 in the FT-7 from 1µF to 47nF (a similar modification applies also to the FT-901).

But he continues to wonder how so many operators can find pleasure in unmodified equipment with poor audio fidelity: "I do not like to operate a rig which causes a headache after using it for about half-an-hour. In contests, it is important to immediately understand the speech, often in a dialect or language to which one is not accustomed. Often I have problems talking to Danish amateurs (the TR-7010 and TS-700 have poor bass responses and it is desirable to insert a 47nF capacitor in series with the microphone) . . . . Why do so many reviewers (except G3SJX) so seldom report on annoying deficiencies? I can understand that amateurs, once they have bought equipment, being motivated by a desire to tell the world what good equipment they have chosen and glossing over the deficiencies, but this should not apply to reviewers".

COMBATING CORROSION

DICK BIDDULPH, G8DPS, in a short item in *TT* (April 1991, p34) drew attention to the need to avoid contact between copper and aluminium in antenna installations, in addition to other rust-prevention precautions such as the application of grease, lanolin or RTV silicone rubber.

This topic crops up also in a detailed article 'Combating corrosion in aerials' by Steve Henderson, ZL1AOC, (*Break-in*, November 1990, pp10-14) covering this important topic in depth. It is based in part on publications of the Building Research Association of New Zealand as well as drawing on examples of corrosion problems in both amateur-radio installations and in the more numerous VHF (Bands 1/III) TV-receiving aerials used in New Zealand, including wideband log-periodic arrays. Most populated areas in New Zealand have a marine atmosphere, with high concentrations of chloride-containing sea salt aerosol (which, like the sulphur dioxide of industrial atmospheres, promotes corrosion).

It should be appreciated that all corrosion involves electcrolytic processes, including that produced by coupling dissimilar metals or by the existence of different concentrations of dissolved salts or gases in the electrolyte at different parts of the metal surface.

In his opening paragraph, ZL1AOC stresses: "All unprotected metal surfaces (except the few 'noble' metals such as gold and platinum) corrode or oxidize to some degree. How long this takes before it becomes a problem very much depends on the working environment. All too often one hears of an antenna where the telescoping tubes of an expensive Yagi array can no longer be adjusted, or a trap in an element has disintegrated. Not only are amateur radio antennas involved; domestic television aerials can also give a great deal of trouble. Antennas are costly items which, with a little effort, can be given good protection that will extend their life."

He lists some typical examples of problems commonly encountered: tinned-copper braided pigtail connections from a balun to a wire dipole completely disintegrated; aluminium-alloy bolts terminating the wire connections to traps in a wire dipole corroded to the extent that some had fractured; telescoping tubes of a Yagi corroded and seized, offering high resistance between sections; element mounting bolts of TV aerials rusted with corrosion to the extent that an element may fall off after only a few months use; two-piece element clamps of diecast metal corroded so that the element sections no longer provide a continuous electrical path. He writes:

"Amateur-radio antenna arrays can have a large number of tubular sections, many of them being required to have telescoping adjustable sections. If these are not protected when they are assembled, it will be impossible to dismantle them at some later date. Hardware supplied with some arrays is electro-plated; with others, stainless steel is provided. The preference is always to use stainless steel hardware on this type of antenna. It is a point worth exploring if one is contemplating purchasing a new antenna."

He stresses that rust is always a problem with hardware, both in the antennas and in the supporting structure. Not only is it a progressive action in reducing the mechanical strength of bolted points but the corrosion also produces a rectifier, leading to the 'rusty bolt' effect and possible EMC problems.

In a section: 'Improving the durability of an antenna', ZL1AOC writes:

"In assembling an antenna for the first time, or after repairs, care should be taken to prepare all sections to prevent the entry of water. If a telescoping section is involved, all signs of corrosion should be cleaned off the metal. The sections should be liberally coated with grease or better still with one of the anti-corrosive compounds. When the position of the sliding joint is finally determined, the surplus compound should be cleaned off and the joint wrapped to seal it completely with a self-amalgamating tape. If you have access to a hot air gun then the joints could be covered with heat-shrink tubing. In assembling the antenna elements to traps or on to a boom, all the nuts, bolts, washers and clamps should be completely coated with a suitable compound. The presence of the compound in a joint does not introduce any electrical discontinuity between sections. There are always sufficient surface imperfections on the metal that maintain contact when a joint is secured with the clamping system. Grease is not entirely suitable in this application as it will weather and finally wash off.

"Always ensure that drain-holes in traps and other components are clear and face the ground, so that any water that may penetrate the trap will drain away. Element tubes with open ends should be plugged to prevent water gaining entry.

"An expensive TV aerial is worth treating before it is first installed (Most of this advice applies to any VHF/UHF antenna - G3VA). All the connecting joints, mounting clamps and hardware should be thoroughly coated with a compound before assembly. If it has been in use for some time and is being reconditioned, have a good look at the hardware. It could have been electro-galvanized and is almost certain to be rusted. Replacement hardware should be stainless steel. Providing the new hardware is given protection it should not give any trouble in future years. It is important to ensure the compound is worked into all crevices at the joint points.

"In one location with a marine atmosphere, an antenna was successfully protected by carefully wrapping all the joints with Denso plumbing tape (a messy process due to the compound on the tape but providing good long-term treatment). The action of covering the joints with an anti-corrosion compound or taping it prevents the moisture-laden solutions reaching the metal and provides a barrier to prevent corrosion taking place.

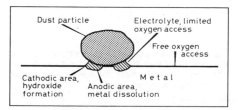

Fig 6: Differential aeriation cell illustrating the role of oxygen in the corrosion process.

"Corrosion is frequently found on die-cast components, including the clamps and die-cast casing of rotators. In one case, the unit was dismantled and the case sections and clamps sand blasted to remove the corrosion and then sent for powder coating. This has the same function as a wet paint application but is tougher and more durable. Outdoor use requires that coatings must be capable of withstanding weathering under all conditions. The coating best able to cope is based on polyester powder. It is necessary to dismantle items to enable the treatment to be carried out, as the coating needs to be oven cured, in some cases at up to 160°C. Powder coating is a specialist application which requires consultation with an expert associated with aluminium joinery components."

ZL1AOC lists a number of materials used for corrosion protection available in New Zealand. He is particularly keen on Lanacote MSG based on 'woolgrease' and presumably a local proprietary form of the lanolin recommended by G8DPS. Other products he lists include Naolox (anti-oxidant preparation for use as a joint compound, particularly with aluminium joints); Corium 89, an aluminium cleaner for removing microscopic corrosion film from stainless steel and aluminium; Corium 209, an aluminium sealer capable of protecting aluminium from chemical action; Denso or Protector Industrial Tape; Polyisobutylene (PIB) self-amalgamating tape which is moisture and ozone resistant (if a rubber self-amalgamating tape is used, finally wrap the joint with good quality PVC tape). Liquid water on the metal surface is needed for corrosion to occur, while oxygen has a special role in atmospheric corrosion because it acts as acceptor of the electrons lost by the metal during corrosion. Atmospheric corrosion usually ceases in the absence of oxygen. However, different concentrations of oxygen at points on a surface, such as inside and outside a crevice, can provide the driving force needed for corrosion. This is termed a differential aeration cell: **Fig 6**.

SMALL MAY BE BEAUTIFUL BUT BIGGER CAN BE BETTER

THE REFERENCE BY LA8AK to the size and weight of the KW.E.a receiver of 1939 (or the AR88 of 1941) struck a chord to which I can respond. As someone whose height is almost exactly one-metre-plus-one-yard (there's a mixture of measurements) and with fingers (and feet) to match, I have never been much attracted to the Tiny Tim scale of current amateur-radio equipment, although fully recognising its attraction for mobile or portable operation. Indeed, the pressure on manufacturers to reduce size is partly a desire to have commonality between mobile and base equipment and partly to economise on enclosures etc. I like my equipment to be large and fairly heavy, with good-sized knobs and switches, with meters that follow my keying, and cabinets that emit the gentle hum of transformer laminations! And free from a massed phalanx of miniature switches.

The consumer-electronics industry is only gradually responding to the growing dislike ('technifear') of over-complex and often confusing (except to the very young) controls. Video recorders so easily set to record the wrong programme on the wrong channel at the wrong time. Teletext units that remain little used. Digital car radios . . . .

Consider the following extract from a letter from a Mike Rogers in *New Scientist* (6 April 1991): "Previously, it was simple, while driving, to cope with two big knobs and six decent-sized push buttons to get a useful selection of (broadcast) stations. Now one is faced with several, barely identifiable minuscule buttons packed side by side or on top of one another. You read the manual - which is nearly as thick as the one describing the car - and try to memorise which button is for what. Then you drive up a motorway at night-time and are left feeling nervously for the said badly illuminated buttons on a radio usually placed at the bottom of the centre console. The discipline of good ergonomics seems to have flown out of the window."

VARIABLE SELECTIVITY AND SIDEBANDS

DAVE LUNN, G3LSL, while browsing through a box of old radio magazines he had been given, came across a fascinating article by the great Professor E V Appleton (discoverer of the 'F' (Appleton) layer of the ionosphere) 'The physical reality of sidebands' (*Wireless World*, March 19, 1930, pp299-300). This was subtitled 'A reply to the Heretics' and was a devastating reply to those who still, in 1930, refused to accept that sidebands really existed and were not just a mathematical concept. The heretics included not only Sir Ambrose Fleming, Baird and his supporters (who believed that television of entertainment value could be transmitted in the medium-wave band without creating chaos) but also Dr Robinson who believed that his 'stenode' receiver, incorporating a single-crystal filter with top-boost, would permit broadcasting stations to be packed together with minimal frequency separation.

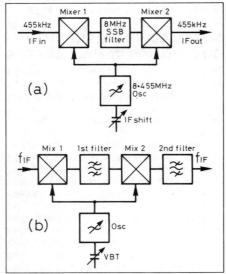

Fig 7: (a) IF shift positions the IF passband but does not change the overall selectivity. (b) The use of a second filter variably aligned with the first filter provides variable bandwidth tuning.

One of the speciously powerful arguments used by the heretics was that it is possible to listen to the harmonics of a broadcast station without the audio frequencies being doubled as they avowed they would be if they really existed at the fundamental. As the professor pointed out, they overlooked the fact that modulation is essentially a mixing process which, as every user of SSB appreciates, can be used to heterodyne a modulated signal to another frequency without affecting the audio-band frequencies. The harmonics are, in fact, themselves generated in the mixing process as unwanted products.

Today, we accept the physical reality of sidebands without question - after all they can be displayed clearly on a spectrum analyser. But this means that, if in an SSB receiver, you strictly limit the bandwidth to say 300 - 2500Hz in a 2.2kHz filter having a shape factor approaching unity, then the audio response of an accurately tuned receiver is inevitably limited to about 300-2500Hz which is bound to reduce intelligibility (as well as making it sound rather unpleasant) to some degree, even for male voices. A 2.7kHz filter sounds

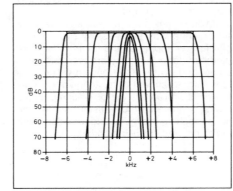

Fig 9: Selectivity curves of the EKO7-80 filter at bandwidths of +/-0.15, +/-0.30, +/-0.75, +/-1.5, +/-3.0 and +/-6.0kHz. Note the similar slope at all settings right down to -70dB.

a little better, but there is still much to be said for having some degree of variable selectivity or bandwidth options that enables an operator to take advantage of band conditions and extend the audio response up to say 4-5kHz when the band is less crowded. For AM broadcast reception of reasonable quality music, the bandwidth needs to be around 12kHz (+/- 6kHz) and even then not to roll off too sharply.

In *QST* (March 1991) David Newkirk, WJ1Z, reminds us of several "Transceiver features that help you beat interference" (more concerned with narrowing than widening the response) including passband tuning (IF shift) and variable bandwidth tuning (VBT), both of which are outlined in **Fig 7**. A de-luxe version of VBT (requiring four extra mixers instead of two) was described in *TT* way back in December, 1969, based on a Rohde & Schwartz professional receiver using their EKO7-80 filter in which two high-grade low-pass-filters at 30kHz, using inductors rather than crystals, were so arranged that they provided a *bandpass* filter, acting on both upper and lower sidebands (**Fig 8**).

As shown in **Fig 9** this filter had an excellent shape factor, giving a bandwidth continuously adjustable from +/-6kHz down to +/-150Hz with substantially similar slope right down to -70dB at all settings, presumably without introducing the non-linearities and limited dynamic range that are seemingly inherent in crystal filters.

This was indeed a deluxe, high-cost system but one suspects that today somewhat similar characteristics might be just about achievable using digital filtering techniques.

For those who believe that there are still new ideas to be explored with analogue technology, I pass along an intriguing though untested idea sent in by Mike Powell, G3IJE as the result of listening to an item on HCJB's amateur-radio/SWL programme of 13 March (HCJB's reduced carrier transmission on 21,455kHz). This described a form of receiver claimed to have been developed by a listener in the USA many years ago, although I am uncertain whether the receiver was ever successfully tested outside the laboratory.

Fig 10 shows what G3IJE believes was the essential idea behind the receiver which was claimed to be immune to adjacent-channel sideband splash permitting (shades of the stenode!) carrier separation of +/-1kHz while delivering audio out to some 7500Hz! As G3IJE puts it, it seems an ingenious way of using the common-mode rejection properties of a push-pull circuit to null out interference. He feels there may well be snags but hopes to give the idea a try. I suspect that it would be more suited to MF than HF - but who knows until they have tried it!

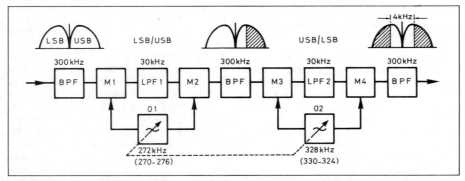

Fig 8: The basic principles of the 1969 Rohde & Schwartz EKO7-80 filter based on two low-pass-filters using inductors and not crystals to provide continuously variable bandwidth.

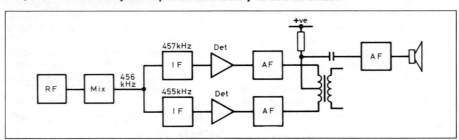

Fig 10: G3IJE's outline of the receiver described on HCJB claimed to eliminate adjacent channel sideband hash from closely spaced carriers.

PHASING-TYPE SSB GENERATORS/ DEMODULATORS

SINCE THE INTRODUCTION of SSB into amateur radio some 40 years ago, there has been continued interest in, but often frustration with, 'phasing-type' techniques for the generation or demodulation of SSB signals. Transceiver manufacturers have for long universally adopted the alternative 'filter' method, following the development of high-performance crystal filters at HF. Originally such filters tended to be limited to frequencies below about 500kHz.

The result has been that for many years, phasing systems have tended to be confined to the home constructor. This is despite their undoubted cost advantages in eliminating the need for an SSB filter, and the ability to select either the upper or lower sideband without the use of two offset oscillators. They also have the advantage that not having sharp-cut-off filters in the exciter, they can provide superior audio quality.

However, although cheaper, phasing systems require the use of stable, close-tolerance components often of critical, uncommon values with long-term stability against ageing, and good short-term stability against temperature variations, plus skill in setting up. The later development of 'third method' (Weaver) and 'polyphase' (Gingell) configurations largely overcame the component-value problem but required the use of four balanced modulators (mixers) and, for Third Method, reasonably good audio filters. Thus, even for home construction, the filter method has generally found favour, with the cost of SSB filters reduced by the use of low-cost colour-TV or 'clock' crystals.

In the early days, it was usual with phasing-type systems to generate SSB directly at the transmission frequency avoiding the (usually) double-conversion of filter-type SSB generated at, say, 455kHz. However, it is now often considered preferable to generate the signal at a fixed high frequency, as with filter-type SSB, and then convert it to the band in use. Phasing-type demodulators for direct-conversion receivers work at the incoming signal frequency although this in practice tends to limit slightly the degree of rejection of the unwanted sideband in multiband receivers.

Fig 11 shows the basic phasing-type system in which the carrier is suppressed by the balanced modulators (mixers), with the AF and RF 90° phase differences resulting in the outputs comprising two sets of each sidebands, with either the USB or the LSB sidebands in phase and the other set 180° out-of-phase. When the signals are combined (added together) the sideband which is 180° out-of-phase nulls and disappears, provided that both the RF and AF networks are almost precisely 90° over the range of frequencies involved. For RF this is not too difficult and can be done digitally by frequency division. For AF networks covering say 300 to 3500Hz or more, networks providing +45° and -45° as in **Fig 11(b)**, the problem of achieving an accurate stable phase-shift network is more difficult, although it has been made simpler by the technique of using all-pass lead and lag networks.

Moreover, even for the classic phase-shift networks it is possible to take advantage of the improved stability of modern components such as metalfilm resistors, multiturn cermet trimmers and polystyrene capacitors. John R Hey, G3TDZ, believes that it was the poorer components of yesteryear which gave the phasing method a bad name. He has adopted the system for the 'White Rose Radio' club constructional project which has been expressly designed to smash through the £1000 'brick wall' that deters many Class B licen-

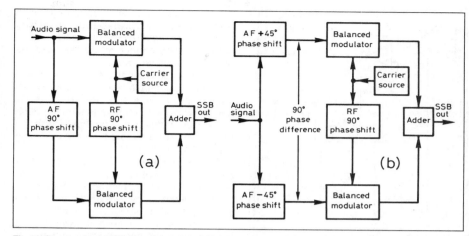

Fig 11: Phasing-type SSB generation. In reverse form the arrangements provide SSB demodulators.

sees from struggling with the Morse test and getting on HF. His detailed description of an HF receiver that can be constructed for around £25 to £30 or so appeared in *Radio Communication*, February 1990, pp-35-39. *[Reprints £5 - Ed]*

G3TDZ writes: "Something not seen in *TT* or elsewhere for some time is the phasing method of SSB generation. Considering the advantage of there being no expensive filters or crystals needed, yet capable of superb SSB audio quality, with generation possible

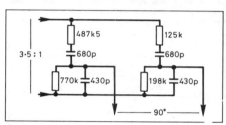

Fig 12: Audio-phase shift network providing output which differ by 90° in phase over the audio speech band.

This diagram can be found on page 314.

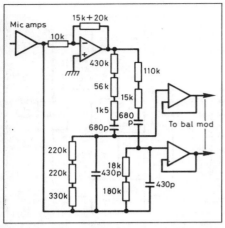

Fig 13: G3TDZ's practical realisation of the audio phase-shift network using standard value components (1%) found to give excellent results between about 150Hz and 4kHz.

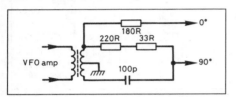

Fig 14: The RF phase-shift network used by G3TDZ for the White Rose constructional project.

This diagram can be found on page 314

directly in-band, perhaps a little regeneration of interest is needed. In designing a matching transmitter for our White Rose receiver project, the phasing method was chosen and has proved to work very well.

"It is a fair guess that it is the construction of the actual phase shift networks which frighten off the average amateur constructor. It is the way these requirements have been solved in our project that prompts this letter; readers may be interested to learn how easy these may be achieved.

"The audio network with its formidable and critical component values were perhaps responsible for the appearance of the Gingell Polyphase network where off-the-shelf component values go some way to simplifying the requirements. This network, however, does use a great number of individual components so it seemed a good idea to take a renewed look at the original network. It was soon found that series combinations of common off-the-shelf values could not only satisfy the values of **Fig 12** but also resulted in an accurate 90° phase differential across the output from about 150Hz to about 4kHz. The 3.5:1 drive requirement is also very easily met with a single op-amp and common resistor values.

"**Fig 13** shows the practical realisation of the audio phase-shift network of Fig 28 using 1% tolerance resistors of common values, and where the 3.5:1 drive is easily accommo-

dated. As with all such networks they must be driven from a low-resistance source and terminated by a high-resistance load.

"The RF phase-shift network is even simpler. Basically it consists of one resistor and one capacitor, although in practice the values are achieved by using series values: **Fig 14**. At mid-VFO frequency, the reactance of the 100pF capacitor is 255Ω.

"While every electronics text book shows the well-known series connection of resistance and reactance formula:

$$Z = \sqrt{(R^2 + X^2)}$$

I had to think long and hard to come up with the formula for the parallel combination:

$$Z = \sqrt{\left(\frac{R^2 \times X^2}{R^2 + X^2}\right)}$$

Or, where R and X are equal, the answer is found using the series formula and dividing the answer by two. With L, C and R in circuit, it is the difference between X_L and X_c which is entered into the above formulae.

"The simplicity of the RF network has caused some constructors to ask the question: 'Surely these values can only provide the required 90° phase shift at one frequency; how can they work over a whole 0.5MHz band?' My answer is that a little calculation (Tan $\varnothing$ = X_c/R) shows that the error angle is only +/- 1° On a band such as 3.5MHz, where only 200kHz are used by SSB operators, the phase error is as little as 0.4°, hardly enough to cause any loss of sideband suppression. In practice the two networks result in an SSB system which gives excellent voice quality with all components off-the-shelf industry standards.

Fig 15 shows the full circuit of the White Rose exciter but without full constructional details or setting-up procedure which one hopes may be the subject of a full-length article by G3TDZ (who can provide a PC board for the exciter for £3.50). Briefly, following the single stage microphone amplifier are diode clippers which are intended as amplitude limiters rather than speech clippers, thereby obviating the necessity of difficult ALC circuits later. Out-of-band audio products are removed by the low-pass filter IC1b. C1 is chosen for low-frequency roll off below 250Hz. The filter with its inverting amplifier IC1c provides drive for the audio phasing networks. These are terminated by followers IC2a, IC2b and R25 and VR1 permitting audio drive equalisation. TR1 amplifies the VFO input to about 1Vp-p and drives the RF phase shift networks. These feed twin 1496 double-balanced modulators with carrier balance about -50dB. Following the combining transformer, either a low-pass filter or a tuned circuit has been provided on the board before the high level mixer which frequency changes the generated SSB signal into the required HF band. A tuned circuit must be included after this and before the power amplifier. This is included on the plug-in power boards together with a low-pass output filter.

VR3 allows adjustment of gain-slope characteristics of one modulator for better balance, thereby achieving excellent SSB generation. Only four adjustments are necessary, VR1 to VR4. The use of modern components including metal film resistors, multiturn cermet trimmers and polystyrene capacitors all ensure long term stability. ❑

'PARASITICS REVISITED' REVISITED

TT, DECEMBER 1990 digested information from Part 1 of a *QST* article by Richard L Measures, AG6K, on 'Parasitics Revisited'. This warned of the damage that can be done to high-power, high-cost transmitter valves by VHF parasitic oscillations which may exist undetected over a long period, intermittently or continuously, due to unwanted resonances.

Part 2 of AG6K's article (*QST*, October 1990, pp32-35) continued the sad saga, showing how VHF parasitics can also damage band-change switches and tuning capacitors. It also provides useful information on improved forms of parasitic suppressors.

He points out that VHF parasitic-oscillation damage to band switches and tuning capacitors stems from the high VHF voltages that are generated by the parasitics in the amplifier anode circuit causing arcing, which melts and/or burns switch and capacitor materials. AG6K writes: "Band-switch damage can occur in two forms:

"(1) Band-switch contacts burned so badly by VHF energy that they no longer make contact. In some cases, the contacts may be missing because the arcing has vaporized them! The fix: Drill out the rivets and replace the burned contacts, or replace the defective switch wafer - after installing better (lower VHF-Q) parasitic-oscillation suppressors, cathode-circuit protection and an HV (high-voltage) fuse resistor in the amplifier.

"(2) Conductive material deposited by the arcing on the surface of the ceramic insulation of the switch. Even if better parasitic suppression is successfully applied to the amplifier, the conductive material must be removed because such paths can arc during normal amplifier operation."

AG6K adds that when the VHF arc vaporizes and burns the contacts, carbon-black and gasified metal are deposited on the ceramic insulation which is indirectly heated by the arc. These conductive substances stick to the ceramic like glaze on pottery and when cooled are difficult to remove:

"If you know where the switch arced, and only minimal arcing occurred, you may be able to remove the metal particles with 400-grit wet or dry silicon-carbide abrasive paper, applied under dripping water. Polish and dry the ceramic, and coat it with suitable HV-insulating paint to reduce the possibility of the arc recurring at the original site. Frequently, however, the only fix is to replace the wafer concerned. (Don't discard the damaged wafer - you can salvage its undamaged contacts to replace damaged contacts on wafers that don't have arc-contaminated ceramic.)"

AG6K explains that arcing can also pit, blister or even partially melt the metal plates of an air-dielectric variable capacitor in a high-power amplifier. This can reduce the working voltage of the capacitor and in severe cases may result in arcing under normal operating conditions. However, such faults can be easily overcome (again after first suppressing the VHF parasitics) by using a thin, flat file inserted between the plates of the capacitor and filing them smooth, rounding off any sharp edges, realigning any bent plates with long-nose pliers and ensuring that the air gaps of fully meshed plates are consis-

tently equal. Do not worry if part of a plate has been destroyed, this will only reduce the maximum capacitance by a minimal amount.

He describes a superior form of parasitic suppressor having a U-shaped (hairpin) inductor: **Fig 1**. This can be used if there is room in the amplifier box. He writes: "This form of inductor offers advantages over a conventional coil: it affords less inductive coupling with its associated suppressor resistor(s) and its inductance can be adjusted without desoldering and adding or removing turns. This is useful if it is necessary to decrease inductance to reduce suppressor-resistor dissipation at 28MHz. The inductance is lowered by squeezing together, or increased by spreading, the two sides of the U."

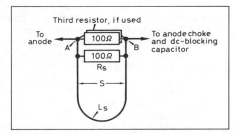

Fig 1: A U-inductor VHF parasitic suppressor recommended by AG6K for use in high-power HF amplifiers. L_s consists of a single loop of No 18 nichrome-60 wire. The network resistor, R_s consists of two or three 100Ω, 2W, metal-film resistors soldered across the U. For typical 3-500Z amplifiers, the wire length between A and B is about 3.5in, producing an L_s of about 60nH. For lower voltage amplifier valves, A-B may be increased to about 4in for an L_s of about 80nH. The maximum spacing between the inductor sides (S) is set by the length of the resistors that make up R_s. See text for adjustment of the inductance by squeezing the sides.

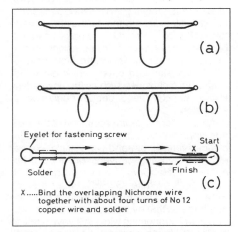

Fig 2: To kill really stubborn VHF parasitics it may prove necessary to substitute low-VHF-Q conductors for existing high-Q anode straps. Parallelled straight and inductively loaded nichrome-60 wire runs are one answer. The loading inductors can take the form of Us as in (a), or single circular turn coils [shown in side view in (b) as loops]. C shows a method of constructing such a low-VHF-Q conductor from a single length of nichrome-60 wire. (AG6K, *QST*).

AG6K provides further information on solving really stubborn cases, for example by the substitution of low-VHF-Q conductors (**Fig 2**) in place of the usual high-Q anode straps fitted in high-power amplifiers.

He also describes the provision of a low-VHF-resistance path to chassis earth at the cathode terminal(s) on the valve socket: for example a metal-film resistor in series with a small-value capacitor. This can be 25pF and 1 - 10Ω; the object being to find a capacitance that resonates with the valve's inductive input reactance at the parasitic frequency. A capacitor without resistor may exhibit a high-Q self-resonance that could aggravate the parasitic problem.

AG6K suggests that this VHF input-swamping technique is especially useful with valves such as the 3CX1200A7 and 3-1000Z "which exhibit about four times more plate-to-cathode feedback capacitance than other valves of similar power capability." For these valves he suggests one RC network consisting of a 10Ω resistor in series with a 245pF capacitor between each filament terminal and chassis.

AG6K also notes the difficulty in tracing intermittent VHF parasitics even with a spectrum analyzer or VHF oscilloscope. Dip meters can reveal resonances in a dead amplifier (unpowered and unplugged). The resonant frequency of the amplifier-box cavity can be measured with all covers in place by coupling the dip meter to the cavity via a small continuous loop passed through the box's ventilation holes.

The above notes, and those in the December *TT*, form only a brief digest of the discussion and suggestions of AG6K's long two-part article, but may serve to show that VHF parasitic oscillation can be, and often is, a very real problem not only in home-built but also factory-built high-power amplifiers. A note from K H Green, moreover, stresses that the general problem of VHF parasitics is far from being confined to transmitter amplifiers. He writes:

"The *TT* item on VHF parasitic oscillation takes me back a few years but I feel sure there is still a lot of it about.

"About a year before I exchanged the soldering iron for a typewriter, I built a handheld absorption-wavemeter-probe with a DC transistor amplifier. Coupled to a 2-turn coil on the end of a feeder from a roof-top three-element Yagi array at Epsom, this would indicate the two carriers from the old Crystal Palace Band I sound and vision transmitters. It covered (and still does) the range 600kHz to 360MHz although it was intended to go lower and all the way up to 1000MHz. Currently I have plans to replace the crystal-diode/DC-amp with a modern op-amp unit but the weeks do not seem as long as they used to. (An age affliction from which I find myself increasingly suffering! - G3VA.)

"The device was built to go looking for parasitics which I had long believed to be the cause of many unexplained and often undetected problems in electronic equipment. If you build four identical audio amplifiers or identical receivers, the chances are that one of them will be a rogue; about 2dB down in gain, about 1 to 2dB up in noise; it will overload just before the others or be unhappy-ish with transients; it will resist adjustments to its input impedance and sound a lot nastier than distortion-measurements say it ought to.

"The firm had a family of 'mains stabilisers' which used motor-driven variacs in buck-and-boost arrangements. They were always fine when first built but would soon become lazy and develop hysteresis effects. Certainly, my probe showed that many of these problems were indeed caused by VHF parasitics but, alas, I departed from that realm before my investigations really got under way.

"The most notable of these 'ossers' however was a UHF sweep oscillator which I developed and built to provide a daily performance check on a string of unattended 400-500MHz recording-receivers. I cannot recall the valve-type but it was used in a resonant-line TATG oscillator around 450MHz part-tuned by a motor-driven 360° capacitor.

"The prototype worked well - eventually - and a draughtsman folded it all up, tidied it away and passed it to Workshops to make the first one. I then had to make it work all over again - and successfully. Workshops then made four more. I wired the first of these and, when it was powered, it oscillated powerfully like any good audio amplifier! The only problem was that I could not find the oscillation frequency.

"Eventually I dug out our latest acquisition in absorption wavemeters and traced it to 960MHz. After two hours of messing about, I had not succeeded in shifting that frequency by even 1%. My problem was out-of-band and I believe that I used a search coil on the none-too-sensitive absorption wavemeter to discover that the very many milliwatts were centred within the very-hot valve envelope.

"The valve electrode assembly was acting as a resonant line and the entire oscillation function was in a world of its own. However, the cure proved to be simple. I lowered the impedance of the feed line (can't remember which) by moving the two copper strips closer together.

"If you translate this experience from a small-signal valve to a high-power transmitting valve, then it is not surprising that valves can suddenly melt-down. My advice to all designers and redesigners would be to keep their grid and anode circuits at low impedance at both VHF and UHF. And always to remember that a capacitor that serves admirably at HF is almost certainly an inductor at VHF, let alone UHF, and that the tank circuit for many parasitic oscillators is labelled in the circuit diagram as decoupling."

While the above notes apply primarily to valves, it is worth emphasising that, over the years, the subject of VHF parasitics in transistor amplifiers (which can result in instant destruction of the device) has been discussed a number of times in *TT* and elsewhere.

HOME CONSTRUCTION AND THE PCB

THE SAD STORY OF THE electronic hobbyist (*TT*, May p29) whose interests spanned from broadcast receivers to hi-fi to computers to computer software (but not amateur radio experimentation) raised, once again, the thorny question of what type of constructional practices are most suited to equipment not intended for mass production in a factory. There can be little doubt that for those who

ZAPPER II AND ZAPPER III ANTENNAS

ROD NEWKIRK, W9BRD was particularly pleased to find the *TT* references to his 'BRD Zapper antenna, the unidirectional version of a single-section, end-fed W8JK array (*TT*, September 1990, pp31-32). He sends along two variations, one of which obviates need for the home-built matching circuit.

He writes: "The simplified approach to phased antenna directivity suggests variations. For example, need for a dedicated matching circuit at the stub can be avoided by using two Zapper arrays in phase (**Fig 3(a)**) for an acceptable match to balanced 300Ω line. A standard balanced-output matching unit can then be used at the transmitter. Directivity reversal must be done at the stubs. Added collinear gain, up to about 3dB, can be realized by spacing the Zappers apart, as limited by the combined stub lengths.

"A vertical version provides switchable unidirectivity in four directions (**Fig 3(b)**). This version requires the single-tap feed approach detailed in the original article (*QST*, June 1990 for full details), a dedicated T-match being recommended. The selectable patterns are cardioidal, broad in the front quadrant, with a sharp rear null. A high-grade rotary switch at the stubs-juncture selects any one of four lobe/null directions. (The sharpness and depth of the target-frequency null suggests VHF benefits for clashing repeaters, etc). Note that while Zapper/W8JK configurations are fundamentally simple, optimum re-

sults depend heavily on proper symmetry and accurate resonance (high-Q). *Ergo*, each half of a double Zapper should be physically identical and identically resonant. Directivity switching then has little effect on matcher settings for unity SWR".

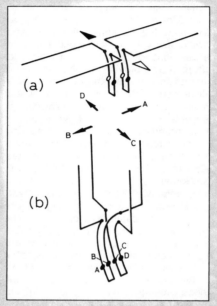

Fig 3: (a) The Zapper II antenna by W9BRD uses two unidirectional Zapper/W8JK arrays. (b) The Zapper III antenna with four vertical elements can provide switched directivity in each of the four quadrants.

wish to build one of the many complete kits that are still on offer within our sector of electronics, the PCBs provided with the kits represent a satisfactory way of reproducing the intended design, and so achieving a specified performance without the need to exercise any design or layout skills.

But when it comes to trying out your own ideas or 'half-copying' a published design, but using available components, the home-made 'one-off' printed circuit board has little to recommend it. *TT* has on many occasions pointed to the advantages - from the standpoint of KISS, flexibility and often performance - of alternative techniques such as the now widely-known W7ZOI 'dead beetle' ('ugly-board') approach.

An excellent two-part appraisal of the various approaches suitable for RF circuits including various pin-and-wire, sticky-copper etc, not involving conventional PCBs, appeared in *RadCom* (February and March 1991) by Ian White, G3SEK, under the title 'How to lay out RF circuits'. It should be emphasised that even 'old-fashioned' breadboard and connecting wires still have a role to play in PSUs etc, easing subsequent modification and repair rather than creating 'throwaway' modules. There is, however, a real danger that newcomers to amateur radio may have already come to believe that the PCB is the *only* effective modern form of c%%onstruction.

Dave Plumridge, G3KMG, feels very strongly on this subject. He writes: "Robert W

Lucky (*TT*, May) remarks on the futility of 'stuffing parts onto boards and soldering the connections' - yet what do I see on the front cover of *RadCom* but one of those wretched boards for a simple PSU regulator! While I would agree that the PCB approach gives a good introduction to constructional practices it is surely the most stultifying procedure ever adopted by home constructors who seem to think it must be the only correct method since all commercial, factory-built equipment is made like that!

"I do hope that young novices will be weaned off the PCB syndrome and on to techniques which allow scope for innovation, experimentation and modification. Then you are no longer a 'board stuffer' but a creative experimenter. Result - *much* more fun and sense of achievement.

"I was glad to see such non-PCB techniques described in the recent two-part article by G3SEK - but please no emphasis in *TT* or elsewhere on 'How to etch your own PCBs'.

"Copper clad board is a wonderfully versatile material. It cuts easily with tin snips, allows tracks to be cut quickly with 'hobby tools', solders easily, makes strong and RF-tight boxes, etc, etc. It also forms a super ground-plane giving enhanced RF performance. Remember the problems that constructors had with the 1988 *RF Design* low-cost spectrum analyser? It emerged that they were making PCBs whereas K2BLA had built his 'dead-bug'-fashion on copper-clad board. My current project is based on the 'High performance communications receiver' by W7ZOI (recent *ARRL Radio Amateurs Handbooks*). W7ZOI found that his prototype built this way had a better performance.

"For this receiver project, I am using small pieces of board, usually about one-inch square, with insulated 'lands' cut very quickly with a 12V drill and burr. I then build up a single stage on this and then mount it on a large board, just anchoring it with the decoupling capacitor leads and any earthy-ended components. I can then very easily try different stages or re-arrange them as required. It's really up to you and your imagination how you develop and apply these techniques - which makes for much more fun. For example, QRP-advocate (and *RadCom* columnist) George Dobbs, G3RJV, uses megohm resistors from 'bargain packs' as 'lands' instead of sticking on little bits of board.

"This brings me to the G3KMG Whistling Dipoles, a KISS hand-portable Doppler D/F I built in the 1980s using what could be called 'surface mount technology - ham style'. (This is presented separately. Unlike the ZS6EF design in *TT*, April 91, there are no FET RF pre-amplifiers and Faraday-link coupling to the antenna elements is used -G3VA). To have made a PCB would have required layout, drawing-preparation, then on to the board with etch resist, messy etching, careful drilling and finally component stuffing and soldering. My way is to lay out the components on a bit of board, stick down the chips or pads, solder up and then cut the board to size with tin snips . . . ."

MORE ON SPERRTOPF COAXIAL SLEEVES

FURTHER EXPLANATIONS HAVE come in confirming the explanation given by G4LQI of the term 'sperrtopf' as a 'blocking-pot', with an amateur radio 'Sperrtopf vertical' marketed for amateur radio use by Antenna Andes. Charles James, G0ILF, also points out that the 'FD4 Windom' is as well-known in Germany as the G5RV is in the UK. Peter Nolte, GW7IZG/DC6BN adds that sperrtopf coaxial sleeve antennas have been produced in Germany for many years as commercial VHF/UHF antennas by such firms as Kathrein Rosenheim and the well-known Rohde & Schwarz.

He explains that in commercial/military communications wide-band characteristics of antennas are essential, with the ratio of length to diameter an important factor. For some sperrtopf VHF antennas in the region of 150MHz some of the elements are 35mm diameter and some about 50mm. Two designs from Rohde & Schwarz (HKO12 and HKO14), both wideband antennas, have the sperrtopf part of the assembly really looking like inverted pots, in contrast to narrower-band versions (about 10MHz bandwidth) which have about 35mm diameter. The R&S designs HK001, 012 and 014 feature additionally a kind of inverted basket in order to reduce further the unwanted re-radiation from the feeder cable. Another feature of some designs is the slightly raised elevation angle of the main radiation for ground-to-air operations, whereas normally radiation from such antennas is in the horizontal plane.

Professor Guenter Beuche, DL6AB, adds

further details of this barrier-pot form of RF choke, emphasising that there is nothing magic behind the 'sperrtopf' which could just as well be called a 'sleeve' and is widely used as a form of balun to facilitate feeding a balanced load with coaxial cable, with the normal arrangement as in **Fig 4**. As used in Fig 2 of the April *TT* (with details of connections shown in (a)) the sole purpose is to suppress RF current on the outer-braid of the coaxial feed-line. Filling with suitable dielectric material, as mentioned, helps to shorten the length of the electrical quarter-wave sperrtopf used in this way.

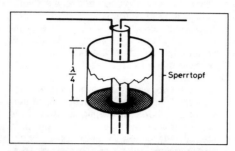

Fig 4: The Sperrtopf (barrier-pot) sleeve used to reduce outer-braid current when feeding a balanced element from unbalanced feedline.

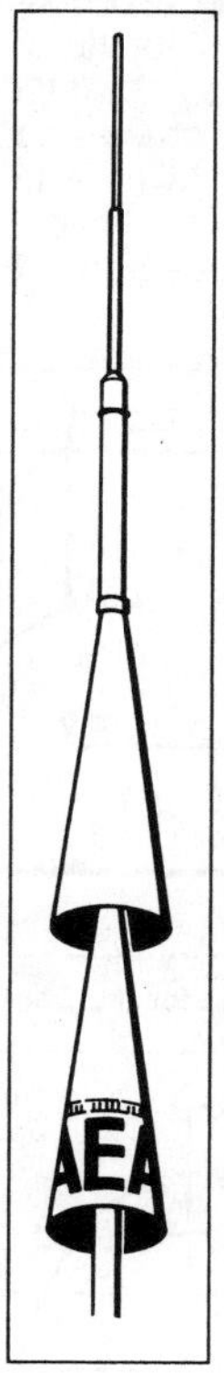

Fig 5: Sketch of the AEA IsoPole VHF/UHF omni-directional base station antenna using two modified Sperrtopf-type 'decouplers'.

He also refers to the 'IsoPole' omni-directional VHF/UHF base station antennas (**Fig 5**) manufactured in the USA by AEA who claim "exceptional decoupling results in simple tuning and a significant reduction in TVI potential" by the use of "decoupling cones offering great efficiency over obsolete radials which radiate in the horizontal plane." They also claim a low SWR across the entire American two-metre band 144 - 148MHz. DL6AB writes: "Although I have not done any analysis of the IsoPole antenna it looks like an application of two Sperrtopf (used inversely) and called by AEA 'decoupling cones' to produce the same effects as the arrangements described by Taguchi (*TT*, April) although with a different mechanical arrangement."

IN-RUSH CURRENT AND THOSE GLOWING VALVES

I STILL USE FOR BROADCAST reception a 30-year-old valve FM tuner (originally forming part of a school installation) that uses valves which are clearly visible since the tuner is no longer in its original enclosure with a gramophone turntable. When first switched on the miniature B9A valves glow so very brightly that at one time I worried that this would shorten their life. However they seem to have survived daily use over many years. I put down the bright heaters simply to in-rush current and left it at that. However, Bob

Pearson, G4FHU, raises some interesting points in considering the general question of in-rush currents and their potentially damaging effect on the heaters/filaments of high-cost power-amplifier valves. He writes:

"A brief reference by Peter Chadwick, G3RZP, to the question of in-rush current in his review of the Heatherlite Explorer Linear Amplifier (*RadCom*, December 1990, p52) made me wonder whether it might be possible to tease a new generation of radio amateurs with an old trick question: 'Why do thermionic tubes glow brightly at the moment of switch-on?' The usual answer is 'Because the resistance of the heating filament is lower when cold than when hot, so an excess current rushes in when you throw the switch, falling to normal when the heater reaches operating temperature.' But this is not good logic. If the heater is cold it cannot be glowing brightly, if it is glowing brightly then it can't be cold! The explanation is more subtle. It is not the *whole* of the heater that glows at switch on, but only the parts that are less well cooled than the bulk. End connections are especially vulnerable since, like cathode straps, they are designed not to allow excessive heat loss via the connection pins in the base. The effect is strongest with indirectly-heated cathodes where most of the heater is contained inside a tubular cathode. The result is that it is usually the ends of the heater wire that are found to have burned out when a heater has gone open circuit. These are the parts that visibly overheat quickly while the rest of the heater wire is still warming up.

"It may be not only the thermal shock but also mechanical shock and the vibration produced magnetically that can cause failures. This is less fanciful but it may seem when typical inrush current for high-power valves are calculated. For example, the heater of a TY125 triode runs normally at 5.4A RMS (7.637A peak) with a (hot) resistance of 1.167ohms. But its cold resistance will be only about 0.15ohms, so with a perfect (zero impedance) 6.3V supply, the in-rush current could reach a peak value of 42A. Such a current can produce a force of the order of a gramme weight, vibrating the filament at twice the supply frequency.

"In the Explorer review, G3RZP speculated about a plan to increase the leakage inductance of the supply transformer to reduce the in-rush current. From AC circuit theory, such a scheme may appear promising, although there could be difficulties in regard to tolerances and, especially, of frequency sensitivity. But further consideration suggests there could be another snag.

"In a reactive circuit comprising resistance and inductance (or resistance and capacitance) there is the possibility of a transient surge at switch-on. The magnitude would depend upon the phase of the supply at the instant of closing the switch and upon the reactance/resistance ratio of the circuit. In the ultimate case where reactance dominates, the surge current could be twice the in-rush current predicted by simple AC theory. Although this does not mean that the arrangement would not offer an overall advantage, it tends to make it less attractive. The use of a DC regulator chip with a slow start circuit added, as used by G4LU to DC power the heaters of two 2C39 valves (*TT*, January

1991, p30) is a convenient solution now that such chips are relatively cheap, but problems mount at large currents, requiring heat sinks and expensive electrolytic capacitors.

"It is a great pity that the choke-input filter for rectifier supplies has not yet returned to the popularity it deserves (mainly because of the lack of availability of suitable chokes). For constant current loads of more than a few amps it has great advantages over the more common capacitor-input filter. It scores on life, reliability and less risk of excess voltage on failure. Also it offers much reduced peak currents in diodes, transformers and the supply mains. This latter point is becoming of importance in impending European legislation (see *TT*, December 1990, p30).

"For amateur-radio applications, there remains little to beat the popular arrangement of a surge-reducing resistor in the supply primary that is manually switched out by the operator (using a self-holding relay and pushbutton) a little while after turning on the main on-off switch. This automatically resets itself when the equipment is turned off. If the relay has a spare contact this can be used to add another panel light to indicate the action; pretty, impressive, and above all, simple!" (In-rush protection circuits of this general type have been described in *TT* etc over the years).

A MEDIUM-COST 'VARIAC'

TT, FEBRUARY 1991 PROVIDED details of a 'Poor Man's Variac' from *Electronics Australia*. This used a tapped 30V/1A secondary winding of a relatively low-power mains transformer that could be switched either to boost or buck the mains supply for equipment drawing up to about 250 watts in order to compensate for poorly regulated mains supplies.

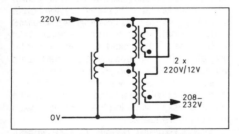

Fig 6: Form of 'Variac' system providing continuous adjustment of bucked-or-boosted AC supplies to compensate for poorly regulated mains supplies.

Basically the same buck or boost technique is used, but in a rather more sophisticated way, by G J Komen, PA0GJK (*Electron*, May 1991, p234). The arrangement of **Fig 6** can provide a continuously variable +/- 12V to the mains supply, ie delivering 220V from a mains supply of 208 to 232V, or 240V from supplies ranging from 228 to 252V using two 12V transformers and a relatively low-power variable auto-transformer. While such an arrangement would cost more to implement than the *EA* arrangement, it would be more flexible and would not require the use of a multi-position switch or a multi-tapped transformer, yet might be expected to be less costly than a high-power Variac.

FETS AS RF AMPLIFIERS

ALTHOUGH, OVER THE PAST few years, *TT* has included a good deal of discussion on,

and examples of, the use of VMOS-type power-FETs as RF power amplifiers, it is many years since information has been included on the use of small-signal FETs and dual-gate FETs as RF/IF amplifiers in HF and VHF receivers.

THE WHISTLING DIPOLES 144MHZ DOPPLER D/F

IN THE 1980s, IN CONNECTION with some 'repeater problems' in Scotland, Dave Plumridge, G3KMG, developed a simple 144MHz Doppler direction-finder and has since produced the MkII version shown in **Figs 7 and 8**. While the basic principles, method of use and so on are the same as those described for the ZS6EF unit in the April *TT*, the absence of RF pre-amplifiers as well as the use of 'surface mount technology - ham style' (**Fig 9**) rather than a PCB for the electronic switch makes this a KISS project for home construction.

The two antennas are switched sequentially to the receiver at approximately 800Hz. Whenever the signals reach the receiver out-of-phase due to slight path length differences, the signal presented to the receiver will be phase-modulated at 800Hz. Only when the boom is exactly broadside to the transmitter will the tone disappear, thus indicating the two possible directions of the transmitter (ie in front of, or behind, the observer). G3KMG reports that the 'null' is very sharp and there may be harmonic effects (due to multipath reflections etc) so that it is necessary to listen for the disappearance of the fundamental 800Hz tone.

He also comments: "Incidentally I was impressed by the accuracy of the design information on helical-wound antennas given in Vol 2 of the *RSGB Handbook*. They resonated almost spot on, and with the balun feed as shown gave a return loss of nearly 20dB, not that it mattered too much in this instance for reception only."

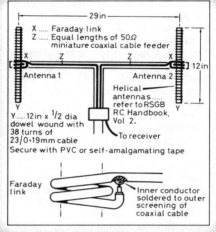

Fig 7: G3KMG's 'Whistling Dipoles' KISS 144MHz Doppler direction finder.

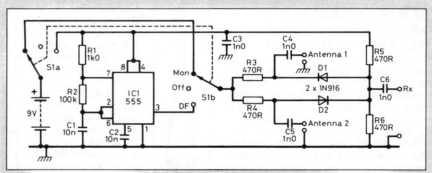

Fig 8: The 800Hz electronic switch for the Doppler D/F.

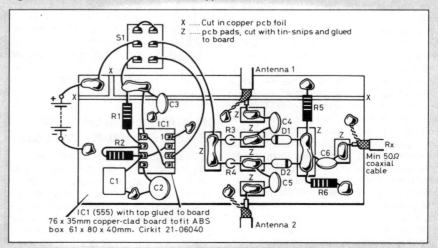

Fig 9: The 'surface mount' form of construction eliminating the need for a home-etched PCB - an approach applicable to other home-construction projects and likely to appeal to those who regard PCBs as a barrier to experimental, flexible constructional projects.

Mike Murphy, VK6KRO, (*Amateur Radio*, May 1991, pp 19 & 30) emphasises that: "Twenty-five years after their introduction, it would be fair to say that FETs are rarely used by radio amateurs except as VHF pre-amplifiers (and sometimes as oscillators - G3VA). This is unfortunate, as they offer many advantages when used properly."

VK6KRO believes this state of affairs is partly due to the belief that FETs are fragile and easily destroyed by electrostatic discharge, and partly because of the belief that since superficially they have characteristics akin to valves, they can be used in basically similar circuits.

He points out that modern FETs are very rugged once they are wired into circuits having an easy, low resistance, path between their gate(s) and earth. He much prefers circuits with a coil connected directly between gate and earth to those with, for example, ten megohm resistances down to an AGC line, akin to valve practice. He says: "I have never blown up a FET and I have used dozens of them." Admittedly, FETs are very vulnerable to ESD (static) when not connected in circuit unless the gate is protected by an internal diode.

If you simply replace a valve by an FET in an amplifier stage you will almost certainly run into difficulties. This is because they have a very high slope g_m of up to 30mA/V (much higher than almost any valve) but also more drain-to-gate capacitance than most triode valves; rather like combining in a single device the high-slope of a frame-grid pentode valve with the inter-electrode capacitances of a triode valve! A sure prescription for self-oscillation if connected into a typical pentode-type circuit.

The saving grace, VK6KRO points out, is that the FET has very low output impedance and can be used as a perfectly stable *low-gain* device, yet providing excellent stage gain from the voltage step-up that can be readily achieved with a resonant input transformer.

For example, the 21MHz pre-amplifier shown in **Fig 10** using the popular 2N3819 FET (g_m = 10mA/V) with a 330Ω resistor as a load has a device gain of only about three, which would hardly be considered worthwhile for some applications. But the input tuned circuit can provide a gain of about 7, resulting in a stable voltage gain of about 21, with the FET's very high input impedance presenting only light loading of the input transformer. A stage gain of some 26dB is achieved without the FET 'getting a chance to oscillate.' (Note that VK6KRO's article does not go into the question of dynamic range, and the effect of a high-gain pre-amplifier in front of a receiver - G3VA).

Again, for the IF amplifier of **Fig 11**, standard transistor-type IF transformers can be used by simply reversing the connections used in bipolar transistor circuits, ie with step-up for both input/device and device/output transformers. It is then the IF transformers that provide most of the voltage gain, the FET providing an impedance change (power gain).

VK6KRO writes: "I built a 455kHz amplifier using MFE131 dual-gate devices (**Fig 12**) and, without any special tuning, got a gain of 10,000 using only two stages and it was absolutely stable. A gain of 10,000 will turn

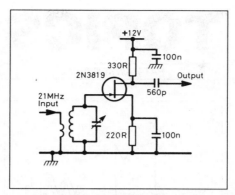

Fig 10: Stable FET pre-amplifier with low-impedance output load and with the main part of the gain coming from the step-up input transformer.

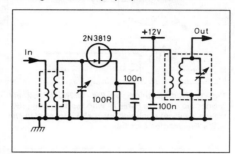

Fig 11: Stable FET IF amplifier using two bipolar transistor-type IF transformers in reverse configuration.

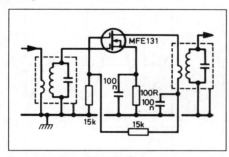

Fig 12: Dual-gate FET IF amplifier.

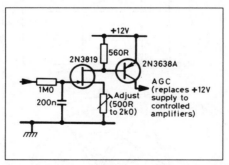

Fig 13: AGC amplifier to provide varying supply voltage to FET RF/IF stages.

10μV into 0.1V, most of the gain needed for a receiver. I also have a receiver which uses three of these stages (to make up for a lossy filter) and it is completely stable. Construction of such an amplifier is not difficult. Normal VHF techniques of mounting all components close to a continuous copper or brass plate and by-passing to the nearest point on it are used. Straight-line signal paths are always a good idea, too; ie don't bring the output back near an input. It is the same arrangement for RF stages and mixer stages: step-up transformers in and out.

"What about AGC? . . . . I tried everything I could think of before I realised how easy it is. FETs work well at 12V but poorly at lower voltages. But 'poorly' just means lost gain, not distortion. You can control the gain of an FET by reducing its supply voltage (to zero if necessary).

"**Fig 13** shows a simple AGC amplifier to control the supply voltages of the stages to which AGC is to be applied . . . . The FET in Fig 61 is biased more negatively by AGC derived from the amplified signal. The FET is effectively a base resistor for the PNP bipolar transistor. As the FET conducts less, the transistor does too, reducing the supply voltage. Oscillators and mixers should be fed from a stable power supply and not from the AGC supply. The arrangement of Fig 61 needs to be pruned to suit the individual FETs - op-amps could do it better and more predictably."

One of the applications for such use of FET devices and circuits, VK6KRO suggests, would be to modify discarded valve receivers for solid-state operation.

BATTERY HAZARDS

DEREK BRANDON, G4UXD, as a chemist, disagrees with the suggestion made by R D Marshall (*TT*, January 1991) that washing soda is twice as effective as sodium bicarbonate for dealing with battery acid spillage. He points out that the RMM (relative molar mass) of sodium bicarbonate, $NaHCO_3$, is (near enough) 84 while that of sodium carbonate (which usually comes as the decahydrate crystals) $Na_2CO_3.10H_2O$, (known as 'washing soda') is about 286. The effectiveness of these two bases in neutralising strong acids, such as sulphuric acid, is proportional to the percentage sodium (RAM 23) that they contain. Thus $NaHCO_3$ (sodium bicarbonate) is about 1.7 times as effective as washing soda, and is also safer to use. Although neither can really be called dangerous, the carbonate, being the stronger base, is more corrosive and dangerous to the eyes.

G4UXD adds: "Many people do not realise how insidious is the effect of even small traces of sulphuric acid in causing cotton to 'rot'. Even tiny spillages on cotton clothes will eventually lead to holes appearing. As suggested in *TT* (August 1990), it is a good idea to keep a battery in a small, cheap plastic bucket to minimise the danger of spillage. It is also, as previously emphasised, an important rule to switch off battery chargers before disconnecting them. ❏

ERRATUM

FIG 7 OF APRIL'S *TT* featured a doppler D/F from *Radio-ZS*. A number of members queried the transistors which should have been marked BF982, not BP982. Several also commented on the apparent non-availability of the BF982 in the UK.

We apologise for the error, of course, but circuits in *Technical Topics* should be regarded purely as sources of ideas, *not* full construction articles, and some specific components may well be difficult or impossible to obtain.

COLINEAR ANTENNAS FOR VHF/UHF MOBILE OPERATION

WHAT APPEARS TO BE A realistic use of the moment method (program not specified) to investigate the performance to be expected from a colinear monopole anna (CMPA) as a 900MHz mobile radiotelephone antenna, or as a dual-band antenna permitting also the reception of Band II (85 - 108MHz) FM broadcasting, is presented in *Electronic Letters* (6 June 1991, pp1103-4) by H Nakano *et al* of Hosei University, Tokyo.

This indicates how the gain of a conventional quarter-wave mobile antenna above an infinite ground plane (in practice a vehicle roof) having a gain of around 1dB can be improved by using two linear wire sections (L_F 0.23λ and L_S 0.5λ) connected by a coil with a diameter of $^1/_{16}$thλ, a pitch angle of P1 7° and a coil wire length of 0.5λ : **Fig 1**. All dimensions are for a λ equivalent to 900MHz. At this frequency, **Fig 1(a)** shows the calculated current distribution along the antenna. The wire radii of both antenna sections and the coil is taken as 1mm.

The Japanese authors write: "It is found that the current amplitude and phase on the first element are close to those on the second element. Because the contributions of both the antenna elements in the far field add constructively, the radiation pattern becomes narrower than that in the conventional monopole antenna, as shown in **Fig 2(b)**. The gain is increased by 3.3dB compared with a conventional monopole antenna. The input impedance is calculated to be 69 - j32Ω."

The Japanese also discuss a double-band version of the CMPA with a further section connected to the top of the 900MHz colinear antenna via a (900MHz) trap coil, with the length of the third section arranged to resonate the antenna in the FM broadcast band (input impedance at 85MHz 21 - j4Ω).

Consideration is also given to the use of a CMPA with four quarter-wave ground wires (radials) rather than an infinite ground plane: "The absolute gain at 900MHz is calculated to be 3.6dB which is significantly higher than a value of 1.4dB obtained by a quarter-wave monopole antenna with ground wires."

LOOSE PINS AND OVER-HOT 3-500Z VALVES

THE HIGH-POWER (AND COSTLY) 3-500Z power triodes used in a number of amateur radio linear amplifiers can occasionally develop loose pin sleeves on their filament pins. According to Bill Orr, W6SAI, (*Radio FUNdamentals, CQ,* May 1991), this problem seems to arise only in amateur practice and not in the many 3-500Z valves used in professional communications and broadcast equipment.

He goes into the causes of loose pins in great detail, but essentially it is a reflection of the problem that is basic to glass-to-metal seals, accentuated by the high filament current (14.5A) and high dissipation of the 3-500Z in linear service. The filament leads are of tungsten which has approximately, but not identical, temperature expansion to that of glass. Whereas metal expands linearly, glass

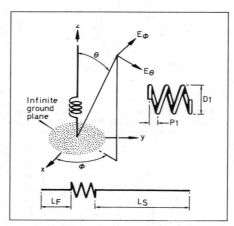

Fig 1: Configuration of the 900MHz colinear monopole antenna (CMPA) with loading coil (180° phase change) analysed by H Nakano *et al* in the IEE's *Electronics Letters.*

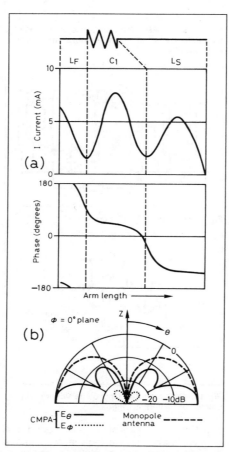

Fig 2: Current distribution and vertical radiation pattern of the 900MHz CMPA. (a) Current distribution. (b) Radiation pattern.

does not: **Fig 3**. W6SAI points out that the useful life of a seal is longest when the seal is heated and cooled slowly. For the 3-500Z, maximum temperature rating of the filament seals is 200°C (the thoriated-tungsten filament operates at temperatures in the range 1800 to 2200K (1527 to 1927°C)). To hold the

seals within 200°C, cooling air *must* be applied to them.

W6SAI suggests that for amateur service, the 5V filament of the 3-500Z should be run at about 4.9V: "This enhances filament life and also permits the filament seals to run cooler than if the filament is run at or above the nominal voltage." Second, he notes that electrical connection to the filament pins should have minimum contact resistance: "Any voltage drop across the contacts represents an 'I²R' loss, which shows up as additional heating at the filament pins". Thirdly, sufficient cooling air must be passed across the filament pins to hold pin and seal temperature below 200°C (this can be checked by means of temperature-sensitive paint or decals applied to the base of the tube directly at the filament seals). All three requirements can be met by carefully measuring (and regulating) the filament voltage, using the proper valve socket, and by applying adequate cooling.

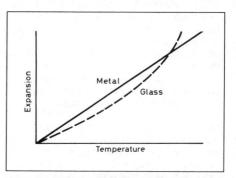

Fig 3: Typical example of how glass and metal expand, showing how differential will increase rapidly when the temperature of a glass seal exceeds the recommended value.

W6SAI notes that extended operation in a DX contest with heavy speech processing can make an otherwise adequate air flow suddenly become insufficient. Pin problems usually occur with only one of a pair of valves, indicating that one of the sockets is receiving insufficient cooling air. A special Eimac SK-410 Air System socket is recommended but is expensive. Ceramic sockets can be used successfully provided extra air to that required for the SK-410 is passed through the socket holes.

In his article, W6SAI provides information on temperature runaway conditions, proper cooling for the 3-500Z, techniques that have been used to resolder base pins and how to reduce the chances of the problem re-occurring. He considers that equipment reviewers should check out the air system of amplifiers, or run the equipment under tough operating conditions to check seal heating, using temperature-sensitive paint or decals. He finds that loose pin problems occur in isolated cases among many brands of amplifier, with no particular factory-built amplifiers having a consistent history of socket/base overheating.

W6SAI provides a check list intended for amateurs who have experienced pin problems, but which also makes good sense for general use with high-power linears:

● Do I run my filament voltage at or slightly below the nominal value?

● Do I operate for long periods with a lot of speech compression?

- Do I carefully retune my amplifier for proper loading when I change bands or frequencies within a (wide) band?
- Do I take care not to overdrive my amplifier valves?
- Do I regularly oil my blower or fan and clean the air passages of the amplifier?
- Do I examine the socket pins at intervals for signs of overheating?
- Finally, do I know the characteristics and air-flow capability of my cooling fan or blower? Is it big enough to do the job?

CAPACITIVE BOTTOM-LOADING OF ANTENNAS

THAT REDOUBTABLE TROIKA OF retired engineers - Arch Doty, K8CFU, John Frey, W3ESU, and Harry Mills, K4HU - did much a few years ago to revive the interest of broadcast antenna engineers, as well as amateurs, in the use of elevated radials and counterpoises rather than extensive and costly buried radials and earth systems (by making thousands of measurements rather than using computer software). They have more recently turned their attention to the use of capacitive bottom loading in order to tune approximately-quarter-wave vertical elements to resonance over a quite wide frequency band, without changing the dimensions of the element, by varying the capacitance of the bottom loading. They have constructed many test antennas at 450MHz and also tried out the system at 144 and 28MHz using quarter-wave folded monopole elements (see *TT*, July 1987); at 450MHz constructed from printed circuit board.

They presented a paper on this subject at the Radio Club of America Technical Symposium in November 1987 of which some parts were published in the July 1990 issue of *Mobile Radio Technology* under the title 'Capacitive bottom-loading tunes mobile antennas'. This emphasised that the technique eliminated the need to change element length for different frequencies or vehicles. K8CFU has sent some selected pages from this article from which the following notes are derived.

"Loading vertical antennas to reduce their physical height is not a new idea. Verticals often are loaded inductively, as with 'top-loading coils' and 'base-loading coils' and capacitively with 'top hats'. The idea of capacitive bottom-loading, although mentioned by K Henny *Principles of Radio*, p462 (John Wiley, 1938) as early as 1938, apparently has not been tested or applied extensively. The authors conducted a series of tests to better define and quantify the capacitive bottom-loading effect. The emphasis in these tests was to determine what range of frequencies could be attained with a fixed height of vertical element by varying the value of the capacitive bottom-loading.

"In deriving the test programme, it was considered that the capacitive bottom-loading effect may be described as follows: As the frequency of operation is raised, an antenna of fixed length looks at its base feedpoint as an increasing resistance in series with a decreasing capacitance. The resulting inductive reactance at the feedpoint must be tuned out, which necessitates the use of capacitive

reactance, which is provided by a capacitor . . . . In the tests, a sufficiently accurate impedance bridge was not available, so VSWR data were taken instead. The data and subsequent tests show:

(1) The resonant frequency of a quarter-wavelength vertical antenna used with a counterpoise varies as the size of the ground system (or plate in the design tested) under the counterpoise (in the 450MHz unit this comprises a circular 'wheel' with many wire spokes), the larger the ground system, the lower the resonant frequency.

(2) The resonant frequency of a vertical antenna used with a counterpoise varies with the distance between the counterpoise and the ground. The greater the distance, the higher the resonant frequency.

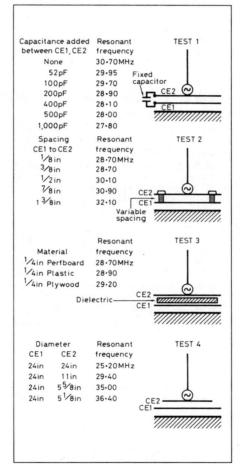

Capacitance added between CE1, CE2	Resonant frequency	TEST 1
None	30·70MHz	
52pF	29·95	
100pF	29·70	
200pF	28·90	
400pF	28·10	
500pF	28·00	
1,000pF	27·80	

Spacing CE1 to CE2	Resonant frequency	TEST 2
1/8 in	28·70MHz	
3/8 in	28·70	
1/2 in	30·10	
7/8 in	30·90	
1 3/8 in	32·10	

Material	Resonant frequency	TEST 3
1/4in Perfboard	28·70MHz	
1/4in Plastic	28·90	
1/4in Plywood	29·20	

Diameter CE1	CE2	Resonant frequency	TEST 4
24in	24in	25·20MHz	
24in	11in	29·40	
24in	5 5/8in	35·00	
24in	5 1/8in	36·40	

Fig 4: The 28MHz version of the capacitive bottom-loaded antenna showing how its resonant frequency can be changed by bottom-loading without varying the length of the vertical element. The arrangement resulting from Test 4, varying the diameter of CE2, provided an antenna tunable from 25.2 to 36.4MHz.

"In other words, the capacitance between counterpoise and ground acts to capacitively bottom-load the vertical element. In these tests, capacitance was added between the feedpoint and the ground system to supply the required capacitive reactance. By varying the value of this reactance, the frequency at which the base impedance of the antenna is purely resistive, ie its resonant frequency, was varied."

Extensive tests of vertical antennas using

this principle have been made on amateur bands from 3.5MHz to 450MHz, including fixed as well as mobile applications. K8CFU has also made some 800MHz versions for use with his (American) cellular telephone: "Each of the antennas boost simple construction because they have fixed, rather than adjustable, whips."

Some test results of various methods of 'tuning' 28MHz antennas are shown in **Fig 4**. It is stated that the 28MHz antenna (presumably the Test 4 version) was tested extensively and found to be tunable from 25.9 to 31.5MHz without changing the height of the vertical element: "On-the-air performance on the amateur 10-metre band was excellent."

EARTHS, COUNTERPOISES AND RADIALS

THE ITEM "LOW RESISTANCE EARTHING" (*TT*, April) outlined the American military "surface-wire-ground" (SWG) system using a series of short, cruciform-shaped stakes as a means of providing a lower DC earth resistance than the traditional 6ft earth rod. It also referred briefly to the important difference between DC earth resistance (important where the system is used as a *protective earth*) and the RF return-current efficiency when the earth is used to provide the missing half of a monopole or Marconi-type antenna, where RF loss resistance can dramatically reduce radiation efficiency.

As emphasised on many occasions in *TT*, there is growing evidence that elevated radials or even a single quarter-wave counterpoise (which may be physically shortened by inductance loading etc) tend to provide better radiation efficiency (ie lower RF ohmic loss) than all but the most elaborate buried earths, which for broadcast applications may consist of 120 or even 150 buried wires in addition to earth stakes.

The detailed measurements some years ago by Arch Doty, K8CFU, and his friends provided a very strong case for using elevated wire(s) and this has since been further strengthened by NEC-software computer studies reported in *TT*.

As a result of the April item, Allan Taylor, G3JMO, has commented in some detail on the question of 'earths' used as an integral part of vertical monopole antennas. He writes: "Although the SWG system apparently bettered the results of earthing by a 6ft rod in terms of DC resistance compared with 6ft rods, I am very suspicious of its use as part of an antenna system based on my own experiences with the vertical antennas used consistently for over 30 years.

"To judge from results of earthing experiments in my own locality (Redcar, Cleveland), I do not think a series of 10in ground rods would achieve very much, in fact any length of rod is nearly useless in ground which will not carry earth currents - and that goes for most of it. The short-ground-rod philosophy appears to be based on the assumption that earth currents travel near the surface which gets the rain (but dries out easily) whereas formerly it was considered that any ground rod less than three-feet long was of very little use. This can suggest only that the subject of earthing is still uncertain, at least in respect of RF ohmic losses.

"It is well recognized that if a vertical radiator of about a quarter-wavelength is to radiate effectively then its efficiency depends upon the earth creating the antenna's 'mirror image' of the quarter-wave element. Provided that the 'return' earth currents flow back to the feeder, then the antenna radiates, but in practice low earth-conductivity means that such current does not flow readily and the antenna radiates poorly with low efficiency. Indeed, in some circumstances the earth forms virtually a dummy load on the end of the feedline, absorbing most of the transmitter output, particularly where the antenna element is mismatched or mistuned.

"There is thus often a large difference in radiation efficiency between a vertical antenna tuned against ground and one tuned with a counterpoise or radial, either as a 'ground-plane-antenna (GPA)' elevated above ground, or with radial(s) at about ground level. I suspect that the improved results of the American SWG system, if they relate to antenna earth rather than protective earths, may be due more to the counterpoise effect of the circular ring of cables than to the actual short earth rods. Indeed, if the 10in rods are as inefficient at linking the wire to the ground as I suspect they are, the wire may well be acting more as a counterpoise than as a 'true' earth. The improved (ie lower) DC resistance compared to 6ft spikes reported by the Americans may, from the figures quoted, still be far too high in areas of poor earth conductivity, to form an efficient antenna 'mirror image' earth.

"In my experience, most antennas work far better isolated from true earth even by a foot or so, rather than being connected directly to earth as part of the antenna system. If a 'true earth' cannot equal or excel the efficiency of a simple counterpoise, which can be isolated from ground and tuned as part of the antenna system, why bother to use ground in the first place?

"However, this does not include the coaxial feeder; by burying the cable a few inches underground, this will kill off the outer-braid common-mode current and may reduce the pick-up of local electrical interference close to the house (recognising that vertical elements are in any case prone to pick-up more interference than horizontal elements)."

G3JMO discusses other possibilities including the use of balun impedance matching transformers with the feeder earthed at both ends but this is a rather different question to that of SWG earths. He does however point out that the cruciform rods used for SWG look familiar, as he uses MetPosts from a garden centre as guy anchors and finds them very effective in holding the guys of his 30ft vertical; but being painted he would *not* recommend them as short earth rods!

L E Newnham, G6NZ, points out that much information on earths, and the configuration of earth rods (but for protective rather than RF earthing systems) can be found in such books as: *Earth Resistances* by Dr G E Tagg (Newnes, pp258) and *Earth Conduction Effects in Transmission Systems* by Erling D Sunde (Dover Publications, New York, pp370 (rather more mathematical)). I tried to find these in some professional libraries but without success.

MORE ON SAFE SOLDERING

THE JUNE *TT* ITEM ON 'Safe Soldering', highlighting the potential problem of 'woodworker's asthma' from breathing in flux fumes resulted in a useful follow-up from Roger Blackwell, G4PMK. He writes:

"Some years ago, when microprocessors first came on the scene, I began making a number of memory boards for my home-brew machine, each of which had nearly 3000 soldered joints. It soon became apparent that I was reacting badly to the fumes of the flux from the solder. The project, indeed any soldering at all, was not really practicable, even with a fan blowing the fumes away.

"Fortunately, I talked to my GP, who was also an electronics enthusiast. He prescribed an inhaler used for asthma sufferers (Intal, diSodium Cromoglycate) which helped a great deal.

"A further positive step was to change to a solder using a different flux - Multicore Xersin. This is available from such suppliers as Farnell. Using this solder, I experienced no problems at all.

"I would therefore suggest that anyone who experiences problems when soldering should consider the use of this type of cored solder, or, if their reaction is severe, talk to their GP."

Roy Hill, GM0IJF, is more careful than he used to be to avoid inhaling fumes. He reports: "Recently I made myself a fume extractor using an old vacuum cleaner - a spherical 'Hovercraft' machine. I kept the felt dust filter and replaced the bag with an active charcoal filter intended for kitchen hoods. A cardboard cone taped to the suction pipe helps to take the fumes away from a suitable area.

"Briefly: (1) The charcoal may not be altogether suitable for solder fumes, but I can't smell what gets through. (2) The normal dust bag could be filled with active charcoal. (3) The machine is noisy, but is needed only intermittently. A foot-operated switch would be useful. (4) Instead of trying to absorb fumes, they could be vented through a window or under the floor boards, although this is not possible with my type of machine. Clearly, there could be many possible variants, based

TWO-TONE TESTING WITH OLD OSCILLOSCOPES

DEL ARTHUR, G0DLN, IS A FIRM believer in the value of two-tone testing for anyone involved in the construction of SSB transmitters and linear amplifiers. He considers such checks should always be carried out before equipment is put on the air. He writes: "Not only does such testing demonstrate the linearity but also enables an amateur to know the maximum PEP that can be run safely before flat-topping occurs. A mildly non-linear flat-topped signal may sound perfectly OK to a listener but could be resulting in RFI somewhere else. A bent cross-over curve may gain 'BBC quality' reports from the station you are working but try telling that to the unfortunate amateur using a nearby channel suffering severe interference from your splatter!

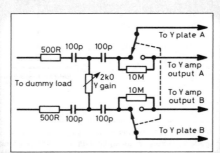

Fig 5: G0DLN's method of feeding RF directly to the Y-plates of an oscilloscope of restricted HF performance for two-tone testing at 14MHz and above.

"Thousands of amateurs have an oscilloscope available but a considerable proportion of these are ancient or have insufficient bandwidth to do a good job on HF. Although for two-tone testing, only a slow sweep rate is required from the time-base, the problem usually lies in the Y amplifier which was not designed to handle higher HF signals. My ancient Cossor single-

beam oscilloscope will just struggle up to about 14MHz but is completely defeated on higher bands.

"With valve-type 'scopes, the problem is easily overcome by connecting the test signal directly to the Y plates, by-passing the Y amplifier. A simple RC network is required and the plates can be disconnected from the Y amplifier for two-tone testing with a double-pole change-over switch (unless this is done the signal will tend to disappear into the Y amplifier causing loss of amplitude on the screen). In **Fig 5** the two high value resistors keep the DC voltage from the Y amplifier on the plates so that the Y-shift control is still operational. Without this voltage it may prove difficult to focus properly. The 500Ω resistors preserve the SWR between rig and dummy load which would otherwise be disturbed due to the low reactance of the capacitors at HF when the gain control potentiometer is set low.

"All component values are nominal but the capacitors should not be of much higher value than shown or hum will appear on the trace. About 5% of the total test power will be dissipated in the network so components should be rated accordingly. A 'sniff' of RF is taken from the dummy load via a very small-value capacitor to the external synch terminal (or hard wire it to the appropriate point in the synch amplifier if you can find it).

"With the component values of Fig 62 I can obtain a usable amplitude of trace with as little as three watts into a 50Ω load; with the gain control set to low gain I can punch in 400W for short periods. Since modifying my old Cossor 'scope in this way, I now enjoy a clear, sharp display vastly better than was possible when using the original Y amplifier. But don't forget that even small 'scopes will bite your fingers if provoked. Take care."

on the type of machine and the particular circumstances."

MININEC - A DOUBLE-EDGED SWORD?

IN RECENT YEARS, there have been many *TT* items on the uses and abuses of computer-modelling of antenna impedances and radiation patterns derived from software based on simplified versions of the Numerical Electromagnetic Code (NEC), using the 'method of moments' developed in the late 1960s and later translated into software. Let me stress that there can be no doubt that NEC and the less powerful MININEC have given antenna designers probably the most important new tool developed in the past 20 years.

Yet, equally, there can, as G3SEK stressed in *TT*, July 1990, be great need for amateurs to be extremely careful in ensuring that, in using the NEC variants, they possess sufficient knowledge of antenna fundamentals and practice to avoid being seriously misled by their computers.

Dick Rollema, PA0SE, draws attention to 'MININEC - The Other Edge of the Sword' by Roy Lewallen, W7EL, (*QST*, February 1991, pp18-22) which is editorially sub-titled 'MININEC antenna-modelling software is powerful and popular. But you need to know about its limitations to use it effectively. Here's the lowdown.' This referred to one amateur whose computer told him that a 3.5MHz dipole erected 0.110ft above poor ground would give him a gain of 45dB!

As W7EL warns: "One of the edges (of the MININEC program) is its ability to help us answer questions about antennas; its other edge is its limitations which, should we fail to recognize and carefully avoid them, can lead us to conclusions that are embarrassingly and profoundly wrong."

As Ian White, G3SEK (the European agent for MN, the enhanced MININEC program written by Brian Beezley, K6STI), very fairly puts it: "I would like all antenna users to have a *realistic* appreciation of both the power and the limitations of antenna software. This field is developing very fast; yet whatever wonders the future may bring, the most important ingredient in successful mathematical modelling will always be the end-user's understanding of how *real* antennas behave!"

KISS 70W POWER AMPLIFIER USING VHF BIPOLAR TRANSISTORS

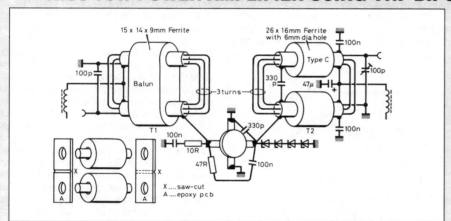

Fig 6: PA0FRI amplifier - detail of ferrite input and output (T1 and T2) transformers. PA0FRI states that suitable ferrite is sold by Barend Hendrikse, Box 314, 7200 AH Zutphen, The Netherlands (telephone Holland 05756-1066).

FRITS GEERLIGS, PA0FRI, has sent me annotated diagrams (**Figs 6 and 7**) of a KISS 70W HF power amplifier using two VHF bipolar power transistors (Mullard/Philips BLW60). He writes:

"It is possible to build this KISS amplifier successfully with the brief information shown on the diagrams. (I would not recommend this for constructors not experienced in sorting out the problems that can arise with high-gain bipolar transistor amplifiers - *G3VA*). Several Dutch amateurs are currently on the air with this design.

"No PCB need be made. Copper clad epoxy (CCE) is used upside down. The copper side forms the 'ground' and cut-out pieces of CCE are glued to the copper as stand-offs/soldering pads etc. The epoxy side is bolted to a heat sink.

"The amplifier performs well with a two-tone test and on-air reports are excellent when using an FT-7 as the driver. I expect the BLW transistors could be replaced by similar VHF-types with similar results."

The above notes plus the annotated diagrams represent the only information available to me. The gain at HF of a VHF bipolar transistor can be very high so that the amplifier must be perfectly stable. PA0FRI's address is: F H V Geerligs, Beverdam 89, 4874 KT Etten-Leur, The Netherlands.

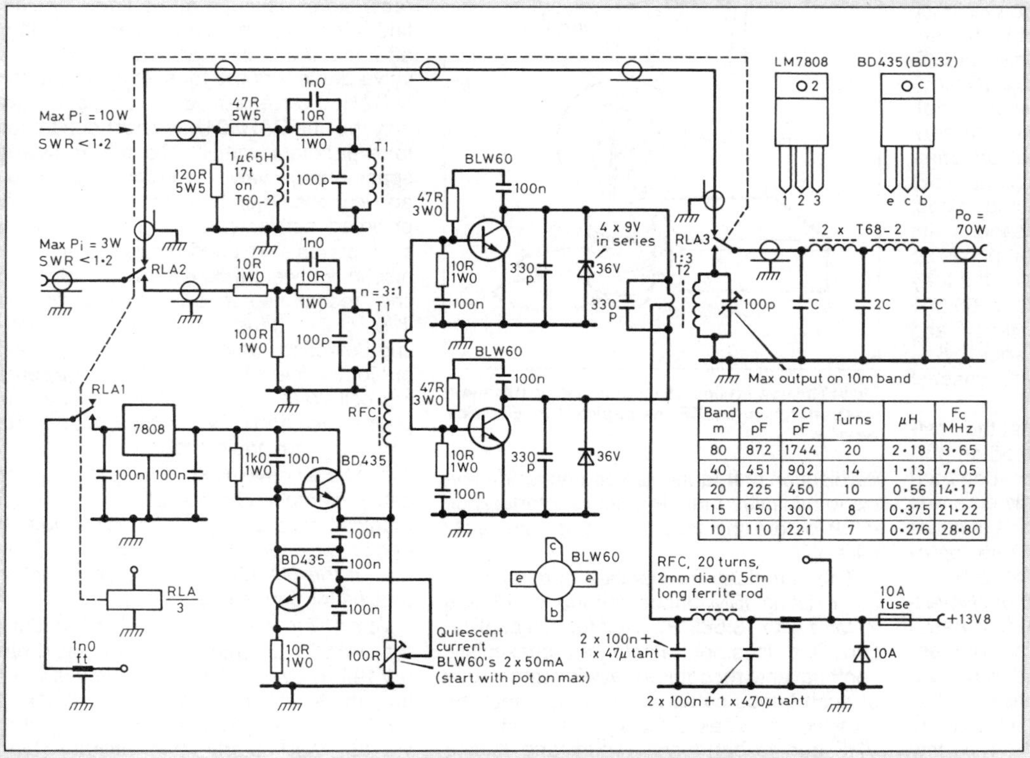

Fig 7: PA0FRI's KISS 70-watt power amplifier using two BLW60 VHF bipolar transistors.

W7EL summarises his long *QST* article as follows: "All modelling tools, no matter how elaborate, powerful and expensive, have limitations. Absolutely none of these can be used sensibly unless you're constantly conscious of their limitations. MININEC is no exception. You must always be alert for answers that don't seem quite right. Are the impedance and gain values *reasonable*? If the antenna is symmetrical, is the pattern symmetrical about the axis you intended to specify? Do the currents change abruptly from one segment to another? Do the results seem too good to be true? *If so, they probably are!*

"We owe MININEC's authors a great debt of gratitude for the pioneering work they have done. They've put fast, accurate antenna analysis within the reach of thousands of amateurs. The programs they have created are very useful for analyzing a variety of antenna designs. Wielded properly, MININEC can be a powerful tool - a weapon against a decades-long void in knowledge about antenna design." His long and detailed article provides an excellent guide that should help MININEC users to avoid the other edge of the sword. But for the amateur-radio antenna erected among all the clutter and metalwork and unexpected resonances of the average urban or residential area, the proof of the pudding still depends on how the real antenna works out in practice.

NEW INDUCTION LIGHT BULBS AND THEIR RFI POTENTIAL

W A BOOTHMAN, G3SWP, and Bill Dykes, G1UKE, have each sent me an article by Tony Sachs, the first from *Electrical Review* (19 April/2 May), the other from the 31 May/13 June issue. Both articles relate to the future marketing in the UK of new, high-efficiency 'induction' or 'electrodeless' light bulbs, developed by Philips as the QL lamp, by GE-Thorn (unnamed) and by Sylvania (IWCF - Induction Wave Compact Fluorescent lamp). These lamps differ to some extent in construction and characteristics but all are energised not directly from 50/60Hz AC mains but from RF energy. They are expected to cost much more than conventional incandescent lamp bulbs (I have seen estimated prices up to about £15 each, at least initially) but they should have an active lifetime of over 60,000 hours (and more at reduced efficiency) and efficiencies (lumens/watt) up to about 65%, equivalent to that of a compact fluorescent tube.

The *New Scientist* suggests that the cost-effectiveness of such lamps (based on purchase price/energy consumption comparisons with conventional bulbs) only emerges when the light is used for thousands of hours per annum (continuous 24-hour use represents roughly 8000 hours/annum) seldom if ever required in a domestic situation. Nevertheless, it seems likely that they will be heavily promoted for both commercial and domestic use on account of their considerable energy-saving ('green') characteristics.

To understand why amateurs are already viewing their introduction over the next few years with some trepidation, it is necessary to appreciate that these lamps have no filament but are excited by induction at a radio frequency which in Europe may be 2.65MHz. The RF causes mercury vapour molecules to strike fluorescent powder on the inside of the bulb; **Fig 8** from one of the *Electrical Review* articles gives an idea of the construction of the Philips QL lamp. An external unit provides the RF power, presumably from a relatively crude form of transmitter-type generator.

To quote from the second ER article: "Another reason for the arrival of the commercial induction lamp is that agreement is close on operating frequencies. The international body which regulates RF allocations has already had one vote to approve RF lamp operation at 2.65MHz. A second vote is needed before this approval can be formalised, probably next year. US suppliers are (already) allowed to use higher frequencies but, says Philips, these are less efficient and will require tighter controls to stay within the allocated band.

"Peter Lees, Sylvania's European marketing manager for fluorescent lamps, believes that there will have to be world-wide stan-

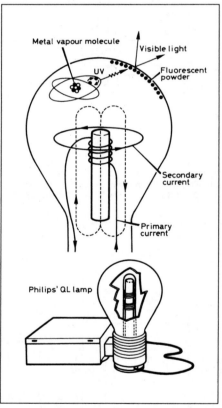

Fig 8: The new Philips QL induction lamp (filamentless) energised by RF. As depicted in *Electrical Review*.

dardisation of frequencies and emission levels to minimise radio frequency interference (RFI) before the induction lamp can really take off."

The American frequencies appear to be the existing ISM bands around 6, 13 and 27MHz with 13.56MHz used for this application. One does not have to be a pessimistic soothsayer to recognise that widespread use of such lamps could significantly affect the reception of weak signals on HF and even VHF due to harmonics, spurii and drifting signals! As G3SWP comments: "Yet more QRM?".

VALVE DATA AND THE DAH50

FIRST, I WOULD LIKE TO acknowledge the safe receipt through Parcelforce of a Flintstones Freezers carton full of post-war Mullard, Brimar, GEC, RCA, Osram, Sylvania valve and valve-application data. There was no indication of the identity of the sender, only an illegible postmark. The parcel has significantly augmented my collection of valve information, thanks!

I can also report that the appeal for information on the interesting Philips DAH50 low-voltage valve with a space-charge grid (*TT*, May, p32) brought a most informative reply from Gerhard Stroessner, DJ2VN, who actually has one in his collection. Enclosed with his letter were articles from German war-time and post-war periodicals (these have been forwarded to Dr Tom Going), some specific to the DAH50, others dealing with space-charge-grid valves in general, including German military types RV2.4T3 and RV2.4P45).

The earliest of these, from the German DASD journal *CQ* (No 3/4. 1941) 'DAH50 - Eine neue Roehre fuer tragbare Geraete' (DAH50 - a new valve for portable radios), was of particular interest as I had previously not been aware that DASD (the pre-war German national amateur radio society) continued publishing its journal in wartime - although I frequently listened (with envy) to German wartime amateur activity (and band-edge beacons) on 3.5, 7, 14 and 28MHz, with German pre-war call prefixes D3 and D4. The *CQ* article had been photocopied by Rudi Staritz, DL3CS, who has written extensively on German Abwehr clandestine radio sets.

DJ2VN writes: "I obtained my DAH50 from a friend in 1942 when he was serving in an air force signals company stationed in Czechoslovakia. He bought the valve from a Prague radio store, although at the time I could not find this valve on sale in Germany. Shortly after the end of the war, about 1948, a local valve-dealer offered for sale a large number of DAH50 valves but quickly sold out. Having only the one DAH50 I have not been tempted to experiment with it. "To my knowledge, space-charge-valves were primarily used for applications other than radio communication or broadcast reception. In the military field, such valves were used in mine detectors and also in lightweight detectors for telephone-line reconnais-sance (military designation: 'Kleiner Drahtlauschempfaenger') as well as line-detecting devices. Small, lightweight audio-amplifiers together with a large searching coil were used to pinpoint buried telephone lines and power cables, with a strong AF test signal applied to the line.

"To date I have no knowledge of any application of space-charge-valves in radio communications or even in clandestine radio. Nor does there appear to have been any industrial use of the DAH50 with only constructional articles for portable receivers."

Apart from the *CQ* 1941 article introducing the DAH-50, an article in *Funkschau* (February 1942) covered valves and circuits for very low anode voltages; *Funk-Technik* (No 13, 1949) provided circuits for space-charge-valves, particularly the military types: *Funkschau*, January 1949 presented some thoughts about space-charge valves.

TOPICS

PAT HAWKER G3VA

DIRECT-CONVERSION CW RECEIVER WITH SIMPLIFIED PHASING-TYPE DEMODULATOR

AS MENTIONED BRIEFLY in *TT* (November 1990, p29), Tim Walford, G3PCJ, has been developing a phasing-type demodulator for use in a CW-only 7MHz direct-conversion transceiver taking advantage of the fact that the accurate quadrature (90°) phase difference needs to be maintained only over the relatively small AF bandwidth involved in CW reception through fairly sharp audio filtering.

His prototype transceiver (**Fig 1**) has its audio bandwidth restricted to about 800+/-300Hz and is based on the use of NE602 double-balanced mixers, BC109 band-pass AF filters centred on 734Hz, all-pass plus and minus 45° phase shifters using a TL072, sharper 734Hz audio filter (TL071) and audio amplifier (LM380). In effect, it requires an extra mixer, filters and audio-phase-shift networks compared to a conventional DC receiver, but reduces the unwanted audio-image sideband by -35dB (voltage). He writes:

"The receiver (**Fig 2**) uses NE602s (or 612s) whose oscillator section can be driven by an external signal from low-impedance RF phase shift networks to obtain +/- 45° phase shift relative to the local oscillator. I used a 3.5MHz VFO with doubler in order to improve stability but this is not essential for the phasing aspect of the receiver.

The incoming signals are fed to both 602 devices, in this case from the two windings on the output of the RF amplifier stage. Outputs from the 602s are filtered with a resonant load (0.1H and 470nF) and further filtered/buffered with a two-pole low-pass filter. These drive the op-amp all-pass phase-lead and phase-lag stages which provide the +/- 45° audio phase shifts required to obtain phase cancellation at the centre frequency of 734Hz.

"The two audio signals are 'added' (combined) at the input to the final narrowband CW filter. The desired audio sideband is most easily selected by changing over one of the 602 outputs to its other output (the two outputs differ by 180°.

"The circuits are set up by tuning a steady signal to produce the undesired beat note at its loudest frequency (which should be about 734Hz) and then adjusting the RF phase-shift trimmer capacitor (65pF) and the audio-balance potentiometer (10k) for minimum signal.

"My measurements show the undesired audio sideband level to be at least 54 times down (-35dB voltage) over the whole audio band compared to the desired 734Hz sideband. While this is not as good as could be achieved by a more complex phasing-type or filter-type receiver it is very good for the small amount of extra circuitry involved. Digital RF phase shifters might be used for a multiband receiver but then the complexity approaches that of a filter rig and is much more complex than the two-capacitors, two-resistors used in this 7MHz receiver.

"At present I am working on a 3.5MHz CW phasing design with improved roll-off of the audio response (hence selectivity for a direct-conversion receiver), and with better strong signal performance by avoiding an RF amplifier stage and incorporating audio AGC. I hope to have this 3.5MHz design available in kit form in the region of £45."

ELECTROMAGNETIC FIELD EXPOSURE

THE PUBLIC IS STILL BEING confused by the wide difference of expert opinion on possible biological (athermal) effects of long-term exposure to electromagnetic fields. An article by Robert Pool in *Nature* (14 February 1991, p554) was headlined 'EMF - cancer link still murky' and pointed out that the mystery surrounding the claimed connection between EMFs and cancer was deepening as more epidemiological studies showed up such odd and inexplicable correlations between childhood leukaemia and black-and-white (but not colour) television and with hair-dryers but not other domestic appliances! One sometimes feels inclined to quote the old adages that statistics can prove anything and that there are 'lies, damned lies and statistics'.

Perhaps more relevant was a BBC Research Report last year (RD 1990/4 'Electro-

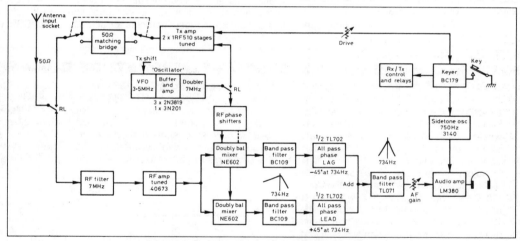

Fig 1: Block outline of G3PCJ's 7MHz CW transceiver incorporating a phasing-type direct-conversion receiver.

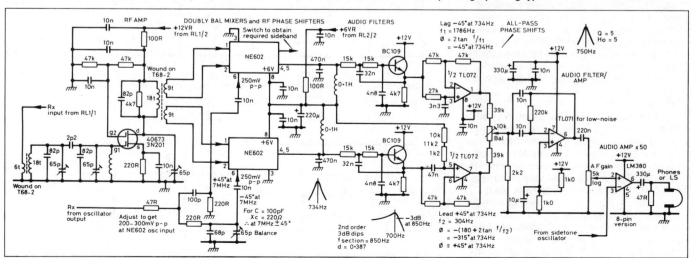

Fig 2: G3PCJ's 7MHz phasing-type receiver which reduces the unwanted audio-image sideband by a factor of 54 (-35dB voltage) measured overall. The 65pF balance trimmer for the NE602s and the 10k balance potentiometer at the output of the TL072 phase-shifters are adjusted for lowest level of the unwanted 734Hz sideband.

magnetic field exposure in broadcast environments' by S Wakeling). To quote from the introductory remarks: "Recently, there has been renewed concern at possible deleterious health effects from exposure to electromagnetic fields with international authorities recommending ever more stringent exposure levels . . . . the areas around broadcast antennas to which a person can safely gain access are becoming increasingly restricted. Broadcasters face a variety of problems when trying to ensure safe operational practices in areas with significant levels of electromagnetic fields, such as exist close to transmitting antennas. The exposure guidelines have become more stringent each time they have been updated . . . . international authorities are tending towards an 'as low as reasonably achievable' principle in the light of inconclusive biological evidence which will create more problems in future . . . . Safety factors are being compounded by incorrect assumptions regarding exposure conditions. The derived field strengths of exposure standards are calculated assuming optimum coupling conditions and far-field, plane-wave exposures whereas, in broadcasting, the potential for hazard is generally confined to the near-field around the transmitting antennas and hence the derived field-strength values are inappropriate for determining true SAR (specific absorption rate) levels and hence the actual level of potential hazard."

SAR is the power (in watts) absorbed per kilogram of tissue, and the BBC Report points out that the biological effect (heating) of a given SAR will depend on the thermoregulatory system of the animal being exposed; humans, it is pointed out, have a very efficient thermoregulatory system.

The Report covers such questions as RF shocks and burns, thermal effects, athermal effects, epidemiological studies etc. It notes that the cancer links have been found only in some studies; others have not found any significant correlation.

An American study, reported by F P Ziemba (*Nature*, 21 February 1991) into possible hazards from the electric and magnetic fields emanating from TV and VDU screens suggests that natural radioactivity (from radon gas) and high electrostatic fields are more likely than EMF to be the cause of various common complaints from computer operators. Radiation levels as high as 6000 alpha disintegrations per minute per 100cm² of viewing-screen area have been detected in computer displays and TV screens. He considers his measurements show that this phenomenon is caused by the electrostatic deposition of charged radon progeny onto the faces of viewing screens. Radon-22 gas is formed by the radioactive decay of naturally occurring uranium-238 and comes from the first metre of underlying soil and rock in many areas. This enters living areas by diffusion, convection and ventilation, with charged clusters of dust and aerosol particles attracted to CRT displays by the electrostatic fields that build up on CRT screens, providing a pumping action that can continue even after the TV or VDU has been turned off. VDU colour monitors show the highest levels of activity.

EARTH LOOP FEEDBACK

AN ARTICLE 'EARTH CURRENTS' by Bob Vernall, ZL2CA, which originally appeared in *Break-in* (date unknown) has been reprinted in *Radio-ZS* (February 1991, p4). It draws attention to what can appear to be a mysterious RF-feedback problem that can occur when a solid-state transceiver *and* an auxiliary unit such as an external speech-processor are fed from the same high-current 12V PSU or battery.

ZL2CA points out that a transceiver rated at 100W RF output fed from a nominal 12V supply may draw up to about 20A at full output which, with SSB, occurs *only* on audio peaks. Even if the wires between transceiver and PSU have a DC resistance of only 5mΩ, then each lead will drop 100mV at the peaks, and this voltage appears between transceiver earth and the mains-earth of the PSU. With a speech processor, handling audio input voltages of about 10mV, connected both to the transceiver earth and the PSU earth line, there can exist the type of earth loop that so often results in problems with assemblies of hi-fi units, but in this case varying along with the SSB waveform. These earth loop cur-

MORE ON THERMISTOR TEMPERATURE COMPENSATION

JOHN BEECH, G8SEQ in describing the most effective VFO temperature-compensation technique using an NTC thermistor/varicap-diode (*TT*, April, p33) wondered whether he could claim genuine originality, or whether the idea had been used in TV tuners or somesuch.

No claims have been received of any use of this technique in professional electronics but Derek Money, G3MKD, who ran the now-closed Hamgear Electronics of Norwich has sent along evidence that he also hit upon using this idea in an amateur-radio VFO in "early 1989" which may or may not have been before G8SEQ began to use it "a couple of years ago". What matters more, is that he also found the system effective. After building a prototype, he advertised "The Hamgear 3-band VFO" intended for use by QRP operators and providing a switched output on three CW bands (3500-3585, 7000-7050 and 10,100-10,150kHz): **Fig 3.**

He still has the prototype built in early 1989 but lost interest in the technique when he received no enquiries from his advertisements. Temperature compensation was optimised at room temperature to around 15Hz per degree shift. Long term stability (3 hours on 7MHz) at room temperature the shift was less than 20Hz.

Postscript: Since writing the above notes, further evidence of thermistors providing temperature compensation of oscillators has come to hand. D A Bundey, G3JQQ, described a similar system to that of G3SEQ in *Two Improvements to the FT7B* (*RadCom*, July 1982, pp582-3). In July 1981, Mike Walters, G3JVL, used an STC G24 thermisor in a stabilised crystal oscilator providing a reference signal at 10,368.000MHz (described shortly afterwards in the *Microwave Newsletter*). The idea of using thermistors to stabilise oscillators (including an 8GHz Gunn diode oscillaor) is discussed in the book *Thermistors* by E D Macklen (1979). Clearly, this idea is an excellent and thoroughly practical method of improving the temperature stability of a VFO and should become an established part of the amateur's armoury.

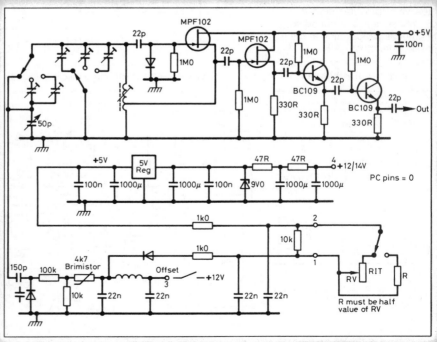

Fig 3: 'Hamgear' three-band VFO with Brimistor (KED 472CY) temperature compensation as announced in 1989 but which never went into production. The prototype built in early 1989 still exists.

rents and voltages can then result in audio distortion not unlike that produced by RF feedback, although in this case RF is not involved and the distortion does not disappear when the transceiver output is fed into a non-radiating dummy antenna.

ZL2CA writes: "A fairly sensitive test of 'power supply feedback' is to use an SSB two-tone tester in place of the microphone. Look for RF envelope variation on an oscilloscope. The two tone signal produces maximum envelope changes and consequently the current drawn from the main power supply is similarly modulated and 'lumpy'. As two-tone drive is increased, look for a form of hum modulation showing up on the RF envelope. If this occurs then it is either a poor power supply or the result of an earth loop causing a form of audio feedback provided that RF feedback is discounted by using a dummy load and provided that the two tone tester is not itself introducing a new earth loop."

If audio feedback of this type is detected, a possible solution is to use genuine double-insulated PSUs for all accessories. These usually have split bobbin transformers, and ZL2CA points out that this is a similar approach to that used for hi-fi audio systems in countering hum loops by using equipment with two-wire mains cords. If the transceiver PSU has negative earth then the station will have all connected accessories earthed, but with a minimum of loops.

For a TNC set-up, a mains isolation transformer can be used to feed power to the computer. An alternative approach is to provide a DC break in every cable that is required to carry low-level audio signals to the transceiver. Audio isolation transformers rated at 600Ω impedance, 1:1 ratio can adequately isolate low or medium impedance audio inputs or outputs. ZL2CA adds that if the PTT control is a DC type (usually grounded to transmit) then an opto-isolator is one of the only ways of providing an equivalent DC signal past a DC break. He also gives further advice on using opto-isolators in connection with TNC installations but points out that each solution usually needs to be customised to the particular combination of TNC and transceiver.

ZL2CA, himself, uses a combination of solutions. An external speech processor has a double-insulated power supply. A TNC cable has 1:1 audio isolation transformers and a 4N33 opto-isolator for PTT control.

I have no idea how common is this problem of 'power supply feedback'. As ZL2CA points out, no such problem exists with SSB linear power amplifiers using valves since the HT currents vary at most by a few hundred milliamps rather than the tens of amperes of all-solid-state transceivers with their external power supplies and connecting cables.

THE UNIVERSAL VFO

IN AN UNUSUAL coincidence, the June 1991 issue of both *QST* and *CQ* included articles on building general-purpose VFOs by the same author (Doug DeMaw, W1FB) with much in common, although some circuit details of the two VFOs differ. In 'Build a Universal VFO' (*QST*), W1FB describes a straightforward VFO suitable for a variety of applications, such as tunable oscillator for superhet

FERRITE-BEAD CHOKE BALUNS

JOHN S BELROSE, VE2CV, in 'Transforming the Balun' (*QST*, June 1991 pp30-33) shows how the W2DU choke 1:1 balun, comprising simply a number of ferrite beads slipped over a short length of coaxial cable, can serve as the basis for excellent ferrite-bead-choke current baluns with 4:1 and 9:1 impedance transformations. He considers that the W2DU balun is: "The best so far devised. By *current balun* I mean a balun that, with each of its balanced output ports terminated in unequal resistances, forces essentially equal, opposite-in-phase current into each resistance. The traditional toroidal balun is a *voltage balun* in that, terminated as just described, it produces equal, opposite-in-phase *voltages* across the two resistances.

"For minimal radiation from a balanced transmission line, the currents on both its conductors must be equal in amplitude and opposite in phase; that is, there must be no current discontinuity on the radiator at the antenna feed point . . . . For antennas fed with a coaxial transmission line, the goal to achieve is little or no current on the outside surface of the coax shield. *In general, these requirements cannot be met without a current balun.*" The original W2DU balun (as described some years ago in *TT*) used 50 beads of No 73 ferrite (eg Amidon No FB-73-2401) on about twelve inches of Teflon dielectric cable, with suitable connectors to make a practical balun for 1.8 to 30MHz.

VE2CV provides a de-

tailed resume of the differences between the performance of toroidal and choke baluns, but also breaks new ground by showing how two ferrite-bead baluns can be used to provide a 4:1 transformation (50Ω to 200Ω-balanced) using short lengths of 93Ω cable (RG62A up to 100W, RG-133A for 1kW level), and three 1:1 baluns for 9:1 impedance transformation (50Ω to 450Ω-balanced) using 150Ω cable (RG-125 is difficult to obtain even in the USA and VE2CV suggests that other impedances can be used rather less effectively). **Fig 4** shows the connections for 1:1, 4:1 and 9:1 impedance transformations.

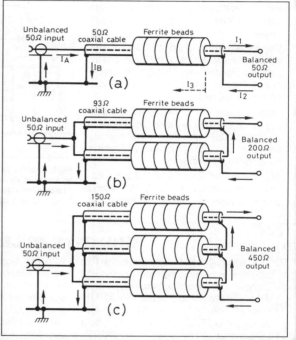

Fig 4: Ferrite-bead choke baluns as described by VE2CV (*QST*, June 1991). (a) The basic W2DU 1:1 choke balun using about 50 ferrite beads threaded on 12-inches of coaxial cable, using 50Ω coax for 50Ω balun; 75Ω cable for 75Ω balun, etc. (b) A 4:1 current balun based on two ferrite-bead coax-shield chokes. (c) Three ferrite-bead-choke baluns can be combined to form a 9:1 impedance transformation.

or direct-conversion receiver, transmitter/transceiver VFO, signal generator etc. His unit covers 2.137 to 2.586MHz but, with an appropriate tuned circuit, can work in any required band between about 1.8 and 10MHz. It has two output levels for driving active or passive mixers; with a 12V supply the 'high' output is about 22.3dBm from an extra bipolar amplifier stage (not in the 6.45 to 6.75MHz *CQ* design) which provides about 6.6dBm (4.2V P-P over 500Ω). Both designs use 2N4416 FETs as the oscillator with a source-follower FET isolating buffer, although the *QST* oscillator is a Hartley with tapped coil; the one in *CQ* is a Colpitts, with a source-follower buffer: **Fig 5**.

W1FB's *CQ* article 'The practical aspects of VFO design plus how to build one' concentrates on the choice of VFO components, advice on obtaining good stability, questions

of short and long-term stability/drift, etc. The following is a digest of some of the points made in this article:

(1) Avoid using silver-mica fixed capacitors in VFOs; although once a popular choice they do not exhibit uniform temperature characteristics. W1FB prefers NP0 ceramic types, with polystyrene capacitors (slight negative drift characteristic) as a low cost second choice.

(2) An 'ideal' VFO would have no magnetic core in the tuning coil but would be air-cored on a ribbed ceramic former, seldom suitable for modern 'miniature' equipment. W1FB uses No 6 material toroid cores (eg Amidon T50-6; yellow) or equivalent slug-tuned core material. Coils after winding should be doped twice with, for example, General Cement polystyrene Q Dope.

(3) Select the right oscillator device: W1FB dislikes bipolar transistors for this application as they tend to exhibit greater changes of internal resistance and capacitance with temperature than a JFET or MOSFET. He considers that the 2N4416 is his favourite device for VFOs since it has a high pinch-off characteristic and gives more output than is available from the MPF102 family of FETs. Dual-gate devices (40673, 3N211, 3N212) provide good performance and gates 1 and 2 can be tied together so that they function as single-gate devices without the need to bias gate 2.

(4) If possible, use a good mechanical tuning capacitor rather than an electronic tuning diode (which changes capacitance with temperature): "Double-bearing capacitors that turn freely are best; avoid using capacitors with aluminium vanes - plated brass or iron vanes are better."

(5) Use 1/2W carbon-film or carbon-composition resistors. Because of their greater physical size they tend to be more stable than 1/4W or 1/8W resistors as they can absorb more heat.

(6) Two-or-more fixed capacitors in parallel (eg two 50pF NP0 ceramic capacitors to provide 100pF) provide more surface area than a single capacitor, minimizing heating from RF current.

(7) W1FB uses single-sided G-10 glass epoxy board material for VFO PCBs and advises against using double-sided PCBs or phenolic-base board material. He thinks that with double-sided boards, the etched-side conductors form unstable low-Q capacitors in combination with the ground-plane side of the PCB. He does not mention constructional practices not based on etched PCBs but see G3KMG's remarks in July *TT*.

(8) Physically separate, with a dividing heat-shield made from PC board, the oscillator from the buffer/amplifier stages. The cover for the VFO box can then be vented above the buffer/amplifier stages with the PCB-stock shield acting as a heat baffle.

(9) Use lowest practicable oscillator voltage (eg 6 to 8V) to reduce internal heating, regulated by a zener diode or a small three-terminal regulator.

(10) Filter the DC leads entering the VFO box with an RF choke and 0.001µF feedthrough capacitor to keep RF energy from entering the VFO circuit.

(11) Do not use low-cost plastic trimmer capacitors in a VFO. Use miniature air trimmers or NP0 ceramic units.

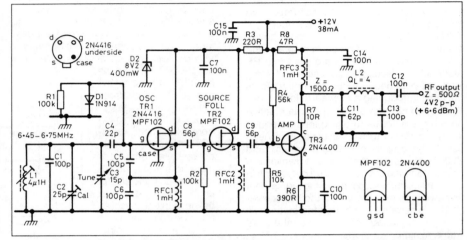

Fig 5: The VFO described by W1FB in *CQ* covering 6.45 to 6.75MHz but suitable for other frequency ranges by appropriate changes to L1/C1. C1, C4, C5 and C8 are NP0 ceramic or polystyrene types. C2 is a ceramic trimmer and C3 a miniature 15pF air variable. L1 is 32 turns of No 28 enamel wire on Amidon T50-6 (yellow) toroid. L2 has 25 turns (No 28 enam) on Amidon FT-37-61 ferrite toroid.

SHUNT-TYPE CRYSTAL LADDER FILTERS

TO THE BEST OF MY knowledge, the first appearance in the amateur radio press of a description of constructing ladder-type crystal MF filters was by J Pochet, F6BQP, in *Radio-REF*, May 1976, with an English-language digest in *TT*, September 1976 (and a full translation in *Wireless World*, May 1977). This was soon followed by the excellent series giving full design data by J Hardcastle, G3JIR (*RadCom*, December 1976, January, February, September 1977). Both F6BQP and G3JIR drew upon the classic paper by M Dishal (*Proc IEEE*, September 1965). Since then, most designs have followed basically similar lines but show that it is possible to cut costs by using low-cost colour-TV crystals (4.43MHz PAL, 3.58MHz NTSC).

"A different approach to ladder filters" by John Pivnichny, N2DCH, (*Communications Quarterly*, Winter 1991, pp72-76) is subtitled 'Another way to make crystal filters'. In effect, N2DCH puts the crystals in shunt with the signal rather than in the usual series configuration. The main difference between them is that the shunt filter has its steeper cut off on the low-frequency side (termed an upper-sideband filter) whereas the series filter has its steep cut off slope on the high frequency side (lower-sideband filter). N2DCH considers that the shunt filter may be preferable for narrow bandwidth filters (eg CW filters) particularly when using relatively low-Q plated crystals in HC-18 holders, although he admits that the series-type lower-sideband filter is usually preferable for the wider SSB filters. He points out that it is possible to create a pair of filters (one shunt, one series) to provide switched sideband selection with just one BFO crystal. N2DCH provides design data for shunt-type filters plus an example of a CW filter designed for 3470Ω termination; **Figs 6 and 7**.

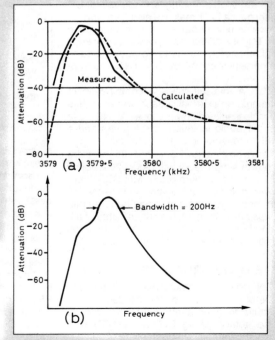

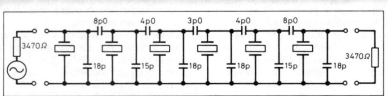

Fig 6: Shunt-type crystal ladder CW filter using six 3.58MHz NTSC crystals designed for 3470Ω terminations. Crystals should be matched to within 100Hz (TV crystals are often only specified as within 300Hz but usually are within 200Hz).

Fig 7: (a) Calculated and measured response curves for the CW filter. (b) Filter response resulting from use of poorly matched crystals.

Performance tests for the *CQ* unit are given for a frequency of 6.7MHz with a room temperature of 70°F (21°C). Short-term drift amounted to 2Hz during the first 5 minutes of operation; over a period of some 35 minutes, the frequency drifted 75Hz lower, then back to within 10Hz of the initial frequency before stabilization occurred. This was with the unit terminated with a 560Ω resistor; when this was shunted with a 10Ω resistor, the frequency shifted by 4Hz showing good isolation. The ARRL Laboratory test on the *QST* unit at around 2MHz gives the frequency drift as less than 4Hz in the initial 4 minutes.

MODIFIED G2DAF LINEAR AMPLIFIER

IT IS NOW AROUND 30 years since publication by G R B Thornley of the G2DAF series of SSB designs, including his high-grade HF receiver, his Mark 1 and 2 SSB transmitters, and the G2DAF 400W PEP linear amplifier. The linear amplifier, first published in the April, 1963 *RSGB Bulletin* (former title of *RadCom*) with additional notes in the May issue, was later published in a condensed form in *SSB Equipment* which also reprinted the G2DAF SSB Transmitter Mark 2: **Fig 8**.

The linear amplifier was based on the passive-grid technique suitable for being driven from an SSB exciter/transmitter of around 50W PEP. The original model used two 4-125A (Mullard QY3-125) valves but it was noted that the method of operation was suitable for any of the commonly used tetrode or pentode amplifier valves including the 4-65, 4-125, 4-250, 4X150A, 4X250B and 813. The valves were operated under zero bias conditions without any of the complications of carefully regulated screen supplies, the screen voltage derived by rectifying a small portion of the input signal in a voltage-doubler.

G2DAF pointed out that "in many ways the 813 is a quite remarkable valve - its performance in the G2DAF amplifier is quite outstanding. With 2.5kV anode potential, it is possible to run *one* 813 valve to 400W PEP output. This is possible without degradation of linearity, and 'on the air' reports indicate that the intermodulation distortion products are at a level 45dB down in relation to the wanted voice sideband signal. This is about 5dB better than the writer's amplifier using a pair of 4-125A valves."

The G2DAF linear amplifier still in the 1990s represents a valid approach but the input circuit may require a minor modification for use with current solid-state transceivers and/or for different valves. A modified 2DAF amplifier has been described by P J Liebenburg, ZS2PL, (*Radio-ZS*, January 1991) with additional suggestions by Lou Gatzke, ZS6AOZ, (*Radio-ZS*, April 1991). ZS2PL, (formerly ZE5JU) has been using a modified 2DAF with two 4X150A valves since 1970, driving it from a Collins KWM-2 transceiver, but then added a 1:3 step-up toroid transformer to avoid a mismatch to his ICOM 730 solid-state transceiver.

Fig 9 shows modification to the original G2DAF design which had two 4-125A valves and a single passive-grid resistor (300Ω) made up from five 1W resistors for SSB operation, The three 50Ω, 50W dummy-load resistors used by ZS2PL would seem very generously rated, even when driven by an

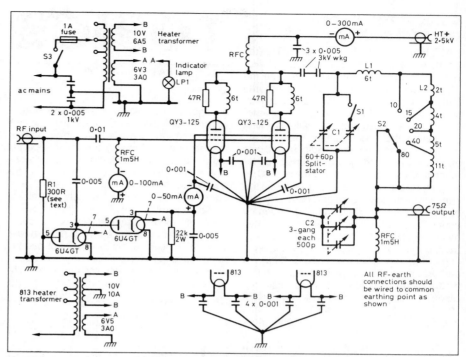

Fig 8: Circuit diagram of the 1963 G2DAF linear amplifier. S1 open for 28, 21 and 14MHz, closed for 7 and 3.5MHz. Fixed capacitors are mica except the three 3kV 0.005uF disk ceramics. The anode RFC should be of the split-winding type without series resonances on any of the HF bands, particularly if the amplifier is intended also for use on 10, 18 and 24MHz.

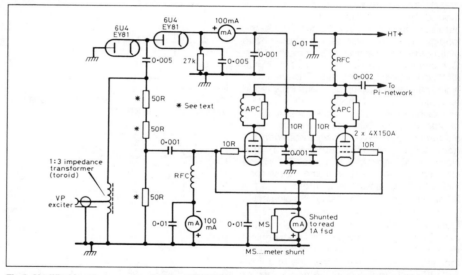

Fig 9: Modified input arrangement of the G2DAF linear as recently described by ZS2PL/ZS6AOZ.

ICOM 730. ZS2PL states: "The 1:3 toroid step-up transformer provides a better match to modern solid-state rigs. The RF voltage at the top of this resistor chain is of the order of 100V or more and is rectified and doubled as an 'audio varying DC voltage' and applied to the screen-grids of the amplifier valves, with excellent linearity. In the absence of RF drive there is no screen voltage and the standing current is very low.

"The reason for the voltage divider input circuit was due to the fact that 3W of drive would destroy the 4X150As (μ = 12mA/V) and the grid drive is therefore taken from the lower end of the chain. This will have to be taken from higher up the resistor chain, even from the top as G2DAF did in his original design, for driving a pair of 4-125A valves.

"This type of linear has many desirable features, including low cost, low component

count, stability due to the swamping effect of the passive grid input load and simplicity of construction. To the best of my knowledge there are no solid state diodes which will reliably handle the RF input voltages, and thermionic diodes are used in the voltage-doubler arrangement as in the original circuit; note that the cathodes and heaters of these rectifiers must not be connected; I have used two EY81 television rectifier valves without failure since 1970 and can recommend them. The meter shunt is earthed right at the amplifier cathodes, and the leads run in shielded wire away from RF to the meter which is mounted in a shielded can."

It must be stressed that a linear amplifier with an EHT supply of around 2.5kV calls for very careful construction and generously rated components as well as stringent safety precautions during setting up and testing, etc. ❑

OSCILLATOR BASICS, CRYSTALS AND THE VXO.

MIKE HALL, G3USC (Euroquartz/Brookes Crystals of Crewkerne, Somerset), was provoked into writing to me by the item on the 'Harris' cathode-follower LC oscillator/Q Multiplier (*TT*, February 1991) - an item which he felt contributed little of value to oscillator technology. But also, to put it briefly, to reflect his feeling that too much of the material published in the amateur-radio periodicals and books tends to ignore the basic fundamentals of oscillators, both crystal and LC, in magnifying the minor variations between the relatively few basic configurations. He believes that many oscillator circuits, presented under the name of the designer, who may have done little more than introduce a minor (but possibly useful - *G3VA*) modification to one of the very few basic circuits: "Had the authors attempted to explain the basic theory a little better instead of trying to make the reader run before he could walk, I know that I for one would have had, much earlier than I did, a better understanding of the fundamental principles involved.

"The two, and only two, conditions which must be satisfied for oscillation to take place at the wanted frequency are the Barkhausen Criteria, namely that the initial gain around the oscillatory loop (the loop gain) must be greater than unity and that the phase shift around the loop at that frequency must be zero. Non linearity or an AGC circuit limits the loop gain to exactly unity after a (short) period of time which is determined by the circuit final Q, having taken into account the Q-multiplier effect of the positive feedback. The amplitude would otherwise build up and something would become exceedingly hot! . . . . All oscillators employing a feedback network consisting only of one inductive element and two capacitive elements (or vice versa) which provide the necessary phase shift of 180° around a single stage of gain, also ideally giving 180° phase shift, can be boiled down to the Pierce (one inductive, two capacitive elements) and the Miller (two inductive, one capacitive elements).

"But what, you may be asking, about the Colpitts, Gourier-Clapp, Hartley, Vackar and others? If you check these oscillators against the basic Miller and Pierce - remembering that the Miller oscillator depends upon the 'Miller Effect' (ie the effective anode-grid or collector-base capacitance) - you will find that the differences are no more than which active-device electrode is at earth potential or, if tuneable, how the tuning is arranged. With transistors, the Pierce had the emitter earthed, but in the Colpitts it is the collector. Similarly the Miller has the emitter earthed; for the Hartley it is the collector. Or, to look at the effective tuned circuit, is it the capacitive arm that is tapped? - a Pierce. Or is it the inductive arm that is tapped? - a Miller: **Fig 1**.

"The bona-fide variants (Colpitts, Hartley, Gourier-Clapp, Vackar etc) do indeed offer advantages for specific applications: for example better amplitude stability over a wide tuning range, or better frequency stability with supply-voltage variation."

But G3USC was far from happy with the claims made for the 'Harris' oscillator which he considers to be merely an unexciting Hartley variant of the Miller, or in another configuration a Colpitts variant of the Pierce, with no particular merits of its own. He believes that the term Class A - if by such is meant good gain linearity over the full operating cycle - can be applied only to oscillators where the amplitude is held at a low level by a separate AGC circuit, an approach that is commonly adopted in high-quality oscillators.

Subsequently, G3USC admitted that his criticisms of the way oscillators are commonly presented in the amateur-radio media were influenced by his professional experience in dealing with enquiries from amateurs who, he considers, usually fail to specify correctly the crystals they order. This has the

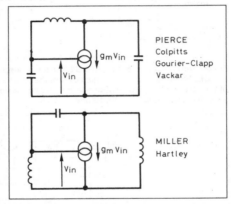

Fig 1: The two basic single active-device oscillator circuits with some derivatives.

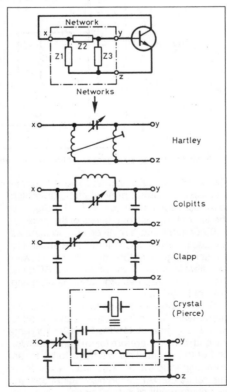

Fig 2: How the three feedback impedances are arranged in Hartley, Colpitts, Clapp and Pierce oscillators.

result that the crystals do not work as intended, often leading to lengthy (and always costly) correspondence advising how to specify crystals for use in specific circuits and applications: "Being myself a radio amateur made me sympathetic to this problem but it sometimes required second-guessing which could result in the crystal still not doing exactly what was required; the result a dissatisfied customer and the risk of acquiring a bad name for my company. Unlike catalogued components which can be bought and sold by part number, the sale of quartz products which have to be made to special order is a hazardous business indeed when dealing with a hobbyist."

It is thus important that amateurs should recognise that crystals behave differently in different circuit arrangements, with different load impedances, with different drive levels, or in series-resonant or overtone oscillators. It would clearly be impossible, each time a different oscillator circuit was published in *TT* or elsewhere, to provide detailed theoretical information at a level capable of being understood by newcomers and old-timers alike, together with a full guide on how to specify crystals, but I can claim to have referred to these topics from time to time.

Some 25 years ago a digest of information from the 1960s booklet *Guide to the specification and use of quartz oscillator crystals* published by EEA (then the Radio Communication & Electronic Engineering Association) was given in *TT* and subsequently reproduced in all editions of *Amateur Radio Techniques*. (The seventh edition - ART7 - has been out of print for several years but has just been reprinted; hopefully one day there may be an ART8). The 1960s EEA 36-page booklet was clearly published in an attempt to overcome the difficulties that resulted from a lack of understanding on how correctly to specify crystals then evident even among professional engineers. It is by no means certain that even today this a problem affecting only radio amateurs!

More recently (*TT*, January 1984, pp40-42) I included some information on crystal basics, the effects of load capacitance, 'sleeping sickness' in crystals, 'rubber crystals' and the use of low-cost crystals and ceramic resonators. Again in *TT*, September 1989, p43, I reproduced a diagram from Professor Mike Underhill's, G3LHZ, IEE Conference tutorial paper 'Fundamental limitations of oscillator performance'. This diagram (**Fig 2**) shows the three basic network components in terms of Hartley, Colpitts, Clapp and crystal (Pierce) oscillators.

Yet undoubtedly there remains some confusion about the basics of crystal oscillators. Recently, for example, Jesper Fogh Bang, OZ1XB, enquired how and why a variable crystal oscillator works. He questioned how it is possible to alter the frequency of a "solid rock" of quartz. Such a question can be answered only by considering the electrical equivalent of a crystal (**Fig 3(a)**) and the recognition that like any other resonant circuit, its frequency can be changed, if only slightly, by changing the external impedance into which it is connected. In effect, in a VXO, one does not change the resonant frequency of the crystal itself, but adds external 'trimming' components in the form of a variable capacitance plus in some cases additional external inductance of as high a Q as possible.

The extent to which one can control the frequency of a VXO is governed by the parameters L, C_i, R, C_o of the equivalent circuit and these will vary with different types of crystal. It will be noted from Fig 3(a) that a crystal provides at the same time both parallel and series-tuned resonant circuits, slightly spaced from each other. A significant difference between a conventional LC circuit and a crystal is the sharpness of these resonances, governed by the Q which, for a quartz plate, may be between about 10,000 and 1,000,000 compared with about 300 for a high-grade inductance/capacitance tuned circuit. Crystals have very high inductance, very low internal capacitance: in rough terms representative values for a 400kHz crystal could be about L = 7.61H, C_i = 0.02pF, C_o = 16pF and R = 400Ω - notice the value in Henrys rather than the usual mH or μH!

With the usual 'parallel-resonance' form of oscillator, the crystal unit is designed to operate as an inductive impedance connected to an amplifier which appears capacitive at the crystal socket. It is this load capacitance which is the main external influence in determining the precise operating frequency. Crystal units are designed for a specific load impedance, with crystals marked with their parallel resonant frequency for a standard value of load capacitance: usually 30pF (formerly 20pF) in the UK, 32pF in the USA.

With a different load impedance, the frequency of oscillation changes slightly, although excessive loading may result in no or unreliable oscillation. For relatively small changes in load impedance, the frequency changes a small amount without affecting the stability and activity of the crystal. This is most easily affected by putting a variable reactance either in series or parallel with the crystal, the choice being decided by the nature of the oscillator circuit. For example, with a Pierce/Colpitts oscillator, the load capacitance can be changed by putting a variable capacitor across the crystal socket or in series with the crystal: **Fig 3(b) and (c)**. The degree to which the frequency changes with a change in load impedance depends in part on the relationship between C_i and C_o. The primary use of such frequency 'pulling' is to provide a trimmer on VHF equipments to compensate for the gradual change of crystal resonance due to 'ageing'. As noted in *TT* (January 1984), a typical HC6/U style of plated crystal with a nominal frequency of 4055.526kHz (series resonance

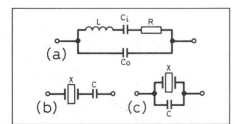

Fig 3: (a) The electrical equivalent of a quartz crystal unit; (b) An external series capacitor tends to raise the frequency of oscillation; (c) A parallel capacitor tends to lower it. Additional frequency shift can be achieved with a combination of external capacitance and inductance.

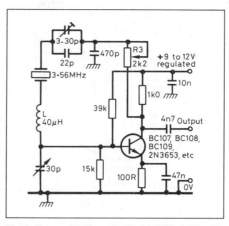

Fig 4: Representative practical 3.5MHz VXO with inductive and capacitive loading providing a tuning range of about 3.5kHz at 3.5MHz without significantly degrading the stability. With some (older) crystals an appreciably greater tuning range can be achieved provided a high-grade, high-Q, mechanically stable loading inductance (see *TT*, June 1984 'The VXO revisited').

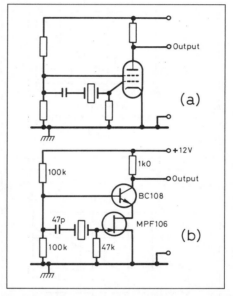

Fig 5: (a) Modified Pierce crystal oscillator using the screen-grid of a tetrode or pentode valve to provide the feedback path but with the output taken from the 'electron-coupled' anode; (b) Using a hybrid cascode arrangement with FET and bipolar transistor to form a solid-state equivalent of (a). (*Electronics Australia*).

4053.960kHz) at a circuit loading of 30pF might have a frequency of 4056.976 for 10pF loading and 4054.518kHz at 100 pF loading, a span of about 2.5kHz. VXO circuits (eg **Fig 4**) are designed to enhance this frequency variation, by adding external inductive as well as capacitance reactance. For HC6/U plated crystals the maximum effective pulling range, without significant degradation of stability, is of the order of 1.5kHz per MHz, ie some 15kHz at 10MHz. The larger, older crystals in air-gap mountings (eg FT243) can give greater range of stable variation but it should be appreciated that individual crystals vary and that departing from the conditions from which a crystal is intended may have other deleterious effects. In any crystal oscillator it is desirable to keep the crystal drive as low as possible: less than 5mW up to 10MHz for HC6/U and similar small plated crystals; less

than 1mW for overtone circuits or crystals above 10MHz. Older non-plated crystals can be driven rather more heavily but, for long-term stability, drive levels should always be kept low.

To round off this rather long section, it seems worth drawing attention to an item in the 'Circuit & Design Ideas' feature of *Electronics Australia* (August 1991, p66) contributed by R H Bennett of Auckland, New Zealand, as follows:

"A crystal oscillator circuit which was often used with tetrode and pentode valves was a modified Pierce oscillator (**Fig 5 (a)**). This is a form of electron-coupled oscillator, the feedback path being from screen-grid to control-grid, with the screen-grid used as the oscillator 'anode'. Output is taken from the anode with no direct connection to the actual oscillator circuit - this aids stability. (It also permits a harmonic tuned circuit to be included in the anode circuit to provide frequency doubling in the one stage - *G3VA*).

The circuit shown in Fig 5(a) is not directly convertible to FET use, because the gates in the FET do not draw current as did the screen grid of a valve. However, using a hybrid cascode circuit with FET as the lower stage and a bipolar transistor as the upper stage, the circuit (**Fig 5(b)**) behaves like the valve modified Pierce oscillator.

MORE ON COMPACT LOOP TRANSMITTING ANTENNAS

INTEREST CONTINUES IN the use of compact loop antennas for transmission, for reception and for direction-finding. This month there is space only to consider the development of HF transmitting loops ('magnetic antennas') along the lines described by Roberto Craighero, I1ARZ, in *Radio Communication* (14 MHz and above, Feb 89, pp38-42; 1.8, 3.5 and 7MHz, Feb 1991, pp38-40) and in the various references quoted in his articles, including many *TT* items since 1967 [see also 'Loop Antennas - Facts, not fiction', *RadCom* last month and this, and this month's *Eurotek* - Ed]. Their use has become well established, with few disappointments provided always that the basic design criteria are followed.

Dick Kelsall, G4FM, has rearranged the equations given by Ted Hart, W5QJR, in the 1988 edition of *The ARRL Antenna Book*. He writes: "Quite a number of amateurs are now using small loop antennas basically along the lines originally developed in the 1960s for the US military and finding them of value, particu-

	14MHz	7MHz
Radiation resistance	0.78Ω	0.048Ω
Loss resistance		
(22mm tube)	0.17Ω	0.012Ω
Efficiency	97.8%	80%
Inductance	4.7 μH	4.7 μH
Reactance	413Ω	206.6Ω
Tuning Capacitance	27.5pF	110pF
Q	435	3443

The last three values are readily calculated from the preceding ones.

Table 1

larly if they have a restricted QTH. The equations given by W5QJR provide a most helpful insight into the design of these loops. A little rearrangement makes them easier to use and to decide on the best size for the bands required.

"In designing a loop it is convenient to think in terms of circumference (S) only and to express the enclosed area of a loop (A) in terms of S: $A = S^2 / (4 \Pi)$. Further it helps to use "S x F" (circumference x frequency) as the variable when plotting radiation resistance (R_r), loss resistance (R_l) and efficiency. Since wavelength (metres) x frequency (MHz) = 300, one can see from the graphs (**Fig 6**) where the practical limits to loop circumference lie (0.125 to 0.25λ). Working in feet, 300 becomes the familiar number of 984.

"For example, a loop to cover 7 to 14MHz would need to have a circumference of about 0.125 λ on 7MHz and 0.25λ on 14MHz. Thus 14 x S = 246 for the quarter-wave on 14MHz, giving S = 17.6ft, ie a loop diameter of 5.6ft." From the graphs, **Table 1** can be produced.

Several novel features are to be found in the loop antennas initially designed by Zygmund Chowaniec, G3PTN, and subsequently also constructed, in a slightly different form, by G H Lucas, G3TWE. Both loops are intended primarily for efficient operation on 7MHz, but function with lower efficiency on 3.5MHz (G3TWE also mentions 10MHz).

G3PTN writes: "I started two years ago with a loop for the higher end of the HF spectrum, made along orthodox lines. My conclusion was that there is not much to be gained in performance in comparison with a good dipole antenna if you have space for this. (A point emphasised in I1ARZ's 1989 article - *G3VA*). However, the situation is different on the lower HF spectrum where there are a number of benefits, size being but one.

"For optimum efficiency, the circumference should be about 5 or 10% less than a quarter-wave at the required frequency. To construct a loop from 25mm or 30mm copper tubing presents a number of problems since, unless the tubing can be formed into a circle, it is likely to be made into a square, hexagon or octagon, introducing joint resistance with consequent lowering of the Q.

"I decided to use coaxial cable, rather than tubing, but instead of using a single loop I constructed two loops in parallel, along the lines of a folded dipole, spaced 3in apart. My cable is standard ¼in (RG8U) coax, 32ft per loop, forming an 8ft square (using quad-like spreaders and a centre pole). This loop is designed for maximum efficiency on 7MHz.

"According to computer calculations, such spaced cables offer a performance roughly similar to that of 3in-diameter tubing. Predicted and measured bandwidths agree.

"Mechanically, it is rather difficult to mount a tuning capacitor at the top of a loop. Current distribution in the loop is approximately uniform but nevertheless there is maximum current opposite the high-voltage open gap across which the tuning capacitor is connected. It is thus advantageous, both mechanically and electrically, to have the capacitor at the base of the loop and the coupling loop at the top, the reverse of the orthodox arrangement. In practice, such an ar-

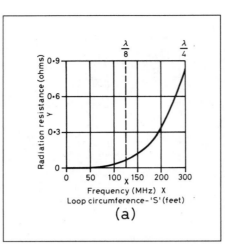
(a)

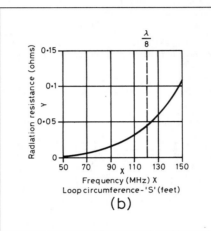
(b)

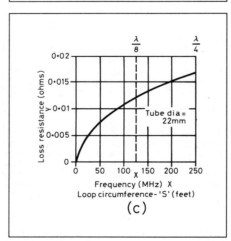
(c)

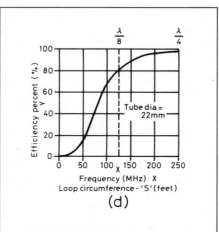
(d)

rangement appears to give improved performance for a given height of the loop over ground. No adverse effect was apparent from the capacitor being at the lower end.

"It appears to be common practice for the coupling loop to be half-shielded rather than a true Faraday shield. The reason may be that this can make it easier to obtain a unity SWR. It is accepted that there is a definite relationship between the conductor sizes of the link coupling and of the antenna loop, a factor of five or ten or so. If the link is made of RG8 cable with 25mm tubing, this will result in a shielded-half of a ratio 25:1. A loop made on the lines as above produced at best a 1.4:1 SWR. A loop constructed of RG8 cable, using outer as a conductor, produced immediately 1:1 SWR. A Faraday shield was made using aluminium foil all the way round, reducing the pick-up of local electrical interference etc with the SWR remaining 1:1."

G3PTN's notes are rather cryptic and it seems useful to add comments made by G H Lucas, G3TWE, even though to some extent these duplicate the statements of G3PTN. G3TWE writes:

"To re-cap, the basic design criteria for a compact loop antenna:

(a) Ohmic resistance must be minimum;

(b) Area enclosed must be maximum, hence a circular loop gives better performance than an equivalent square;

(c) The Q must be maximum even though this will result in very low bandwidth at the lower frequencies; any attempt to earth the main loop at the current node will degrade the Q;

(d) The tuning capacitor *must* be of the highest quality, with wide spacing and preferably split-stator. This is expensive, if bought new, but costs can be re-couped in the construction of the main loop; my 3.5/7/10MHz loop cost £85, the cost of the capacitor and its motorised drive;

(e) The diameter of the conductor of the main loop must be as large as possible, preferably about 50mm copper tubing with no soldered connections or joints, where only a single loop is to be used.

"The problem presented by (e) can be overcome by using two 10m lengths of good coaxial cable, inners and outers strapped together in parallel and spaced by about 4in.

Fig 6: A useful series of graphs by G4FM to aid the design of compact loop transmitting antennas. (a) Radiation resistance; (b) Radiation resistance (expanded for low frequency x circumference products); (c) Loss resistance (25mm tubing); (d) Efficiency; (e) Inductance.

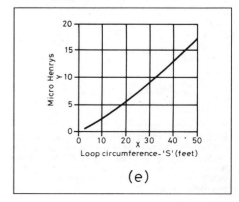
(e)

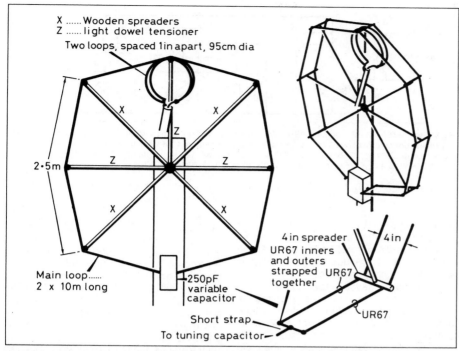

X ......Wooden spreaders
Z ......light dowel tensioner
Two loops, spaced 1in apart, 95cm dia

2·5m

Main loop......
2 x 10m long

250pF variable capacitor

4in spreader
UR67 inners
and outers
strapped
together   UR67

4in

UR67

Short strap

To tuning capacitor

Fig 7: G3TWE's version of the two-coaxial-cable loop antenna originally developed by G3PTN.

This, to RF, will look like 50mm or more copper tubing. G3PTN uses RG8U, I use UR67, the conductors being braced by diagonal spreaders to form a square, and then tensioned further by light-weight spreaders to push the complete assembly into the form of an octagon, thus nearly satisfying (b) above: see **Fig 7**.

"The capacitor assembly in its box weighs about 2kg. It seems poor engineering practice to have this waving about at the top. As with the G3PTN original, the whole antenna is turned upside-down: the capacitor at the bottom, the coupling loop at the top. It must be remembered that there maybe up to 5kV of RF at the tuning capacitor - the antenna should be sited or protected so that there is no likelihood of any person (particularly children) or pets etc coming in to contact with high RF voltages.

"The diameter of the coupling loop is not critical; anything between 10 to 20% of the diameter of the main loop should be satisfactory. What is critical is the ratio of the size of the materials used in the loops (compare to the principles of gamma matching for Yagi arrays). Anyone who is unable to obtain a better SWR than about 1.3:1 with an accurately tuned loop is probably using the wrong gauge of conductor in the coupling loop. My coupling loop is again fabricated from two turns of the same UR67 cable used in the main loop, inners and outers strapped and spaced about 1in. This spacing may be varied to adjust the SWR for optimum on the highest frequency band, the lower bands will then follow.

"The loop will work with normal inductive coupling and it is unnecessary to go to the complication of using Faraday or half-Faraday coupling until development work is completed. SWR and transmitter performance will not be affected. However, there is considerable advantage to be gained in terms of static and electrical noise level in the receive-mode by using a full Faraday screen on the

coupling loop. G3PTN has achieved this by threading the coupling loop through a length of garden hose and wrapping the whole issue in aluminium foil.

"Mounting: If the loop is to be mounted horizontally then it should be well up in the air - preferably a half-wave above ground. In most cases, however, such a loop will be mounted in the vertical plane and can be just a few feet above ground. My loop has its bottom about 1m off the ground, with the top about 4m high, partly concealed in fruit trees and mounted on the side of a garden shed. As with any high-Q antenna the loop should be in the clear as far as is possible. There is an advantage in elevating the assembly off the ground.

"Despite the satisfactory performance of this type of loop antenna, I still feel that it would be outperformed by a really good half-wave dipole in the clear, by one or two S points. But where real-estate is limited and a low visual impact is considered essential, a well-engineered loop is capable of surprisingly good results."

MORE ON SPACE-CHARGE 'TETRODE' VALVES

IT IS STRANGE how often an odd enquiry such as Dr Going's search for background information on the Phillips DAH-50 diode-heptode low-voltage valves (*TT*, May and August) reveals unexpected byways of radio technology. I have rashly assumed that the 1940 DAH-50 marked the introduction of space-charge-grid valves. In fact, by then, such valves had been around in Europe for almost 20 years. If only the index in my copy of *Saga of the Vacuum Tube* by Gerald F J Tyne (1977) had been more informative, I would have discovered far earlier that "the (Phillips) type D V1 was a space-charge tetrode which had originally been marketed under the designation Q in 1921 ... the anode and space-charge-grid was 2 to 10 volts". The

bright-emitter tungsten filament operated at 3.5V 0.5A. Then, in 1924, the Phillips Miniwatt series with dual-emitter filaments (4V, 0,1A) was extended to include the A441, again a space-charge-grid tetrode for an HT of about 15V.

Another Dutch valve manufacturer, M Heussen & Co of Arnhem (sold in the UK under the brand name Champion) from July 1922 marketed a space-charge-grid valve, type VE, which had a 3.8V filament and 8V anode, But this type of low-voltage valve never seems to have much impression in the UK.

Further information on these valves, including the DAH-50 has come from Dick Rollema, PA0SE, including an article describing the construction of a small portable receiver with built-in loop antenna ('A 1940 Walkman' - PA0SE) which used two DAH-50 valves, weighed 1.3kg, and ran from four 4.5V torch batteries; this was in the Dutch magazine *Radio-Expres*.

PA0SE who was a schoolboy in occupied Holland actually made 'covert' use of the A441 in the later stages of the war. He writes:

"When, in May 1943, the Germans confiscated the radio sets of Dutch citizens, my parents handed in our beautiful 1936 Radio Bell superhet. For my father, I built, as a substitute, an 0-V-1 (two valve, regenerative detector/audio amplifier) short-wave receiver using 4V filament valves. The set ran from a rechargeable battery (accumulator) for the filaments and the HT came from a mains PSU. Later, possibly 1944, the domestic mains supplies were cut altogether because of the shortage of coal in the power stations. (This was probably after the Dutch railway strike that began in early September 1944 leading to the ghastly famine of the 'hunger-winter' of 1944/45 - G3VA). My father had good contacts at Phillips and at my suggestion returned from one of his business trips to Eindhoven, while still under German control, with two A441 space-charge-grid valves. I made a new 0-V-1 HF receiver with these two valves and plug-in coils on valve bases. At first the 4V accumulator could still be charged at the Stork engineering-works at Hengelo, where we lived, and which had its own power plant. But this facility came to a sudden end, thanks to precision bombing by the RAF. The radio was then run from hard-to-get 4.5V dry batteries (my father knew the owner at the local battery factory). Since the set needed only 15V 'HT', the set could be run from four or five 4.5V batteries.

"The set brought us news from the BBC and from Radio Oranje (the Dutch service broadcast from London) until the end of the war in May 1945. As we were the only family in our street lucky enough to be able to listen to the news, my father staged a 'news conference' for our neighbours every night in our home. What the German military dentist who occupied one of our upstairs rooms thought about this daily event and the fact that my father regularly spent time every morning and afternoon in our attic (where the receiver was hidden in a bookcase) remains a mystery, but he caused us no trouble and turned out to be a decent chap when it was all over. I wish now I had preserved this set but that is not something one thinks about when young!"

PA0SE is still puzzled that space-charge-grid tetrodes, with their low HT requirements, were not more widely used. (Possibly the major reason was the fact that they could not provide enough power for a loudspeaker and were thus only suitable for headphone reception - G3VA). He believes that they enjoyed some popularity in the Netherlands in the 1920s, and also in France and Germany. J Wolthuis, PE0RTX tells him that the German RV2.4P45 (see August *TT*) a pentode with space-charge-grid was used in some German wartime military radios. PA0SE adds:

"A remarkable application of the space-charge-grid tetrode was a two-terminal oscillator. This was found independently in 1924 by two Dutch experimenters and hence became known as the Numans-Roosenstein oscillator: **Fig 8**. It seems that John Scott-Taggart (2ST in the '20s) published a similar oscillator in 1922 using a valve with two anodes (Negatron). The circuit comes from a 1929 Dutch book on short-wave radio reception.

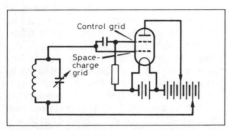

Fig 8: Two-terminal Numans-Roosenstein oscillator using A221 space-charge-grid tetrode as described for a wavemeter in a 1929 book published in Holland. (PA0SE)

"The oscillator functions as follows: When the control grid goes more positive the anode current increases. As the total current from the cathode (filament) remains about the same, the current flowing towards the space-charge grid decreases, although since this grid is connected to the control grid it becomes more positive.

"A decreasing current with increasing voltage represents a negative input resistance and the similarity with the later Transitron negative-resistance oscillator is obvious. The circuit oscillates readily with only a few volts 'HT' and works down into the audio-frequency range given a suitable tuned circuit.

"The Dutch amateur P Bakker has thoroughly investigated the space-charge-grid tetrode, and has also tried using modern pentodes in this way. This turned out to be possible provided that the control grid was connected to the cathode, the screen-grid used as a space-charge grid, and the suppressor grid used as the control grid - an interesting possibility for any collector restoring an old set using space-charge valves, or wishing to demonstrate that valves can be used at 'solid-state' voltages."

10A PSU WITH THREE-TERMINAL IC REGULATOR

MIKE FODEN, G3UPA, PROVIDES details of a simple, low-cost power supply unit providing 10W output at about 14.5V using a 78M12, 0.5A voltage regulator IC (or equivalent) in conjunction with a 2N3772 series pass transistor: **Fig 9**.

He writes "It is fairly common knowledge

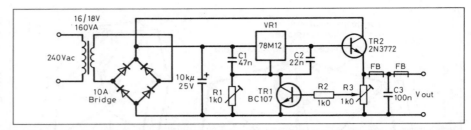

Fig 9: Simple 10A, 13.8V regulated PSU using standard fixed-voltage IC regulator. Note that it is advisable to provide some form of over-voltage protection to guard against failure of the series-pass transistor TR2. Components: TR1 BC107/8/9, TR2 2N3772, VR1 78M12 0.5A, 12V IC regulator, R1, R3 1K0 potentiometers, R2 1K0 1/4W. Disk ceramic capacitors: C1 0.47µF, C2 0.22µF and C3 0.1µF.

that the range of fixed-voltage IC regulators can give a higher voltage output than their designed ratings by simply adding a resistor in their common lead. This principle can be carried a little further by adding a small signal transistor and a suitable series pass transistor to provide a high-current regulated supply with a low component count.

"Operation is as follows: A variable resistor, R1, is connected in the common lead of the IC regulator, VR1, to increase voltage output from 12V to about 14.5V. A small-signal transistor, TR1, is connected in parallel with R1 with its base connected to the main output. The current in the regulator common line is now divided between R1 and TR1. If the output voltage tries to fall under load, the current through TR1 will fall, causing more current to flow through R1, hence increasing the output voltage of VR1. This is because the quiescent current in the common lead of VR1 is constant.

"Setting up is quite straightforward. Set R3 to the zero voltage end of its travel and then adjust R1 to the required maximum output (eg 14.5V). Then adjust R3 to give the required output voltage from the PSU, that is 13.8V. The PSU is then capable of supplying an output of 10A at a regulated 13.8V.

"The maximum current available is governed mainly by the transformer and rectifier. A 2N3772 pass transistor is capable of running at 20A and 150W, subject to temperature limitation. The pass transistor requires a substantial heatsink. A rating of less than 2° per Watt should be adequate for 10A output. C1 and C2 are the usual anti-parasitic components recommended for all fixed-voltage regulators. C3 and the ferrite beads offer some protection against RF getting back into the supply.

"I have been using the system for two years to run my HF transceiver, using two pass transistors and a 25A transformer with no problems. However it should be noted that the supply, as shown, does not include over-voltage protection against failure of the pass transistor etc. In my own PSU, I have added a 25A-rated relay which operates should the output voltage rise above 14.5V, giving some degree (non-instantaneous) of over-voltage protection. A conventional thyristor-type over-voltage protection circuit would give faster-acting protection."

CONSTRUCTIONAL TIPS AND TOPICS

Two useful suggestions have been received from Dick Biddulph, G8DPS, of the RSGB's Technical and Publications Advisory Committee:

Marking Printed Circuit Boards

When building a piece of gear on a complex PCB, I have found it useful to mark some of the tracks so that it is easier to place the right components in the right holes. The so-called 'Magic Marker' is quite good but, to the best of my knowledge, is available only in two colours plus black. Staedler, the drawing-office people, make pens for overhead-projector foils. The waterproof ones, called 'Lumocolor' permanent, come in five colours plus black and make a clear mark on a PCB. It can be soldered through but, for a *concours d'elegance* project, the marks can be removed by meths. - *Dick Biddulph, G8DPS.*

A Different Way with Veroboard

Veroboard is not too good at VHF when used as the makers intended. But if it is glued strip-side up to a piece of plain copper-clad board which then forms an earth-plane, it is quite good. It is necessary only to make .25in (6mm) holes at intervals to connect the ground-plane to one or two of the strip conductors. DIL (dual in-line) packages can be used with their legs spread out as large surface-mounted devices. - *Dick Biddulph, G8DPS.*

ADD-ON SPEECH PROCESSOR

THE ABILITY TO USE speech processing to increase the 'talk power' of transceivers, which may well in future be enhanced by the prospect of increasing use of digital signal processing techniques, has long been recognised. Many of the add-on processors however have tended to result in 'hard limiting' using, for example, back-to-back diodes to slice off the audio peaks; a process which tends to result in a rich harmonic output and which unless corrected can lead to distortion and some loss of intelligibility. An alternative approach is to use rather milder forms of dynamic-range compression in which an amplifying stage has its gain throttled back on the speech peaks, thus providing automatic level control.

A 'Speech processor for transceivers' by Rob Evans (technical editor of *Electronics Australia*) appears in the September 1991 issue of that magazine (pp72-77). This provides full constructional and adjustment details of an add-on unit that connects in-line with an existing microphone and acts as a preamplifier, compressor and speech filter. The unit also incorporates a tone oscillator which automatically generates a short 'beep' each time the push-to-talk (PTT) button is released, although circuit details for this have been omitted from the simplified circuit shown in **Fig 1**.

Operation is as follows: The gain of a TL072 dual op-amp pre-amplifier is automatically varied by means of an opto-isolator constructed from a combination of a 5mm LED and an OP-12 miniature light dependent resistor (LDR) assembled together in a short piece of heat shrink tubing: **Fig 2 (a)**. **Fig 2 (b)** shows the audio compression curve this provides for the pre-amp (note that although the shape of the curve remains fixed, the values along each scale will depend on the setting of RV1 and RV2 - miniature PC-mount horizontal trimpots, 50k and 5k respectively). Filtering and screening is used to suppress RF input to the unit and to shape the audio response roughly to about 300Hz to 3kHz. A 'compress' LED2 flashes to indicate compression on the speech peaks.

TECHNICAL
TOPICS

PAT HAWKER G3VA

Before connecting the unit to a transceiver it should preferably be checked on a high-gain audio-amplifier/loudspeaker to check the quality of the output signal.

Rob Evans includes a section on 'possible changes' that may be found necessary in some cases where the processor may not perform quite as expected, despite the fact the circuit is operating correctly. He notes that while RV1 can be used to alter the gain over quite a wide range, the final output level *does* depend on the strength of the microphone signal and the light sensitivity of the LDR.

He has found that with different LED/LDR combination, with 2mA flowing through the LED (as in the circuit of **Fig 1**), the LDR may present a resistance anywhere between 10k and 50k. These are within the adjustment range of RV1. However, for microphones providing an unusually low or high output, the value of R11 may have to be adjusted. It is useful to test the opto-isolator action before installing it in the unit.

It should also be remembered that when a speech processor is used on an SSB rig, the duty cycle of the power amplifier will be significantly increased, possibly calling for a chunkier power supply unit and/or improved cooling. It is better to compress an audio signal too little than too much so as to avoid the danger of flat-topping and hence radiating an excessively broad signal. Remember that peak-limiting and/or compression represents a form of signal distortion and needs to be carried out with care if it is not to impair signal intelligibility. Broadcasters use dynamic compression on both AM and FM transmissions without introducing excessive distortion, although it is interesting to compare the quality of Radio 3 FM (virtually no compression) with the other UK Band II signals (moderate compression), or the heavy compression on the BBC medium-wave World Service transmissions (and other international-broadcasting transmissions) with the less heavy processing on domestic AM services.

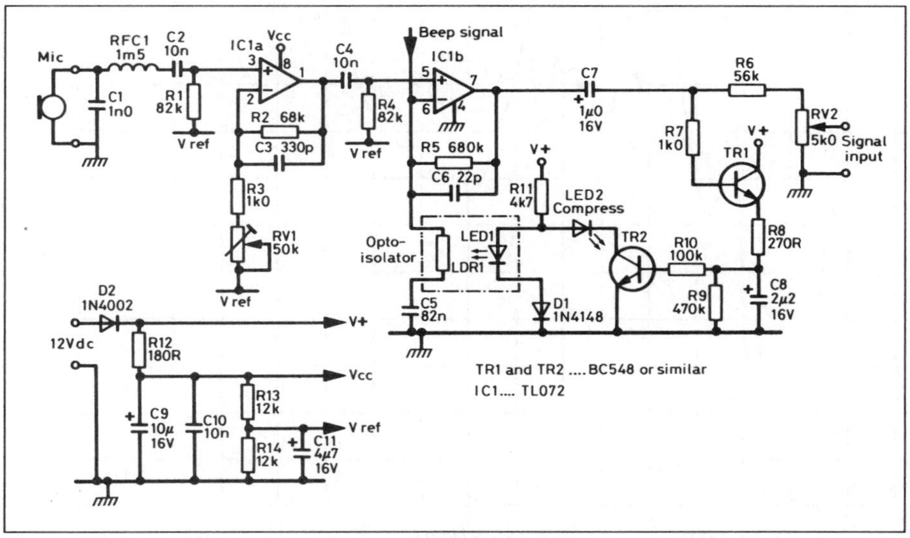

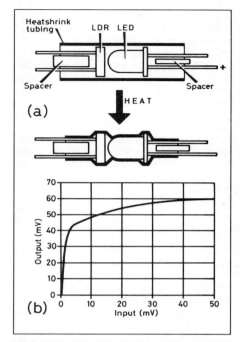

Fig 2: (a) Construction of the opto-isolator. The components are slid into a piece of heatshrink tubing and heat applied. (b) Audio compression curve. Note that the shape of the curve remains the same but the values along each scale depend on the settings of RV1 and RV2.

THE GOOD OLD DAYS?

SOMETIMES ONE TENDS TO THINK that amateur radio (like the old grey mare) "ain't what she used to be many long years ago". But in many respects one should say thank goodness it ain't! Consider for example the terms of the standard amateur/experimental licence in the UK circa 1925: "The power must not exceed 10 watts and messages may be sent only on waves of 150 to 200 metres (Tonic train, CW and Telephony) and a further fixed wave of 440 metres (CW and Telephony only) . . . . Messages may be sent at any time, but the time occupied in transmission must not exceed two hours during any consecutive period of 24 hours. The use of the 440-metre wave is not allowed between 5pm and 11pm on weekdays or during the Sunday transmissions of the BBC. Except with the sanction of the Postmaster-General, messages may be transmitted only to stations in Great Britain or Northern Ireland which are actually co-operating in the licensee's experiments . . . . No single transmission may last more than 10 minutes, and must be followed by a period of three minutes listening-in on the wavelength used for transmission . . . . " Hardly the Good Old Days!

COUNTERPOISES AND ELEVATED RADIALS

THE AUGUST ITEM 'Earths, counterpoises and radials' emphasised that there is growing evidence (I am tempted to write 'proof') that buried earths, even when there are a large

Fig 1: Simplified circuit-diagram of the *Electronics Australia* speech processor (PTT-operated beep generator circuitry omitted). The gain of the microphone pre-amplifier (IC1a and IC1b) is reduced on speech peaks by the action of the opto-isolator (LED1 and LDR1). Note that some electret microphones require a DC voltage not provided in this circuit.

number of buried radials or several deeply-sunk earth rods, should be avoided wherever possible as part of an antenna system. The remarks on this topic from Allan Taylor, G3JMO, in his criticism of the American 'surface wire ground' (SWG, *TT* April 1991), rang a bell for Arch Doty, K8CFU, who has done so much to re-awaken us to the advantages of the nearly forgotten 'counterpoise' approach. He writes: "Several years ago some of the data we collected on earth conductivity was published by the IEEE and in *QST* but was largely ignored (I suppose only real antenna nuts can be expected to show much interest in the topic of earth conductivity!). The data based on my daily measurements showed clearly that even in areas of relatively good earth conductivity this varies significantly over a period of months: **Fig 3**. If short ground rods are used, as with the US Army SWG system, it is obvious that, if used as part of the antenna system, the return ground currents (which vary with earth conductivity and on which the efficiency of the antenna will depend), will be unpredictable, to say the least. I feel that G3JMO's conclusions are right on the mark!"

G3JMO, himself, in a follow-up letter, traces the concept of using the earth as part of an antenna system back to the era of very long wave communications (wavelengths of thousands of metres) as used by Marconi in the

first decades of the Century: "From there it was natural that amateurs should carry on this practice for '200 metres and down' since it is not easily recognised that the shorter the wavelength, the less efficient and less appropriate becomes the use of the Earth as part of a radio transmission system. To some extent amateurs were lead astray in carrying on long-wave practice down into the short-wave region.

"If radio had developed directly from the dipole-like 'antenna' structures of Hertz who in the pre-Marconi era experimented with spark equipment on very short wavelengths, it is possible that the concept of using the Earth as part of a tuned antenna (eg Marconi Antenna or verticals at ground level) would never have caught on.

"That a number of amateurs in the 1920s appear to have recognised the value of antenna systems not directly connected to earth can be seen from George Jessop's all-too-short but fascinating *Bright Sparks of Wireless* (RSGB) where references to the then popular and clearly effective 'conterpoise' approach appear on pages 15, 26, 27 and 37 - not bad considering the relatively few stations described. It would seem that amateurs in general have, over the years, been using very-long-wave techniques for short-wave radio and paying the price in terms of efficiency and unpredictability."

The early stations referred to as using counterpoises in G6JP's book were those of H W Pope, PZX (later G3HT); E J Simmonds, 2OD (one of the most active and successful pioneers of the short waves in the early twenties); the receiving station of W R Wade of Clifton for the 1921 Transatlantic Tests (although in this case the counterpoise was buried); and that of Jack Partridge, 2KF who was the first British amateur to make two-way contact with the USA on 200 metres and who used "a five-wire counterpoise mounted some 7ft above the ground with an antenna of the L-type with three wires 60ft long in parallel at a height of 50ft."

The single-wire counterpoise remained popular in the 1930s and I recall using one for Top Band in 1938 and also putting one up at Helmond, Holland in 1944 for use with a Whaddon Mk III transmitter. The popularity of a large number of buried radials stems from Dr George Brown's classic study of *medium-wave* broadcast antennas in the 1930s.

BALANCED ACTIVE RECEIVING LOOPS

J A LAMBERT, G3FMZ, in a full-length article 'A directional active loop receiving antenna system' in *RadCom*, November 1982, pp944-949 described in detail the development by C&S Antennas Ltd of a novel form of resis-

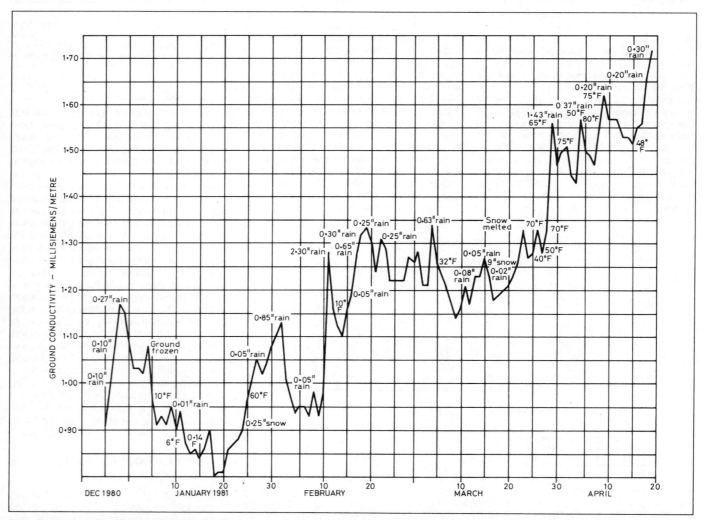

Fig 3: Ground conductivity measured over some four months during 1980-81 at K8CFU's test site at Fletcher, North Carolina shows that conductivity varies significantly under different weather conditions.

tance-loaded compact receiving loop antenna with an associated 2 - 30MHz wideband matching pre-amplifier. This provided a cardioid (heart-shaped) horizontal radiation pattern rather than the usual figure-of-eight pattern. Such loops were then (and possibly still are) being marketed for use at professional receiving stations, usually with a number of loops forming an endfire or broadside directional array suitable for permanent, temporary or portable use. G3FNZ provided constructional details of an experimental loop with an 0.5W carbon non-inductive resistor (value between 47 and 100 Ohms) connected across the top of the loop with the matching amplifier across the base junction: **Fig 4**.

Dick Rollema, PA0SE had his attention drawn by PA0EZ to a contribution to the IEE's *Electronics Letters* (18 July 1991, pp1320-21) by P V Brennan and Y Valverde of University College, London. This shows how the C&S type of unbalanced loop can be changed into balanced form by using two resistors and a balanced feed arrangement, maintaining the cardioid pattern but not suffering from the problems associated with the requirement of an unbalanced antenna for a solid ground connection, which becomes particularly important in the lower HF spectrum.

To quote their introductory remarks: "An antenna with a cardioid radiation pattern can be produced by taking an electrically smaller circular loop and introducing an imbalancing resistance in the top of the loop, as shown in **Fig 5**. This is the basis of a commercially produced antenna for HF reception purposes which includes a low noise amplifier mounted at the base of the loop.

"The antenna, being electrically small, has a very low radiation efficiency, but this is of little concern in HF reception applications, because the system is usually limited by external noise . . . . The antenna relies on a ground plane connection to one side of the loop, without which a figure-of-eight would be obtained, and this can often be difficult to achieve in the HF band. A stake may be driven into the ground for this purpose or the trailing coaxial cable may be used as a pseudo-ground plane; in both cases it is found that the antenna pattern varies quite considerably depending on the quality of the ground connection and/or the position of the coaxial cable. For this reason, it is attractive to consider a balanced version of the antenna that does not require a ground connection".

Of interest also is that they describe a scaled down prototype antenna of this type suitable for use between 40 and 600MHz, presenting measurements made between 150 and 200MHz which shows that a good performance may be obtained without the need for a ground connection or careful placing of the feed cable. It would thus appear that this technique might be useful, for example, for 144MHz D/F.

Their prototype antenna (**Fig 6(a)**) consists of a printed rectangular loop, of 3mm track width, with a 180° hybrid for the balun and an MMIC amplifier mounted within the loop. The resistor values required for a good cardioid pattern were found not to be critical and were in the same range as for the original unbalanced antenna, The antenna was measured in a relatively small anechoic chamber, using a dipole as the source antenna. **Fig**

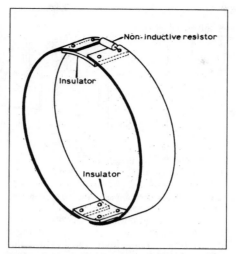

Fig 4: The experimental 3 - 30MHz HF unbalanced active-antenna described (with associated matching pre-amplifier) by G3FNZ in *RadCom* **November 1982. The 1m-diameter loop is made from a 150mm-wide strip of 16SWG aluminium, cut into two parts and then rejoined using two blocks of insulating material. The amplifier is mounted and connected across the lower insulator, with a 47 to 100-Ohm non-inductive resistor across the top insulator. Cardioid horizontal radiation pattern.**

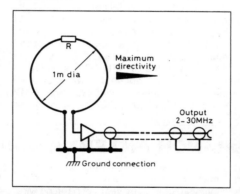

Fig 5: Unbalanced HF active loop receiving antenna system as originally described by G3FNZ of C&S Antennas Ltd.

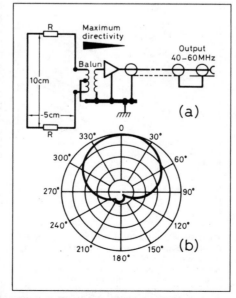

Fig 6: (a) Balanced form of the prototype active VHF/UHF loop antenna as a scaled down version intended for HF reception. (b) Radiation pattern of the prototype at 200MHz showing operation without the need for an earth or ground-plane.

6(b) shows the radiation pattern (linear scale) at 200MHz, with a front-to-back ratio of some 17dB and the field pattern dropping "quite convincingly" to -6dB at +/- 90° from the main beam direction.

Incidentally, Dick Rollema, PA0SE questions the mathematics (not given in the *TT* digest) of the Canadian VHF D/F loop with half of the coaxial-cable screening braid removed (*TT*, June 1991 p29) which is claimed to give a cardioid pattern with a single deep null. He points out that in their paper it is assumed that there is uniform current distribution on the loop; however since this is a 'half-wave' in circumference this cannot be the case, although it would apply to electrically very small loops. I am not clear whether this error in any way affects practical results and it would be interesting to learn whether anyone has any comments based on a practical test. In fact the authors seem to have tried to put together possible theoretical explanations to fit their practical results, so possibly this theoretical error is of little practical consequence.

CRYSTAL OVEN

ABOUT A DOZEN YEARS AGO, *TT* included a couple of items on the use of proportional control to stabilise the working temperature of crystals for applications requiring high frequency stability. In both cases the control systems used solid-state devices both as sensors and to provide the heating, in one case with discrete transistors soldered directly to the metal cover of an HC16/U crystal and in the other (contributed by G3SEK) based on a National Semiconductors LM3911 IC temperature controller and a heating transistor both mounted on a copper clip which was then slid over an HC6/U crystal. These ideas are in *ART7* pp178-9. [*Amateur Radio Techniques*, 7th edition is now back in print again by popular demand, see *Bookcase* pages - Ed].

Such temperature controllers can be installed for example in an existing frequency counter without the requirement for fitting them in an 'oven'. Nevertheless crystal ovens still have their place, particularly for crystals with a zero-coefficient temperature of around 70°C.

Bob Parker ('Circuit and Design Ideas', *Electronics Australia*, September 1991, p67) describes a homebrew oven with a solid-state temperature sensor and controller but with a resistive heating element (**Fig 7**). He has installed this in an elderly counter in conjunction with a custom-ground 3.579545MHz 75°C HC6/U crystal which gives a stability of better than one part in two million. He writes:

"The crystal lives in a plastic foam-lined 35mm film canister, sandwiched between a power resistor to heat it and a BC178 transistor to sense the temperature. I used the BC178 because it has a quick temperature response from its metal can, which is earthed. But a BC558 would probably work just as well (and BC178s are becoming hard to find). The sensing transistor is connected so that it amplifies its own temperature-dependent emitter-base voltage drop, and the 741 op-amp compares this voltage with the approximately 5.1V derived from the zener diode.

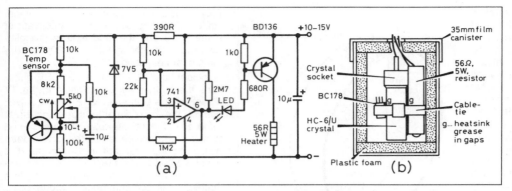

Fig 7: Details of the electronic temperature controller and the mechanical details of the Australian crystal oven.

"The 2.7M resistor provides hysteresis to ensure that the 741 switches sharply. The 1.2M resistor and 10uF capacitor combination has the effect of turning the circuit into a low frequency variable-duty-cycle oscillator, once the crystal temperature stabilises. This gives better temperature control than a simple on-off circuit. The LED indicates when the heater is on, and its voltage drop ensures that the BD136 switching transistor switches fully off.

"I calibrated the original by attaching leads to a 1N914 diode, sleeving it with heat-shrink tubing and connecting it to a digital multimeter on a 'diode' resistance range, I immersed the diode in 75° water and noted the meter reading, then temporarily attached the diode to the crystal in its oven and adjusted the 5k pot until the meter gave the same reading - the tricky part is finding a thermometer which can read up to 75°C. I used a dairy thermometer.

"If it is found that the circuit keeps going from full-on to full-off instead of stabilising in the oscillating mode, then reducing the value of the 1.2M resistor should solve the problem. The circuit could be useful for other applications requiring an electronic thermostat".

A Q-GATE VFO STABLE TO 39MHZ

GEORGE SOUTHGATE, VK5QG (ex-G3LXO), was delayed by ill-health from pointing out that unfortunately the 'corrected' diagram of his Q-GATE oscillator (Fig 5(a) of *TT*, March 1990) still differed from his original drawing in showing the output taken from the source rather than the drain (my profound apologies for the SNAFU - *G3VA*). Although the circuit as then shown resembles the oscillator described by Dr Mike King, G3MY, (*TT*, November 1990), VK5QG following tests

remains convinced that his intended circuit, without G3MY's source resister but with low supply voltage, as (hopefully) in **Fig 9**, gives better results. He found that G3MY's circuit tends to stop oscillating if loaded with less than 2000Ω, even with a 12V supply, with a frequency shift measured in kHz. He writes:

"I offered my circuit to the QRP and KISS fraternity as it gives excellent frequency stability under varying load conditions due to having good isolation from the tuned circuit and a very low impedance, all with a minimum of components. I have now completed my receiver with 10.7MHz IF which was what started me investigating oscillators and led to the Q-Gate Circuit. The receiver tunes amateur bands from 1.8 to 29.7MHz with 10kHz resolution per revolution of the tuning knob (less on some bands). In a series of 8-hour runs in a room whose ambient temperature changed from 14° to 25°C the oscillator frequency at 39MHz showed a frequency stability of better than 26ppm/°C with the receiver staying tuned to 28MHz SSB transmissions throughout long contacts without having to touch the tuning.

"I have taken all the usual precautions in making the tuned circuit as stable as possible. The coil former is ribbed ceramic 0.75-in diameter and the 20SWG wire was preheated so that it shrunk on the former under tension when cooled. The coil has several taps taken off and is switched with a small ceramic switch. Temperature compensation is accomplished with a mixture of fixed ca-

TREE-BRANCH ANTENNA SUPPORTS

THOSE OF US WHO USE trees to support one or both ends of wire antennas soon come up against the problem of getting a cord or wire over a sufficiently high and strong enough branch, without the antenna becoming entangled in the lower branches etc. An accepted and effective solution involves the skilled use of a good bow and arrow - fine if you or a friend are 'into' archery and the tree(s) are sufficiently in the clear to avoid an errant arrow damaging people or property! Personally, I have always tended to limit the height of my ambitions to around 20-30ft using either a weight attached to a thin cord and then thrown over the branch (more proficient throwers could improve on my results!) or, more recently, creating a lightweight 'pole' from bamboos etc with, at the top a V-shaped aluminium guide designed to allow a weighted thin line to be 'put' over the branch so that it drops to the ground, the 'pole' recovered and then used to guide the final antenna support wire beyond the reach of the lower branches. This has proved superior to my poor throwing performances but I would not recommend it for branches much higher than 25ft or so, above which makeshift lightweight poles tend to become too whippy and unmanageable.

Ron Grant, G3XPH, has tackled the problem more elegantly (and more effectively) while still avoiding the requirement for the

use of professionally made archery equipment. He writes: "Details of my system, evolved after many years of hanging wire antennas between trees and in pursuit of

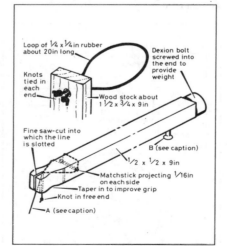

Fig 8: Details of G3XPH's homemade 'catapult' and associate wooden arrow used for shooting a line across the high branch of a tree. A - Make sure the line passes *over* the wrist of the hand holding the arrow which should be fired from the side of the tree where the antenna will hang. B - Wood-screw let in for the elastic to hook behind. Make sure the screw does not pinch the elastic or the arrow will wobble on release. Preliminary practice may be advisable.

even greater height, are shown in **Fig 8**. Briefly, I use a catapult - a simple affair in the form of a sling, not needing a Y structure. This fires a cross-bow type of arrow or bolt, a piece of wood about 9 by 0.5 by 0.5 inches. This carries a fine nylon monofilament line aloft but to avoid festooning the trees with bits of tangled nylon I have developed a crude release mechanism. This is a portion of matchstick pushed transversely through the arrow.

"With the arrow fired up into the tree, if all goes well a few jiggles on the nylon line causes the arrow to carry the line smoothly to the ground, where it can be unhitched and a halyard bent on and then pulled back over the branch. Sometimes however, I haul a white plastic gardening tape back through the tree so that I can study it through binoculars to see whether it looks useful.

"If, however, the line or arrow snags then a few jiggles on the line will disengage the line from the arrow which falls to the ground and one can then retrieve the nylon line ready flaked out to shoot again."

G3XPH does not mention the heights he achieves but clearly this can be much better than my lightweight pole! But some preliminary practice in safely using and aiming this type of catapult/sling would seem highly advisable. A metal-loaded wooden bolt fired from quarter-inch rubber elastic could prove a formidable weapon!

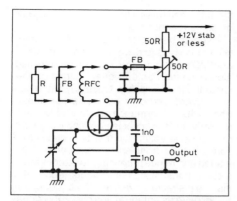

Fig 9: The Q-Gate FET ocsillator - hopefully this at last shows the correct connections for the output, taken from between drain and chassis.

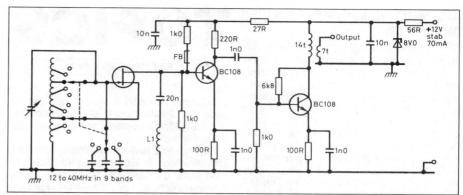

Fig 10: The final oscillator circuit used in VK5QG's HF communications receiver and capable of holding 28MHz SSB transmissions throughout long contacts without retuning.

pacitors, those of negative coefficient being of the polystyrene type.

"The oscillator circuit, as used in the receiver, is shown in **Fig 10**. L1 is a small coil of 4 turns (1/8in in dia) of 22SWG wire and forms a filter with the 20nF capacitor resonating at about 5.6MHz. This adjusts the output for maximum amplitude and minimum distortion. If not included the output is very low and varies greatly from band to band. If this inductance is made too large, the output is high but distorted. I found the optimum value by winding the coil just large enough to be able to insert a ferrite bead on the end of a toothpick and then watched what happened on a CRO (for those without an HF CRO I suggest that L1 should be adjusted for the purest T9 note on a receiver). Some FETs produce a cleaner waveform with a diode connected from gate to ground (eg 1N914 etc diode).

"I have also recently checked to see if the basic oscillator could be located remotely from the buffer amplifier and the main heat-producing equipment. I found that I could run the oscillator at the end of a 60ft length of coaxial cable (the longest single length to hand at the time) with no problem at all: **Fig 11**. I have not tested frequency drift but I feel the configuration should give advantages. The 3k resistor should be adjusted to a value that just maintains oscillation over the full tuning range, measured and then a fixed-value resistor substituted. The collector transformer for the BC108 in both Figs 10 and 11 is wound on a small toroidal core. While compiling the drift figures for my receiver VFO it was winter time with the shack temperature raised from 14°C to a maximum of 25°C or so, although the temperatures compensation components had been selected the previous summer with a shack temperature between 30-35°C. I intend to make further checks in summer conditions and expect the drift in ppm/°C be even better.

MORE HOSTILE ENVIRONMENT?

A RECENT ANNOUNCEMENT by government scientists suggests that the ozone depletion over Britain and Europe (due largely it is believed to the CFCs used in refrigerators, air conditioning, aerosol sprays etc) is double that of previous estimates. We were warned of the increased danger of skin cancers and eye cataracts stemming from over-exposure to the more intense UV rays resulting from the thinner ozone layer. Apparently, the UV light reaching the ground has been increasing by about 1% per annum since 1980, with ozone levels now about 8% lower than a decade ago.

For radio amateurs, this means more rapid deterioration of plastic ropes, plastic coverings, plastic tapes etc used in outdoor antenna installations, or indeed all materials exposed to strong sunlight. As noted in *TT* (June 1985) in an item 'Reducing ultra-violet radiation damage': "Deterioration caused by UV has always to be taken into account with materials used in full sunlight, as shown by the deterioration of the outer covering of coaxial cable. Similarly, plastic rope often used for mast stays becomes hardened and brittle after to exposure to sun and rain."

It was suggested that good quality outdoor paint can provide useful protection; white materials and cables tend to be more resistant to UV than coloured materials; UV-resistant marine varnish can be used on metal items; white adhesive tape can be wound round cables; self-amalgamating tape tends to be particularly vulnerable and should be protected by layers of thicker conventional tape.

TT (March 1991) noted that polypropylene lines or monofilament (nylon) fishing line deteriorates progressively in sunlight due to UV radiation and suggested a number of alternatives. The vulnerability of polypropylene rope was confirmed by Ernie Sumpton, C53GS/G3DQL, writing from The Gambia who found that in the strong tropical sunlight polypropylene ropes tend to lose all strength in less than a year.

Les Parnell, G8PP, operates quite often in Australia and also in Labrador where he found that the outer plastic cover on some British coaxial cable (he took the first time) could not withstand intense cold - after a couple of months his feeder consisted of the outer braid fully exposed to the elements. Since then, when visiting Labrador, he uses the 'local coax' which treats −40°C with contempt.

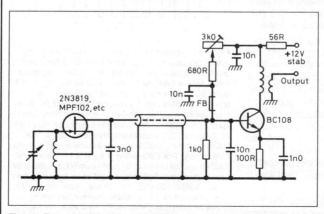

Fig 11: Test circuit used by VK5QG to investigate the possibility of locating the Q-Gate oscillator remotely from sources of heat, etc. He achieved successful results with 60ft of coaxial cable.

BIG MOUTH, LINEARITY & SPLATTER

PROPERLY CONDUCTED two-tone testing of an SSB transmitter will show the maximum level to which a power amplifier can be driven before the onset of 'flat-topping' - in other words the point where the intermodulation products (IMPs) begin to spread the signal out into the adjacent channels as well as distorting the in-band speech. As Bill Orr, W6SAI, explains in 'Intermodulation Distortion (Or why does Big Mouth take up half the band?), *CQ* (Sept 91, pp56-58, 60-61): "Big Mouth doesn't know (or doesn't care) that all SSB transmitters have an overload point. Operating beyond this point won't make the signal louder or more readable. It just takes up more space on the dial and actually wastes useful power in the splatter! . . . . IMD is created whenever a complex signal (such as speech which is composed of many audio tones simultaneously) overloads an amplifier or mixer stage of a transmitter . . . . a CW signal is a single-frequency entity and does not create IMD" [But a poor keying waveform can create clicks which similarly cause the transmission to occupy excessive spectrum - *G3VA*].

While the two-tone test with a conventional oscilloscope display is extremely valuable in obtaining an appraisal of the overload point, to obtain a quantitive measure of the performance of an SSB transmitter requires the use of a spectrum analyser (professional instruments are usually well beyond amateur budgets!). A spectrum analyser can show (**Fig 1(a)**) the third-order and higher-order IMPs and allow an observer to determine how far down in decibels these are from either one or both tones, (if measured from one tone, this gives a result six decibels less than from the transmitter PEP level). The majority of amateurs, without spectrum analysers, are dependent either on the manufacturer's claimed specification or preferably, an independent equipment review such as those of Peter Hart, G3SJX.

But watch the small print. An amplifier measured at its full rated output will be judged more harshly than when, for example, displayed at 80% (a level used by some reviewers). **Fig 1(b)** from W6SAI's article shows how a 100W local SSB signal, representative of many current transmitters, if received at 20dB over S9 on a receiver of wide dynamic range, would have splatter extending over some 28 to 30kHz. In a section 'Observations on IMD', W6SAI writes:

"Rough rules of performance can be outlined as far as IMD goes. These rules are based upon countless observations on various SSB transmitters. Older rigs using sweep tubes (6LQ6 etc) have IMD third-order figures in the -21 to -25dB range (measured from PEP). That's not very good, judged by today's standards. Other rigs using 6146-type valves exhibit IMD ranges falling between −24 and −28dB below PEP. The famous Collins S-line (which incorporates RF feedback) can better these figures by about 4 to 6dB. That's very good for a tube-type exciter.

"Solid-state rigs seem to run from −34dB to −40dB third-order products, depending upon the amount of RF feedback used and the voltage applied to the amplifier stages. That's

good performance for equipment falling in the price that amateurs can afford! Of course, when Big Mouth operates any of these rigs, all bets are off."

I cannot help feeling that W6SAI is being a little charitable in his assessment of current solid-state transceivers, particularly those running directly off 12V - at least to judge from

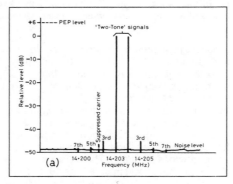

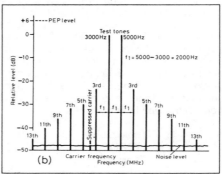

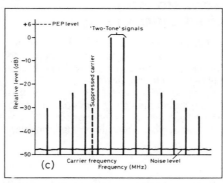

Fig 1: (a) Spectrum analyser presentation of a high-grade (probably professional-type) SSB transmitter driven by a two-tone test signal. Carrier suppressed 45dB below level of tones (51dB below total PEP output). Third-order products 45dB down on test tones with fifth-order products about 48dB down and seventh-order products barely above noise level. Still-higher-order products cannot be observed in this test. (b) Representative of a fairly typical 100W amateur SSB transceiver shown with tones 2kHz apart. The 13th-order products are down only 45dB from the tones and would easily be audible by local amateurs. Splatter would thus be produced over some 30kHz or more spectrum. (c) Representative of an older transmitter using TV "sweep" valves and with no RF feedback. Improperly loaded or over-driven such a transmitter would disrupt reception for many miles around. (W6SAI, CQ)

the IMD measurements reported by G3SJX on some recent transceivers.

It should be appreciated that when a transceiver is used to drive a high-power linear, any IMD products in the drive will be amplified along with the wanted signals no matter how linear the final amplifier. Once any stage has been overdriven or is otherwise non-linear, poor IMD performance is inevitable. But, similarly, before accusing any local amateur of excessive splatter you should check that your receiver front end is not being overloaded and hence producing splatter even on a clean transmission. If in doubt reduce the input to the receiver with an RF attenuator (or a short wire as antenna) and check the signal at, say, S9.

Alex Allan, G3ZBE, was interested to note that in the item on the 30-year-old G2DAF valve linear in the September *TT*, the IMD performance for a single 813 was given as some 45dB down with a screen supply voltage derived (with voltage-doubling) from the RF drive. He writes:

"What struck me is that in the past few years we have seen a lot of discussion and recommendations about the need for very stiff screen supplies in order to get good intermodulation performance, especially in connection with the use of 4CX250 valves, yet here we are saying it is possible to get 45dB down on PEP with an 813 with the screen voltage varying at syllabic rate! Why this advice about needing something better than gas stabilisers or zeners? Admittedly the screen voltage in the 2DAF amplifier is normally in phase with the driving signal and not causing a varying voltage drop across a screen resistor. In the case of a correctly loaded 4CX250B the screen current is, we're told, sourcing current! I feel the screen-supply business is being over-stated. I have an ex-RAF Collins SSB linear which has no screen stabilisation at all and equalises the standing current in the two 4CX250B valves by varying the screen resistors, yet still claims excellent IMD figures."

It may well be that the Collins linear uses effective RF feedback and other linearising techniques. Then again, I seem to recall that the advocates of extremely stiff screen supplies were thinking in terms of VHF/UHF operation where the noise-floor is much lower than on HF so that much higher-order products can still be a source of interference. With the G2DAF linear the voltage drops as drive drops.

A section in the 1960 3rd edition of *Fundamentals of SSB* published by the original Collins Radio Company has the following notes on grid-driven tetrode power amplifiers (p7.5): "**Fig 2** is a simplified schematic of a grid driven tetrode power amplifier. This amplifier, operating class AB1 produces 250W per tube using the 4X250B tetrode. In general, the same design considerations exist for tetrode amplifiers as for triode amplifiers. That is, grid circuit swamping is required to hold the input impedance constant if the tetrode is driven into the grid current region, and neutralisation is generally required if the tube is to operate over the entire HF range. However, since the plate-to-grid capacitance is small in the tetrode, neutralisation is much simpler. The tetrode amplifier, being a high-gain tube, requires relatively little driving power and a relatively small grid swing for operation. This permits the paralleling of tubes with a common input network and a common output network which reduces the number of stages and simplifies tuning. In the tetrode power amplifier, *the screen voltage has a very pronounced effect on the dynamic characteristic of the tube*. (Italics added).

"By lowering the screen voltage, the static current required for optimum linearity is lowered. This permits greater plate RF voltage swing which improves efficiency. The use of lower screen voltage has the adverse effect of increasing the grid drive for class AB2 operation and lowering the power output for class AB1 operation. The tetrode tube can be used in the cathode-driven circuit and can be so used without neutralisation in the HF range."

To judge by this passage, there would seem to be distinct advantages in providing a varying screen voltage derived from the RF drive as in the G2DAF linear - but this is a debate in which I do not feel qualified to enter!

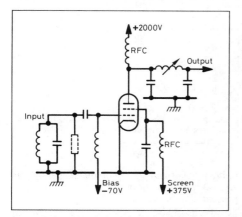

Fig 2: Simplified circuit of a grid-driven tetrode (4X250B) power amplifier. (*Fundamentals of SSB*)

HORIZONTAL LOOPS PLUS 1.8MHZ

WHILE THE 'SUNSPOT MAXIMUM' year of 1989 was, on the whole, rather disappointing in not yielding exceptionally good HF propagation periods, this has not been true of 1991 when the rich mixture of sunspots, geomagnetic activity and solar flares has seen periods when it has been possible to enjoy worldwide contacts with low-power or 'pieces of string' antennas or even both! This means that one may have to discount slightly some claims for antennas put up during 1991.

Nevertheless, there seems little doubt that the large horizontal loop has now established itself as a reliable performer on all bands from 3.5 to 28MHz (and probably also on 50MHz). *TT*, September 1990 and February 1991 presented some of the attractions of the large loop for multiband operation, even when suspended from supports considerably lower than the 50ft masts used by W1FB. As illustrated again in the September 1990 survey, the attractions of large wire loops in either the horizontal or (quad type) vertical planes were outlined by S M de Wet, ZS6AKA, as long ago as June, 1972 (and even earlier by G2PL when he reported excellent results using a quad antenna with its reflector element resting on the ground). Today, at last, this type of antenna is enjoying considerable popularity

even among those with only limited-size gardens.

Mike Hollebon, G4HOL, is particularly enthusiastic. He writes: "Following the *TT* items on horizontal loop antennas I put one up early this year (1991). A whole new world of DX has opened up for me. Using the familiar 1005/F formula, I cut mine for 3.55MHz, with resonances at approximately 7.1, 14.2, 21.3 and 28.4MHz.

"In switching checks on 3.5MHz in conjunction with my well-trusted 0.25λ sloper (66ft support) the loop was consistently some 9dB better - a tremendous boost for my 50W FT7B transceiver. The DX rolls in on 28/21/14MHz and I flabbergast 3.5/7MHz operators when I tell them I have only a FT-7B. My loop is an irregular four-sided affair fed at one corner with 300-ohm slotted-ribbon feeder. I can tune it nicely from 3.5 to 28MHz with my Nevada TM1000 ATU. As it is only 21ft above ground level, I am patiently waiting for the supporting trees to grow . . ."

A new twist to the use of a modified horizontal loop has come from Jean M Bourdereau, F1LCI, (Champniers, France) who has investigated methods of using his horizontal loop as a top-fed grounded Marconi antenna on 1.8MHz well suited to his attic shack, and with some affinity to the G3BDQ 'Steeple' antenna (or the earlier G8ON 1.8MHz antenna), making it a 'top-fed, top-cap antenna for top-band'.

His ideas took shape in 1990 but he has since upgraded the system and also completed an analysis with ELNEC software. His QTH, with a useful sized garden, is in a small village but near the Angouleme airfield so that a low profile approach is an advantage. He realised that he could take advantage of ZS6AKA's observation that "when the input is balanced, the furthest mid-point may be earthed" (originally adopted to form a static leakage path in thunderstorm-prone South Africa). F1LCI saw that earthing the loop and shorting the balanced feeder would transform the loop antenna into a top-fed inverted-L antenna with, in effect, capacitance loading by the two sides of the loop, providing a vertically-polarized component for DX operation on 1.8 and 3.5MHz etc.

He writes: "My loop is one full wavelength for 3.5MHz, and rectangular (18 by 24m) to fit my garden. Its mean height is 12m (varying between 8 and 14m). The higher (further) end is now grounded and supported by a fishing rod and telescopic mast, placed on a large aluminium plate (1m squared), to which are connected 20 radials and the neighbours' fences (**Fig 3**). The opposite end is connected to open-wire twin-line running 10m to the house roughly horizontally. It comes into the attic where there is a relay which provides the option of two transmission lines to my rig (my shack is in another part of the attic). The relay gives the options of: (a) open wire line and inductive coupler in the shack for 3.5/28MHz, which gives a horizontal loop antenna, grounded against static; and (b) the relay short-circuits the outdoor open-wire line

and connects it to coaxial cable, providing the 'vertical mode' for the lower frequency bands. A 2nd 'matchbox' (SPC) tuner is in the shack, but could be moved close to the relay.

"Results: Immunity to static with no more sparks in the inductive coupler due to the permanent grounding of the antenna. In the horizontal mode, grounding the loop at a current maximum does not effect performance and pattern (as stated by ZS6AKA and verified with ELNEC). In the vertical mode, which I prefer to consider as a 'top-fed Marconi' rather than a 'half loop' à la VE2CV, since the size is not right for a half-loop and one leg is in the house. There are some points in common with G3BDQ's 'steeple antenna' (*RadCom*, August 1986, pp556-568, 575) which I tried without as much success, as this design.

"Vertical-mode operation is of no interest above 14MHz. On 10MHz it permits filling in some notches in the horizontal-mode pattern. On 7 and 3.5MHz the vertical mode has less high-elevation gain but noise is stronger; again the major lobes are 90° apart. On 1.8MHz the horizontal loop is practically unusable for transmitting. But the ground connection and shorting the feeders (ie vertical mode) makes it function like a top-loaded vertical. The horizontal pattern is quasi-circular, the vertical one seems closer to a pure vertical than a conventional inverted-L, as if the two paths in the loop tend to cancel some radiation from the cap."

F1LCI has provided much information and comments on the ELNEC computer analysis of this antenna but this would require considerable space to reproduce. He does however also provide some constructional tips, as well as mentioning that one of his projects will be to try adding some short counterpoise wires.

On construction, he writes: "Fishing rod (fibreglass cheaper than carbon fibre): choose a non-telescopic one and discard the last segment. Flexibility provides resistance to French gales provided that three levels of nylon cord guys are used. With the loop stretched, the end will stay lightly bent. Inside, use the biggest wire available (eg piece of hi-fi 'esoteric' loudspeaker cable - very expensive - or similar less costly wire).

"Loop: no precise dimensions but the two arms must be equal. One approach is to take a 100m reel and fold it; solder the mid-point to the vertical, with the remainder (after forming the loop) used for the open-wire line (any spacing). The whole system can easily be erected by one man, provided the wires do not get entangled in branches. Make connections between copper wire and aluminium with stainless steel bolts and washers."

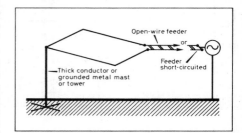

Fig 3: The 84-metre multiband horizontal loop used by F1LCI from his attic shack. It can be switched to form a vertical-mode top-fed Marconi antenna for 1.8MHz DX working.

OSCILLATOR STABILITY WITH VALVES AND FETS

ONE OF THE VERY FIRST widespread applications of solid-state technology in amateur radio was to provide an LC oscillator that reached thermal stability from switch-on in a matter of seconds rather than the 20 minutes or so often required for valve oscillators. But this did not - and does not - mean that a bipolar or FET oscillator is immune to changes in ambient temperature, either changes in shack temperature or changes resulting from the heat generated within high power stages whether thermionic or solid-state. FETs with their high internal capacitance (Miller effect) and silicon construction can be difficult to compensate effectively over the temperature cycling that occurs in practice, whereas the valve with its much greater self-generated heat tends to settle down after its (very long) warm-up period and then becomes much more resistant to changes in ambient temperature.

Ray Cracknell, G2AHU, - formerly ZE2JV of transequatorial propagation (TEP) fame - was prompted by the September *TT* item on 'The Universal VFO' to recall an experiment he carried out five or six years ago after finding in practice considerable discrepancy between the stabilities quoted for FET VFOs and their performance outside laboratories or temperature-controlled buildings. He writes:

"At the time, my shack was in the loft and suffered from wide swings in temperature. The results are evident from the graph of **Fig 4** based on a purpose-built VFO using 2N3819 FET inverted Hartley oscillator and 2N3819 source-follower operating at the fundamental frequency of 11MHz. It will be seen that the output frequency swung from plus 3kHz to minus

3kHz when slowly heated from 20°C to 60°C over a period of 140 minutes (including a change of some 4kHz in the first 20 minutes). As a result, I built myself a purpose-designed shack!"

"While I agree that the FET VFO has many advantages and especially the lack of pronounced warm-up drift at switch on, I found that I could not replace the 1970 receiver that had stood me in good stead through the Sunspot Cycle 21 TEP tests at ZE2JV with a FET oscillator. It could not match the 18 - 20MHz VFO that used a 6J6 Kalitron oscillator with 6CW4 (nuvistor) cathode-followers feeding the frequency counter and through the triode section to the mixer section of the 6U8 which had an E88CC front-end and independent 4-gang tuned RF.

"I found that the long-term stability of FET oscillators was inferior to the 6J6 Kalitron oscillator which can also produce a T9 note on considerably higher frequencies than 18 - 20MHz. But then we can't turn back the clock, can we?"

In providing (*TT*, November) further information on VK5QG's 'Q-Gate FET oscillator' I gave only the overall drift with the changes of temperature experienced in his shack, omitting the detailed table provided in his letter. However as G2AHU has raised the subject of FET stability it may be of interest to include now **Table 1** which represents average room temperature and average frequency taken over three runs on three different days. The frequency counter used a 1MHz crystal oscillator in an oven at 72°C plus/minus 0.5°C. Zero time was after one-hour warm up time in a room at 14°.

Small frequency shifts in a receiver (or transmitter) need to be minimised for SSB and data modes. The extent to which intelligibility of speech is impaired by the frequency shifting due to slight mistuning or drift was investigated many years ago. A USAF-Montana State College Report

quoted at the time that the use of SSB was being investigated for Airborne Mobile Communications (ARINC Characteristic No 533A issued March 11, 1966). The following notes are taken from appendix 6, III, Conclusions:

Part 1: Frequency-shifting of speech in the presence of noise produces marked deterioration of intelligibility dependent

Elapsed hours+1	Room Temperature(°C)	Frequency (MHz)
0.0	14	38.996
0.5	16	38.998
1.0	17	39.000
1.5	19	39.001
2.0	20	39.003
2.5	21	39.003
3.0	23	39.004
3.5	23	39.005
4.0	24	39.005
4.5	25	39.006
5.0	25	39.007
5.5	26	39.008
6.0	26	39.007
6.5	26	39.008
7.0	26	39.008
7.5	25	39.008
8.0	25	39.007

A span of some 12kHz over a temperature change of 12°C, ie better than 26ppm/°C - a very good figure for a free-running VHF oscillator

TABLE 1

upon direction and extent of the frequency shift. Downward frequency shifts produce greater deterioration in intelligibility than do upward shifts. As listening conditions deteriorate the tolerable amount of frequency-shifting is reduced. For optimum listening conditions (S/N ratio = 16 or more) frequency-shifting upward 400Hz or downwards 300Hz appears tolerable for most communication requirements (intelligibility levels of 85% or more). For average listening conditions (S/N ratio = 0 to 8) frequency shifts of +200 or -100 appear to be the tolerable maxima for normal communication requirements (intelligibility levels of 70% or more). For poor listening conditions (S/N ratio = 0 or less) shifts of more than 100kHz are unsatisfactory for normal communication (intelligibility levels less than 60%).

Part 2: The 0.3 to 3kHz bandpass filter appears optimum for frequency-shifted speech. Removing the lower portion of the 0.3 to 3kHz spectrum by means of a 0.5kHz high-pass filter reduces intelligibility of frequency-shifted speech. Extending the 0.3 to 3kHz spectrum by use of a 5kHz low-pass filter reduces intelligibility of frequency-shifted speech. Both removing the lower portion of the 0.3 to 3kHz spectrum and extending it upward to 5kHz produces the maximum deterioration in intelligibility of the filter conditions under study.

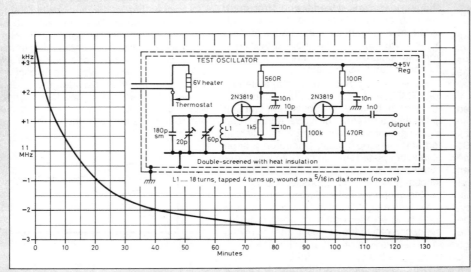

Fig 4:. Variation of frequency with temperature over a range of 20°C to 60°C over a 140-minute period of the FET test oscillator. As measured by G2AHU.

GAIN OPTIMIZATION OF YAGI ARRAYS.

OVER THE YEARS, AMATEURS have built some very large and complex antennas, but I cannot help feeling that the recent efforts of a troika of veteran Californian amateurs (combined ages total 178 years) would take some beating. Jack Hachten, Bud Ansley and Dan Bathker (W6TSW, W6VPH and K6BLG) have drawn on their professional expertise and Method of Moments software in building a gain-optimised 13-element, divided-boom, Yagi array for 14MHz, in an area 10 by 100 metres, with the elements 25 metres above ground. This is briefly described in 'A Modern Giant Yagi' (*IEEE Antennas & Propagation Magazine*, June 1991, pp19-21).

The structure, using MININEC, has thirteen widely-spaced elements mounted on six towers as a fixed beam. It is located in Southern California with a boresight 15 degrees East of True North, a great-circle heading to cover selected portions of Europe and Asia. The azimuth beamwidth is slightly less than +/- 15° to the 3dB points. First used in February 1991, it very quickly became evident that the performance in both transmission and reception equalled or exceeded all expectations. The elements are arranged for a considered balance between forward gain, sidelobe level, impedance level, bandwidth, structural wind survival and construction economies, with emphasis on forward gain. Using Brian Beezley's, K6STI, MN-software some 15,000 machine-aided EM design iterations were made, although it is emphasised also that 'indispensable human judgement, experience and strategy remained necessary ingredients'. But without such (PC-implemented) method-of-moments analysis and weighted, multi-parameter optimization, such a project would not likely to be initiated. The wire and optimization codes have enabled such a large undertaking to be approached with high confidence.

According to the authors, the 100m (divided boom) antenna operates at a centre frequency of 14.150MHz. The design provides a comfortably-high feed-point resistance (30Ω) with an impedance bandwidth (VSWR = 1.5) somewhat more than 2%. In free space, the predicted directivity is +15.8dBi. The predicted directivity is fully +21.5dBi at a favourably-low elevation angle, when arrayed over low conductivity (in fact, good dielectric) ground. The actual power gain is 0.1dB less at the feed point, due to calculated element dissipations, and 0.5dB less again, due to the loss in the 55m of cable between the feed point and the transmitter/receiver. Each element is built with heavy-wall aluminium tubing, starting in the centre with 32mm diameter, stepped twice, and ending with 19mm diameter at the tips. Each of the six, 75mm-diameter boom segments (on the six towers) measures 9m. To assure EM field purity in the six-tower environment, the topmost tower guys are dielectric. A conductor-free zone of a half-wavelength (minimum) radius is thus provided for the intended horizontal polarization.

This monster has been tested in comparison with an adjacent, well-constructed and widely-spaced five-element rotary Yagi, having a similar high feed-point resistance and overall efficiency - an antenna that I guess most of us would be more than content with!

As somebody who continues to believe in KISS and simple, negligible-cost wire antennas (tree and house supported), I nevertheless believe that a remarkable project such as this Californian monster antenna has a valuable role to play. This is emphasised in the accompanying editorial by W Ross Stone, editor of the *IEEE A&P Magazine*: "I once designed and built a professional one-kilometre long, 32-element, vertically-pointed array of crossed Yagi antennas. In doing so, I came to understand just how crazy I really was. It is thus with true awe that I present to you the article on a 100 metre Yagi . . . . (This) is important for two reasons. First, it provides unequivocal proof of the power of the Yagi design - as well as of the knowledge, the design tools, and the engineering expertise of the authors. Second, it is a testament that the amateur radio roots of our profession are alive, flourishing and continuing to set examples (or, at least, landmarks!) for us."

In the same issue of the *IEEE A&P Magazine*, David K Cheng (Syracuse University) reviews his work in the 1960s on 'Gain Optimization for Yagi-Uda Arrays' (pp42-45) that shows clearly why it has taken some 60 years really to come to grips with this deceptive simple-looking antenna. He writes: "Although the geometrical arrangement of a Yagi-Uda array appears simple, it's optimization is a different problem, mainly because there are many interdependent variables . . . . Since all the elements are electromagnetically coupled, the adjustment of any one of these variables changes the current distributions on all the elements. The optimization process cannot follow a one-variable-at-a-time procedure; all variables must be adjusted at the same time."

He notes that: "Many early studies of Yagi-Uda arrays made the basic assumption that the current distributions along all the array elements were sinusoidal. This assumption is not true, and the deviations from sinusoidal current distributions are critical in the calculations of the conditions for optimum gain . . . ."

He concludes: "The evolution of the research work that my former students and I carried out . . . . went through several stages, and we overcame a number of difficulties. With both spacing and length perturbations, we were able to find the optimized array analytically in a systematic way - some examples having gain increases of nearly 80%. The effects of finite dipole radius and mutual coupling were included in the theoretical treatment. Yagi-Uda arrays are used extensively in practice; but manufacturers have not been pressed to offer arrays with an optimum gain, because most users have scant idea of what gain or directivity is. It is hoped that our work will eventually have an impact on the design of Yagi-Uda arrays.

"We have, in fact, more recently looked further into the problem of increasing the gain of Yagi-Uda arrays, based upon an observation by Landstorfer, that properly-shaped wire antennas (**Fig 5**) longer than a wavelength, could yield a higher directivity than straight dipoles (see *TT*, December 1982). By assuming a sinusoidal distribution that did not change with the shape or the radius of the dipole, he obtained a dipole geometry for maximum directivity by a piecewise-linear approxima-tion. He also found by experimentation that a 3-element Yagi-Uda array of shaped wires, each 1.5λ long, could be adjusted to yield a maximum gain of 11.5dBi (**Fig 6**). We managed to put Landstorfer's results on a firm analytical basis, by applying the method for function minimisation. We found the optimum shapes (bent like bows), as well as the positions of the array elements, both of which depend on the radius of the wire dipoles. The calculated current distributions on the shaped dipoles differ markedly from sinusoids (*Electronics* Letters, September 1982 pp816-818 and *IEEE Trans Ant & Prop*, May 1983)."

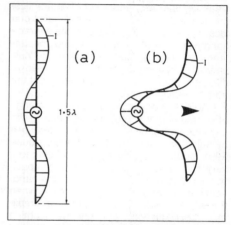

Fig 5: The current distribution on (a) a straight 1.5λ dipole where the phase reversal reduces radiation normal to the axis of the dipole; (b) A 1.5λ dipole with a gain-optimized shape producing maximum radiation in the forward direction (F M Landstorfer, 1982).

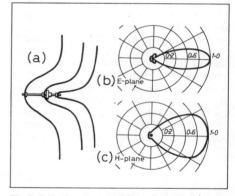

Fig 6: A Yagi array using three Landstorfer gain-optimized 1.5λ elements. A VHF array of this type provided a gain of 11.5dBi, sidelobe attenuation better than 20dB, and a front-to-back ratio of 26dB.

POSTSCRIPT ON 144MHZ D/F SYSTEMS

SOME USEFUL COMMENTS have been received on the 144MHz handheld D/F systems described in the April and July *TT*.

Dick Rolema, PA0SE, mentions that Helmut Liebich, DL1OY, has pointed out that this type of 'Doppler' direction-finder is suitable only for use with vertically polarised signals, whereas many of the popular European 144MHz 'fox hunts' specify the use of horizontal polarization in order to allow even simple dipole antennas to function as crude D/F antennas. However, this is not universal. It also does not apply, for example, where there is a need to sort out 'repeater problems' for which the G3KMG 'whistling dipoles' were originally developed.

If you turn these antennas through 90°, as PA0SE comments, you can find the elevation of an incoming signal but not its bearing! This is not the case with the various Yagi type antennas often used in fox hunts, or for example the directional miniature twin-loop antenna that formed part of the ZS6EF 'sniffer' system (antenna *TT*, September 1990; receiver *TT*, March 1981).

The ZS6EF sniffer system was intended primarily for use quite close to the transmitter, although the antenna itself responds well to weak signals. As ZS6EF noted, a practical problem with most D/F systems is that strong local signals can be received on the average handheld receiver virtually without an antenna, making it difficult to obtain a good 'null' unless two systems are carried: one for weaker distant signals, the other for sniffing out the transmitter in the final stages of the hunt.

PA0SE has drawn my attention to a means of overcoming this problem, eliminating the need for a separate sniffer receiver, described by Anjo Eenhoorn, PA0ZR, in *Electron*, June 1991, pp309-310). His elegant solution to a very real problem consists of a compact, screened, add-on unit, attached to the hand-held receiver and then brought into use when the signal is strong. It comprises a simple mixer/oscillator which converts the incoming signal to a different 144MHz channel, spaced some 500kHz from the channel used by the hidden fox transmitter: **Fig 7**. The mixer is a 1N4148 with a simple diode mixer, a BSX329 as 500kHz oscillator and an emitter-follower BC107 arranged to provide variable oscillator injection. By varying the oscillator signal applied to the mixer, by means of a slider pot, the conversion loss (attenuation) of the signal applied to the handheld receiver proper can be reduced by tens of dBs. In this way, the signal strength indicator becomes useful over a range of more than 100dB.

As PA0SE explains: "At the beginning of the hunt the antenna is connected directly to the handheld receiver and the 'fox' received on its correct frequency. When the signal becomes too strong to enable a clearly de-

fined minimum, the antenna is transferred to the add-on unit but the receiver remains on the fox channel. The injection control slider potentiometer now drives the diode as an adjustable attenuator with a range of about 12 to 26dB. When, as one closes in, the signal becomes so strong that this amount of diode attenuation is insufficient, the hand-held is retuned to one of the two mixing products,

$$f(mix) = f(fox) \pm f(osc).$$

The oscillator frequency can be chosen more or less at will. PA0ZR uses 500kHz which means that at least one of the mixer products will be in the range 144 to 146MHz yet sufficiently removed from the fox frequency to minimise breakthrough/overload problems. With a low oscillator frequency, stability will not be a problem. The unit is powered by a single 1.5V 'button' alkaline battery and consumption is only 0.7mA at 1V. A nice feature is that, when near the transmitter, conversion loss is increased so that the output signal on the fox frequency reaching the receiver is also attenuated. Although the receiver is not tuned to the fox channel, its front-end stages could otherwise still be overloaded by the extremely strong signals when very near the fox transmitter".

H J Benjamin, Z21FB writing from Harare, Zimbabwe, questions the use of the term 'Doppler' to categorise the type of D/F system outlined by ZS6EF and G3KMG (the principles of operation of which were outlined in the April, 1991 *TT*). He writes: "My understanding of the term is that the 'Doppler Effect' occurs when a static observer receives an audio or RF signal arriving from a moving object with a frequency which changes depending on whether it is coming towards or moving away from the observer. With these electronically switched antennas neither the transmitter nor the observer is moving.

"This is not the way these direction finders operate. The oscillator switches the output of each antenna element in turn. When the elements are at different distances from the transmitter, ie not pointing at the transmitter, the radio wave will arrive at the first antenna before it arrives at the second, inducing unequal signal amplitudes due to the phase difference between them (ie because the signal is arriving at slightly different times). If the unequal outputs of these two antennas are now summed, then an output will be produced being the incoming carrier wave phase modu-

lated at the rate of the switching oscillator. This signal will produce an audio tone of the switching oscillator in the receiver. But when both antennas are equidistant from the transmitter, the signal arrives at the antennas at the same time, producing an equal signal at the summing point thereby cancelling the output. Therefore no carrier wave is passed to the receiver, hence no audio output".

I do not agree with this final paragraph. The electronic switch connects each antenna to the receiver in sequence, so in fact there is no summation of the outputs. There is no cancellation of the carrier wave at the receiver. However, because there is no phase difference between the signals, the receiver sees the carrier as an unmodulated carrier, and hence the audio tone disappears. Since, in effect, the antenna is moved back and forwards by the action of the electronic switch, it does produce a sort of artificial 'Doppler Effect' justifying the use of the term 'Doppler D/F', though perhaps others may disagree. In any case "a rose by any other name would smell as sweet".

However, Z21FB does raise another matter of practical significance. He writes: "I would also like to comment regarding the spacing of the two antenna elements. Neither ZS6EF nor G3KMG commented on the significance of this spacing and their spacing was different, although this would not have been important in their antennas. However, if cognisance is taken of the effect of the spacing, then by suitable adjustment, use can be made of the properties of a parasitic array to resolve the 180° ambiguity.

"Considering each antenna in turn, the dormant one (ie the one not switched through to the receiver) as a parasitic element affects the radiation pattern of the active element so that it is no longer omnidirectional. Instead it becomes that of a two-element parasitic beam pointing sideways on to the transmitter (both dipoles equidistant to the transmitter). If the spacing is now set for about 0.2λ then the resulting received pattern can be used to determine whether the transmitter is at 0° or 180° relative to the antennas.

"The audio output from the receiver is fed back into the unit and used to control a switch giving an output on a centre-zero meter. It can then, by correct phasing, be arranged to show the output from each antenna on the left or right of the meter. Because of the directional characteristics of the antennas, by simply rotating them by a small amount, the antenna most forward to the station will produce more output on that side of the meter, showing immediately if the transmitter is ahead or behind.

"If the meter is to the left, then turning left until the needle centres will show that the transmitter is ahead. Conversely, if the needle is centred and turning in either direction causes the needle to move in that direction, then the station will be behind.

"I developed and manufactured a system based on this technique in Zimbabwe (pre-1980) for use in aircraft operating on a frequency between 118-136MHz. If readers are interested in further information I will be pleased to send the circuitry". His address is H J Benjamin, Z21FB, P O Box 1215, Harare, Zimbabwe.   ❑

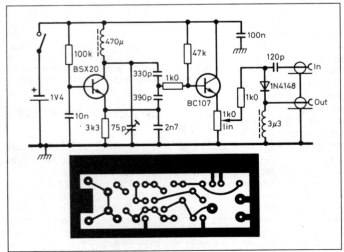

Fig 7: PA0ZR's add-on channel translator/attenuator provides an elegant solution to the problem of using a handheld receiver as a combined strong-signal 'sniffer' and weak-signal direction-finder, enabling the system to cope with a 100dB variation in signal strength.

AN INDOOR 'VK2ABQ-TYPE' 28MHZ BEAM

IT IS VIRTUALLY impossible to predict how well or how badly an indoor transmitting antenna will behave among so many lossy materials: electrical wiring, water tanks and radiators and general domestic metalwork. Roof-space and attic-room antennas usually work reasonably well, rooms lower in a building or in tower-block apartment can vary from just acceptable to downright poor, compared with a similar antenna erected outside the house. For VHF operation, an antenna - foil or wire - taped to a window can give excellent results in the directions away from the building but tend to be pretty poor in the opposite directions where the building and contents will tend to attenuate signals by some 10dB or so - more in a reinforced concrete structure. Nevertheless, DX operation on HF is often possible. *TT* (September 1990, pp31-32 and July 1991, p26) gave brief information on W9BRD's 'Zapper' antennas (a form of unidirectional W8JK driven array) which he finds effective for working into Europe from the Chicago area.

Tony Baker, G3JSF, has found early retirement an incentive to get back on the bands with his TS520 transceiver after an interval of some eight years. One result is that he has devised a novel form of a single-band VK2ABQ compact array that gives his signal some gain and directivity, while fulfilling his belief in low-cost KISS philosophy and the value of lateral thinking.

In effect, he uses a fixed VK2ABQ-type of square wire structure arranged so that he can direct signals towards any one of the four quadrants simply by changing the feed point and inserting a 'jumper' wire across the opposite gap. As shown in **Fig 1**, the antenna comprises four quarter-wave lengths of wire - AB, BC, CD and DA - arranged with gaps at the points A, B, C and D. The array can be fed at any of the four points, A. B, C and D from 75Ω cable terminated with a couple of crocodile (alligator) clips. If fed at A, a jumper wire (about 2") similarly with crocodile clips is connected across gap C. Then to change direction in steps of 90°, the feedpoint and jumper are changed as required.

G3JSF writes: "I am currently using crocodile clips on the feeder and on the jumper wire. By using coax with no balun and then reversing the 'inner' and 'outer' connections at the feed-point, some slewing of the main lobe can be achieved. Direction of fire can be changed in about 30 seconds. My Monimatch SWR meter indicates an almost perfect match to 75Ω cable, flat from 28.3 to 28.7MHz. Standard DIY connecting strip is used to fix this beam horizontally to the ceiling of the room next to the shack, fixing the corners also with the same connector strip. This allows a good mechanical/electrical connection as the feed point is changed. Used with a home-brewed ATU and low-pass filter there is a complete absence of any TV/radio/telephone breakthrough and I find that I can put out a signal on 28MHz with around 90% success rate on the first call.

"Results have included RS58-9 from the Falklands, Brazil, etc. 59+ East Coast USA, 55-8 West Coast, RS58 Japan, 52 New Zealand, 59++ short skip. When not in use, the coaxial cable is simply coiled up and put away. If white PVC covered wire is used for the elements together with the clear connecting blocks for fixing, the beam itself is unobtrusive. The beam also provides a great talking point with my contacts!"

Clearly such a 28MHz beam could be put up in quite a small room sized some 9ft by 9ft. A 21MHz version would often be possible, although a 14MHz version would need a fair-sized room or a roof-space with easy access. But with different sites, different buildings, there can be no guarantee of achieving the same DX results as G3JSF. It can also prove difficult to clear EMC problems when using indoor antennas. But it should not cost more than a few pounds to give the idea a try-out should you be unable to put up an outside antenna giving the required directivity.

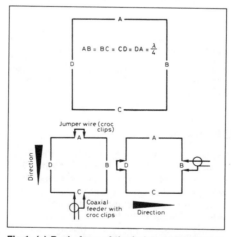

Fig 1: (a) Basic form of the indoor VK2ABQ-type antenna developed by G3JSF. (b) Showing how the directivity is changed by changing the feeder point and the jumper wire to form a driven element and reflector.

RF PROTOTYPING

ADDING TO RECENT discussions on forms of construction that do not involve the etching of one-off PCBs, Dave Lauder, G1OSC writes: "Various techniques for prototyping RF circuits have been described in *RadCom* recently, including those in the two-part article by Ian White, G3SEK (February and March 1991 issues) and the technique briefly mentioned in *TT* (October 1991, page 33) by Dick Biddulph, G8DPS, of combining Veroboard with an unetched piece of copper-clad board to form a ground-plane. Like G3SEK, my favourite technique is pin-and-wire with a ground plane. Although it takes longer than techniques such as 'dead bug' ('ugly construction') the result is neat, robust and easy to repair or modify. Having to drill all the holes for the Veropins is rather tedious, however,

and it is necessary to plan the layout precisely before starting.

"When I worked as a design engineer for Marconi Avionics, we used pin-and-wire construction on what we called 'ground-plane Veroboard' (ie copper-clad board drilled as Veroboard). This was obtained on special order from BICC-Vero as "0.1 inch matrix SRBP Veroboard, pierced but not milled". It is an intermediate stage in the manufacture of the normal copper-strip Veroboard, after the holes have been pierced but before the strips have been milled out. Unfortunately, although relatively inexpensive and ideal for RF prototyping, it is not currently available to amateurs because of the large minimum-order charge which, some years ago, was £250. However, similar material may be available in the USA since a 1982 article in *CQ* magazine describing the home construction of a satellite TVRO refers to 'copper-clad perfboard' as 'ideal because you put the clad portion on the top and do the wiring at the bottom'.

"I have tried on several occasions without success to persuade BICC-Vero sales representatives that there is a market here for this type of board but they suggest that I should use Vero 'Microboards'. These are glass-fibre Eurocard boards with a 'colander' ground plane on the component side, ie the ground plane is etched around each hole to clear component leads. A similar product is available from RS Components, No 434-841 but costs over £10 plus VAT for a 100 by 160mm ground-plane board. Microboards are thus an expensive way of RF prototyping and the ground-plane is covered with solder resist which has to be scraped off to make a connection to ground. Perhaps, through *TT*, BICC-Vero might be persuaded to make copper clad perforated board available as a stock item. Or, alternatively, perhaps the Society might buy a batch from BICC-Vero for sale to members in small quantities? Or an enterprising trader could trace the USA source and import some for sale?

"Finally, on the subject of pin-and-wire, I would offer some constructional hints:

(1) When clearing copper away from holes for non-grounded pins, turn the board upside down and tap it sharply to remove all copper shavings to avoid being plagued later by shorts to ground!

(2) If fitting IC sockets to a board with a bare ground plane, ensure that there is a layer of insulating material under the socket to avoid shorts to the ground plane.

(3) If screening between the base and collector of a transistor is required, drill a hole in the board and mount the transistor upside down in the hole so that a screen may be soldered across it.

(4) Pins can be pushed in without force by heating and pushing them with a soldering iron".

A 144MHZ UNIPOLE ANTENNA

THE CONVENTIONAL quarter-wave 144MHz vertically-polarized rod antenna for repeater/mobile operation with horizontal radials (or metal ground plate) has a feedpoint impedance of under 20Ω. This can be raised either by sloping the radials downwards or by lengthening the element slightly so that it is no longer an electrical quarter-wave. Another rather more elegant solution is the 'unipole' (folded-monopole element) which has the added advantage of increasing the bandwidth of the antenna.

Constructional details of a 144MHz unipole antenna are given by Des Greenham, VK3CO in the WIA's *Amateur Radio* (October 1991, p14). He writes:

·"Performance of this antenna (**Fig 2(a)**) has been found to be marginally better than a normal quarter-wave vertical, and the impedance match (SWR) is certainly better with a broader frequency range. The construction is simple using readily available components along with some 'junk box' bits. The main component is a standard CB-type 'mirror mount' bracket used to mount whips on the heavy-duty mirrors of trucks, and is readily available from CB shops: those with workshop facilities, however, could easily fabricate a suitable bracket from 3/16" aluminium plate along with suitable 1/4" U-bolts.

"A standard PL259 flange type chassis socket is mounted on the bracket using four machine screws, reaming the hole slightly if necessary. This requires the use of a small file and some muscle. Place a solder tag under one of the mounting screws to terminate one end of the antenna. The radials are made from aluminium tubing of any diameter between 1/4" and 1/2" (scrap from old TV antennas is suitable). The radials are attached to the bracket with pop rivets, self-tapping screws, or small 1/8" diameter machine screws. Radials need to be mounted solidly as they are likely to be used as bird-perches.

"The antenna proper can be made from

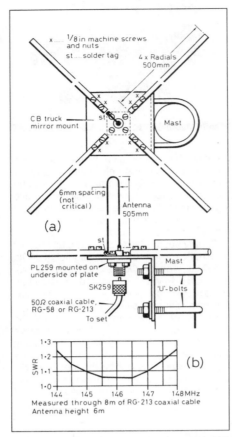

(a)

(b)

Fig 2: (a) Constructional details of the VK3CO 144MHz unipole antenna. Note that dimensions of element and radials are centred on 146MHz to suit Australian 144-148MHz band. For the UK it would be better to make them slightly longer to resonate at 145MHz.

any available suitable material such as aluminium, wire or brass. Salvaged copper wire should have a diameter of at least 1.5mm, thinner wires will be too fragile. Perhaps the best solution is to use 1/8" bronze welding rods, available in various lengths. If one length is not enough to form the folded element, a soldered joint can be easily made at the top bend. Bronze solders well and a good connection can be made to the PL259 socket and earth tag secured under the mounting screw. A good clean with steel wool will make for easier soldering. Don't forget to waterproof the exposed end of the coax cable at the antenna to prevent water entering the cable and ruining it. Finally mount the antenna on a mast at the maximum possible height and in the clear (eg chimney mounted mast).

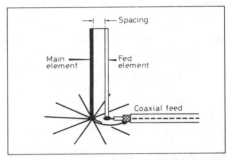

Fig 3: Basic form of the folded-monopole (unipole) antenna. Step-up ratio of feedpoint impedance compared with single quarter-wave element is approximately 4:1 for equal-diameter conductors in fed and main element.

If in the clear, such an antenna should give good 'omnidirectional' performance, but remember it is intended for working stations using vertical polarisation. *TT* July 1987, p497 and August 1991 gave more information on the fundamentals of folded monopoles, including the work of Arch Doty, K8CFU, and his colleagues on their use for HF, VHF and UHF, as well as their technique of bottom-loading. One of the advantages of the folded element is that by using different diameter wires or rods in the main and fed element it is possible to design into the antenna almost any required feed-point impedance for 50 or 75Ω cables etc. **Fig 3** shows the basic structure. VK3CO uses the conventional four radials but as *TT* has pointed out in the past, it should be possible to obtain virtually the same performance using only three or even two radials.

SITING VEHICLE ANTENNAS

TT HAS REFERRED several times to the paper and book by Melvin Weiner *et al* (the paper in *IEEE Trans on Ant & Prop*, May 1987, pp488 to 495) and the book *Monopole Elements on Circular Ground Planes* (Artech House, 1987)). These sources showed how the vertical radiation pattern (VRP) of a quarter-wave monopole antenna depends to a significant extent on the dimensions of the ground-plane (including a vertical with zero ground-plane) as noted in *TT*, November 1987 and March 1988. It has long been recognized that the low-angle radiation from verticals is also greatly affected by ground conductivity, but it was seldom fully appreciated that with certain dimensions of ground plane (as found for example when the metal-

RF SWITCH FOR FAN ETC

JAY F HAMLIN, WB6HBS, (*QST*, August 1991) describes a simple way of automatically turning on a fan during transmissions from a compact high-power VHF transceiver; such a system could also be used to indicate that the rig is delivering RF to the antenna. As shown in **Fig 4** a pick-up coil (L1) comprising a few turns of hook-up wire, is wound around a typical (leaky) coaxial feeder cable.

The RF is rectified by D1 and turns on the power transistor, TR1, for which he uses an "ultra reliable" National Semiconductor LM395 which has built-in thermal-overload protection and current and power

limiting. R1, in the absence of RF, pulls the base back to ground and turns TR1 'off'. *TT* has in the past pointed out that most modern co-axial cables do not have 100% braid screening and thus leak out some RF. WB6HBS finds that with L1 about ten turns, 5W of RF into Tandy RG8-M (foam-dielectric miniature RG-8) cable will reliably turn on a small fan he has fitted in the transceiver.

Other cables may require some experimentation to find a suitable number of turns for the power involved. Such an RF-operated switch could also be useful for mobile operation by illuminating a 'transmitter on' display or pilot-lamp to overcome the problem of the microphone PTT being lodged between car seats etc and so jammed 'on' - a far from unknown occurrence in commercial PMR networks, causing a channel to be jammed out for long periods until the offending mobile can be traced.

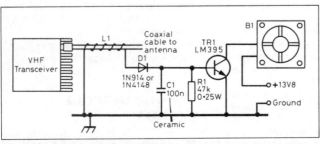

Fig 4: WB6HBS's arrangement for switching on a fan during transmission-only by sensing RF leakage or outer-shield current on the coax feeder cable. Alternatively the switch could operate a 'transmitter-on' indicator, etc.

work of a vehicle is used as the ground plane) the maximum radiation lobe may be at a high angle above the horizon.

In 'Reception - a function of radiating structures' (*Radio-ZS*, September 1991, pp4, 6-7), B N Jansen of Mikorntek summarises Weiner's findings (**Fig 5**) as part of an investigation into the factors affecting the performance of mobile antennas, including the effect of broadcast antennas and the mounting position of the mobile antenna on the vehicle. He demonstrated to SARL members the variation in the HRP at an Antenna Test Facility although emphasising that the results presented represent a demonstration only and do not come from detailed antenna measurements made under optimised conditions.

The demonstrations included the use of two types of antenna (a quarter-wave and a five-eighths-wave element) each tested separately on 149MHz in six different positions (**Fig 6**) on an Opel Monza car, using in effect the boot, the roof and the bonnet as ground-planes. **Fig 7** shows the composite results for all six positions: (a) being for the 5/8-wave antenna and (b) for the 1/4-wave. B N Jansen also provides six further diagrams, each representing a comparison of the results of the two antennas for each position but these are omitted here to save space. The patterns of Fig 7 are those 'seen' from above the car with the front of the car at 0° and the driver side of the car at 90°. He points out that: "The efficiencies and losses of the antennas are assumed to be of the same order of magnitude.

This implies that it cannot be said, purely on these tests, that the one antenna is better than the other just based on the radiation patterns. However, some conclusions can be drawn by seeing what effect the different positions will have on the antennas, and to what extent the ground-plane affects the pattern".

While personally, I would hesitate to draw firm conclusions on the effect of ground-planes from this test, it is certainly interesting to note that while the quarter-wave antenna shows a directivity variation of some 12dB, that of the longer antenna exhibited a variation of 6dB. It also seems that the roof positions, as might be expected, tend to be

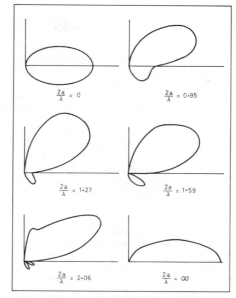

Fig 5: Elevation directive gain patterns (VRP) for any azimuthal direction of a quarter-wave element mounted on a solid ground plane of radius a (based on Wiener *et al*) as given in *Radio-ZS*.

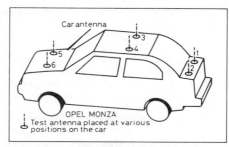

Fig 6: Test antenna positions on the vehicle used for the South Africa demonstrations.

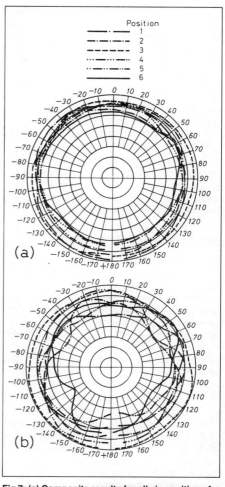

Fig 7: (a) Composite results for all six positions for the five-eighth-wave antenna. (b) Composite results for the quarter-wave antenna.

superior to the boot or bonnet mountings. Even with roof mounting, the broadcast antenna has some influence on the patterns.

B N Jansen suggests that the variations can be attributed to one of the following possible causes: "(1) The broadcast car antenna plays a role in acting as either a director or reflector with respect to the test antenna. (2) The relative size of the ground-plane plays a role. For the specific car, three sub-ground-planes can be identified, ie the boot, the roof and the bonnet. The sloping down to ground on the edges of the ground-planes may also contribute to the lowering of the pattern in that particular direction. (3) The physical length of the antenna plays a role. For the same ground plane, antennas of different lengths will have different radiation patterns".

EEA GUIDELINES ON SOLDERING-FLUX HAZZARDS

THE JUNE 1991 *TT* ITEM 'safe soldering' drew attention, not for the first time, to the fact that solder-fluxes containing colophony (rosin) have been shown, for more than a decade, to present, particularly for heavy users in poorly ventilated areas, a very real risk of becoming sensitized to 'woodworker's asthma' as noted in *TT*, November 1979. Subsequently, the August *TT* included a note from Roger Blackwell, G4PMK, pointing out that Multicore Xersin flux appears to be free from this problem; he also found an asthma inhaler (Intal, disodium cromoglycate) useful for sufferers.

By coincidence, in late August, the Electronics Engineering Association (EEA) published a 12-page (A4-format) booklet *Guidelines on the use of colophony (rosin) solder fluxes in the electronics industry*. This booklet is intended to assist employers whose staff use resin-based fluxes, to help prevent ill-

ness as a result of exposure to solder fume. It does not cover risks that may arise from the involvement of other materials such as zinc chloride, lead, isocyanates (polyurethane coatings) or cadmium - some of which were mentioned in the *QST* article by NU1N.

The booklet (including detailed information on the requirements imposed by the Health & Safety Acts, and priced at £11 post free to UK destinations, from EEA, Leicester House, 8 Leicester Street, London WC2H 7BN), is clearly not aimed at the amateur-enthusiast. It has been produced by the Electronics Industry Working Group - a joint industry, trade union and Health & Safety Executive committee. It does, however, add some further information on the effects of colophony fume: "Colophony fume can give rise to respiratory irritation and in some persons it may also cause respiratory sensitization. Sensitization means that after an initial period of exposure, breathing problems such as asthma may occur which are triggered by very low levels

of fume whilst colleagues are unaffected.

"Exposure of skin to colophony can also result in the development of allergic contact dermatitis . . . . The sensitizing effect of colophony is not caused by a single indentifiable constituent of rosin. A number of allergens appear to be present in both colophony and in pyrolysis products formed during heating or soldering".

The booklet noted that "some fluxes are available which do not contain colophony and these should be used where reasonably practicable, care being taken not to substitute a risk by a greater one". Colophony (rosin) is widely used as an adhesive and mastic in cold processes, but the main use of heated colophony is in the electronics and electrical industries: in liquid fluxes for wave soldering; as part of the core of solder wire 7/8 and in solder paste for application by screen printing or syringe dispensing. For the amateur, cored solder-wire is the main source of colophony fume.

The booklet covers legal requirements for employers and the choice of exhaust systems for workplaces. It is pointed out that "fume from hand soldering will rise vertically on thermal currents, entering the breathing zone of the worker as he or she leans over the work". Control is normally achieved by means of effective local exhaust ventilation. Details are given of (a) exhaust nozzle fitted to the soldering iron; (b) captor hood; (c) individual fume control units; and (d) exhaust ventilated benches.

A bibliography lists, inter alia, ten references to papers and articles in medical and trade magazines dating back to 1976, suggesting that the industry has not been in a rush to produce its guidelines!

NATTY FRONT PANELS - II

MY TECHNIQUE FOR finishing aluminium front panels is somewhat simpler than that of KA3RRF (*TT*, March 1991, p30-31). A 'brushed' finish can be achieved by rubbing an aluminium panel in one direction with 600-grade or finer 'wet and dry' abrasive paper on a block used wet with white spirit turpentine, then wiping with cellulose thinners to remove any oily residue from the white spirit. But beware, both these solvents are flammable and cellulose thinners contains xylene which is harmful by inhalation or skin contact.

Letraset can be put straight onto the aluminium followed by several coats of clear lacquer. I have found RS Components aerosol clear lacquer (568-477) suitable for this. However, a word of warning - some types of aerosol lacquer are not suitable for front panels as I learned to my cost.

One day I had no RS lacquer and bought some Holts 'Dupli Color' aerosol clear lacquer from a local car accessory shop for the front panel of my home-brew hi-fi tuner-amplifier. It looked very smart for a few weeks, then it started to develop an unsightly frosted effect around the most-used control knobs. This turned out to be small traces of natural skin oils which caused the Holts lacquer to develop a mosaic of tiny cracks. I was able to prove that a trace of any type of oil or grease - from Flora margarine to 3-in-1 oil, and especially skin oil, caused it to crack. Clearly this lacquer is totally unsuitable for front panels and should be used only for applications free of any traces of oil or grease and not touched by hand! I had to remove all the lacquer and lettering with cellulose thinners and start again with RS lacquer which has now stood up well to several years of daily use. *Dave Lauder, G1OSC.*

HERE AND THERE

PETER CHADWICK, G3RZP, in commenting on the April *TT* item about strong RF fields affecting voltage measurements, writes: "As far as RF in power supplies, test meters and the like is concerned, I've found that the ubiquitous 723 regulator suffers very badly in this respect. One of my friends had to rebuild his 12V PSU because the RF from his FT747 shut down the 723 regulator. In the end, he used a 741 op-amp to drive a string of discrete amplifiers, and a zener for reference.

"I have a 12V 5A supply that can be shut

CHEAPER SOLAR POWER?

THE USE OF SOLAR CELL arrays to provide electrical power to charge storage batteries in conjunction with radio equipment has become established in professional communications in remote areas, particularly where the sun shines more predictably than in the UK. In *TT*, October 1988 ('Low cost systems aid the third world') it was noted that Dr S A G Chandler, G3UDD, was implementing in Sierra Leone a network of 'village' radiophones using low-cost 27MHz CB transceivers under microprocessor control with the batteries kept charged by solar arrays costing about £100 per station. But to provide sufficient charging power for regular operation of, say, an HF 100W transceiver, suitable solar arrays do not come cheaply.

In the 1980s, the Japanese launched a long-term project with the aim of bringing the cost of solar power down to about $1/Watt but that target does not seem to have been achieved.

A new possibility of reducing the cost of solar power - though still only on the horizon - seems to be opened up by a recent announcement in *Nature* (24 October 1991) of a novel form of photovoltaic cell created from low to medium purity materials and low-cost processes.

Brian O'Regan and Michael Graetzel of the Swiss Federal Institute of Technology, Lausanne writes: "The large-scale use of photovoltaic devices for electricity generation is prohibitively expensive at present: generation from existing commercial devices costs about ten times more than conventional methods". They describe a cell based on a 10-micrometres-thick, optically

transparent film of titanium dioxide particles a few nanometres in size, coated with a monolayer of a charge-transfer dye with an overall light-to-electric solar energy conversion yield of 7.1 - 7.9% in simulated solar light and 12% in diffuse daylight.

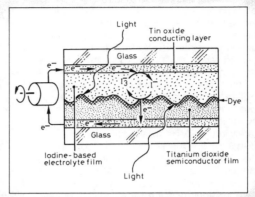

Fig 8: The form of solar panel announced by the Swiss Federal Institute of Technology could open the way for low-cost chemicals turning double-glazing into a solar generator at much reduced cost to silicon solar cells.

Following up this report, Andy Coghlan in *New Scientist* (26 October 1991) suggests that: "Buildings could be made much more energy efficient by fitting their windows with a new type of transparent solar panel (**Fig 8**) rather than glass". It is estimated that panels producing around 150W/m² might cost around £40 - £80 compared with around £400 for conventional silicon solar arrays: "The sandwich arrangement of the Swiss panel mimics the way that plants make their food by gathering energy from light through photosynthesis". There would still be the capital cost of the solar windows and storage batteries but solar energy then comes for free.

down by putting the antenna of a 144MHz handheld on low power about 3-in from the 723. Oddly enough, no amount of bypassing seems to cure the problem. This suggests rectification of the strong electric field is taking place somewhere on the chip itself, although the electric field from 200mW of RF can't be that great - there is certainly not enough to light a neon - an old-fashioned but extremely useful item of test gear. Another is a loop-lamp." (Two items of test gear that have retained their usefulness at G3VA over the years since 1938 and before that at 2BUH!)

Doug Allerston, G5PQ, in *TT*, March pp29-30, warned of low-cost 90° cable elbows he had bought at a rally and which proved to have only "a horrible little black metal spring" connecting the plug and socket ports, not even soldered. The same form of construction is reported by Barry Collins, W4TLV (*QST*, May 1991, p46) in a BNC-type 90° adapter (UG-646/M-359A) for PL259 sockets bought from a Californian mail order firm. Used at a 144MHz repeater station it resulted in the destruction of the power amplifier: "The elbow adapter had a coil spring made of 24-gauge wire slipped on (not soldered) to the input and output connections. Not only does

this have the limited current-capacity of 24-gauge wire but it also adds inductance in the form of the coil spring. Running 100 watts at 146MHz through the connector caused the spring to heat up, slide off one of the connectors and arc every time the machine keyed up. In short order, the repeater's final amplifier was destroyed.

"Next time you're tempted to go for low-priced, no-brand-name connectors and adapters, think about this type of construction. In my opinion, they're not even adequate for audio use, much less RF."

Geoff Pendrick, G6BEI, has found a use for a small item that is readily available, in most cases free. He writes:

"As a keen constructor of QRP equipment, I am always looking for ways of keeping down costs. When constructing a project recently I needed a quantity of small pillars to support the circuit board on the chassis. On looking through my scrap box I came across four old spark plugs discarded from the last service. On looking at the plug tops (which unscrew) I found that these were just the right height for mounting the board. There was sufficient clearance around the board for isolation purposes and with a small drill to enlarge the hole

I found they could be installed using either a nut and bolt or a self-tapping screw.

The interesting point was that when I enquired at my local garage to see if they had any spare old plug tops, I was given 100 of them free of charge. Pillars designed for this purpose are surprisingly expensive."

Mark Rogers, G4RGB, draws attention to Parafilm 'M' Laboratory Film made by the American Can Company which he uses for his professional work in a laboratory for sealing test-tubes, flasks etc so that they can be shaken. He finds this material is very pliable and both weather and waterproof. He suggests it could have its uses for sealing the entry of co-axial cable into antenna connection boxes, for stretching around exposed electrical connections to keep out water, etc. He adds: "I have found that insulation tape tends to undo itself and lose its stickiness, PTFE is awkward to work with and tends to go into fine strands - so, hopefully, Parafilm may have its uses in amateur radio. It is available in the UK from laboratory suppliers in a variety of widths/lengths, for example from Gallenkamp, Bolton Road West, Loughborough, Leics LE11 0TR (Tel 0509-237371)". G4RGB does not mention whether this material lasts long when exposed to UV radiation.

Another tip for waterproofing co-ax fittings comes from VE7FLA in W6SAI's *CQ* column (October 1991): "An easy way is to use non-contaminating heat-shrink tubing. It is not as messy as coax tape".

In *QST*'s *Hints & Kinks* column (October 1991), Bob Raffaele, W2XM, suggests an unusual substitute for glass or porcelain insulators for temporary antennas for field days etc: "If great strength is not required and the installation is temporary, I use Wiffle practice golf balls. They work well and are far less expensive than porcelain insulators". I wonder if this applies to equivalent UK products?

TT has included in the past some brief details of the series of DC/AC inverters published in *Electronics Australia* permitting the operation of mains appliances from 12V or 24V vehicle batteries. An American design

providing an output of up to 40 watts appears in *Radio-Electronics* (April 1991 pp43-44 & 68). This uses six of the relatively low-cost IRF511 power-FETs as switching devices providing a 75Hz square-wave output at about 120V (adjustable), but could clearly be easily modified for 240V or 220V by substituting a suitable transformer.

It draws about 5A full-load and about 0.5A off-load, making it suitable for use from the vehicle 12V cigarette-lighter socket, to enable a soldering iron, oscilloscope or other mains-operated appliances to be used in the field; it could also power a mains battery charger for a transceiver or camcorder etc from the vehicle battery, provided care was taken not to run down the battery while stationary. Although the output is square-wave rather than sine-wave, the RMS and peak voltage is the same as for a sine-wave supply, the 75Hz frequency (derived from a 300Hz clock) reduces the likelihood of saturating the core of the appliance transformer.

The number of public and private museums in the UK devoted to early 'wireless' receivers and communications equipment seems to be growing (see *RadCom* August 90 for details of some - *Ed*) though it is a pity that both the Science Museum and the Imperial War Museum and their field stations now impose entrance fees that tend to discourage casual or frequent visits.

In the USA, a relative newcomer is the Historical Electronics Museum, set up in 1980, which displays historical artefacts in communications, radar, counter-measures and space electronics. Located at 920 Elkridge Landing Road, Linthicum, Maryland, near the Baltimore-Washington International Airport (BWI) and not too far from the famous Smithsonian Institution museums in Washington DC. Among the exhibits is an S-Band (10cm) SCR-584 in working order, claimed as the first automatic tracking radar in the second world war and one of the first 'true weapons systems'. This type of radar was used at Anzio, Battle of the Bulge and in the UK as a very effective means of shooting down V1 buzz-bombs. There is also the SCR-270 (105-110MHz) which on Opana Point, Oahu, Hawaii detected the incoming Japanese planes which attacked Pearl Harbour in December 1941, but due to a human SNAFU did not alert the air defences.

Jim Brown, G0KZV, noted the brief obituary of John Bardeen in the May *TT*, and was reminded of a classic case of lost opportunities in sending along a *Wireless Engineer* abstract (reference 1683) of April 1939 of a paper by Hilsch & Pohl 'Control of Electron Currents with a Three-electrode Crystal, and a Model of a Barrier Layer' (*Zeitschr. f. Physik*, No 5/6, Vol III, 1938, pp399-408) which begins "Some experiments are described in which crystals of potassium bromide are used as a model of a barrier-layer rectifier and its control by means of a built-in grid; a 'three-electrode crystal' is devised which behaves in a manner analogous to a three-electrode valve." As G0KZV puts it: "Doesn't it prove there is nothing new under the sun? Had Hilsch and Pohl been interested in amplification and not rectification at that time, history might have been different." Or at least we might have had transistors a whole decade earlier! **G3VA**

DIY SHELVES + TABLE = OPERATING POSITION

NOT ALL OF US ARE sufficiently skilled in carpentry to tackle the construction of a complete operating desk. But Larry Hill, AA4DJ (*CQ*, February 1991, pp34-36) shows that it is often possible to acquire a second-hand or auctioned off office table or disused kitchen table at a low-cost and then to add DIY wooden shelving custom-designed to accommodate transceiver(s), ATU, VDU, books etc in a manner acceptable in a domestic environment. He provides very full constructional details of the arrangement shown in **Fig 9**, made from a single panel (4ft by 8ft) of 3/4inch birch plywood for the shelves, supports and back with a little solid birch for trim. I will not attempt to digest his working notes since I suspect that those with sufficient experience of DIY carpentry would be capable of producing a suitable structure, while those, like myself, whose shelves always seem to collapse or wobble, would be better off adopting an alternative approach. But it seems a good idea.

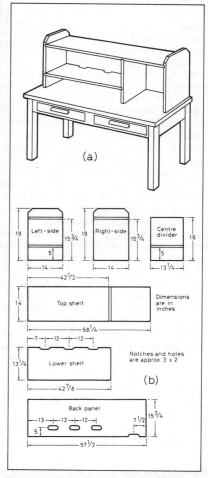

Fig 9: (a) AA4DJ's completed operating position with DIY shelving assembly placed on a strong table. **(b)** The parts as cut from a single sheet of plywood, but the design could be adapted to suit individual station requirements.

RESONANT MEANDER ANTENNAS

SPACE RESTRICTIONS in the average domestic environment have always resulted in amateur radio interest in methods of shortening the overall span of resonant HF antennas, as well as finding ways of the efficiency of loaded vertical whips: loading coils, capacitance hats, L- and T-antennas, ends dropping down, (**Fig 1(a)**) or bent sideways as in the VK2ABQ type of compact array. It is becoming increasingly difficult to think of a configuration that somebody has not already thought of and tried, often as long ago as the 1920s or 1930s. Even planar (linear) loading elements can be traced back some 60-plus years to the Franklin Uniform Antenna, although in this case used for phasing rather than loading 1.5-lambda dipole elements or 0.75-lambda monopoles.

TT, November 1984, p965, presented two relatively novel methods of shortening the overall span of half-wave dipoles without significant loss of efficiency or directivity: the zig-zag element and the meander-line element: **Fig 1(b) and (c)**. These came from a paper 'Shortening Ratios of Modified Dipole Antennas' by a team of Japanese engineers at Hosei University, Tokyo (*IEEE Trans on Ant & Prop*, April 1984, pp385-6). It was noted that a meander-line element can use up to about 0.7-lambda of wire to achieve 0.5-lambda resonance but can result in shortening the span by 30% compared with a conventional dipole and with a radiation resistance still as high as 43 ohms.

Soon afterwards (*TT*, March 1985, p190), Les Moxon, G6XN showed how a form of planar loading, attributed to VK5HA and using a string of one-turn loops as in **Fig 2(a)**, could be used to fold a half-wave dipole element into about one third of its normal length at the cost of only some 15-20% increase in total wire length. G6XN who used this technique in some of his 'Claw' antennas commented: "This is a big improvement over a helix (loading coil) or another alternative such as a form of 'meander' system shown recently in *TT* (see above) as means of reducing the overall span of dipole and which can be implemented as in **Fig 2(b)**".

While G6XN believes that VK5HA loading loops are near optimum, a detailed discussion of meander-type loading has recently been presented by Jalil Rashed (University of Seestan and Baluchistan, Iran) and Chen-To Tai (University of Michigan, USA) in 'A New Class of Resonant Antennas' (*IEEE Trans on Ant & Prop*, September 1991, pp1428-30). The abstract of this paper is as follows: "A new class of wire antennas called meander antennas is introduced as possible elements for size reduction. Efficiency is affected only by the ohmic losses in the wire, and cross-polarization is negligible.

"An increase in the number of meander sections introduces less size reduction in return for an improved bandwidth. These antennas can be used to reduce the size of

the existing wire antennas such as Yagi-Uda antennas and log-periodic dipole arrays".

In view of the Japanese 1984 paper it seems a little strong to claim meander-type

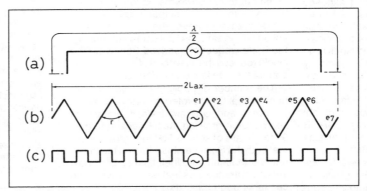

Fig 1: Significant shortening of the overall span of a half-wave dipole element can be achieved without significant loss of efficiency or directivity. (a) Ends dropped down or bent inwards. (b) Zig-zag element where e1 = e7 = 0.0208λ and e2 = e3 . . . = e6 = 0.0416λ. (c) Meander-line element as discussed by Japanese engineers in 1984.

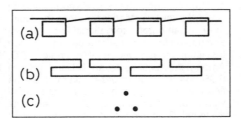

Fig 2: (a) VK5HA-type planar loading as recommended by G6XN in 1985. This involves a string of one turn loops which may be implemented using three cords as in (c) with appropriate spacers. With three loops each side of centre, he was able to fold a half-wave dipole into about one-third of its normal length, at the cost of an increase of only some 15-20% in total wire length, a big improvement in size reduction compared with a helix or meander elements as shown in (b).

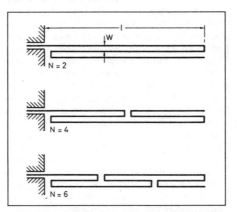

Fig 3: Some special cases of meander antennas (shown in monopole form) discussed by Rashed and Tai. N = 2 corresponds to half a meander section while N = 4 constitutes a complete section. See also Table 1.

elements such as a new class of resonant antenna, particularly when implemented in the form that has been used for some years for 7MHz quad antennas under the term 'planar loading'. However the recent paper does provide new insights in to these forms of element shortening. It is noted that, in general, any attempt to reduce the physical size of a monopole (ie half a dipole) while preserving the same resonant frequency ends up with deficiencies such as bandwidth deterioration, pattern distortion and reduction in efficiency. The authors present theoretical and experimental data (UHF model antennas) on some special cases of meander antennas, as shown (in monopole form) in **Fig 3** and **Table 1**. N is in effect the number of meander sections, with N = 2 corresponding to half a meander section while N = 4 constitutes a complete section. In general the lower the N, the greater is the reduction property but at the cost of a lower resonant radiation resistance and bandwidth. The authors write:

"By means of a sleeve, one is able to match the antenna to any desirable impedance level. Unlike most of the size reduction techniques such as lumped loading and the use of dielectric materials, the efficiency of the meander geometry is comparable to that of a conventional monopole. Since meander dipoles have a resonant length less than half a wavelength, and the separation W is negligibly small, they have essentially a figure-of-eight pattern and unlike many size reduction schemes, the undesirable radiation for horizontal portions is negligible . . . . Meander antennas can be used in the existing wire antennas; especially large arrays with long elements. As an example, a log-periodic dipole array (LPDA) is compared with its meander version (LPMDA). A 35% reduction in element size is obtained with an average loss of 2.5dB in the gain of the antenna over a 5:3 band: J. Rashed-Mohassel 'A Miniaturised Log-periodic Dipole Array' presented at ICAP89 (IEE Conference Publication No 301, part 1 - *Antennas* pp403-406). A whip antenna with partial meandering in the base of the whip is another example with the advantage of higher efficiency in comparison to lumped loading . . . . The meander geometry can be applied equally to other existing wire antennas such as Yagi-Uda arrays".

Antenna type	N	Resonant frequency (MHz)	Band-width (%)	Efficiency (%)	Calculated Radiation Resistance (ohms)
Monopole	-	545	9.5	99.1	36.5
Meander	2	922	3.0	96.7	13.5
	6	1050	7.0	97.8	17.0
	10	1110	7.5	97.9	19.0
	14	1180	8.0*	98.0	21.5

*Approximation from extrapolation

TABLE 1: Experimental data based on model antennas made from a 13.5cm length of wire (diameter 0.8mm). The height of the meander antennas (ie l shown horizontally) is 4.5cm with a small separation W less than 0.3cm (W/l = 0.06).

TOROIDAL CORES, BALUNS AND ATUS

MANY YEARS AGO, *TT* noted that ferrite cores when used in wideband baluns could result in serious power losses - a fact made only too clear by the large heat exchanger fins fitted to professional baluns of this type. Indeed several readers advised against using ferrite-cored baluns at least with simple dipole antennas, although it was generally agreed that baluns not based on toroidal cores have a significant role to play in preserving the desired radiation patterns of multi-element beams and in overcoming some RFI problems where these result from radiation from the outer-braid of coaxial feeders.

Since then there has been increased use of coaxial-cable baluns and ferrite bead chokes to reduce outer-braid currents. The use of toroidal-core baluns has tended to decrease, although such components still turn up in antenna matching transformers and ATUs, as well as in end-of-feeder baluns.

It is some years since this subject has cropped up in *TT* but now George Moorfield, GW3DIX, suggests that the following notes could prove an educational surprise to those who still consider that the ubiquitous balun is a panacea for many ills. He writes: "The use of toroidal-cored baluns in antenna matching units has been progressively less popular in recent editions of the ARRL's *Radio Amateurs Handbook*. Indeed the ARRL now actively discourages such use of these devices, as may be inferred from the following notes that can be found on pages 28-18/19 of the 1992 (16th) edition of the *ARRL Antenna Book*:

"Broadband transformers of the type found in many transmatches are not suitable for use at high impedances. Disastrous results can be had when using these transformers with loads higher than, say, 300 ohms during high power operation. The effectiveness of the transformer is questionable as well. At high peak RF voltages (ie high-Z load conditions such as 600-ohm open-wire feeds or an end-fed random length antenna), the cores can saturate and the RF voltage can cause arcs between turns or between the windings and the core material. If a balanced-to-unbalanced transformation must be effective, try to keep the load impedance at 300 ohms or less. An air-wound 1:1 balun with a trifilar winding is recommended over a transformer with ferrite or powdered-iron material".

GW3DIX adds: "The most important fact, however, to be observed in connection with the use of these devices - and one which seems to have escaped those who manufacture some ATUs containing them, as well as home constructors, is the following note from the same source as above: The principles on which baluns operate should make it obvious that the termination must be essentially a pure resistance in order for the proper impedance transformation to take place. If the termination is not resistive, the input impedance of each bifilar winding will depend on its electrical characteristics and the input impedance of the main transmission line: in other words, the impedance will vary just as it does with any transmission line, and the transformation ratio likewise will vary over wide limits.

"From this, then, the observation may be

50-OHM "QUAD-LOOP" ANTENNA

THE ONE-LAMBDA square-loop, mounted either in the vertical or horizontal plane, is a deservedly popular form of antenna. However, with a feed-point impedance of roughly 120-ohms it can present SWR problems when fed directly from 50 or 75-ohm feeder unless a quarter-wave matching transformer is interposed between feeder and element (eg an electrical quarter-wavelength of 75-ohm cable between 50-ohm feeder and the 120-ohm feed point). Bill Orr, W6SAI, in his *Radio FUNdamentals* column in *CQ* (November 1991, pp56-57) shows how by changing the shape away from a square into a rectangle it is possible to achieve a feed-point impedance very close to 50-ohm [or with less elongation of the square close to 75 ohms - *G3VA*]: **Fig 4**. A horizontal loop of this type retains the figure-of-eight pattern of a dipole but with some extra directivity resulting in slightly more broadside gain (at the cost of radiation off the ends). W6SAI points out that feeding a balanced element from unbalanced coax may bene-

fit from slipping some ferrite-beads on the line at the feedpoint or by using a balun. But he adds that "The experimenter will hook the coax directly to the quad loop, see how it works, and then determine if he has to go to the bother of adding a balun or beads on the line".

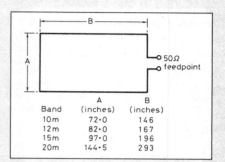

Band	A (inches)	B (inches)
10m	72·0	146
12m	82·0	167
15m	97·0	196
20m	144·5	293

Fig 4: W6SAI's suggested oblong quad loop antenna providing a feedpoint of 50-ohms resistive, a roughly figure-of-eight dipole-type radiation pattern but with some extra directivity and gain.

made that the use of such toroidal devices should be confined to matching fixed impedance sources one to the other, say 50 to 75 ohms, or 50 to 300 ohms, bearing in mind that any transmission line involved must be a flat line.

"Finally" adds GW3DIX, "it is most encouraging to note that the ARRL have 'put their money where their mouth is' and altered all the circuits in their various new books in accordance with the above comments. And those comments also serve to reinforce the recommendation of the construction and use of a properly balanced matching unit, together with open-wire feeders, as the best way of feeding wire antenna systems, either small or large, from 1.8 to 144MHz".

MORE ON G2DAF LINEARS

DICK BIRD, F6IDC (G4ZU), notes with interest the ZS2PL/ZS6AOZ modifications to the 1960s G2DAF linear amplifier (*TT*, September 1991, p33). These make this amplifier, with passive-grid drive from which the screen-voltage is derived by means of a voltage-doubler circuit using two small EY81 diodes, more suitable for use with modern solid-state transceivers.

He writes "In 1990 I published a series of seven articles on linear amplifier design in the Australian magazine *ARA* and am now working on a linear amplifier booklet, part one of which is presently in the hands of *Practical Wireless*. This includes a description of my own linear amplifier which uses a circuit very similar to that of Fig 9 in the September *TT*.

"However, because of the voltage step-up from the added input, I was able to eliminate the complexity of a voltage doubler arrangement, with a simple thermionic diode proving more than adequate to provide the required screen voltage. There would be obvious attractions in replacing the EY81 with a solidstate diode since it would provide instant availability at switch-on. An HF power transistor

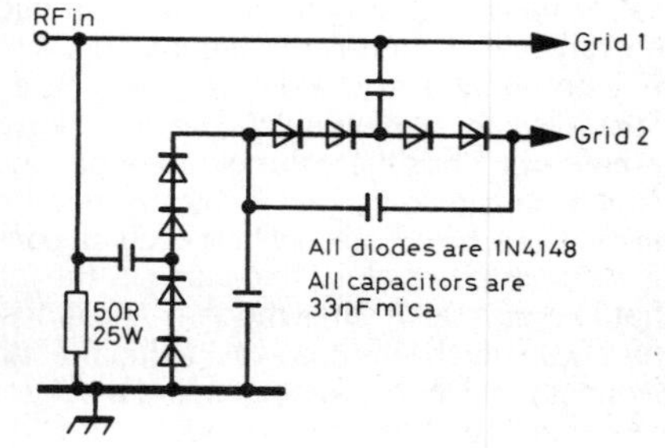

Fig 5: VK2ANO's drive/screen-voltage arrangement for a G2DAF-type linear amplifier using solid-state diodes in place of thermionic diodes. As reported by F6IDC (G4ZU).

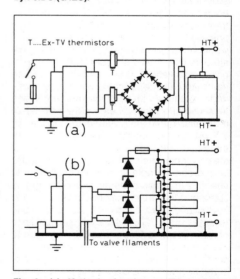

Fig 6: (a) Method of using ex-TV-set heater thermistors as inrush limiters to reduce switch-on stress on rectifier diodes and filter capacitor. (b) Typical arrangement used in commercial designs with series resistors rather than thermistors resulting in poorer voltage regulation on peak load. (F6IDC/G4ZU).

strapped as a diode would be a possible but rather expensive solution.

"A more attractive solution, devised by VK2ANO, is shown in **Fig 5** and uses eight low-cost 1N4148 diodes. I would recommend that if adopted it should be mounted in a position where it is not subject to a stream of hot air from the cooling system, and that the diodes be mounted on a copper-faced circuit board which then acts as a 'heat sink'".

F6IDC (G4ZU) also provides a hint for high-voltage power supplies: "Feed to a high voltage bridge is via a pair of 'inrush-limiting' thermistors, recovered from old, series-heater valve-type TV sets: **Fig 6**. The HT voltage rises slowly at switch-on, limiting stress on both the rectifier diodes and the smoothing capacitor. Elimination of the usual series resistors gives improved voltage regulation on peak load". F6IDC also prefers to use a separate filament transformer in a linear in order to permit precise adjustment of heater voltage - a useful precaution aimed at achieving a long operating lifetime for high cost power valves as mentioned a number of times in *TT*.

EDDYSTONE USERS GROUP

THERE IS A SOLID BODY of people (including myself) who have retained a liking for the classic valve receivers of the now fast-receding heyday of thermionic technology. This may be partly due to a dislike of paying out hard cash for a new solidstate receiver or transceiver while the older gear keeps functioning satisfactorily (aided by the ease of repair when the occasional fault occurs), partly due simply to nostalgia, and partly by the fact that like so many other modern appliances there was much less cost-saving (cost-effectiveness) and less skimping on the mechanical aspects of these older models, traditionally 'built like battleships'.

Admittedly, the technical specifications of modern solid-state receivers, at least on paper, have steadily improved from the days when solid-state front ends crumpled in the presence of strong signals, while even low-cost frequency synthesizers now result in less phase-noise that mars near-in selectivity. It would be rash to suggest that the best solid-state models are in any substantial way inferior to the valve models of twenty or more years ago. Perhaps that is why valve-aficionados or those with nostalgic memories tend to seize upon instances where solid-state may fail to make the grade. In the December *TT*, G2AHU noted that FET oscillators, although quickly reaching switch-on thermal stability, nevertheless in the long-term tend to be more vulnerable than valve oscillators to changes in ambient temperature - though he conceded that we cannot put the clock back.

Similarly, Ted Moore of the Eddystone User Group (EUG), with 22 years experience of radio in North Africa, was not surprised to learn that the US military, during the Gulf conflict, suffered severely from the effect of static on their solid-state radios and had to recall back into service the more resistant front-ends found in many of their 'antique' Collins valve-type equipments.

This seems a good opportunity to draw attention to the EUG and its bi-monthly newsletters which are crammed with information

'USING ELEVATED RADIALS with ground-mounted towers' by Al Christman (KB8I and Grove City College) and Roger Radcliff (Ohio University) in *IEEE Trans on Broadcasting*, September 1991, pp77-82) reflects the continuing saga of the move to use a few elevated radials as a counterpoise in order to replace the extensive 120 (or more) buried radials which, for many years, have been standard for medium-wave broadcast installations. An earlier paper by KB8I on his computer studies was digested in *TT*, August 1988. For this further paper, computer-modelling studies (backed up by some full-scale experiments) were used to investigate several different methods of attaching radials to ground-mounted (insulated) towers, along with variations in radial height, radial length etc. Limited full-scale outdoor tests on several of these configurations have been carried out by William Culpepper, a consulting radio engineer. The preliminary results show good agreement between the measured data and the computer predictions although it is stated that Mr Culpepper plans to present the measured data separately soon.

The computer predictions, as with the earlier modelling, indicate that 'it is possible to use four elevated radials together with a conventional ground-mounted, base-insulated tower for MF broadcasting purposes, and achieve the same level of performance which is normally obtained from a classic 120-buried-radial system.'

Such an approach would clearly be most suitable for use by amateurs on the 1.8, 3.5 and 7MHz bands for verticals; on the higher frequency bands it is already conventionally adopted in the form of the popular ground-plane antenna (GPA).

The paper is based on MF broadcast systems with quarter-wave towers 75m or 84m in height, insulated at the base with the following elevated radials: radials with

45° sloping ends, at heights of 5m and 10m; radials with steeply-sloping ends at heights of 5m and 10m; and an elevated feed method (fed at 5m and 10m) with the radials horizontal over their full length. The four radials are similarly about 75m (quarter-wave) in length. There appears to be relatively little difference in performance between the different systems (**Fig 7**) but it is recognized that much more experimental verification work needs to be done.

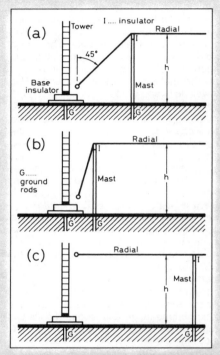

Fig 7: Elevated radial systems investigated by KB8I using computer-modelling to simulate a typical base-insulated broadcast quarter-wave tower antenna. Each of these configurations was modelled for radial heights of 5m and 10m above ground.

on the many Eddystone receivers produced since the 1930s. They were first produced by Stratton & Co Ltd and then from July 1965 by Eddystone Radio Ltd as a manufacturing-subsidiary of the Marconi Company (initially as part of the English Electric group of companies and then more recently as part of the GEC group). With over 250 members in 16 countries, EUG is by no means exclusively valve-orientated though it is clear that it is the older receivers (from the ECR in 1939 and wartime 358X) and particularly the 500/600/700/800 series of models that attract the most interest.

It is also evident that, at least for medium-wave DX broadcast reception, valve receivers with their double (or triple) tuned IF transformers and good pre-mixer selectivity still tend to outperform the current solid-state models available to SWLs and amateurs.

Ted Moore, himself, has a very large collection of Eddystone models (and hopes one day to initiate an Eddystone museum) and has assembled a substantial store of informa-

tion not only on the long history of Eddystone from its entry into radio in 1922 (see *TT*, June 1988), but also technical/servicing/restoration information on this unique range of major British-made receivers. The non-profit-making newsletter has reached double figures, although experience has shown that it is difficult for user groups to keep going (it would appear that the former Collins and Racal groups are dormant). There must be many readers with a personal interest in Eddystone equipment and components; for information on EUG they should contact: Mr W E Moore, Moore Cottage, 112 Edgeside Lane, Waterfoot, Rossendale, Lancs BB4 9TR.

DIGITAL COMMUNICATIONS RECEIVERS

SOME SIX YEARS AGO I included a *TT* (May 1985, pp359-360) notes on the Rockwell-Collins receiver type HF2050, which was the first professional VLF/HF communications receiver to be based on digital signal processing (DSP). The HF2050 was a hybrid analogue/digital receiver with the 2nd IF signal at 3MHz converted into digital form with quadrature processing on the bit stream after sampling the 3MHz signal using a 12MHz clock. Single-sideband selectivity was achieved at the direct-conversion 'OkHz' signal and thus the equivalent of analogue AF filtering in a phasing-type direct-conversion demodulator/filter arrangement.

In this form of digital signal processing, the final receiver bandwidth, ripple and selectivity are all determined by programmed data within the signal processors which consist of very large scale integrated circuits (VLSI). In the HF2050, two CW, two AM, SSB and ISB bandwidths were implemented within the two (I and Q) VSLI filter processors.

It was pointed out that the several major firms, American and European, were developing hybrid analogue/digital receivers, based on various architectures, with the eventual aim of having a fully digitized signal-path, with incoming signals at RF converted into a digital bit stream; although then (and now) this still seemed a fairly long-term ambition due to the limited dynamic range and the limited usable clock frequencies of VLSI A/D converters.

Nevertheless the hybrid receivers did seem to offer the attraction of the well-shaped selectivity curves of DSP at a lower cost than a full complement of analogue bandpass filters as commonly fitted in high-grade professional receivers. Digital technology was seen as offering a lower component count, an easier assembly and (potentially) the lower costs of digital designs based on standard devices. However, there has not been many signs of rapid progress being made in receiver digitization during the past six years, at least for high-grade HF receivers with their stringent requirements.

Richard Groshong (Collins Defense Communications) and Stephen Ruscak (Analog Devices Inc) have taken up the challenge in two articles in *Electronic Design* (May 23, 1991 and June 13, 1991) which have been brought to my notice by Rex Beastall, G1LRI. In their introduction they state: "Digital techniques offer some inherent advantages in communication receiver design. These advantages, however, have been offset by both the cost and dynamic range limitations of analogue-to-digital converters (ADCs). Consequently designers continued to use analogue circuitry despite its associated complexity and lack of flexibility. But recent introductions of low-cost, highly linear ADCs, combined with a technique known as undersampling, make digital processing the architecture of choice."

The first article "Undersampling techniques simplify digital radio" is subtitled "By sampling below the Nyquist rate with a new type of ADC, designers can exploit the benefits of digital radio." The authors outline the requirements of a high performance HF receiver: it must be sensitive enough to receive a 0.5uV (-113dBm) signal at the receiver input (50-ohms) with a 10db signal-to-noise ratio (SNR) in a 3KHz bandwidth, adding "However, the receiver must also be able to receive a 1V signal (+13dBm) without significant distortion. Consequently, in-band dynamic range must be at least 126dB".

In a practical analogue/digital receiver, (**Fig 8**) with analogue front-end, the receiver's dynamic range is adversely affected by the fact that the bulk of the receiver gain must be ahead of the ADC in order that this should function satisfactorily, whereas a conventional analogue receiver the main gain normally occurs after the second IF bandpass filters. This means that for the digital receiver the designer must supply both analogue and digital gain control since the ADC cannot possibly support the required 126dB of dynamic range. In other words, much of the dynamic range will not be instantaneous dynamic range but depend on AGC control of the front-end - by no means a desirable characteristic when trying to copy a weak narrow-band signal immediately alongside a very strong signal.

The authors point out: "In the digital design, the positioning of the gain means that undesired out-of-band signals can pass through the wider-bandwidth front-end and saturate the amplifier and ADC. This must be avoided because ADC saturation generates many aliased in-band harmonic and intermodulation products that can block a weak signal. The solution lies in automatic gain control (AGC) and the use of large-wordlength, highly-linear ADCs."

Conventionally, for digital sampling, the sampling frequency must be at least twice the highest signal frequency as stated in the Nyquist law. However, a low sampling rate is a key factor in the overall performance of a digital receiver, the authors point out that in the case of a bandpass signal, designers can use undersampling which means sampling at a rate less than twice the highest frequency being converted (**Fig 9**) and this approach is described in detail, with particular reference to two Analog Devices sampling ADCs type AD679 and AD779.

In the second of the two *Electronic Design* articles 'Exploit digital advantages in an SSB receiver' - the authors cover the design of a receiver using undersampling linear ADCs in

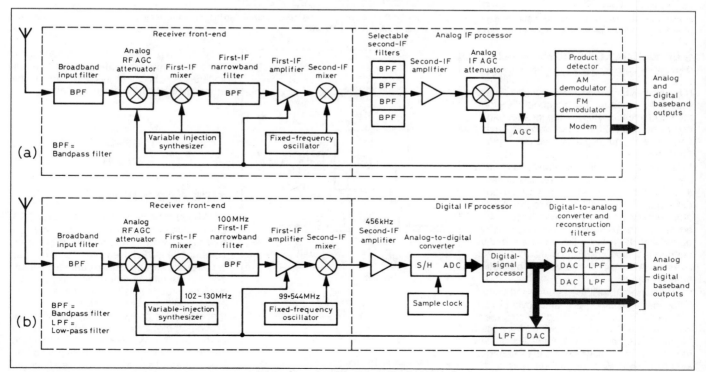

Fig 8: (a) Outline of typical 'professional' analogue communications receiver with several bandpass filters and demodulation circuits for the different modes. **(b)** Use of a software-reconfigurable digital signal processor at the 456kHz second IF potentially reduces cost by eliminating the multiple bandpass filters etc. (*Electronic Design*)

greater detail, although is not made clear whether such a receiver is (or will be) marketed by Collins as a military radio.

The authors consider that "The digital IF processor's high integration level is indicative of the future of SSB equipment. As the performance of the ADC improves, it will be placed close to the receiving antenna in the analogue front-end. The ultimate goal is to digitize the incoming signal directly from the antenna and implement the remaining digital functions in custom ASICs (Application Specific Integrated Circuits - see *TT*, August 1990)."

It seems rather unlikely that we will see this degree of digital signal processing in amateur-budget receivers in the near future - furthermore it is clear that there must be some risk of low-cost DSP degrading rather than improving the performance of good analogue receivers. But it is a technology we need to be aware of.

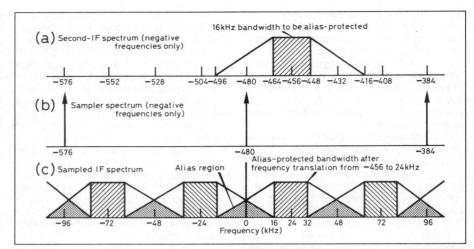

Fig 9: Undersampling the second 456kHz IF signal with a 96kHz sampling frequency to provide the full 16kHz bandwidth free of aliasing requires that the first IF filter must have no more than an 80kHz-wide stopband. (*Electronic Design*.)

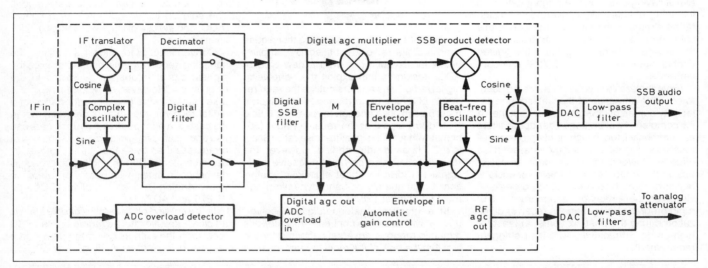

Fig 10: SSB filter, AGC and demodulator are implemented with the DSP VLSI chip. The system's sample rate is first reduced by a factor of ten in the decimator to produce enough instructions cycles between samples to perform the required algorithms.

OLD OSCILLOSCOPES AND TWO-TONE TESTING AGAIN

N P CHEASLEY, GM4RDB thoroughly agrees with G0DLN about the value of two-tone testing of linear amplifiers and the problem of doing this with older oscilloscopes having only limited frequency response (TT, August 1991, p30).

However, he draws attention to what is, in his opinion, a simpler solution which he has to found entirely satisfactory and which does not require any modifications to the 'scope. This approach was described in his 1981 edition of the *ARRL Radio Amateurs Handbook* (page 12-18) as follows: "An alternative method is to use an RF probe and apply the resulting AF signal to the vertical deflection amplifier input".

In his case, GM4RDB has arranged a small probe inside his antenna change-over switchbox and connected to a simple high impedance detector: **Fig 11**. The probe is arranged to pick up approximately equal RF voltages from the switch box when this is switched to either dummy load or antenna. With the 'scope's Y-amplifier on its 100mV/cm range a peak amplitude of about 2cm for a transmitter output of 100W is obtained.

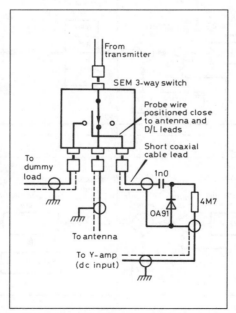

Fig 11: How GM4RDB arranges his RF probe inside his antenna/dummy-load change-over switch-box, with an external high impedance detector and output connection to the Y-amp socket of his 'scope of limited HF perfomance.

GM4RDB points out that the advantage of this arrangement is that no high RF or DC voltages are involved in connection to the unmodified 'scope, making it safer!

TIPS AND TOPICS

NORMAN WILKINSON (G4HVT/LA0FG) adds to the hints on projecting antenna-support cords over the branches of trees (*TT*, November 1991, p31). He writes: "Like others, I was worried about possible damage to neighbours and their property when using the next-door-teenager's bow and blunted arrow and also found that I needed more weight to pull the cord over and down. My four-year-old granddaughter supplied the answer: a semi-hard, and heavy enough, 1.5in diameter 'super-ball'. With a suitable hole drilled half-way through, it was a tight fit on the arrow, and also gripped the end of the line. The only snag (my granddaughter considered it an advantage) was that the ball had to be replaced."

WIDEBAND 'BIG MOUTHS'

THE DECEMBER *TT* item 'Big Mouth, linearity and splatter', based on W6SAI's notes in *CQ* (September 1991), emphasised the harmful effects of driving a power amplifier beyond the point at which intermodulation products (IMPs) start to become evident due to non-linearity (flat-topping) of the stage. It was noted how two-tone testing, particularly in conjunction with a spectrum analyser, can show how SSB signals spread out, resulting in serious splatter interference either side of the frequency channel in use This may occur when any stage of a transmitter is overdriven. It was also pointed out that while most discussions of IMPs and splatter tend to relate to HF transmissions, the problem can be even more serious at VHF where the receiver noise floor can usefully be much lower than on 'noisy' HF.

This item has resulted in a helpful letter from Steve Thompson, GW8GSQ who works at his home, near Bridgend, South Wales as a power-amplifier designer and consultant. He highlights a form of wideband interference that arises from incorrect operation of automatic level control (ALC) but can pass undetected during a two-tone test. He writes: "The piece on 'Big Mouth' came to mind when I encountered the signals of a couple of local amateurs who visited a nearby high site, a few miles from me, to take advantage of good conditions on 144MHz. The signal levels at my house long ago prompted me to rebuild the front end of my TS700 to cope with strong signals, and it now seems to withstand almost anything my modest antenna picks up.

"Station A was operated by a friend who has recently completed a home-brew PA. On his signals there were two forms of spreading, one was the normal muffled IMD from speech, about 20kHz wide; the other was much wider and took the form of a click at roughly syllabic rate over a much wider bandwidth (about 100kHz). I call this form of spreading 'spitch' rather than 'splatter'. I verified that both forms of interference were on the transmission and not generated in my receiver by feeding the antenna into my 'professional' spectrum analyser. I spoke to the operator of Station A who said he had spent some time with a two-tone source and a spectrum analyser setting the bias throughout the transmitter chain to arrive at a compromise where low order IMD was higher than ideal, but high order IMD was well suppressed. He could not understand the wider-band interference which had been totally absent during his testing.

"Later the same day, Station B, using an FT726, visited the site and promptly wiped out most of the bottom half of the band with 'spitch'. On the spectrum analyser, a curtain of interference some 300-400kHz wide could be seen building up on a storage display at only 25-30dB below PEP; each click appeared to be of very short duration. I called him and explained the situation. He responded by reducing his microphone gain and this dramatically reduced the problem.

"Station A uses an FT221 for his exciter, which I know has ALC acting on the audio input. I know little about the FT726 used by Station B (except I feel it has far too many knobs!). I suggest that the wideband interference from both transmitters would not show

up under two-tone testing. It is my guess that during the short period before the ALC acts, the transmitters are, in effect, being grossly overdriven, resulting in an output with a fast-rising edge, similar to a key click. There is also the possibility of a short duration spike with some of the characteristics of an impulse. I also postulate that, in general, ALC applied to an audio stage takes longer to control the final output than when it is applied to an RF stage (especially if it is post crystal-filter).

"I find that wideband interference is much more of a nuisance than close-in IMD from speech; the opposite may be true on a crowded HF band, Monitoring techniques other than off-air receivers can easily miss this form of overload and interference. Perhaps it is worth reminding readers to operate with the minimum required microphone gain and drive levels, forgoing the 'comfort' of a flickering ALC meter needle".

The action of an audio-derived ALC system for SSB transmitters is directly analogous to audio-derived AGC in receivers. Last year *TT*, (April and June, 1991) presented the thoughts of LA8AK on the shortcomings of audio derived AGC and showing how in some cases this can produce wideband noise in receivers in much the same way as outlined by GW8GSQ above. LA8AK emphasised that really good AGC systems still represent 'a difficult technique'. All of this bears out GW8GSQ's advice that operators should not rely on ALC to offset excessively high microphone gain!

THE 7MHZ DIPOLE ON 21MHZ

IT HAS LONG BEEN accepted that a 7MHz half-wave dipole may be used as a 1.5-wave dipole on the 21MHz band. This approach can often work satisfactorily, even without an ATU, particularly with older valve-type rigs that are happy to 'see' a moderately high SWR. Remember that unless an HF coaxial feeder is very long, a reasonably high SWR does not represent significant lost power. But with modern solid-state rigs that may begin to throttle back the power with an SWR above about 1.5 or 2.0:1, so the 7MHz antenna can prove unsatisfactory in practice.

Bob Raffaele, W2XM in 'Hints and Kinks' (*QST*, December 1991) points out that 'end effect' causes a half-wave dipole resonant at 7.1MHz to resonate as a 1.5λ dipole at about 22MHz and not 21.3MHz: **Fig 1**. Furthermore the feed-point impedance of a resonant 1.5λ dipole tends to be higher than that of a half-wave dipole. His suggestions include using a compromise antenna length of 67ft and feeding the antenna via a coaxial feeder that includes a 21MHz quarter-wave matching section between the antenna element and its 50Ω feed line; this 21MHz impedance transformer should have little effect at 7MHz. He uses 7ft 7in of RG-59 cable as the Q-section. Since different cables of a common impedance vary in capacitance per unit length, the length of the matching section may have to be changed slightly. With this compromise arrangement W2XM provides a lower SWR at the low end of 7MHz and the high end of 21MHz.

In an editorial comment, WJ1Z notes that at a height of 25ft (about 0.2λ) above ground, a flat-top half-wave 7.1MHz dipole exhibits a radiation resistance of around 65Ω. A 50Ω feed line connected to such an antenna should exhibit an SWR of about 1.3:1. Operated as a 1.5λ dipole, the same antenna (0.5λ high at 21MHz) exhibits a radiation resistance of about 110Ω at resonance, resulting in an SWR of about 2.2:1 when fed with 50Ω cable. Resonance is at about 22MHz, so that the SWR may be unacceptable (without an ATU) when operating at the low-end of the 21MHz band, unless some compromise solution, such as that suggested by W2XM is adopted.

POWER SUPPLIES, RF AND THE 723 REGULATOR

'RICK' STERRY, G4BLT, agreed with G3RZP's comment (*TT*, January 1992, p39) that the ubiquitous 723 regulator chip is susceptible to disruption by strong RF fields. However he considers that all is not as hopeless as it may seem. Indeed, on page 33 of that same (January) issue there is a design for a medium-to-high power HF amplifier featuring a 723 regulator actually on the same PCB as the PA transistors!

"I have built many PSUs using the 723 chip over the past 15 years or so, and many times I have noticed the output voltage waver about when there was RF in the vicinity. However, at VHF/UHF, I have found the cure to be simple in every case. First of all, I always use a metal case; if the PSU is built in a plastic one then you are inviting trouble! Secondly, I by-pass the two DC output terminals to the case with 470-1000pF ceramics, using short leads. Thirdly, I by-pass the unregulated supply to

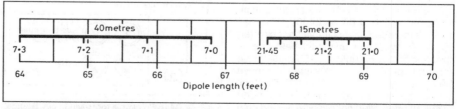

Fig 1: The resonant frequency of a harmonic antenna as a function of length in feet. Calculated from the formula 492(n- 0.05)/f where f is frequency in MHz and n is the number of half-waves in the antenna, so that n is 1 for a half-wave dipole and 3 for a 1.5-wave dipole. For example, a dipole resonant at 7.1MHz is not resonant at 21.3MHz but at nearer 22MHz. The radiation resistance of a typical horizontal 7MHz antenna at a typical height will also differ significantly as a 1.5-wave dipole at 22MHz.

the 723 with a third 470-1000pF capacitor, close to the IC, ie across the +ve and -ve connections. So far I haven't found any need to use ferrites. For protection at HF, it is advisable to fit additional capacitors of a higher value, say 0.05μF.

"During 144MHz contests, my local society runs a meaty 400W PEP valve linear amplifier in close proximity to my 12V PSU (which uses a 723) with no problems. Indeed, all my efforts to couple as much RF into the PSU as possible, eg wrapping the antenna feeder round PSU and 12V leads, have failed to provoke the slightest reaction. I am not claiming that my suggestions will cure all such problems, but I do think it makes sense to fit these components whichever type of regulator(s) are used".

240V AC POWER RELAY

PETER MURLAGH, IN *Electronics Australia* (January 1992, pp92-95) presents full constructional details of what he calls a '240V Power Relay' - a simple project that monitors the power drawn from a 'master' socket and then, when current is detected, automatically switches power to a 'slave' socket. The design stems from a rather similar project described in *Popular Electronics* (September 1991) as a 'Socket Sentinel'.

One can think of useful applications of such a device in an Amateur Radio shack since it would allow several separate pieces of equipment to be turned 'on' or 'off' by the operation of the switch on just one of the units - eliminating the common problem that when one turns off the main transceiver it is very easy to forget to turn off every other item of ancillary equipment unless they are all wired up to one master power switch. It should perhaps be stressed that from a safety viewpoint each unit connected to a power relay (**Fig 2**) should either be unplugged or at least switched 'off' by its own double-pole switch before doing any maintenance work etc.

In operation, the power relay detects the voltage drop across a series of back-to-back silicon diodes (0.7V per section) and uses this to switch on a TIC236N triac which can deliver 12A at 800V. In practice the power diodes have to carry the current delivered through the master socket, and the triac carries all current taken through the slave socket(s).

In the *EA* unit, IN5404 power diodes rated at 3A are used with a total load current (master and slave sockets) well below the 5A fuse rating. For higher-power loads and multiple slave sockets the ratings of both diodes and triac may need reconsidering, and the fuse rating increased. For low-power slave loads, a rather lower-power triac would be possible but Peter Murlagh advises a minimum triac rating of 6A and 400V. The triac must be mounted on a suitable heat sink (eg 60 by 37 by 31mm universal heat sink is specified for the *EA* unit). A 275V metal oxide varistor (type V275LA20A) is fitted to remove mains voltage transients. The RFI filter coil (L1) comprises 520mm of 1mm diameter (B&S 18) enamelled copper wire wound on a ferrite former (23mm length of 10mm diameter broadcast aerial rod).

A possible hitch that showed up during the design of the *EA* unit was that the computer

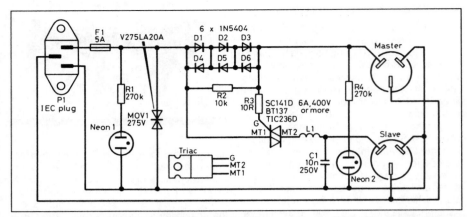

Fig 2: The circuit diagram of the *Electronics Australia* 240V power relay. The 'master' current flows through the diode network and turns on the 'slave' socket. The current for the slave socket flows through the triac. The MOV protects against mains spikes.

powered from the master socket had three RF-filter capacitors totalling 1.5μF across its power switch on the active side. This meant that the AC leakage current was high enough to keep the slave socket turned on, even when the computer was turned off. However, such high-value filter capacitors should not be found in modern equipment as these values are much higher than those recommended from a safety viewpoint.

In the *EA* design the complete unit is enclosed in a plastic jiffy box 50 x 90 x 150mm with the master and single slave socket mounted on the box. As in any unit involving 240V AC mains supplies close attention should always be given to safety aspects.

CUTTING 'ISLANDS' IN PCB MATERIAL

RICHARD COOK, G4XHE, adds an alternative suggestion to G3KMG's advocacy of non-etch use of PCB material (*TT*, July). He writes: "I have been using the following technique to produce circuits on single or double-sided boards. But instead of gluing small pieces of PCB material on to the board, I have produced a simple tool that cuts the islands directly onto the board. It consists of a good quality screwdriver blade modified with a needle file to the shape of a fork with three prongs (**Fig 3(a)**).

The two outer prongs are slightly shorter than the centre one, which is there solely to prevent the tool from skating around the board. The modified blade is then placed into a drill and an almost perfect island can then be cut anywhere required. The major advantage is that pads can be added in exactly the right

place as the board progresses, making a neater job than stick on pads. Results so far have been very good indeed; it has even been possible to mount integrated circuits using a smaller version of the cutter that cuts pads around 2mm in diameter.

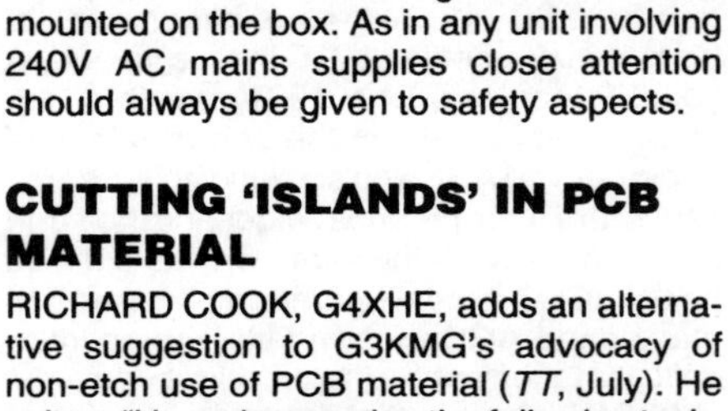

David Jones, G4FQR has recently used this method to construct a 7MHz transceiver with pads on the underside of the board used for DC connections. Results on stages checked so far are "most encouraging".

BRYANT-CLARK 'SWEET-SPOT' PROPAGATION

ROGER CROFTS, VK4YB (who has also been licensed as G3UPK and as ZB2/ZD8/ST2/TJ1 with call letters AY) writing from Queensland, Australia draws attention to a most interesting form of propagation, affecting primarily 1.8MHz and the lower HF bands. This has been unravelled by two enthusiastic Australian broadcast-band listeners, John Bryant and David Clark. It appears to endorse some of the notes which appeared in *TT* (and later *Amateur Radio Techniques*,) many years ago on the 'whispering-gallery mode' etc and which shows that, contrary to accepted wisdom, it is sometimes possible to work 1.8/3.5MHz DX using low, horizontal-dipole antennas that provide only high-angle radiation.

VK4YB writes: "In these days of high sunspot activity, our lower frequency bands have been somewhat neglected, especially 160 metres. It's not much fun listening through heaps of static for extremely weak or non-existent DX signals. There is, however, one DX path on 1.8MHz which continues to provide amazingly reliable and frequently very strong long-distance signals. This path is from Australia to West and Mid-West North America, but only during the months May to August. This propagation path has been enjoyed by many VK, W and VE operators over the years, without too much thought as to why it occurs so reliably only during the northern summer. After all, the path is in total darkness for all the year at the W/VE sunrise.

"Now, exciting work being done by John Bryant and David Clark has shed new light on the phenomenon. They are avid HF Broadcast DXers and their initial observations were made in the 60, 90 and 120 metre 'tropical broadcast bands'. Painstaking research has revealed that the location of the origin of the enhanced signals corresponds to the part of

Fig 3: (a) G4XHE's simple tool used to cut 'islands' directly on PC boards. It consists of a good-quality 5mm screwdriver blade modified with a needle file to the shape of a three-pronged fork. (b) Results before and after soldering. The tool forms an insulated 'moat' around the 'island'.

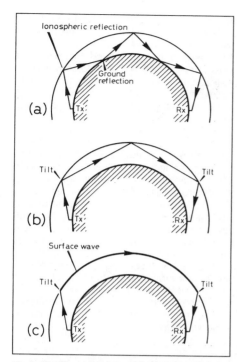

Fig 4: (a) Conventional HF multihop path with two ground and three ionospheric reflection points all reducing the strength of the signal. (b) Chordal hop propagation with no intermediate ground reflection points can occur when there are suitable ionospheric tilts - as in the classic dawn-dusk grey-line path. (c) Another possible form of chordal hop/ducting propagation.

the ionosphere experiencing the 'Spread F' effect associated with Travelling (Tropical) Ionospheric Disturbances (TIDs). These usually occur around 2100-local-time in tropical latitudes. The term 'Spread F' refers to the smudging or smearing in the presentation of the F-layer reflection as seen on an Ionogram. Under these conditions, the exact height of the F layer is indeterminate. The effect declines at higher latitudes. In 1991, VK4 had trans-Pacific openings on 95% of days in the season, compared to 60% for VK3 (further south). These statistics are available thanks to the 'SEANCE Net' (South East Australia to North America Communications Exchange Net) which operates on 1832kHz, daily at 1100GMT, from May to August. Out of season, the TIDs move rapidly north and propagation returns to 'normal' levels.

"So what is happening in the TIDs? None of us is sure, but it does appear that high-angle radiation is somehow coupled into the 'single-sided duct ' or 'whispering-gallery' mode. I say high angle radiation because low dipoles, on average, outperform full-size verticals. Once in the duct mode, the signals propagate along the underside of the F layer with very low attenuation. John Bryant and David Clark theorize that the signal level could actually increase after 10,000km, because the great circle routes would then begin to reconverge (That is 'ionospheric focusing' as discussed some years ago in TT - G3VA). At the eastern end of the circuit, the signals are nudged earthward by the downward tilting of the F-layer at the dawn terminator, giving rise to the well-known dawn (grey-path) enhancement.

"The bad news for British amateurs is that it would appear that the British Isles are too far north to experience a 'sweet spot' of

Spread-F enhancement overhead. Furthermore at max dawn, the position of the sweet spot is such as to provide excellent propagation to a totally unpopulated region of the eastern Pacific! Perhaps this goes some way to explaining why John Bryant could find no mention of the phenomenon in Amateur Radio literature".

It was in the 1960s that a great deal of interest was generated (as a result of 'round-the-world echoes') in the various forms of chordal hop and whispering gallery modes, and the effects of ionospheric tilts (**Figs 4 and 5**). (See also *ART7,* and *HF Antennas for all Locations* by G6XN). VHF enthusiasts are also likely to see the apparent links between this 'sweet spot of Spread-F enhancement' affecting frequencies as low as 1.8MHz and the well-documented 'Trans-Equatorial Propagation' (TEP) modes on frequencies up to at least 50MHz (with the UK again too high in latitude to benefit directly). In *TT* and *ART* in a section 'When long-path is better', I concluded that there are several lessons to be learned which appear also to apply to the Bryant-Clark mode:

(a) Longer may be louder.

(b) Going up in frequency may put your signals down in strength.

(c) The traditional amateur 'dawn/dusk' (greyline) periods of optimum DX are directly linked with the regular appearance of ionospheric tilts which occur because of the difference in effective layer height in darkness and daylight. Fig 4(b) shows how a chordal hop propagation may occur when the signals hit a tilted layer.

(d) When the tilts are roughly overhead, one can launch a satisfactory chordal hop signal even with an antenna providing a high angle of radiation. (*ART7*, p327). The new work seems to confirm that tilts in layers also occur in tropical regions during Spread F conditions.

SONYA'S REPORT

THE RECENT PUBLICATION *Sonya's Report,* is a book originally published in East Germany in 1977, and now translated by Renate Simpson (published by Chatto &

The Great Survivor. A recent photograph of Ruth ('Sonya') Werner who, in her thirties, as Mrs Ursula Beurton, with a young family and an English husband in the RAF, successfully operated undetected between 1941 and about 1950, a clandestine radio circuit from the UK for Russian Military Intelligence (GRU). Her book *Sonya's Report* includes several references to Amateur Radio. *(Photo courtesy of Chatto & Windus)*

Windus, 1991, 318 + vi pages). While not adding greatly to our knowledge of radio communication, this must surely be of interest to anyone who wonders what it must have been like to operate a clandestine radio in various countries in the 1930s and 1940s, as a spy for the Red Army - and get away with it! Well worth borrowing from a library (ISBN 0 7011 3801 7).

'Sonya' is still alive and came to Britain for the publication of her memoirs and was born in Berlin in 1907 as Ruth Kuczynski. She has been a life-long communist, who in the early 1930s, while living in Shanghai, began to assist Richard Sorge and was recruited through him into the GRU (the Russian Military Intelligence service). Subsequently she became one of the most skilled and accom-

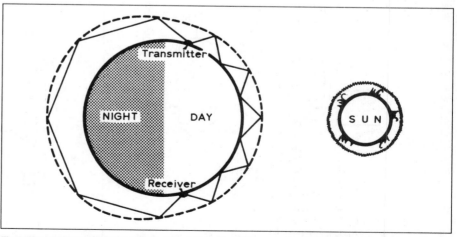

Fig 5: The change of effective height of the ionospheric F layer around dawn and dusk produces the tilts that make possible chordal-hop transmission over the 'long-path' with the low attenuation in darkness conditions and no ground-reflection losses. This provides stronger signals than the short-path with its multiple hops. The Australian work on 1.8MHz reported in the text suggests that signals can also be induced into chordal-hop paths by Spread-F travelling ionospheric disturbances in the tropical regions at certain seasons of the year.

plished secret radio-agents and almost certainly the only one to operate undetected in rural England from 1941 to about 1950. Whatever you may think of the damage she did to a country that gave her and other members of her family a home - for example, she provided communications for the atom-spy Karl Fuchs - one must surely acknowledge the resolution, daring and skilled tradecraft she showed in operating radio transmitters (some of which she built herself) in China, Poland, Danzig, Switzerland and from several villages in and around Oxford and the Cotswolds.

Within the GRU she eventually held the rank of a Red Army Colonel - emphasising some remarks I made in writing about clandestine radio in *Wireless World* (January/February 1982). As I pointed out, in the main Russian intelligence networks the radio operator was traditionally nearer to the centre of things than those of British or German networks, where the radio operator was often regarded as a minor character. Admittedly there is a considerable difference between a highly-trained peacetime agent and the large number of Russian radio operators dropped or infiltrated into their wartime Partisan groups. In 1933 Sonya was trained at the Russian special training centre near Moscow: "I settled in quickly, building the apparatus was fun, and I held my own in Morse, but I did not get on at all well with the theory, where I must have been a willing but untalented pupil. I built transmitters, receivers, rectifiers (power supplies) and frequency meters, learned to

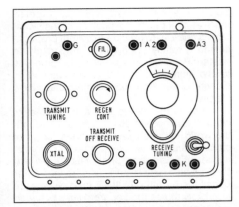

Fig 6: Front panel of the wartime Russian clandestine radio Model Belka M-2. (*DL3CS archives*).

speak Russian and found the political lectures stimulating."

The radio-agents were not always well served by their Controllers often being allowed or even encouraged to stay on the air for many hours at a time, working diligently through the night. She had several near escapes. Once in Danzig the wife of a Nazi official told her that her husband was convinced that the frequent interference to their broadcast radio was caused by a secret radio transmitter and enquired whether Sonya, then living in the same apartment block, had suffered similar problems. Sonya promptly claimed she always went to bed early - and hurriedly changed location. Another time, in

Switzerland, she was reported to the Swiss police as a radio-spy by someone who had seen a Morse key in her house. In fact the key had been a toy one, used to train fresh operators and she was able to convince the police that she was training a youngster about to join the Swiss Army. The key she really used was made from a metal ruler and was dismantled when not in use.

In England, Sonya clearly ran rings around the Security Services. In fairness to the Radio Security Service, they were too busy intercepting and looking for German and Italian transmissions to worry about signals using the different Russian procedures - from June 1941 to 1945 the USSR was, after all, an ally! MI5 made some desultory investigations following the return of Alexander (Allan) Foote who had been trained as a radio operator by Sonya in Switzerland in 1939-40 and who took over her 'Lucy-ring' transmissions to Moscow when she departed to England.

Her brother, also a dedicated communist agent, while living in London in 1944 acted as an adviser to the American OSS and was able to persuade them to employ several communists. Teams, organised by William Casey (later Director of the CIA), were dropped into Germany in 1945 carrying the miniature Joan-Eleanor hand-held UHF radio-phones for talking to Allied aircraft equipped with wire-recorders. Joan-Eleanor was a major breakthrough in miniaturisation and the GRU were delighted to receive early technical details of this equipment, passed to them via Sonya!

At first, in the UK, Sonya used one of her

PRACTICAL SPREAD SPECTRUM SYSTEM

JAMES VINCENT, G1PVZ, believes that he may have recently carried out the first amateur-radio experiments in the UK on the feasibility of using a military-type spread-spectrum modulation on the 435MHz band. He has constructed a direct sequence frequency modulated (DFSM) transmitter and receiver/correlator with a spread bandwidth of 6.8MHz (**Fig 51**): The transmitter uses a pseudo-random sequence at a clock rate of

3.4MHz to bi-phase shift key an NBFM carrier; this creates a noise-like spectra centred around 435MHz which has a low spectral power density.

At the receiver the signal is amplified and then de-spread using a similar circuit with an identical pseudo-random code and correlator. The system is based on ideas from Andre Kesteloot, N4ICK, with Andre and Chuck Phillips, N4EZV, providing assis-

tance and advice. The system was field tested in Yeovil on January 19 with G6TIJ providing a monitoring receiver. These techniques have mainly been used by the military to provide anti-jam and low probability of intercept protection. The FCC have permitted American amateurs to experiment with spread spectrum techniques and recently the RA granted G1PVZ authority to test a spread spectrum system on 70cm.

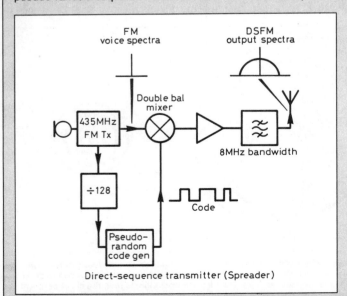

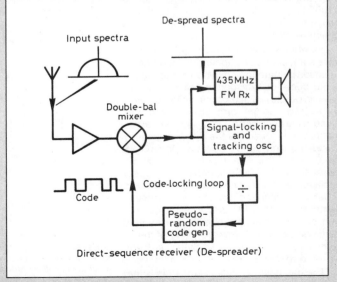

Fig 7: G1PVZ's direct sequence transmitter/receiver based on N4ICK's pseudo-noise spread spectrum system.

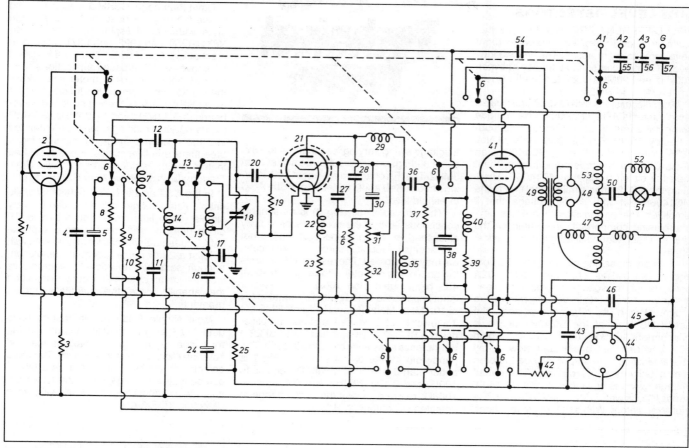

Fig 8: Circuit diagram of the Belka M-2 three-valve HF transceiver.

home-built transmitters but was later provided with one of the series of Russian-agent radios, probably brought into the UK in a diplomatic bag. Details of a number of these radios have been assembled by Rudi Staritz, DL3CS, and I also have a copy of a secret 1943 German publication on direction-finding written for the ORPO teams of the Funkabwehr (kindly supplied to me by Dick Rollema, PA0SE) with a chapter on agent-radios of Allied countries. Together, these sources describe such Russian models as Nobla, Sewer, Tensor, Jack and the Belka M-2.

The Belka M-2 (**Figs 7 and 8**) was a very simple but ingenious 3-valve transceiver with the audio-output valve used as a crystal-controlled keyed oscillator for transmitting. The regenerative 'straight' receiver had an untuned RF stage that would not have contributed much gain, but would have reduced the oscillator voltage to the antenna on receive and made the regenerative detector much more tame by eliminating antenna resonances etc.

NOT-TOO-SIMPLE PSUS

EINSTEIN ONCE DECLARED that everything should be as simple as possible, but not simpler. In *TT*, October 1991, p33 details were given of G3UPA's 'simple low-cost 13.8V, 10A PSU'. Due warning was given that, as presented, this did not include overvoltage protection against failure of one of the series-pass transistors (a not unusual fault).

Dave Lauder, G1OSC, adds that, from a designer's point of view, several other aspects of the design deserve comment even

though G3UPA reported that he had used his unit to run his HF transceiver for some two years, using two series-pass transistors and a 25A transformer, with no problems.

G1OSC writes: "First, there is no resistor between base and emitter of the series-pass transistor, TR2. It is often assumed that leakage of silicon transistors is insignificant but this may not be the case if power transistors reach a high junction temperature at full load during a long 'over'. If, at the end of the over, the current consumption drops to a low enough value on receive, there is a possibility of overvoltage at the output caused by the PSU losing regulation due to collector-base leakage current of TR2. The 78M12 regulator can drive current into the base of TR2 but I doubt whether it can pull collector-base leakage current out.

"It is a wise precaution to include a low value resistor (such as 100Ω) from base to emitter of the pass transistor(s) in any series regulator. Overvoltage protection is also wise but prevention is better than cure! All the power supplies which have appeared in *TT* in the past few years have had such base-emitter resistors other than the Australian 'Moonrabin Mk IV' unit outlined in the January 1989 *TT*.

"Secondly, as the 2N3772 used in the G3UPA PSU is specified as having an h_{FE} of 15 to 60 at 10A collector current, a transistor with minimum h_{FE} would require 667mA of base current rather than the 500mA-maximum rating of the 78M12.

"Thirdly, the only form of current limit is that the TR2 base current is limited by the 78M12 regulator and the effectiveness of this de-

pends on the h_{FE} of TR2. If TR2 has a relatively high h_{FE}, this form of current limiting would not be effective and TR2 and the transformer would not be protected in the event of an output short-circuit. It would, however, be worth mounting the 78M12 on the same heatsink as TR2, not to keep it cool but to warm it up! Then, if the heatsink gets too hot the 78M12 would go into thermal shutdown, limiting the TR2 base current. This could provide some over-temperature protection but not safe-operating-area protection as the latter would probably require 'foldback' current limiting." **G3VA**

LOW-LEVEL DETECTORS

TWO DIFFERENT ARRANGEMENTS that can provide low-level detection down to 40mV have come to my attention. The first is a low-level AGC detector suitable for use between 200kHz and 20MHz from Jan-Martin Noeding, LA8AK. He writes:

"After discussions with OK2ZZ and DJ8ES about suitable AGC detectors, I have made some experiments based on an idea published by PA0KDF in *Electron* (Oct and Nov 1986). Whereas he used the MC1495 as an audio CW synchronous-demodulator, I first tried his circuit using the MC1496P. However, the SO42P has similar functions to the MC1496P but with the advantage that it simplifies the design since there are several biasing components integrated on the chip and I subsequently adopted this device: **Fig 1**.

"With an increasing input signal, DC voltage on pin 3 rises while pin 2 falls. IC2A converts only the voltage difference between these two points into a voltage referred to ground. When the difference is zero, the actual DC level at the SO42P outputs is unimportant. IC2B is an amplifier with a gain of 4 and has fast attack and slow decay characteristics. The output may be buffered with a unity-gain 741 op-amp. The output voltage swing is suitable for Plessey 1600-series ICs, as well as MC1349/1350 and PIN-diode regulators. With a PIN-diode regulator,

a voltage swing varying less than +4 to +8V, some 80dB gain variation may be achieved at 9MHz. The IF-voltage varies about 4dB, leaving about 4-5dB audio variation over the AGC threshold level.

"This characteristic (**Fig 2**) is reasonably continuous so that the problems previously discussed in *TT* in respect of the abrupt characteristics found in some modern receivers may be avoided. The resistor RA controls the gain of the detector with 0Ω giving about 4dB higher gain than 100Ω. The detector input impedance is 1KΩ with RA equal to 0Ω at 10.7MHz. Mean IF level is 40mV RMS but if a lower level is desired, a simple amplifier using a BFR90 or BF199 (similar to BF224) will increase sensitivity by up to 20-26dB. The bandwidth for the circuit shown in Fig 1 is better than 0.2 to 20MHz with RA equals to 100Ω, and 0.4 to 20MHz with RA equal to 1000Ω, referred to less than 5% change in detected DC output level."

Dave Plumridge, G3KMG, was interested to see the detector used in 'A field-strength meter with decibel display' by Ralph Fowler, N6YC (*QST*, Jan 1992, pp33-37). He considers that a detector which can linearly detect RF above 40mV has useful applications in the RF voltmeter and power meter field. While the N6YC meter has an input comprising a tuned RF amplifier covering switched wavebands of 3-11MHz and 11-30MHz, G3KMG points out that readings could be extended into the microvolt range by substituting a broadband amplifier such as those described in the *ARRL Handbook* or in *Solid State Design*. [Both available from RSGB - Ed.]

In the *QST* article, N6YC notes that while usable field-strength indicators can be very simple (often little more than a simple RF diode detector and meter), more sophisticated measurements call for instruments with at least a 20dB range, adequate resolution, enough sensitivity to allow measurements well outside an antenna's induction field and the capability for relative quantitative measurements.

Most simple field-strength meters have detectors that operate at least partly outside their linear regions, lack dynamic range, and have insufficient detector sensitivity. The more complex meter he describes uses a diode-compensated RF detector of the type illustrated by J Grebenkemper in 'Calibrating diode detectors' (*QEX*, Aug 1990).

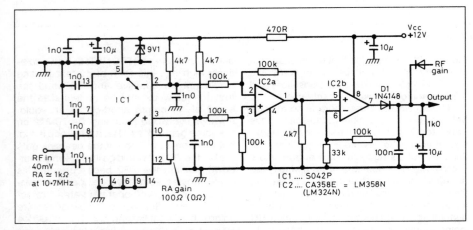

Fig 1: LA7AK's low-level AGC detector, 0.2 to 20MHz.

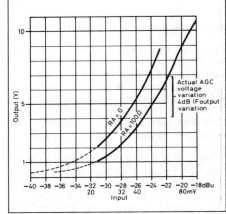

Fig 2: Characteristics of LA7AK's detector.

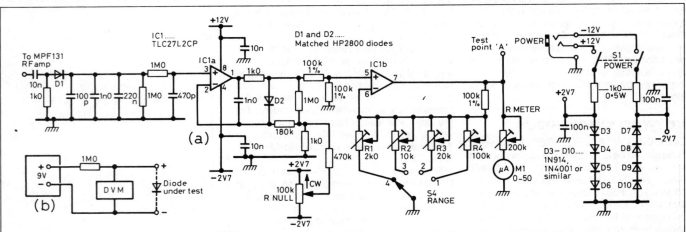

Fig 3: (a) Detector and DC amplifier section of N6YC's field-strength meter with a detector that linearly detects RF above 40mV and is thus suitable for use with an output meter providing a decibel display. It uses matched HP2800 or 1N5711 hot-carrier diodes, D1 and D2. (b) test set-up for matching D1 and D2 to within a few millivolts of each other.

N6YC writes: "The beauty of this circuit (**Fig 3(a)**) is that with low-barrier-voltage diodes, it can linearly detect RF inputs between about 0.04V peak and the saturation limits of the DC amplifiers IC1A and IC1B - a range of at least 45dB. Although Grebenkemper suggests using diodes with 200mV barrier potentials (1N5711s) I find that HP2800s (barrier potential of 500mV) work quite well in this application and I expect them to be only slightly less sensitive. As Grebenkemper points out, matching the diodes (to within a few millivolts of barrier potential) is important. Generally, hot-carrier diodes are already pretty well matched, but I suggest selecting diodes with similar forward drops for optimum performance. You can match diodes using the circuit shown in **Fig 3(b)**. A two-stage TLC27L2CP op-amp DC amplifier, gain-switched in four 10dB ranges, amplifies the detector output."

G3KMG was also glad to note in the construction section of the article more reinforcement for his prejudice that for amateur one-off projects 'ugly construction' is the best! (See G3KMG's *TT* item 'Home construction and the PCB' July 1991, pp26-27). He writes: "The copper clad board provides an unbroken ground plane for better stability and performance - plus it is so much quicker and easier to knock up circuits. In addition, the inevitable improvement or modification causes so little hassle compared with PCB construction."

N6YC built his first prototype using point-to-point (dead bug) construction. His next model, built on a PCB, never worked - "it seemed to lock-up with no offset control. For the third (current) version, I went back to 'ugly' construction and again achieved success. In retrospect I believe that stray pin-to-pin currents plagued my PCB version . . . . So, proceed carefully if you choose to fabricate a PC-board."

HRODDITIES

ALTHOUGH IT IS NOW some 45 years since I last used an HRO receiver built by the National Company of Malden, Mass, this set remains in my mind as the classic valve communications receiver designed for the amateur radio market. Perhaps this is just a nostalgic prejudice that stems from the five busy years (1941-1946) spent spinning the unique PW dial of HROs (up to three at a time) for Special Communications, but the sound design of these sets is reflected in the number that are still in good working order, even if the electrical performance can no longer match some aspects of the latest solid-state transceivers/receivers.

There also seems to be always something new to learn about them. For example, it was not until I read Hugh Skillen's *Spies of the Airways* (the story of the Army's tactical Y-Service) that I discovered that the HRO was widely used by the Special Wireless Group units of the pukka British Army, designated by the Army as the R106. This book also sheds new light on the German 'copy' of the HRO - their KST receiver. Hugh Skillen writes: "According to Fritz Trenkle, the HRO (R106) was well-known in Germany before the war and it was manufactured under licence by the German radio manufacturer Koerting, proba-

bly from 1938, with the original dial, (four-gang) tuning capacitor and plug-in coil assemblies (imported from the USA until 1941 via Portugal) but with German steel valves and known as the KST receiver. The main users were the diplomatic services and Admiral Canaris's Abwehr within the Wehrmacht".

An interesting account of the development of the HRO and other National receivers appears in *Communications Receivers: the vacuum tube era: 50 glorious years, 1932 - 1981* by Raymond S Moore (ex-K1DBR). He considers that the excellent mechanical design of the National receivers can be attributed to James Millen, trained as a mechanical engineer, who was with the company from 1928 to 1939 when he left to set up his own component-manufacturing company. His leaving, unfortunately, led to the decline of National as a leading innovator in communications receivers, although they continued manufacturing HRO designs until the 1960s.

To quote the book: "Late in 1933 work began on a communications receiver which was destined to become the most famous in history, a receiver which remained in production in recognisable form for 30 years. The electrical design was farmed out to Herbert Hoover Jr, W6ZH (W6ZH was the son of the President of the United States whose term of office unfortunately included the Wall Street crash of October 1929 - *G3VA*). The mechanical design was done at National's plant in Maldon, MA. The receiver was the HRO and was first mentioned in print in Jim Millen's column in *QST* in August 1934. The first advertisement in *QST* October 1934 had a picture of a prototype which was quite different from the final version which started deliveries in December . . . . Changes were apparently made late in the design . . . . The PW dial and gear drive, the ganged capacitors and the ganged coils and (plug-in) coil compartments are classics of mechanical design."

Ray Moore's book (112 pages large format with soft covers and many illustrations) was first published several years ago but Ray kindly sent me a copy in April 1990. I wrote an appreciative review for *RadCom* but unfortunately this somehow disappeared down a black hole somewhere along the line from Dulwich to Potters Bar. For those interested in the history, collection or use of the valve receivers that did so much to raise the performance of our hobby this is a book to savour. It contains potted details (valve complement, IF, date, original prices etc but no circuit diagrams) of some 700 receivers and kits marketed for radio amateurs from 1932 to the final 'hybrid' Drake R-4c which was finally phased out in 1980-81. Over 50 American manufacturers are represented, including those well-known to UK amateurs such as Collins, Drake, Hallicrafters, Hammarlund, Heath, National, RCA, RME etc and others whose products seldom appeared in the UK. It does not include receivers made specifically for the US services such as the BC312, BC342, BC348 etc. The book also contains brief but interesting notes on the major companies and their designers. Sadly, as far as I am aware, not one of these major companies is still producing receivers for the amateur market - even Heath of kit fame has recently announced its withdrawal.

The book is published by Ray Moore (RSM Communications), PO Box 218, Norwood, MA 02062, USA. Price UK and West Europe surface mail $17.29, air mail $22.

REUSABLE ALKALINE MANGANESE (RAM) BATTERIES

TT (JUNE 1990, p33) DREW ATTENTION, not for the first time, to the use of 'dirty DC charging' for both zinc-carbon and manganese-alkaline cells normally regarded as 'disposable' after being used once. As explained then, suitably dirty DC can be produced simply by connecting a resistor (example 200-300Ω) across a single-diode rectifier. This technique for recharging dry Leclanché (zinc-carbon) cells, although rarely used, dates back to the mid-1950s and possibly earlier. It is particularly effective with larger zinc-carbon cells provided they are put on charge before being completely exhausted and one must always emphasise that due care must be taken (eg limiting the maximum charging current according to the type of cell) to avoid the risk of explosion due to 'gassing'. This applies to any form of sealed cell. When attempting to recharge cells intended by their makers to be used once only, there are a number of rules that should be followed (see for example the June 1990 *TT* item).

But if it is possible to recharge alkaline manganese cells why not market them as such? Interestingly, Frank Harris, G4IEY, has sent along an article from *Batteries International* (Jan 1992) stating that a number of battery firms around the world are shortly expected to begin marketing alkaline-manganese cells specifically designed as high-energy rechargeable units. These should show a relative cost of energy factor which provides a significant advantage over nicad cells, and even some cost advantage over lead-acid cells. One of the firms licensed to manufacture these RAM cells is Ray-o-Vac, covering manufacture in the USA, Mexico and the UK.

To quote from *Batteries International*: "The public conception of cylindrical 'dry' cells is that they cannot be recharged. But to a limited extent, they can, particularly the alkaline-manganese variety. Back in the 1960s, Dr Karl Kordesch, who invented alkaline manganese cells, persuaded Eveready(US) to market a rechargeable version. At that time, Eveready made and sold them for portable TVs and lanterns. No-one needs telling that the single-use alkaline manganese quickly became an outstanding commercial success. But the rechargeable version was withdrawn after a few years due to limited market growth and concerns about adequate protection against end-user abuse. Either they short-circuited internally and died, or they gassed on recharge and presented an explosion hazard.

"But recent advances in separators, gassing suppressants and gas recombination technology have made the technology come alive again. Karl Kordesch has been working with a Canadian company, BTI, to perfect the technology, supported by research at the Technical University of Graz in Austria."

The article emphasises the advantages of RAM cells over nicads (cylindrical spiral type) and flat-plate lead-acid cells as used in car batteries: see **Table 1**.

Some of the points made are that an AA-size RAM cell made as a bobbin can now produce 2000mAh of energy, compared with 500-600mAh for industry-standard nicads, 800-1000mAh for high-performance nicads and 1100mAh for Ni-MH cells. RAM cells (**Fig 4**) cost little more than single-use alkaline-manganese cells to manufacture; it should therefore be possible to market them at about half the price of nicad cells, size for size. RAM cells are claimed to be ideal at 2-3 hour discharge rates (ie relatively high current loads) and are thus well suited for Walkman, portable computer and presumably hand-held transceivers. Using cells in series-parallel, or spiral-wound, the high-rate performance is good enough for power tools and electric vehicles.

Property	Ni-Cd (spiral)	RAM (bobbin)	RAM (flat plate)	Lead-acid (flat plate)[a]
Energy density, Wh/kg	27	47	32-52[b]	35
Power density, W/kg	72	30	215-430[b]	150
Cycles, shallow	500	300	100	300-400
Cycles, deep	100-200	100	40	20
Relative cost	2.5	1	1	1.2
Relative weight	1	1	1	2.3
Operating voltage	1.2	1.2	1.2	2.0
Charge retention (20°C)	3-6months	2-3years	2-3years	3-6months
'Memory' effect	yes	no	no	no
Toxicity of components	toxic	non-toxic[c]	non-toxic[c]	toxic

[a] typical SLI vehicle battery
[b] lower figure has been achieved, upper figure appears readily achievable
[c] mercury-free version

(Condensed from *Batteries International*)

Table 1: Characteristics of rechargeable cells.

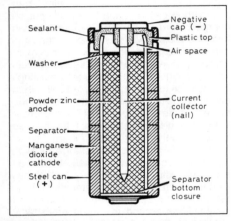

Fig 4: A bobbin form of reusable alkaline manganese (RAM) cell as proposed for AAA, AA, C and D sizes. It is uncertain when such cells will be marketed in the UK, but manufacturing licences have been issued.

G4IEY also draws attention to the Yuasa NP range of 'maintenance-free' sealed lead-acid batteries which are manufactured in Wales. This includes 4, 6 and 12V rechargeable batteries offering a choice of 25 models covering 0.8Ah to 65.0Ah.

BROADBAND RADIALS

THE AVAILABILITY OF FIVE amateur HF bands between 14.0 and 29.7MHz, including bands without any harmonic relationship, provides an incentive to develop broadband antennas capable of efficient operation over at least an octave of spectrum. A well established method of increasing the effective bandwidth of any antenna element is to increase the diameter/length ratio, as for example in the once popular caged dipole.

One practical form of broadband antenna exploiting this technique is the vertical biconical monopole, despite its rather complex structure. Way back in the *RSGB Bulletin* (now *Radio Communication*) of May 1966, pp305-306, an amateur example of a biconical antenna, originally described by W5WEU in *CQ*, January 1966, was presented in *TT* together with details of a professional antenna of this type as used at a number of Royal Navy HF coast stations (described by H P Mason of the Admiralty Surface Weapon Establishment (now Admiralty Research Establishment) at a 1963 IEEE HF Conven-

tion) and implemented in three forms: for 2-5MHz, 4-11MHz and 10-26MHz. The W5WEU and ASWE designs are shown in the 7th editon of *Amateur Radio Techniques*, p277.

It was then emphasised that, as for any monopole antenna, it is necessary to use the best possible ground plane. For the ASWE designs, 36 buried radials about one quarter-wave long at the lowest frequency were used. Interestingly, I find that I then added the comment: "What I have never yet found is any detailed comparison between the effectiveness of a ground radial system and that of the three or four-wire up-in-the-air technique which we associate with 'ground-plane' antennas - and how much the ground conductivity below such sloping ground-plane systems affects low angle radiation". That was in 1966 and since then both these topics have been well aired (and answered) with some assurance!

It is now widely accepted (and in increasing evidence for amateur 1.8MHz practice) that a few elevated radials can be every bit as

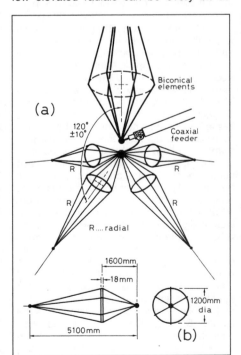

Fig 5: UT5YB's use of broadband radials in conjunction with a biconical vertical antenna covering 14-30MHz continuously with low SWR on the coax feedline.

effective as a massive buried earth system (although the very low angle radiation will be much attenuated in either case in areas of poor ground conductivity extending out to some 50 wavelengths). But when used with a broadband radiating element it is clearly desirable that elevated radials should also be broadband in order to achieve equal efficiency and a similar radiation pattern over the full frequency range.

What appears to be an effective means of implementing such an approach appears in the Russian *Radio* No 12, 1991, page 19, in a short article by UT5YB in conjunction with a biconical monopole antenna originally described by UW4HW in *Radio* No 9, 1981: see **Fig 5**.

If my guesses at the Russian text are correct, then UT5YB claims that fed with 75Ω coax feeder, the antenna shows an SWR of only about 1.05 to 1.2 throughout the band 14 to 30MHz. Each of the radials is similar to the vertical element, 5.1m (5100mm) long.

MORE ON 1.8MHZ 'SWEET SPOT' PROPAGATION

IN *TT*, MARCH 1992, pp36-37, a letter from Roger Crofts, VK4YB, commented on the remarkably reliable 1.8MHz 'openings' between Australia and North America. These have been observed by the SEANCE net between May and August in recent years. One of the North American participants, Bob Eldridge, VE7BS of Pemberton, BC confirms the curious fact that horizontally-polarized antennas having relatively high-angle radiation usually considered almost as a sine qua non for 1.8/3.5MHz DX.

But first a correction. VE7BS points out that the two 'tropical bands' broadcast DX enthusiasts who have been unravelling this apparently chordal-hop form of 1.8MHz transequatorial propagation are not, as I wrongly assumed, Australians. John Bryant is in Oklahoma and is publisher of *Fine Tuning's Proceedings* and Davis Clark is in Ontario and writes for *DX Ontario*.

A personal observation: VK4YB suggested that the UK is too far north to experience a 'sweet-spot' of the tropical Spread-F enhancement that appears to form one of the two ionospheric tilts, and thus would be unlikely to benefit directly. But I note that Pemberton BC is around latitude 50° North, roughly the same latitude as say Plymouth or Torquay in south-

LOW-COST SOLAR CHARGER

THE POSSIBILITY THAT WE may yet see cheap solar power stemming from work at the Swiss Federal Institute of Technology was noted in the Jan 1992 *TT* p39. But currently, solar arrays are still relatively high-cost items, even if required only to provide a few watts for keeping a small nicad or lead-acid battery, used intermittently, up to scratch.

Electronics Australia (Feb 1992, pp 72-75) however, publishes a constructional project for a solar charger suitable for use with batteries of up to 12V and claimed as "probably the cheapest solar charger project ever published". This is based on amorphous-type solar panels rated at 6V, 1W output (more in brightest sunshine) costing $A14.00 (roughly £6), or using enough photovoltaic solar cell 'offcuts' to make a 6V, 1.5W panel at about half the price. A DC-DC converter (**Fig 6**) is then used to push the charging voltage up to that required for batteries of between about 7.5 to 14V, making it possible to construct the charger for about £8. A complete kit, including PCB, is marketed in Australia for this project by Oatley Electronics but the components are probably available in the UK.

The charge to a 12V battery varies between 400mW and 1W, representing a charge current ranging from 30mA to over 80mA depending on sunlight conditions. This is sufficient to maintain the charge of a vehicle battery etc, if this is to be left unattended for long periods and then used only intermittently. The unit can also be used to charge nicad cells. Six cells should charge at between 50 to 100mA, sufficient to fully charge a set of AA cells in some 12-14 hours: see **Fig 7**.

The DC-DC converter is based around a 400Hz oscillator (IC1a) which after amplification switches the complimentary germanium output transistors (AD161, AD162) with two 'charge pump' voltage doublers which together give an output of up to four times the input voltage. Batteries of less than 12V are best connected between B+ and B- while 12V lead-acid batteries between B+ and earth.

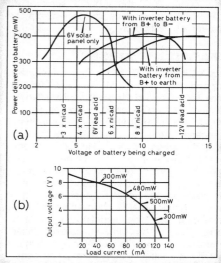

Fig 7: (a) Power transferred by the solar charger with a solar panel rated at 6V 1W measured in Australian winter conditions. Power transfers of over 1W expected under Australian summer conditions. (b) Power transfer directly from a 6V 1W solar array under different load conditions. Optimum power transfer with load currents of about 100mA. Possibly twice the power under Australian summer conditions.

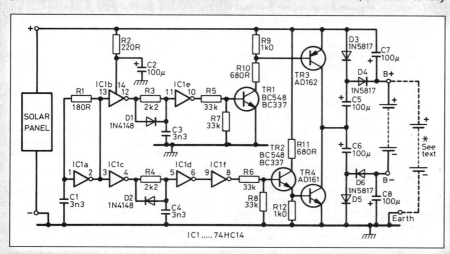

Fig 6: The *Electronics Australia* low cost solar battery charger with 400Hz DC-DC converter. A 12V battery is best connected as shown by dotted connection.

west England while, say, Rio de Janeiro is near the Tropic of Capricorn which runs through Queensland, Australia, where VK4YB has been located. There would thus be dawn and dusk tilts available to UK amateurs with the possibility of South American amateurs taking advantage of tropical Spread F. So what are the chances of a similarly reliable summer path on 1.8MHz between PY and the UK?

But back to the question on vertical radiation patterns. VE7BS queries the accepted wisdom that high-angle DX signals must always imply multi-hop propagation with its associated ground (or sea) reflection losses and thus less likely to get through the low-angle signals. He writes: "On 1.8MHz I use a delta loop antenna much the same as the one shown in Fig 8(b) of *TT*, November 1989. The apex is about 115ft above the physical ground and the base wire about 0.4λ. It is fed near one bottom corner about 0.25λ from the apex using 75Ω coax direct feed. The resonant frequency can be raised by lifting the centre of the base wire. I also use a full wave horizontal loop (highest point about 80ft, lowest about 40ft) for response to higher angle signals and for changing from vertical to horizontal polarization, switching from one to another for reception as needed and usually transmitting on both in parallel and sometimes receiving similarly on both, disconnecting one or the other if the signals fade.

"For several years I have operated through our summer on 1.8MHz around our sunrise and have data on the reliability of the path to VK - the 1991 chart is shown as **Fig 8**. VK4YB MCs the VK end and from mid-May to mid-August had propagation to North America on 95% of the days. Many of the Australians use dipoles relatively close to the ground and many stations on both ends of the path find that as sunrise approaches dipoles perform better than efficient monopoles. VK4YB is the most consistently strong signal (often perfect S9+ copy on SSB) and his phased dipoles at about 100ft are almost better than his 100ft vertical plus radials".

VE7BS, however, feels that the 1.8MHz path between Pemberton and Australia is very different from 50MHz TEP. He can find

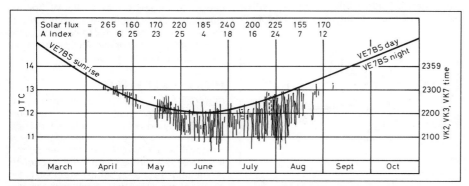

Fig 8: VE7BS's record of the 1.8MHz openings from Australia to British Columbia during the 1991 'summer season'. Propagation to VE7 on 114 days; no propagation on 18 days; uncertain 10 days. Start times are influenced by the fact that VK4YB called CQ each day at 1100z.

very little correlation between propagation on 1.8MHz even with that on 1620kHz and 2325kHz.

He writes: "Playing with some ray-tracing programs written by NM7M, I think I can see that at the critical time one ray goes right through, one comes right back down, and the 1.8MHz ray refracts and glances at whatever. I believe that the unstable-E condition that Raymond Fricker considers unreliable is the one that allows me to get over the hill and along to VK . . . . VK4YB will be in VK6 for about 18 months, and we do not yet know whether anyone else will take on regular supervision of SEANCE. But we have worked VKs consistently through our summer on 1.8MHz for several years, so I guess the experiment will go on".

"PARFICK" MORSE?

AS A DEDICATED USER OF old fashioned up-and-down manual Morse keys, I was interested to read in *Morse Magnificat* (No 22, Spring 1922) a letter from Gordon Brown, VK1AD, claiming that 'perfect' Morse in not necessarily the most readable Morse, particularly at higher speeds. He claims: "Hand-sent Morse is superior to machine generated Morse . . . . When [we] old pros were taught Morse . . . . it was impressed on us most emphatically that in letters such as 'y', 'q' or 'w', or anything that finished with a dash, the final dash must be held on just a little bit longer than normal. Only a couple of milliseconds, but definitely longer than a dash in the middle of a letter . . . . With machine-generated 'perfect' Morse you are not quite sure at high-speed whether you hear a 'y' or a 'c', a 'q' or a 'z', and so on. This was first noticed about the time Mr Wheatstone invented his Morse tapes and high-speed transmitter . . . ."

This is an interesting concept and I suppose that with fully microprocessor-controlled electronic transmission it would be possible to generate such accented Morse. But the human flexibility that is possible with manual sending on a straight key, with variations in speed to emphasise words or symbols, or in the formation of letters, is all par for the course! Similarly speed can be adjusted to suit band conditions.

Incidentally, Tony Smith, G4FAI (1 Tash Place, London N11 1PA, Tel 081 368 4588), the consultant editor of *MM* is compiling detailed information on the many varieties of the popular 'wartime' Services Morse key, known generally as type 'WT8 Amp' but manufactured by a number of firms in different countries and under different Mark numbers etc. He has already identified over 40 different versions made in six countries (Australia, Canada, England, New Zealand, South Africa and the USA) in different years.

He is seeking further identification legends (eg KEY WT8AMP No 2 - N.E. Co 1941) and then has a form helping the owner of the key to list the various characteristics of the particular model (eg number of bridges, shape of base corners, type of tensioner, etc, etc). An article in *MM22* by Jim Lycett, G0MSZ, describes and illustrates eight of the basic variations as well as the original W B Morse key introduced in 1938 by Whiteley Electrical Radio Ltd that appears to have been the first of this large family of WT8AMP keys.

FORECASTING BAND CONDITIONS

A RECENT ITEM IN THE monthly newsletter of the Thames Valley Amateur Radio Transmitters Society by John Pegler, G3ENI/G3TVS, provides a handy means of translating basic propagation forecasts into likely band conditions - although one should remember that weekly or monthly forecasts may not always be reflected in the real-time state of the ionosphere.

G3ENI writes: "Amateurs who have been active for many years over several sunspot cycles may develop an instinct for judging band conditions. Routine checking of DX broadcasting stations on adjacent bands is often helpful, as are the 28MHz worldwide and 14MHz sequential beacons. However, it is possible to carry out basic forecasting oneself to supplement and update the propagation information given during the *GB2RS* Sunday news bulletins. Ignoring the multiplicity of solar events which cause variations in the ionosphere, we need to consider to main items. First, the 'solar flux' which is noise measured on 2800MHz each day and which ranges from a minimum of about 66 units to a maximum of about 300 units. Good conditions on the higher HF bands require a high flux. Second, 'geomagnetic activity' which acts against the benefits of high flux and may be presented as either 'A' or 'K' units.

"The latest flux, geomagnetic level and other information can be obtained from the US National Bureau of Standards station WWV which provides these at 18 minutes past each hour simultaneously on 2.5, 5, 10, 15 and 20MHz. If these are all inaudible, the information can be obtained at the cost of an international telephone call to 0101 303 497 3235. The prerecorded information is passed in under

one minute. **Fig 10** shows, in approximate terms, the relationship between solar flux and geomagnetic activity to determine expected propagation conditions. On the chart, solar flux is plotted vertically. The geomagnetic index is shown horizontally with the two scales: the K scale is based on readings taken eight times a day, each covering the previous three hours. The A scale is based on the eight K values for the previous day. The intersection of the flux and geomagnetic activity values determines the expected conditions, divided into eight zones as given in the caption".

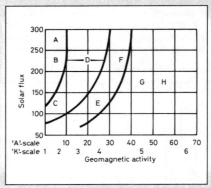

Fig 10: Chart relating solar flux and geomagnetic activity to likely band conditions as published by G3ENI in the *TVARTS Newsletter*.
Zone A: Above normal, 50MHz open, 21 to 28MHz open up to 24 hours
Zone B: Above normal, 21 to 28MHz open up to 24 hours
Zone C: 21 to 28MHz alive
Zone D: Normal conditions
Zone E: Below normal, unsettled
Zone F: Below normal, disturbed
Zone F: Disturbed, sub-storm level, aurora may form
Zone H: Storm level, auroras

SOFT START FOR HIGH VOLTAGE PSU

JEREMY CARROLL, G3NFW, writes: "The February *TT* (Fig 6) showed further ways of soft-starting high-voltage power supplies. An alternative is shown in **Fig 9**. This circuit provides a slight delay before the soft-start 200Ω series resistor is shorted out by the relay contact. A feature of this arrangement is that the relay will only operate reliably if the secondary is lightly loaded at the moment of switch-on. Otherwise the voltage drop across

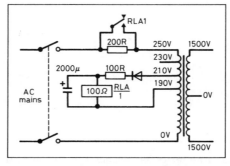

Fig 9: G3NFW's soft-start circuit used for many years with a 2kV PSU for a linear amplifier.

the 200Ω resistor may be such that insufficient voltage develops across the primary winding for the relay to operate.

"With a short-circuit on the secondary side, only minimal voltage will develop across the transformer primary and hence the relay will not operate. Whilst this provides some protection for components on the secondary side of the transformer, it introduces a problem on the primary side where the series resistor, with almost full mains voltage across it, attempts to dissipate around 250W (for the value shown). Suitable precautions need to be taken to avoid problems; nevertheless the circuit has operated uneventfully in my linear amplifier for almost 20 years."

HERE AND THERE

BOB CONNELL, G4JQY, draws attention to the Swedish TWC battery charger marketed in the UK by Aqua Marine for boat batteries. The charger cycles the charging voltage between 14 and 14.6V and it is claimed that this "creates a stirring effect in the electrolyte, preventing the charge being held close to the battery plates. Helping to distribute the charge in this way enables a 100% charge to be achieved." It's a new idea to me. **G3VA**

ANOTHER COMPACT VK2ABQ 14MHZ ANTENNA

IT IS NOW ALMOST 20 years since *TT* presented the original VK2ABQ three-band (14/21/28MHz) wire beam antenna, first published as a short letter in *Electronics Australia*. Since then, Fred Caton, VK2ABQ (formerly G3ONC) has followed this with a number of other ideas, submitted directly to *TT*, including several modified forms of his original design which has become well-established (see *ART7*) and which has been endorsed by Les Moxon, G6XN in his book *HF Antennas for All Locations* (available from RSGB sales). I must admit that I sometimes wonder what professional antenna specialists such as VE2CV would make of the jottings which Fred sends along to explain his ideas.

A recent letter is no exception and I can only hope that I have understood at least the gist of this new design which dispenses with the open-wire phasing line used in the original VK2ABQ design, and has the driven element fed directly from a coax feed-line. The dimensions shown are for 14MHz, and should be divided by two for 28MHz. A 14MHz antenna can be used on 21MHz as an extended-element array, but the feedpoint impedance will rise and become reactive, so that an ATU will be necessary.

In effect, **Fig 1** shows a KISS recipe for a simple 14MHz two-element array. The unidirectional 135° phase shift is achieved using equal-length elements without a phasing line but with critical coupling.

Take a 71ft length of lightweight plastic-coated wire (bare/enamelled copper wire would need to be rather longer). First check for resonance with the wire fitted on the wooden frame, using a GDO. Then fold the 71ft wire into four, and touch the plastic with a hot soldering iron to identify where the sides are to be cut. The frame can be constructed from four 11ft 6in dowels ($^5/_8$in diameter) or garden canes, mounted on a square piece of board with about 15in sides (as in the original VK2ABQ designs). In placing the wire on the framework, make sure the two current-focus sections are placed an eighth-wave apart (2.5m on 14MHz) with the voltage-tips adjustable to 4in gaps in order to provide the quarter-cycle (90°) phase-shift between L1 and L2. The 90° critical coupling between L1 and L2 plus the 45° current loop spacing gives the required 135° phase-shift between the two elements resulting in an effective unidirectional two-element array with a satisfying front-to-back ratio, useful forward gain and sharp side nulls. VK2ABQ stresses that the gaps between the elements are critical in achieving critical coupling, in his case he found 3.75in optimum.

Fig 1(b) shows the piece of flat plastic material used as an insulator at the element feed point. The 0.25in coax cable is then routed down through the hole in the centre-board. Seal and 'gunk' the feedpoint, using for example *black* bitumen paint or similar. A nylon cord is loosely connected as a stabilizer between the feed-point insulator and the centre rear of the L2 current loop. VK2ABQ likens the array to an old-style critically-coupled IF transformer with lumped-components, but opened-up to tickle the ether and provide a simple, cheap, compact but effec-

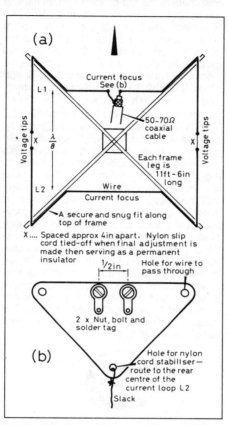

Fig 1(a): The VK2ABQ KISS 14MHz array. (b) Feedpoint insulator with nylon cord stabiliser.

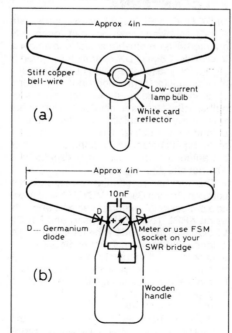

Fig 2(a): Simple current sampler. (b) More sensitive current sampler.

tive two-element beam. To adjust the coupling, a simple current sampling gimmick can be used as in **Fig 2(a)**. Provided that the loop of the device is very small in terms of wavelength, it will not respond to the electric (voltage) field. **Fig 2(b)** shows a similar device but with a meter to increase sensitivity. With the antenna at shoulder height, and with the aid of a helper, the gaps at the voltage tips can be adjusted for equal current in both elements, indicating a 90° phase shift. Overcoupling will be indicated by more power in the reflector element, undercoupling by more power in the driven element. When power is shared equally, the coupling will be providing the correct 90° phase-shift. It should be appreciated that a VK2ABQ-type array is basically a form of driven array rather than a Yagi parasitic-reflector array.

Adjustments may be carried out with one person standing in the middle of the shoulder-high array using the current sampler, and with a few watts of 14.05MHz RF fed to the antenna. The helper then adjusts the spacing at the voltage tips, but moves *well away* from the voltage tips after adjusting the spacing to instructions. Any large object near the voltage tips will nullify the adjustments.

Finally, VK2ABQ endorses the value of a tip that appeared many years ago in *TT* and elsewhere, and is applicable to all dipole-type antennas with low-impedance feeder. A 20KΩ carbon resistor soldered across the element feedpoint has no effect on the operation of the antenna but allows an ohmmeter check to be made in the shack as a warning against a broken feedline. VK2ABQ has used such a resistor (well covered in 'gunk') for some 25 years.

Incidentally, at the age of 74 years, Fred no longer feels able to correspond with readers seeking further advice on his antennas. He hopes that the information provided here will enable readers to achieve satisfactory results.

ANTENNA GAIN AND EFFICIENCY

JOHN BELROSE, VE2CV, as a professional antenna engineer, is clearly concerned at the looseness and inexactitude of much of the terminology and information that appears in the amateur radio periodicals (including, I must confess, those in *TT*). For example he was disturbed to read the suggestion by G4HOL (*TT*, December 1991) that "his horizontal loop at 3.5MHz has 9dB more gain than his quarter-wave sloper". VE2CV comments: "Great. Should he throw out his sloper? Maybe not? When on 3.5MHz I switch from my dipole to my half-delta loop, which has an overhead null, the signals received from stations a few hundred kilometres away decrease by up to three S-units (15dB); whereas the signals from DX stations a long way away, on the west coast of Canada, increase by up to three S-units, depending on propagation conditions (angle of arrival of the skywave signal). No wonder amateurs do not understand antennas. They read so much conflicting information."

In pleading *mea culpa* I would suggest that this is an age-old problem not made easier by the fact that the whole subject of antenna gains and losses offers enormous scope for sophistry, semantics and what is known in the trade as 'specmanship' - ie why say your antenna has a gain of 6dB when with some subtle redefinition you can say the gain is 12dB? For those of us who are not professional engineers, antennas are not easy to understand even in purely pragmatic terms! Think of the signal leaving the antenna and spraying out in many directions, possibly boosted by ground reflection according to polarization. Then consider the tiny percentage of the original power that actually tickles the receiving antenna, as found only by accurate ray-tracing of the signal over the specific path concerned and the actual height of the reflecting layers. It then becomes evident that the performance of an antenna may bear little relationship to a single definition of gain without reference to the lobe patterns of both horizontal and vertical radiation. The development of computer-modelling based on NEC codes has made it easier for professional-amateurs and some others to assess antenna performance without actually engaging in practical trials - but most of us still depend on subjective assessments.

Tony Henk, G4XVF, has shown clearly that the overall efficiency of small transmitting loop antennas in terms of the amount of power actually radiated compared with the output power of the transmitter is usually quite low with more energy being lost in the matching components including the capacitors than in the actual loop element.

Rightly, he warns against spending a lot of money on a remotely tuned loop if you have sufficient space to erect a more conventional transmitting antenna. But the small loop can be a useful addition to the amateur antenna armoury. I seem to be bombarded with enthusiastic letters and information from amateurs who have developed or used such loops (I will try to find space to include some of this information before too long). And for those who would wish to experiment with low-cost loops, a reminder that the idea can be tried out without remote tuning or expensive high-voltage capacitors using 'capacitors' formed from parallel rods (as in a *CQ* design from the Dec 1991 and Jan 1992 issues) or from lengths of coaxial cable etc. Certainly, many of those who have built small magnetic loop antennas have been pleasantly surprised how well they work, even though they tend to be inherently 'low-efficiency' antennas. They bestow a number of useful characteristics both for medium and long-distance operation.

John Brodzky, G3HQX, uses both a small loop and a full-wave (3.5MHz) more-or-less horizontal loop antenna formed by conversion from a long-wire antenna by continuing it back up his garden, across the house and back to where it started, fed at one corner with 300-ohm ribbon and through a 4:1 balun to his ATU. He considers the large loop is "the best wire antenna that I have ever used". It works well on all bands up to 28MHz. On 3.5MHz the low height means that it radiates at a high vertical angle primarily suitable for medium-distance contacts but able to get across the Atlantic at times. Above 14MHz he works anything he can hear. But he was not satisfied with the performance on 7MHz after hearing UK stations working JA and ZL stations that he could not even hear. He was

attracted by the idea of introducing some further vertically polarized components into his signal and studied the F1CLI antenna but he decided that it would not suit his location. Instead he hit on the idea of bringing down near the ground a point that was removed from the feed-point by 3λ/4. He felt that the two arms of a V (see **Fig 3**) formed by this alteration would now be at about 45° and carrying currents in phase, with a current maximum at the top of each arm. In making this change the overall length of the loop had to be increased by 12ft and the feed-point moved down one of the legs to get the bottom of the V to come to the bottom centre of his garden. The increased length has shifted the loop resonance to the CW end of 3.5MHz and at 7MHz it is also at the preferred frequency. The overall length of the loop is now 286ft.

I am not sure what computer-modelling (or VE2CV) would make of this arrangement - and one may have to discount the unusually good HF propagation conditions early this year - but G3HQX reports that since he made the changes he finds that on 7MHz most mornings he can work ZL, JA, VE (including VE7) and plenty of Ws (including West Coast W6s). He bases his operating times on 'gray-line' propagation as described in the book *Low-band DXing* by ON4UN (available from RSGB) using his computer to predict sunrise and sunset times at the home QTH and those of the areas of interest. It is unlikely that others will wish to duplicate an arrangement designed to fit a particular location, but it is interesting to note that good 7MHz DX is possible with a large loop having a height varying between 12ft and 24ft.

VE2CV'S COMMENTS ON THE F1LCI ANTENNA

IN *TT*, DECEMBER 1992, Jean Bourdereau, G1LCI, showed how he had effectively adapted an 84-metre horizontal loop antenna to provide 1.8MHz DX operation by grounding the far-end (centre-point) of the loop via a thick conductor (or grounded metal mast) and by connecting the open-wire loop feeders together at the attic transmitter end to form what was termed a top-fed grounded Marconi antenna on 1.8MHz. On other bands, by restoring the balanced feed, the operation of the antenna as a multiband horizontal loop was not affected: **Fig 4**.

The item has resulted in correspondence between Dr John Belrose, VE2CV (well-known as a professional antenna specialist who acts as an ARRL Technical Adviser) and F1LCI. VE2CV was intrigued by the idea of a single antenna that could be switched between: (1) a horizontal rectangular loop and (2) what is technically more accurately described as a form of vertical electromagnetic ground-plane loop (akin to the VE2CV half-delta loop as described in *QST* etc).

His own interests centre more on the 3.5MHz band than 1.8MHz. He writes: "Since both short and long distance communication is possible on this band, one would like to

have more than one antenna with a switch to choose between antennas matched to the distance or azimuthal direction requirement. For near-vertical-incidence-skywave (NVIS) signals, out to several hundred kilometres, we want an antenna that favours high-angle skywaves, such as a dipole or horizontal loop at a height of about a quarter-wave (or less - *G3VA*). For distant stations, we want an antenna that has a vertical-plane pattern that favours low-angle skywaves; a null for NVIS signals is useful in order to reject nearby strong interfering signals, man-made radio noise and radio noise from nearby to medium-distance thunderstorms."

Consequently, VE2CV computer-modelled (ELNEC) the F1LCI antenna with reference to 3.5 and 7MHz as well as for its intended 1.8MHz. He comments as follows:

(1) The description of the antenna as (a) 'horizontal mode' and (b) 'vertical mode' is somewhat a misnomer. Both arrangements when used for the higher frequency bands are electrically large, and both polarizations (horizontal and vertical) are radiated by each arrangement. The change of pattern with frequency for the EMGP arrangement is particularly complicated.

(2) With the shorted-feed line, the antenna is *not* 'a top fed Marconi antenna' (the same applies to G3BDQ's 'steeple antenna'). It is a kind of electromagnetic ground plane (EMGP) loop; a rectangular half-loop top-corner-fed, excepting that there are two top wires, and this makes the difference between this EMGP loop and thin-wire half-loop. The grounded metal mast or

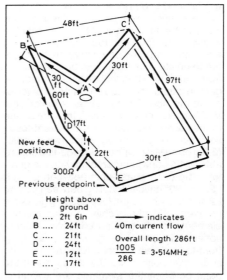

Fig 3: The large multiband loop antenna as modified by G3HQX to improve DX performance on 7MHz by adding the V-shaped section.

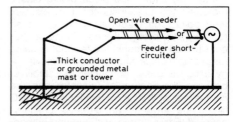

Fig 4: The F1LCI antenna as described in the December 1991 *TT* with option of a short-circuited feeder for 1.8MHz operation.

QRP - A TRANSMITTING MORSE KEY

IN *TT*, JULY 1990, p31, in describing some of the small 'AP' series of Polish clandestine radios designed and built at the Polish Radio Centre Workshops, Stanmore in 1941-45, I noted that: "In 1945, in the final months of the war, the Poles developed the prototype of what may have been the smallest (complete, mains-operated) HF transmitter-receiver of all - the AP7 using miniature valves and the whole not much larger than a 20-pack of cigarettes . . . ." The AP7 was in fact designed to fit into two 'pocket' metal containers (6 x 5 x 2.5ins) with a 4.5 to 8MHz superhet receiver. It used four 9001 and one 9002 miniature valves and a crystal controlled transmitter, using a 117N7 high-voltage-heater valve as power oscillator and mains diode rectifier. This resulted in approximately 3W RF output, and the entire transmitter-receiver weighed some 3lb.

I was reminded of this 47-year-old design by a photograph in *QST* (Dec 1991) of a 3.5MHz SSB 1-watt transceiver dubbed the Neomyte by its builder, Joe Stipec, VE7TX of Whiterock, British Columbia.

This little rig is shown alongside (and of similar size to) a pack of 20 du Maurier cigarettes. I would guess it's size to be about half that of the AP-7, although in this case battery-operated and requiring antenna, headphones and 12V power source to bridge the transcontinental distance between VE7TX's home and Quebec. The microphone is built into the front panel.

Most of the smaller war-time equipment had a built-in key (preferably silent in action) and SSB phone was not contemplated. CW is, however, still very much in evidence for modern QRP operation. In *CQ* (February 1992), the *World of Ideas* column by Dave Ingram, K4TWJ, describes a 'QRP key' in which a 1.5W, 7MHz CW transmitter is built onto the base (1.25 x 0.87 x 2.25 in) of a small brass Morse key: **Fig 5**. The FT-243 crystal plugged into the side is comparable in size with the transmitter enclosure. WA8MCQ who built this transmitting key uses $1/_8$ Watt resistors, ultra-miniature trimmer capacitors and a 0.25in toroid. With no room for a heat sink, the bottom cover of the box is left off during operation.

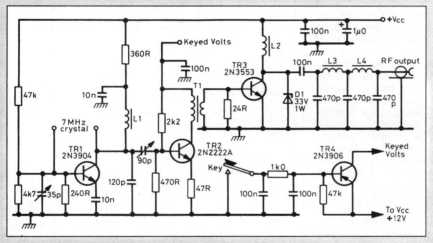

Fig 5: Circuit diagram of WA8MCQ's 'QRP-key' with a 7MHz transmitter built in a small box on which the brass key is mounted. D1 is 33V, 1W zener diode to protect TR3. L1 15 turns on ferrite toroid core type FT-23-43. L2 20 turns on FT37-61. L3, L4 16 turns on FT23-43. All coils wound with No 28 or No 32 enamelled copper wire. *CQ* also provides details for 10MHz conversion.

tower at the far end of the horizontal loop and the 'ground wire' to the transceiver chassis-ground both carry current and are connected to real earth. It is thus an EMGP loop no matter how you look at it.

If you insulate the end of the horizontal loop from the grounded mast or ground wire, the antenna truly becomes a top-fed Marconi antenna or inverted-L. This is a perfectly good antenna and the lack of success with it on 1.8MHz reported by F1LCI is undoubtedly because the transceiver 'ground wire' which forms the vertical element of the inverted-L is inside the house.

(3) According to ELNEC, the EMGP loop is resonant at about 1.72MHz. Its radiation pattern for 1.9MHz is not unlike that for a thin wire half-quad, diamond or delta loop.

larization. The azimuthal pattern is a complicated mixture of the two polarizations. According to ELNEC the impedance is not particularly attractive for matching purposes.

VE2CV summarises that the EMGP loop is a good antenna for 1.9MHz (the band for which F1LCI intended it - *G3VA*), but he is not impressed with either impedance or pattern when used as an EMGP loop on other bands. He feels that it is not a suitable candidate to complement his own 3.5MHz antenna system. But notwithstanding these comments, he recognizes that the system is, in principle, a neat idea. He adds some further suggestions:

"One problem with large horizontal loops is that as frequency increases the antenna's azimuthal pattern breaks down into many lobes, which in my view is undesirable. The ability to switch between two different arrangements could give the ability to hear a station that might otherwise have been missed in a pattern null. The following remarks refer to the method of feed and the function of the 'ground wire' to the attic-located transceiver. When the open-wire transmission line is fed in the balanced mode, this ground connection is unimportant since little current will flow on the wire. It might even be better to let the transceiver chassis-ground float, from the viewpoint of the antenna's response to local man-made radio noise. The horizontal loop is grounded at the far end, and it is sometimes better that antenna systems which are physically large have only one earth-ground, so that a noise current will not flow between two earth-grounds.

"When the open-wire feeder is shorted at the end, and the antenna is fed as a form of EMGP loop, the equipment ground becomes very important. This wire will carry a radiating current, and unfortunately the wire will usually be inside the house as at F1LCI. In this case the transceiver will certainly not be at RF ground. It would be preferable to modify the method of feed. The EMGP should be tuned to 1.9MHz by means of a series capacitor and this tuned loop fed by a current balun. The loop would connect to one of the balanced terminals of the balun and the 'ground wire' to the other balanced terminal of the balun, which could be a W2DU type of current balun. This comprises a short length of transmission line with ferrite beads to kill current flow on the outside of the shield of the ferrite-loaded transmission line. The transceiver ground-wire should connect to the 'shield' of the W2DU transmission line balun on the balanced side, and the transceiver chassis ground should be connected to the 'shield' on the unbalanced side. This avoids forcing the balun to work in the phase reversal mode, and connecting the balun this way means that the transceiver chassis ground will be tied to DC (and 50Hz) ground, but leaving the chassis ground floating with reference to RF ground. There will be little or no RF voltage on the chassis ground of the equipment. The 'ground wire' should be insulated since it will have RF voltage on it, and currents can be coupled into the electrical wiring of the house, and into water pipes if a water heating system is used. This ground should be a heavy wire running down the outside of the house, and tied to a good earth system."

That is the direction of fire is broadside to the plane containing the loop, and the radiated field is almost entirely vertically polarized. However, this is clearly not the case for 3.5MHz.

(4) At 3.75MHz the pattern is quite different, not unlike that for a horizontal dipole or a full-wave horizontal loop, except that the input impedance is not particularly easy to tune or match. The field radiated is analogous to two dipoles fed in phase - a broadside pattern horizontally polarized. The azimuthal pattern resembles that of a broadside array.

(5) The radiation patterns for 7.15MHz are more complicated. At this frequency the sides of the loop are approximately a full-wave long and therefore there is a null in the broadside direction for horizontal po-

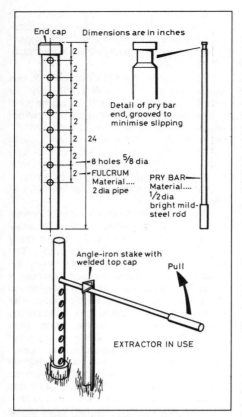

Fig 6: G1TPS's extractor for removing guy-rope stakes from hard ground.

REMOVING GUY ROPE STAKES

SOME TIME AGO R SMITH, G1TPS, came up with an idea for removing stakes from hard ground. With summer on the way, it seems an appropriate time to find room for his notes. He wrote:

"On a number of occasions over the past few years, I have participated in National Field Day events and Special-Event stations where we have been operating in the field with masts supported by the usual guy ropes made-off to stakes driven at an angle into the ground. At the end of the day, these stakes often require much straining to extract them, with a high risk of damage to the stakes and/ or the person trying to lift them. For several years, reduced rainfall has meant that the ground has been particularly hard making the task of extraction more difficult and led me to make an extractor to ease the task: **Fig 6**.

"The pry bar is a two-foot length of half-inch steel bar, grooved at one end to prevent slipping out of the fulcrum hole, with a length of shrink sleeve or similar at the other end to form a handle. The fulcrum consists of a length of 2-in scaffold pole or water pipe, about two feet long, with a line of 5/8-in holes drilled every two inches to furnish a variety of fulcrum heights and with an end plug to act as a base.

"In use, the fulcrum is placed alongside the stake, spaced about three inches away, and the pry bar then inserted into a convenient hole. The bar is positioned under the projecting top of the stake, the fulcrum pole being angled to match the angle of the stake, thus aligning the lifting force in the direction where it can do the most good. Then an upward pull

on the end of the pry bar should apply sufficient force to lift the most stubborn stake. If the head of the stake is different from that shown in Fig 6, the pry bar can be modified or an adaptor, perhaps an 'S' hook, could be employed to engage with the stake.

AURORAS AND MAGNETIC STORMS

SOLAR CYCLE 22 HAS HIGHLIGHTED the dramatic effects of major magnetic storms, including extensive power failures, the under-

---

OVERTONE OSCILLATOR SPURII

RECENTLY, IAN BRAITHWAITE, G4COL, having bread-boarded a 116MHz crystal oscillator checked its output on a spectrum oscillator. This disclosed what he at first took to be spurious oscillations. He writes:

"However, I found that the oscillations were very stable and could not be shifted by dabbing a small capacitive probe at various points on the circuit. This made me suspect the crystal itself, a suspicion confirmed by warming the crystal with my fingers. As the temperature rose, the 'spurii' came and went in turn, and obviously were temperature sensitive.

"**Fig 7** shows the plot of the output with and without the unwanted signals. The 'clean' trace used a lower analyser bandwidth to give a larger dynamic range, though this is not evident from the plotted parameters due to an error on my part.

"Looking at the signals in more detail showed that the unwanted components were in the form of sidebands, spaced from the 116MHz carrier by about 45 and then a further 25MHz (I was not attempting to measure to great precision). When I checked the crystal itself, the light dawned a little further. The 116MHz frequency is the crystals 5th overtone, with the 3rd at 69.6MHz (46.4MHz away) and the fundamental at 23.4MHz.

"I believe that the crystal, run at a high drive level, was be-

having non-linearly and producing sidebands related to the 3rd overtone and fundamental frequencies. The sidebands disappeared when the drive level was reduced by reducing the standing emitter current in the oscillator transistor.

"I have not seen this effect before and wonder if any members can offer any enlightenment."

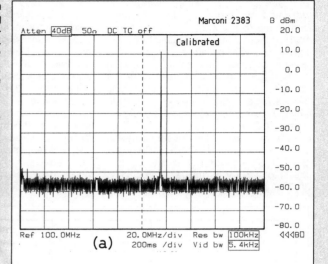

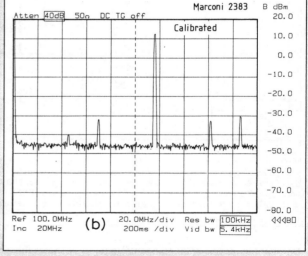

Fig 7: Analyzer plots of G4COL's 116MHz overtone crystal oscillator. (a) Clean plot with lower analyser bandwidth. (b) Plot showing the unwanted sideband 'spurii'.

---

mining of navigation systems and, of course, the disruption of radio communications. One result has been increased scientific interest in attempting to determine the loose association that appears to exist between solar activity and terrestrial magnetic storms. A note in *Nature* (5 March 1992) by W S Kurth of the University of Iowa, surveys recent work which suggests that "extreme southward magnetic fields in and in front of flare-associated coronal mass ejections that intercept the Earth's magnetosphere, are most likely to generate the largest events . . . . Minor variations in the (solar) wind speed or solar magnetic field direction result in minor fluctuations of the magnetosphere and drive nearly continuous auroral displays at high latitudes. Major disturbances in the solar wind, however, can severely distort the configuration of the magnetosphere (**Fig 8**), even to the extent of pinching off part of its long tail, resulting in a relaxation of the stretched field lines and the subsequent dumping of energy stored there in the form of spectacular aurorae moving to abnormally low latitudes."

It is the major auroral events that result in displays visible in the south of England or even in Texas. However it appears that the work of the two teams attempting to identify the most effective features of flare-associated disturbances in generating storms (Gosling *et al*, Tsurutani *et al*) has not yet positively identified a unique set of necessary and sufficient conditions for a major magnetic storm. It would seem that the coronal mass ejections often do not lead to significant magnetic storms, whether or not accompanied by a shock or southward magnetic fields. This would seem to account for the fact that some of the warnings of major magnetic storms have proved false. It is still extremely difficult to forecast with certainty the onset of a major storm with an auroral display visible in low latitudes - desirable though this would be.

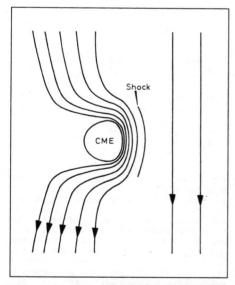

Fig 8: Diagram of a coronal mass ejection (CME) from the Sun moving from left to right showing the compression and draping of solar magnetic fields in a southward-directed configuration ahead of it. This can result in a major terrestrial magnetic storm, with aurora displays visible at relatively low latitudes.

GOING MOBILE - SAFELY

STEVE FORD, WB8IMY, an assistant technical editor of *QST*, contributes 'Going Mobile - Part 1' in the December 1991 issue of the ARRL's journal.

In this he discusses the use of hand-held portables in cars, including their use with externally-mounted antennas and with the addition of an external power amplifier, with both hand-held and amplifier connected directly to the vehicle's battery.

However, he warns: "Do not attempt to power a hand-held directly from the vehicle's electrical system without consulting your owner's manual first. Some hand-helds permit a direct 13.8V connection but others do not".

A side panel emphasises safety aspects applicable to all mobile installations: "Safety Always. In whatever mobile configuration you decide to use, make safety your top priority. Install all wires and cables neatly. Keep them away from areas where entanglements could have serious consequences. Place your transceiver in a suitable position that allows you to manipulate the controls without taking your eyes off the road for long periods of time. Make sure you have a bracket to hold your microphone or headset when you are not using it.

"Mobile operating is fun, but it should never take precedence over your most important task: driving safely. If traffic is heavy and you're uncomfortable holding a QSO, sign off as quickly as possible and tell the other stations you'll return when the situation improves. They'll understand . . . ."

A section headed 'Penetrating the Great Wall' notes that most amateurs shudder at the prospect of running wires through the firewall:

"This is actually not as difficult as it sounds. Open the hood and examine the firewall at the rear of the engine compartment. You'll find at least one large grommet where a bundle of cables make their entry into the passenger compartment. If there is more than one grommet, choose the one that is closest to the driver's side.

Many manufacturers install electronic control modules along the passenger side of

the vehicle, making it an undesirable location for your wiring harness. Your dealership or service centre should be able to show you the locations of these modules.

"Threading a stiff piece of wire through the grommet will provide a flag to assist you in locating the entry point within the passenger compartment. Finding the opposite end of the wire may require the removal of a section of the dashboard, but in most cases this isn't necessary. At worst you may have to bend and stretch a bit to reach the wire from underneath.

"Once you've located the interior side of the grommet, you'll discover that there is usually enough extra space to accommodate your power leads. Feed the wires through the grommet and secure them along the driver's side of the engine compartment.

According to most automobile manufacturer's guide-lines, the negative and positive leads for the transceiver and the amplifier should be individually connected to the battery. This means that you'll be running four separate wires to the battery. (Do not use the chassis as a short cut for the negative ground return). In addition, be sure to use heavy-gauge wire for the amplifier leads. Remember the amplifier will be drawing a substantial amount of current through a significant length of wire.

"To reduce the possibility of interference to the electronic systems in your automobile, keep all power leads as far as possible away from control modules and their associated cables. Also, keep the wires together in a tight bundle as you route them through the engine compartment. If the battery is on the passenger side of the vehicle, then the power leads should cross in front of the engine (see **Fig 9**).

"Making connections to the battery terminals can be as easy as removing the cable clamps, sliding the stripped ends of the power leads into the clamps and then repositioning the clamps on the battery posts. (Be sure to place the positive leads on the positive terminal and the ground leads on the negative terminal. Doing otherwise may reduce the life span of your equipment from many years to a few nanoseconds!) If your cable clamps feature lugs for connecting additional wiring, so much the better. For an extra measure of protection, place fuses in both the negative and positive power leads for your amplifier and hand-held".

Note that while the above notes provide useful guidance, they refer specifically to American cars with their left-hand drive and negative chassis and this must be taken into account when dealing with British cars. WB8IMY also covers such matters as avoiding UFOs - unrestrained flying objects:

"Most amplifier manufacturers provide mounting hardware for securing the amplifier to the automobile. For your own safety, use it.

Another good reason to avoid under-seat locations concerns air-bag control modules. Some newer designs place these modules beneath the seats, making this area a poor environment for a warm, bulky amplifier. Generally speaking, amplifiers are best kept in the trunk. Although this entails greater wiring hassles, it is unquestionably the safest location".   *G3VA*

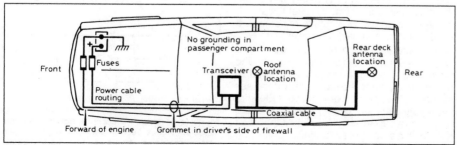

Fig 9: Typical wiring diagram for mobile transceiver installation. Note that the diagram and text are based on American left-hand-drive cars rather than British cars with right-hand-drive and positive earth battery connections.

THE EXTENDED DOUBLE ZEPP ANTENNA

THE UNEXPECTEDLY RAPID decline in solar activity during March would seem to foreshadow some years during which 14, 18 and 21MHz rather than 24, 28 and 50MHz will be of major interest for long-distance daytime working, with 1.8, 3.5, 7 and 10MHz increasingly useful during the hours of twilight and darkness - though it is much to be hoped that 28 and 50MHz will continue to be well occupied for medium-distance Sporadic E, extended local operation etc.

Recent *TT* items have underlined the usefulness of such multiband wire antennas as the large horizontal loop, but there are many locations where loops tend to be difficult if not impossible to fit into narrow gardens, even where there are long enough to accommodate a single span of say 70 to 100ft. In such circumstances, as past *TT* items have frequently emphasised, a centre-fed dipole fed with open-wire feeders and a flexible ATU with balanced output will work well on any band, whether or not the top span is resonant. Admittedly, the horizontal radiation pattern will differ on the various bands, splitting into multi-lobe patterns on the higher frequencies.

A well-established, but seldom used, configuration of this general type is a centre-fed antenna designed as an extended double-zepp antenna for a favourite band (providing a broadside gain of an extra 3dB over a half-wave dipole) but eminently usable on other bands with various radiation patterns and gains.

A timely reminder of the usefulness of the EDZ appears in *QST* (Feb 1992) as a *Hints & Kinks* item from Bob Baird, W7CSD, supported by editorial addenda. W7CSD writes: "Although the extended double zepp (EDZ) antenna (**Fig 1**) has been in just every antenna handbook since the year one, hams seldom use it. Its overall length is 1.28λ and it is bidirectional broadside. Fed with open-wire line and a balanced antenna tuner, an EDZ also makes a fine multiband antenna. Let's look at an EDZ for 18MHz. We can calculate the overall length in feet as (984 x 1.28)/f(MHz) from which an 18.15MHz EDZ works out to be 69.4ft long. At this frequency the EDZ exhibits 3dBd gain in a figure-of-eight pattern with two major and four minor lobes. It still performs usefully when operated on several bands lower in frequency. At 14MHz, an 18MHz EDZ acts as two slightly long half-waves in phase, exhibiting between 1.6 and 2dBd gain. At 7MHz, it is a slightly long half-wave dipole. All these modes are directional broadside if the EDZ is positioned at least a half-wave high at 7MHz. At 21MHz, it exhibits a four-leaf-clover pattern, with minor lobes broadside; at 28 and 24MHz, it is close to two full waves in phase and produces a pattern similar to that at 21MHz. It can even be used as a short 3.5MHz dipole - not bad for a 70ft piece of wire! . . . . There's nothing magic about the EDZ. It's a tried-and-true dipole that offers useful gain at its design frequency and good multiband performance."

W7CSD does not mention the 10.1MHz band but a good performance could be expected from an 18MHz EDZ. On 1.8MHz it could be used either as a very short dipole or with the open-wire feeder strapped together

as a T-antenna fed against earth (or a counterpoise), with a high T-antenna providing vertically-polarized radiation.

TRIP SWITCH (ELCB) TROUBLES

ON A NUMBER OF OCCASIONS in the past, *TT* has referred to the use of 30mA and 15mA earth-leakage circuit-breakers (ELCBs) as a safety measure to protect against severe electric shock from mains supplies. In *TT*, July 1981 (pp628-9) it was pointed out by G3HWR that a problem can arise with these devices where mains filters having capacitors of the order of 10.1µF or more are fitted to equipment. Modern filters should have much lower value capacitors (of the order of 0.01µF) but older filters and indeed capacitors in older equipment may result in continuous leakage currents large enough to trip the more sensitive 15mA ELCBs. G3HWR provided information on a modified filter configuration that overcomes this problem: **Fig 2**.

'Dud' Charman, G6CJ, has encountered the related but rather different problem of ELCBs affected by switch-on surges. His notes on this topic, originally written for the FOC *Focus* newsletter are as follows:

"I don't know what happens in other countries, but in G-land we have a protective system in which the electricity-mains wiring comprises three wires: Phase (Line); Neutral; and Earth. A trip switch is provided which will fire if there is any substantial potential difference (causing a leakage current to flow) between Neutral and Earth.

"So far so good. I have had some alterations made to bring my ancient house wiring up-to-date and this has involved a new set of the Company's input switchboard instruments. In the past the potential difference between N and E was reasonable, but the legal PD has now been reduced to 30mV!

"The result with the new switchboard instruments was that every time I tried to switch-on my rig, the trip fired. After some considerable work, it was realised that the charging (in-rush) current of any capacitor across the line would cause a trip. The only way to get the station on the air was to reset the switch by hand (in an awkward place of course). It would then hold-in past the surge.

"Virtually any piece of radio gear has a capacitor connected from Line to Earth and for a time it seemed I was condemned to manually re-setting the trip, a pretty hopeless situation. Then I discovered that the Electricity Supply company could provide an ELCB with its own built-in 'shock-absorber' that does not trip on a surge but still provides protection against continuous leakage. Joy at last!

"So if you move into a new house fitted with one of these 30mV switches, or have been

obliged to have one fitted, make sure that the Company fits one with a shock absorber. It will still be the property of the company, so you will not have to pay for it, though there may be a charge for the work of installing it."

1.8MHZ TO THE SOUTH ATLANTIC

IN COMMENTING ON THE reliable 1.8MHz chordal-hop path during the months of May to August between the West Coast of North America and parts of Australia (*TT*, April and March, 1992) I suggested that there could be a good possibility that a similar 1.8MHz path could exist between the UK (or at least the South-Western areas) and parts of South America around the Tropic of Capricorn (Brazil, Paraguay, Peru). This would make use of the dawn ionospheric tilts and the tilts that appear to exist during Spread-F conditions in the tropics as well as the now recognised tilts of the Grey Line paths.

These comments have brought forth a most interesting letter from Peter Hobbs (G3LET/VP8GQ/RS84049). He writes:

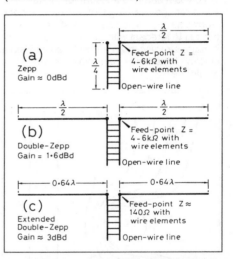

Fig 1: Evolution of the extended double zepp antenna. (a) Classic zepp antenna, originally developed for use in the Zeppelin airships but now considered uncertain in behaviour due to the unbalanced connection of the element to the resonant balanced transmission line. (b) Double zepp (two half-waves in phase) provides a broadside gain of 1.6dBd. (c) By extending the dipole element lengths to 0.64-wave, the gain is raised to 3dBd with two major and four minor lobes. It is termed an extended double zepp (EDZ) antenna.

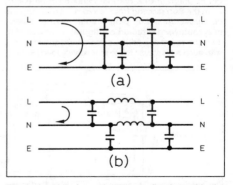

Fig 2: (a) Unbalanced currents flowing with the capacitor values used in some mains filters can present problems when a sensitive earth leakage circuit breaker (ELCB) is fitted. (b) Modified filter configuration suggested by G3HWR in 1981 overcomes this problem.

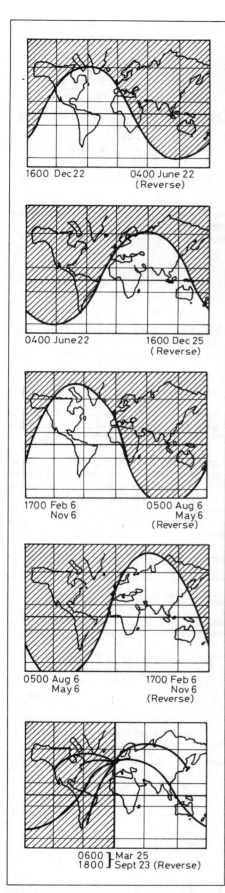

Fig 3: How the twilight boundary (grey-line path) varies at different seasons of the year. Times are GMT for the UK. Computer software for determining time of sunrise and sunset grey-line paths from the UK to locations throughout the world has been published.

"Your April piece on 1.8MHz propagation stirred a distinct chord (no pun intended!). I came to very similar conclusions on the reliability of trans-equatorial solstice propagation on the band back in the early 1960s when, as VP8GQ in the South Orkneys (latitude 60° South), I spent many hours investigating the possibility of Top Band contacts with the UK.

"The antenna in use was a rhombic with 250ft per leg on 40ft masts, built for the BERU contest and fed, on Top Band, with strapped feeders against ground. At that time, the German coastal station DHJ was a well-known occupant of the lower end of the band, available virtually continuously as a 1.8MHz beacon signal - forming one of the first beacons that I had come across. At the appropriate times, his signal strength in the South Orkneys was roughly equivalent to that of DL1FF and G3GRL when they were around.

"As suggested in *TT*, 50° or 60° of latitude, North or South, should, by rights, be rather high for classical trans-equatorial propagation but my VP8GQ logs show that DHJ was at least audible virtually every day during June and July and again in December and January. Between five and ten days in each of those months, the path would be so good that local contacts between G-stations around dusk would be of good strength for an hour at a time, although raising them from VP8 was another matter. I often wondered about the then accepted wisdom of multi-hop propagation with signals of such strength and always felt that there must be some other mechanism at work.

"My motivation at the time, of course, was to achieve that elusive first 1.8MHz VP8-G contact. Eventually, I persuaded Paddy, EI9J with whom I kept a daily sked at midnight on 3.5MHz to spend a couple of days off the air reorganising his station for Top Band and give it a try. We succeeded in making contact at the very first call. After that, the word spread and I had quite a busy time making QSOs on 1.8MHz.

"So, for what it is worth, another anecdotal confirmation from 30 years ago that chordal hop propagation does work on 1.8MHz (MF) and can extend, with reasonable reliability, to quite high latitudes. The main, and possibly only, reason that this was and is not more widely recognised is lack of amateur activity along the open paths. In all the time I listened on 1.8MHz from VP8, a period of five solstices between 1961 and 1964, I only heard one South American station, ZP9AY. I believe he worked W1BB (who did so much to encourage 1.8MHz DX in the post-war period - *G3VA*) and a few others one night and that was it".

Old-timer Ted Cook, ZS6BT, (a long-time HF enthusiast but now at 88 years restricted to VHF/UHF operation) in commenting on the March item, appears to have gained the impression that the 1.8MHz VK/W6 transequatorial contacts were thought to have been made via 'long-path' - an impression possibly fostered by my inclusion of Fig 5 (page 37) intended only to illustrate the difference between multi-hop and chordal-hop propagation (my use of Figs 4 and 5 was in fact strongly criticised by John Branegan, GM4IHJ, on the grounds that they distorted the height of the ionosphere in relation to the scale of the Earth and thus wildly distorted the actual

signal path geometry, but I am sure that this would have been obvious to readers and make no apologies for including them).

Long-path propagation, almost invariably by chordal-hop, is indeed a most valuable mode, much exploited in morning G-VK and afternoon G-W6 contacts, as a feature of 'grey-line' propagation along dawn/dusk and dusk/dawn boundaries. But chordal hop paths also occur along dawn/dawn and dusk/dusk boundaries or indeed, as in the 'sweet-spot' 1.8MHz contacts, where there are suitably located ionospheric tilts to put signals into and out of the chordal-hop mode: **Fig 3** shows the twilight (grey) boundary at various seasons.

ZS6BT points out that long-path grey-line propagation from Johannesburg to the West Coast of North America via Australia is possible (usually on 14MHz), with an alternative path via the South Pole on 21MHz during the summer solstice. He also points to the useful signal enhancements brought about by the focussing of signals at or near the antipode of the transmitting location.

This topic was touched upon in *TT* (Jan 1973) in an item 'Thoughts and facts on chordal hop' with reference to a paper by Gary Bold of the Radio Research Centre, University of Auckland, New Zealand (*IEEE Trans on Ant & Prop*, Nov 1972, pp741-6). The antipodes are the two locations precisely opposite one another on the surface of the Earth so that times and seasons are exactly reversed. All radio paths along Great Circle routes, no matter in which direction they take off, all come together again at the antipodal point, in other words a broad-lobe antenna can be every bit as effective as a narrow, highly-directional beam; there is no long-path or short-path since all paths are approximately the same length.

Gary Bold showed that 15MHz transmissions from a Voice of America relay at Tangiers built up rapidly in signal strength (by up to 30dB) over a half-an-hour period at its antipode in New Zealand during local dawn (around 2000GMT) at times when the critical frequencies were too low to support multi-hop propagation at 15MHz.

The exact antipode of the UK is unfortunately a virtually blank stretch of the South Pacific south of New Zealand, although, as ZS6BT points out, France is a near exact antipode to New Zealand and the UK is near enough often to benefit from antipodal focussing. Johannesburg is a near antipode to Hawaii. He writes: "We here are fortunate enough to be almost exactly antipodal to WWVH and we are able to hear all four frequencies simultaneously *and*, at the same time, make contact on 21 and 28MHz". ZS6BT believes that it is time that more attention was paid by amateurs to basic propagation.

G3IPV'S SELF-NEUTRALIZED FET AMPLIFIERS

TT, JULY 1991, pp28-29 GAVE information on the problem of avoiding instability in small-signal FET amplifiers based on a review by VK6KRO in *Amateur Radio*, May 1991. The problem arises from the combination of a high-gain device, large internal capacitances and the vulnerability of FET devices to destructive self-oscillation in RF amplifiers.

VK6KRO showed that one solution is to operate the device itself with low gain but to achieve a reasonable overall gain by achieving high voltage gain with a step-up resonant input transformer.

A British amateur who over a number of years has experimented with FET pre-amplifiers primarily as a means of providing very sharp signal-frequency selectivity (using crystals or LC circuits) ahead of the first mixer stage is P W Hallett, G3IPV. A number of his radical ideas have been described over the years in *TT*. (For example February 1986, pp109-110 and July 1985, pp541-2) illustrating his search for unconditional stability while using high-Q resonant circuits.

Last year, before the appearance of the VK6KRO article, G3IPV sent along a further contribution to this topic in the form of a new version of his self-neutralized internal-feedback amplifier which he believes makes it easier to vary output power from radio transmitters, provide low-noise gain for radio receivers and which could also find application in other types of RF equipment. He writes:

"**Fig 4** shows the first self-neutralized controlled internal feedback amplifier developed at G3IPV. The selectivity, gain and internal feedback of this amplifier are controlled by two pairs of coupling capacitors, C1-C2 and C3-C4. Tuning is varied (over a small range) by capacitors C5-C6 and C7-C8. Once the four coupling capacitors, C1-C2 and C3-C4 are set below a critical value the amplifier becomes unconditionally stable. This to some extent is variable with different input and output load impedances. A key feature of this amplifier is that if the input and output inductances are placed in series with its input and output, the internal feedback drops to a low value. It has been found that if the tuning capacitors are also in series with input and output of the amplifier then a much improved amplifier is produced especially at VHF where the earlier amplifier did not have satisfactory gain and selectivity.

"This new version (**Fig 5**) has been tested for small-signal purposes at HF and VHF in receiver front ends and also using high-power MOSFETS in linear amplifiers. It is my belief that this version represents possibly the finest high-selectivity amplifier so far developed. In Fig 5, C1-C2 and C3-C4 are coupling capacitors which control internal feedback, gain and selectivity of the amplifier. When they are below a critical value they ensure that the amplifier is unconditionally stable and also that input/output tuned circuits act as peaking bandpass filters and not as notch filters. This is an unusual feature of this amplifier and was not foreseen. The input and output L/C tuning circuits can be replaced by quartz crystals when very high selectivity is required, for example in the front end of receivers intended primarily for operation at or around fixed frequencies (see *TT*, July 1985).

"Another feature of this amplifier is that its gain can be controlled by varying supply voltage with little distortion to the output signals. This makes it easier to vary power output from radio transmitters and the gain of radio receivers etc. Note that the gain of this type of amplifier is lower than for conventional amplifiers so that additional stages may be needed to achieve as much gain; however

since they contribute very little noise this is not a significant problem and does not affect those applications where the primary purpose is to obtain good pre-mixer selectivity."

READABLE MANUAL MORSE

F L U RITSON, G5RI, was interested to note the comment by Gordon Brown, VK1AD (*TT*, Apr 1992, p40), reprinted from *Morsum Magnificat* No 22, that 'perfect' machine Morse is not necessarily the most readable Morse, particularly at higher speeds. I also expressed my liking for the 'old-fashioned' up-and-down manual Morse-key, even though at times I have spent many hours practising and/or using semi-automatic ('bug') keys, electronic keyers and iambic squeeze keyers.

G5RI found support for the views of VK1AD in a 50-year-old letter from an L J Voss in *Wireless World* ('Thoughts on Morse Operating', Sept 1940, p393). In considering the question of telegraph operators who initially learned to use sounders or the single-needle railway telegraph system, he wrote:

"Operators with much experience of wireless all agree that it is most important to get the dashes clear and distinct, if necessary spinning them out beyond their precise three-dot length. *Never* clip the dashes; when interference or atmospherics are bad, the good operator instinctively sits on his dashes a little more, and is grateful if the other fellow reciprocates . . . 'Machine' sending is only really suitable for machine reception. Personally, I dislike the 'bug' for this reason; as a multitude of ordinary Post Office operators used to have no difficulty in working at a steady 30 (WPM) without fatigue or cramp, with a burst up to 40 if required, one fails to see any reason for using a bug at all, when the normal key will take anything one gives it."

L J Voss suggested that anyone who has copied much press (ie machine telegraphy in those days), as distinct from scrappy messages with breaks between them, has experienced that maddening feeling that comes from the monotony of the machine - or the soulless, machine-like hand telegraphist, adding: "Holding the key is ruled by the size and shape of the knob and by the set and length of the operator's fingers. My own handwriting was ruined in early life by a schoolmaster who insisted (with a stick) on

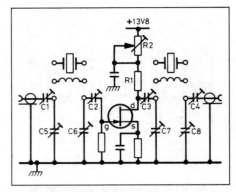

Fig 4: G3IPV's first form of controlled internal feedback FET RF amplifier.

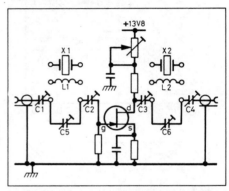

Fig 5: G3IPV's new version of the self-neutralized controlled internal feedback FET amplifier.

REPRODUCIBLE TONE-BURST OSCILLATOR

B WALTERS, GW3XHD, writes: "With ex-commercial equipment still coming on the market, there is a continued need for small projects to modify the equipment for amateur-radio use, including the fitting of 1750Hz tone-burst generators. I have found CMOS devices are sometimes unpredictable in this application and often need obscure component values. I consider the generator shown in **Fig 6** using two discrete bipolar transistors, one PNP

and one NPN, is repeatable however built. Using modern components I have managed to build it on a PCB the size of two postage stamps. Diode D1 isolates the key line from the microphone key line, TR1 switches the voltage to the oscillator and a 0V on the tone-key line starts it up. The variable resistor fine tunes to 1750Hz. Feeding the tone output into the microphone line is quite effective, or it can be fed straight into an op-amp input."

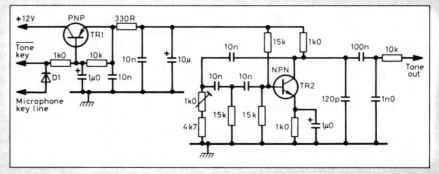

Fig 6: GW3XHD's 1750Hz tone-burst generator using small signal transistors NPN and PNP.

SOLAR POWER AND THE LEMON-DROP KIDS

I AM NOT SURE WHETHER children today still read a book that I recall from my own early days - *The Swiss Family Robinson* - in which a shipwrecked family sets about providing themselves with many of the amenities of civilisation by utilising the local materials, plants, flotsam and jetsam. Today, of course, it would be advisable to take along a well-stocked survival pack including *inter alia* some electronic components and a solar array to provide a modest supply of electricity, if only to play those eight *Desert Island Discs*!

Even in Wales, R W Mander, GW4DYY, has for several years used a solar charger incorporating a DC-DC converter along the lines of the *Electronics Australia* low-cost solar battery charger outlined in the April *TT*. He uses an ex-equipment DC-DC converter from a Pye radio (believed to be from a hand-held car amplifier/charger type AT27148) which, with a 12in by 12in solar panel, is used to top up his caravan battery. He finds it a very useful piece of equipment.

Across the Atlantic, Bob Culter, N7FKI and Wes Hayward, W7ZOI, nursing an ambition to do something in amateur radio

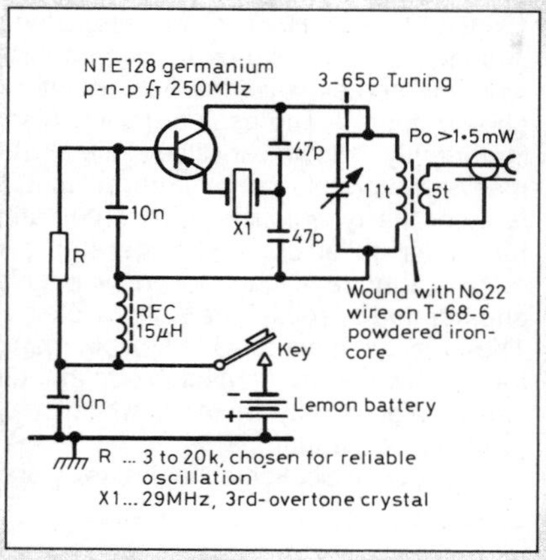

Fig 7: The micro-power transmitter used by W7ZOI and N7FKI to make the first contact using a lemon-juice battery.

for the very first time - and believing that solar-powered transmitters are now relatively 'old-hat' - have succeeded in making a 29MHz CW contact over a span of some two miles using a battery in which the electrolyte comprises the juice of a lemon!

As described in *QST* (March 1992, pp18-19) a primitive cell was made first by piercing the lemon with a zinc-coated nail (negative terminal) and a 3/16in-diameter copper tube (positive). This gave an open-circuit output of 0.93V dropping to 0.6V with a 2KΩ load with depolarization effects soon reducing this further.

A more practical battery was then constructed by layering a 5 x 7in zinc-coated shingle, a similar-sized paper towel separator soaked in lemon juice and a slightly smaller rectangle of copper-clad circuit-board. Two of these in series gave an open-circuit voltage of 1.9V (initial short-circuit current of 64mA) dropping to 1.35V when delivering 4.7mA output to the micro-QRP transmitter (**Fig 7**) giving an RF output of rather over 1.5mW. Contact was made over a distance of some two miles, ending when depolarization effects began to result in a poor-quality signal.

Since fruits other than lemons also contain citric acid, one might see a rush to gain a 'Worked All Fruits' certificate were it not for an unfortunate connotation in North America!

---

our resting two fingers on the pen; that suited his own hand all right, but he could not see that most of us had a middle finger appreciably longer than the index, and so needed to rest it at the side of the pen for comfort, the essential factor for good writing as for good telegraphy. And writing is an important matter to the telegraphist whether or not a typewriter is normally used."

His remarks on 'bug' keys reflects well the controversy that, in those years, raged among both professional and amateur operators on this side of the Atlantic and the then official dislike of any form of semi-automatic or side-swiper type of key. I recall a friendly contest held at Hanslope Park in early 1942 between a Post Office telegraphist (Bill Windle, G8VG) and Des Dowing, GI3ZX, one using a manual key, the other a bug. I fancy the decision was a draw. While experienced telegraphists could certainly reach a steady 30 or so, I cannot help feeling that bursts of 40WPM on an up-and-down manual key is a bit of a fisherman's tale - though certainly some of the operators at the Coast Stations and those on the large trans-Atlantic passenger liners of the 'thirties, sending masses of telegrams on the old 2100-metre shipping band, could certainly lick along! And their Morse was far from 'Soul-less'.

TOROIDAL CORES DEFENDED

THE ITEM 'Toroidal cores, baluns and ATUs' (*TT*, Feb 1992, p37) noted that the balun-type broadband impedance transformers with toroidal ferrite or powdered-iron cores of the type still found in many transmatches (ATUs) are not suitable for use at high or reactive impedances: at high power cores are prone to saturate while at high impedance the RF voltage can cause arcs between the turns or between the windings and the core material. GW3DIX also noted the decision of the ARRL actively to discourage use of these components for such applications.

This has resulted in several letters pointing out that it is wrong to condemn outright the use at relatively high powers of toroidal cores. Used correctly such components still have a useful role to play, several correspondents suggest.

For example, Bob Pearson, G4FHU, writes: "While I agree with much of this item, it would be a pity if it were to cause unnecessary dismay among those who could nevertheless use ferrite or iron-dust cored baluns and transformers successfully.

"It is often quite practicable to connect a balun on the transmitter side of an ATU, so that the balun drives a resistive impedance of

a suitable magnitude. The ATU need not then be a balanced configuration even though it feeds a balanced line. But it does need to be fully insulated. For output powers up to about 100W PEP the ATU components can be physically small enough to fit into a plastic box of reasonable size, and shaft-insulation can consist of substantial control knobs with recessed and plugged grub-screw holes.

"For example, a single variable capacitor and a tapped inductor can cope with a wide variety of matching requirements. The simplest arrangement uses terminals or wander plugs and sockets to permit a variety of configurations (see **Fig 8**). It is remarkable how small a suitable toroidal core can be, even for quite high power transfer, as long as the balun load impedance is correctly adjusted by the ATU before full power is applied.

"The minimum core size can be estimated as follows: Most suitable ferrites have a saturation flux density of about 0.2 tesla to 0.5 tesla (2000 to 5000 gauss). Suppose we permit a peak flux density of no more than a tenth of the lower figure (ie 0.02 tesla or 200 gauss) and assume a winding of no less than about ten turns across a 50Ω load.

Peak envelope power $P = V^2\text{rms}/R$
$= V\text{pk}/2R$

Peak flux $\Phi\text{pk} = V\text{pk}/Nw$ where N=number of turns and $w = 2\Pi f$

Therefore $\Phi = BA$ where B=flux density and A = core cross sectional area.

Then finally $A = (1/2\Pi f\, N\, B_{pk}) \times \sqrt{(2RP)}$

More familiar as $A = \sqrt{(RP)}/4 \cdot (4f\, N\, B_{pk})$

Compatible units are in mm², MHz, tesla, Ohm, watt.

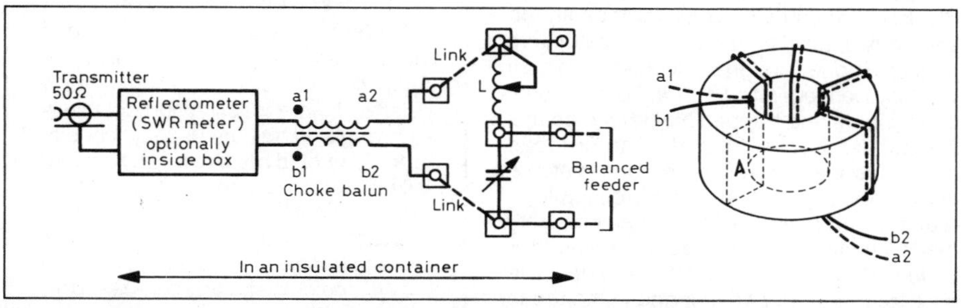

Fig 8: G4FHU's method of using toroid balun transformer with unbalanced ATU to feed a balanced transmission line without contravening the guidelines for using toroid cores

Results on this basis are shown in **Table 1**. Commonly available toroids need be no longer than about 2-inch diameter to satisfy the highest figures shown. A 1-inch diameter core easily meets the 100W PEP 3.5MHz requirement, though one could select a slightly larger core to minimise the number of turns of wire needed and to give a comfortable winding space".

Power	Lowest frequency of operation (MHz)				
(W PEP)	1.8	3.5	7	14	28
1	4.42	2.27	1.14	0.57	0.28
2	6.25	3.22	1.61	0.80	0.40
5	9.89	5.08	2.54	1.27	0.64
10	13.98	7.19	3.60	1.80	0.90
20	19.77	10.17	5.08	2.54	1.27
50	31.26	16.08	8.04	4.02	2.01
100	44.21	22.74	11.37	5.68	2.84
500	98.86	50.84	25.42	12.71	6.36
1000	139.81	71.90	35.95	17.98	8.99

TABLE 1: Minimum cross sectional area (mm²) for magnetic core with peak flux density of 0.02T (200 gauss) and 10-turn coil effectively in parallel with 50Ω resistive load. For higher flux or more turns, core area proportionately less. But required area increases as the square root of load resistance.

HANDHELDS AND YOUR EYES

IN DIGESTING THE guidelines suggested by WC2S ('Health Hazards: Tougher Guidelines', *TT*, January 1990), I noted that a worrying aspect of the WC2S survey is that "he suggests there is a growing body of opinion that not all handheld transceivers with less than the usually accepted figure (endorsed in the ANSI-C95.1 safety standard of 1982) of 7W RF output are safe if held near the operator's head, and that more stringent guidelines may be introduced in this area."

The WC2S guidelines, as originally published in *QST*, Oct 89, include: (9) Handheld radios should be used on the lowest power setting needed to carry out communications. (10) Handhelds should be kept as far from the head as possible when operating. (11) The use of a separate microphone or similar device is recommended. (12) Transmissions using a handheld radio should be kept as short as possible". *TT* has in the past noted that some transceivers marketed for amateurs are specified as having an RF output of up to 5W, approaching the 7W exclusion clause of the ANSI safety standard.

The rationale for stringent guidelines is that in most cases the 'rubber duck' antenna during transmission is only a few inches from the operator's eyes. These are known to be particularly vulnerable to proven thermal effects of RF radiation. A rise of temperature of a few degrees Centigrade (from the normal 37°C to about 42°C) can result in irreversible effects leading to cataracts. The lens is particularly vulnerable because it has no blood supply and hence only poor thermal conduction paths; it also has a high water content.

A further warning that the 7W exclusion clause of the ANSI standard for low-power communications equipment needs to be revised downwards is given in a paper 'Energy Absorption Mechanism by Biological Bodies in the Near Field of Dipole Antennas Above 300MHz' by Niels Kuster (Swiss Federal Institute of Technology) and Quirino Balzano (Motorola) which appears in *IEEE Trans on Vehicular Technology*, Feb 92, pp17-23. This

DIY FINGER MORSE KEY

CHARLES SMITH, G0ICA passes along a suggestion for a novel 'twin-paddle-type' Morse key which he finds comfortable to operate and easy to make. Also, importantly, it costs very little since all the main components come from an ex-BT relay of the type which, in recent years, have been pulled out of Strowger step-by-step telephone exchanges now largely superseded by solid-state digital systems. These relays have reliable flexible members with excellent contact points at their tips of high-quality material which may prove to be platinum.

The original electromechanical relay and the way this is converted into a finger-operated Morse-key are shown in **Fig 9**. G0ICA writes:

"In use the entire hand can rest on the operating table, with only the index-finger and the fore-finger used to operate the keys, in a manner rather similar to playing a piano or using a typewriter: in other words to consider the action similar to drumming your fingers on a table whilst resting the palm on the table. This avoids the tendency with conventional keys of experiencing wrist ache due to keeping the lower arm, wrist and fingers locked in one position, arched above the key."

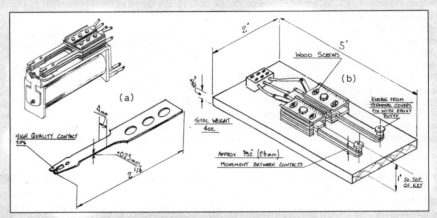

Fig 9: (a) Standard GPO/BT electromagnetic relay as now discarded in large numbers from old Strowger-type telephone exchanges, with well proven reliability. (b) Finger-type (dual paddle) Morse key based on parts from the BT relay as built by G0ICA. It has no bearings and movement depends on flexing of the upper steel member (4mm wide by 0.25mm). Approximate pressure 0.5oz.

detailed study shows that the 7W exclusion clause is not always consistent with the ANSI safety limits for the spatial local peak SAR (specific absorption rate) recommended for the controlled environment (8mW/g).

For the uncontrolled environment (1.6mW/g) the exclusion directly contradicts with the peak SAR limits. The authors provide a telling example. They state: "Assume that the feedpoint current of a 7W 1.5GHz transceiver 2.5cm from the eye tissue is increased to about 350mA due to feedpoint changes, this would result in a spatial peak SAR averaged over 1g of tissue of over 40mW/g. Further note that in the close near field, the SAT is not directly related to the input power but to the antenna current distribution.

HERE AND THERE

PETER CHADWICK, G3RZP, recently observed two 'locals' (about ten miles distant) putting in good S5 signals on 28MHz when in fact they were operating on 14MHz with home-brew linears and trapped multi-band beams. A reminder that with a multiband or broadband antenna that retains a good match to harmonics any that are generated will get radiated - and this is likely to arise in factory-made amplifiers as well as the home-brew variety. G3RZP points out that a simple filter such as that of **Fig 10** inserted in the feeder when transmitting on 14MHz (be sure to remove it when using higher bands!) will give

about 25-30dB of rejection on 28MHz. Although an ATU is an alternative, G3RZP considers that unless it is designed for a working Q of 10 (which an L-network would not be) this would not help much. **G3VA**

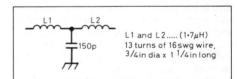

L1 and L2 ..... (1·7µH)
13 turns of 16swg wire,
3/4in dia x 1 1/4in long

Fig 10: G3RZP's simple filter for reducing the 28MHz harmonics generated by a 14MHz amplifier fed to a multiband antenna

CORRECTION: 'SWEET SPOT' 1.8MHZ PROPAGATION

Unfortunately an error appeared in the first paragraph of this item (*TT*, April 92). The line '. . .horizontally-polarized antennas having relatively high-angle radiation usually considered. . .' should have read '. . .horizontally-polarized antennas having relatively high-angle radiation, often outperform antennas designed to provide the low-angle radiation usually considered. . .'. We apologise for any confusion this may have caused.

TWO-BAND QUAD-LOOP ANTENNA

LES MOXON, G6XN has shown (*HF Antennas for all Locations*) how a quad-loop element can form a multiband antenna by the use of stubs, etc. Many years ago there was included in *TT* and later *ART* a more conventional dual-band quad-loop antenna for 14 and 21MHz with a 75Ω coaxial feeder connected directly across a common feed-point of two resonant, one-wavelength loops. Originally published in *73* (Sept 1965), W6WAW claimed that this had proved effective in spite of the fact that the theoretical feed-point impedance of a loop element is approximately 125Ω.

Al Akers, ZS2U, (*Radio-ZS*, Feb 1992, pp5 and 8) uses a basically similar arrangement as a lightweight quad-loop antenna for 14 and 21MHz portable operation from the Ciskei, but with a ingenious matching network designed to provide a good match between a 50Ω cable and the 125Ω element impedance: **Figs 1 and 2**. His antenna is claimed to be easy to erect, dismantle and transport and uses garden canes for spreaders with an aluminium centre piece and aluminium mast, with no traps, etc to catch and damage among bushes and trees.

ZS2U writes: Fig 1(a) shows the antenna. L1 is the 28MHz loop and is 10.9m in length. The centre plate A is shown in Fig 1(b) with U-clamps used to fasten it to the mast (not shown are four saddles which fasten the pipes to the plate, also a centre piece which serves to hold these pipes and to block off their ends. The support arms are garden canes (2m long) and are epoxied onto lengths of 16mm outside-diameter aluminium tubing which make up the extra length needed. These pipes plug into the pipes on the mounting plate.

B is an ABS box, 15 x 8 x 5cm usually available from local electrical emporiums. It is used to house the acceptor-rejector circuits and L-match networks. The box is fastened to a 32mm PVC waterpipe about 80mm longer than the box and slotted for about 50mm. The pipe slides onto the mast and a hose clamp round the slotted section serves to clamp it to the mast.

In Fig 2, L1, C1, C2 and L2, L3, C3 form the two acceptor-rejector circuits. L4 and C4 is the L matching network for the 21MHz loop and C5 and L5 is the L matching network for the 14MHz loop. The upper acceptor-rejector circuit forms a series-resonant circuit on 21MHz (very low impedance) and a parallel-resonant circuit on 28MHz (very high impedance). The lower circuit functions similarly providing very low impedance on 28MHz and very high impedance on 21MHz.

ZS2U adds that he used silver mica capacitors, two in parallel in each case to make up the required value, and that these are standing up as well to the 50W output from his FT7B transceiver. The coils were air-wound with 14SWG copper wire, 22mm in diameter and 4mm-per-turn spacing. He used 3 turns for L2 and L3, 4 turns for L1 and L5 and 5 turns for L4. Adjustments were made by varying the coils in length, most of them requiring some spreading: "Orientate the coils so as to minimise inductive coupling between them. Start with L1 and C1 only. Resonate on

21MHz, then connect C2 and resonate on 28MHz. C3 and L3 are resonated on 28MHz, then L2 connected and adjusted to resonate on 21MHz. Wire up the whole unit and test. Probably minor adjustments will need to be made to the L matches. I used an SO239 socket at the bottom of the box for feedline attachment". ZS2U concludes his article as follows: "You may think, as I did, that this antenna will be difficult to make and adjust and, with all the coils etc, would be rather inefficient. I found that it was not difficult to adjust and it has proved itself in operation. It is a useful antenna where space is limited and has the advantage that it is directional".

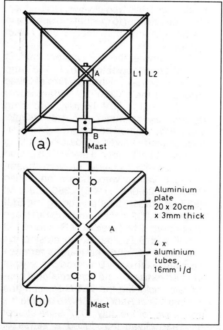

Fig 1: (a) ZS2U's two-band quad-loop antenna for portable operation on 21 and 28MHz. (b) Detail of the centre plate (see text).

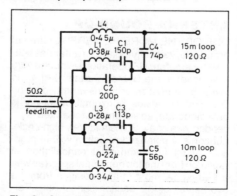

Fig 2: Acceptor-rejector matching networks providing good matching between a single 50Ω feedline and the separate 21 and 28MHz quad-loops.

VIVE LA LAMPE DE RADIO

THE MODERN WORLD OF tiny surface-mounted devices, application-specific ICs, HEMT low-noise microwave transistors and gold-bonded UHF power bipolars and FETs is gradually enveloping us all, even if, with high-power transmitting valves and the ubiquitous cathode-ray tube, we are still not quite in the all solid-state era. But it is coming inexorably. The UK's first high power solid-state UHF television transmitters have recently been installed for ITC/ITV by NTL (formerly IBA Engineering) at Stockwell Hill, Devon and Waltham (East Midlands). An IEE lecture/demonstration by Dr S Kataoka (Sharp Corporation) on 'Recent developments of black and white and colour LCDs and their applications' showed clearly the continuing developments of liquid-crystal television flat-screen TV display panels, including their use for large-screen projection displays. However, it seems pretty certain that the CRT which had its origins in the late 19th Century will still be in wide use in the early 21st Century - and I guess that there will still be some thermionic power valves in the linear amplifiers of amateur-radio transmitters. All of which means that we still need to understand how to get the best life out of devices which are of increasing rarity and cost.

Roland Martin (Z21HF) in *QUA* (Newsletter of the Mashonaland Branch of the Zimbabwe ARS) lists a number of useful hints on how to get maximum lifetimes out of power valves, especially the TV 'sweep tubes' such as 6JS6, 6KD6, 6LQ6, 6DQ5 etc. Remember that these valves were never intended for HF service as power output valves. Z21HF does not claim to be an expert on valve-based equipment but his running a station on a limited budget has given him experience that could help others in a similar position. He writes:

To get maximum life out of sweep tubes:

(1) Do not exceed the usual recommended maximum tune-up time of ten seconds, especially when the transmitter loading/plate settings are out of resonance and the anode currents are high.

(2) A quiet fan on the power-valve enclosure is a good investment, as a lower valve envelope temperature will much improve the operational life of both the valve and the surrounding components. If you don't have a fan make sure all air-vents are kept clean and clear of obstructions.

(3) Check the heater/filament voltage actually at the valve sockets. They should be within a 5% tolerance or preferably better (6.3V for the above types). If they are not within the specification check that the equipment is wired for the correct local AC mains voltage (240V UK, apparently 230V in Zimbabwe, 220V in most mainland European countries).

(4) When purchasing new power valves, matched pairs are preferable in order that the load is shared equally between them. Non-matched pairs can differ significantly.

(5) Again, when purchasing tubes, particularly sweep tubes, check that the manufacturer is compatible with your equipment. FT101 and FT200 transceivers are a case in point, as these were designed to

use Toshiba 6JS6C valves but will also work with NEC valves. On the other hand, valves from other manufactures may produce unpredictable results.

(6) Correct neutralisation of power valves is vitally important. Unless you have a 'sure fire' procedure, refer to the manufacturer's manual for the correct method.

(7) Do not run power valves for long periods with the heaters powered but with no HT on the anodes; this may result in cathode poisoning causing loss of emission and in effect destroying the valves.

(8) Efforts should be made to limit heater/ filament inrush current, especially for high power linears using such valves as the Eimac 3-500z, as the magnetic field can in extreme cases warp the grid structure. It is important to note that filament transformers are often designed so as to reduce such current surges. Replacement transformers (especially if up-rated) may not provide inrush protection.

(9) Before replacing any power valves, always check the voltages on the socket(s) against those in the manual. the conditions which caused the previous set to fail may still be there! Owners of FT101 should take note!

Z21HF recognises that an increasing problem is that the correct replacement valves may no longer be available, or have become too expensive. He notes that some TV sweep tubes appear to be interchangeable. The obvious thing to do is to check that the proposed substitute has the same base, the same physical size and the same pin connections. It may be useful to obtain or borrow a manual for an equipment in which the proposed substitute is used. Check this against your equipment: (a) heater/filament; (b) anode and grid voltages; (c) values of neutralising capacitors; (d) values of loading/anode and tank coils.

He adds that it is possible to substitute commercial transmitter-type valves such as the 6146B (still usually available) for TV sweep tubes. However, (a) the chassis may have to be modified (ie bigger cut outs made to accommodate the valves; (b) for a given power output a higher anode voltage is almost always needed; and (c) grid voltage will probably have to be changed to suit the new valve.

How much work and expertise will be involved depends upon the particular transceiver. As an example, Z21HF cites the example of an FT200 transceiver with FP200 power supply modified to accommodate a pair of 6146B valves in place of a pair of 6JS6C valves; (a) The valve sockets were changed to 8-pin octal types; (b) the neutralising capacitor was changed to 500pF; (c) a stabiliser valve was installed to provide 220V to the screens, against 150V for the original 6JS6Cs; and (d) the bias was reset to give 60mA anode current.

The result was a drop in power, 180W PEP input against 240W PEP input with the original valves. However, this reduced power represents only a fraction of an S-point received signal. the plus point was a completely reliable transceiver using transmitting-type valves which are still around in reasonable numbers.

THE UK AND THE BEAM-TETRODE

IN *TT*, OCT 1986, p782 under the heading 'The valve that changed everything' it was noted how, 50 years earlier, in 1935-36, a team of RCA engineers, led by Otto Schade, developed a new metal-type power valve. This had a tetrode structure but used aligned grid and screen electrodes and beam confining plates connected to the cathode that, like the pentode, eliminated the kink in the characteristics of the earlier screen-grid tetrode valve. So came to us the 6L6 and then late in 1936 the glass 6L6G and the improved RF version, the 807 - a family of valves that truly changed everything for amateur-radio transmitters.

In my review of BREMA's *The Setmakers* (*Radcom*, June 1991, p52) I noted that the author Keith Geddes explained that the original work on beam-tetrodes could be ascribed to C S Bull and 'S Rodder' of EMI at Hayes, Middlesex who had been given the task of circumventing the Philips patent on the pentode, but with British valve-makers unwilling to tackle the mass-production of this type of valve. Ivan James, G5IJ, pointed out to me that the spelling in the book is wrong: 'S Rodder' was in fact Sidney Rodda.

Furthermore, the 6L6 was not the first type of 'beam power tetrode'. In 1935, the relatively small British valve firm of Hivac introduced the HY220 (2V battery valve) and the ACHY (4V heater), providing respectively an audio output of 580mW and 2.4W, claimed as superior to comparable pentode valves - and both featuring Harries 'critical anode distance' electrode structures with 'focussed' electron stream.

These valves were based on British Patents 328,680 (1929), 380,429 and 385,968 (1931), thus preceding the EMI Patent 423,932 in the names of (Sir) Isaac Shoenberg (EMI Director of Research), C S Bull and S Rodda. Being outside the powerful BVA 'ring' the Harries tetrodes were not taken up by British setmakers but were advertised in the constructional periodicals, including the *T & R Bulletin* (the original title of *RadCom*). For example the front cover of the July 1937 issue stated: "In 1935 Hivac introduced a series of Hivac Harries 'critical anode distance'

beam power tetrodes. Since their introduction several new types have been added to the range. May we send you full particulars?" The advert showed the electrode structure: **Fig 3**.

The Harries tetrodes were described by their inventor, J H Owen Harries in *Wireless World* (2 Aug 1935) but seem to have vanished with the coming of the war in 1939 without ever reaching the popularity soon achieved even in the UK by the American beam-tetrodes. I recall that Owen Harries, a prolific inventor in the 1930s in the fields of radio and television, became disillusioned with his attempts to have his ideas taken up by major manufacturers, emigrated after the war to the United States and eventually settled in Bermuda. Whether or not his form of beam-tetrode was as good as, or even superior, to the RCA electrode structure is no longer of practical importance - my junk box contains a few 807 valves but no Hivac beam-tetrodes. *Sic transit gloria . . . .*

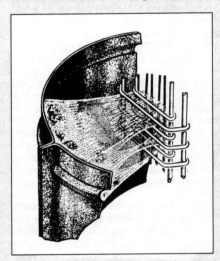

Fig 3: An illustration from the front-cover Hivac advertisement in the July 1937 *T & R Bulletin* showing the manner in which the electron stream was 'focussed' in Harries 'critical anode distance' beam power tetrodes. Unlike the RMI/RCA 6L6 beam power tetrodes there were no beam forming plates connected to the cathode. The Harries/Hivac tetrodes reached the market ahead of the 6L6 in 1935.

ANTENNA ROUND-UP

ONE OF THE MORE POWERFUL forms of broadside, vertically-polarized antennas suitable for amateur HF operation (although very little used) is the Bobtail Curtain: **Fig 4**. Its low-angle radiation provides a hefty gain on DX. The broadside horizontal directivity is only moderate, an advantage for a fixed, suspended wire array. Some relatively high-angle, horizontally polarized radiation will, in practice, result from imperfect cancellation of radiation from the top horizontal span (as with a T-antenna, most of the radiation from the two halves of this section cancel out). Perhaps the most obvious disadvantages are that it is basically a single-band array, requires a matching network at the base of the

central vertical wire to provide a voltage (high impedance) feed and a site that can accommodate a full-wave span at a height of just over a quarter-wave.

In the NRRL journal *Amator Radio* (4/92), LA5UF has a short note on a simple variation which, although no longer a true Bobtail, should provide a simple DX antenna that can be fed directly from 50Ω co-axial cable, providing a mixture of horizontally and vertically polarized radiation: **Fig 5**.

Dave Plumridge, G3KMG, has some useful thoughts on feeder radiation and RF current measurement. He writes: "Recent comments on baluns and the controlled feeder radiation antenna have made me realise that nowhere have I noticed (handbooks included)

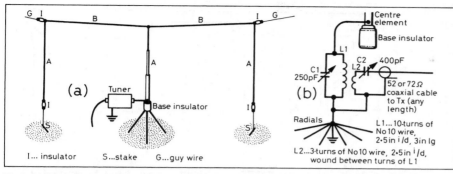

Fig 4: (a) The Bobtail-curtain antenna as described in many Handbooks. This design comes from VE1TG (*Ham Radio*, July 1969) as reproduced in *ART7*. Dimensions for 14MHz A 16.5ft, B 33ft (7MHz A 33ft, B 66ft). (b) Tuner used by VE1TG on 7MHz. For 14MHz L1 and C1 about half the values shown, C2 about the same.

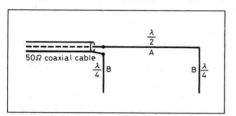

Fig 5: The simple DX-antenna described by LA5UF in *Amator Radio*. A = 75/f (MHz) in metres, B = 150/f.

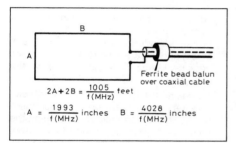

Fig 6: Elongated quad-loop antenna as implemented by G3BDQ.

any information on how to measure or even check the magnitude of current on the outer braid of a coaxial line. The last time I can recall antenna current being mentioned was many years ago in *TT* when a device involving a spring-type of clothes-peg with two half toroids which could be clipped round a coax cable to form a current transformer with diode rectifier and meter was described (Despite a lengthy search I cannot trace the issue in which this appeared - *G3VA*). (But see 'Remote Reading RF Ammeter', *RadCom* June and July 92 - *Ed*.)

"I needed to check a loaded 7MHz dipole made for a local blind amateur to use as an indoor antenna. On testing it in my attic I was plagued by RF feedback. I wanted to confirm whether it was just the close proximity of the antenna or outer braid radiation from the feeder. To check the RF on the feeder I made a current transformer with one of the large 'braid breaker' ferrite toroids of the type available from the RSGB (see *Book Case* pages - *Ed*). This consisted simply of 20 turns of wire wound on the toroid, a 47Ω load resistor with a simple diode detector (the *QST* detector shown in the April *TT* would allow accurate measurements!). The large toroid allows coax plugs to pass through without any need for disconnection or a split clothes peg toroid. The device was calibrated by coupling to the inner of the coax feeding the station power

meter and dummy load and noting the voltage at various power levels. A bit of maths gave the RF current for a given detected voltage.

"Application of this meter to the dipole feeder showed the presence of a large current on the outer braid. A balun choke made by coiling the coax at the feed point into six turns at about 10in diameter reduced the current significantly and eliminated the RFI problems. Out of interest, a further 'coil balun' a few feet away from the feed point reduced the current on the outer braid to a negligible level. Such an RF current meter can thus give a quantifiable measure as to the effectiveness of a balun. On a controlled feeder radiation antenna the ratios of 'antenna' to 'feeder' currents could be quantified to check theory with practice.

"When my parallel dipoles, fed via an ATU with 75Ω twin feeder, seemed to be playing up badly on 21MHz only, a check with the current meter showed a large unbalanced current on this band with next to nothing on the other bands. Lowering the antenna showed there was a break in the 21MHz dipole near the feed point.

"A further application came with a desire to try a ground-plane antenna on 21MHz. Remembering the suggestion in *TT* that the requirement for 'four' radials is something of a modern myth with the inventor, the late George Brown, originally being satisfied with only two, I used only two radials, making the installation much less messy with fewer wires hanging about. Apart from the SWR and performance being fine, the current meter showed negligible current on the outer braid - so who needs four or even three radials?"

John Heys, G3BDQ tried the flattened-loop antenna noted in the February *TT*, p37 using the dimensions given by W6SAI but found they did not give unity SWR on the design frequency and found that on 21MHz his formula gave a loop that resonated at 20.5MHz. Much trimming eventually gave unity SWR at 21.2MHz. G3BDQ considers that the total wire length should be that used for a normal quad-loop element:

1005/f(MHz) ft with the side lengths chosen as shown in **Fig 6**. He finds that this gives a perfect match and an antenna that has worked 'really well' when with the lower side some 10ft from the ground.

It would appear that G3BDQ has his quad-loop in the vertical plane. The design is equally suitable as a horizontal loop and this may account for the lower resonant frequency found by him due to proximity of the lower element to ground.

BLOW (PIPE) UP YOUR ANTENNA

TT, NOVEMBER 1991 INCLUDED an item showing how Ron Grant, G3XPH, uses a homemade catapult-sling as a means of shooting a line across a high branch of a tree, as the first step in putting up a wire antenna. I pointed out that G3XPH had not mentioned the heights he achieves with his rather formidable weapon that shoots a metal-loaded wooden bolt. He has since written to say that the trees he uses are about 90ft high and that as he can clear these with his bolt, he guesses that it would be possible to reach 110ft or so - a truly impressive height.

He also brings to attention an alternative idea (brought to his notice by Ed Hughes, G0IOB). This, although incapable of putting a line across such high branches, combines reasonable performance with less chance of causing injury or damage to anyone else! The idea stems from an article by Ray Fry, VK2FRY, in the Australian magazine *ARA*: 'Dipole installation made easy'. The idea is to use an improvised blow-pipe formed from a piece of plastic conduit about 0.75in (20mm) in diameter and about four or five feet (1.5m) long. The projectile is a rolled-up sheet of semi-stiff paper rolled into a long narrow cone, measuring 20mm at its opening and tapering to a point at the other end. The 20mm end is formed so that it slides nicely into the pipe, a piece of sticky tape helping to keep its shape.

Next take a fishing line with a sinker attached and sticky tape it to the point of the cone. Then insert the cone into the plastic tube and shake it down until it almost comes out the other end. The paper cone forms the dart.

With an assistant standing alongside, holding the remaining line on a cork, end on, towards the tree, the person with the strongest 'puff' places the tube in his mouth and aims at the desired location in the tree. The 'blower' takes a deep breath and gives a sudden, sharp puff into the conduit. With luck the dart will shoot up and across the chosen branch, and then it is only a matter of tying a stronger cord to the line and carefully pulling this into place with the nylon line. VK2FRY and his sons have used this blowpipe several times, achieving deadly accuracy to heights of about 15m. The Australian believes it would be possible to blow harder and go further but has never needed to exceed this height. The lead sinker used was about the size of a large bean, sometimes known to (Australian) fisherman as a 'bug'. The only problem encountered was the tendency of the very light nylon line to snap while the heavier cord was being dragged through the tree.

BATTERIES AND A LEAD-ACID BATTERY CHARGER

ACCORDING TO AN ARTICLE by Andy Cogan in *New Scientist*, April 25 1992, new ranges of 'wafer-thin' disposable lithium batteries will soon be marketed by a number of Japanese (eg Yuasa) and European firms. The batteries can be made a fraction of a millimetre thick and in any shape to fit portable phones, pager devices, laptop computers and video camcorders. The developers of solid-state lithium batteries believe they can reach a target of between 150 to 200 Watthours per kilogram, compared with about 35 to 40 for conventional lead-acid and nickel-cadmium batteries. All the batteries under development have solid electrolytes made of a polymer. In each cell, a sheet of the polymer is sandwiched between one electrode of lithium and one made from a mixture containing vanadium oxide, parts of the electrolyte, lithium salts and a binder to increase conductivity. The 'sandwich' is sealed to prevent leaching of lithium. In the past, a problem with lithium cells is the potential hazard of explosion if overheated. It is stated that the new batteries should be safe because the flat construction makes it easier for potentially dangerous heat generated if the battery is short-circuited to radiate away from the broad surface. Dowty Batteries of Abingdon has developed a prototype stack that fits onto a miner's belt to power the light on safety helmets: "These batteries are very safe because there is no liquid electrolyte. Lithium is a very reactive metal but the construction is such that you don't get very much lithium exposed if the battery is cut open. At the molecular level, the polymeric electrolyte flows round the lithium and shields it." according to Colin Newnham, the group project leader at Dowty.

TT has on several occasions referred to the practice of zapping away the whiskers that tend to develop in nicad cells and cause short-circuits. A rather different, and more drastic, cure is suggested in a letter in *New Scientist* (April 25 1992) by Michell Bell: "If you drop a 'tired' battery about a foot onto a concrete floor a few times it renews the battery wonderfully. The theory (folklore?) is that a layer of crystals builds up around the electrodes and dropping the battery breaks the crystals. Whatever the truth of the theory, it certainly works." An editorial note warns: "Be careful - you may cause the battery to leak, which could damage your equipment".

An item 'Low cost battery charger using regulator' by A D V N Kularatna (University of

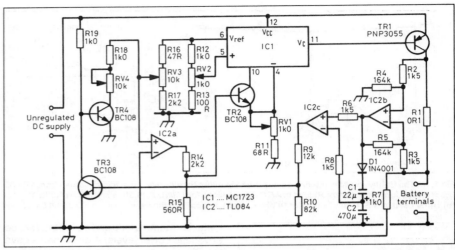

Fig 8: Circuit diagram of the battery charger as implemented for use with a 6V, 5.5Ah lead-acid battery.

Moratuwa, Sri Lanka) in the Applied Ideas feature of *Electrical Engineering*, February 1992, p28 describes the use of a MC1723 precision regulator to configure a charger providing optimal characteristics for ordinary lead-acid batteries: **Figs 7 and 8**. The charger initially feeds the battery at a constant current until the terminal voltage reaches a value around 2.33V/cell. Then the circuit automatically configures into a constant voltage mode, and charges the battery until it reaches about 0.8 to 0.95 of its Ah capacity. When this stage is reached, the circuit once again reconfigures into a trickle charge stage (2.23/cell) minimizing gas formation. The circuit shown in Fig 8 is a design for a 6V, 1A charger for a 5.5Ah, 6V lead-acid battery. The values for constant current, constant voltage and trickle charge can be adjusted to suit individual cases with potentiometers PR1, PR2, PR3 and PR4. The author provides a detailed description of the functions of the regulator and associated components.

FRONT PANEL LETTERING

R C ARNOLD, G8DZU, suffered over some years from lettering falling off the front panels of his constructional projects and decided that the time had come to develop a foolproof technique that would provide a permanent non-destructible form of lettering that cannot be damaged or fall off just after the equipment has been finished. He describes as follows his technique:

(1) Panel preparation: Wire wool key the aluminium panel. Wash panel under a hot tap to remove any grease or debris, then dry the panel.

(2) Apply undercoat: Use grey undercoat spray paint. Allow it to dry for a minimum of *two* hours in a warm atmosphere.

(3) First top-coat: Apply first top-coat of spray paint. Allow to dry for minimum of *two* hours.

(4) Apply lettering: Use Lettraset or Dryprint, as required.

(5) Protective finish: Apply draughtsman Magic Tape over each piece of lettering. Do not worry about cutting into the paint surfaces already applied as they will automatically be retouched with the application of the second top-coat.

(6) Second top-coat: Spray second top-coat over the entire surface including the now protected lettering to the required final finish, and allow to dry as before. You will find the Magic Tape unaffected by the spray paint.

(7) Revealing the lettering: The lettering can now be revealed by taking a rounded-blade, sharp craft-knife and scraping the paint off the surface of the Magic Tape. The original lettering will now be seen in its permanent form.

HERE AND THERE

JOHN TAYLOR, G0AKN, poses an unusual question involving rubber bands, insects' wings and VLF radio waves (!). He writes: "I recently received a VLF receiver from Conversion Research of Descanso, California and at the beginning of March took it into the country to an area relatively free of mains hum in order to try it out. All went well, but I noticed that a rubber band that had originally secured the whip antenna in transit had been left around the case of the receiver. When I went to remove it, I distinctly heard in the receiver's headphones a strong twanging noise as I stretched the band.

"I removed the rubber band and, thinking the twanging might be due to capacitance effects from my hands, I persuaded someone else to stretch it and pluck it at a distance of two metres. I received in the headphones, a powerful sound just like an electric guitar. The Conversion Research's receiver handbook mentions that the receiver can pick up the buzz from insects' wings. They state that the cause is not known but they postulate electrostatic charges. So I wonder if vibrating rubber bands are emitters of VLF radio waves? Do other vibrating strings, for example on a violin, do this?

Mike Whitaker, G3IGW, noted the March *TT* item on the use of 7MHz dipoles on 21MHz with the problem that, because of 'end

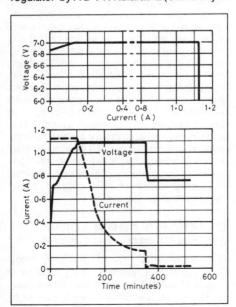

Fig 7: Characteristics of the *Electronic Engineering* low-cost battery charger (lead-acid batteries) using an MC1723 precision regulator which operates in constant-current, constant-voltage and trickle-charge modes.

MAGNETIC LONG-WIRE BALUN

A LETTER FROM DEREK MORLEY (ex-YB0ADW) reported that he had recently bought (from Lowe) a 'magnetic long-wire balun' made by RF Systems Inc. The associated sales leaflet made strong claims for the device as being the ultimate way of matching any long-wire antenna to 50Ω coaxial feeder. Derek wrote: "I don't know about the theory behind it but in practice it works well - about 1.5 to 3 S-points up on a traditional long-wire antenna as comparison, with greatly reduced noise."

I must admit I was misled by that YB0ADW callsign. As a long-time user of a 40m long-wire antenna at G3VA my eyes lit up. This

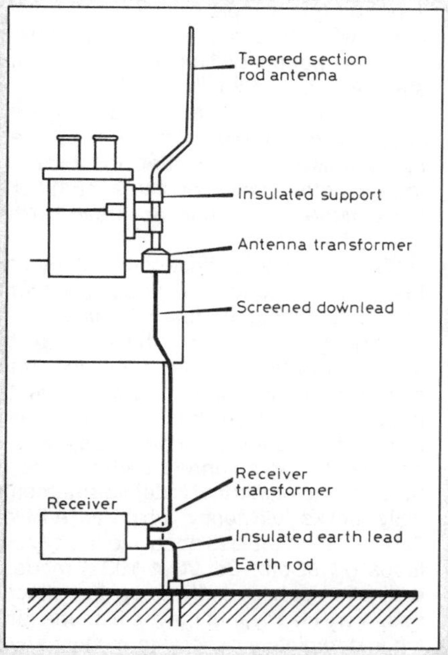

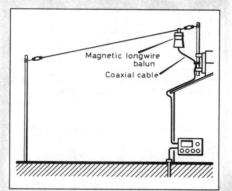

Fig 9: A wideband noise-reducing antenna installation for broadcast reception as marketed in the UK many years ago. The second receiver transformer was necessary since broadcast receivers had a relatively high input impedance of about 400Ω.

seemed just what I and many others wanted. I could replace that part of my long wire that passes through the roof space and down to my upstairs rig with coax!

But then my scepticism about baluns and wideband toroidal cores returned, with their tendency to saturate and overheat, and their power losses. Had RF Systems really come up with the long-awaited answer to end feeding a multiband antenna with coaxial feeder?. G6XN has indicated a partial solution with a capacitor loaded end-fed Windom intended for single-band operation. (*TT*, August 1988).

It took some minutes for the penny to drop. What RF Systems have developed is a wide-band, impedance matching transformer for *reception* - useful for enthusiastic SWLs and possibly for those amateurs who are prepared to use separate antennas for reception and transmission but not, alas, a device that could make the long-wire transmitting/receiving antenna more popular than ever.

My mistake and not the manufacturers! Indeed, wideband impedance-matching transformers were, over 40 years ago, an inherent part of the 'noise-reducing aerial

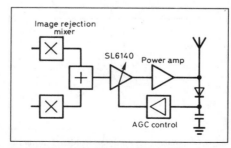

Fig 10: A receiving antenna system as suggested by RF Systems and using their magnetic long-wire balun.

systems' offered by such firms as Aerialite Ltd, matching a vertical whip antenna to a screened downlead: **Fig 9**.

But to return to Derek Morley's notes on what he felt would be of interest to *TT* readers (**Fig 10**). He wrote: "However, I examined the balun before installation. I could foresee problems of weather-proofing the PL259 connector. So I hit on the modification as shown in **Fig 11**."

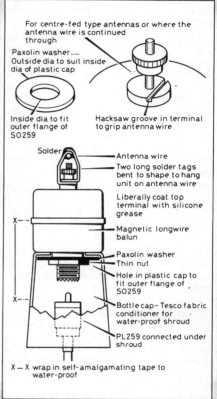

Fig 11: Modifications to improve the weather-proofing of the socket for the magnetic long-wire balun.

effect' antennas do not resonate exactly on harmonically-related frequencies. He writes: "It is probably not widely recognised that the 5th harmonic of a 3.5MHz dipole comes out roughly at 18MHz and the 7th harmonic at roughly 24MHz. After allowing for 'end effect' the dipole length for mid-band resonance on these two WARC-bands would be 134.4ft and 137.1ft respectively.

"A compromise length of 136ft would have a fundamental resonance at about 3.43MHz although if cut for 3.65MHz (the middle of the 3.5 - 3.7MHz band) would be some 8ft shorter. However, in practice, a 136ft dipole would cover much of the 3.5MHz band before there would be a cut-back of power output (due to rising SWR) when using a typical solid-state transceiver, and would thus be effective on 3.5, 18 and 24MHz bands. Furthermore, a 3.5MHz dipole is also quite effective on the 10MHz WARC-band, although on this band there is considerable reactance needing to be tuned out by means of an external ATU."

Antennas for the lower-frequency bands

when used on higher-frequency bands will have multi-lobe radiation patterns. Unless some half-wavelength high, they will tend to be virtually omnidirectional on their fundamental frequency. For general use, multi-lobe patterns are seldom a disadvantage and G3IGW was pleasantly surprised to work 101 countries in 30 days on 18MHz using a 3.5MHz dipole 40ft high. He comments "18MHz is a wonderful band".

John Greenwell, G3AEZ, sends along a clipping from one of the electronics magazines showing how the Plessey SL6140 AGC IC chip can be used as a fast-attack, slow-decay AGC system on the power stage of SSB transmitters. The SL6140 is pin-compatible with the Motorola MC1590 but has enhanced frequency performance (SL6140 up to 400MHz, MC1590 less than 100MHz) as well as mil-spec type temperature performance (-55 to +125°C).

According to the clipping: "The SL6140 has been used as shown in **Fig 12** taking an AGC input from a peak detecting diode and through an AGC control circuit to operate the ALC control pin on the SL6140. The SL6140 AGC amplifier is most suitable in this type of application as its balanced design does not 'thump' (produce a spurious output) when the AGC is activated. The input to the power amplifier in this SSB application is an image rejection mixer, but could equally well be any other input circuit requiring a power output stage with accurate control of output power."**G3VA**

Fig 12: Use of the SL6140 AGC amplifier chip as ALC control of an SSB power amplifier.

THE FOLDED-TEE ANTENNA

IN *TT*, JULY 1987 and again in August 1991, some details were given of the investigation by Arch Doty, K8CFU, of the advantages of the quarter-wave folded monopole antenna, including the possibility of feeding such antennas directly from 50Ω coaxial cable feeders (or 75Ω cable with different diameter conductors) and the reduction of ground losses brought about by the higher feedpoint impedance. But, as noted then, a 1.8MHz monopole requires a height of some 115ft (35m) - a height not really feasible for the vast majority of amateurs. Even for 3.5MHz a quarter-wave monopole needs a height of some 66ft (20m) or so.

Anthony Preedy, A45ZZ/G3LNP, a professional broadcast-antenna engineer writing from the Sultanate of Oman, has come up with an effective way of reducing the height of folded monopoles with an original design - the 'folded-Tee antenna'. This design was first proposed for use in Saudi Arabia to enable MF transmitters to be tuned rapidly to various frequencies but would seem to offer significant advantages for amateur operation on 1.8MHz and the lower HF bands. Tony Preedy writes:

"DX operation on the lower bands usually calls for a vertical antenna. The height of a self-resonant quarter-wave or half-wave antenna for 1.8MHz is generally beyond the facilities available to most amateurs.

"An 'L' or 'T' configuration is the usual solution to this problem. The 'T' is preferred because, otherwise wasteful high angle (horizontally-polarized) radiation is conserved by cancellation between each half of the horizontal section. But a single wire 'T' for 1.8MHz with a 'reasonable' height of, say, 15m will have a feed resistance of only about 10Ω and requires a matching network if coaxial feeder is to be used. A tuned network will considerably reduce the effective bandwidth of the antenna.

"**Fig 1** shows how a 'folded-Tee' antenna can be derived from the quarter-wave folded monopole as described in the standard handbooks or *TT*, July 1987. This is a special form of 'T' antenna developed for MF broadcasting, and largely retains the significant advantages of the folded monopole which are bandwidth, a static discharge path to earth and a moderate feed resistance.

"With similar diameter conductors, the feed resistance of the folded-Tee is four times that of a simple 'T' and varies as the square of the height as shown in **Fig 2**. A match to 50Ω coaxial feeder requires a height of approximately only one-tenth of a wavelength, although this is dependent to some extent on earth loss resistance. Earth resistance should be minimised for optimum efficiency as with any vertical antenna driven against ground.

"Adjustment is simple and this feature made the antenna attractive for MF broadcasting during the 1991 Middle East conflict. Determine the height which provides 50Ω feed resistance, then trim the top lengths symmetrically at the centre for resonance.

"Dimensions for a 1.85MHz antenna are shown in **Fig 3**. This requires supports a little over 15m high and should cover the whole band with low VSWR without the need for

Pat Hawker's
Technical Topics

base matching networks. The dimensions can be scaled for other bands with final top lengths trimmed for minimum VSWR".

It is interesting to note that a folded-Tee antenna for 7MHz DX with support heights of one-tenth wavelength would have a height of only about 4 to 4.5m. It should prove effective in any location having reasonable earth conductivity, or alternatively could be used with elevated resonant radials or counterpoises.

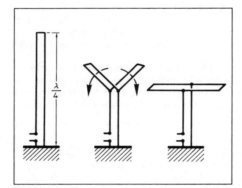

Fig 1: The derivation of the G3LNP/A45ZZ folded vertical quarter-wave monopole antenna.

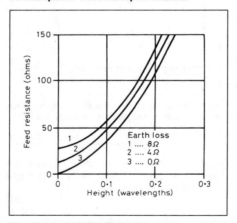

Fig 2: Resonant feed-point resistance versus height for the folded 'T' antenna.

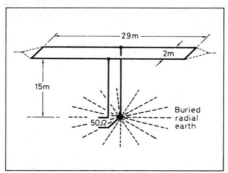

Fig 3: Dimensions for a 1.85MHz folded 'T' antenna. Dimensions can be scaled for higher-frequency bands.

EFFICIENCY OR EFFECTIVENESS?

SEVERAL COMMENTS HAVE been received concerning the criticisms levelled generally by Dr John Belrose, VE2CV, at the looseness of terminology found in amateur-radio publications with particular reference to the comments in *TT* (December 1991) on the G4HOL horizontal loop antenna.

Dr Brian Austin, G0GSF, felt that VE2CV was too severe in his criticisms of *TT* and of G4HOL's comments on the performance of his loop on 3.5MHz but also brings out the important difference between antenna 'efficiency' and antenna 'effectiveness'. He writes:

"G4HOL didn't say in *TT* that his new loop had 9dB more gain than his sloper but simply that it 'was consistently some 9dB better'. That surely is completely fair comment since that is what he observed on the signals and over the period of time concerned. At no stage was gain actually mentioned.

"I certainly agree with VE2CV when he says that there are probably more erroneous statements made and written about antennas than any other aspect of amateur radio but in my experience *TT* has not been guilty of many, if at all.

"One example of loose terminology which I see and hear often involves the concept of efficiency. Frequently one will hear amateurs comparing antennas on the basis of their 'efficiency' when, in fact, they don't mean efficiency at all. If they had said 'effectiveness', I would have been entirely satisfied since effectiveness can be a subjective assessment of an antenna's performance. It is not a characteristic that is defined mathematically, unlike 'efficiency' which is. AJ Henk, G4XVF, in his articles about electrically small loops (*RadCom*, Sept/Oct 1991) made the distinction between efficiency and effectiveness very clearly, but maybe it needs restating in completely general terms lest anyone thinks that only such small antennas can be inefficient.

"Mathematically the gain, G, of an antenna and its directivity, D, are related by the radiation efficiency or just the efficiency, e, thus G = eD. As in all cases where efficiency is involved in engineering we mean the ratio of output power to input power, usually expressed as a percentage. Since the output power from an antenna is a measure of how well it radiates, we would expect the radiation efficiency to involve the radiation resistance R_{rad}, and the overall loss resistance, R_{loss}, of the antenna. Hence:

$$e = R_{rad}/(R_{rad} + R_{loss}) \times 100 \text{ per cent}$$

"For most antennas that amateurs use in a fixed installation, the radiation efficiency will be very close to 100%, in which case gain and directivity can be used interchangeably. However, mobile whips with sizeable loading coils and any other antenna containing significant amounts of lumped loading may well be rather inefficient: the so called Australian Dipole and the T2FD which have become popular again because of their broadband performance by trading efficiency for bandwidth. In both cases their radiation efficiencies, which vary with frequency, are typically less than 50 per cent and considerably less than that at the low end of the HF band".

If I have understood G0GSF correctly (and to save protests from users of Australian dipoles and T2FD antennas which use resistive loading) he is emphasising that antennas which have only low or moderate efficiency can yet prove quite effective in certain applications. For example, the small loop in those situations where an antenna of dimensions comparable to half-wavelength is impracticable; or the Australian dipole where multiband operation matching adjustments are more important than radiating every watt of transmitter output - 50 per cent efficiency, after all, represents a drop of only 3dB, or less than one S-point. After all, it is only the power radiated towards the target area, at the right elevation angle for the propagation conditions at that moment, which governs the signal strength.

ANTENNA MODELLING WITH ELNEC AND MN-PRO

DR BRIAN AUSTIN, G0GSF, as we have noted in *TT* over the years, was one of the early users of computer-modelling of antennas based on the Methods of Moments including pioneering work in validating derivatives of the original Numerical Electromagnetic Code (NEC) software programs.

His studies have recently been expanded to include two MININEC programs that have been written by radio-amateurs - ELNEC written by Roy Lewallen, W7EL, and MN written by Brian Beezley, K6STI. G0GSF writes:

"I've noticed in a number of *TT* items of late that the MININEC-derivative programs, such as ELNEC and MN, are becoming increasingly popular. As you will remember I've long been a user of MININEC from its very first version, which was written for the Apple computer in the early 'eighties, through each development since, including THE MININEC SYSTEM and MININEC from the original developers of the code. Within the past few months I've been able to use both ELNEC and MN-PRO. Without a doubt these two very similar 'amateur' programs, leave the 'professional' codes in the shade as far as 'user-friendliness' is concerned. In fact, once one has experienced the ease with which a virtually unlimited range of wire-type antennas can be analyzed using them, I see no need to go back to the 'professional'; PC-based programs.

"Both benefit enormously from having very useful graphics capabilities 'built-in'. Whereas THE MININEC SYSTEM does too, it is a tedious business to use it and even then the graphics available are somewhat limited. ELNEC and MN-PRO have graphics which form an inherent part of the programs and which are very easy to access by just a couple of keystrokes.

"Anyone who has used the earlier PC Moment Method codes to analyze antennas will no doubt have encountered the problem of inaccuracy when modelling any antenna containing wires which join at an acute angle, such as the inverted vee. It was realized quite some while ago, when many people were 'validating' these codes, that the accuracy could be greatly improved by tapering the segmentation scheme used on the wires,

particularly in those regions where the current distribution was known to be critical. For those unfamiliar with what is meant by this it should be realised that the program works by treating a wire as consisting of a number of short elements, called segments, which are joined in series. If the length of these segments is progressively reduced along the wire then the segments are said to have been tapered. This process is quite tedious to do manually but is most necessary if an accurate value is required for the input impedance of an antenna.

"Both ELNEC and MN-PRO contain automatic tapering facilities, selectable by just one or two keystrokes, for performing this task. To show just how effective they are in computing the accurate impedance, see **Fig 4**. This shows the calculated input impedance of a halfwave inverted vee antenna, in free space, for various values of included angle. This theoretical curve is from "Analysis of the symmetric centre-fed V-dipole antenna by J E Jones (*IEEE Trans Antennas & Propagation, AP24,* May 1976, pp316-322).

"Also shown on the graph are the values for input impedance computed by NEC (the large main-frame moment method program) and by MININEC without tapered segments, and then after using the automatic tapering scheme mentioned above. It will be noticed that all the programs compute the resistive component accurately but that the untapered MININEC shows an increasing error in the reactive term as the included angle is decreased. Note that how both NEC and the tapered MININEC schemes produce excellent agreement with Jones' results.

"I've subjected these new codes to a fairly extensive set of my own validation tests and they've been shown to produce very good agreement with results from NEC, experimental data and the antenna 'literature'. Of course, any computer-based analytical technique is just as capable now, as they ever have been, of producing results which are clearly nonsense (ie GIGO - Garbage In =

Garbage Out) if the user makes inappropriate or simply incorrect decisions when setting up the model. So, as previous *TT* warnings have made clear, a good understanding and 'physical feel' for how antennas behave is still necessary when using these new antenna codes".

Al Christman, KB8I, is another amateur concerned with engineering education who has underlined the value of computer modelling of antennas using MININEC and ELNEC. In 'Phased Driven Arrays for the Low Bands' (*QST*, May 1992, pp49-52), he shows how arrays of driven monopoles and also inverted-vee arrays offer great promise for directive low-band arrays when the various elements are fed at the correct amplitude and phase. This is an approach long used for directional broadcast MF arrays but in the past usually considered difficult for amateur designers. He presents ELNEC-computed horizontal and vertical radiation patterns over real earth for four-square, three-in-line and cross vertical arrays, and the three-in-line inverted-vee array: **Fig 5**. He provides references to the literature on the design of suitable phasing networks while expressing the hope that some enterprising amateur will manufacture and sell a phasing box making it easier to experiment with multi-element driven arrays.

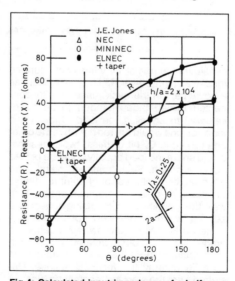

Fig 4: Calculated input impedance of a half-wave inverted-vee antenna showing the extremely close correspondence between the 1976 theoretical curve of J E Jones (*IEEE Trans A&P*) and computer-modelling using NEC and ELNEC + taper whereas the MININEC program shows significant divergence on the reactive component. Note that all three programs agree in the resistive component.

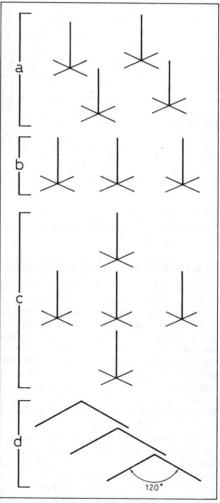

Fig 5: Four types of directive arrays subjected to computer-modelling by KB8I in the May *QST*. (a) Four-square array of monopoles. (b) Three-in-line array. (c) Cross (five-square) array. (d) Three-in-line inverted-V array.

THE FRINEAR 400 LINEAR - A KISS VERSION

TT, FEBRUARY 1990, p30 included a 400W linear amplifier from Frits Geerlings, PA0FRI, which he had developed from an earlier 100W design based on a single PL519 (or PL509) television line-output (sweep) valve. The 1990 design used three PL519 valves in parallel with some quite complex ancillary circuitry in order to obtain the full legal output from the three valves.

PA0FRI has now sent along a simpler, lower-cost version of his amplifier using four instead of three valves but with otherwise an appreciably reduced component count: **Fig 6**. As from his earlier designs, he has condensed constructional information into a single annotated diagram plus a minimum of additional notes. Care should be taken to use suitably rated components etc and to

remember always that any equipment using lethal high-voltages (1250V with a peak current of over 1A) must always be handled with extreme care. Note also that in this amplifier the series heaters of the PL519s are powered directly from the mains supply.

PA0FRI adds that, compared with the 1990 design, the extra PL519 provides as much or more output with lower anode dissipation per valve; however forced air-cooling using a quiet computer fan is advisable. The input capacitance of the valves must be tuned out in order to obtain drive and low SWR by the grid-drive multiband impedance-matching system. This offers a simple 'remote' front-panel mounting with solely a 5mm hole for the 50ohm cable in the amplifier enclosure. The input twin-gang variable

capacitor (2 x 320pF) is from an AM broadcast radio. For an amplifier intended for use only on 1.8 and 3.5MHz the input tuning network can be omitted.

The screen-grid and cathode resistors help to equalise the loading of the four valves. Output on 28MHz is reduced by the relatively low efficiency, which in turn is a result of the lay-out, the PL519's input capacitance and the minimum capacitance of the output tuning capacitor. To achieve maximum output power on the 28MHz and WARC bands, the taps on the output filter need to be adjusted experimentally.

PA0FRI reports that the amplifier shows up well in a two-tone test and that on-the-air reports are encouraging. He drives it with a Yaesu FT7.

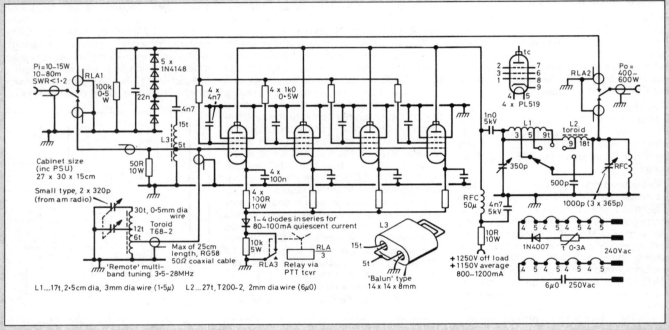

Fig 6: The 'Frinear 500' high-power linear amplifier using four PL519 TV valves (F H V Geerlings, PA0FRI).

MATCHED PAIRS OF VALVES

THE RECENT *TT* ITEM based on Z21HF's guide on how to get maximum life out of sweep tubes (TV line output valves) stressed that when buying replacement valves it is preferable to use 'matched pairs' in order that the load is shared equally between them and that non-matched pairs can differ significantly. Z21HF also noted that with the increasing rarity of some TV valves, a good case can be made for modifying a transceiver so that transmitting type valves (still available) such as the 6146 can be fitted.

Some interesting additions to the subject of matched pairs is to be found in Bill Orr's, W6SAI column, 'Radio FUNdamentals' (*CQ*, May 1972). His many years with Eimac has left W6SAI with an excellent insight into the whys and wherefores of valves and valve amplifiers. This time he explores the recent trend for advertisers to offer matched pairs of transmitting type valves such as 6146s, 572Bs, 3-500Zs etc. W6SAI, not unnaturally,

considers the use of TV valves not intended for use as high-power RF linear amplifiers as a 'royal pain in the neck' since parallel-connected sweep tubes needed to be hand-selected to equalize the load: "More often than not, one would run red hot while the other one ran cool. By hit or miss, two tubes that would share the load equally could be picked out of a bunch. Such 'matched pairs' were often daubed with a spot of paint to identify them and then sold at premium prices. That was the penalty paid for using tubes in a service for which they were not intended".

He adds: "When the sweep tubes were gradually phased out of amateur equipment, the popular 6146B tube took its rightful place as a linear amplifier for SSB service. Designed from the start as transmitting tubes, it was not necessary to match them, as manufacturing tolerances were held tight enough so that all tubes worked equally well in RF service - true enough when the tubes were made by reputable manufacturers: RCA, General Electric, Sylvania, et al.

"Those days are gone forever, however! Everybody is making tubes that are branded 6146Bs. Some are good and some are bad, but they all sport the 6146B label. The mavericks of the bunch seem to be those imported from China. At last count there were over a dozen companies in China making transmitting tubes. One or two of the companies produced rather good products . . . some of the other Chinese manufacturers vary in quality and operating characteristics to a marked degree. They do not seem to have the quality control and knowledge necessary to produce world-class products.

"Regardless of quality, transmitting tubes are being imported in large numbers into the United States and other western countries from China and sold under recognisable brand names the copyrights of which have expired.

"I recently examined a bunch (perhaps 20) of 6146Bs from China made by various manufacturers and all imported by one distributor. The height of the glass envelope varied from one bunch of tubes to the next; some of the worst examples would not fit into the amplifier compartment of a Kenwood TS-830, for example, as the tubes were too tall.

"Mechanical assembly varied. Just by looking at the tubes it was easy to tell which ones were poorly made. Testing them at maximum plate current rating revealed that the operating characteristics varied widely. Such tubes have to be sorted out as to manufacturer and then separated into 'matched pairs' by testing under full load - I wonder how many importers have the desire, the test equipment and the knowledge to do this. The bottom line is that properly made transmitting tubes do not have to be matched for amateur service. The fact that many of the imported tubes sold today have to be matched is a sad commentary on overseas techniques and also on the US tube manufacturers who have deemed it not cost-effective to remain in the business. Transmitting valves are now imported into the USA from several European and South American countries, the ex-Soviet Union and China. Some overseas tubes are fine products. Some are not".

STATE OF THE ART SHF TRANSISTORS

TO THOSE WHO REMEMBER the first difficult days of solid-state devices which could only occasionally be persuaded to function at HF let alone VHF, the continued progress of the technology must excite wonder - with low noise devices now available at reasonable cost capable of operation well up into the SHF spectrum.

A paper 'Ultra-high-speed modulation-doped field-effect transistors: a tutorial review' by L D Nguyen, L E Larson and U K Mishra of Hughes and the University of California (*Proc IEEE*, April 1992, pp494-516) shows that ever since the first demonstration of mobility enhancement in modulation-doped heterostructures in 1978 "we have witnessed an explosion of research and development of the Modulation-Doped Field-Effect Transistor (MODFET) - also known as the High Electron Mobility Transistor (HEMT), Selectively-Doped Heterostructure Transistor (SDHT) and Two-Dimensional Gas Field-Effect Transistor (TEGFET) - for microwave and millimeter-wave device and circuit applications." Probably, the term HEMT will be the most familiar in view of their use in 12GHz low-noise amplifiers for the reception of direct satellite broadcasting (DSB).

The authors point out that "At the present time, and for the foreseeable future, the MODFET is the fastest three-terminal semiconductor device in the world. In five years alone (1984-89) the speed of state-of-the-art MODFETs, which is commonly characterised by their current gain cut off frequency (f_T), has increased by a factor of five; from 50GHz in 1984 to 250GHz. As a result of these improvements, the frequency bandwidth that is accessible for communication and data processing by transistor circuits has grown by a factor of five. We expect this trend to continue at roughly the same pace during the early 1990s, resulting in MODFETs with f_Ts as high as 400GHz."

The paper discusses in detail the various ways in which these improvements have been brought about. **Fig 7** shows the noise figure of experimental and commercially-available low-noise MODFETs.

"On system applications, the authors note that one of the most popular system applications of low-noise MODFETs is in DBS at Ku-band (11-12GHz) in Europe and Japan. Due to their extremely low noise, discrete MODFETs are almost always used as the preamplifier in a typical DBS receiver, followed by one or more GaAs MESFET monolithic microwave integrated circuits (MMICs). The use of the low-noise MODFET preamplifier has resulted in substantial improvements in system performance at little additional cost (typically $2-$5 for a packaged, 0.25μm gatelength device).

"As described by Konishi, a Matsushita Low Noise Downconverter consisting of a 0.25um MODFET and three GaAs MMIC chips is capable of achieving a system noise figure less than 1.3dB with an associated gain of 62 +/- 2dB from 11.7 to 12.2GHz, which is quite a remarkable achievement for a commercial, low cost, high-volume system."

A futuristic form of semiconductor device seems to be foreshadowed by current work at the Universities of Nottingham, Glasgow, etc by M W Dellow, and also by S Gregory, D M Lutz, et al, as reviewed by Sean Washburn, in 'Single atoms as transistors' (*Nature*, May 21, 1992, pp199-200). Recent experiments indicate that the limits to making transistors smaller may be reached only at the level of single atoms:

"Three independent groups of researchers now show that electrical current can be controlled by the configuration of an individual atom's quantum-mechanical state and that the state itself can be switched on and off." Such truly micro-tiny devices, it is foreseen, could find application for gigabit computer memories!

FEEDBACK

AN UNFORTUNATE PRINTING SNAFU made nonsense of the two mathematical statements in 'Toroidal cores defended' (*TT*, June 1992, p39) although the results as shown in Table 1 were correct. The formulae should have read:

$$\text{Peak envelope power P}$$
$$= V^2_{rms}/R = V^2_{pk}/2R$$
$$\text{And A} = \sqrt{(RP)} / (4.44fNB_{pk})$$

Similarly the 'commonly available toroids' need be no larger (not 'longer') than approx 2in diameter to satisfy the highest figures shown in the Table.

Dick Biddulph, G8DPS, spotted my lack of knowledge of modern automobile electrics in the item 'Going mobile safely' (*TT*, May) where I suggested that British cars have positive earths - a memory from some 40 years ago when I ghosted a book on automobile trouble tracing! G8DPS writes: "I take issue with you because I can't think of any British car less than 20 years old that has a positive earth. Also, no common British car has air-bag restraints although I expect that they will be with us before too long".

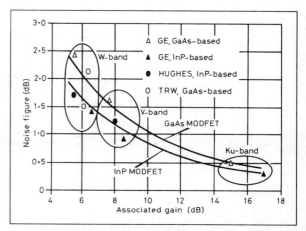

Fig 7: Noise figure of state-of-the-art low-noise MODFETs versus their associated gain. (*Proc IEEE*, April 1992)

REMOVING GUY ROPE STAKES WITHOUT EFFORT

CLIFFE SHARPE, G2HIF noted the item by R Smith, G1TPS on using a specially-made extractor to remove stakes from hard ground (*TT*, May 1992, 40). He writes:

"I have been removing stakes from hard ground after field-day and /P events for the past 40 years and have long since abandoned the use of a G1TPS-type extractor in favour of a 'more powerful with less effort' system.

"The only equipment required is a standard car jack of the type which has a short arm that plugs into the side of the car chassis. **Fig 8** is self-explanatory. I can vouch for the effectiveness of this approach having recently removed four 5ft stakes from my garden clay. If the stake is longer than the extension, a few bricks under the jack is usually sufficient to extend the pull in two or three goes."

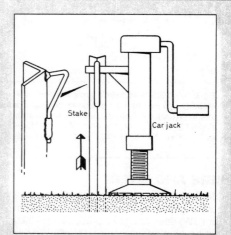

Fig 8: G2HIF's recommended method of removing stakes from hard ground with the use of a standard car jack of the type which has a short arm that plugs into the side of the car chassis.

GW0GHF MOSFET PRE-AMPLIFIER

BRIAN D WILLIAMS, G0GHF, was interested in the *TT* (June, pp37/38) item from G3IPV concerning the stability problems that can be encountered with FET signal frequency amplifiers. As a keen believer in home-brew, he had encountered similar problems in the construction of VHF MOSFET pre-amplifiers using off-the-shelf devices from advertisers in amateur radio magazines. Despite his use of meticulous layouts and good constructional practices at VHF, there were problems with instability and self-oscillation.

However, he has found an easier solution to building VHF pre-amplifiers than that suggested by G3IPV which does involve a number of variables that might daunt many constructors. His solution is shown in the annotated circuit diagram of **Fig 9**. He has used this arrangement daily over the past two years and finds it well behaved with no hint of feedback, spuriae or other deleterious effects. He writes:

"The special thing about this circuit is the untuned output, impedance-matching stage using a bipolar transistor. I find that in most homebuilt gear, the biggest single problem tends to be feedback (instability) that occurs when the tuned circuits are peaked. Yet, these days, as G3IPV infers, it is desirable to precede any pre-amplifier with one or more high-Q tuned circuits in order to reduce strong off-frequency signals. But the output of the pre-amplifier is far less critical and, in any case, will be feeding a tuner front-end which preferably will be tuned to the incoming signal-frequency.

"My circuit provides the advantage of a MOSFET signal-frequency stage without hassle. For those who may be inclined to criticise the inclusion of a bipolar device in a pre-amplifier of this type, I would like to point out that it acts purely as a buffer and an impedance-matching device and there is therefore no problem in so far as dynamic range is concerned. Since the bipolar transistor uses the emitter-follower configuration its voltage gain will be less than unity."

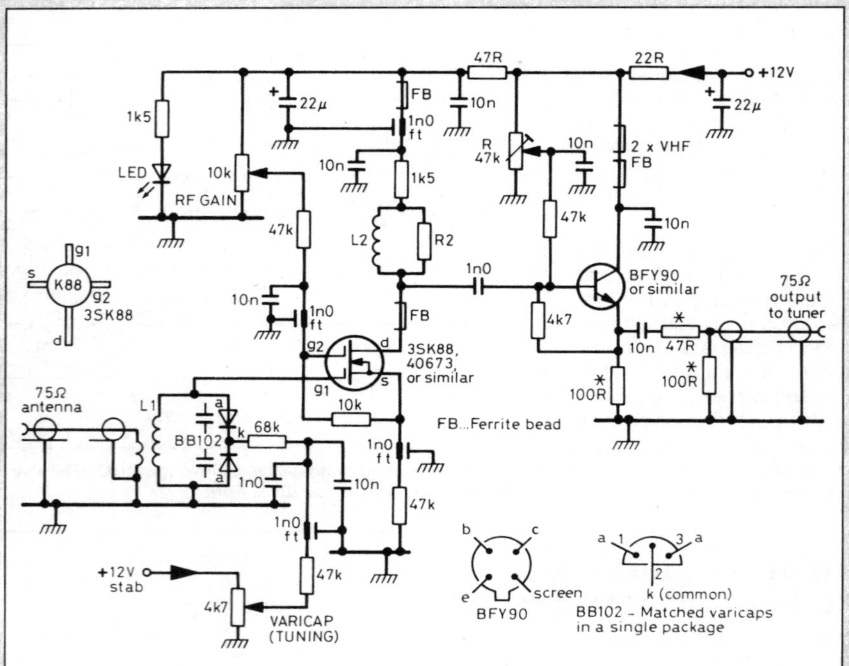

of about twelve turns just before the feed point.

Suspicion fell on the choke-balun and this was discarded and replaced by a length of RG213 cable. Thereafter, near unity SWR on 5W. He concluded: "The whole problem appears to have originated from contamination of the RG8 coiled length of cable and was strangely being exacerbated by the low output power.

Robert J Ruplenas, W1DDO, (Hinks & Kinks, *QST*, May 1992) noted that his TS-830S sometimes lost sensitivity when returned to receive after transmitting. He deduced that the contacts on the antenna relay were becoming erratic because of increasing resistance caused by oxidation - as can happen with relay contacts that run 'dry' without any appreciable current being switched. The relay cover precluded easy access to the contacts.

His solution was to pass a small DC current (derived from an analogue ohmmeter on its lowest resistance range - digital meters do not source enough current) through the receive contacts, while switching several dozen times between receive/transmit after making sure that no RF was generated during transmit by turning 'Mic' and 'Carrier' controls to minimum). This proved entirely successful and could prove a useful dodge for relay and switch contacts that run dry.

TIPS AND TOPICS

WITH THE INCREASING use of the 18 and 24MHz 'non-harmonic' WARC bands, the problem of multi-band operation of a centre-fed, fixed-length dipole can be successfully overcome, as many amateurs are finding, by the use of open-wire feeders and a suitable low-loss ATU with balanced output variable over a wide impedance range. Over the years a number of ideas for constructing low-cost feeder spreaders have been given in *TT* but a further idea is presented by David Gosling, G0NEZ, in *Sprat* Nr 68, Autumn 1991, p14. He suggests using standard A4 plastic-end binders as available from most stationers, singly or in packs. These are about 10-inches long but can be easily cut to required length (eg each binder cut in half to provide two spacers) using a Stanley knife or similar.

He advises: "Cut the required length then drill the sealed end. Slide over your feeder and the closed edges trap the wire quite securely: **Fig 10**. More effective security can be had by using a spot of superglue". *G3VA*

Fig 9: GW0GHF's MOSFET pre-amplifier using a bipolar emitter-follower stage to achieve good stability and freedom from spuriae. *For 50Ω cable, change the value of these components to 68Ω and 27Ω (top). R2: Adjust value on a weak, stable signal for best signal/noise. Emitter of the BFY90 should be about 1.7V. For 40-100MHz the L2/R2 combination consists of a 10k 0.25W resistor on which is wound about 10 turns of 26SWG enamelled wire.

HERE AND THERE

TONY TURTON, ZU1AT/ZR6CST, with a South African Novice licence (maximum power 5W) describes (*Radio-ZS*, March 1992) how he recently bought a good quality 28MHz monoband array which had previously been used for only a few days on a DX-pedition to Penguin Island. Connected to his TS120V (maximum power about 10W) the SWR was near unity but as soon as the carrier power was reduced to 5W the SWR climbed up-

wards, back on 10W it remained briefly low and then suddenly climbed to infinity.

He felt that a logical explanation was corroded electrical contacts between element joints and indeed found fairly severe corrosion from the few days use in a salty environment. After cleaning every joint the SWR seemed excellent but again very soon climbed back 'through the roof'. The array is fed via two Beta stubs with no balun fitted but with the RG8 coaxial cable formed into a choke balun

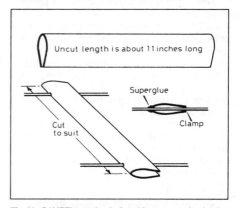

Fig 10: G0NEZ's method of making open-wire feeder spacers from A4 plastic binders. (*Sprat*).

MAINS TRANSFORMERS - ARE THEY HAZARDOUS?

THE OTHER EVENING I had an unpleasant surprise when I went back to the 'shack' after a meal break. My ancient valve transmitter (LG300) - long past its 'use by' date but easy to keep running when the occasional fault materialises - has a separate PSU for the built-in VFO. Since this takes some 20 minutes or so to reach thermal stability, I often leave the VFO running while out of the shack for a time.

To cut a long story short, when I opened the door I found evil smelling smoke pouring out of the VFO PSU and it was clear that the transformer was close to going up in flames (Note; perhaps one should one consider putting a smoke detector in the shack?). Subsequent examination showed a considerable area of charred windings and both primary and secondary short-circuited to the screen foil. What had brought about the fault, and in what order, remains uncertain. The transformer, although many years old, was an apparently well-built component with a large core and was running well below its design loading. There was no question of the core over-heating (at least until the fault occurred) and I can only presume that the enamel insulation on the primary winding had failed and connected the mains supply to the screen without blowing the mains fuses.

Over the years, I have had a number of mains-transformers go down, although not with a comparable fire hazard since the PSU of a Whaddon MkIII transmitter similarly came near to catching fire at Eindhoven in early 1945. The recent incident was a timely reminder that enamel-insulation can deteriorate over the years, particularly in humid conditions.

It also recalled a debate that emerged recently in the 'Forum' column of *Electronics Australia* (Feb and May 1992). Originally, a correspondent suggested that the use of toroidal mains transformers should be avoided in constructional projects. This was rebutted by later correspondents representing firms manufacturing or selling toroidal transformers who insisted that toroidal types, if of reputable make, were as safe as those based on the older type E-I cores.

The difference, apparently, is that there is normally no 'screen foil' between primary and secondary windings in toroidal transformers and they cannot meet the more-stringent Australian 'fail safe' or 'inherently short-circuit protected' standard (nor for that matter do most transformers with E-I cores).

A British transformer-manufacturer got dragged into the debate, with Terry Monaghan, a designer at Antrim Transformers, commenting: "It is unfortunate that some constructors have a tendency to have cheapness, rather than safety as their main criterion for choosing a particular power transformer. Like your correspondent, we have seen a fair share of badly constructed power transformers over the years (E-I types included). Even our bulk standard toroids are double insulated; some are even triple insulated. At the crossover point, where the primary windings pass through the secondary, not only are the leads double insulated, but a high creepage distance is maintained between the windings.

Pat Hawker's
Technical Topics

"There are several options available to further improve the safety aspect of the transformers if deemed necessary. These include: (1) Triple insulation between primary and secondary to comply with AS3108 requirements. (2) Thermal cutouts or thermal fuses to limit temperature rise under fault conditions. (3) Copper foil earth safety screens between the primary and secondary windings. Regarding mounting: a large dished steel washer is used to spread the pressure on the windings, plus neoprene washers and polymeric insulation are used to absorb any stress that could damage the windings . . . Alternative mounting arrangements are available - eg potted inserts in the centre or totally potted construction. It must be said however, that thus far we have not seen any evidence of transformers damaged due to the mounting arrangements."

Back in the early 1950s, when I was editing the massive *Radio and Television Engineers' Reference Book*, I recall including an item on 'Heat-operated or Temperature Fuses' as follows: "The primary purpose of a temperature fuse is to reduce fire risk by breaking a circuit when the temperature of a component such as a transformer exceeds a certain limit. **Fig 1** illustrates a typical temperature fuse fitted to a mains transformer. A copper strip, B, is well insulated and fixed between the HT and heater windings, the order of winding being: primary, screen, HT, heater and rectifier heater. It projects at both ends of the coil, having a lug at one end to which the start of the primary winding is soldered, and at the other end is jointed to a phosphor-bronze spring, A, by a fusible alloy of low melting point (95°C). The other end of the spring is secured to the insulated tag jacket of the transformer by a tag which also serves as connection to one mains lead.

"If the temperature of the transformer rises sufficiently to cause the heat conducted along strip, B, to melt the fusible alloy, the spring A, separates from the strip, thus breaking the mains circuit. This arrangement has been arrived at after experiments to ensure that whichever winding or part of a winding be short-circuited, the temperature rise of the

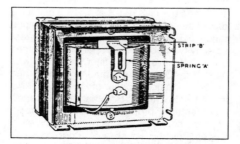

Fig 1: Temperature-fuse as fitted to a mains transformer in the early 1950s. (*Radio & Television Engineers' Reference Book*).

hottest part of the transformer cannot exceed 135°C when measured two minutes after the fuse has opened."

I have never come across this type of thermal fuse in practice, but glass encapsulated thermal fuses for various temperatures are marketed (for example by RS, who also supply resettable sub-miniature thermal circuit breakers in a plastic case with a reset button) and could be taped to a transformer core etc.

Transformers are normally impregnated to prevent moisture from entering, but where a winding operates at a positive potential with respect to the core and/or another winding, electrolytic action may remove copper from any bare places on the wire such as 'pin holes' in the enamel, provided something in the nature of an electrolyte exists. Corrosion occurs, eventually resulting in a break in the winding. This type of problem is not common with AC mains transformers but used to affect audio output, modulation and IF transformers in the valve era resulting in a 'green spot' at the point of the break. Impregnation alone is useless in preventing this type of fault.

It does appear that both toroidal and E-I transformers need to be chosen and used with care in order to minimise hazards. And, if my experience is anything to go by, even what appears to be a robust, well-made, varnish-impregnated transformer with a generously sized core run under derated conditions may eventually fail for no obvious reason! I must admit that in my case the component, acquired ex-equipment some 20 years ago, was probably about 40 years old.

Incidentally, a good deal of information on power transformers, both with toroidal and E-I cores, most of it stemming from John Brown, G3EUR, appeared in *TT*, March 1986. There is also a detailed article 'Toroidal transformers' by Terry Monaghan in *Electronics & Wireless World*, March 1987, pp225-258 that reviews their advantages, disadvantages and applications.

HRO VARIANTS & THE HAMMARLUND SUPER-PRO

THE APRIL *TT* ITEM 'HROddities' recalled some of the impressive background to the HRO receiver which was manufactured by National in various versions from 1934 for some 30 years until the mid-1960s, plus models using the same basic tuning arrangements made in Germany and Japan. This has prompted Barry Kirkwood, ZL1BN, to add to the saga - recalling that at least two lines of HRO-clones were produced 'down under' in the 1940s when there was a desperate shortage of communications receivers. He writes:

"Two close relatives of the HRO were the 'Kingsley' AR7 which closely resembled the HRO and which was manufactured in Australia to a very high specification - arguably superior to the original; and the Collier & Beale Model 949 manufactured in New Zealand. Both closely followed the HRO concept and used the famous PW4 ganged capacitor and dial from the National factory, plus trays of plug-in coil assemblies fitting through the front panel. Valve line-up and circuitry were also similar to the HRO.

"The Model 949 was widely used for many years after the war by the New Zealand Post

Office and also by the NZ Civil Aviation Department. I have an almost mint example, and Jock White, ZL2GX, has a collection of variants of the 949 including some documentation on them. An interesting feature of the 949 is that, save for the gang and dial, it was built around components used for domestic broadcast receivers rather than purpose-built components. The IF transformers are standard, and the front-end coils are wound on half-inch-diameter bakelised paper forms, supported by leads of 18g bus-bar in the middle of the spaces in a rugged die-cast catacomb. Very efficient, very inexpensive, works better than the original!

"The set has no AGC or crystal filter, but most sport a full-wave diode detector which is very linear. Transformer coupling gives a degree of audio selectivity. The cathodes of the RF and IF amplifiers are unbypassed, reducing gain and Miller effect, and usually eliminating any need for realignment when valves are changed. The unit is designed to run on 180V HT and valves last a long time.

"I feel fortunate to be the owner of an almost mint 949 and find it a superb CW receiver by any standards, especially on the lower bands."

A receiver which, in various 'marques', was actually manufactured over an even longer period than the HRO is the 'Super Pro' a top-of-the-range communications receiver introduced by the Hammarlund Manufacturing Company of New York City in 1936 (later production at Mars Hill, North Carolina). This superseded their 'Comet Pro' (one of the very first general-purpose superhet communications receivers introduced in 1932). The SP-10 model of 1936 was followed by the SP-110, and then in 1939 the SP-210 series which formed the basis of a large number of US military receivers under such designations as the BC779, BC794 and BC1004. Two Super Pros were normally fitted in the famous American SCR299/SCR399 signals vehicles alongside a BC610 high-power transmitter based on the Hallicrafters HT4 transmitter designed for amateur radio. Super Pros were also used on some of the earliest military RTTY HF links in North Africa.

The line-up of the SP-200-X was impressive: Two 6K7 tuned RF amplifiers; 6L7 mixer; 6J7 HF oscillator; 6K7 1st IF amplifier (with six-position crystal filter); two 6SK7 IF amplifiers; 6H6 and 6N7 noise limiter; 6SJ7 BFO; 6SK7 AGC amplifier; 6H6 diode detector; 6C5 AF amplifier; 6F6 driver; and two 6F6 push-pull output; plus PSU.

Some of the wartime models, such as the BC-779B, were low-frequency plus HF (to 20MHz) receivers, but when these were sold as surplus to amateurs a number were converted by removing the 100 - 200 - 400kHz coils and inserting in their place 1250 - 2500kHz and 20 - 40MHz coils although Hammarlund did not recommend this since an entirely different tuning unit was employed in the BC-779B than was employed in receivers that tuned to 40MHz.

Post-war Super Pros included the SP-400 series introduced in 1946 and the still-highly regarded SP-600 series that came along in 1950 and continued in production until about 1973, although the original Hammarlund company was sold to the Giannni Scientific

FISHING FOR ANTENNAS WITH MONOFILAMENT LINE

AS NOTED RECENTLY IN *TT*, a whole battery of weapons can be used to shoot a thin line over a high branch of a tree: bow-and-arrow; catapult-sling (Nov 1991); even a blow-pipe (July 1992). They form an alternative to the usually less-effective method of attaching a weight to the line and throwing it over a suitable branch.

A less warlike approach is suggested by Bill Glung, KC3XO (*QST*'s 'Hints and Kinks'): "If you are a proficient fisherman with the ability to cast a line, a fishing rod and heavy sinker is an excellent way to throw a line where you need it. I pulled a nylon line over with the fishing line, then a rope with the nylon line - result a newly erected 3.5 and 7MHz sloper antenna."

Sounds easy - but Norman Bonnet, G0NNA/DL, warns that any method involving monofilament fishing line can result in a nasty tangle unless care is taken. He writes:

"Monofilament fishing line is a truly wondrous material *but* it needs a little forethought in use:

(1) You need to buy the strength of line you want. 50kg line will give a truly strong support but will bring its own problems. A better weight is in the range 5 - 15kg depending on what you are going to heave or pull.

(2) Take the length you want and (exactly as for copper wire) put one end in the vice and stretch the line. This helps to defeat the desire of fishing lines to form themselves instantly into coils. The working strain of the line is marked on it so there should be no breakages as can happen with copper wire.

(3) *Wearing a strong pair of gloves* start at the vice end and run the whole length

of line through your fingers to remove finally any remaining coils.

(4) Normal 'Boy Scout knots' are of little use with fishing line as there is too little friction for them to hold. It is better to use a knot as shown in **Fig 2** which has never lost me a salmon or trout!

(5) While buying your line at a tackle shop, you can also buy very neat beachcasting weights.

(6) Small cut-off pieces of fishing line are deadly to small animals and birds, so ensure that you remove all such pieces which should then be destroyed.

(7) When throwing (or casting) the line do not lay it on the grass and hope it won't snag the grass or small twigs. Instead, lay it on a large sheet of plastic and then coil it in as concentric a circle as you can manage.

(8) Do not be tempted into thinking that fishing line is inert. You will find it has a mind of its own and will try to form itself into a bird's nest. If this happens, years of fly-fishing have taught me not to attempt to unravel it, but to replace and destroy it painlessly indoors.

"Use the above tips and problems should disappear!"

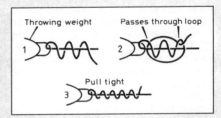

Fig 2: G0NNA's recommended knot for fixing sinker to monofilament fishing line.

Company in the 1960s. The Super Pro was thus in production for almost 50 years, almost ten years longer than the HRO.

Some of the above information comes from Raymond Moore's *Communications Receivers*. There are still quite a few SP-200 and SP-600 receivers in the UK - although since it was never, as far as I know, used widely by the British Services it is far less well-known here than the HRO, but a number of amateurs still speak highly of these receivers and a number are still in use (a product detector can be fitted). Some of the features of the Super Pro were used in the lower-cost HQ-120-X of 1938 and the HQ-129-X of 1945 (I still have one of these in working order), with only one tuned RF amplifier but including switched-selectivity similar to the Super Pro and based on an effective crystal filter. The firm was started by Oscar Hammarlund in 1910 and became a major supplier of HF components in the 1920s when as Hammarlund-Roberts it manufactured broadcast receivers. Unusually for a communications receiver, the early Super-Pros had a push-pull output stage (2 x 42 or later 2 x 6F6). The SP-150 was even fitted in a console type cabinet with a 15-in high-fidelity loudspeaker!

LETRASET ON METALWORK - AN ALTERNATIVE VIEW

A CLEMENTS, G4KDZ, NOTED the item 'Front panel lettering' in the July *TT*. Here, G8DZU offered advice on a non-destructible form of lettering that cannot be damaged or fall off just after equipment has been finished. G4KDZ is not convinced that G8DZU's method is the easiest or best method of preparing metal work for eventual Letraset or similar finish. He offers the following procedure:

(1) First, cut out and drill any necessary holes that may be required.

(2) Wash the aluminium workpieces with hot water and Fairy Liquid, rubbing the panels down with wire-wool to remove any surface grease.

(3) Dry the workpieces and fill any major cuts or dents with car cellulose filler where necessary. At this juncture it may be necessary to spray the panels with a cellulose putty filler to fill in any minor cracks or scratches on the metalwork.

(4) When dry, rub down with fine wet-and-dry paper until you obtain the required finish.

(5) Apply an undercoat to the metal work (Car spray primer: light colour if top coat is to be light; dark if top coat is to be dark). Allow to dry and then apply a top coat - gloss (car spray) colour of your choice.

(6) When dry, apply a light coat of clear lacquer (spray) such as Aerosol lacquer (RS Components 567-496) or 101 Letraset spray or similar product.

(7) When this is dry, you can apply your Letraset lettering, removing any laid in error by the use of masking tape.

(8) When entirely happy with the application finish add a final spray of clear varnish over the lettering and allow to dry. The panels will now be well protected against normal handling. Depending on your art work, the finish will look professional too.

G4KDZ adds: "I find that people let their projects down by being rather indifferent in this area. They tend to put their project in the first box or enclosure they find. Similarly, few go to the bother of re-calibrating meter faces using Letraset. Yet it is quite simple and does give the finished project a touch of class. I remove the existing meter face (very carefully) and mark the outer perimeters of the existing arc using a light touch from a centre punch at these points. The meter face is then rubbed down with a fine grade wet-and-dry paper and Fairy Liquid, dried and sprayed with a white primer.

"Usually, either side of the meter face can be prepared. When this is dry a new arc is drawn to the meter using a compass and sharp soft pencil. The small punch marks made earlier form an arc guide. The scale is then divided into the respective divisions, marking each with a Letraset marker, and the whole is finally finished with appropriately sized numbering on the scale. No varnish spray is needed as the meter will be protected when re-assembled. Needless to say, it is important to be careful during re-assembly since with one wrong move the meter could be damaged beyond repair."

FEEDBACK

NOTE THAT THE 3SK88 source resistor for the GW0GHF MOSFET pre-amplifier (Fig 9, *TT* August, p41) should be 470Ω and *not* the 47K shown. GW0GHF has supplied details of the input coil, L1, to tune about 45-75MHz: 10 turns, about 22SWG enamalled wire on 5mm former with slug, spaced about one-wire diameter. Antenna coupling link is one and a half turns wound over the 'cold' end of L1. He finds his varicap tuning pot needs resetting a few minutes after switching on, but then stays put; cause unknown.

MORE ON USING 7MHZ HALF-WAVE DIPOLES ON 21MHZ

ROBIN MOSELEY, WA3T, WITH REFERENCE to the March item 'The 7MHz dipole on 21MHz' points out that there are two methods of forcing a dipole antenna to be simultaneously resonant at any two desired frequencies: one in the 7MHz band and the other in the 21MHz. He writes: "One solution is to use capacitive loading as described by NJ2L in *QST*, June 1991. Another is to use a small amount of inductive loading, positioned approximately at the centre of each of the 'outside' halfwaves of the 21MHz 1.5-wave di-

---

MAKING NON-REVERSIBLE LOW-VOLTAGE CONNECTORS

TT HAS BEEN RUNNING for over 34 years and it is not surprising that occasionally a previously described idea turns up in a new guise. But since there are always new readers as well as old-timers, occasional repetition seems justified.

SA (Dick) Fox, G0MZI, for example, points out that non-reversible low-voltage connectors seem hard to find. He writes: "A simple solution is to use 'choc blocks' of appropriate size. Fit the 'live' block with a prong for the negative connection and the 'fed' block with a prong for the positive connection: see **Fig 3**. The screws holding the prongs should be tightened and made 'blind' or 'capped' with Araldite or Blu-Tack. The standard small size block takes wire up to 3mm in diameter, the next size takes prongs from old round-pin 5A mains plugs. Cut the prongs the same length as the block. Mate the two and tighten the socket screws."

The idea seemed familiar and a little searching unearthed an item 'D-I-Y general-purpose connectors' (*TT*, October 1977, p785) in which Les Mitchell, G3BHK, described home-made connectors made from off-cuts of the widely-used terminal blocks, with 'plugs' formed from brass or copper nails of suitable size with the heads cut off. G3BHK wrote: "By using these connectors (**Fig 4**), which (then) cost around 10p each, you can match any

cable to any other. I mark the screws to be loosened or tightened by dabbing a hot soldering iron on the side of the terminal block adjacent to the screw involved. Perhaps an even better system would be to cut off some of the plastics sleeves above these screws in order to indicate the ones needing a screwdriver to make or break the connections. The only safety point to watch is that on the output connector from a power unit the positive side ends in a 'non-nail' connection, with the nail making the negative connection.

"I have found this a most useful dodge; for instance if you have a pair of headphones with a large jack plug that will not fit a receiver having a small socket, it is possible just to break this connector and fit the lead to a small jack plug in a matter of seconds. Or again, one power unit will connect to any of a number of units each with their own different socket arrangements - a real boon to the experimenter."

At the time, I did add a comment that, from the viewpoint of safety, it may not be advisable to use the same type of connector for low and high voltages. Such connectors are best restricted to low-voltages.

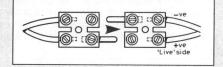

Fig 3: G0MZI's non-reversible low-voltage connectors using 'choc blocks'.

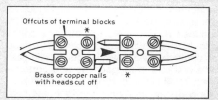

Fig 4: G3BAK's 1977 version of the non-reversible connectors made from terminal strips. The screws marked * indicate the ones to be loosened or tightened.

---

pole. The inductors should be positioned near the maximum-current points in the 21MHz dipole. When operating at 7MHz they carry only half the maximum current. Taking this and the frequency difference into account, the inductors present about six times more loading effect on 21MHz than they do on 7MHz. Thus they increase the electrical length correspondingly more on 21MHz.

"In a practical antenna, the two design and adjustment variables are the inductance of the loading coils, and the overall length of the dipole. Rather than worry too much about putting the inductors at the exact maximum-current points for 21MHz, I suggest they be positioned 20ft from the centre, and the final length adjustment made in the outer section without changing the position of the inductors.

"A good value for the inductors is 0.5μH, corresponding to four turns on a 1.5in plastic tube, spaced over about 1.3in. A good starting point for the overall length is 66.5ft.

"For an antenna height of 30ft, MININEC predicts a 21MHz resonant impedance of 82Ω, giving an SWR of 1.65 on a 50Ω line. A 75Ω quarter-wave section could be used (as suggested by W2XM in the March item) to

reduce this mismatch to about 1.3. The 'ideal' antenna impedance when this arrangement is used would be 112Ω, but the good news is that over-compensation at resonance will widen the SWR bandwidth, somewhat offsetting the inevitably narrower bandwidth of a long antenna. Note that these inductors are not 'traps' merely slight loading to adjust the electrical length. The bandwidth of the antenna is not significantly affected by their presence."

CONSTRUCTIONAL HINTS AND KINKS

A SERIES OF INTRODUCTORY ARTICLES 'Build it yourself from QST' by Bruce S Hale, KB1MW/7, has been running in *QST*. Part 2 in the May, 1992 issue, has some interesting notes on the use of 'ground-plane construction' - the technique that has been advocated many times in *TT* under its colloquial name of 'ugly construction'. It has been suggested that such construction is more suitable for one-off, home-built projects and for experimental prototypes than the commonly used home-etched printed circuit board.

KB1MW/7 introduces ground-plane construction as follows: "Ground-plane, sometimes call ugly construction, is simple: You build the circuit on an unetched piece of copper-clad circuit board. Wherever a component connects to ground, you solder it to the copper board. Ungrounded connections between components are made point-to-point.

"Once you learn how to build with a ground-plane board, you can grab a piece of circuit board and start building any time you see an interesting circuit. It's easy to trace and modify a ground-plane circuit. Ham designers generally also find that building on a large copper ground plane makes most MF/HF circuits more stable than building them on a PC board - at least until the PC board version goes through several iterations to cure circuit instabilities.

"Building a ground-plane board is fun, and I think it's more rewarding than simply stuffing and soldering a PC board. Ground-plane construction is something like model building, connecting parts using solder almost - but not exactly - like glue. Because you build the circuit directly from the schematic, ground-plane construction can help you get familiar with a circuit and how it works much better than etched-PC-board construction can.

"Ground-plane construction is very flexible because you can build subsections of a large circuit as small ground-plane modules and string them together into a larger design . . . . Don't be bashful about how your ground-plane projects look. It probably won't look as slick as an etched-PC-board circuit or factory produced rig . . . . Part of the philosophy behind ground-plane construction is that you don't have to build 'pretty' to build radio gear that's first-rate in ruggedness and performance . . . . Building is supposed to be fun."

One of the problems facing home-construction as well as factory-produced HF equipment is the ever-rising cost of specialised high-voltage components. A useful trip for keeping the cost of high-voltage variable capacitors (of more than about 150pF maximum) within reason is given by Sherman L Lovell, WY7F, in *QST's* 'Hints and Kinks' May 1992, p74. WY7F points out that some TUs etc require 350pF capacitors with the plates spaced great enough to handle high voltages - difficult to find in boot sales or rallies and now horrendously expensive new.

His solution is to cut glass microscope slides (purchased at his local college bookstore) to the correct length with a common roller-type glass cutter, and slipping the cut slides into the gaps between the plates of a 100pF or 150pF high-voltage capacitor. The high dielectric constant of glass will about double the maximum capacitance while improving rather than reducing the voltage rating of the capacitor (provided that this is limited by the inter-vane spacing). A quick application of general purpose silicone sealant serves to secure the slides. Its rubbery texture provides some isolation from mechanical shock. The glass chosen should fill the air gap between the vanes as much as possible to assure maximum capacitance increase. Barry Kirkwood, ZL1BN, mentions that the 'Dr Gary Bold' credited in the June *TT* (p37) as the author of the 1972 IEEE Trans Ant & Prop paper on the focussing of HF signals at the antipodes is ZL1AN who now writes a regular column ('The Morseman') in

ALUMINIUM DRINKS-CAN BATTERIES

JOHN BEECH, G8SEQ, NOTED the recent items on solar power and lemon juice batteries with interest. Normally he uses a foot-square solar panel to float charge the 7Ah nicad battery that runs his QRP rig. This allows several hours operation at up to 10W output on 50 or 144MHz.

But he considers that lemon-juice batteries too juvenile an approach. In 1972, in an era of power cuts, he investigated ways of providing a little light without resorting to candles or other smoky fuels and overcoming the shortage of batteries. He writes:

"The batteries I made used aluminium film cans and stranded copper wire as electrodes. For electrolyte I first tried salty water. The cells generated plenty of voltage but didn't last long due to lack of a depolariser. It was then I realised that there was a cheap, readily available depolarizing agent in the house - bleach!

"I have since then demonstrated at a special-event station how to run a 2W 144MHz transceiver using a battery of aluminium drinks-can cells to recharge the nicad pack in the transceiver at about 50mA. After recharging the nicad for about an hour I could monitor continuously at low volume (squelched receiver) and transmit at 100mW or 2W for brief periods. If I had recharged the nicad overnight I could have had several hours of normal operating.

"More recently (June 1992) I have repeated the experiment in order to show a Novice-pupil how it is done. Using a drinks can with the internal coating scratched off

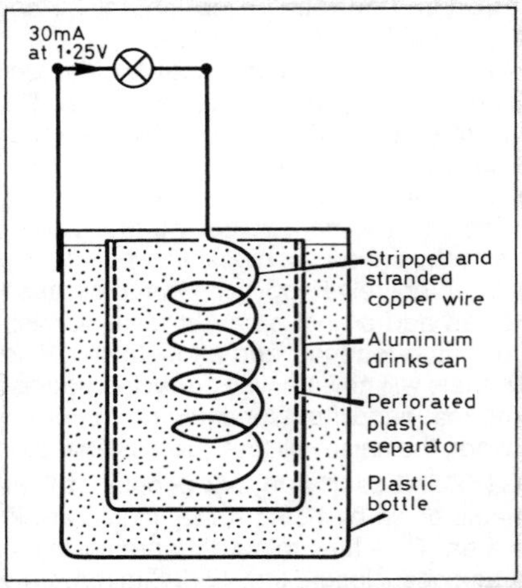

Fig 5: G8SEQ's home made battery using aluminium drinks cans (empty first!) inside plastic bottle. Two in series provide enough power to light to full brightness an 'ultra bright LED' (no need for a series resistor). The aluminium and the bleach become used up. A carbon electrode (Barbecue charcoal) might give a higher output voltage.

and bits of plastic and gravel as separators I constructed a cell which would deliver 30mA at 1.25V *continuously* and with a short-circuit current of some 300mA peak settling to 80mA at a terminal voltage of about 0.15V. I suspect that even higher currents could be achieved by burning off the internal coating of the can and using more concentrated electrolyte (I added about a tablespoon of salt to 500ml of bleach). **Fig 5** shows details."

Break-in, and who has also developed an excellent computer-aided learning system to teach Morse.

TIPS AND TOPICS

In the November *TT*, I raised the question of the performance of the Canadian VHF D/F loop with internal sensing (*TT*, June 1991). However even before this note appeared, Dave Lauder, G1OSC, reported his experiences. Incidentally, these seem to bear out some of the November *TT* comments on the problems associated with unbalanced loops. It also highlights other difficulties that seem to reduce the value of this design other than for fixed-frequency operation for which it was evidently designed. G1OSC writes: "I built one of these loops and found that the length of the coax has to be an electrical half-wavelength before half the screen is removed. I found it impractical to tune by trimming the cable, even using a spectrum analyser with tracking generator and directional arrangement which can cover 145MHz plus/minus 1.3MHz: see **Fig 6**. "Even when tuned, it did not stay precisely tuned as the URM43 coax I used was not phase-stable enough. I also found that it has a very narrow bandwidth and while it may be suitable for fixed frequency operation, it can only cover a small portion of the 144MHz band (about 200kHz) without retuning. Within this range I found the direc-

tion of the null varies significantly with frequency, so each time it is used it needs to be tuned, then calibrated with a signal in a known direction on the same frequency that is to be used for direction finding!

"Another problem is that the counterpoise for the unscreened omnidirectional part of the antenna appears to be the feeder cable. When I fitted a quarter-wave coaxial sleeve balun to suppress currents on the outside of the feeder coax, I could no longer get a cardioid response. The only use I can see for it is as a sense antenna to resolve the 180° ambiguity of another antenna such as an ordinary D/F loop". G1OSC wonders whether others have been successful.

Sheer nostalgia: George Young, ZS1Y, in a two-part *Radio ZS* article on 'when radio was fascinating' writes: "In the 1990s with everybody from delivery boys, traffic cops, doctors to sports referees spouting into portable R/T, and the ham bands 90 per cent SSB, and QRL every weekend with CQ TEST which switches everybody else off, the romance has gone. What Morse we hear is canned stuff from a machine - a dying talent in an age of satellite communications and telex . . . . After 55 years of punching the same (manual) Morse key it will have to see me out . . . . The six spare 6146 tubes will keep me on the air since those now in my transmitters have been going for 20 years and still emit the same signal strength." **G3VA**

W2DU-TYPE CURRENT BALUN

CONSTRUCTIONAL DETAILS of a wide-band W2DU-type choke-balun for minimising outer-braid current on coaxial feeders connected to dipole-type balanced elements over the range 2 to 30MHz are given in "Reflecties door", PA0SE, (*Electron*, April 1992, p189) reproduced from "Le Balun W2DU" by Maurice Limes, F6ELM (*Radio-REF*, October 1991): **Fig 7**. The 50 ferrite beads are Amidon type FB-73-2401 (outer diameter 9.7mm, inner diameter 5mm, length 4.8mm, permeability about 2500) and are slipped over a length of RG141 (50ohm) coaxial cable using two spirals of Teflon thread to secure them. This is then sealed (waterproofed) into a length of PVC tubing with an inner diameter of 16mm, using a rubberized adhesive filler given as Dow Corning Silastic 7338 (or UK equivalent). Impedance of this choke balun is stated to be more than 800Ω throughout the range 2 to 30MHz, peaking to about 1500Ω between 7 and 10MHz.

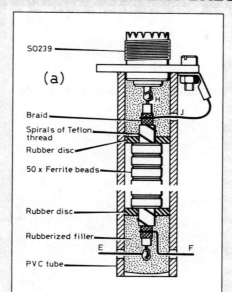

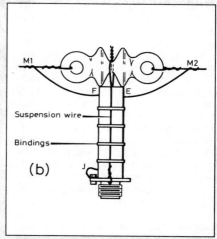

Fig 7: (a) Mechanical details of the W2DU-type wideband choke balun as constructed by F6EIM. (b) The balun suspended to feed a dipole-type wire element.

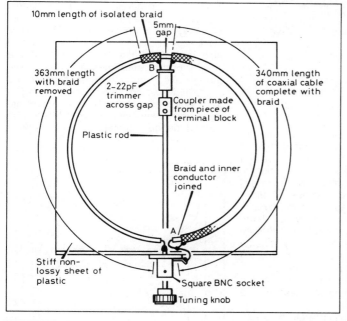

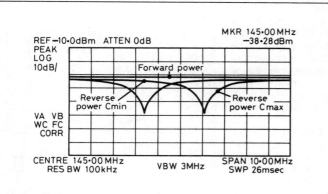

Fig 6: G1OSC's modified form of tuneable Canadian D/F loop but still presenting the need for calibration of the null at the specific frequency use. The critical factor proved to be the length of the coax with the braid on. This appears to need to be an electrical quarter-wave so that it transforms the short-circuit at point A to a high impedance at point B. Coax is URM43 with good quality woven braid. Cheap RG-58-type cable with sparse braid does not work.

PLIERS-TYPE RF CURRENT PROBE

IN THE JULY *TT*, p39, Dave Plumridge, G3KMG, mentioned that he had seen "many years ago in *TT*" a device involving a spring-type of clothes peg with two half toroids which could be clipped round a coax cable to form a current transformer with diode rectifier and meter, that could be used to measure the current flowing on the outer-braid of a coax feeder cable (or the RF current flowing in an antenna wire-element or an open-wire feeder).

This has brought in some correspondence. Colin Greenaway, G3UGG, Eric Sandys, GI2FHN, and Malcolm Horton, G4DMH, explained why I had not been able to trace the item in *TT*: the reason was simple - it was not in *TT* but described in an article by M R Irving, G3ZHY, 'The peg antenna meter' (*RadCom*, May 1972, pp297 and 301). G3ZHY pointed out that he had used a small toroid that would fit over a wire conductor or small-diameter coaxial cable but the two halves would not close on thicker cables, and his device had not been intended to work above about 3.5MHz. He had noted that "the only items needed are those components shown in **Fig 1**, some fixing cement such as Plastic Padding, together with a hand-drill, hacksaw and a small file. A little patience is required when cutting the ferrite ring, and two attempts were necessary by the author before obtaining a satisfactory clean break. Those seeking perfection should try to obtain the use of a jeweller's diamond saw."

Dick Rollema, PA0SE, also noticed G3KMG's remarks and has sent along full details of a rather more ambitious pliers-type RF current probe (Photo and **Fig 2**) that he described in his 'Reflecties door PA0SE' column in *Electron* (VERON) in July 1990. He writes: "Such devices are widely used by the 50Hz power people. In German it is called a stromzange, in Dutch a stroomtang (ie current pliers).

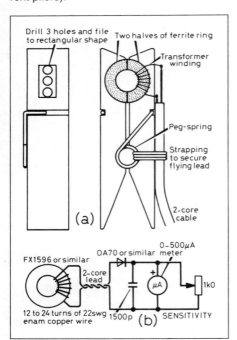

Fig 1: (a) Basic constructional details of G3ZHY's peg sensor as described in 1972. (b) The complete ferrite ring RF meter.

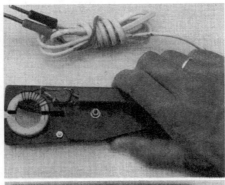

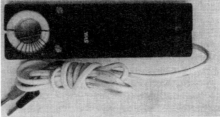

The PA0SE pliers-type RF current probe.

"When the toroid is clamped over a conductor the latter acts as a one-turn primary of a current transformer, the winding on the toroid core forming the secondary. Thus, in Fig 2 the secondary current flows through R resulting in an RF voltage across R. This is rectified by diode D, and after the bypass capacitor C fed to a high-resistance voltmeter; a digital type is easy to read. [Note that the voltmeter must be far enough away from the source of RF to ensure that there is no direct pick-up - *G3VA*]. To make the reading independent of frequency, the reactance of the secondary winding should be at least 5R = 5 x 56Ω = 280Ω.

"I used a 'violet' Philips toroid of 38mm outer-diameter, 4C6 ferrite, μ = 125. The measured self-inductance of the winding is 15.6μH, (before splitting the ring it was 17.7μH, showing the effect of the two airgaps, even though the two halves fit together perfectly). The 15.7μH inductance results in a reactance of 345Ω at 3.5MHz so is more than enough. On 1.8MHz, the reactance is only 177Ω, introducing an error of almost 5%, but nevertheless still a useful sensor.

"The difficult part is splitting the ring. First, make two sharp notches opposite each other, using a file (a thin diamond disc would be ideal if you are on good terms with your dentist). The toroid is then clamped with its lower half in a vice. A piece of wood is put against the upper half and struck a blow with a hammer. With luck, a clean fracture . . . . without it, try again. My second try was successful. After the secondary winding has been wound on, the two halves are fitted to the 'pliers' with some epoxy.

"I made my 'pliers' out of paxolin, but other materials such as perspex, suggest themselves. The toroid is kept closed by a spring and opens when the 'pliers' are squeezed. Keep the two halves in the closed position while the epoxy cures. Be very careful that no epoxy gets into the gaps between the two parts of the ring (voice of experience)!

"To calibrate the sensor, I used the arrangement shown in **Fig 3**. The sensor is clamped over the upturned U-loop. The transmitter should have variable CW output. R is a 50Ω dummy load. If the meter, V, shows a voltage of U_{dc} then the current through the loop is $I_{rms} = (0.707 (U_{dc} + 1.2V))/50Ω$. The 1.2V accounts for the voltage drop across the two silicon point-contact diodes. By varying the transmitter output (do not exceed the maximum permissible voltage across the diodes) the DC output voltage of the sensor can be plotted against the primary RF current. I found a perfectly linear response when the RF current was 50mA or more. Below that value the diode in the sensor introduces some non-linearity. The conversion factor in my case worked out at 5VDC per 1A RF current. The response proved frequency independent up to at least 30MHz.

"I have found this RF current probe a most useful device. I use a long-wire antenna about 37m long on 1.8, 3.5 and 7MHz. The wire is fed directly at one end via an L-network. The 'cold' side of the network is connected to a radiator of the central heating system. The current sensor shows that indeed most of the current flows via the radiator pipe to earth. But considerable current also flows via the mains-cord of the transmitter with even some via the earthed triangular metal mast that supports

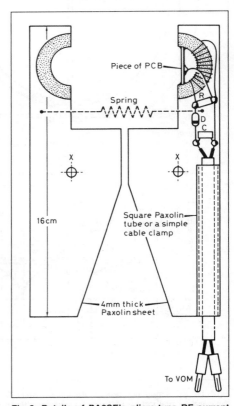

Fig 2: Details of PA0SE's pliers-type RF current probe. R is 56Ω 0.25W. D is germanium point-contact diode. C is 10nF ceramic. Philips toroid OD 37mm, Ferrite 4C6 μ125, violet. Winding 10 turns of 27SWG enamelled wire. Inductance is about 15.7μH.

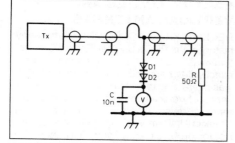

Fig 3: Arrangement used for calibrating the probe. D silicon point-contact diodes, R 50Ω, C 10n ceramic capacitor.

one end of the antenna. It is interesting to note that the current does not divide evenly over the structural elements of the mast!

"I have also used the current probe to check the current in the loops of my 'Optiquad' antenna. It was gratifying to note that on 28, 21 and 14MHz, where I made my measurements, current maxima occurred at the expected positions and also that the current in the left and right halves of the loop were equal. This showed that the baluns were performing correctly although I already knew that because the sensor detected no current on the outside of the coaxial feeder cables connected to the baluns (the baluns used by PA0SE were described in *Eurotek* by G4LQI, *RadCom*, August 1992, p51).

"To sum it up. I consider that an RF current probe of this type is a must for serious antenna experimenters."

Wire-loop current probes and their uses are described by Les Moxon, G6XN, in *HF Antennas for all locations* (p237) and a ferrite probe with a fixed gap in the toroid was included in *TT*, November 1984, stemming from Dick Kelsall, G4FM. This was basically similar to the PA0SE probe but without the advantage of being able to open and close the gap so that it could be used with large diameter cables etc. G4FM also experienced the problem of cutting ferrite cores without fracturing them. His solution was to cast the ring in polyester resin (from a glass fibre repair kit) inside a suitable piece of plastic tubing resting on a sheet of glass laminate. When the resin was set he was able to file a slot through the resin and ferrite core without difficulty.

DECOUPLING CAPACITORS - WHY USE TWO WHEN ONE WILL DO?

SOME COMMON CIRCUIT TECHNIQUES tend to be accepted as the thing to do without anyone questioning them. Once the technique becomes common practice it acquires an air of authority and a momentum of its own. One such technique could be the use of a parallel combination of large-value and small-value capacitors to extend the effectiveness of RF bypassing over an extended frequency range.

The technique probably stemmed from the long established system of connecting an RF-type capacitor (ceramic or mica etc) across an high-value electrolytic capacitor when it is necessary to provide RF bypassing/decoupling. This was (and is) an effective system since electrolytic capacitors tend to be very ineffective for RF bypassing, although provid-

FULL-WAVE ENVELOPE DETECTOR

FERGUS VEITCH, G4LEV, draws attention to an item in the 'Ideas for Design' feature of *Electronic Design*, May 14, 1992, pp94-95. This is entitled 'Envelope Detector is Very Simple' by Thomas J Schum.

This points out that envelope detectors are simpler and less expensive than synchronous detectors but have non-zero rectification thresholds and are thus less sensitive. Schum presents a two-transistor circuit (**Fig 4**) that is claimed to provide the best of both worlds: it offers the virtually zero rectification threshold of a synchronous detector, but without the complexity. The arrangement is described as follows: "The circuit is an amplifying full-wave envelope detector that has two transistors connected in parallel except for their bases, which are driven by RF signals that are 180° out of phase. For biasing purposes, the two transistors are treated as a single Class A device.

"The method of driving the transistors out of phase with one another has two main effects. First, thanks to emitter coupling between the transistors, this type of detector smooths the portion of the conduction function near the zero crossing, where control passes from one transistor to the other. Second, due to collector coupling, the circuit eliminates the positive excursions of the output, allowing only the negative half of the amplified envelope . . . . Because the detector can amplify, it can be made extremely rugged by keep-

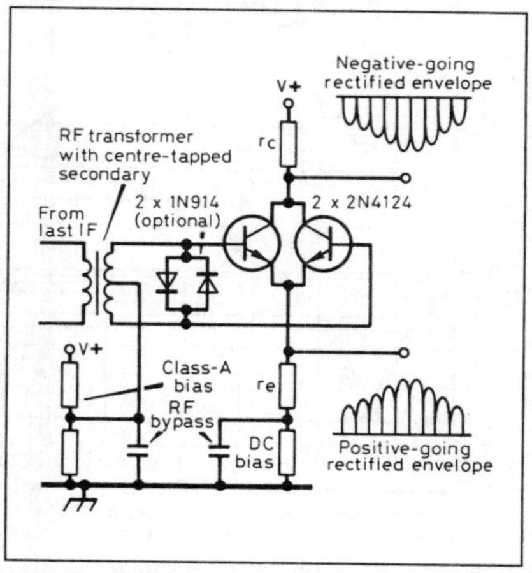

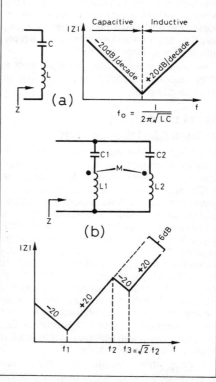

Fig 4: Claimed as simple yet sensitive, this amplifying full-wave detector circuit has almost zero rectification threshold and presents a highly linear RF load to a final IF stage. The gain for the collector output is given approximately by r_c/r_e. The emitter output gain is slightly less than unity.

ing the average input voltage below 0.1V and by placing clipping diodes across the RF input as shown in Fig 4. Because the detector threshold is virtually non-existent, it presents a highly linear RF load to the final IF stage. That feature, together with the fact that the detector can work with very low level signals, can significantly simplify the design of the final IF stage."

ing low impedance at 50-100Hz and audio frequencies. It must therefore have seemed logical to adopt this approach when providing RF bypassing in low-impedance solid-state circuits such as power amplifiers when an RF decoupling capacitor may need to be of the order of 0.1µF or so and capable of passing significant RF current.

But should such capacitors be augmented by a second, lower-value capacitor? This is common practice and a typical arrangement is shown, for example, in the 15 Watt linear amplifier in the highly-respected ARRL book 'Solid State Design for the Radio Amateur' (Chapter 4) [Available from RSGB; see p78].

Dr Brian Austin, G0GSF, draws attention to a paper 'Effectiveness of Multiple Decoupling Capacitors' by Clayton R Paul (University of Kentucky) in *IEEE Transactions on Electromagnetic Compatibility*, May 1992, pp130-133. This calls into question the effectiveness of using a parallel combination of large-value and small-value capacitors to increase the effectiveness at the higher frequencies and to overcome the effect of lead inductance. With detailed mathematical analysis, computed and experimental results, the author shows that this scheme is *not* significantly effective: **Figs 5 and 6**. The improvement at high frequencies is at most 6dB over the use of a single large value capacitor.

The paper concludes that the use of a small-value capacitor in parallel with a larger-value capacitor only minimally reduces the high-frequency impedance of either capaci-

Fig 5: (a) The effect of lead inductance on capacitor impedance with minimum impedance at the self-resonant frequency. (b) Equivalent circuit for parallel decoupling capacitors and the Bode plot of impedance.

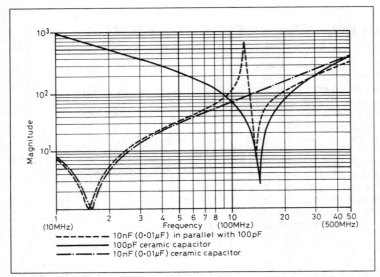

Fig 6: Measured impedances of a 0.01μF and a 100pF ceramic capacitor individually and in parallel from 10 to 500MHz. (*Source Paul, IEEE Trans EMC*).

tor. A rather large reduction in impedance occurs only over a very small frequency range. Component and installation variations can cause this narrow range to vary in frequency so that the seeming benefit cannot be relied upon: "Therefore this scheme does not significantly improve the high-frequency impedance of capacitors above their self-resonant frequencies. Between the self-resonant frequencies of the two capacitors, the impedance of the parallel combination exhibits a resonance where the impedance is actually larger than that of either capacitor. Above the self-resonant frequencies of both capacitors, the impedance of the parallel combination is reduced at most by 6dB. This high-frequency reduction of some 6dB may not be worth the expense of the additional capacitor or its installation and could be attained by using only the larger value capacitor while simply cutting its lead lengths in half!"

As G0GSF puts it: "This paper presents a good case against doing what we have all taken for granted."

ANGLO-POLISH CLANDESTINE RADIOS

IN *TT*, JULY 1990, p31, I gave some background information on the highly-regarded series of clandestine radios designed at the Polish Radio Centre Workshops at Stanmore between 1942 and 1945, including some details of the AP5 transmitter-receiver that had a 16W 6L6 transmitter and 6K8/6SJ7/6SC7 superhet receiver. Since then it has become clear that there are still quite a few of the AP-series equipments around but that collectors find it difficult to identify positively which model they hold. It has also emerged, thanks to F C P Flanner, G3AVE, that many of these transmitters were built in Birmingham by Monitor Radio Company, located at Stechford Birmingham, a firm with which a number of local amateurs were involved.

Although there also appears to have been a few models that do not fall into any of the main types, the majority of sets were as follows (the AP classification was adopted by 1943 to avoid confusion with SOE models A-1, A-2 and A-3). All the Polish A/AP models

used a similar metal enclosure as illustrated in the July 1990 *RadCom*, with a single 6L6 as transmitter, and 5Z4 rectifier, but differed in frequency coverage, receiver line-up and component placement. The receivers all had regenerative detectors (the super-gainer form of superhet) with an IF of about 1.5MHz:

A-1, 3.5-9.5MHz, 2 valve superhet 6K8-6SC7

A-2, 3.5-15MHz (Tx 4-8 and 8-16MHz), 3V 6K8-6SJ7-6SC7

A-3, 2-8MHz, 2V superhet 6K8-6SC7

AP-4, 2-8MHz, 3V superhet 6K8-6SJ7-6SC7

AP-5, 2-16MHz (3 wavebands), 3V 6K8-6SJ7-6SC7

The AP4 models were used for medium-distance working, for example for UK-France links, whereas the AP-5 for the longer distance UK-Poland links. Some of the Polish 15/16MHz sets were also dropped into Czechoslovakia. The higher-power BP3, BP4 and BP5 sets used a 829 double-tetrode with a power of some 60 Watts. BP3 and BP5 covered 2-8MHz, the BP4 4-16MHz. All BP models used a four-valve superhet receiver: 6K8-6SK7-6SQ7-6SC7 with an IF about 1.5MHz.

Many of the AP5 sets seem to have been built by Monitor Radio under guidance of Polish technicians who regularly visited the factory. The company, set up in 1939 or 1940, was located at the Parkinson Stove Company, Stechford, Birmingham in a building formerly housing the Gas Lamp Street Lighting Department of Parkinson's whose street lighting business had been reduced by the black-out restrictions. Monitor also manufactured Eureka 210MHz beacons which were dropped into Europe to guide Allied aircraft to agent dropping zones or to special bombing targets. The Eureka/Rebecca system as used in this way was a form of secondary radar with the Eureka transponder forming the ground element and Rebecca the airborne component. It was designed at TRE and a later version was used by paratroops during the Normandy campaign.

According to G3AVE, among those associated with Monitor Radio were Colonel Colley (licensed amateur but callsign unknown), George Brown, G5BJ (who introduced VHF radio to the Birmingham Police in 1942), George Flanner, G3KBA/T, Ken Field, G3PVT, Bruce Raynor, G4FYN etc.

EARTHS, LOSSES AND VERTICAL ANTENNAS

RECENTLY, I WAS CHECKING ON the early history of the BBC's original 'Empire Service' that was launched from Daventry almost exactly 60 years ago, in November 1932. It was interesting to find that the quite complex series of vertically-polarized directional antenna arrays, plus some omnidirectional Franklin Uniform vertically polarized antennas for the 49, 31, 25, 19 and 16m bands, had proved unsatisfactory. They provided weaker than expected signals into the various target zones from the two 10kW STC transmitters, and as a result the BBC engineers began a series of experiments with horizontally-polarized dipoles. These were initially strung from the 500ft masts used for the original 1600m Daventry long-wave station opened in 1925. This has since been relocated to Droitwich.

As described in Edward Pawley's *Engineering History of the BBC, 1922-72*: "Early in 1933 it became clear from reports from listeners that the Daventry transmissions were not being received as well as might be expected and poor performance of the transmitting aerials appeared to be a likely cause. A series of experiments with different types of aerial was undertaken, the first step being to suspend simple horizontal dipoles from the 500ft masts carrying the Daventry long-wave aerial and to compare their performance with that of the existing low vertical aerials. The first test was made in May 1933 to compare directly a high horizontal half-wave dipole (10 wavelengths above the ground) dimensioned for an operating frequency of 11.86MHz - with one of the low vertically-polarized non-directional aerials.

"The results of this comparative test were quite definite and showed the high aerial to give a gain of 5 to 10dB in the strength of the signals received in Buenos Aires and Bermuda. In December 1933 a high horizontal half-wave dipole dimensioned for 9.7MHz was compared with a low vertical four-element aerial operating on the same wavelength and oriented on India. The high dipole was found to give equal strength signals in Ceylon (Sri Lanka), on the centre line of the directional transmission, although the theoretical gain of the four-element aerial was 9dB above that of the non-directional dipole. At this time it was not known whether the superiority of the horizontal aerial was due to its polarisation or to its height above ground."

Pawley describes how further tests were made between October 1934 and March 1935 with eleven different antennas on 12MHz, using 350ft towers, in order to determine the choice between horizontally and vertically polarized antennas and to discover the minimum mast height for optimum reception with a given transmitter power. The conclusion reached was that, at least at Daventry, horizontally-polarized antennas were better than vertical, that it would be unnecessary to have more than four horizontal radiators stacked vertically at half-wave intervals, and that the lowest element should be not less than one-wavelength above ground.

Since then, to the best of my knowledge, HF broadcast antennas have been horizontally polarized for sky-wave transmission whereas medium- and long-wave broadcast antennas are almost invariably vertically-polarized in order to provide maximum ground-wave coverage, although I recall a *TT* item about a Telefunken MW T-antenna design that could be switched at night to horizontal polarization for medium-distance skywave coverage.

Radio amateurs, of course, are seldom able to have their antenna elements a full wavelength above ground - at least on most of the lower frequency bands - and have learned how to make reasonably effective use of vertically-polarized antennas including ground-planes and phased arrays of monopoles. It should however always be appreciated that vertical antennas close to the ground, whether tuned against real earth, elevated radials, or as vertical dipoles, have a performance that is significantly affected by ground conductivity and the presence (in domestic environments) of many vertical 'lossy' objects. It is partly for this reason that amateurs usually find that elevated ground-plane type antennas perform significantly better than monopoles, even where these have a good earth-screen. All those text books that show monopoles with optimum radiation right down to zero elevation are, for most amateurs, just wishful thinking, unless operating /MM.

In *TT*, January 1985, Les Mitchell, G3BHK, underlined that, for most amateurs, the domestic environment includes many lossy, conductive and semi-conductive objects, the majority of which tend to be vertically inclined (**Fig 7**) and to have a significant effect on either the radiated pattern of an antenna, or else absorb and dissipate a significant amount of the energy radiated from the antenna. It should be appreciated that whereas a resonant insulated guy wire, for example, will re-radiate most of the energy it picks up (affecting the radiation pattern but not the total power radiated) lossy objects, such as a tree trunk, a building, poorly-conductive earth, etc, will dissipate a large proportion of the energy induced or fed into them. This loss tends to be significantly greater for vertically-polarized antennas than those horizontally-polarized.

However, Les Moxon, G6XN, has recently sent along some notes on an improved form of a type of vertically-polarized antenna that has been featured a number of times in *TT* following my use of it in the early 1970s: the inverted ground-plane (or Vertical-Tee). The following notes and **Fig 8** will eventually appear in a new edition of his *HF Antennas for All Locations* book:

"Starting from ground level an increase of height of ground-plane antennas with suitable attention to loading and tuning can be expected to result in greater efficiency due to the disappearance of ground losses. Up to 3dB of gain due to height can be expected, as well as a better chance of clearing obstructions. This process, pursued to its limit, results in antennas such as the inverted ground-plane: Fig 8(a): the two-wire form shown at Fig 8(b) improves bandwidth, reduces end-voltages, and assists with matching to coaxial line. It may be noted that this method requires shortening of the radiator by about one-sixteenth of a wavelength, a matter of little consequence since R is reduced by only 15%.

"The arrangement of Fig 8(b), which scores

heavily in terms of convenience, was compared experimentally with the Zepp feed form shown in Fig 8(c), with and without a G6CJ-type balancing stub. Apart from establishing the credentials of the new method, the results were highly instructive. Differences in field strengths were small provided the current on the outer of the coaxial cable was sufficiently low, a condition achievable in the case of the Zepp by using *either* the stub *or* the more convenient linear trap. As this was a one-off experiment it should not be assumed to apply in other cases without further checking, but it would appear that the absence of any path to ground ensures that the same current has to flow in both feeder wires. In the case of Fig 8(b) the trap was needed only in the event of maladjustment of L. Bandwidth was adequate for coverage of the 21MHz band even in the case of the Zepp feed.

"If vertical polarization is favoured and two supports are available the inverted ground-plane antenna of Fig 8(b) can be recommended. This can also be used as a horizontal half-wave dipole or a top-loaded ground-plane antenna at half the frequency."

Les also mentions that at long last the ARRL have accepted his 20Ω figure for the radiation resistance of a ground-plane antenna, as this has now been backed by their own computer study. The recognition that, as he has often pointed out, the GPA is a form of dipole and not a form of monopole antenna has a devastating effect on a large number of sacred cows but, adds G6XN "it may be more than a coincidence that the large numbers of radials demanded by some authors ties in very closely with the mesh size requirements specified by Proctor 'Input impedance of horizontal dipole aerials at low heights above the ground' (*Proc IEEE*, part 3, May 1950) - a very important reference since it is possible to extrapolate from **Fig 9** etc to get an idea of ground losses in horizontal wires generally. Vertical wires do not induce significant losses. The reference also shows effect of ground screens."

My 1970s version of the inverted ground-plane antenna was derived as a single-element version of the Bobtail array mentioned and illustrated in the July *TT* (p39). This has encouraged Bill Wheeler, G3BFC, to comment as follows: "When *TT* first referred to the

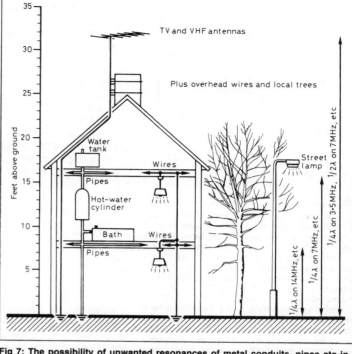

Fig 7: The possibility of unwanted resonances of metal conduits, pipes etc in a typical residential environment as suggested in *TT*, January 1985, by G3BLK. The houses can also have broadband resonances. Energy induced will be re-radiated by a lossless 'element' but will be absorbed by 'lossy' conductors, including the earth, building, tree trunks, etc.

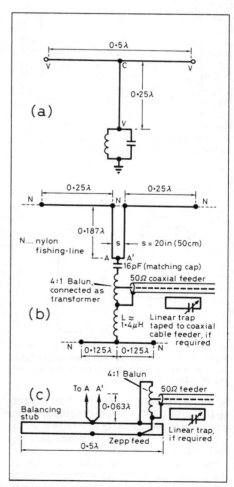

Fig 8: (a) Basic inverted ground-plane (also known as Vertical-Tee) antenna. (b) G6XN's recommended method of end-feeding from coaxial-cable. (c) Zepp form of feed as tested by G6XN.

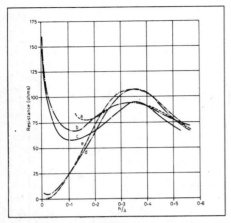

Fig 9: Measured input impedance of a resonant horizontal half-wave dipole above ground where h is height above ground. (a) Calculated for soil permittivity of 6. (b) Dry ground. (c) Wet ground. (d) Conducting mat (large, fine-mesh copper mat representing perfectly conducting ground for comparison purposes). (e) Calculated for infinite permittivity. Results quoted are for an open site covered with short grass and having a gravel subsoil, of which a sample measured a value of six after a long spell of fine weather. Above the dielectric ground there is a large increase in the radiation resistance of the antenna as it approaches ground-level. Close to the ground the radiation resistance is about double that of a similar antenna in free space. (Source: Proctor, *Proc IEE*, Part 3, May 1950)

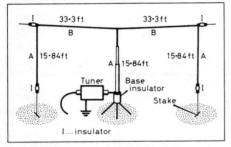

Fig 10: Bobtail curtain for 14MHz as originally used by G3BFC at 9Y4BFC in 1970.

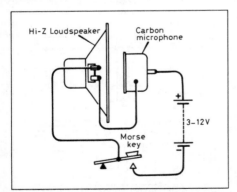

Fig 11: KISS form of Morse code practice oscillator using the howl-round between carbon microphone and speaker or headphone.

Bobtail in 1970, I was living in Trinidad and operating 9Y4BFC. I constructed the antenna as shown in **Fig 10** using four radials and a tuned LC circuit. It performed well over the 4500-mile path to the UK in the evenings on 14MHz. Later, back in the UK, I returned to the Bobtail using the same approach as at 9Y4BFC. My near neighbour, Bill Sykes, G2HCG, suggested that I omit the radials and LC and replace them with a tuned closed stub - this worked well. Then along came 'Con-

trolled feeder radiation' (CFR) by G2HCG in *RadCom*, May 1990 and July 1991. So my Bobtail was made simpler still using CFR in accordance with the July, 1991 article again with good performance. However, size was then reduced to two vertical elements instead of three, but with each carrying equal current rather than the original version in which the two outer of the three elements carried half the current of the centre element.

"Fig 5 of the July, 1992 *TT* showed a two vertical element form of Bobtail directly fed at the top with 52Ω co-axial cable although I consider the dimensions given in this account should be read in reverse. I have found a 28MHz version seems to work well when compared with a three-element monoband beam (not as well since the comparison is hardly a fair one).

"To sum up, of the various Bobtail-type configurations I have tried, the two element version using a tuned toroid as described in the two *RadCom* articles by Bill Sykes (the founder and Chairman for many years of Jaybeam Ltd) is well worth considering."

It seems to me that the G3BFC version with the 'reversed' dimensions changes the arrangement from a broadside array to an end-fire system, though both approaches seem logical enough.

While on the subject of vertically-polarized antennas, it seems worth noting a comment from C W ('Mick') Cragg, G2HDU, about my comment in the August *TT* that a folded monopole has lower earth losses than a simple monopole (not claimed by Tony Preedy, G3LNP, for his 'folded-tee' antenna). He writes: "This has been stated many times, and in many places, but I have never seen an acceptable proof. It seems to be taken for granted, but a little thought will show that in fact the earth current is the same as with a simple monopole, so that for a given earthing system the loss is the same. There is no question that the feed point impedance is higher since only half the current flows in each side of the folded monopole. However, both of these half currents flow in the earth so that the total earth current is the same as with a simple monopole. I would be interested to learn whether the antenna pundits agree."

While one could use two separate earths for a folded monopole putting the earth currents in 'parallel', this would be unusual and G2HCG appears to have a valid point, although there seems evidence that in practice the efficiency (as well as the effectiveness) of the folded version may be significantly higher.

AN EARTHED HOME?

DENNIS UNWIN, G0FMT, has come up with a novel solution to the problem of providing an effective earthing system for a 1.8MHz Marconi-type antenna. He writes: "I have a garden much too small for a λ/2 antenna on Top Band but can just manage a rather bent λ/4. A good earth is therefore needed. I started with two aluminium earth stakes just outside the shack window. This resulted in a feed impedance of 58Ω. Since the impedance of a quarter-wave antenna is of the order of 15Ω, this suggests an efficiency of about 15/58 = 26% (the figure of 15Ω was arrived at following extensive tests).

"I attempted to improve the efficiency by

increasing the number of earth stakes to five. This lowered the feed impedance to 46Ω, giving an efficiency of about 33%. A much folded counterpoise produced similar results, but using both earth stakes and counterpoise gave no further improvement. I then tried the effect of a length of wire draped around the floor of the shack on the ground floor of my bungalow. This resulted in a noticeable improvement, the feed impedance dropped and received signals increased slightly.

"My bungalow has solid floors over which carpet tiles have been laid. Some tiles in the shack, hall and a bedroom were lifted and two strips of self-adhesive copper foil, 20mm wide, were laid throughout this area, each about 15 metres long, and the ends connected to the ground point. With this arrangement the impedance had now dropped to 25Ω so efficiency was now about 60%. Used on its own, the copper foil earth was slightly superior to the five outside earth stakes but best results were obtained by using them together. If in fact my estimate of antenna impedance (15Ω) is too low (as has been suggested) then the figures become even more impressive.

"The copper strips seem too short to be acting as a counterpoise and calculations of the likely capacitance of the copper foil earth produced figures much too small to account for its performance. It was then realised that the concrete floor contains steel mesh reinforcement, and it is assumed that the foil is acting as capacitance coupling to the steel mesh ground sheet thoughtfully provided by the builder. It would perhaps have been just as effective to have used a layer of aluminium cooking foil covering the shack floor, but the system now works so well that I am not prepared to change it. I wonder how many other amateurs are literally sitting on an effective earthing system without realising it."

TIPS AND TOPICS

THERE CAN BE NO DOUBT that computer studies based on the Method of Moments software are providing antenna designers with a most valuable new tool. But such programs need to be used with care and a good understanding of basic antenna theory and practice. Also they need to be confirmed by practical experiments. There seems to be a growing tendency for some amateur-radio publications to publish designs based solely on computer studies. As Les Moxon, G6XN, puts it: "I'm afraid my attitude to computer studies tends to be highly sceptical. It is essential for conclusions to be reconciled with all the known facts. I feel there are far more computer addicts than experimenters with adequate factual knowledge, plus the necessary programming skills.

Roger Davis, ZS5L, in *Radio-ZS*, May 1992, p3 writes: "It amazes me that people go to extreme lengths to make the most complicated oscillators on which to practice Morse Code when with an old carbon microphone, a high impedance loudspeaker, a battery and a Morse key, an oscillator can be constructed that gives a good tone and works first time: **Fig 11**. The high impedance speaker can be replaced by an earpiece from an old pair of headphones or, once again, from an old telephone headset. An 8Ω speaker can be used but a 22Ω current limiting resistor must then be placed in series with the circuit. *G3VA*

THE ULTIMATE KISS RIG

TEN YEARS AGO (*TT*, November 1982, p961) I described the Whaddon wartime Mk VII/B ("Paraset") as about the simplest practical transmitter-receiver of the valve era. The Mk VII has a two valve regenerative 'straight' receiver (2 x 6SK7) and a crystal-controlled power-oscillator (6V6) that provided an output of about 4-5 watts RF between 3 and 8MHz. Later (*TT*, June 1987, pp409-410) a Dutch amateur, S Pauwe, described how he had 'modernized' the design to make it more suitable for use as a simple amateur rig on 3.5 and 7MHz by adding bandspread, sidetone, audio limiting and filtering, adding a 39V zener to maintain more constant HT on the screen of the regenerative detector, and upping the power output by using a 6L6 in place of the 6V6.

A few months later (*TT*, October 1987, pp748-749), Des Vance, GI3XZM, described a simple solid-state straight receiver that used a FET as an infinite impedance detector in conjunction with a bipolar Q-multiplier, using a total of just four active devices. The GI3XZM design has proved popular and a number of simple receivers have been described in *TT* and *Sprat* based on this approach.

Chris Garland, G3RJT, in conjunction with an article he wrote for the club magazine of the Denby Dale (Pie Hall) Radio Society - starting off with a simple crystal set but continuing with what he calls "An Active Crystal Set Receiver". This was inspired by the GI3XZM design but further simplified by substituting a 'drain bend detector' (akin to the once popular anode bend valve detector) for the infinite impedance detector. The extra gain meant that G3RJT could dispense with the two stages of audio amplification in the GI3XZM design and use a pair of high-impedance headphones fed directly from the FET, reducing the number of solid-state active devices to just two: **Fig 1**.

In practice, with a few other modifications, G3RJT found the performance good enough to use the design as the receiver section of a very simple 7MHz CW QRP rig that he calls "The Ultimate KISS" (**Fig 2**). The two-stage transmitter section with an RF output of about 5 watts uses a BFY51 driving an IRF510 low-cost power-FET.

G3RJT writes: "I call this rig 'Ultimate KISS' in the belief that it cannot be effectively simplified further. For example, the crystal oscillator has a level adjustment that operates only on receive, and permits the level of the oscillator signal picked up by the receiver to be adjusted so that it can be used as a stable BFO, very useful for working stations a few hundred Hertz away from the transmit frequency! It is doubtful if this would be possible if the transmitter had just a single power oscillator. The 'netting' facility it also provides of positively identifying the relationship of the transmit frequency to those of adjacent stations is similarly vital to satisfactory operating.

"For the receiver circuit of Fig 1, I also made some other modifications to the GI3XZM design with a view to achieving maximum performance from the Q-multiplier. I use a trimmer capacitor to couple the Q-Multiplier to the tuned circuit, so that the degree of coupling can be adjusted to the minimum necessary to obtain oscillation. This trimmer (CT1) is used in practice as a pre-set range adjustment for the reaction (regeneration) control, and eliminates the need for an expensive ten-turn potentiometer. I have also selected a high gain (greater than 400) sample for the Q-multiplier transistor (TR1). This also helps to minimise the coupling between the Q-multiplier and the tuned circuit, the aim being to achieve the highest possible Q before oscillation occurs.

"I use a moveable link to couple the antenna to the tuned circuit. This is adjusted to achieve sufficient coupling for satisfactory reception, thereby minimising the damping effect of the antenna. I have also introduced T/R switching facilities.

"The receiver is more fully described in the Denby Dale journal as a logical progression from a crystal set, and is, I believe, a highly suitable 'Novice' home-construction project, since it combines absolute simplicity with quite remarkable results! It has provided the most effective piece of simple electronic circuitry I have encountered in my entire career as an electronics engineer and radio amateur. I feel it might even be called a 'two transistor communications receiver'.

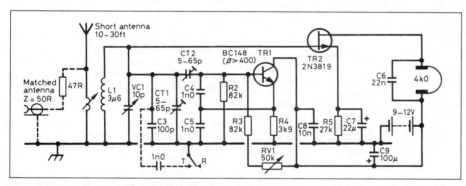

Fig 1: G3RJT's "Two-transistor communications receiver" or "Active crystal-set receiver" based on the 1987 design approach of GI3XZM but using a higher gain drain-bend detector that permits the omission of the two-transistor AF amplifier provided that high-impedance headphones of good sensitivity are used.

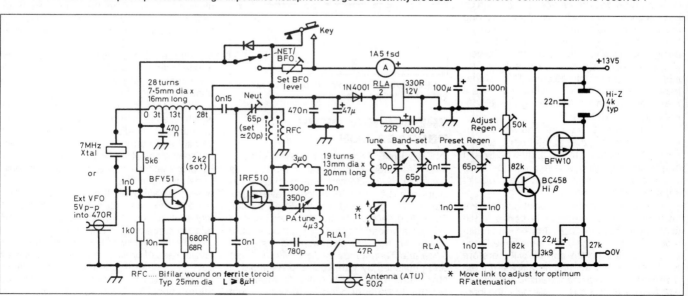

Fig 2: How G3RJT uses the simple receiver as the basis for his "Ultimate KISS transmitter-receiver" with a two-stage transmitter using a low-cost power-MOSFET to provide some 5-watts CW output on 7MHz.

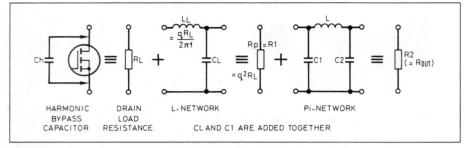

Fig 3: Development of the L-Pi tank circuit used in the Ultimate KISS rig.

"But a word of warning. It does require a good pair of sensitive, high-impedance headphones. I have two pairs, once of which is noticeably better than the other. Results with an indifferent pair of headphones could prove disappointing, and require the addition of an audio amplifier as in the original GI3XZM design.

"There appears to be no special precautions needed for circuit layout, other than those one would observe when constructing a VFO in the interest of stability. I would suggest that construction be kept as simple as the circuit itself. The receiver could be built on a single piece of copper clad board drilled to take the panel controls. the copper clad side (if single sided) would face rearwards, and the circuit would be constructed on it using the 'ugly construction' or 'dead bug' method, where all grounded components are soldered direct to the copper, and are used as stand-offs to support the remaining circuitry. Components could be stuck down with 'Blu-tak' if so desired. The copper cladding forms a ground plane."

With regard to the transmitter section as shown in Fig 2, the PA tank circuit is an L-Pi network, which simultaneously provides impedance matching and harmonic filtering of the output: see **Fig 3**. The L-network transforms the very low drain load resistance of the power-MOSFET up to a value conveniently high to form the input resistance of a pi-network, which can be adjusted for output impedances over a wide range, but has been designed to match 50Ω. G3RJT has provided details of the design method he uses which he describes as somewhat simplistic but giving useful results usable to 144MHz and also with bipolar transistors. However the formulae and design steps involved, although relatively simple to use, are not really suitable for inclusion in a monthly column. The component details shown in Fig 2 should provide a reasonable guide for 7MHz using the IRF510, in conjunction with Fig 3.

G3RJT adds: "CL is combined with C1 in a variable capacitor that tunes both L and Pi networks simultaneously. C2 may be fixed if operation into 50Ω only is required, or made variable if output matching over a range of impedances is required.

"At this point some words of caution are appropriate. the L-network is series tuned with respect to the MOSFET drain load resistance, and will exhibit a minimum impedance at resonance. The PA current will therefore *peak* when correctly matched; it will *not* exhibit the familiar dip characteristic associated with a pi-network circuit. Conversely, the input impedance of the L-network is high and harmonic frequencies and harmonic currents will induce large, even destructive voltages across it. A harmonic by-pass capacitor C_h is therefore connected from drain to ground. This capacitor is initially given a value of $1/(2pi fC_h)$ = $5R_L$. Provided that its reactance is kept greater than $5R_L$ (which is 14Ω for Vcc = 12V and Pout = 5 Watts) it will not significantly affect the component values required for the L network. The MOSFET drain capacitance will form part of C_h, and for some devices will form all of it. This is also true for bipolar transistors operating near their cut-off frequency (f_T). Once the transmitter is working, the value of C_h can be optimised by experiment for best efficiency."

MOVABLE BENCH SPOTLIGHT

G R POLLARD, GW8DOA, has sent along a sketch and brief description of a versatile spotlight that he finds useful in his workshop: **Fig 4**.

He writes: "The assembly is simple and cheap, but is versatile and can be used for several spotlights. It can be mounted horizontally or vertically and consists of a suitable length of water pipe, plastic or copper, held in place by two suitable plastic clips as used for radiator pipes. The spotlight can be a clip-on type and the cable is taken through the tube and fed either from the normal lighting circuit or through a plug."

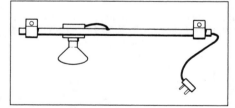

Fig 4: GW8DOA's versatile moveable bench spotlight based on a low-cost assembly.

THE SCIENCE OF HF PROPAGATION

IN THE JUNE *TT*, I noted the remark of old-timer Ted Cook, ZS6BT, that he believes it is time that more attention was paid by amateurs to the basic modes of radio wave propagation. The following month, Brian Austin, G0GSF, drew my attention to a new book on HF communications that had just been published, entitled *HF Communications - Science and Technology* by John M Goodman and published by Van Nostrand Reinhold of New York, 1992, ISBN 0-442-00145-2. He felt this to be very good, reflecting current thinking on HF propagation; a major plus factor from a research point of view being the extensive list of references at the end of each chapter.

This sounded interesting. But when I discovered that this hard-cover book is available in the UK from Chapman and Hall at the not inconsiderable price (even for a 650-page book) of £54.50, I decided to restrict my efforts to seeking out a library copy to have a look through. Eventually I was successful (IEE Library, London) and would recommend anyone genuinely interested in HF propagation to do the same. It would be possible to take photocopies for personal use of particular sections for a more modest outlay!

The author believes that "HF has suffered from an inferiority complex for a number of years, having been afflicted by the presence of new and advanced satellite communications schemes . . . . satellite communication has an insurmountable edge over HF over most of the globe. Nevertheless, in remote areas where satellite terminals, undersea cables, and radio relay are either non-existent or sparse, HF will remain the communication system of necessity. Furthermore because of relatively low capital investment, HF will continue to be an important medium of communication in the developing countries for some time to come. Since geosynchronous satellite coverage is not reliable in the near-polar regions, HF service is important there as well . . . . HF radio, which requires no costly space segment, has remained a major component of the hierarchy of military communication systems essential for maintenance of requisite command and control functions."

Although the book is primarily concerned with HF propagation as it affects professional communications systems, including the latest adaptive and other emerging systems such as spread spectrum and real-time channel evaluation, the author notes that: "Radio amateurs have contributed significantly to our understanding of skywave propagation over the years. More importantly, amateurs provide an invaluable service during periods of time when normal telephonic or satellite communications systems are disabled. Such periods may occur during massive earthquakes, floods, hurricanes, and other natural disasters . . . . The frequency prediction *requirements* of radio amateurs are obviously less formalized than those of the civilian, broadcast and military sectors. Still, the interest is there . . . . there is a vast reservoir of HF amateur radio operators which may serve as a resource during disasters. This resource should be nurtured."

He regards the ionosphere as 'a satellite which doesn't fall down even though it may appear to be unreliable at times. Coping with ionospheric variability at HF is a traditional problem. Many of the historical concerns about HF propagation, especially that element which depends upon the ionosphere, are being overcome although they cannot be totally removed from consideration . . . . The advantages of HF communication arise from its relative simplicity, its ability to provide near global connectivity at low power without relay, its ease of proliferation, and its moderate cost . . . . satellite communication systems provide the bulk of existing and planned-future capability. Even so, HF will continue to have a special role to play, even in peacetime."

Considerable space in the book is devoted to near-vertical-incidence-skywave (NVIS) propagation with the ability of such systems to provide: (1) omni-directional communication; (2) generally constant signal level over coverage area; (3) no skip zone; (4) local terrain effects are minimized; (5) effective for valley-to-valley and 'nap-of-the-earth (NOE); and (6) its use in electronic warfare (ie jamming etc). There is also discussion of the effects on HF communication of high-altitude nuclear explosions which result in electromagnetic pulses (EMP).

In connection with EMP, Richard Buckby, G3VGW, draws attention to an article in *Flight International* of 25 August - 1 September 1992 reporting that the UK as well as the USA and Russia is studying 'the feasibility of a microwave bomb'. this would be based on a hollow travelling-wave tube in which a radio standing-wave resonates at a fixed frequency. An explosive charge is detonated at one end, causing the tube to collapse and resulting in a massive amplification of the RF pulse. Upon detonation such a device would create a localised EMP that could burn out unprotected electrical circuits and could (like high-altitude nuclear explosions) represent a major threat to communications, radar and weapon systems. The bomb might produce a one gigawatt pulse lasting around two pico-seconds. Not long, but presumably long enough to break down solid-state receiver front-ends, etc in the vicinity of the explosion!

John Goodman's book mentions north-south 'grey line' propagation but only briefly. Interesting letters on this subject have come in from David Reynolds, G3ZPF, Ted Cook, ZS6BT, and Ray Cracknell, G2AHU and I hope to return to this topic soon.

GOODBYE HEATHKIT - FAREWELL LEICESTER SQUARE

IN *TT,* MAY 1991, p29, under the heading 'Sad Story of an Electronic Hobbyist', some extracts were given of an *IEEE Spectrum* (July 1990) contribution by Robert W Lucky, who, until his retirement, was one of the distinguished group of electronics scientists at Bell Telephone Laboratories. His theme was that modern technology had all-but killed off the home-construction of electronic equipment, including the radio receivers, then hi-fi amplifiers, home computers and finally home-written computer programs that had given him so much pleasure in the past: "I went to a computer flea market that has been a source of experimental junk . . . . I found myself looking at 500 stands all selling the same two dozen commercial products. What was I doing there? I hear that enrolment in electronic engineering has been dropping steadily. I'm looking at my keep-your-hands-off clone. Do you think there is any connection?"

I had been careful to point out that "As radio amateurs we are still, if only on a much reduced scale, survivors of the golden age of electronic do-it-yourself. It is still possible to experience the satisfaction of making a unique piece of equipment or trying out your own antenna ideas, even if most gear now comes from the factory in black boxes." Our Editor added that Robert Lucky's pessimistic view of

GROUND PLANE ANTENNAS CLOSE TO EARTH

A RECENT *TT* ITEM from Les Moxon, G6XN, has emphasised that the usual form of elevated ground plane antenna with two, three or four quarter-wave wire radials, as normally found in the Amateur Service, needs to be considered as a form of dipole rather than a vertical monopole antenna. As he pointed out "this has a devastating effect on a large number of sacred cows".

However, antennas for the lower frequency bands - including medium-wave broadcast antennas and antennas for 1.8 and 3.5MHz - consist of a vertical radiating element and a large number of wire radials buried in close proximity to the surface of the earth or elevated just a few feet above earth. These radials which form the 'ground plane' may or may not be resonant lengths. Such antennas are normally analysed as 'monopole' antennas.

Dr Brian Austin, G0GSF, has drawn attention to "a particularly interesting set of computed results" that has been published in *Electronics Letters*, 30 July 1992, pp1550-51. This is 'Radiation efficiency and input impedance of monopole elements with radial-wire ground planes in proximity to earth' by M M Weiner, S Zamoscianyk and G J Burke of The MITRE Corporation and Lawrence Livermore National Laboratory. A number of earlier *TT* items have reported briefly on earlier publications by Dr Weiner on aspects of ground-plane antennas.

The results have been computed using the NEC-GS program (an optimisation for radial-wire ground planes of NEC-3) based on an antenna geometry consisting of a vertical monopole element, of length h and radius b, on a groundscreen consisting of N equally-spaced radial wires, of length a and radius b_w, at a depth of z_o below a flat lossy Earth surface of defined dielectric constant and conductivity. The monopole element and the radial wires are assumed to have infinite conductivity.

Results are presented in **Fig 5(a), (b) and (c)** for parameters with fixed values of quarter-wave height, b and b_w equal to 0.00001 wavelength, Earth dielectric constant of 15 and frequency-dependent conductivity, for a varying number of wire radials at a height of 0.0001 wavelength (ie a 'negative depth') above lossy Earth. The radiation efficiency, input resistance and input reactance are plotted in the graphs shown in Fig 5. Radiation efficiency is the ratio of the far-field radiated power to the available input power and is a measure of the power loss in the particular characteristics chosen to represent the lossy earth since the monopole element and radial wires are assumed to have infinite conductivity.

While clearly one needs to interpret these results with care - and I hesitate to give my own interpretation - they appear to show that radiation efficiency with radials a few feet above ground is virtually independent of the number of radials, at least for ground screens of normal size. This seems a further justification of the work initiated over a decade ago by Arch Doty, K8CFU, which showed, from hundreds of actual measurements, that a few elevated wire radials were as efficient as the standard broadcast practice of using 120 buried radials. The input resistance seems curiously high and presumably reflects earth losses.

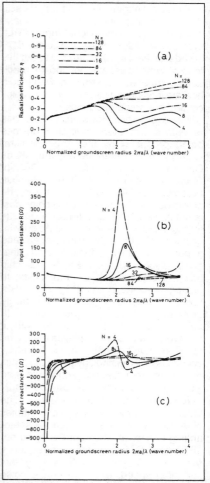

Fig 5: **Computerized results shown by M M Weiner et al in** *Electronics Letters* **in connection with the radiation efficiency and input impedance of monopole elements with radial-wire ground planes in proximity to earth. (a) radiation efficiency; (b) input resistance; and (c) input reactance for varying numbers (N) of wire radials at a height of 0.0001-wavelength above a 'lossy' Earth of specified dielectric constant and conductivity.**

the death of electronic d-i-y was not entirely supported by the number of ads in *RadCom* for kits.

Recently in *IEEE Spectrum*, July 1992, p22, Dr Lucky has returned to the passing of his (non-amateur) golden age in a piece

'Goodbye, Heathkit' with the following opening paragraphs:

"The other day a small company in Benton Harbor, Michigan, announced that it had closed down one of its lines of business, and would henceforth concentrate on other products. In the business community, this event passed without notice. Had Wall Street reacted, the analysts undoubtedly would have cheered the elimination of an unprofitable division. Smart decision, they would have said, and the stock would have risen.

"For engineers, however, the decision of that little company signified the passing of an era - the end of a time when it was fun and profitable to tinker with electronics. The product that symbolized the electronics hobbyist is no more. It hurts to say it, but say it we must: goodbye, Heathkit! We shall miss you . . . .

"I remember studying the new Heathkit catalogues, weighing my limitless cravings against my available dollars. I remember the thrill of seeing the big boxes waiting for me at home. I also remember the great satisfaction in sorting through the little bags of parts, and slowly beginning to create order out of chaos . . . . As the kit neared completion, the expectancy would grow, until the final moment of pregnancy and doubt arrived, and all that remained was to turn on the power. The thrill of victory, the agony of defeat - one of them lay just ahead.

"Because of very-large-scale integration or because of modern manufacturing technology, building a kit does not make sense any more [Not necessarily true of all types of amateur radio equipment! - G3VA] . . . . Still, it must be said: I miss that big box of little parts. I miss the growing check marks in the yellow manuals. Bravo, Heathkit. Thanks for the memories. Thanks for a job well done."

It is some time since Heathkit first pulled out of its UK operation and then withdrew from the amateur radio market, but the loss is still felt - and there are quite a few Heathkit rigs still operating on the bands.

Dr Lucky mentions how his previous article brought letters from engineers lamenting the closing of 'Radio Row' in lower Manhattan, New York where electronics hobbyists could wander from store to store in search of surplus parts, test equipment, and kits of all sorts - now occupied by the building complex known as the World Trade Center.

For UK amateurs living within reach of Central London, much the same sense of loss can be felt when walking past the Chinese restaurants that now fill Lisle Street, off Leicester Square - a Mecca for radio amateurs (and those of an older profession) for more than 50 years, starting in the 1920s. I still use a large 'roller coaster' variable inductor, doorstop transformers etc bought there for a few shillings. Then there was Proops in Tottenham Court Road (originally at Kingston-on-Thames) so convenient when I lived in Bloomsbury. Then there was Charles Brittain in St Martin's Lane, which was an easy lunchtime step from an office in Tower House, Southampton Street. Farewell Leicester Square and those surrounding streets of beckoning surplus!

Dr Lucky quotes an engineer who got a major thrill in 1977 when BASIC came up on his kit-built computer and announced 'Ready' on the screen, adding: "Last year I purchased a new IBM clone, brought it home and plugged it in. That was about the same level of excitement as buying a washing machine."

Let us make sure, even without those Heathkit rigs and the bits and pieces from the surplus shops, that we retain at least some of the excitement of experimenting with equipment and antenna systems and all those little bits and pieces that can still find a use alongside a 'black box' transceiver. We need to hang on to d-i-y experimental amateur radio!

LOWER-COST DIRECT DIGITAL SYNTHESIS

TT, DECEMBER 1988, pp957-958 drew attention to the potential advantages of direct digital synthesis, and in the December 1990 issue of *RadCom* there was a full-length article on this subject by Dr PH Saul, G8EUX, - one of the UK's leading professional experts on this form of oscillator which can provide much lower phase noise than the conventional form of PLL synthesiser. Unfortunately, the cost of DDS boards, at least in 1988, tended to put this form of synthesiser well beyond the reach of most amateur constructors who would hesitate long before investing in VSLI chips costing hundreds of pounds.

However, Colin Horrabin, G3SBI, has recently drawn attention to DDS devices being produced by the American firm Qualcomm and marketed in the UK by Chronos Technology Ltd, Upton Bishop, Ross-on-Wye, Herefordshire, HR9 7UL (telephone 0989 85471). In particular, he points out that the Q2334 DDS chips cost about £50 in one-off quantities. The Q2334 features two DDSs in one package with choice of 20, 30, 50MHz clock speeds and a patented noise reduction circuit that gives -76dBc spurious: **Fig 6**. The chip has to be used with external digital to analog converters etc. (**Fig 7**). G3SBI notes that the 32-bit accumulator range gives fraction of a Hertz resolution at HF and that a synthesiser can be built at relatively low cost. He believes that using the Sony DAC (8-bit) CXD1171M at £4 each puts DDS technology within the reach of the Amateur Service and could lead also to many commercial applications.

A Qualcomm brochure claims: "The Q2334 DDS produces digitized samples of a sine wave that drive a digital-to-analog converter. With our DDS you obtain extremely fine phase and frequency resolution, broad bandwidth, very fast switching speed, excellent phase noise performance, and lower power and size made possible by advanced full-custom VLSI CMOS technology. Two unique features are patented. One is the noise reduction circuit which allows you to specify less expensive DACs without the expected increase in spur levels. The other, algorithmic sine lookup, provides improved spurious performance and requires so little silicon area that a second independent DDS is included in each package. With two DDSs per package you can design non-drifting I&Q (quadrature) or any other phase or frequency offset outputs, or generate two independent signals for completely separate circuit function."

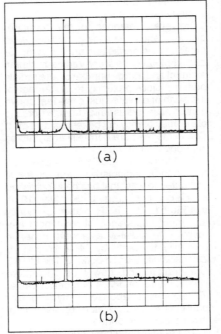

Fig 6: A patented noise reduction circuit is incorporated in the Qualcomm Q2334 dual direct digital synthesiser chip. (a) Shows spectrum output with the noise reduction circuit off showing significant level of spurs. (b) Spectrum output from a Q2334 chip generating a 4MHz fundamental at a 30MHz clock frequency. Sony CX20202A 8-bit DAC used with DDS noise reduction circuit on. In both diagrams, X-axis is 0-15MHz and Y-axis is 10dB per division.

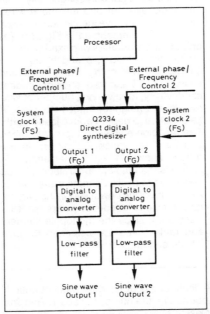

Fig 7: Block diagram of the Qualcomm Q2334 DDS system.

SUPPRESSING POWER SUPPLY SURGES

IN NOTING (*TT*, Sept) THE SAD FACT that even well-made power transformers eventually tend to fail, mention should perhaps have been made of the basic problem facing all electronic equipment connected to the mains supplies - the very high voltage transients that momentarily change 240V ac into kilovolt sources.

Many years ago we noted in *TT* (and subsequently in all editions of *ART*) that a Mullard investigation at Dudley, Worcs, during a period of six weeks recorded the following substantial overvoltages: 35 of 20-40% above normal; 7 of 40-70%; and 1 of over 100%. At Cheam, Surrey, during a period of 12.5 weeks, recorded overvoltages amounted to 27 of 20-40%; 4 of 40-70%; and 8 of 70-100%. Such transient overvoltages may only last a few microseconds and seldom had much effect on valve rectifiers and power supply units, but became of increasing importance with the many solid-state appliances and equipments that began to be installed in homes during the 1960s.

High transient overvoltages generally arise from switching operations in the mains-supply network or from lightning strikes (particularly important in the case of overhead power cables in rural areas), but transients can also be created by local switching. As Gary S Tighe, KN4FY, points out in a four-page article 'Basic steps toward suppressing power-supply surges' (*QST*, July 1992, pp25-28) even turning something as simple as a table lamp on and off can cause a line-voltage surge capable of confusing a computer and damaging electronic gear. The article covers in some detail how the problem of overvoltages arises and methods of protecting equipment from them

KN4FY includes details of an investigation of line-transients at typical Swiss locations (220V lines) carried out by L Regez, Landis & Gyr, Zug, and relates these to American 120V mains supplies: **Fig 8**. The conclusion

is drawn that even 120V homes may experience peak instantaneous voltages exceeding 1000V more than 100 times per year. The Swiss farmhouse supplied by an overhead transmission line would have to cope with some 10 transients exceeding 10,000V peak per year!

It is pointed out that the effects of surge voltage and noise on mains supplies can be reduced by *diverting* it (shunting it around the equipment you want to protect) or *attenuating* it (reducing its strength) before it reaches the equipment.

The article shows that bypass capacitors can divert transient energy around equipment, and a crowbar circuit provides brute-force protection by taking equipment off the line. KN4FY believes that attenuating transients by clamping them to a non-destructive level is probably the best first-line defence. While zener diodes are used for clamping DC circuits, there are a number of advantages to using metal-oxide varistors (MOVs) for power line clamping. They are fast-acting, have large junction areas that are capable of dissipating large amounts of transient power, and can be installed on AC and DC lines because they are not polarized. Because they leak little current below their clamping thresholds, they take little power from the circuits they protect.

However, should an MOV fail this usually results in a short-circuit, unlike zener diodes which usually fail open circuit. KN4FY points out that this means that MOVs should be fused for safety - actually a plus because a blown fuse or open circuit breaker can guard against subsequent surges by crowbarring the protected equipment off the supply.

An MOV possesses considerable capacitance and needs to be applied carefully in any high-frequency logic or linear circuits in which the added capacitance could compromise circuit performance. For most power-line applications, however, the capacitance (from about 150 to 2500pF in 130V MOVs) has no effect on system performance. For 240V AC mains, the usual MOV operating voltage is 275V (about 360V DC), although V250 and V260 types are also used. Suitable components are available from a number of suppliers. KN4FY stresses that "MOVs are a proven, cost-effective solution to the problem of power-supply transients. All you need to do is select and install them!"

To protect 12V DC supplies, use an MOV

rated at 14V DC (10-11V AC) but note that for 13.8V DC supplies the MOV should be rated at 18V DC (14V AC). The peak current rating of the MOV determines the price, but as KN4FY points out, low-cost MOVs (under $2 each for 130V rating in the USA) will cope with transients far greater than those which may be encountered on domestic supplies. The personal computer explosion has vastly increased the demand for transient suppression and surge-protected power outlet accessories are widely available. Most of these, according to KN4FY, use some type of MOV and may also include bypass capacitors and/or filter inductors. **Fig 9** shows how MOVs can be installed to protect equipment from power line transients as given in an earlier item on this subject (*TT*, Jan 1987).

HERE AND THERE

VALVE TECHNOLOGY seems suddenly to have become almost respectable. Harvey Collett, G3KI, noticed the article 'Go backwards - and glow with pride' (*The Daily Telegraph*, September 5) singing the praises of high-fidelity amplifiers based on valves (a costly business for those without well-stocked junk boxes but then hi-fi aficionados still seem prepared to spend hundreds of pounds on the dubious advantages of special loudspeaker cables!). *Electronics Australia* (September 1992) has Part 1 of a construction project 'High quality stereo amplifier using valves'. The interesting Diamond Jubilee Issue of *Practical Wireless* (October 1992) has Part 1 of a series of articles by Phil Cadman, G4JCP: 'Using those versatile vacuums'.

Jim Cookson, G4XWD noted the July advice on carefully checking the heater voltage applied to power valves and rectifiers but was reminded of the very different treatment meted out to the valves in some of the 1940s American juke boxes where it was important that the amplifier using push-pull 6L6 valves was fully warmed up from cold within 8-10 seconds of switch-on. To achieve this the heaters were initially fed with 9.8V. When the 6L6s began to conduct, a relay, acting as bias resistor, became energised and switched the heater voltage to the normal 6.3V. G4XWD recalls that despite this "barbarous technique" the valves lasted surprisingly well, although switched on and off every few minutes as punters selected their favourite discs.

John Wightman, ZL1AH (ex-G3AH), was interested in the item on the Hivac-Harries beam-tetrodes (*TT*, July) as from the days of his interest in BCL/SWL receivers at the age of ten, he used two valve regenerative sets (with a swinging reaction coil!). He became very keen on Hivac valves when he found he could buy them more cheaply than those made by the BVA firms. In 1936, he changed his output valve from a Hivac battery pentode to the Harries-Hivac HY220 battery tetrode. He used this when licensed as G3AH in November 1937, until February 1939 when he acquired a Hallicrafters Sky Champion, becoming one of those who achieved WAC and WBE (Worked British Empire) on a two-valve battery set (I never quite made WAC (missed Asia) on my pre-war two-valve battery set but did contact VK, ZE, LU, PY, VO and W etc - G3VA).

G3VA

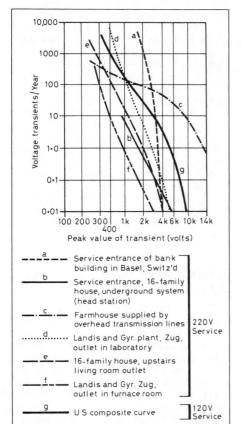

Fig 8: Frequency of line-transient occurrence versus peak transient voltage for several Swiss sites (220V service) and composite curve for US (120V service). In many homes instantaneous peak transient voltages of 1kV may occur quite frequently.

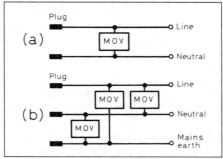

Fig 9: Diagram showing how metal oxide varistors (MOVs) can be installed to protect equipment from power line transients. (a) two-wire system with single MOV. (b) Use of three MOV devices to protect fully a three-wire system. The supply should always be fused ahead of the MOVs since they can fail as a short-circuit.

SURVIVING HELL AND HIGH WATER

IF THE WORST HAPPENS and electronic equipment is subjected to such catastrophes as domestic or vehicle fires, floods, lightning strikes, battery acid spills, electrical shorts etc what are the chances of it ever working again?

An article 'Surviving hell and high water' by Marvin Kurland (Trenton State College) in *IEEE Spectrum*, May 1992, pp44-47 claims that electronic equipment can often be rehabilitated after a fire or flood at a cost of only 15% or so of replacing it "but it helps to design it so as to minimize damage in the first place". Apparently there is a UK company - Imbach UK Ltd of Aldridge, West Midlands, that specialises in coping with large electronic installations as experts in damage management and reclamation.

It is pointed out that the most common type of damage is the sooty film that smoke leaves on equipment, even in rooms not touched by fire. The next most common is damage from water from building sprinkler systems, fire hoses, or even leaking radiator pipes in the ceiling overhead. Corrosion proceeds most rapidly right after exposure to fire, smoke, or water. The longer the exposure lasts, and in the case of fire, the higher the temperature reached inside the equipment, the less likely the hardware is to survive.

The first step in stopping corrosion is immediately disconnecting the damaged equipment from the power supply. This rules out further damage from electric shorts. It also erases any voltage potentials within the circuitry that would otherwise plate contaminants onto circuit boards and backplanes. Next, the ambient humidity must be reduced to below 50%. Although smoke does little damage while a fire is raging, the particulate residue left after the smoke has dissipated contains chlorides (from burning PVC insulation and cabling and from some fire extinguisher compounds in high temperatures) and sulphides from burning paper. All are corrosive by-products of combustion that eat away at metal contact surfaces in the presence of oxygen and moisture - reducing humidity slows corrosion. Ideally equipment should be moved to a clean, air-conditioned, and humidity-controlled environment.

The *Spectrum* article shows how damage-management companies go about the task of reclaiming high-cost electronic data processing installations but there are a few ideas that might prove suitable when tackling radio equipment - although in bad cases this would seem to be a job for a professional expert. To quote the article by Marvin Kurland:

"Once the necessary test samples are taken - a procedure taking up to a couple of hours - the damage management team will probably spray connectors, backplanes, and circuit boards with a water-displacing protective oil. The oil leaves a thin but easily removable coating to help prevent oxygen and moisture from contributing further to corrosion. Contrary to popular belief, water in itself does not permanently ruin electronic equipment, which can be splashed or sprayed with it, or even submerged in it without irreparable harm. Water alone is quite innocuous - indeed, deionized water (which has about the same

low surface tension as alcohol and essentially no conductivity) is used in cleaning much damaged equipment. The trouble is due to corrosive impurities from pipes or soot that mix with the water - hence the use of a water-displacing oil to limit the occurrence and extent of corrosion.

"As soon as possible, cabinet doors should be opened, side panels and covers removed, and chassis drawers pulled out to drain the water off, something a user can do. Never, ever, should water-damaged equipment be placed in cardboard packing boxes or any other material that will trap moisture inside the chassis.

"A damage management team will probably set up fans to move room-temperature air through the equipment to dry it out, taking care to keep the damp air flow away from other equipment. Technicians may also direct compressed, deionized air at low pressure (about 0.l7 Megapascal) to blow out trapped moisture or direct heated air from handheld driers onto connectors, backplanes, and circuit boards.

"Chassis and large pieces of equipment are disassembled and may be spray-cleaned by deionized water at low pressure. Circuit boards could also be washed by hand and gently scrubbed with a clean, soft brush in a continuous left-to-right, top-to-bottom motion to avoid any recontamination. If the equipment has been exposed only to chlorides, it may be washed with deionized water and mild detergent and rinsed with deionized water. If it has also been exposed to sulphides, it may also be washed with a solution of alkaline and deionized water. In any case, the rinse is followed with a low-pressure spray of alcohol to drive out the water. The units are finally baked dry at 100°C in special ovens, so as to remove all trace of moisture."

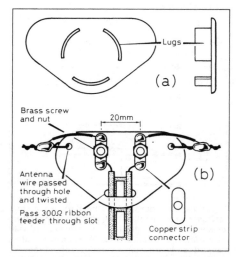

Fig 1: Simple dipole centre made by GI4JTF from kitchen cupboard blanking plates.

Labels: Lugs — (a); Brass screw and nut; 20mm; Antenna wire passed through hole and twisted; Pass 300Ω ribbon feeder through slot; (b); Copper strip connector

Pat Hawker's Technical Topics

The article includes advice on how equipment could be designed to facilitate reclamation and lists a number of publications giving further advice. It notes that one of the first books published on the feasibility of using water to clean smoke-damaged electronics without hurting their reliability was *Effects of Corrosive Smoke on Electronics* by S T Olesen, published in January 1984 by the Danish Public Research Institute.

TIPS AND TOPICS

BRIAN JOHNSON, G3LOX, reminds us that an old car-ignition sparking plug, fitted into an 18mm diameter copper tube forming an earth stake, provides an effective static discharge system for antennas - a tip he discovered some years ago when using balloon supported antennas. He also points out that a spare car wheel can provide an excellent temporary base for a vertical antenna such as a 14AVQ which conveniently fits into the centre hole.

Dr E H Squance, GI4JTF, while looking for a dipole centre for a G5RV antenna he was building, noticed some blanking plates inside some old kitchen cupboards (Hygena): **Fig 1(a)**. He cut the lugs off and super-glued the two plates back to back. They were then drilled and finished as in **Fig 1(b)**.

Julian Jablin, W9IWI, in the 'Hinks & Kinks' column of *QST* (July 1992) writes: "An article on repairing meters that cautioned against losing tiny screws and springs reminded me of an old watchmaker's trick. The working area on the bench must be scrupulously clean, of course. Attached to the front of the bench, just in front of the working area and extending over the floor, is a wooden frame about 18 inches wide and 12 inches deep, with a loose rectangle of thin cotton material tacked to its underside. This can be temporary, and held in place by C clamps. An old picture frame, with a smooth kitchen towel tacked loosely where the glass would be, works fine. When a little screw or spring drops out of the meter (or whatever small device you're working on), it rolls off the bench (Murphy's Law in action), but instead of hitting the floor and disappearing it is caught in the cotton gadget and is easy to retrieve". A simpler version of basically the same idea is also provided by Jim Harrison in *Sprat* No 71: "For table top construction a wooden board with a piece of beading pinned round is most useful, so that components do not roll onto the floor!"

USING SCRAPS OF COAXIAL CABLES

SOME TIME AGO, I RECALL including in *TT* an item on using the cylindrical insulation of scraps of coaxial cable to form stand-off insulators, coil formers and the like. This idea turns up again - but in more detailed form - in a 1991 issue of the *Mid-Sussex Newsletter* (taken in fact from a reprint in *Airtime*, June 1991, Newsletter of the Southdown Amateur Radio Society). This provides a 'Topical Techniques' feature but the original author is not credited. The text is as follows:

We all have many odd short lengths of coax lying around the shack, but these usually end up in the rubbish bin the next time we wipe down the bench. Old UR67 and similar 'half-inch' cable is, however, a most valuable raw material, for lengths of even less than an inch can be put to good use for stand-off insulators or coil formers.

The first task is to remove the outer sheath, braiding and centre conductor. This can be done by any of the usual techniques. Then, for stand-offs, cut the inner insulation into lengths of half to three-quarters of an inch. For coil formers, cut to about 1.5 to 2in (38 to 51mm).

There are two methods of making the stand-off: **Fig 2**. The simplest is to attach a couple of solder tags to one end using a short self-tapping screw and then using another similar screw to fasten the stand-off to the chassis or PCB. Provided that the gap between the tips of the two self-tapping screws is more than a quarter of an inch, these stand-offs should cope with up to 5000 volts.

An alternative method is to drill a 1/16th inch hole through one end of the insulation and force through a tight hairpin of copper wire (the discarded inner conductor is ideal). Where it comes through, open up the hairpin into a small loop and pull back until it is tight against the insulation. Cut one of the 'legs' of the hairpin on the other side to around 3/16th inch and bend back round the insulator to secure and form the longer leg into a loop of similar size to the first. The wire can be made more secure by applying just sufficient heat to melt the insulation around the wire. Again attach to the chassis or PCB with a short self-tapping screw. Making a coil former uses exactly the same procedure except that two loops are fitted, spaced sufficiently far apart to permit the required coil to be wound between them. **Fig 3** shows how the formers are made, together with a graph plotting frequency against turns for formers made from the inner insulation of half-inch coax, with capacitances of from 15 - 140pF, using 20SWG enamelled wire.

Rather longer lengths of discarded coaxial cable (that has not been ruined by moisture) can also be used to form fixed high-voltage, high-Q capacitors of any required low value provided that the cable's capacitance per inch is known or can be determined.

Another application of stripped cable insulation that has been suggested in the past is to form spreaders for balanced open-wire line using short self-tapping screws to hold short lengths of binding wire.

G8VXB'S SURFACE MOUNT TIPS

THE PROBLEM OF DEALING with surface-mount chips has been described by P J Roberts, G1VUV in *Television* (September 1992): "The need to remove and replace surface-mounted components, especially ICs is becoming more common. Those little flat square chips with millions of legs are a particular problem. Getting them off the board is hard enough, let alone putting them on." Some notes by Dave Young, G8VXB, on handling surface-mount components also appeared in *Cats Whispers* - the newsletter of the Coulsdon Amateur Transmitting Society - September 1992.

G8VXB notes that an increasing amount of equipment is using surface mount technology: although a number of suppliers sell specialised equipment for surface mount

working, these all involve a large outlay. The main differences between surface mount and standard components are: (a) No component pins or PCB holes. (b) Approximately half the size. (c) PCB tracks and pads are smaller.

For anyone contemplating the repair of surface mount equipment, he considers that a number of tools are required which may be absent from most toolboxes. He lists these as follows, based on Farnell catalogue numbers, although similar tools from other distributors may be substituted:

- Wire cutter (Farnell 108-713). These need to have small jaws, but strong enough to cut an IC pin.
- Long nose pliers (Farnell 276SEB). The tips of the pliers are required to be able to grip a surface mount IC, but long enough to keep any heat away from the hand.
- Soldering iron (Farnell C250). For the small pads and tracks a low power, miniature iron is ideal. The regulated irons are better, but a good deal more expensive.
- Iron tip (Farnell 10, 1106). This needs to be as small as possible for soldering and a 1mm bit for use with solder wick.
- Tweezers (Farnell VEN7A). These are ideal for the smaller surface mount devices. Do not buy the cheaper tweezers, as they are not suitable for surface mount use.
- Solder wick (Farnell AA). Use the smallest size of this product.
- Solder (Farnell SMAR26). Silver-loaded solder should be used on surface mount components, to stop the connections from deteriorating.
- PCB cleaner (Farnell PCC01L). There are a number of suitable cleaners.
- Anti-static area (Farnell 175-818). Static precautions should be taken where necessary, especially if the circuit contains unprotected FETs. This product is not suitable for mains operation.
- Heat gun (Farnell 107-261). This is used for the removal of the larger ICs. For smaller ICs a gas soldering iron, used as a heat gun, may be used.
- Anglepoise lamp (Farnell 401). A number of such lamps are suitable.
- Magnifying glass (Farnell 201-870). A plastic-lens version is usually sufficient.
- Component holder. This can be made from a small piece of plastic rod with some double-sided tape on the end.

If the above list has not already discouraged any attempt to repair or build SMC boards, G8VXB adds that "Before any work is carried out, ensure that: (1) The PCB is firmly held on the work surface (insulating tape works reasonably well). (2) There is enough illumination to see the soldering area clearly.

While soldering, due to the small track size, a minimal amount of heat is required in order not to damage the PCB or the components.

(a) Keep any soldering to less than three seconds per pad.

(b) Use a 1mm iron tip when using the soldering wick.

On the question of removing surface mount devices, G8VXB divides this into procedures for (A) Two and three terminal devices; (B,C)

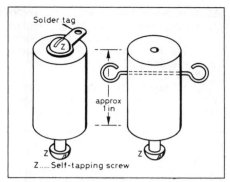

Fig 2: Construction of stand-off insulator from short lengths of scrap coaxial cable.

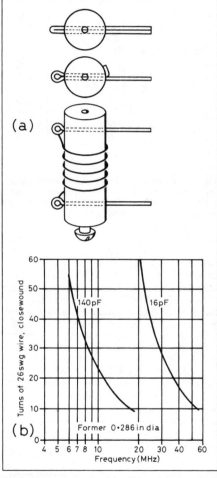

Fig 3: (a) Construction of coil formers from half-inch coax. (b) Plot of frequency against turns for formers made from the inner insulation of half-inch coax with capacitances between 15 and 140pF.

Two methods for dealing with multi-pin devices:

(A) 1. Remove solder from terminals using solder wick. 2, Heat device with iron while holding in tweezers (or heat one terminal, then quickly the other, while holding in tweezers). 3, Rotate in the plane of the PCB when solder has melted. 4, Remove surplus solder with solder wick. 5, Remove any glue deposits.

(B) Multi-pin devices, first method: 1, Cut IC pins using cutters. 2, remove IC and pins using tweezers. 3, Remove surplus solder with solder wick. 4, Remove any glue deposits.

(C) Multi-pin devices, second method: 1, Heat IC pins using heat gun. 2, Remove using long-nose pliers, rotating in the plane of the PCB. 3, Remove surplus solder using solder wick. 4, Remove any glue.

G8VXB notes that Method B requires a certain amount of experience and recommends initial practice on some surplus PCBs.

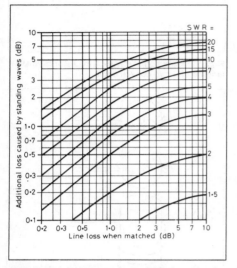

Fig 4: Graph showing by how much (or at HF usually how little) additional feeder loss occurs with a moderate VSWR on the line compared with the same line having an accurately matched 1:1 SWR.

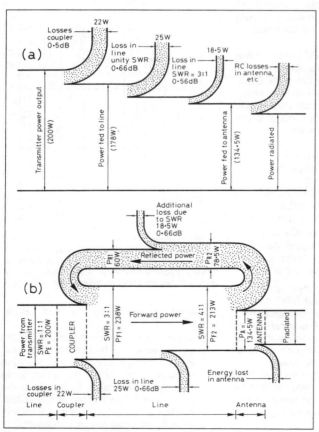

Fig 5: An ingenious diagram originated some years ago by a French amateur that illustrates the effects of a mismatch between antenna and transmission line. Although with even moderate SWR a significant amount of power may be reflected, most of this subsequently returns back up the feeder. Note that forward power, as measured in the feeder can be appreciably more than the true output power of the transmitter.

Method B however is the recommended approach since with Method A the tracks may be damaged when cutting the IC pins.

His technique when installing surface mount devices is as follows: 1, Pre-tin one pad (if a dual-in-line component choose a corner pad). 2, Hold device in tweezers, and line up on PCB. 3, Press lightly on component with holder. 4, Heat pad until solder flows around pin. 5, Solder the opposite pin. 6, Solder the pins on alternative sides. 7, Clean with PCB cleaner and inspect. 8, Redo connections if necessary and clean. NB A minimal amount of solder is required.

PERSISTENT SWR MYTHS

DESPITE THE EXCELLENT explanations given a decade or so ago by Walter Maxwell, W2DU, in a series of articles in *QST* and later in his book *Reflections - Transmission Lines and Antennas* published by ARRL, many of the myths that have long surrounded SWR and the use of SWR meters continue to persist. For example, the idea that in the presence of a mismatch between the antenna element and its feeder, reflected power represents lost power dissipated in the transmitter. There is no doubt that an SWR meter is a useful accessory, and virtually essential in the case of a transmitter with a solid-state power amplifier where protection circuits will begin to reduce the output power when the SWR reaches or exceeds about 1.7:1. However it should always be remembered that it is often misleading to attempt to evaluate antenna performance on the basis of 'the lower the SWR the better'.

In the past, based on the writings of W2DU, *TT* has emphasised such points as:

(1) Reflected power does not represent lost power except for the (usually modest) increase in line attenuation over the matched line attenuation (**Fig 4**). In a lossless feeder line no power would be lost because of reflection no matter how high the SWR. At HF with low-loss cable, reflected power loss is usually insignificant; at VHF it may become significant; at UHF it may be extremely important.

(2) Reflected power does not flow back into a transmitter and cause excessive dissipation and other damage. The damage often blamed on a high SWR is usually caused by improper output-coupling adjustments and not by the SWR.

(3) Attempts to reduce SWR below 2:1 on any coax line on HF generally represent wasted effort from the viewpoint of increasing the radiation from the antenna - although may be needed to prevent output reduction of solidstate amplifiers arising from the action of the protection circuits.

(4) A low SWR is not evidence that an antenna system is a good one or that it is working efficiently. On the contrary a lower than normal SWR over a significant bandwidth is reason to suspect that a dipole antenna or a vertical antenna is being affected by resistance losses that may arise from poor connections, poor earthing systems, lossy cable or other causes.

(5) The radiator of an antenna system need not be self-resonant length to achieve maximum resonant current flow, nor need the feed line be of any particular length. A substantial mismatch at the junction between feeder line and radiator does not prevent the radiator from absorbing all the real power that is available at the junction. Where suitable matching (ATU etc) cancels out the reactance presented by a non-resonant radiator and a random length of feeder, mismatched at the antenna junction, then the system is matched and all the real power may be radiated effectively.

(6) The SWR on the feed line is not affected by any adjustment of an ATU (or the length of the cable see below). A low SWR achieved by this means is usually an indication of a mismatch between the transmitter and the input to the ATU.

(7) With an effective ATU and a good openwire feeder a 132ft centre-fed dipole does not (contrary to general belief) radiate significantly more power on 3.5MHz than an 80ft dipole fed with the same transmitter power. A dipole self-resonant on 3750kHz does not radiate significantly more power on 3750kHz than on 3500kHz with any normal length of feeder, although the SWR may rise to about 5:1 and the coax cable will then, in effect, be working as a tuned feeder.

(8) High SWR in a coaxial feeder resulting from a severe mismatch at the antenna junction does not in itself produce common mode currents on the line or cause the line to radiate.

(9) The SWR in a feeder cannot be adjusted or controlled in any practical manner by varying the line length.

(10) Of the various types of dipoles (thin wire, folded, fan, sleeve, trap or coaxial) none will radiate more field than another, providing that each has insignificant ohmic losses and is fed the same amount of power.

It is however worth noting that where a mismatch exists between a feeder and the input impedance of a receiver, then reflected incoming signals will be re-radiated from the antenna element and lost. Optimum SNR of received signals thus does depend on good matching between feeder and receiver.

It seems worth publishing again an ingenious diagram stemming from a French amateur illustrating the effects of a mismatch between feeder and antenna element: **Fig 5**.

This shows incidentally that forward power in a feeder, as measured in the feeder may actually be significantly more than the real output power of the transmitter!

My excuse for attempting, once again, to destroy some of the common myths about SWR is that misleading information continues to be published in some periodicals and books. A letter 'SWR and the feed line' from Phil Winter, KM4OD in *QST*, September 1992, pp88-89, expresses concern that an article in *QST*, April 1992 on a five-band, two-element quad - although generally extremely useful, seemed to imply that adding three feet of coax to a quarter-wave feed line 'cured' a 4:1 SWR on 7MHz. KM4OD shows that on 7MHz three feet of coax would have a negligible effect on impedance and no effect on SWR.

He writes: "I strongly suspect that the real culprit was not the quarter-wave feed line or the reactive load, but current flowing on the outside of the coax shield. This could lead to a 4:1 SWR indication on the shack SWR. Maxwell states 'Since there is no practical way to determine the impedance of arm 3 (outside of the coax shield), the true antenna impedance and SWR cannot be calculated from the measured data'. Adding three feet of coax could have altered the impedance on the outside of the shield so that a lower SWR reading was indicated . . . . If we are to get the most out of our stations, we must make sure we understand what's going on in that black stuff that runs out the wall and up the tower. Firstly, SWR does not change as the feed-line length is altered, discounting attenuation effects. If we do measure an SWR change as the feed-line length is changed, then current must be flowing on the outside of the coax shield, rendering any SWR measurement inaccurate. Secondly, line loss aside, no single length of coax is any better or worse than another. Make your feed line long enough to reach your antenna, turn on your rig and make contacts."

Perhaps a more typical example of the misleading nature of antenna measurements brought about by RF current on the outer shield was reported in the Technical Correspondence column of *QST* a few years ago by Scott M Hower, K7KQ, as follows:

"Antenna construction and experimentation can sometimes be very confusing, with measurement yielding results that change and do not seem to make sense. Most amateurs use an SWR indicator or perhaps a noise bridge, both of which generally provide useful data for HF antenna measurements. There is one situation, however, that will result in meaningless readings from either device, that being when the outer shield of the coaxial transmission line becomes part of the antenna system. My antenna is a 14MHz vertical ground plane, consisting of a quarter-wave vertical radiator mounted at the peak of the roof. Four radials, each a quarter-wave-length long, run out from the base of the antenna along the roof. A short length of coax connects the antenna to the radio equipment on the top floor, immediately beneath the ground plane system.

"Two major problems I encountered were constantly changing SWR-meter (or noise-bridge) readings and lots of RF in the shack, creating a hot chassis, microphone and so on. Several attempts to detune the transmis-

sion line by using different line lengths had no effect on the problem of RF in the shack. Changing the transmission-line length did, however, have an effect on the SWR readings. The clincher occurred when I observed that the SWR readings changed when the headphones were plugged into the rig!

Finally, I realized that the outer shield of the transmission line was contributing to the composite load, made up of the shield and the antenna itself. Further, all of my radio equipment - SWR meter, linear amplifier, coaxial cable jumpers, even the headphones and microphones - would add to the total length when connected.

"One might think that a good earth connection would solve the problems, but a good earth is hard to obtain from the third floor of a house. Turning to *The ARRL Antenna Book*, the solution became obvious. A portion of the coaxial transmission line was wound into an RF choke, 5 turns, approximately 6in in diameter - right at the base of the antenna. The addition of the choke cured both problems completely."

It may be useful to add that the problem of a 'hot' chassis in an upstairs shack can be successfully overcome by the connection of a quarter-wave length of wire to the 'earth' point of the ATU - a dodge that has been mentioned several times in *TT*. Similarly the choke current-balun could be of the ferrite-ring type, using the constructional details shown in the September *TT*.

WHEN MULTIPLE BYPASS CAPACITORS MAY BE NEEDED

THE OCTOBER *TT* NOTED an IEEE paper by Clayton Paul that showed that it is unnecessary to use two capacitors when bypassing lines to prevent EMC problems. However, G0GSF suggested that this line of thinking could be applied also to bypassing solid-state power amplifiers. Bob Price, GW3ECH, feels that, for this application, G0GSF may have overlooked a valid reason for using multiple capacitors. He writes:

"Anyone who has tuned a VHF power amplifier into a load whilst watching the output on a spectrum analyser will have seen that under certain tuning conditions, parasitic (low frequency) oscillations can occur which then look like sidebands spaced either side of the amplified frequency. The principal reason for this is the very high gain of VHF transistors at relatively low frequencies. Small values of impedance in common paths to two stages or in supplies which also feed bias stabilising circuits (to just one stage) can lead to the right conditions for (parasitic) oscillation, ie a loop gain exceeding one and 360° phase shift around the loop.

"One small value but low inductance capacitor is used to decouple the stage at the amplified frequency. The second (and often third) capacitor(s) then decouple the stage at lower frequencies at which parasitic oscillations are likely to occur. It is not unusual to find a relatively high value polyester capacitor and an electrolytic capacitor used, not to improve the frequency response of the decoupling at signal frequencies but to minimise the risk of oscillation at one or more low frequencies."

EARTHS AND MARCONI ANTENNAS

IT IS NOTICEABLE THAT every time the topic of earths and earthing as part of a vertical monopole or Marconi-type antenna crops up in *TT*, it produces correspondence from those who hold diverse views. It sometimes seems that the subject can be as controversial as that of the antenna itself! John Heys, G3BDQ, for example, crosses swords with Dennis Unwin, G0FMT, in connection with his in-built earthing system for his quarter-wave Marconi antenna (*TT*, October). While personally I am not persuaded to start digging or laying an earth mat by G3BDQ's suggestions (surely with a resonant quarter-wave Marconi or monopole vertical the feed impedance is assumed by convention to be directly related to the radiation resistance and the more RF current that you can push into the antenna for a given transmitter power then the more efficient the antenna), it seems only fair to reproduce G3BDQ's remarks:

"I must cross swords with G0FMT. He is wrong in assuming that efficiency is directly related to feed impedance on a quarter-wave wire. You can juggle about with feed impedance in many ways (usually by lengthening or shortening the wire) but this will have little effect upon the efficiency of the system. The only way to increase the efficiency is to raise the radiation resistance of the antenna and/or reduce the earth resistance.

"This latter factor is the thing we can do ourselves. Running wires around the house, along the floor or putting in earth rods is almost a waste of time and effort. Salt water all around the antenna for a considerable distance, a copper sheet of enormous dimensions represent the ultimate . . . . earth rods are 'no-go' and buried wires unless very long and very numerous are not very good either. I find that an effective compromise is a comprehensive 'earth mat' of galvanised 'chicken wire'. this must cover a considerable area all around the antenna. As my 'mat' was increased the efficiency of my antenna was raised dramatically. I certainly did not try to equate efficiency with feed impedance.

"An earthing system must have a very low resistance return for the earth current back to the antenna base. The late Dr George Brown (*Proc IRE*, February 1935) states: 'In the operation of the usual transmitting antenna, the conduction current in the antenna diminishes as we proceed upward along the antenna. This is explained by displacement currents which are assumed to flow in the antenna, through space to the conducting plane below. This conducting plane completes the circuit by forming the return path to the base of the antenna. If this plane is not a perfect conductor, some power must be expended in returning the current to the base of the antenna'."

While one would not quarrel with the general tenor of the later comments, it does seem to me that they at odds with the now widely held view that, for example, a monopole antenna with a few radials elevated a few feet above ground and forming a counterpoise has been shown to be as effective as the usual form of broadcast antenna earth with 120 buried radials. Les Moxon, G6XN (*HF antennas for all locations*) shows clearly (page

THAT FULL-WAVE RECTIFIER

BOB PEARSON, G4FHU, was interested in the October *TT* item on a full-wave envelope detector first described in *Electronic Design* (May 14, 1992) but was puzzled by the claim of the original author that it offers the virtually zero rectification threshold of a synchronous detector.

G4FHU writes: "In fact this is not true! It does indeed work well as a full-wave rectifier when the input signal is sufficient to turn one transistor off but that needs rather more than 100mV peak-to-peak.

"If the transistors are well matched (as they need to be for good full-wave rectification) they draw an almost *constant* current via the collector and emitter loads while they are both conducting because increase in one transistor is balanced by a corresponding decrease in the other.

"In case I was in error in my conclusion, I connected the matched pair of transistors in a CA3045 integrated circuit array

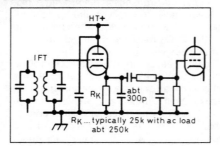

Fig 7: Basic circuit of infinite-impedance AM detector.

and added a balancing circuit to adjust the input to give equal adjacent peaks at the collector when operating as a full-wave detector. I then plotted changes in collector direct voltage against input signal level and this showed the anticipated 120mV peak-to-peak input offset in the rectifier characteristic: **Fig 6**.

"The CRO showed that below that level, the waveform deteriorates progressively. Paradoxically, a mismatch then helps to improve the low level rectification by 'half-waving', but the penalty is then the loss of precise full-wave operation everywhere else.

"I make the point only to save disappointment if the circuit is used for low-level signals. It is still of course well worth consideration for other applications."

On the subject of low-distortion envelope detectors, I would draw attention to the 'infinite-impedance detector' (**Fig 7**) which was developed by RCA in the mid-1930s and which I recall formed an extremely effective detector for broadcast receivers, with far less distortion of heavily modulated signals than with the conventional diode envelope detector. I am not sure whether this form of detector with its very high input impedance can be readily implemented with a bipolar transistor, but it certainly can with an FET as, for example, in the GI3XZM HF 'straight' receiver (*TT*, October 1987, etc), although I have no idea whether this would show the same low distortion over a wide dynamic range as when implemented with a valve.

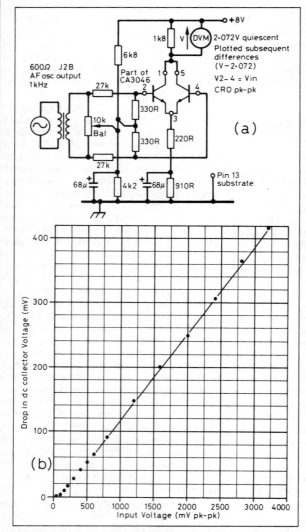

(a)

Fig 6: Full-wave envelope detector as tested by G4FHU showing that such an arrangement works well on signals of more than about 100mV peak-to-peak but does not meet the original designer's claim that "it offers the virtually zero rectification threshold of a synchronous detector". Below about 100mV the waveform deteriorates progressively, although a mismatch may help to improve low level rectification by "half-waving".

4) that "high efficiency can be achieved with very short radials or counterpoises . . . ." The important thing is to make sure that the currents flowing to and from the feed line are maximised. In the old days, before we worried about SWR and power meters, an RF ammeter in the antenna wire or the earth wire formed a valuable guide to antenna radiation. If altering the earthing or counterpoise system increases the current then one could safely assume that the radiation efficiency had been increased. While a large earth mat made from chicken wire *does* form an effective earth it is not the only approach that yields high radiation efficiency. One method may well be the in-built system used by G0FMT that could save a lot of back-breaking digging.

HERE AND THERE

A LONG 'MINI-REVIEW' PAPER 'Auroral and Polar-Cap Ionospheric Effects on Radio Propagation' by Dr Robert Hunsucker (University of Alaska) in *IEEE Trans Ant & Prop*, July 1992, pp818-828, provides a detailed description of how disturbances in the auroral and polar-cap ionosphere can have profound effects on radio signals transversing the high-latitude ionosphere (auroral oval) including for example HF paths between the UK and much of North America. the paper reviews salient past results and presents developments in this field for the period 1970—91 during which considerable efforts have been made to model and predict the parameters of the auroral and polar-cap ionosphere and to develop HF propagation programs which include these important effects.

Wilf Boothman, G3SWP, in connection with the notes on recharging dry batteries, draws attention to an article in the May 1992 issue of *Electrical Review* which tells how pupils at Westray School in the Orkneys found that a battery charger design intended for recharging nicad cells could be modified for dry batteries. Some 250 chargers were sold with the profits used to buy computers for the school, but then the British Battery Manufacturers' Association warned the local trading standards authority of the possible dangers of recharging dry cells and the lower efficiency compared to using nicads. The BBMA secretary denies that BBMA's objection to dry cell chargers is motivated by possible losses of sales.

Gerry Openshaw, G2BTO, reminds us that he described 'An easily constructed audio oscillator' using a GPO carbon microphone and headphone earpiece for Morse practice - similar to the arrangement shown in the October *TT* as long ago as April 1947 (*RSGB Bulletin*, p166). This type of simple oscillator was also used by S Pauwe as a sidetone oscillator in his modernized Mk VII transmitter-receiver (*TT*, June 1987).

BENCHLIGHT WARNING

LAWRENCE BROWN, G7LQO, considers the GW8DOA Movable Bench Spotlight (*TT*, November) potentially dangerous. He writes: "If a plastic or copper tube is used, the cable *must* be grommeted at the entry and exit points. If the tube is copper, then it *must* be earthed. Otherwise it could be extremely dangerous."   *G3VA*

VALE - WILLIAM HALLIGAN, W9AC (HALLICRAFTERS)

WHILE THE TOP HF communication receivers of the 1930s were undoubtedly the HRO and Super Pro models noted in the September *TT*, the more widely known and most famous name in amateur radio receivers for many years was indisputably 'Hallicrafters', the firm founded by William J Halligan, W9AC, in 1933 and which he ran until he retired to Miami, Florida in 1975. From ARRL comes the sad news that the founder of Hallicrafters died on 14 July, 1992, aged 93, after a life which spanned the whole history of radio.

He was first licensed as 1AEH in 1914, served as a ship's radio operator when still a teenager and as a US Navy operator at NAE on Cape Cod during WW1. He then worked for a time as a journalist before opening a radio store in Boston during the 1920s. In 1928 he moved to Chicago forming a partnership Chambers-Halligan selling retail radio components.

When, during the American depression, the firm failed, he formed his own company Hallicrafters, and was soon making and selling communications receivers ranging from the low-cost Sky Buddy (which sold in the UK for around £9), the Sky Champion with a stage of tuned RF amplification (UK around £15), to a series of higher performance Skyriders, Super Skyriders and Ultra Skyriders (coverage up to 79.5MHz) and Sky Challengers. From 1937, there was also a series of Hallicrafters AM/CW transmitters, starting with the 50 watt (100W CW) HT1 and from 1938 the HT4 (325W phone/400W CW) that became the basis of the US services' excellent BC610 transmitter used in the signals vehicles SCR299/SCR399 mentioned in connection with the Super Pro.

The British Y-services made good use of Hallicrafters S-27 VHF receivers tuning 27.8 to 143MHz (S-27B 36 to 165MHz) introduced in 1940, and also a high-performance HF receiver in the Super Skyrider series (SX-28 and military version SX-28B) dating from 1941. Post-war, in 1946, the low-cost S-38 was in effect a replacement for the Sky Buddy, with the S-40 replacing the Sky Champion, but import restrictions meant that few came to the UK.

With all the surplus receivers on the market in the late 1940s and 1950s, communication receiver firms found in tough going and, for example, Hallicrafters began making television receivers. Nevertheless, they still catered for the amateur market with a succession of models and some kits, pioneering a number of technical firsts and in 1962 becoming the first firm to market an amateur transceiver with a fully-transistorised receiver section (FPM-200). One of the best known postwar models was the SX71 double-conversion receiver introduced in 1950.

The following month, August, saw the passing at the age of 80 of (Colonel) Jerry Parker, G1SML, who played an important role in the wartime SOE Signals Directorate, organising clandestine radio links from Cairo and from the UK. In *TT* (June 1987, p409) I told how in Cairo in the early 1940s, dissatisfied with the equipment provided by British Intelligence, he bought from special funds a number of the Collins 18M-5 transmitter-receivers which had

Pat Hawker's Technical Topics

been developed originally for one of Admiral Byrd's Antartic expeditions. These were supply to General Mihailovic's Chetniks in the days before British support swung behind the partisans of Marshal Tito (Josef Broz). Jerry Parker was later involved with the links with Denmark that used the 'Telephone Directory' set designed by Lorens Duus Hansen, OZ7DU and built secretly in Copenhagen. Jerry once described how the first time Hansen came secretly to London to meet him, he was brought out of Denmark in a high-speed launch which picked him up from the pier that jutted out from and was used by the Gestapo headquarters in Copenhagen.

IMPEDANCE/POWER METER

C W FARRELL, G8GS, having used a thermo-couple ammeter and 75Ω dummy load to measure transmitter output to a matched antenna, decided to make another instrument. This incorporated a peak voltmeter to enable measurement of circuit impedance (Vpk x 0.7/Irms) in addition to RMS power (I x I x R) and sinewave PEP power (2 x I x I x R) using simple arithmetic. **Fig 1** shows his circuit - the meter is calibrated in peak and RMS volts with the aid of another test meter. The peak voltmeter uses three 1N914 diodes in series to cope with the peak inverse voltage, and capacitors of 0.01μF, 350V working for his transmitter output of about 45W RMS.

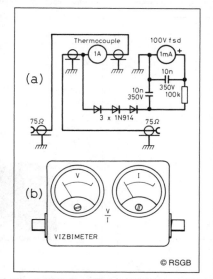

Fig 1: G8GS's 'Vizbimeter' has a peak voltmeter added to a power-meter using a thermo-couple ammeter and 75Ω load.

IONOSPHERIC PROPAGATION ON VHF

WHEN, IN MID-1985, the DTI accepted the recommendation of the Merriman Committee that the band 50-50.5MHz should be allocated to British amateurs, this was hailed in *TT* as "a valuable acquisition" (*TT*, September 1985 pp706-8). It was stressed that "50MHz is uniquely suitable for all those interested in the exploitation of an unparalleled number of different propagation modes. For 50MHz, rather than 30MHz, stands at the critical junction between HF and VHF and is a frequency more responsive to the ionosphere than the lower troposphere that dominates propagation on 70 and 144MHz. It combines many of the features of HF and VHF, external noise levels are significantly below those on 28MHz, antenna arrays are more compact, yet it is suitable for less critical and demanding equipment than the VHF and UHF bands."

"Just consider", I wrote, "the possibilities offered by the following basic propagation modes: (1) Worldwide F2 ionospheric propagation in daylight at periods of very high sunspot activity, with occasional, though possibly rare, openings towards the south in most phases of the cycle. (2) Transequatorial and field-aligned F2 propagation (TEP) in the evenings, even though the UK is often considered too far north for this to be at all common. (3) Ionospheric scatter modes (with very high power) can provide reliable 24hr communication over distances of from 500 to 2000km. (4) Almost the optimum frequency for sporadic-E and meteor burst communications. (5) Reasonable for auroral propagation. (6) Some degrees of tropospheric bending, ducting and tropospheric scatter modes, though less pronounced than at 144MHz and above. (7) Significantly better propagation over hills and down into valleys than at 144MHz."

It was also then noted that HF operators could expect to be reliably warned of sporadic-E and/or high MUF on 50MHz by the presence of short-skip signals on 14, 21 and 28MHz. Perhaps the one disadvantage of 50MHz, not mentioned in the 1985 item, is its susceptibility to local man-made electrical interference, including the all-too-common RFI from computer-based IT equipment.

Seven years later, there seems no reason to revise or amend this list of possible 50MHz propagation modes. Indeed the work by amateurs worldwide on this part of the radio spectrum is beginning to influence the professional radio physicists and the classic texts on HF/VHF propagation. A contribution by three Australian engineers - Peter Dyson and Juan Chen (Latrobe University, Bundoora, Victoria) and John Bennett (Monash University, Clayton, Victoria) in *IEEE Transactions on Antennas and Propagation*, July 1992, pp841-3 'Single-Hop F2 propagation above 30MHz and over distances greater than 4000km' clearly draws on the experiences of Australian amateurs (who have for years exploited the Australia/Japan path on 50MHz).

The abstract notes that "During recent years of increased solar activity there has been an increase in the number of reports of communications at 50MHz over distances exceeding 4000km. This has led to discussion of the propagation modes and to suggestions that the 'standard textbook explanation' fails to explain that such propagation can occur via single-hop F2 modes. We point out that in fact, the 'standard textbook explanation' based on parabolic layers does predict such modes."

The authors write: "Long-distance propagation occurs mostly at HF, so textbooks usually couch their discussions in terms of these frequencies. However, descriptions of propagation via ionosphere make clear that the range of frequencies that can propagate in any mode depends on the properties of the ionosphere. Thus it is apparent that frequencies in the VHF band can propagate if appropriate conditions occur. Even so, other mechanisms involving scatter are more frequent causes of VHF propagation via the ionosphere and this has probably led to the mistaken impression that the 'standard textbook explanation' does not explain that VHF F2 propagation is sometimes possible."

The Australian writers show how 'Bougere's Law' can be used to determine the maximum frequency reflected from a specific height in

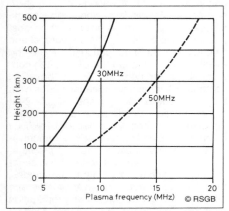

Fig 2: Diagram shows plasma frequency required to reflect 30 and 50MHz signals at various heights of the layer.

the ionosphere and the relationship between the critical (plasma) frequency (the maximum frequency that will be reflected directly downwards) and the maximum usable frequency (MUF). They show that 30MHz signals can be propagated if the plasma frequency is 10MHz at a height of 386km so that propagation at 30MHz will almost invariably occur if foF2 is at least 10MHz: "Much higher plasma frequencies are required to reflect 50MHz. For example, the plasma frequency must be at least 13.6MHz at a height of 250km. Since the peak height of the F2 layer is often greater than this, foF2 will often need to be as much as 15MHz or greater for single hop F2 propagation to occur at 50MHz."

They note that data recorded by K Davies and published in the 1966 book *Ionospheric Radio Propagation* show that at mid-latitudes, the noon value of foF2 is about 10-11.5MHz when the sunspot number is high - thus propagation in the lower VHF band around 30MHz can be expected at these times at mid-latitudes. Davies also presents some data from the high latitude station of Adak, Alaska, showing values of foF2 as high as 15MHz. Perhaps surprisingly this indicates that 50MHz propagation is more likely at higher latitudes: "Relatively high values of foF2 also occur at the equatorial anomalies, increasing the likelihood of VHF propagation near the equator. Of course, other ionospheric features, such as ionospheric tilts or horizontal gradients, may lead to VHF propagation via the F2. This is particularly true near the equator where transequatorial propagation can occur due to gradients associated with the equatorial anomaly and with equatorial bubble irregularities. VHF propagation can also result from reflection from sporadic E layers."

Fig 2, from the paper, shows the plasma frequency required to reflect 30 and 50MHz signals at a given F2 layer height.

The paper notes that the calculation of the range of single-hop propagation is more com-

plex. Davies showed that propagation over ranges of 4000-6000km can occur for single-hop F2 modes with the greatest range occurring when the M factor (the factor by which MUF is greater than foF2) approaches 3, giving as an example an oblique ionogram in which propagation between Ottawa and Slough, a path of over 5000km, occurred at frequencies up to 48MHz.

Fig 3 shows power contours for propagation via a quasi-parabolic layer at a height of 375km and with Ym representing the divergence of the layer from a true parabola. The M factor for this layer is 3.05 so that FoF2 must be at least 16.4MHz for (conventional) single-hop propagation to occur. **Fig 4** shows how the power contour can be affected by underlying E and F1 layers. The formulae on which these contours are based are given in the paper.

The paper is summarized as follows: "The main requirement for VHF single hop propagation via the F2 layer of the ionosphere is that foF2 must be sufficiently high, as occurs at times during years of high sunspot number. For a spherically stratified ionosphere, the highest frequency propagated depends on the combination of foF2, peak layer height and layer shape. Other factors, such as horizontal gradients, can also affect the highest frequency propagated via the ionosphere.

"The distances over which single hop F2 modes propagate can be significantly increased by underlying E and F1 layers. It has been shown that the presence of E and F1 layers can extend single hop F2 propagation well beyond 4000km for a wide foF2 is sufficiently high for them to be reflected from the ionosphere.

"Since VHF can propagate by other modes, (eg via sporadic E, transequatorial and scatter modes), careful consideration of prevailing ionospheric conditions is needed to positively identify VHF single-hop F2 modes over long distances."

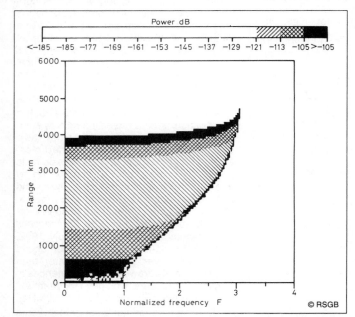

Fig 3: Power contours for single hop propagation via a single quasi-parabolic layer at a height of 375km. For such a layer the plasma frequency (F) for 50MHz propagation would need to be over 16MHz. However layer heights may be significantly lower than this making 50MHz propagation possible at lower plasma frequencies.

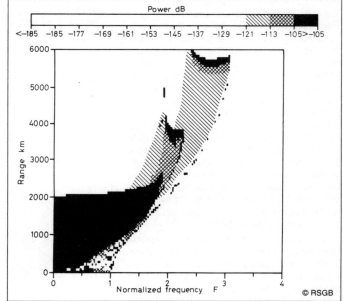

Fig 4: Power contours for single hop propagation via an ionosphere consisting of E, F1 and F2 layers based on layer parameters at Darwin, Australia at 1500 hours local time during March with a sunspot number of 150. The data comes from a paper 'Single Hop F2 Propagation above 30MHz and over Distances Greater than 4000km'.

MORE ON SLEEVE BALUNS

THE 1:1 CHOKE CURRENT-BALUN may be formed either by coiling a few turns in the coaxial feeder at the element end. Alternatively it can be constructed in the form of a ferrite-bead sleeve section as shown in *TT*, Sept 1992. A basically similar device but designed to fit to the base of the 300Ω section of a G5RV type antenna is regularly advertised in *RadCom* by Ferromagnetics of Mold. These are finding increasing popularity as a means of reducing common-mode RF current on the outer braid of coaxial cable feeders.

Most sleeve baluns comprise some 40-50 small ferrite beads slipped over a short section of thin diameter cable such as RG303/U or RG141 cable as shown in the September *TT*. However an alternative approach for use where such cable is not readily available is described by Bill Orr, W6SAI, in his 'Radio FUNdamentals' column in *CQ*, October 1992. He writes:

"The current balun can consist of a number of turns of coax wrapped into an air coil, or wrapped around a ferrite core. The air coil is bulky (about six turns of coax, 8 inches in diameter for RG8/U or RG58/U serves on the 14-30MHz range). This is an inexpensive choke coil, and it can be a portion of the feedline, held together with cable ties. For best results it should be placed at the antenna (element) terminals.

"Wrapping coax around a ferrite core is difficult, as anyone who has tried this can affirm. The bulky air coil is better.

"Taking an idea from the VHF solid-state world, Doug DeMaw, W1FB, proposed in 1980 that ferrite 'sleeves' passed over a coax line could serve as an RF choke, or current balun, to decouple the line. Shortly thereafter, Walt Maxwell, W2DU, built and measured such a decoupling sleeve made up of a number of ferrite beads on a length of the coax. The W2DU HF balun consisted of 50 type-73 beads on a foot-long length of 50Ω Teflon dielectric cable. The only fly in the ointment with this design is that the specified RG303/U cable is not available from most amateur radio distributors. The suggested alternative cable, RG141/U, is also not a household word!

"A practical and inexpensive balun can be either of readily available RG58/U or RG8/U (or similar European cables). Luckily, toroid beads (sleeves) having inner diameters of 0.5in and 0.25in that will pass the coax lines are available in either 43 or 77 ferrite material. The original W2DU design used 73 material which is similar to 77, but large cores that slip over coax lines are presently available only in 43 and 77 material **(Table 1)**.

"Test baluns were constructed using the two available types of ferrite and the baluns were tested using a General Radio RF impedance bridge. Each balun was made of a short length of RG58/U and tested using the set-up recommended by W2DU.

"It was arbitrarily decided that the impedance presented by the choke balun should be about ten times the coax line impedance over the operating range of the balun, 500Ω for a 50Ω cable.

"My conclusion was that the balun using 77

HERE AND THERE

IN *QST* (AUGUST 1992), Zack Lau, KH6CP/1, offers the following answer to the question whether 6146B RF power valves can be substituted for the earlier 6146 valves: "In most cases you can, although the B suffix version has slightly higher grid-to-plate capacitance which may cause problems if the range of the neutralization circuit is marginal. In addition, while the anode dissipation of the new tubes may be greater, do not try to squeeze more power out of the circuit. Your power supply may not survive the additional stress! For tube type amplifiers it is often the power supply that limits the amplifier, not plate dissipation." KH6CP offers many other useful hints on "Substituting parts" in building or repairing amateur equipment.

Mitchell Lee, KB6FPW, in offering advice (*QST*, August 1992) on handling and storing lengths of coax-cable suggests these should not be longer than 100ft since longer pieces are hard to manage in terms of both weight and length. Lengths should be tagged with a note of their length. He adds: "When rolling up the coax, start the roll by making one loop and secure it with electrical tape. Then continue the roll by turning the loop while walking towards the other end of the coax. Do not feed the coax on by coiling it onto the roll - this is guaranteed to make kinks: see **Fig 5**. After rolling up the coax, finish off with more electrical tape to secure the loose end. Selflocking nylon cable ties are also useful for this purpose, and can be

used to secure the roll in several places. If the coax has been used in a wet or dusty environment, it is a good idea to hose it off and lay it out in the sun to dry. Blow moisture and dirt out of the connectors with compressed air. If the coax is really dirty, you may want to unroll it and wipe it down with a wet rag. To store the roll, either lay it out flat or hang it up. Always store it in a cool, dry location, away from direct sunlight. If you choose to hang the coax, use a large radius hanger such as a garden hose hanger but make sure that it will not subject the coax to abrasion from sharp edges. When it is to be used, unroll it in the same way as it was rolled up - like a wagon wheel instead of pulling it off the coil sideways, so as to prevent kinking and frustrating tangles.

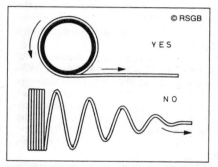

Fig 5: The right and wrong way to coil and uncoil lengths of coaxial cable. Always wind and unwind the cable tangentially in order to avoid kinking.

---

material performed best below 10MHz and that using 43 material was better above 10MHz. In both cases excellent current balance was obtained in the load, even when the load itself was purposely unbalanced.

"A ferrite sleeve balun can be built by sliding six (sleeve) beads of the proper size over the coax at the antenna end of the transmission line. The beads can be held in position against each other by application of heat-shrink tubing. Use the 77 beads below 10MHz and the 43 beads above 10MHz. If you don't mind a slightly poorer balance at the low frequency end, the 43 beads can be used down to 3.5MHz." I feel that to rely solely on heat-shrink tubing protection might result in UV problems for antennas in sunlight. Zack Lau, KH6CP/1 has pointed out in *QST* that it is difficult but not impossible to differentiate the various ferrite materials by colour and texture: "For example, type 43 material has a pronounced metallic sheen compared to type

72. Type 75 material usually appears to be dull and dark."

It is perhaps worth emphasising that, at least for dipole-type antennas, a balun may not be necessary, and may make very little difference to performance. Before going to the trouble of making or buying a sleeve balun it is worth checking that, without it, there really is significant RF current flowing back down the outer side of the braid on all or some bands and causing unwanted effects such as RFI or high levels of RF in the shack.

MORE ON THE ZS6BKW/ G0GSF MULTIBAND DIPOLE

JUST OVER A DECADE AGO, *TT*, May 1982, pp412-3, presented an item 'Potential of the G5RV antenna' which brought to the notice of amateurs the computer-aided work of Dr Brian Austin (ZS6BKW and more recently G0GSF). He showed how the dimensions of the multiband dipole antenna popularised by Louis Varney, G5RV, some forty years ago could be modified to extend its performance to the 18 and 24MHz bands. A few years later, Dr Austin provided a full-length description (*RadCom*, Aug 1985, pp614-617, 624) of this antenna. Computer aided work showed how such an antenna could be dimensioned so that, even without an ATU, an effective match could be obtained on most bands from 7 to 28MHz. With the aid of an ASMU (ATU), operation on 3.5, 10 and 21MHz was possible.

Amidon Part No	Outer dia (in)	Inner dia (in)	Length (in)	Fits cable
FB-77-1024	1.0	0.5	0.825	RG8/U
FB-43-1020	1.0	0.5	1.112	RG8/U
FB-77-5621	0.562	0.250	1.125	RG58/U
FB-43-5621	0.562	0.250	1.125	RG58/U

Nomenclature	Permeability	Material
Type 77	2000	Manganese-Zinc
Type 43	850	Nickel-Zinc
Type 73	2500	Manganese-Zinc

Table 1: Characteristics of Amidon toroid sleeve-type beads as given by W6SAI.

Surprisingly, relatively few UK amateurs seem to have taken advantage of this modified design which eliminates the disadvantages of traps, multiple wire elements etc, yet still provides a coaxial feed into the shack. Also, it can be used as a readily transportable wire antenna for field events, expeditions etc. It has, however, been attracting increasing attention overseas, and also for non-amateur communications.

Fig 6 as given in the Danish journal *OZ* (10/92) and initially in Rothammel's *Antennabuch*, shows **(a)** the standard 'G5RV' antenna together with two modified versions, **(b)** as proposed by W5ANB in *QST*, Nov 1981, for 7, 14 and 28MHz, and **(c)** the ZS6BKW/G0GSF arrangement discussed below. **Fig 6(d)** shows one form of ATU that can be used with any of these antennas on bands where the VSWR without a tuner is more than about 2:1. The Danish article by Rick Meilstrup, OZ5RM, gives results of measurements made on the original G5RV antenna now being marketed by DeeComm, although normally a wire antenna can be constructed at lower cost than a packaged product.

In the New Zealand journal *Break-in*, May 1992, Rick Hill, ZL1OK presents some SWR measurements made on what he describes as "a very useful cheap antenna that thrashes the pants off a G5RV . . . . The main disadvantages are the lack of 15m band coverage, the 10m resonance is rather high in the band and the antenna is de-tuned somewhat by heavy rain."

ZL1OK writes that his antenna has a feedpoint impedance close to 50Ω on five bands - "operation on all or part of the 40, 20, 17, 12 and 10 metre bands is quite practical using a solid-state rig with no tuner. I have built several versions of this antenna. Results have been good with the antenna in the inverted vee configuration with the apex 12m above the ground. He gives measurements made on a lightweight version using slotted low-loss TV ribbon (300Ω) for the matching section and 0.55mm² hookup wire for the 'top'. It is possible to optimize SWR for your favourite portion of your favourite band by adjusting the dipole length, but this may result in the 'loss' (without an ATU) of one of the other bands."

A recent IEE colloquium on 'Multi-band Antennas' was concerned primarily with antennas for the microwave and millimetre wave bands, but provided also a forum for Brian Austin, G0GSF, to describe his version of the G5RV type antenna as a solution to the problems of tactical HF one-hop communications. He emphasised that ionospheric propagation mechanisms used at HF involve diurnal, seasonal and sunspot cycle variations that make multi-frequency operation obligatory if 24-hour contact is required over any given path.

"This requirement places quite considerable constraints on the antenna systems used and would suggest that either a multiplicity of antennas or a single broadband configuration is required . . . . If operational requirements (eg tactical situation or non-permanent installations) preclude the use of large broadband antennas then a viable alternative is the multiband antenna.

"A configuration which achieves multiband performance, at high radiation efficiency, was

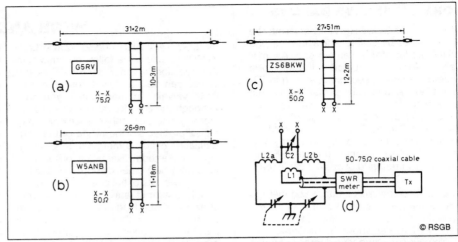

Fig 6: Three versions of multiband dipoles providing low SWR on the coaxial cable feeder on a number of HF bands. (a) The original 'G5RV'; (b) version proposed by W5ANB; (c) the ZS6BKW/G0GSF antenna discussed in the text and (d) a suitable ATU for all versions for use on bands not providing low SWR.

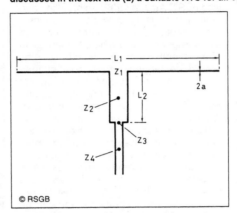

Fig 7: Basics of the multiband wire antenna.

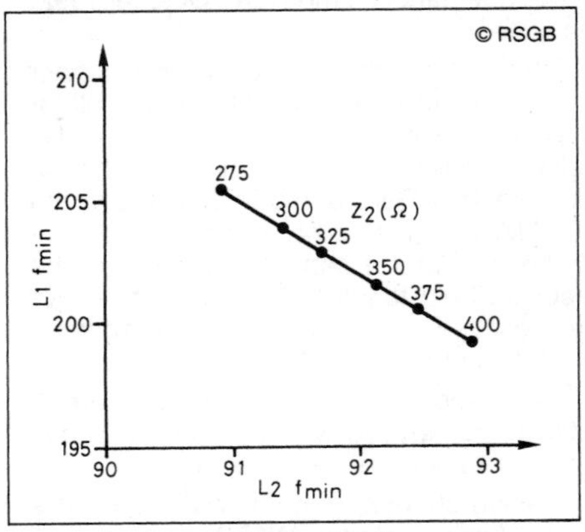

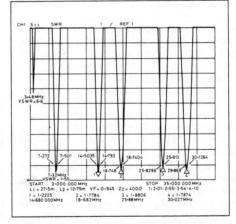

Fig 8: 'Design line' for the multiband antenna.

first used in the 1930s, then popularised for radio amateurs by Louis Varney, G5RV, (*RSGB Bulletin*, Vol 34, No 7, 1958, pp19-20) and more recently optimized in terms of its VSWR performance (B A Austin, 'An HF multiband wire antenna for single-hop point-to-point applications', *J.IERE*, Vol 57, No 4, 1987, pp167-173).

"The antenna is shown in **Fig 7**. The transmission line section L2 acts as a series-section impedance transformer whose function is to transform Z1, the driving-point impedance of L1, into a suitable value Z3 which will match the characteristic impedance Z4 of the system transmission line to the terminal equipment. The performance criterion used is the VSWR on that cable (usually coaxial with Z4 equal to 50Ω). An acceptable match exists when VSWR is equal to or less than 2:1 . . . . In general, the relationship between L1, L2 and Z2 when the VSWR with respect to Z4 is shown in **Fig 8**."

In the IEE colloquium digest No 1992/181, Dr Austin presents two relatively simple manual methods to analyse the performance of this antenna (see also the *J.IERE* reference given above). He shows that where Z2 is greater than 275Ω and less than 450Ω an acceptable impedance match will occur at a number of frequencies in the HF range. The optimum value of Z2 lies between 325-400Ω. Within this range the matching performance of the antenna is basically independent of Z2, and a simple design equation for the antenna is $L1 (f_{min}) = 473.44 - 2.95 L2 (f_{min})$ where f_{min}

is the lowest frequency at which the antenna is to operate, constrained by the requirement that $\pi L1/\lambda$ is greater than 1.

For any given values of f_{min} and Z2, there are specific lengths L1 and L2 which will satisfy the matching criterion. The frequencies at which this match occurs are related by the following series which varies slightly for different values of Z2: f/f_{min} = 1: 1.99: 2.53: 3.49: 4.07: 5.62: 7.18.

Dr Austin has designed and tested a number of these antennas in various practical situations. **Fig 9** shows the VSWR for an antenna providing resonant frequencies just outside amateur bands with L1 27.5m, L2 12.75m, Z2

Fig 9: VSWR vs frequency for multiband antenna.

400Ω (velocity factor 0.95) and Z4 50Ω. With these dimensions five bands of frequencies in the HF band, between 3 and 30MHz, yielded VSWRs less than 2:1 with f_{min} equal to 7.32MHz and the matching series 1: 2.01: 2.55: 3,54: 4.10. A ferrite sleeve balun, consisting of 40 ferrite beads (type 73 material, permeability 2500) was used at the intersection between the balanced line L2 and the coaxial cable Z4. Its effect on the measured impedance Z3 and hence on the VSWR was minimal. He concludes: "It would appear, therefore, that the use of a balun is not justified in this application."

A KISSLESS FUTURE WITH VSLI/DSP?

WHEN FRANK WELLS, G3ATJ, enquired as to the meaning of the abbreviation KISS (Keep it simple, stupid) in 'The last word' (*RadCom*, Nov 1992, p77) the Editor, in supplying the meaning, added "It is generally used in connection with home construction" - a comment that conceals a disturbing, if understandable, trend in the development of new technology for professional communications and broadcasting. For KISS was originally coined by professional engineers but increasingly is being disregarded in commercial practice. The trend is towards complex very-large-scale-integration (VLSI), with tiny application-specific chips containing thousands of active devices. A far cry from the days when even professionals hesitated to use more than about 20 thermionic valves and preferably fewer in a receiver or transmitter.

The latest move towards vastly more complex systems, based on the wonders of digital signal processing, can be seen in the current effort being put into digital audio broadcasting (DAB) and digital transmission of high-definition or 625-line television within terrestrial UHF channels. Several such systems have already reached the stage of field trials in Europe including the UK. Similarly, work is at an advanced stage for digital mobile radio systems. In all these systems, a key factor is the lower bit rates that are possible using digital compression - with the enormous redundancy of video signals making it possible to transmit coded digital video signals in bandwidths much narrower than is possible for analogue video signals. Digital speech combined with error correction can, for communication purposes, be transmitted with a total bit-rate of around 5-9kbit/s in bandwidths determined by the modulation mode.

Digital signals can be regenerated many times without introducing any additional quantisation noise and DAB, for example, can provide multiple channels from one transmitter of CD quality stereo music. In the European-developed system this can use a single channel allocation for a country-wide terrestrial complex, representing much greater spectrum efficiency than a comparable VHF/FM network. But the susceptibility of high-speed digits to multipath effects has required the adoption of a complex modulation system called COFDM (coded orthogonal frequency division multiplex). This is related to multi-tone telegraphy with similarities to the Piccolo HF system of the 1960s. This was used for many years by the Foreign Office but has now been largely abandoned in favour of satellite systems for FCO diplomatic communications.

But where will digital speech systems leave amateur radio? Packet radio has shown the advantages and disadvantages of digital systems on the amateur bands, particularly on HF. Will it be long before we see bandwidth-compressed digital speech and digital video? Technically and economically this seems likely once the necessary chip sets are available at consumer electronics prices. But whether digital transmission systems such as OFDM with its large numbers of closely spaced carriers individually modulated will be feasible (or even desirable in amateur radio) remains to be seen. One thing is certain, they would break the rules of KISS! Equally important, they would make the hobby even more of a 'black box' activity than it is at present.

Will we soon need to understand such concepts as 'Codebook excitation linear prediction coding (CELP)' or for video 'Motion compensated hybrid discrete cosine transform coding (MC-DCT)' not to mention the Reed-Solomon systems of forward error correction?

Terrestrial DAB as demonstrated on several occasions by the BBC (most recently during Open Days at the BBC Research Centre, Kingswood Warren) clearly offers significant advantages over VHF/FM for mobile reception of multiplexed broadcast channels. But there remains the problem of acquiring 'parking spectrum' (possibly in the old Band III around 200MHz) for use until such time as it is politically possible for DAB to replace VHF/FM in Band II. And this at a time when the BBC is still encouraging listeners to equip themselves with three band LW/MW/FM receivers and have promised to complete their FM network before taking Radio 4 off the AM bands! But there can be little doubt that

the future of personal and mobile cellular radio-telephones lies in digital rather than the current analogue systems.

So far, for amateur radio, DSP has been thought of primarily in terms of high-performance selectivity filters working at audio frequency although this is just one of the many potential applications. The cover of the September 1992 issue of *QST* proclaims: "DSP: The Future is Here" to mark an article 'Low-cost digital signal processing for the radio amateur' by Dave Hershberger, W9GR. He describes a multipurpose digital signal processor based around the TMS320CI0 DSP CPU (see **Fig 10**). It functions as linear-phase super-sharp CW filter, an adaptive noise filter and an advance multiple automatic notch filter, all under software control. But even in this form it is hardly KISS technology.

RE-CYCLING COMPONENTS

MY ACCOUNT IN THE September *TT* of how one of my old mains transformers came to a dangerously smoky end that might have been avoided if it had been fitted with a temperature fuse of the type described and illustrated in the 1950s *Radio & Television Engineers Reference Book* (in a section by L Driscoll who was at the time in charge of the Murphy Radio Receiver Design Laboratory) attracted more comment than I had expected. A subsequent search through circuit diagrams of British-made broadcast receivers of the early 1950s revealed temperature fuses fitted to only a few top-grade Murphy receivers such as their 'baffle-cabinet' Model A188c with push-pull audio output. Possibly other British firms fitted them, but if so I cannot trace any.

Bob Currell, G4EIK, suspects that the transformer may have been sealed with shellac as widely used for sealing coils etc. He points out that it is widely known in the antique restoration trade that shellac is not a stable material. It has a limited shelf life when in an alcoholic solution of about two years and only lasts about 80 years without care when applied to a surface as French polish. After about this time interval, which is variable with storage conditions, it tends to flake off, crack and become hard and brittle causing it to scratch very easily and deeply. G4EIK adds: "Inside a piece of electrical equipment the warm dry conditions coupled with the thermal shock from the heating and cooling cycles would exacerbate any tendency to crack and cause breakdown of the insulation - this could be a possible explanation of the failure of the transformer."

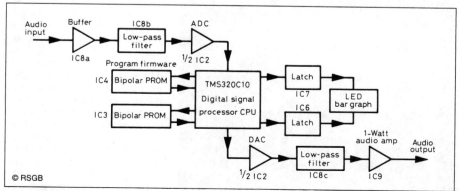

Fig 10: W9GR digital signal processor - block diagram.

SATELLITE TV - A SOURCE OF REVERSE TVI

DR BRIAN AUSTIN, G0GSF, recently mentioned that he has been suffering from interference to HF reception and had found the source to be the 'outdoor' 11GHz LNB converter unit of a satellite TV receiver. I had not previously come across this problem but G0GSF has sent me a copy of an article 'In the workshop with the Optoelectronics Handi-Counter 2300' by Rob Mannion, G3XFD, the Editor of *Practical Wireless* in his August 1992 issue.

It describes the use of this hand-held frequency counter as a means of tracking down sources of interference. In particular, one such source affecting the 14MHz band was traced to the UHF modulator used in an early computer in his daughter's bedroom. This was radiating spurious signals on HF, VHF and UHF but the problem was cured by replacing the modulator by one purchased for £1 at a rally. He continues:

"I then recalled a problem I had helped solve for another radio amateur during 1991. This to cut a long and sad story short, involved a satellite TV low noise block (LNB). The amateur concerned could not operate on the higher HF bands at all because of very bad interference. He had tried everything except changing the LNB which fortunately (or unfortunately!) had been installed for the benefit of his disabled and housebound wife. After I suggested that someone with a portable spectrum analyser should be brought in, the culprit was found and changed.

"Remembering the 1991 incident, I walked along the road where I live, taking the Handi-Counter with me. I soon found other LNBs radiating signals on HF strong enough to be locked onto by the Optoelectronics 2300. After some research, I have discovered that the problems are probably caused by the high level of local oscillator injections on satellite LNBs.

"I had also come across the problem in the USA while attending the Dayton HamVention, where the hotel dish feeding the 'piped' TV was just below my bedroom window. With spurious signals making the HF bands virtually useless, even trying to hear the BBC World Service was a painful process!"

It thus seems that this problem is universal and likely to become of increasing importance as the number of satellite-TV installations increases. At present, despite the EC EMC Directive, there appears to be no legal requirements that LNBs (or other similar sources of reverse-TVI) should not interfere with reception on the amateur bands, although G0GSF does point out that his local RA inspector is watching the situation.

Pat Hawker's Technical Topics

ROOF-SPACE DUAL BAND MAGNETIC LOOP

SOME MONTHS AGO, FOLLOWING the publication of a number of items on magnetic loop antennas (both in *TT* and as full-length *RadCom* articles), I began to feel that the subject deserved a rest. What more could be written - it had been shown that such antennas were capable of achieving good results, particularly on the lower frequency HF bands, for amateurs without sufficient space or high enough supports to allow the erection of an antenna providing the higher radiation resistance that makes for good efficiency at low cost. It did seem, at least to me, that the models that had appeared on the market were costly compared with a simple wire dipole, while home-constructed models called for good quality tuning capacitors welded to an extremely low-resistance loop, with the complication of accurate remotely controlled

GI2FHN has constructed this dual loop in his roof space.

motor tuning. Nevertheless, well made compact transmitting loops do work surprisingly well and represent a valid approach for those without space. From a number of contacts made with stations using small loops, it does appear that they compare well with, for example, trapped verticals mounted on the ground.

Roberto Craighero, I1ARZ, with much personal experience of using loops, writes: "I confirm once more that the radiation efficiency of a short loop antenna having a circumference slightly less than 0.25-wave approaches the efficiency of a half-wave dipole a half-wave above ground. It is clear that having sufficient space to erect a dipole at such a height provides a more convenient antenna than a compact loop. However, it is clear that most amateurs wishing to work the lower frequency bands find it difficult to erect long dipoles at the required height. In such cases the compact loop is certainly better than a dipole at a very low height in terms of wavelength.

"But I wish to stress once again that to obtain good results with a compact loop, the materials employed must be of good quality. An excellent split-stator capacitor must be used to tune the loop. Welding must be accurate to keep ohmic losses to a minimum.

"In my experience a ground plane improves the overall efficiency of a compact loop even if not directly connected to the antenna. An 80cm loop mounted over the roof of my car, but not connected to the car body, showed a significant improvement due to the ground plane provided by the roof of the car. With my large square loop for the lower frequency bands, I could notice an improvement when the surface of the flat roof is wet following rain. [But is rain water electrically conductive? G3VA].

"I can confirm DK5CZ's remarks (*Eurotek*, Oct 1991, p39) that the high loop currents tend to heat and thereby distort the thin metal in vacuum capacitors and consequently detune the loop. With my large low-frequency loop which has a vacuum capacitor, I find that on SSB (about 60W PEP) with its low power factor there is no need to retune the antenna. But when I use CW with its greater power factor, there is a need to retune the loop from time to time.

I1ARZ also drew attention to a loop described by Sergio Clauser, IV3RLL, in *Radio Rivista*, 7/91, using a length of low-loss UHF Heliax cable. This has an external diameter of 41mm after removing the internal nylon spiral and inner conductor to provide a very light but solid copper conductor of large diameter that can be bent into a circle by hand. Such bending is possible since this type of cable has copper tubing with a special knurling that permits bending and increases the electrical surface of the antenna by about

20%. Such cable is very expensive but it is sometimes possible to acquire short end-of-reel lengths at much reduced cost since short lengths have low commercial value. I1ARZ also mentions the use of 3in elliptical waveguide.

Eric Sandys, GI2FHN, has been making good use of a multiband form of magnetic loop that borrows a dual tuning technique from the Z-match tuner: **Figs 1 and 2**. He writes:

"On 14, 18, 21, 24 and 28MHz, L1 is tuned by C1A and C1B in series. As L3 is high impedance at these frequencies, it can be ignored. On 3.5 and 7MHz, L3 is tuned by C1A placed in parallel with C1B through L1. The coupling links L2 and L4 are connected in parallel and RF is fed in through a 1:1 choke balun. The sizes of the coupling links were

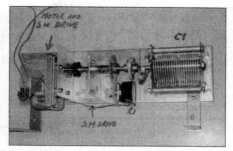
The loop's tuning unit with slow-motion drives.

selected to give the lowest SWR which is better than 1.5:1 on all bands. If coverage of the 10MHz band is required, L4 needs to be reduced slightly in size.

"The same diameter coaxial cable is used for the loops and coupling links. Note that the connections between the two coupling links should not be transposed. A should go to C and B to D. Failure to observe these points can result in degradation of the SWR.

"The loop is housed in the roof space using a timber framework to provide the necessary support. All functions are carried out from a control box (Fig 9) at the operating position. Changing bands is made easy by using a Wheatstone bridge to give a visual indication on M1 of the travel of C1. The variable arm R1 is gear driven from the shaft connecting the motor and reduction gearing to C1.

"Direction of rotation is controlled by S1, a DPDT switch (centre-off). Fine tuning is provided by a speed control R2. A current probe enables exact resonance to be established at the operating frequency.

"Results have exceeded all expectations and the arrangement can be recommended for anyone who does not have space for a fullsize outside antenna."

MORE ON THE G5RV/ZS6BKW ANTENNAS

THE JANUARY *TT* drew attention to the growing interest overseas in the ZS6BKW/G0GSF antenna developed from the G5RV but offering a reasonable match (without ATU) on five bands: 7, 14, 18, 24 and 28MHz. It is interesting to note that Bill Orr, W6SAI, in his *Radio FUNdamentals* column in *CQ* (November 1992) also presents information on both versions under the heading 'The G5RV antenna revisited - again'.

In addition, he traces some early history, writing: "To go back a bit, the G5RV antenna is an offspring of a 3-band antenna (80-40-20 metres) designed by Art Collins (ex-W9CXX) and L M Croft and described in detail by Croft in the December 1935 issue of *Signal* magazine, the house publication of the old Collins Radio Company . . . . The idea behind the antenna was sound, but the execution was a failure because the antenna used a 300Ω section made of two 82.5ft lengths of aluminium tubing hanging from the centre of the 103ft flat top. The weight of the installation made it heavy and impractical. Signal gain of this antenna was about 1dBd.

"In the early 1950s the antenna reappeared in modified form in England, redesigned and popularized by Louis Varney, G5RV. The Varney antenna functions as a 1.5-wave antenna on 14MHz with a feedpoint impedance

slightly over 100Ω. The matching section of heavy tubing is replaced by a 450Ω open-wire half-wave line. This light-weight (Matching section) transformer closely matched the antenna feedpoint impedance to an 80Ω transmission line on 20 metres . . . . it was quickly found that the G5RV would function quite well on other bands if an antenna tuning unit was used at the transmitter. No one worried much about SWR in those days . . . ."

Curiously enough, the highly-respected Walt Maxwell, W2DU, in his book *Reflections - Transmission lines and antennas* (ARRL, 1990) commits one of his very few errors in dismissing as "one of the myths and confusion concerning the G5RV" that it can yield a low SWR [admittedly not 1:1 but below 2:1 - *G3VA*] on bands other than 14MHz. He states categorically that "there is no length of open-wire line of any characteristic impedance Zc that will transform the antenna impedance Za to an impedance that is even close to presenting a match to 50 or 75Ω coax, except on 20 metres". May I humbly suggest to W2DU that before the next edition is published, he should carefully read the various papers by G0GSF mentioned in the January *TT*.

ADVANCES IN HF RECEIVERS

IN THE ERA OF BLACK BOX transceivers, there is a danger that most of us, unless professional design engineers, will gradually lose touch with the finer points of modern HF receivers. There is a pertinent cartoon in the December 1992 issue of the Australian 'Amateur Radio'. It is a drawing of an amateur speaking into the microphone of his transceiver with a 'Black Box Operator certificate' hanging on the wall. He is saying "Yes, I got the certificate. Now I'm going for the fifty knob endorsement!"

It seems that the trick nowadays is to learn how to use the knobs rather than to have any clear idea of what they do and why they actually work - not to mention whether they are really necessary, and whether the facility they provide may be at the cost of more desirable performance characteristics. It has to be admitted ruefully that in many respects, at least for CW operation, the HF receiver of today is unlikely to be significantly better and may be significantly worse than the best designs of over 30 years ago.

On the other hand it has also to be admitted that if a manufacturer were rash enough to attempt to market a replica of receivers such as the Collins 75A4 or 51J4, the Hammarlund SP600 Super Pro or even the 1940s RCA AR88, the price tag would be way up in the stratosphere! Recent articles have shown that in 'real terms' the cost of 'economy-class' amateur HF transceivers has continued to fall although top-of-the-range models with ever more built-in facilities (and even more knobs) have risen significantly. **Fig 3** shows representative block diagrams of modern receivers.

Currently, in the professional and to some extent in the amateur receiver world, the main talking point is the increasing use of digital signal processing as part of the trend towards the true digital-radio. Digitization is still confined to post-detection baseband (audio-frequency) signals as in **Fig 4** or to IF signals at relatively low-frequency by using sub-Nyquist sampling.

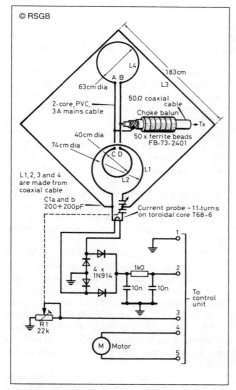
Fig 1: GI2FHN's dual magnetic loop antenna covering 3.5 to 28MHz erected in the roof-space.

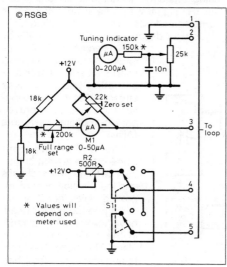
Fig 2: Control unit for tuning the loop antenna.

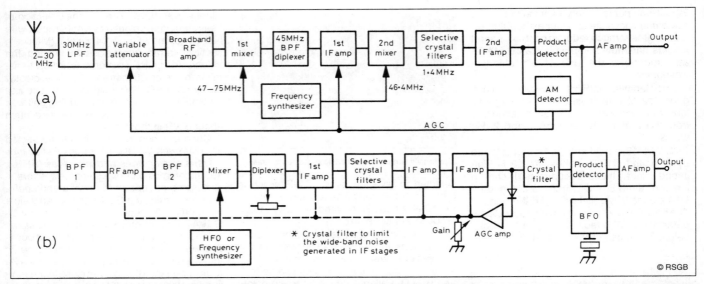

Fig 3: Representative architectures of modern communication receiver designs. (a) General coverage double-conversion superhet with up-conversion to 45MHz first intermediate frequency and 1.4MHz 2nd IF.(b) Single-conversion superhet, typically for amateur bands only, with an IF in the region of 9 or 10.7MHz.

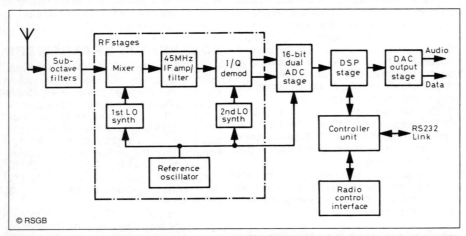

Fig 4: Outline of prototype high-performance analogue/digital professional communication receiver with baseband digitization following a two-phase (I/Q) demodulation. (*Roke Manor Research Ltd*)

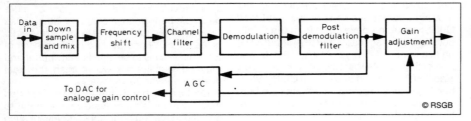

Fig 5: Software structure of the STC receiver.

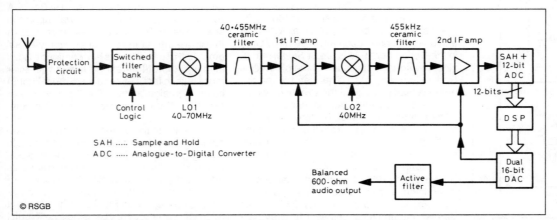

Fig 6: Block diagram of the STC marine HF band analogue/digital receiver with sub-Nyquist sampling of 455kHz IF.

These forms of 'digital' receiver are making progress - for example during 1991, STC engineers described "A low cost digitally implemented marine HF band receiver" of which it was claimed that "Digital signal processing (DSP) has been supplied in radio receivers for a number of years, although mostly for specific military applications where high levels of flexibility are required, and cost is less of an issue . . . . However, this technology has now reached a stage where all the advantages gained in digital implementation can be realized at a lower cost than using conventional analogue techniques - and on a single PCB.

"This paper reports on one such radio, an HF receiver for maritime use, which combines an analogue RF front end with a digitally implemented IF section performing the channel filtering, demodulation and automatic gain control: **Figs 5-6**. Four operation modes - AM, SSB, CW and FSK - have been programmed, all of which are contained within a single Motorola DSP56001 integrated circuit."

The STC design digitizes the IF signal at 455kHz taking advantage of sub-Nyquist sampling of signals already bandpass filtered using analogue techniques. In practice a 455kHz signal with a bandwidth of 6kHz is sampled at 44kHz. This sub-sampling technique was described in *TT* (Feb 1992) by Collins and Analog Devices engineers for a design with a final IF of 456kHz and 96kHz sampling rate. It was stressed that the key to digital radio lies in improved analog-to-digital converters (ADC).

The STC paper concluded: "The advent of low-cost SP integrated circuits and the development of improved radio algorithms, reducing the computation load, have finally put digital radio in the commercial market place. This radio is cheaper to produce and gives a better performance than its analogue counterpart. However, it will still be some time before an 'all-digital' radio becomes a commercial reality, although research into the parts required to make this a reality is progressing."

Thus, at least for the time being, the analogue front end of high performance HF receivers remains important. It is clear that many of the changes that have stemmed from the substitution of electronic for mechanical technology (except in the most complex and high cost receivers) may have improved some aspects of the specification (eg frequency stability) at the expense of others.

A long article 'Recent advances in shortwave receiver design' by Dr Ulrich L Rohde, KA2WEU/DJ2LR, has been published simultaneously in English and German texts (*QST* and *CQ-DL*, Nov 1992). Dr Rohde has a long-established reputation as a designer of high-performance HF receivers for professional and defence applications, His article stresses that extended dynamic range in amateur MF/HF receivers is particularly important today because receivers are frequently operated in hostile environments like contests, or at antenna sites subjected to extremely strong signals. Novel approaches discussed in his article include:

● Multilevel, microprocessor-driven menus as operator control interfaces.

● Fast, low phase noise, PLL synthesizers, including digital direct frequency synthesis (DDS).

● Analog and digital tracking front-end filters.

● Ultra high-level double-balanced mixers with MOS transistors.

● Low-noise, advanced AGC-controlled feedback amplifiers.

● High-isolation IF-filter-switching stages;

● IF amplifiers with low in-band intermodulation distortion (IMD) properties.

● High-performance sampling product detectors.

● Adaptive squelch circuits.

Dr Rohde notes that "Some signal processing can be implemented digitally, and a few well known ham transceiver suppliers have begun doing so. Such techniques are becoming increasingly important. For now, however, those in the general amateur community who are interested in building their own radio hardware may have more interest in the analogue circuit details on which this article concentrates."

A number of the circuit approaches described are based on their use in high-cost professional receivers made be AEG Telefunken and Rohde & Schwarz. My own feeling is that some of the design approaches used in such receivers are really too complex to be implemented in home-built projects, but that nevertheless the basic design principles would be helpful for those seeking to build even relatively simple high-performance receivers. However, we should not accept them uncritically.

For a number of years, most HF receivers have adopted an up-conversion first mixer with an IF of 40 or even 70MHz since this not only meets the criteria that for a general coverage receiver the IF should be outside

the frequency range and high enough to minimise spurious responses including image response, even with broadband input filtering, but also simplifies implementation of frequency synthesis.

My own feeling is that the amateur home-built receiver need not (and possibly should not) follow this approach, since continuous coverage, even in these days of WARC bands, is not an absolute requirement. What is needed is pre-mixer RF selectivity and the absence of the phase noise from a PLL synthesizer. Sufficient stability for most amateur radio requirements can be achieved either by the use of a crystal-controlled HF oscillator with variably tuned IF or, with care, by a free-running band-switched HF oscillator as used for example in G4DTC's 'ultimate' receiver (*TT*, December 1987).

On frequency synthesis, Dr Rohde writes "Another important point I have noticed in recent designs is the trade-off between coherent analog (phase-locked-loop) and digital frequency synthesis. Switching speed and synthesizer signal purity work against each other. The faster a PLL synthesizer must switch, the wider its loop bandwidth must be. It will thereby be 'noisier'. Direct digital synthesis (DDS) is relatively easy, but it must be implemented properly to retain its advantages over traditional PLL approaches."

"In spite of recent advances in shortwave transceiver design, not all possibilities in improving the dynamic-range electrical performance have been implemented by commercial manufacturers . . . . The widespread use of some approaches, like diode switching of input filters and IF filters, has caused more headaches than it has solved."

Personally I feel there is still much to be said for the 'old-fashioned' concept of achieving good pre-mixer selectivity with high-Q tuned circuits using variable capacitors rather than electronic tuning diodes. One reason why this is no longer used is the difficulty of ganging a frequency synthesizer with tuned signal frequency circuits without the introduction of microprocessor-controlled motorised tuning systems.

Dr Rohde continues: "While the concept of having sub-octave input filters is laudable and the filters are necessary, the use of such filters has led to problems because the switching diodes usually used introduce intermodulation distortion that the filters they select cannot cure! There is an easy fix: Replace all the front-end filter switching di-

odes in a transceiver with Hewlett-Packard 5082-3080 or -3081 PIN diodes. Changing 15 or more such diodes as a cost of $3 per diode makes this proposal less than exciting. But installing these diodes can reduce the intermodulation distortion products traceable to the replaced diodes by 18dB or increase the receiver's input-intercept point by 6dB . . . . Another common approach that works against receiver dynamic range is the use of transmit-only antenna tuners. Check your transceiver's schematic carefully, and you may discover that its automatic antenna tuner is switched out during receive. If an antenna tuner is necessary to match a transceiver to a feed line, it should be used in transmit and receive to add to the transceiver's receiver-front-end selectivity . . . .

"Many articles have been written on how to improve a receiver's input intercept point. The design of low-noise, double-balanced diode mixers (particularly using hot-carrier diodes) and ring arrangements of FETs and bipolar transistors has generated a lot of speculation, technical publications and, at times, emotional reaction regarding actual performance. The four leading contestants are:

(1) Double-balanced mixers using high-level hot-carrier diodes. The highest achieved iP3 values for this topology are about 40dBm, accompanied by 6dB of insertion loss.

(2) Active FET ring modulators using four symmetrical FETS, such as in the U350 quad manufactured by Siliconix. For reasons of cost, and because these mixers are more sensitive than diodes to changes in termination (more to changes in reactance than resistance) at the output for third-order intermodulation (distortion) (IMD3), they have not become very popular. A more popular version of this is a push-pull arrangement with N-junction FETs or dual-gate MOSFETs. Both provide similar performance. The dual-gate MOSFETs have slightly more conversation gain, higher intercept points and higher isolation, but most Japanese manufacturers prefer the single-gate combinations.

(3) High-level ring-type mixer arrangements using bipolar transistors . . . . as implemented by Plessey in the SL6440 IC. Because of its high DC supply requirement, this approach has not been implemented in many designs.

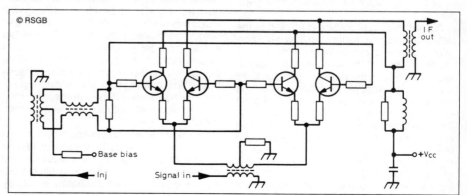

Fig 7: A doubly-balanced active mixer using bipolar transistors in a degenerated version of the balanced transconductance mixer. This approach is used in the Plessey SL6440 high-level IC and in the Motorola low-level MC1596 IC. (*Radio Receivers - Gosling (ed)*)

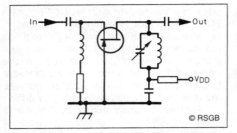

Fig 8: Simple grounded-gate FET amplifier which can provide 2dB noise-figure, 9dB gain in a 50Ω system for a 45, 70 or 100MHz up-converted first IF stage. (*Radio Receivers - Gosling (ed)*)

(4) Use of DMOS switches like the Siliconix SD210. This approach, with wideband termination, has been implemented in commercial radios from AEG Telefunken and Rohde & Schwarz [The complex circuit diagram of the input stage of the ultra-high dynamic range Telefunken E1800 receiver is given in the *QST* and *CQ-DL* articles - it uses four SD210 dual-gate FETs plus a U310 FET plus 8 bipolar devices to form the mixer and first (42.2MHz) IF stage! - *G3VA*].

"Third-order intercept points up to 45dBm have been measured in such circuits. The intercept point depends somewhat on the manufacturing quality of the devices and, of course, their termination. It is important to note that this mixer acts as a switch and exhibits an insertion loss of 6 to 10dB - much as with the high-level diode mixers . . . . The gate signal level required to switch these transistors (several volts) translates into approximately 1-watt of local-oscillator power."

For home-construction, with the virtual disappearance of the 7360 beam-switched mixer valve used by G4TDC, there would seem to be much to be said for the SL6440 IC. In *Radio Receivers* edited by Dr W Gosling and published as one of the IEE's Telecommunications Series 15, a double balanced mixer illustrating the use of bipolar medium power transistors (as in the SL6440) is described (**Fig 7**): "The circuit is that of a pair of transconductance mixers with emitter resistors added for IM improvement. Resistors in the base and collector leads add loss of ultra-high frequencies to suppress parasitic oscillations caused by resonances formed by circuit and transistor capacitances together with the leakage reactance of the associated transformers. Injection is supplied through a balancing transformer to the bases which are overdriven, resulting in signal switching-action.

"Collector supply voltage is applied to the output transformer centre-tap through a parallel resistor-inductor to further suppress oscillation. Although the transistors are operating as injection-controlled signal polarity switches, the impedance ratio between the signal emitters and the IF output collectors results in a modest gain of a few decibels. This can be very desirable when noise figure requirements make the loss of the diode mixer unattractive. Using transistors such as the Motorola MRF517, this active mixer will give a 3dB gain, 9dB noise figure, and +25dBm input intercept over the 2 to 30MHz band as an upconverter to the 100MHz range.

This type of mixer is also available in integrated circuit form, the Motorola MC1596

being a low-level device and the Plessey SL6440 being a high-level receiving mixer."

A practical front-end for a simple 3.5MHz superhet receiver using an SL6440 mixer with 2N5770 local oscillator was given in *TT*, May 1991 as a means of up-grading receivers using the NE602 device as a combined mixer/oscillator chip. An introduction to the SL6440 was given in *TT* as long ago as the combined June/July, 1980 issue based on information from our current RSGB President, Peter Chadwick, G3RZP, who wrote the Plessey Application Note for the SL6440 (AN1007) and presented a number of papers on the device at professional conferences in the UK, USA etc. As a linear mixer the device was stated to be capable of a 30dBm intercept point, +15dBm 1dB compression point, low noise (about 12dB for best IMD performance) and a conversion 'gain' of about -1dB.

It should be noted that with any mixer operating directly on the incoming RF signals without pre-mixer amplification, the IF amplifier that follows the mixer, either directly or after a roofing filter, must have a low noise figure and a high intercept figure (**Fig 8**), with a diplexer arrangement often used to achieve constant input impedance over a broad band of frequencies.

HERE AND THERE

YOU MAY REMEMBER that in November *TT* Jim Cookson, G4XWD, referred to the advice given in July *RadCom*, on carefully checking the heater voltage applied to power valves and rectifiers and offered some advice on dealing with this problem.

A similar facility was required for mobile transmitters and in the 1950s 'quick-heating valves' were marketed with several special forms of heater construction. One form consisted of short, coated ribbon of large cross-section; another a number of thin oxide-coated wires connected in parallel; and a third method thermally bonded the heater to the cathode to allow heat to reach the cathode by conduction. Such valves enabled a mobile transmitter to function within about one second from cold. There was some cost in valve reliability!

G4EIK, as someone who believes in home construction and home maintenance, greatly dislikes the current practice of unnecessary miniaturisation when applied by the factories to such equipment as 144MHz mobile rigs. He writes: "I can see the need to make handheld equipment small and the use of leadless components for microwave applications but why make a 144MHz mobile rig with PCBs that will fit in a matchbox, most of these have to be treated as 'throwaway' items (but not at throwaway prices). The amount of repairs that can be done to surface mount boards is limited even with professional facilities. What should be simple routine repairs can take hours and if done commercially may cost around £50 because of the time they take."

As someone who still builds all of his own equipment, he believes that the limited amount of what he calls 'real amateur radio' carried out by most amateurs is seriously downgrading the regard in which the hobby is held by non-amateurs.

The problem of dealing with surface-mounted chips is well covered in an article by

P J Roberts, G1VUV, in *Television* (September 1992, p801): "The need to remove and replace surface-mounted components, especially ICs is becoming more common. Those little flat, square chips with millions of legs are a particular problem. Getting them off the board is hard enough let alone putting them on. Unless, that is, you adopt the correct approach using the right tool - rework spray solder flux, 29SWG enamelled copper wire, solder cream, a hot-air soldering iron such as the Jetmatic Station, and lots of patience.

"Various ways of going about it have been suggested. I've tried them and found them wanting, eventually adopting my own approach . . . . the method I recommend is as follows: Take two lengths of copper wire, each about six inches long. Feed each one through the gap between the body of the chip and its legs (on the sides of the chip with the most pins). Lift the wire ends at one end of the chip and twist them together. Repeat at the other end of the chip then twist all the ends together. Spray around the IC to be removed with rework flux. Apply light tension to the copper wire while using the hot-air iron, set to 360°C, air flow 5 with the small nozzle, to heat the chip's legs and the solder in an even manner. You will feel it when the chip starts to come away from the PCB. At this point reduce the tension on the wire. If you apply too much tension via the wire as the chip comes away you might lift the PCB print . . . . Having removed the faulty chip, use desoldering braid to clean any excess solder from the print lands. When the PCB has cooled down, clean off any flux with a brass pencil (pencil RS No. 514-868, brass refill RS No. 514-880)".

G1VUV then goes on to describe how to fit a replacement chip and to list a number of problems that can be experienced while learning how to use a hot-air soldering iron. To read them you must refer to the *Television* article but I feel that the above extracts underline the difficulties likely to be experienced by anyone attempting to replace multipin surface-mounted components without professional tools - even if they have the necessary patience to, as G4EIK puts it, "fiddle about soldering in components the size of rice grains even when professional facilities are available".

Some time ago, a firm specialising in supplying kits to familiarise constructors with SMT devices kindly sent me a little audio-amplifier board to try my hand at. I must confess that I quickly decided that this form of construction was not for me even with a pair of binocular magnifiers (*TT*, February 1983, p138) to help my tired eyes. Wonderful technology no doubt but everyone to their own taste as the French say!   **G3VA**

PHASING OUT INTERFERENCE - ANOTHER LOOK

A DECADE AGO, *TT* (August 1982, pp684-5) drew attention to the renewed interest then being shown in overcoming the problem of losing wanted signals due to another, much stronger signal or nasty noise coming up on the same channel. Such interference tended to blot out the wanted signal no matter how good the selectivity characteristics of the receiver.

It was pointed out that the idea of phasing-out an unwanted signal dated back many years and in the 1930s had been utilised in the so-called 'Jones noise-balancing arrangement'. This was described in early editions of *The Radio Handbook*, edited by Frank Jones, W6AJF: **Fig 1**. The aim was to phase out local electrical interference by means of pick-up on an auxiliary antenna used to provide a balancing (180° out-of-phase) signal to the receiver. The system required careful setting up but, it was claimed, could reduce a specific unwanted source of interference by several S-points while reducing the wanted signal by only about one S-point.

Unlike noise-blanking techniques (which are suitable only for pulse-type interference), noise-balancing/null-steering systems can be used to reduce interference from any type of interfering signal provided that it is strong enough to be picked up on the auxiliary 'noise antenna' and is of reasonably consistent strength. In the 1960s a professional MW/LW system for use by broadcasters etc was developed by Christopher Henn-Collins, GU5ZC, which could place a very deep rejection notch (over 55dB) on an unwanted signal.

The 1982 item drew attention to the work of John K Webb, W1ETC, of the American defence-communications firm, The MITRE Corporation as presented at a 1982 IEE Conference on HF communication systems and techniques (*IEE Conference Publication No 206*): **Figs 2 and 3**. Subsequently, W1ETC described his work on interference-cancellation in *QST*, October 1982, including constructional information on a 'null steerer' using coiled lengths of coaxial cable to provide phase-shifting. He presented a compact, relatively low-cost null steerer located alongside (or incorporated into) a receiver or transceiver which could generate deep nulls against a chosen single source of interference. The arrangement was not affected by multipath propagation over the range 2-30MHz, and manual adjustment by the operator used just two knobs. In effect, by adjusting the phase and amplitude of signals from a main and an

auxiliary antenna element, a variety of complex directional patterns was obtained. A breadboard model was claimed to show nulls of over 50dB at 30MHz.

In the QST article he summarized the results he had obtained after many hours of null-steerer use throughout the HF spectrum as including:

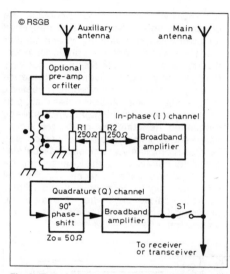

Fig 2: Functional diagram of the electronic null steering unit for use in conjunction with an HF receiver or transceiver (S1 is a relay contact to disconnect the system during transmission) as described by John K Webb, W1ETC, of the MITRE Corporation in 1982.

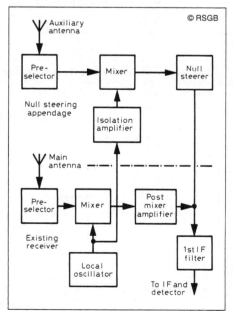

Fig 3: W1ETC's suggestion of how a null steerer might be implemented at intermediate frequency and incorporated within a receiver having dual front-end circuits.

(1) The available null depth in signals propagated over short paths of up to 20 miles is large and stable, limited only by how finely the controls are adjusted.

(2) Nulls arriving over short skywave paths of up to a few hundred miles are in the order of 30dB, provided there is a single mode of propagation and one direction of arrival. Nulls are usually stable.

(3) Signals propagated over paths of 10 to 100 miles may arrive as a mixture of ground wave and skywave. A single null is thus ineffective.

(4) Signals propagated by skywave over long distances frequently involve several paths each having a different number of reflections. A single null will have little effect.

(5) Broadband radiated noise can be nulled as deeply as any radio signal. This seems to be a more effective counter to noise than any blanking or limiting technique .
. . . When the desired signal is of a type that nulls poorly, then it is almost certain that only interferers will be nulled. Close, strong interferers have the deepest nulls.

He found that broadband electrical noise, such as leakage from American 60Hz power lines, could be deeply nulled. This was provided the interference was being directly radiated to the receiver antennas and not entering the receiver in a less-directional manner (for example re-radiation from mains cabling etc).

W1ETC reported that 90° phase shifts could be obtained by using a series of fixed time delay lines that on the higher frequencies could take the form of coiled lengths of co-axial cable. For example, the range 10-14.4MHz used a quarter-wave line at 12.5MHz providing a 20 nanosecond delay from 4m of cable with a velocity factor of 0.66; or for 18.0-29.7MHz, a quarter-wave frequency of 25.0MHz gave 10 nanoseconds delay from 2m of cable.

In the late-1980s an item of factory equipment called 'QRM Eliminator MkII' was marketed in the UK by SEM, reviewed in *Ham Radio Today* (June 1990), at a cost approaching £100.

The 1982 *TT* item emphasised a problem with many such mulling techniques. The problem is that they can prove difficult to adjust quickly enough to be of value to an operator when a strong interfering signal of electrical noise suddenly pops up in the middle of a contact.

Two recent articles on the use of interference null-steerers have appeared in the Australian *Amateur Radio* by Lloyd Butler, VK5BR (September 1992 and January 1993). The first article 'An interference cancelling system for your receiver or transceiver' presented the circuit details of a practical unit which made use of resistance-capacitance (RC) phase shift networks to adjust the relative phase of the wanted and unwanted signals over the necessary 360° of phase. In his second article: 'More on interference cancelling, and a new circuit', VK5BR makes use of the phase shift that occurs when a tuned circuit is set off resonance. His new circuit, **Fig 4**, despite its simplicity, can be adjusted over a full 180° of

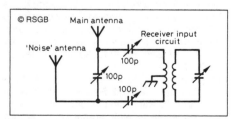

Fig 1: The original Jones noise-balancing arrangement as shown in early editions of *The Radio Handbook*. Local electrical interference could be phased out by means of pick-up on the auxiliary 'noise' antenna. Although it could be effective it required very careful setting up.

phase with a single tuning control, with the remaining 180° accessible by operating a phase-reversing switch.

VK5BR introduces this form of interference-cancellation as follows: "The idea is to use an auxiliary antenna (almost any random length of wire) in addition to the main receiving antenna. As the two antennas are physically spaced from each other and also unlikely to have similar field patterns, the amplitude and phase of signals induced into the two antennas by an interfering signal can be expected to be different. This particularly applies to a localised interference source which is largely coupled into the antenna by induction. This induction field follows a different law of signal attenuation versus distance from that of the radiation field by which the distant desired signal is being received.

"The two antenna outputs are combined after modifying their relative signal levels and phase such that the interference signal from one antenna is equal but opposite in phase from that from the other antenna. The interference signal is cancelled but, as the two desired signals have a different amplitude and phase relationship, a resultant desired signal component is retained. Of course, for all this to work, the interference waveform must be continuous and reasonably stable in its shape and amplitude. From my own experience, the system works extremely well for power line noise and frequency dependent noise bars generated by TV line time-bases and computers".

In Fig 4, L1-C1A and L2-C1B are the two tuned circuits coupled by resistor R2. L1 and L2 are identical and C1A-B a ganged variable pair. VK5BR states that in practice, tracking of tuning does not appear to be critical and there is no need to be too concerned about precise matching of the inductors. The circuit, as shown, runs fairly low Q and almost any identical pair of inductors can be used provided they are selected with the right inductance for the frequency coverage concerned. VK5BR uses miniature RF chokes which are convenient because they are no larger than a resistor or small capacitor, can be bought in precise values and save the effort of having to wind the coils. With 10 microhenrys and a 15-280pF the tuning range covers 3.5 and 7MHz; bandswitching can be added as shown in **Fig 5**. For 1.8 and 3.5MHz use 39µH; for 7 to 14MHz use 2.7µH; and for 14 to 28MHz use 0.68µH. **Fig 6** shows how diode protection can be added when used in conjunction with a transceiver.

VK5BR writes: "To set for a balance, the phase and amplitude controls are adjusted for lower noise, one after the other a number of times, until an interference null is achieved. If a null is not found, or the null is not very definite, the phase is reversed with the reversing switch and the procedure repeated". In the earlier article, VK5BR notes that apart from the forms of local interference already mentioned, he found that on the MF broadcast band a distant (interstate) station was normally completely swamped by a local station. After balancing out the local station, the distant station could be received quite well with only a slight amount of sideband splatter from the local station. In effect, it is rather like obtaining the benefit from swinging the null of a good frame/ferrite-rod antenna.

ANTENNA LORE MK2

THE DECEMBER *TT* ITEM on 'Persistent SWR myths' attracted several supportive comments and it does appear that the whole subject of antennas and feeders is still for many of us surrounded with an air of mystery. *QST* (November 1992) has recently published a five-page article by Kenneth Macleish, W7TX 'Why an antenna radiates' providing what is described as "a searching look at the mysterious process by which our antennas hurl energy from here to there". As a starter it challenges the reader to answer "true" or "false" to four statements:

(1) In a centre-fed, half-wave dipole, electrons surge back and forth from one side of the antenna to the other.

(2) It is possible for a perfect insulator to radiate.

(3) Unlike ohmic resistance, 'radiation resistance' has significance only at the feed point of an antenna or antenna system.

(4) The ground around a transmitting antenna radiates.

W7TX puts the answers in a footnote at the end of his article but, to save any embarrassment, the first and third are false; the second and fourth are true. I won't ask how many you got right! Fortunately, it is not necessary to know exactly how an antenna works to make or use one, but it helps when it doesn't seem to work in the expected manner!

In the 'Lab Notes' column of the December, 1992 *QST*, Zack Lau, KH6CPI/1 of ARRL technical staff, provides in question and answer form some practical, two-page guidance on 'limited space antennas', including the use of indoor antennas on HF. He notes for example that antennas squeezed into small apartments may have relatively low losses in wood-frame buildings, very high in concrete and steel structures, with stucco and wire mesh frames also bad. The practical way to determine such losses is by trial and error since there are usually too many factors involved to evaluate indoor antennas with theoretical models. He advises against running high power to an indoor antenna on the grounds that "while studies have not conclusively linked low-level RF exposure to health problems, it is prudent to limit such exposure".

If a resonant dipole attic or indoor antenna which has been carefully cut to textbook length shows an SWR in the region of, say, 4:1 it is probably being detuned by nearby objects. The length could be adjusted by the use of a GDO or noise bridge, or alternatively one could use a flexible ATU. KH6CPI also comes up with a number of other suggestions but it seems worth opening the discussion to HF antennas generally, by selecting some items from a list drawn up 14 years ago by ZL2AKLW and reproduced in the March 1979 *TT*:

(1) A dipole cut for the centre of the 3.5MHz band and fed with 50 or 75ohm coax via an ATU will be just as good at the band edges as it is at the resonant frequency of the dipole element.

(2) The same dipole, fed with 300ohm ribbon or open line, again via an ATU, will work on any band from 1.8MHz to 29.7MHz.

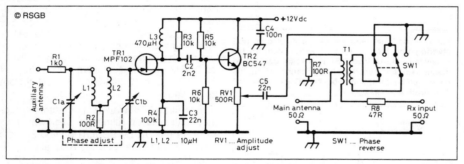

Fig 4: VK5BR's Mk 2 interference cancelling circuit as described in the January 1993 issue of *Amateur Radio*. As shown this covers roughly 3.5 to 7MHz. C1-2 ganged 15-250pF variable capacitor or similar. L1, L2 miniature 10uH RF chokes. T1 11 turns quadfiliar wound on Amidon FT50-75m toroidal core.

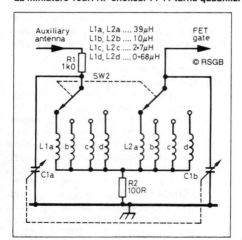

Fig 5: Bandswitching modification to provide 1.8 to 30MHz in four ranges.

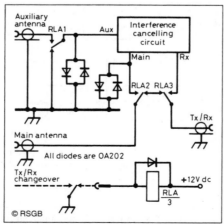

Fig 6: Transmit-receive switching with protection diodes for use of the VK5BR interference cancelling circuit with a transceiver.

(3) Unless higher than 150ft, it hardly matters on 3.5MHz in which direction a horizontal dipole points: more significant will be obstructions, trees etc which absorb some of the power.

(4) A long antenna provides more receiver microvolts than a short one (ie less than a half-wavelength long) but a transmitting antenna radiates all the power that can be fed to it (except IR losses).

(5) Antennas, and the equipment connected to them, can confidently be expected to provide better and better results on HF as a sunspot cycle goes up and up.

(6) The result of doubling your RF output power will be virtually unnoticeable, but halving your input power may well be noticeable since output efficiency may be affected.

(7) A loosely-loaded transmitter sounds awful when overdriven.

(8) A tightly-loaded transmitter, when overdriven, sags at the knees and output may even be reduced.

(9) A properly tuned system is when the antenna correctly loads the transmitter.

(10) A poor antenna is always a poor antenna; but when conditions are good it will work.

(11) There are no magic formulas or magic boxes able to improve the performance of poor antennas, but it is easy to reduce dramatically the efficiency of a good antenna.

(12) A bought antenna is not a better antenna but merely a more expensive antenna; a better investment is a good book on antennas.

(13) Is your best friend afraid to tell you?

THE FIRST BEACONS

THOSE OF US WHO listened on the amateur bands during the 1939-45 war, either for personal interest or as Voluntary (or SCU3) Interceptors, soon became aware that, after an initial close-down, a number of pre-war German amateurs with D3 and D4 callsigns were permitted to resume CW operation on the HF bands. From 1942 these included a number of beacon transmissions (D4WYF2 3600kHz; D4WYF3 7000kHz; D4WYF4 14,130kHz; and D4WYF5 28,000kHz). A note on these transmissions was even published in the *RSGB Bulletin*, October 1944, p55, stemming from Frank Watts, G5BM, in connection with a report on propagation conditions on 28MHz. He noted that "These stations send V's followed by their calls continually throughout the 24 hours. They are very useful for checking frequency meters, besides providing an indication of the skip length on the various bands."

Now 50 years later, the story of why and by whom these first beacons were built has been told by Waldemar F Kehler, DL1IX, (pre-war D3FBA) in 'The Origin of Amateur Radio Beacons' (*CQ*, November 1942, pp17-18). To quote briefly from this interesting account: "In 1942 the German Wehrmacht was spread over most of the continent of Europe. This situation often resulted in difficult if not impossible communications links between frontline units and German headquarters. Faced

VERSATILE CRYSTAL TESTER

MANY YEARS AGO I included in *TT* and subsequently *ART*, circuit details of a simple bipolar transistor crystal oscillator that could be used as a simple means of testing the activity of assorted crystals. A rather more sophisticated unit capable of checking the activity of crystal and ceramic resonators over the range of about 40kHz to 20MHz has been described recently by M J Salvati of Flushing Communications in the 'Ideas for Design' feature of *Electronic Design* (July 9, 1992): **Fig 7.**

He points out that there are several reasons why crystal oscillators may fail to work. It may be due to faulty or low-activity crystals, or poor design. It is thus a good idea to check the crystal before starting to trouble shoot on the equipment (similarly it may be wise to check ex-equipment or even new crystals at the time of purchase). The arrangement shown can work with a wide variety of crystals and ceramic resonators; if used with a frequency counter it provides a check on the parallel-resonant oscillation frequency.

M J Salvati writes: "The crystal 'sees' approximately 30pF of circuit capacitance. The basic oscillator is a Pierce type that uses the first pair of MOSFETs in the CA4007A dual complimentary pair plus inverter, CMOS IC. The remaining MOSFET pairs form a meter driver and a low-impedance output driver. The meter is the primary indicator of the crystal performance. Any low-cost microammeter with about 200-500uA FSD will do (this is the ideal application for that 'tuning' meter from a discarded stereo etc).

"The resistor (R) in series with the meter is selected to produce about 90% FSD with an active crystal. Low-activity crystals of any frequency will generate less meter deflection, as will the good crystals at the upper frequency limit of this device. The low-impedance output can drive a frequency counter or oscilloscope through a terminated cable. Aside from their forming part of the Pierce oscillator, the network of resistors around the first MOSFET pair protects the MOSFET gates from electrostatic and leakage damage. To illustrate its ruggedness, this circuit has not experienced a failure after several years of use, even though the input leads are extensively handled in connecting the crystals or ceramic resonators that do not fit the holder."

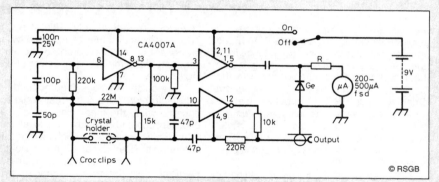

Fig 7: Versatile crystal/ceramic-resonator tester (M J Salvati, *Electronic Design*).

with the problems of selecting reliable shortwave communications frequencies, the idea arose to build and operate continuously a transmitter (called a Richtsender) near Berlin . . . . The basic design was the responsibility of Herbert Salzbrunn, D4WYF who was employed by the German High Command (OKW). He designed two-stage and three-stage transmitters using tubes types RL12P10, RL12P35 and a P50 (input power 50 watts).

"The transmitter was built by a technician in a workshop at Ludwigsfede, a village south of Berlin (site of a monitoring station for foreign broadcasts) from where they were operated except for a short break when the station was bombed during the night of January 1, 1944 . . . . tests were made with a portable 20-watt transmitter in the German Embassy in Madrid . . . . the first two beacons were D4WYF2 on 3.5MHz and D4WYF5 on 28MHz. Later we added two additional beacons, in the 40m and 20m bands. These two were installed in the former office building of a German insurance company (Allianz-Versicherung) at

Fehrbelliner Square in Berlin-Wilmersdorf, a building that became well-known in connection with the attempt on Hitler's life on July 20, 1944 after which General Thiels, head of German Signals Intelligence was executed in 1944. [Presumably this is a misprint for General Fritz Thiele who together with General Erich Fellgiebel, the Signalmaster of OKW, was executed in 1944 for their participation in the assassination plan - G3VA].

"A plan to open a beacon, D3FBA2, in East Prussia was abandoned. The Berlin beacons finally closed down in February 1945 when the Russian Army closed the ring around Berlin . . . . During the 1970s, amateurs rediscovered the idea of beacons, thereby proving the old adage that there is nothing new under the sun".

LOW-COST CHOKE 1:1 BALUN

TT, SEPTEMBER 1992 and January 1993, has provided information on two ways in which the increasingly popular ferrite-loaded sleeve baluns can be implemented and used to minimise RF current flowing along the outer surface of the braid of coaxial-cable feeders connected to the balanced feed-point of resonant dipole-type antenna elements.

An alternative technique which does not depend on the use of ferrite beads and a length of small diameter cable or sleeves fitting over conventional cable is described by Curt Wilson, W0KKQ, in *QST*, November 1992. This depends on the use of fine steel wool to attenuate any RF on the outer braid.

He writes: "For many years, I've used choke baluns made of cardboard (and more recently, PVC) tube stuffed with steel wool . . . and placed them along the coax feed line to attenuate RF energy outside the coaxial shield. Wanting to approximate the performance of the W2DU-type ferrite choke balun on a budget, I began a search for a cheaper material that could do the job of Type 43 ferrite. I tried numerous materials before returning to fine steel wool (US grade 000 or the finer 0000)!

This material proved to be ideal in three important categories. First, its RF attenuation properties are excellent. Second, steel wool is mechanically pliable and a distinct pleasure to use. Thirdly, these fine steel wool pads may be purchased at very reasonable prices from almost any hardware store." **Fig 8** shows the balun design.

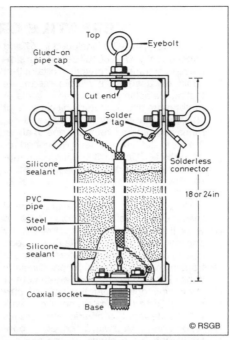

Fig 8: The low-cost 1:1 choke balun as implemented for outdoor use by W0KKQ using fine steel wool as an RF attenuator in place of ferrite rings.

W0KKC uses an 18in length of white (US Schedule 40) plastic tubing with an inside diameter of approximately 1.5 inches with two PVC caps to fit the ends of the tube. He provides very detailed constructional details but the basic arrangement should be clear from the diagram. 'Hints & Kinks' editor, David Newkirk, WJ1Z, adds two pertinent comments: (1) Since UHF series coaxial connectors are not designed to be weatherproof you can avoid having to seal your balun's jack and cable plug against the elements by using N connectors instead of SO-239s and PL-259s; and (2) especially in closed compartments, caulking compounds that liberate acetic acid vapour as they cure can severely corrode susceptible metals (such as steel wool) so avoid using such products when you build your balun".

One effective means of presenting outer-braid RF from feeding back into the shack and at the same time minimising EMC problems and the pick-up of local electrical interference is to bring the feeder cable vertically downwards from the antenna element and then to bury the remainder of the feeder before it reaches the house or outside shack. Unfortunately, as some have found, conventional coaxial cable, even if has a noncontaminating jacket, deteriorates rapidly when buried un-

THOSE COAXIAL CABLE SCRAPS

IN THE *TT* ITEM 'Using scraps of coaxial cable' (December. 1992, pp29-30) I noted that the information came to my notice from the *Mid-Sussex Newsletter* where it had been reprinted from *Airtime*, but with the original author not credited. A letter from Brian Kendall, G3GDU, provides the answer: the material was extracted from an article 'More uses for old coaxial cable' which he wrote (under the pen name 'Ken Williams') for the late-lamented British publication *Amateur Radio* (September 1990).

The original article included additional information, including advice on the not-so-easy-as-it-looks task of stripping the cable: "The first task is to strip the coaxial cable into its component parts. It might be thought that the simplest technique would be to run a sharp blade along the outer insulation to open up the cable, but this would destroy a useful component.

"The preferred method (**Fig 9**) is to cut 12-18in lengths of cable. About 1in of the outer covering is then removed with a knife and the braiding pushed back. The polythene inner insulation is then firmly gripped in a vice and with a cloth to protect the hand, a firm grip is taken of the outer covering and, relaxing the grip to allow the hand to slip, an attempt is made to pull off the outer cover.

"On the first attempt hardly any movement will be noticeable, but after the second or third attempt the braid and outer cover will have moved an inch or so. Two or three more pulls and the cover and outer braid will be free. A gentle pull should now be sufficient to remove the braid from inside the outer cover.

"Removing the inner conductor follows a similar pattern, but this is more firmly attached than the outer layers. Therefore, it is

advisable to remove only 6-9in at a time. This process can often be assisted by applying a hot soldering iron to the inner conductor for a minute or so before clamping it in the vice".

The resulting sections of outer braid provide useful high-current, low-resistance conductors, while the inner pieces represent excellent insulators usable up to at least 100MHz for applications such as those described in the December *TT*. An application for the outer braid suggested in the *Amateur Radio* article is to form a common earthing

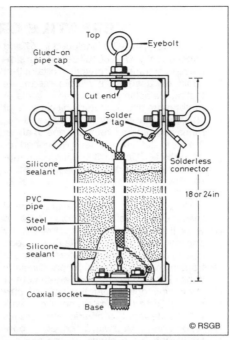

Fig 9: Construction of earthing braids or high current power cables from short lengths of coaxial cable. (a) Braids removed from cable and flattened, laid on bench and ends tinned. (b) Braids and flexible wire placed together, soldered and 0.25in holes drilled. (c) Outer cover pulled over braids.

bus: "One aspect which is often suggested by equipment manufacturers but rarely implemented by radio amateurs, is to attach a common earthing bus to all equipment. For this purpose the outer braiding is ideal.

"Take three or four equal lengths of braiding and lay them on the bench. Make sure that they are not stretched and flatten them so that each one forms a flexible strip about 0.5in wide. Heavily tin about 1in at the end. Take a similar length of flexible wire, strip 1in of insulation from each end and lay parallel with the braids.

"Now lay the braids on top of each other with the flexible wire between, and apply heat with a large (at least 60W) soldering iron at one end so that the braids and wire solder firmly together. Repeat this process at the other end. Drill a 0.25in hole through each end and apply a file to 'tidy up' the end.

"Tie a strong cord through one of the holes, pass it through a length of coaxial outer insulation which is 2in shorter than the braids and 'pull through' the braids so that only the tinned sections show.

"Such braids are capable of carrying extremely high currents and, if several are used to link equipment together and to the station earth, will fully answer all common earthing bus requirements. They can also be used to form low-resistance power feeds to high-power amplifiers, etc. 'Ken Williams' concludes this section as follows:

"With the very high current capacity of the braids, you may wonder why the flexible wire is included? The reason is that this maintains the braid at a constant length. Without it the braids will stretch beyond the length of the outer covering and cause insulation problems if used as a low-voltage power lead."

less further protection is devised. A note in the 'New Products' section of *QST*, December 1992, p28 draws attention to a RG8-type cable designed for direct burial in the earth:

"A common misconception regarding coaxial cable is that a non contaminating jacket means a cable is designed for direct burial. The non-contaminating jacket compound is distinctly better than regular Class 1 PVC, and under similar conditions will last twice as long, making it worth the small increase in cost. This however doesn't provide the additional protection necessary for direct burial. . . A truly 'buriable' RG8-type cable for amateur and professional applications is Flexi 4XL BURY-8.

"The size (0.405in) of familiar RG8 coax, the new cable has a thick, tough, moisture-impenetrable polythene jacket over a 'flooding' compound that self-seals small penetrations and discourages more, such as rodents, soil and gravel abrasion, freeze-thaw cycling and so forth. The two shields are tinned copper braid (95%) and aluminium-mylar foil (100%). The dielectric is sealed microcell polyethylene foam and the centre conductor is 9.5AWG 19-strand copper. Loss rating 2dB per 100ft at 150MHz, velocity factor 84%, capacitance 24pF/ft. The US retail price is given as $0.82/ft for 100ft lengths (The Wireman Inc, 261 Pittman Road, Landrum, SC29356, USA which also has a useful catalogue of products priced $1)."

UK cable makers and distributors have cables intended for wired-TV systems that are suitable for direct burial but I suspect these are even more costly than the above. Anyway, the main purpose of this note is to draw attention to the susceptibility of conventional cables, rather than necessarily to encourage budget-conscious readers to buy buriable cables.

RADIO - AN AGEING TECHNOLOGY

AS WE APPROACH the centenary of the start of Marconi's experiments in radio-telegraphy (usually ascribed to 1894), it is not surprising that more and more amateurs are tending to look back on the technology of the past rather than the future, though clearly there are dangers inherent in such nostalgia. But it is necessary to remind ourselves - and the young entrants to the hobby - that many of the ideas, if not the actual components, that we use today were originally conceived, many of them by professionals who had started as amateurs, many years ago. Just how long ago, often comes as a surprise.

A ONE VALVE TRANSCEIVER OF THE 1920S

I THESE DAYS OF 'black box' stations, it is worth remembering that many of the famous names in radio engineering started off and became interested in radio as young amateur experimenters: Marconi ("You know I have always considered myself an amateur" - 1936); Howard Armstrong; Art Collins; George Brown and many, many more, particularly in the USA.

From an account in Proc IEEE (August 1992) of the lifetime achievements of 90 year old Harold Arden Wheeler, including his development in 1925 of "automatic volume control" (ie AGC), one learns that he obtained the amateur callsign 3QK in April 1920. Similarly, Charles W Harrison, long prominent in antenna engineering, recalls his early interest in radio as a teenager - later holding the call W3CGB in the 1930s - in *IEEE Antennas & Propagation Magazine* (August 1992). His first 'transmitter' based on a Ford spark coil proved capable of wrecking all AM reception in his home town, and was discarded in favour of a one-valve 'transceiver' providing 'phone in the medium-wave band: **Fig 10**. This "worked well, permitting communication around town. Many radio stations then signed off at 10pm, so one tuned in the station while it was on the air. After 10pm, conversations began!" Clearly 'transceivers' are not as recent a development as many of us imagine. At the age of 16 years, he submitted a paper to the professional IRE that gave a mathematical proof of the existence of sidebands (then still in dispute) but was told by the Editor that it should have been sent to *QST*!

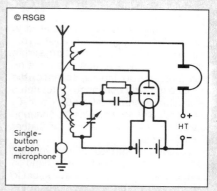

© RSGB

Single-button carbon microphone

Fig 10: American schoolboys discovered how a simple one-valve regenerative receiver could be used as a low-power transmitter to talk around town in the 1920s by letting the valve oscillate and connecting a carbon microphone in the earth lead! As recalled by an eminent American antenna engineer Charles W Harrison Jr.

An example arising from recent items in *TT* will illustrate this. In the October 1992 issue I included a KISS form of Morse code practice oscillator used by ZS5L based on the howl-round between a carbon microphone and a loudspeaker or earpiece. This stirred Gerry Openshaw, G2BTO, to recall that he had published such an arrangement in the *RSGB Bulletin* as long ago as April 1947. But this has now been upstaged by a reminder from Don Graham, VK6HK, that the UK Patent 290 issued to his great-grandfather's brother - Alfred Graham of Graham Amplion Ltd fame - covered precisely this form of acoustically coupled oscillator. The abridged specification notes that "The apparatus consists in a telephonic receiver A and transmitter C arranged in a simple circuit with a battery B and key E. When the circuit is closed at E the two instruments react on each other, producing a continuous sound . . . ." Oh yes, and what was the date of the patent? Just over 99 years on January 5th, 1894!

It was Alfred Graham's son Edward who established a name for 'Amplion' loudspeakers and others in the 1920s although his father had demonstrated the first practical loudspeaker in 1887 and began to market them as Graham Loudspeakers in 1893. It was in 1920 that the 'Amplion' trade mark was registered and the firm began producing speakers intended for 'wireless': **Fig 11**.

The premature death of Edward in 1926 led to the firm Graham Amplion being sold off. VK6HK sent along copies of a few pages from 1926 and 1927 issues of the 'Amplion Radio Magazine' ("published monthly in the interests of better radio reproduction") possibly the first Hi-Fi magazine! An editorial 'The Experimenter' warned against assembling a mere "agglomeration of components without a definite guiding principle going through it from start to finish . . . . One of the reasons why the home building of wireless sets has steadily declined is not because it involves any serious amount of labour, but because experience has shown that in taking a selection of a vast variety of components, and combining them into one complete set, the odds are almost infinite against really good results being obtained . . . . Faithful reproduction is the most difficult of all things to obtain in radio".

VK6HK wonders where there are any *TT* readers who had a close connection with Amplion in those distant days? **G3VA**

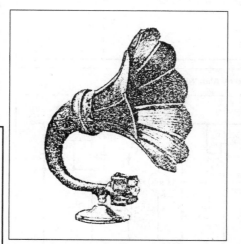

Fig 11: The 1920s was the era of the 'horn' loudspeaker in which the sound from a large headphone-type transducer was acoustically amplified by a massive horn. This is a drawing of the Standard Dragon type AR19 manufactured by Amplion, as illustrated in *The Amplion Magazine* of December 1926.

DIRECT-READING CAPACITANCE METERS

IN THE MAY 1976 ISSUE of *Television*, Alan Willcox described a flexible direct-reading capacitance meter suitable for values from a few picofarads up to about 10µF. It seemed well-worth reproducing in *TT* and subsequently in several editions of *Amateur Radio Techniques* including the reprinted 7th edition. The design was also reproduced in *Electronics Australia* (October 1976) and *QST* (January 1983).

The principle of this type of meter is to charge the unknown capacitor to a fixed voltage (4.5, 5 or 6V) and then to discharge it into the meter circuit; the average current is directly proportional to the capacitance; the whole process being continuously repeated by the astable operation of a 555 timer IC. The meter needle remains steady, although some vibration can be seen on the higher capacitance ranges.

To avoid overloading the meter movement, large value capacitors should not be used on the low-capacitance range. It is advisable to arrange the switch so that one starts at the highest value range, rotating the switch clockwise until reasonable deflection is obtained. The value can then be read off.

In the original design (**Fig 1**), the five range switch (S1) positions gave FSD ranges of 1µF, 100nF, 10nF and 100pF. There was also a x10 range extender switch (S3) effective on all ranges, and a divide-by-two switch (S2) facility which lowered the accuracy of the readings but permitted an estimation of values down to 1 or 2pF. The divide-by-two

facility was omitted from the *QST* design, with W6QB finding it difficult with this type of unit to achieve good stability below about 200pF.

Trevor King, ZL2AKW, in *Break-in* (September 1992), presents a modified version of this capacitance meter: **Fig 2**. He explored the stability aspect in some depth, as a result of which his meter incorporates the following modifications:

(1) 5k6 resistor from pin 5 of the 555 to earth.

(2) 6V three-terminal voltage regulator (7806) instead of the more temperature and current sensitive zener diode.

(3) Plastic cabinet body to avoid stray capacitance of the metal front panel.

(4) Timing resistor on the 50pF range is adjusted for the individual 555 after the other ranges have been preset, so as to provide a customized accurate full scale reading.

(5) It is also convenient, although not essential, to have an adjustable resistor for the 500pF range.

ZL2AKW gives several practical hints: "Short internal wiring is recommended and the IC PCB mounted right at the test termi-

nals. For peace of mind, the 555 is socketed. For calibration, use a good 47nF capacitor on range three to set the 50kΩ calibrator to give a reading of 47µA. Then set the x10 range (using appropriate switch settings) with its preset to read 5µF full scale. Next, adjust the 50pF and 500pF controls. You are now able to see accurately the difference between 2.7pF and 3.3pF. The unit has a small mains power supply providing between 9 and 14VDC after rectification, but could be run from a 9V alkaline battery provided the voltage regulator is included."

ZL2AKW built his unit in a 195 x 115 x 60mm plastic cabinet, with a 50µA Micronta meter with 3500Ω internal resistance, but equivalent meters could be used. The 10nF polystyrene timing capacitor is the heart of the 555 circuit so it is worth finding a really good component, preferably the larger 250V size as the miniatures have less area and thinner polystyrene. The voltage regulator needs 0.1µF capacitors mounted directly on the pins to keep RF energy from the station equipment and to guarantee stability. For the filter capacitor, 16V 220µF is adequate. He checks calibration from time to time using a few 2% capacitors of known value as reference.

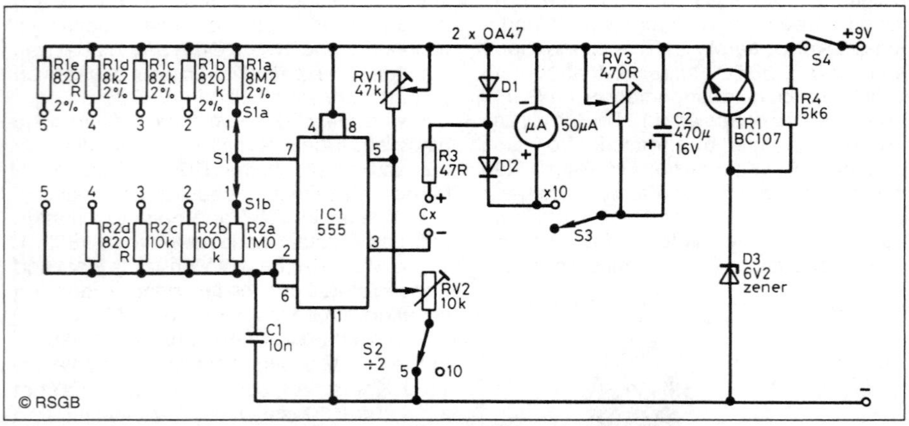

ANTENNA AND SWR FOLLOW-UPS

THE DECEMBER ITEMS 'Persistent SWR myths' and 'Earths and Marconi Antennas' both attracted considerable interest and a number of relevant comments have come in - only some of which can be dealt with briefly this month.

Also, it seems appropriate to draw attention to a recent American publication, *Aerials*, by 'Kurt N Sterba & Lil Paddle' (noms de plume of a husband and wife team) a 94-page compilation of articles that have appeared during the past decade in *Worldradio*. It is based on the well-founded belief that transmission lines, standing waves, antenna matching, reflected power and ATUs are all topics that have attracted myths and old-wives tales in abundance, despite all the efforts of Walt Maxwell, W2DU (who contributes the foreword to this book), and others. The articles reproduced contain hard-hitting, sharply-aimed rebuttals, targeting many of the misleading or ludicrous statements and claims that still appear in amateur radio literature, editorial as well as advertisements, and manufacturers' catalogues.

The book is not a 'how to do it' saga - indeed there are virtually no illustrations, the style is deliberately abrasive and the collected articles are a shade repetitive. As the *QST* reviewer puts it: "Their debunking of common myths and pronouncements - most of which are right on the mark - will make many readers cringe, writhe and quiver with outrage . . . . as they slash away at the waist-deep barrage of 'conventional wisdom' . . . . whether you laugh at, learn from or loathe their writing, you'll find *Aerials* hard to put down." A fair enough comment and warning. It is available for $10 + $2 postage (VISA accepted) from 'Worldradio', 2120 28th Street, Sacramento, CA 95818, USA (916-457-3655).

But back to our own correspondents: Tony Plant, G3NXC, professes surprise at how

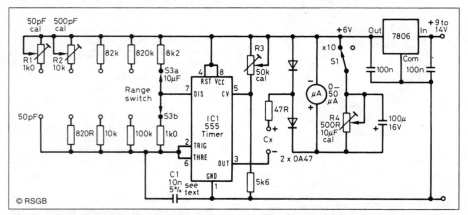

Fig 1: Direct-reading capacitance meter as described by Alan Willcox in 1976.

Fig 2: The ZL2AKW direct-reading capacitance meter. All fixed resistors are 5%, 0.25W carbon types. R1 1k, R2 10k and R3 50k are PC-mount trimmers. S1 SPST switch, S3 2-pole, 5-position rotary switch.

often many of the SWR myths appear in various articles, including those by people who really should know better. He writes:

"I often think that the ubiquitous SWR meter is to blame for many of the myths because it implies that SWR can be measured at a single point on the line and is a phenomenon that can be attributed to that point. This then leads to the belief that SWR can actually vary along the line, simply because the meter shows different readings at different points. Once it is realised that SWR relates to the ratio of two voltages (or currents) spaced a quarter-wave apart on the line then many of the myths crumble to dust. Try asking exponents of 'trim the SWR by varying the line length' to draw the standing wave pattern that this concept implies!

"Let us start a campaign to erase all non-linear SWR scales from meters and substitute linear reflection coefficient scales. It would then become difficult for anyone to argue that the amplitudes of reflected or forward waves can vary along a line, other than as a result of losses or discontinuities. I suppose we might even go for 'return loss' as the displayed parameter although I suspect this would then be used to justify the 'reflected power is lost power' myth.

"Another cause of misunderstandings is use of the expression 'output impedance' when talking about the output socket of a transmitter or transceiver. Too often this is taken to be synonymous with 'source impedance' which then leads to the idea that reflected power is absorbed because the output socket is thought to be matched to the line. We should abandon the use of 'output impedance' in favour of something like 'design load impedance' - better still change 'impedance' to 'resistance' since few transmitters would be happy with a load of 0 + j50 ohms!"

G3NXC points out that there are valid reasons, apart from the action of protection circuits with solid-state power amplifiers for trying to get a low SWR at the transceiver socket:

(1) Low pass filters have characteristics that can be very dependent upon the load impedance that they 'see', and

(2) the terms of the Amateur Radio Licence specify the RF power delivered to the antenna.

Most, if not all, the in-line power meters are calibrated on the basis of a 1:1 SWR, in other words with a 50Ω resistive load on the output. Any divergence from this condition affects the calibration: a 2:1 SWR could result in an error of 12.5% in power measurement, in addition to all the other sources of error.

In the case of simple voltage sampling 'power' meters the measurement errors could be as high as +100% or -50% for the same 2:1 SWR and the reading will (and should!) vary with line length. As a final comment, G3NXC adds: "If an SWR meter does not give the same reading for all lengths of line then it can't be relied upon to give a sensible reading for any length."

It should be noted that G3NXC recognises discontinuities in the line as a potential cause of SWR varying with line length, and this tends to become important at VHF and more so at UHF. B Sykes, G2HCG, points out that in the real world, SWR readings may change

as feeder length is altered, even in the absence of any outer-braid current, even at HF but more so on VHF/UHF. He writes: "The reason can only be that cable, plugs, even the SWR meter are not their stated impedance. The word 'nominal' is used on most cable specifications for example. A 'good' cable may be quoted as 48 to 54Ω. That wretched thing so wrongly called a 'UHF' plug (PL259) is a classic example of a non-50Ω plug having an impedance around 20Ω. Unfortunately, we live in a real world where an unqualified statement that (measured) SWR does not vary with feeder length needs some amendment."

Dennis Unwin, G0FMT, believes (as I do) that G3BDQ (*TT*, December) misread the original item on the earthing of his 1.8MHz Marconi antenna and failed to appreciate that the changes were only to the earth or counterpoise and not to the length of the antenna itself. G0FMT stresses that he was using feed impedance solely to indicate the effectiveness of the earthing system without making any changes in the antenna itself. He still

considers this a reasonable way to proceed but adds:

"Your remarks about the use of RF ammeters induced me to make one and connect it in the antenna lead. I soon discovered that you have to be very careful to adjust the ATU following every change in the earthing system, and also to standardise the output level. I was unable to duplicate all my earlier measurements (*TT*, October) since the wire counterpoise has been removed, but the five earth stakes and the underfloor system could still be compared. The current (in arbitrary units) using the five earth stakes was 5.43 and the current using the underfloor system alone was 5.99.

This appears to confirm the finding based on impedance measurements that the efficiency of the underfloor earth was slightly better than the earth stakes. the current using both together was 7.66. If we compare this with the five earth stakes alone, clearly the aerial current has substantially increased. Since we are measuring current, the improvement in power would be 20 x log (7.66/

EFFICIENT VOLTAGE LIMITING REGULATOR

TIM WALFORD, G3PCJ, WRITES: "For operation of a rig on either batteries or from mains supplies, I wanted a non-switching voltage regulator with very low input-to-output voltage differential but which would remain hard on when the input voltage fell below the desired maximum output voltage. The required input voltage range was 10 to 30VDC (from batteries or rough rectified AC) with an output of about 12V (or lower when the input voltage was less than 12V). It needed to handle up to about 2A and, when input was below 12V, to have very low 'on' resistance.

"The key to achieving this specification is to use power P-type Mosfets with their very low 'on' resistance of the order of 0.2Ω, thus dropping only 0.4V when passing 2A. This can provide a lower differential than 'low drop out' regulators of the LT10xxx type and makes for more efficient/cooler-running PSUs.

"**Fig 3** shows a basically simple regulator circuit with a P-type Mosfet controlled by a common-base NPN error amplifier. Since the Mosfet is voltage controlled

there is very little wasted current; load currents of up to tens of amperes are possible given adequate heatsinks!

"Regulated output voltage is $(V_{ref} - 0.6)$ x $(R1 + R2)/R2$. V_{ref} needs to be less than $(V_{out} - 5V)$. In my case V_{ref} is provided by a 78L05 integrated 5V fixed voltage regulator which can handle the input voltage range to 30V.

It can also provide an additional 5V regulated output. Line and load regulation are both about 0.5%. The output 100µF capacitor improves the transient response but is not essential. Over-current limiting (with an extra 0.6V drop) and remote voltage sensing can be added as shown in Fig 3, although my application did not need them. Because it was available, I used a 2SJ221 Mosfet but a 2SJ174 would be better and can handle up to 20A and input voltages to 60V, with an 'on' resistance of 0.13Ω and maximum dissipation of 75W.

"Finally, the circuit can easily be modified for other fixed or variable output voltages. R1 and R2 are best kept in the range 1k to 10kΩ.

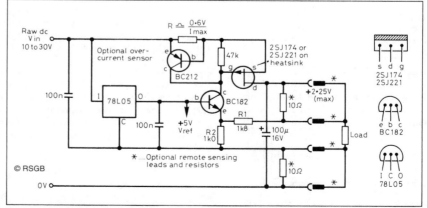

Fig 3: G3PCJ's efficient voltage limiting regulator drops only 0.4V for low input voltages.

5.43) = 2.99dB, indicating that the radiated power had almost doubled. My previous estimate based on impedance measurements was that efficiency had increased from 33% to 60%. It is power this time, so 10 log (60/33) = 2.6dB, a remarkably close agreement between two very different measurement techniques. It does also highlight the value of the 'old-fashioned' RF current meter in settling antenna arguments."

For my part I have always used RF current to optimise tuning up 'long-wire' and some other antennas, using torch bulbs shunted with a loop of wire as a crude and inexpensive form of 'current meter'.

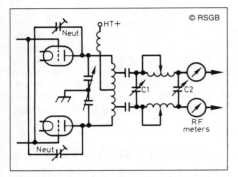

Fig 4: One form of the original Collins Universal Coupler that provided balanced output over a wide range of resistive or reactive impedances.

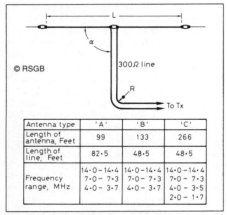

Antenna type	'A'	'B'	'C'
Length of antenna, Feet	99	133	266
Length of line, Feet	82·5	48·5	48·5
Frequency range, MHz	14·0 - 14·4 7·0 - 7·3 4·0 - 3·7	14·0 - 14·4 7·0 - 7·3 4·0 - 3·7	14·0 - 14·4 7·0 - 7·3 4·0 - 3·5 2·0 - 1·7

Fig 5: The Collins multi-band dipole antenna of 1935.

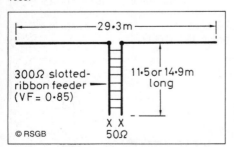

Fig 6: The 1992 G0FAH all-band dipole antenna.

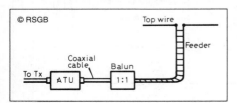

Fig 7: Use a simple current balun and L-network ATU where an SWR of less than 2:1 is needed for solid-state transmitters or for 1.8MHz.

This approach has always served me well in finding the correct inductance and correct capacitance and showing the significant difference when using various lengths of 'counterpoise' as an upstairs 'earth'.

MULTI-BAND AND ALL-BAND HF DIPOLES

AS A PRE-WW2 AMATEUR, I soon became acquainted with the idea of open-wire feeders for resonant elements (both end-fed and so-called centre-fed Zepp) and also low-impedance feeders (often twisted electric flex before coaxial cable became readily available). But I was not really aware of using open-wire transmission lines to non-resonant elements.

Exactly 50 years ago, I arrived at a radio station at Upper Weald, near Stony Stratford, from where we keyed transmitters about a mile away at Calverton. It was something of a surprise to find that fixed-length dipole (doublet) transmitting antennas with open-wire feeders were used on all frequencies between about 3 and 10MHz with the aid of ATUs - probably based on the original balanced form of Collins Universal Coupler (pi-network): eg **Fig 4**.

In recent years, particularly since the arrival of the WARC non-harmonic bands, the attractions of open-wire feeders (or the slightly more lossy 300Ω ribbon feeders) have become ever more evident. It is convenient, though not essential, where the ATU sees a reasonably low (current fed) impedance rather than a voltage fed. It is for this reason that multiband dipoles based on the G5RV/ZS6ABW principle have special appeal.

The February *TT* quoted Bill Orr's belief that the G5RV is an offspring of the 1935 three-band antenna originated by Art Collins, ex-W9CXX, and L M Croft. However, I had forgotten that a few months earlier, Dean Manley, KH6B, writing from the Hawaiian Islands, had sent me details of the Collins antenna as reprinted in *Electric Radio* of April 1991 by Bill Stewart, K6HV. The reprint included the original data as shown on a Collins Radio Company drawing of March 1935. K6HV pointed out:

"I think Varney came up with the idea not knowing of Art's work." Art Collins's design brought the 300Ω transmission line all the way to the transmitter, whereas a feature of Louis Varney's design has always been the connection of the shortish 300ohm section to any length of (70Ω) coaxial cable.

From the original Collins Radio drawing it is clear that the antenna (**Fig 5**) came in three versions. 'A' had an element (L) length of 99ft, with 82.5ft of line, intended for 14.0-14.4MHz, 7.0-7.3MHz and 3.7-4.0MHz. 'B' with 133ft top, 48.5ft line for 14.0-14.4MHz, 7.0-7.3MHz and 3.7-4.0MHz and 'C' 266ft top, 48.5ft line for 14.0-14.4MHz, 7.0-7.3MHz, 3.5-4.0MHz and 1.7-2.0MHz. It does seem however that L M Croft in his *Signal* article also recommended 103ft for L, very close to the full-size G5RV.

The Collins work sheet shows L comprising No 10 B&S hard drawn enamelled copper with six inch insulators at ends and centre, supported 40ft or more above ground. The transmission line, as mentioned in the February *TT*, was formed from 0.25 inch copper or aluminium tubes spaced 1.5in by means of

isolantite (a ceramic material) or impregnated maple blocks at intervals of 20in with bends (R) not less than 1ft radius.

Bill Wright, G0FAH, has drawn my attention to his 'All-band dipole' published in *Sprat*, Spring 1992, as "One antenna for every band - almost!": **Fig 6**. This antenna draws on the work of ZS6AKW/G0GSF in using computer modelling to optimise the number of bands on which the impedance seen at the transmitter is reasonably close to 50Ω and can be connected to coax cable via a simple 1:1 current balun.

The problem of covering 10MHz and 21MHz is solved by changing the length of the 300Ω feeder from 11.5m to 8.8m. With a good ATU it will also work on 1.8MHz either 'as is' or as a top loaded vertical.

With a 'top' length of 29.3m and 11.5m of 300Ω slotted ribbon (velocity factor 0.85) the computer results were:

Frequency (Mhz)	Resistance (ohms)	Reactance (ohms)	SWR into 50ohms
3.56	6.7	-4	7.6
7.03	35	+28	2.1
14.06	40	-3	1.2
18.07	39	+69	4.3
24.90	98	-31	1.9
28.06	46	+81	3.5
With Feeder Length 8.8m			
10.1	27	+234	1.8*
21.06	24	-4	2.0
With Feeder Length 14.9m			
10.1	52	-422	1.0*
21.06	24	+3	2.0

* Negative reactance is capacitive (positive is inductive) in series with the resistive part of the impedance. To get a good match on the 10.1MHz band it is necessary only to tune out the series reactance - with 8.8m feeder a 130pF capacitor put in each leg of the feeder right at the base (with 14.9m feeder inductors of 3.3μH in each leg).

Efficiency should remain good with any SWR below about 10, although for solid-state transceivers this can be reduced by a 1:1 balun followed by a simple L network ATU: **Fig 7**. The current choke balun can be formed by coiling up a length of the coax, or a ferrite or steel wool. Alternatively, the one-coil Z-match ATU could be used without a balun.

Howarth Jones, GW3TMP, who, after experimenting with fitting ferrite sleeved baluns to G5RV antennas over several years, eventually marketed his 'choke balun' under the name Ferromagnetics, queries the comments by G0GSF (*TT*, January) that fitting such baluns is not justified since "Its effect on the measured impedance Z3 and hence on the VSWR was minimal."

GW3TMP writes: "I would have been very surprised if there had been any effect on the measured impedance or the VSWR. The insertion of the balun at the junction of L2 and Z4 will have no effect on line impedance or VSWR but it has a marked effect on the current balance on the output side of the balun as measured in the balanced line L2. The other significant difference is in the current flow on the coaxial screen outer on line Z4. If this is measured before and after insertion of the balun, using a current probe, it will be found that without it there will be quite a large amount of current flowing on the braid outer on some bands. The ferrite sleeved balun will stop this happening. It is this outer braid current that causes most problems with TVI or RFI etc. Many of my customers have solved their EMC problems by fitting sleeve baluns . . . ."

THE PASSING OF 'MR B–2'

ONE OF THE SADNESSES of compiling a *RadCom* column for 35 years is that inevitably many of those who contribute to the column - and who in the process establish a friendly relationship with your columnist - must inevitably become Silent Keys. But the recent death of John Brown, G3EUR, leaves a particular void.

It was not until 1975 that I had the pleasure of meeting him in person when he invited Tom Ivall (then Editor of *Wireless World*) and myself to the Special Forces Club in Knightsbridge, bringing along some of his many photographs of SOE communications equipment and stations. These included the 'suitcase sets' and 'miniature communications receiver (MCR1)' for which, as an officer in SOE's Signals Directorate, he had been responsible between 1941-45.

These included his still famous B-2 (Type 3 Mk 2) transmitter-receiver which I had first used at Nijmegen in November 1944 during a brief stay with the escape and evader unit IS9 (now known as MI9), who at that time were still bringing back more survivors from the Arnhem disaster, hidden by the Dutch Resistance. Some 7000 B-2 suitcase sets were built by SOE at their factory at Stoneleigh Park, Northwest London and many were used for paramilitary as well as clandestine operations.

After the war, many came into the hands of amateurs as low cost and extremely good value 'surplus' - a few are still in use, others are to be found in private and public collections. The two-stage EL32-6L6 transmitter with pi-network has an output of some 15-20 watts between 3 and 15.5MHz. The four-stage superhet receiver has loctal valve types 7Q7-7R7-7Q7-7R7. Total weight in its suitcase about 32lb (14.5kg). It was sturdy and reliable, rather than lightweight, but truly outstanding for a 1943 design. (A B-2 is in the RSGB Museum in fine condition.)

At that meeting, he told us about the 30th anniversary dinner of the SF Club at which Prince Charles had been guest of honour and where there had been a special display of SOE's communication and power generating equipment. SOE even had a steam generator fuelled from charcoal or wood blocks, although few have survived. It proved a fascinating and revealing discussion since my own wartime involvement with clandestine radio was with the rival Special Communications organisation as an operator rather than an engineer.

Since then, John has proved a unique source of information not only on clandestine equipment but also on such matters as voltage doubling circuits for PSUs (see, for example, *TT*, October 1989) and mains transformers with toroidal cores (*TT*, March 1986). But undoubtedly it was his SOE work at The Frythe, Welwyn, and his subsequent membership of the Special Forces Club, that remained closest to his heart. *Vale* Mr B-2, we shall miss you.

NEW MIXER NEEDS LESS OSCILLATOR POWER

THE FEBRUARY *TT* in the item 'Advances in HF Receivers' drew attention to Dr Ulrich Rohde's belief, expressed in *QST*, November 1992, that "The design of low-noise, double-balanced diode mixers (particularly using hot-carrier diodes) and ring arrangements of FETs and bipolar transistors has generated a lot of speculation, technical publications and, at times, emotional reaction regarding actual performance".

The requirement for mixers of very wide dynamic range has been emphasised by modern design practices that result in large numbers of strong signals - particularly those stemming from 500kW HF broadcast transmitters - reaching the broadband mixer(s). Without good pre-mixer RF selectivity, even in the absence of any signal frequency amplification, solid-state mixers and noisy synthesizers have become, in effect, the 'Achilles heel' of modern HF receivers.

Peter Chadwick, G3RZP, has commented in detail on commutative (switching) mixers based on bipolar transistors, as in the SL6440 chip, and on the phase noise of synthesizers. I hope to return to his letter another time. For the moment, it may be helpful to quote his summing up:

"An interesting question is 'How much dynamic range do you need?' We all know that the more the better, but what is the requirement? As I said in my lecture at the Dayton Hamfest last year, a +20dBm third order intercept appears adequate, even on 7MHz at night. More of a problem can be phase noise, especially with some modern rigs - the LF Cumulative Contests show up the transmitted phase noise of some modern rigs quite well, although whether the owners are happy with receiver performance on strong close-in stations is another matter.

"I still maintain that antenna attenuators are an admission of defeat of the ability to design good front-ends. As far as pre-mixer RF gain is concerned, I have wondered about my very much modified FT102. However, on a recent day when the external noise on 28MHz was very quiet and with my beam pointing in the quietest direction (not that there was much to choose from as it was quiet in all directions!), the difference in the receiver between the connected antenna and a 50-ohm load was about 5.5dB, so that receiver noise (measured as a 9dB noise factor) seems nothing to worry about. Listening to the difference, I would not have believed it this great."

TT has commented a number of times on the problem of synthesizer phase noise affecting close-in dynamic range due to reciprocal mixing, and I was interested to learn from a BBC TV engineer that they regard current levels of UHF phase noise in domestic-type synthesizers as a formidable problem. This will have to be overcome if the digital system developed in conjunction with Thomson-CSF of France using 64-QAM digital modulation of some 500 OFDM closely spaced carriers (resulting in the extremely high spectral efficiency of about 7.5bits/s per Hz) is ever to become operational.

Getting back to the topic of mixers, it seems

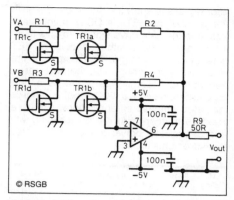

Fig 8: Basic form of the Kushnik double-balanced FET switching mixer.

worth drawing attention to an article in the September 1992 issue of *RF Design*: 'An ultra low distortion HF switched FET mixer' by Eric Kushnik of the American LTX Corporation. It is claimed that this new mixer design, based on an SD5000 quad FET device, is capable of superlative performance in providing excellent intermodulation distortion yet requiring relatively low oscillator power injection.

Kushnik notes that diode ring double balanced mixers (DBMs) are capable of third-order intercept points of +25 to +35dB but this needs oscillator power levels in the +20 to +30dBm range for diode ring DBMs, and in the range of +10 to +15dBm for switched FET DBMs even when using resonant drive circuit techniques which tend to be inconvenient for broadband mixers [Note the resonant drive FET mixer was developed by Ed Oxner, KB6QJ, of Siliconix and described in *TT*, March 1986 pp 187-8, with the relevant Siliconix Application Note 'Designing a super-high dynamic range double-balanced mixer' AN85-2 mentioned in *TT*, August 1986, p574 - G3VA].

Kushnik stresses that a requirement for a high level of oscillator power means more local oscillator design problems, and more shielding and filtering to prevent oscillator noise leaking into the IF stages or RF radiation from the antenna etc. There thus remains a need for a mixer that can achieve high dynamic range, as measured by its third-order intercept point, while operating on relatively low oscillator power.

He then discusses why Mosfet switching mixers require high level injection in spite of the fact that Mosfet gates do not consume or dissipate power. But they require a large switching voltage for the mixer to operate properly: "The problem is that there is considerable signal voltage across the FET switch, and considerable signal current through the FET switch . . . . The solution can be found, without driving the FET gates with higher voltage, by not allowing signal current to pass through the FET, and not to allow signal voltage to appear across the FET."

Fig 8 shows the basic arrangement of his double-balanced FET switching mixer while **Fig 9** presents the practical design as built and assessed. R6 is chosen for input matching (approx 56Ω for a 50Ω system). T1 accomplishes the signal inversion from V_A to V_B ($V_A = -V_B$). T1 has a 6dB loss due to its turns ratio, so R2 and R4 have been made twice the value of R1 and R3 to make up for this. Transformers T3 and T2 take the local oscillator signal and apply it in the proper phase to the gates of the FETs. A DC bias voltage is added to the gate drive signals to give them the proper DC level with respect to the FET gate threshold voltage. The output of the circuit is taken through R9, the 50Ω series terminating resistor. This produces a 6dB drop when driving a 50Ω load. Kushnik's tabulated measurements show that a +25dBm intercept point can be achieved with a local oscillator power of -3dBm. Selected measurements include:

LO (dBm)	Vbias (V)	i/p each tone (dBm)	o/p each tone (dBm)	3rd order products (dBm)	3rd order inter-cept (dBm)
+13	3.4	9.5	−5.2	−76	44
+13	2.2	2.7	−6.8	−67.4	33
+3	2.4	2.7	−10.9	−83	38.7
−3	2.2	2.7	−11.8	−67.4	30.7
−3	2.2	2.7	−5.7	−49.2	25

IMAGE REJECTION MIXER

THE CURRENT POPULARITY of up-conversion to VHF in the first mixer of HF receivers has resulted in a return to multi-conversion designs. It has long been considered that subsequent down-conversion mixer stages should not change the frequency by more than about 10:1, or preferably less, in order to minimise the 'image' response. Thus a receiver with a first IF of the order of 70MHz and a final IF of, say, 455kHz or less (in order to take advantage of digital signal processing etc) will conventionally require an intermediate IF of, say, 9 or 10.7MHz. With triple or even quadruple conversions, it becomes increasingly difficult to achieve a design free of spurious responses and of wide dynamic range.

A review of the Drake R-8 receiver by Scott D Prather, KB9Y, (Communications Quarterly, Fall, 1992) draws attention to the use of an image-rejection mixer (IRM), based on a pair of double-balanced mixers, that permits the first 45MHz IF to be directly converted down to the second and final IF of only 50kHz. **Fig 10** outlines the basic configuration of this unusual mixer which was originally developed over 20 years ago for microwave applications by G P Kurpis and I J Taub 'Wideband X-band microstrip image rejection mixer' (IEEE Trans on Microwave Theory and Techniques, December, 1970, pp 1181-2) but which does not appear to have been used previously for HF communications receivers except in the form of two-phase SSB demodulators.

KB9Y writes: "One of the benefits of eliminating a mid-IF stage is an improvement in the receiver's dynamic range. . . . Eliminating an additional mixer stage and its associated IF amplifiers helps to improve the dynamic range and minimize the generation of spurious responses. Another benefit is that by converting to 50kHz directly, no expensive bandpass filters are required for a second IF in the 2 to 9MHz range. L/C filtering that provides excellent selectivity is easy to design for an IF frequency this low, eliminating the cost of expensive mechanical or crystal filters in the IF altogether. [It would also be possible to utilise DSP with analogue to digital conversion at 50kHz although this is not done in the R-8 which appears to be intended as a general coverage HF receiver (with synchronous AM demodulation) for shortwave listening, etc - G3VA].

KB9Y provides a circuit diagram of the IRM as used in the R-8 but note that full copyright is retained by the R L Drake Company. He

describes the front-end design as follows: "Most of the front end in the R-8 appears to have been borrowed from the design of the R-7. Nine PIN-diode switched Chebyshev bandpass filters provide selectivity for the RF preamp and mixer. Drake also use the same transistor for the RF preamp in the R-8 as they did in the R-7. A roofing filter to improve the first IF rejection precedes the first mixer.

"As with the R-7, Drake use a DBM to up-convert to a 45MHz IF . . . . A non-AGC-controlled JFET amplifies the 45MHz IF from the DBM before it's routed to a four-pole crystal filter. This filter provides a 12kHz (-3dB) bandwidth. From the crystal filter, the 45MHz IF signal is routed either to the AM or the FM IF chain . . . . and routed to the pair of SBL-1X double-balanced mixers forming an IRM."

Unfortunately no laboratory measurements on, or operational critique of this receiver, introduced in 1991, are included in the article, but it was reviewed by Peter Hart, G3SJX, in RadCom, February 1992 [Reprints available from RadCom office price £1.50 to members - Ed]. The use of an IRM circuit based on two double-balanced mixers is an interesting development for a model which, in a Drake advertisement, is claimed to outperform "receivers costing much, much more."

MATTERS ARISING

SEVERAL READERS HAVE CHIDED me for not correcting the use by G8GS (Impedance/power meter, TT, January 1993, p41) of the spurious term 'RMS power'. As Bob Pearson, G4FHU, puts it: "It seems a shame that this error has been repeated down the decades. The product Irms x V_{rms} x cos phi is in fact the average power (averaged over a number of complete cycles).

It all went wrong after WWII when, in competition with foreign manufacturers, British makers of loudspeakers and amplifiers got fed up with foreign rivals quoting peak power ratings instead of the single tone average. Attempts were made to point out that with a single tone rating, the peak power is twice the average but then, some advertiser thought the RMS suffix looked good as a way of spiking the opposition and used it incorrectly.

"But alas, almost every advertiser since has followed the daft practice. Further complications arose later with other terms used to bamboozle buyers of audio equipment: 'music power' for instance. The irony of course is that for a loudspeaker, the ability to tolerate a high power may not be a desirable feature at all, especially if it arises because of poor sensitivity". I must take at least part of the blame for using 'RMS power' since I now recall that many of the points made by G4FHU have already been raised in TT - about a decade ago!

There was also an error in the circuit of the ATU providing balanced output (Fig 6 (d) of the Jan TT in which the 'hot' end of L2b is shown joined to the outer of the coax feed to the SWR meter instead of a 'cross over'.

Amateur Radio (February 1993) has published a correction to the circuit diagram of the VK5BR interference cancelling circuit (TT, March, Fig 4). R4 the source resistor for the MPF102 should be 1000Ω not 100k. **G3VA**

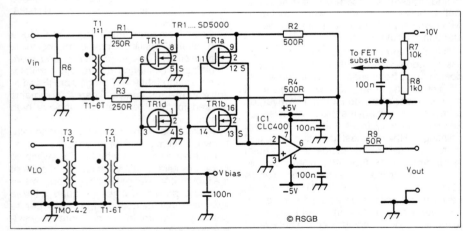

Fig 32: Practical design of the mixer built and investigated by Eric Kushnik as described in RF Design (Sept 1992).

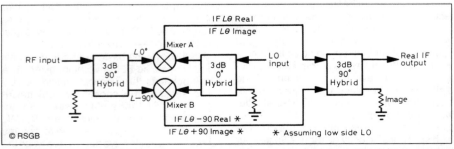

Fig 32A: Microwave image rejecting mixer, from Microwave Solid-state Circuit Design by Bahl & Bhartia (1988) akin to the two-phase SSB demodulator.

THE PA0SE COMUDIPOLE MULTIBAND HF ANTENNA

RECENT *TT* ITEMS have underlined the value of simple multiband dipole-type HF antennas including the G5RV and the derivatives based on the work of G0GSF/ZS6AKW. Also the use of open-wire feeders with a non-resonant 'top' in conjunction with a flexible ATU providing balanced output over a wide range of resistive and reactive impedances. Although as mentioned in the March *TT*, this latter type of 'doublet' antenna was quite widely used more than 50 years ago, Lew McCoy, W1ICP, in *CQ* Magazine has recently resurrected this form of antenna using a horizontal or inverted-Vee radiator of random length. This is preferably not less than about 40% of the lowest wavelength for which it is to be used and is centre fed with open-wire line. He has even rechristened this classic antenna a 'McCoy Dipole'!

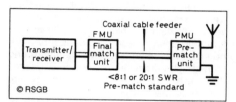

Fig 1: The two-stage tuning and wide range matching philosophy advocated by G3LKZ in 1981.

Dick Rollema, PA0SE, notes that it is not always convenient or practicable to bring the open wire feeders into the shack. Instead, he has drawn inspiration from a paper presented by Dr Mike Underhill, G3LHZ, (wearing a Philips Research Laboratories hat) at an IERE Conference 'Radio Receivers and Associated Systems' at Leeds University in July 1981. His long paper 'Widerange antenna matching networks' (*IERE Conference proceedings No 50*, pages 101-135) was briefly summarised in *TT*, September 1981, pp818-819).

As pointed out many years ago: "When an antenna element presents to the transmission line an impedance other than its characteristic impedance, the impedance offered to the transmitter at the input end of the line may be quite different from either the characteristic impedance of the line or (unless the line is an exact multiple of an electrical half wavelength) the impedance at the antenna junction. The impedance represented by the line then depends on the length of the feeder (which acts as an impedance transformer). In such cases unless a suitable matching network is interposed between transmitter and transmission line, the impedance may be of a value (in the form R + jX) with which the transmitter output circuit cannot cope. But, if the reactance is cancelled out and the impedance falls within the values suitable for the transmitter output circuit, (now invariably 50Ω since the demise of the pi-network tank circuit), then the antenna system

is matched and all the real power delivered by the transmitter (other than the usually modest losses in the transmission line and resistive losses in the antenna) will be radiated. It is the job of the ATU both to balance out the reactive element and to make the resistive impedance

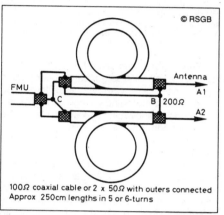

100Ω coaxial cable or 2 x 50Ω with outers connected
Approx 250cm lengths in 5 or 6-turns

Fig 2: A pre-match unit (PMU) in the form of a 50-200Ω coaxial wideband balun transformer as described in the 1981 IERE paper by Dr Mike Underhill, G3LKZ.

suitable for the transmitter output. The problem with designing a flexible ATU is that ideally it needs to cope with a very large range of impedances, both very low and very high, and transform them to around the 50Ω suitable for most modern transmitters. Basically only one capacitor and one inductance are required to do this, but amateurs soon discover that to cover many bands and many possible impedances a very large value, high voltage variable capacitor is needed and preferably a very large and expensive variable (roller coaster) inductance. In practice, most ATUs represent configurations that help to reduce these components to reasonably manageable proportions.

At Leeds in 1981, G3LHZ showed that practical and versatile wide range antenna matching networks can be designed based on a 'two-stage' philosophy: **Fig 1**. This depends on having a pre-match unit (PMU) at the antenna junction (which can consist of a wideband coaxial-cable balun transformer: **Fig 2**) in order to limit the demands on the final match unit (FMU) in the form of an ATU at the transmitter end of the transmission line.

G3LHZ described an FMU which, in conjunction with the 4:1 coaxial balun PMU, was capable of matching a military transmitter to a whip antenna over the entire range of 1.5-30MHz. This required the use of an inductor with a maximum value of 28.3μH and two 2200pF variable capacitors but Mike Underhill later pointed out (*TT*, November 1981, p1034) that these large values were required only for the lowest frequencies between 1.5-1.8MHz, and that for the lowest amateur frequencies (ie 1.8MHz), these values could be reduced to 24.5μH and 1600pF, or less, if the antenna was only intended to cover 3.5MHz upwards: **Fig 3(a)** shows the 1.8-30MHz FMU which can be switched to provide the network configurations shown in **Fig 3(b)**.

PA0SE has adopted G3LHZ's two-stage PMU/FMU approach for his 'comudipole' (coaxial cable fed multiband dipole) but with a simplified FMU. He writes: "G3LHZ again suggests a radiator of approximately a half-wavelength or slightly less on the lowest frequency band to be used. Matching to the transmitter takes place in two stages; by a PMU between the centre of the antenna and the coaxial cable transmission line and an FMU between the cable and the transmitter. The PMU is a 4:1 balun made of coaxial cable, similar to one I used for feeding the two loops of my seven-band 'Optiquad' (see Eurotek in the August 1992 *RadCom*). [This is basically similar to that used by G2LHZ and shown in Fig 2 but Eurotek gave constructional details using 75Ω cable scraps left over from cable-TV installations wound on 110mm OD PVC waste pipe - G3VA].

The advantage of such a balun over those using ferrite or powdered-iron toroids is that there is no danger of saturating the core, resulting in losses and harmonic

Fig 3: (a) The flexible final-match unit (FMU) with component values modified by G3LKZ to cover 1.8-30MHz rather than the full military specification of 1.5-30MHz. (b) The network configurations of the matching unit in the various switching positions.

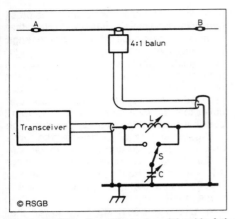

Fig 4: PA0SE's Comudipole (coaxial cable fed multiband dipole). The length AB can be of any value, but preferably not less than about 40% of the wavelength on the lowest frequency band to be used. L can be a roller-coaster or a coil with multiple switched taps. C can be one of the old style three-gang (3 x 500pF) receiver capacitors with the three sections in parallel (the PMU reduces the need for a special high voltage capacitor). If a proper match cannot be obtained with S in one position, the other position should be tried.

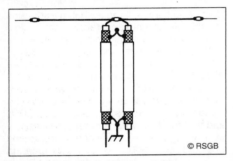

Fig 5: An alternative method of feeding a multiband dipole with parallel coaxial cables used to provide a balanced transmission line less affected by nearby metal objects than open wire line. Radiator should be at least 40% of the wavelength of the lowest frequency to be used. The cables can have any characteristic impedance and in principle can be of any length, but experience has shown that it is advisable that they should be somewhat longer than a quarter-wave of the lowest frequency to be used (ie about 17m for 3.5MHz with cables having a velocity factor of about 0.66). In practice this form of multiband dipole has not been found by PA2ABV as satisfactory as the single coax-fed Comudipole.

generation etc. (Additionally, toroidal baluns are not really suitable with reactive loads). A coaxial balun can tolerate very high standing-wave ratios and/or high power. The only limiting factor is the maximum voltage the cable can withstand and this is considerable with the cable noted in the Eurotek article.

"The PMU takes care of the transition from balanced to unbalanced feed and at the same time limits the SWR on the cable to a maximum of about 20:1. This may seem high but the FMU reduces it to 1:1 at the output port of the transmitter. The losses in the cable remain quite low provided that feeder length is not excessive and a cable with a low-loss under matched conditions is used. Even if the extra loss due to the 20:1 SWR on some frequencies amounts to a few decibels this is a small price to pay for the convenience of a simple all-band antenna without traps, fed by coaxial cable. Should an extremely long feeder have to be used, it is advisable to select a type with minimal inherent loss, such as the new Aircom Plus.

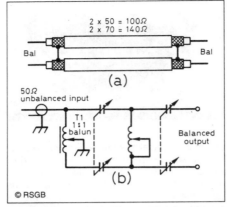

Fig 6: (a) Showing how two coaxial cable lengths can be used as a balanced transmission line. (b) Flexible ATU providing balanced output from 50Ω unbalanced input in such a manner that losses in a 1:1 ferrite balun tend to be minimised. Choke 1:1 baluns would be preferable.

"The rather complicated FMU unit devised by G3LHZ can for amateur bands be replaced by a simple L-network with a switch (S) to change from matching to high or to low impedances as shown in Fig 4 which shows the complete comudipole antenna system."

PA0SE adds: "Following publication of the system in Electron (December 1992) this form of multiband dipole is now being used successfully in The Netherlands by several amateurs. One is Ton Verberne, PA2ABV, who lives on the second floor of a five-storey apartment building. On the roof he has an inverted-Vee dipole of about 2 x 19m and a 4:1 coaxial balun as described in Eurotek, August 1992, but with the connection between the flange of the coax socket and the boom of the quad deleted. From there some 30m of RG-213 coax leads to the shack where an L-network takes care of matching to the transceiver. In practice PA2ABV can match perfectly on all nine amateur bands from 3.5MHz-50MHz. Even on l.8MHz a match is possible but efficiency is low. On all bands 28-3.5MHz results are excellent (and much better than the previously used double-coax balanced feed system shown in Fig 5).

Further information on the use of twin co-axial cables to form balanced line is shown in Fig 6.

RADIATING LIGHT BULBS

AN ITEM IN THE August 1991 TT, 'New induction light bulbs and their RFI potential' drew attention to the development of high-efficiency, long-life electric light bulbs in which there is no filament and which are powered by RF energy from compact generators (trans-

mitters) working in the ISM (industrial, scientific and medical) bands at either 2.65MHz or 13.56MHz. At the time I concluded "One does not have to be a pessimistic soothsayer to recognise that widespread use of such lamps could significantly affect the reception of weak signals on HF and even VHF . . . ."

The item included information on the Philips QL and the Sylvania (IWCF - Induction Wave Compact Fluorescent) lamps based on articles in Electrical Review and New Scientist but it was made clear that at that time such lamps were still in the development stage. Also, their high cost would tend to make them financially attractive in situations where lamps are switched on for thousands of hours per annum, a situation seldom found in domestic situations. But I added the warning that: "Nevertheless, it seems likely that they will be heavily promoted for both commercial and domestic use on account of their considerable energy saving ('green') characteristics."

A year later, QST (August 1992) ran a short item 'Amateurs concerned about RF lightbulb's design' which noted a Californian firm, Intersource Technologies Inc, had announced their intention to manufacture and market high-efficiency bulbs powered by some 25 watts of 13.56MHz RF. QST reported that in reply to the concern expressed by many radio amateurs a company spokesman claimed that the bulbs should not be a matter of concern for amateurs. The bulbs would use a crystal oscillator, power amplifier and a coil-type antenna to "couple high-frequency electrical energy into a mercury vapour plasma" as shown in Fig 7. The bulbs, it was stressed, were expected to meet FCC Para 15 rules regarding incidental interference.

Evan Heaton-Jones, G3CJ, was far from convinced that amateurs have nothing to fear from the introduction of RF-powered fluorescent light bulbs - even those designed to minimise EMC problems. In the October 1992 issue of his local Cheltenham club newsletter he foresaw a time when a town of some 100,000 inhabitants could be generating up to a total of some 10MW of RF power and that if only 1% of this radiates it would represent some 100kW.

In residential areas of London, I have been bothered by intermittent, unstable ISM signals for many years. I suspect these largely emanate from medical equipment or possibly industrial equipment at some distance. Fortunately the interference largely disappears outside working hours and hopefully will gradually reduce as more ISM equipment becomes crystal-controlled rather than using very crude and unstable power oscillators.

But I cannot help feeling that with RF-energised lamps - no matter how carefully

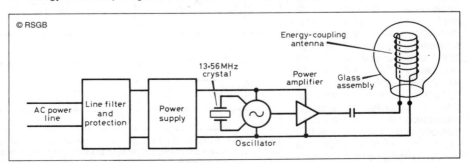

Fig 7: Block diagram of the RF energised lightbulb as developed by Intersource Technologies.

designed (and G3CJ points out that there is the real danger that future low-cost designs from the Far East could dispense with crystal-control and other EMC precautions) - it seems inevitable that a 25W 13.56MHz 'transmitter' in the immediate vicinity of the shack would at least *desensitise* most solid-state receivers with broad-band or even sub-octave RF input filtering in their front-ends, and that covers virtually all current HF transceivers, tuned to the 14MHz band. This would presumably not infringe the European EMC directive since it could be argued that blocking, cross modulation and intermodulation characteristics are inherently 'receiver faults'.

Even the compact fluorescent lamps now marketed in the UK can be a problem - possibly even more troublesome than future RF-powered types. Tim Saxton, G3LJR, writes: "For some time I have been slowly exchanging the filament lamps in my house with the new miniature fluorescent replacement types now available. Initially, these were Philips units about the size and weight of a half brick. They worked well, but their size/shape seriously limited where I could use them. They had an inductive choke and normal neon starter.

"More recently 'electronic' units have come along in which the choke and starter functions are achieved electronically. I put a 23W unit - light output equivalent to a 100W filament lamp - made by Osram in the shack some months ago with no problems. In March, I discovered that my local supermarket was selling a new range made by Mazda (GE Lighting Ltd) at significantly lower cost than most of the others. I bought some 4-tube and 2-D 13W units (equivalent to 60W filament lamps).

My son soon discovered that it was impossible to use his portable radio tuned to the Irish long-wave station *Atlantic 252* (252kHz) within several feet of the Mazda lamps. Even VHF/FM stations received on the portable's whip antenna showed significant noise. I suspect that it is radiation from the gas since the cable to the lamp did not appear hot. On LF the effect is an unpleasant 50Hz buzz, at VHF more like 'white noise'.

With a scanner receiver (50MHz AM) I checked the lamps throughout the house. All units with an inductive choke and normal starter caused no noticeable noise. The German Osram electronic unit produced measurable noise on 50MHz only if the antenna was within a couple of inches of the tubes; the Mazda units could be detected at 12 inches. Only the Mazda units wiped out *Atlantic 252* which was not affected by any other lamps. The Mazda units appeared to produce very broad-band noise with a peak about 90MHz. Admittedly this was only a crude test. It would be interesting to analyse results using an RFI testing room.

"Perhaps this indicates that RFI standards are still higher in Germany than in the UK. When I took the Mazda lamps back to the shop I had no problem but was told nobody else had complained. I'll stick to the more expensive but *quieter* types in future."

POTATO SOLDERING AID

VIC SAVIN, RS43387, writes: "A young friend was finding it extremely difficult to solder a six

200W FM/CW AMPLIFIER FOR 70MHZ

DAVID BOWMAN, G0MRF, writes: "70MHz is one of the few popular bands where home construction and home conversions of ex-PMR equipment still accounts for most of the amateur radio activity. Recently, a large amount of PMR equipment has become available at low cost and a number of articles have appeared on 70MHz conversions, resulting in a number of my friends joining in the exodus from the crowded 144MHz and the setting up of local communication links and packet stations in the relative peace and tranquillity of 70MHz.

"Unfortunately, the output power on some PMR equipment can be as low as 4W, marginal for packet particularly in London where high-gain antennas tend not to be used on this band. This has encouraged the development of a solid-state amplifier using two relatively low cost SD1407 bipolar transistors, providing a gain of some 13dB and producing 200W output. Since these transistors are not specified as VHF devices they are reasonably priced (currently available from Richardson Electronics Europe, Tel: (Lincoln) 0522 542631). The pair I used were not matched, but did come from the same production batch as identified by a number on the ceramic cap.

The amplifier (**Fig 8** and **Table 1**) should be built symmetrically using identical inductors and track lengths for sides; this along with two resistors coupling the bases and collectors (R2, R3) ensures that the two devices are balanced. I produced a small PCB with the two transistors mounted side by side, approximately 35mm between centre. The output trimmers are l00pF film types with PTFE dielectric. Good quality mica compression trimmers would also be suitable. The series output trim-

Cl	6-65pF film trimmer
C2,C5,C7	10-100pF high voltage
C3,C6,C8	47pF silver mica (350V)
C4	4 x 100pF (each base has 400pF to ground)
Cx	100µF + 0.01µF + 1nF in parallel
R1	10R 0.5W
R2	47R 1W
R3	100R 2W (R1, R2 and R3 carbon film resistors)
L1,L2	2t 18SWG, 10mm ID
L3,L4	8t 22SWG, 2.5mm ID
L5,L6	6t 18SWG, 6.5mm ID
L7,L8	2t 16SWG, 10mm ID
RFC	2t 22SWG enamel copper through FX1115 ferrite bead.
TR1,TR2	SD1407

Table 1: Component list for 70MHz Amplifier

mer tunes very broadly and could be replaced by a parallel combination of fixed values.

"The SD1407 transistors require a 28V collector supply. I used a simple, unregulated supply with a 12 + 12V toroidal from which I removed four turns to give the correct on-load voltage. The circuit for a similar power supply was given in my HF amplifier article in the March 1993 *RadCom*.

"At 200W the amplifier dissipates approximately 100W of excess heat. I chose to use a small heatsink rated at 1.4°/watt, with an 80mm fan to cool it. This combination works perfectly, even for 15-minute key-down periods. Switching 200W needs careful consideration with hot switching out of the question. I used a 15A PCB mounted relay from RS Components and used the PTT line for switching. Whatever system is used, the output relay must be fully closed before power is produced."

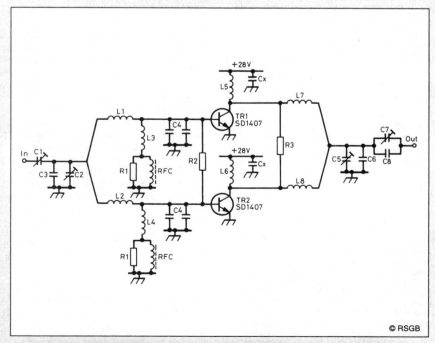

© RSGB

Fig 8: G0MRF's 200W FM/CW amplifier for 70MHz. Components are given in Table 1.

COAX OFF-CUTS AND MOBILE ANTENNAS

PAT PAINTING, G3OEC, adds a further suggestion on the use of odd short lengths of coaxial cable. For many years he has been constructing mobile antennas for 1.8MHz or other bands using the outer braiding of scrap cable and the top section blanks of fibre glass fishing rod with its light weight, flexibility and good strength. He writes: "Obtain a 4ft long tapering hollow or solid fishing rod top section (bland): **Fig 9(a)**. Remove the centre core from a length of 50 or 75Ω coaxial cable, preferably using the method described by G3GDU in the March *TT*.

"Push the point of the rod blank through the outer braid from which the plastic outer cover has been removed: **Fig 9(b)**. Varnish with clear polyurethane varish.

"Then a useful l.8MHz mobile whip can be constructed with the braided fibre glass rod mounted above a 90cm length of plastic electrical conduit wound with sufficient turns of 18SWG enamel wire to resonate the whip antenna as in **Fig 9(c)**."

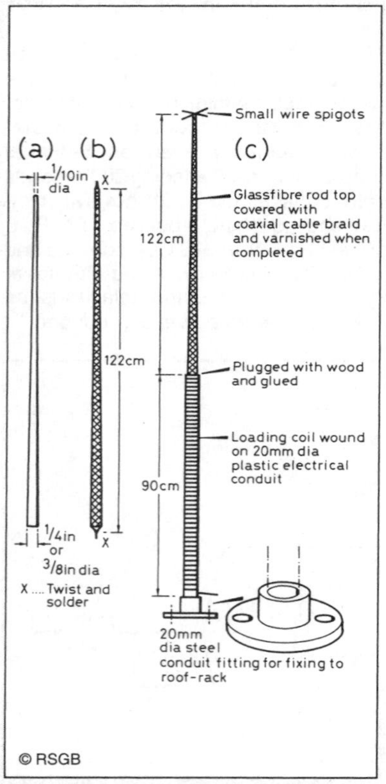

Small wire spigots

(a) (b) (c)

1/10in dia

Glassfibre rod top covered with coaxial cable braid and varnished when completed

122cm

122cm

Plugged with wood and glued

Loading coil wound on 20mm dia plastic electrical conduit

90cm

1/4in or 3/8in dia

X ... Twist and solder

20mm dia steel conduit fitting for fixing to roof-rack

© RSGB

Fig 9: How G3OUC uses the copper braid from off-cuts of coaxial cable for 1.8MHz mobile antennas (the same principle could be used for other HF/VHF bands). (a) 4ft length of tapered, hollow or solid fishing rod(top section, blank). (b) The point of the rod is pushed through the copper braid and this is then varnished. (c) The finished 1.8MHz antenna with the rod section mounted above the loading coil. Wire spigots at the top form a small capacitance cap and can be used for small changes of frequency (wires bent down to raise frequency).

core flex to a six pin DIN plug. He was using a small vice and a 15W iron and experiencing the problem that most of the heat was being lost via the vice or melting the phenol-type plastic body. He sought my help.

"I asked him to give me a potato which I cut in half, placing the cut end on the work-bench the DIN plug was pressed into the top where it was firmly held. I then had no difficulty in soldering the six cores without any overheating or burnt fingers etc. The potato starch was removed from the pins using a switch-cleaning fluid. Sockets may be held similarly by inserting a few pieces of wire into the socket leaving enough length to press into the potato."

"I have used this method successfully for sixty years when soldering various components."

NON-EQUALISING POWER-SUPPLY RESISTORS

HARRY LEEMING, G3LLL, points out that a common fault in valve power amplifier rigs is the short-circuiting of the HT rectifiers resulting, if you are lucky, in the blowing of a fuse; if you are unlucky you find too late that a previous owner has fitted the wrong fuse resulting in the blowing of the mains transformer.

He warns against just replacing the rectifiers without finding out why they short-circuited in the first place after working satisfactorily for years. Most high voltage power supplies depend on the use of four, eight or twelve silicon diodes in various full wave or bridge arrangements. The peak inverse voltage rating is then increased by connecting two or more diodes in series across each arm with, typically, 470k resistors across each diode in order to equalize the voltages across each diode. Similarly there are often a number of series connected electrolytic smoothing capacitors, typically 500V working voltage, again with equalizing resistors.

The problem often lies in these resistors. Composition-type resistors tend gradually to increase in value in situations where they carry current, even when this is within their rated value (note also that most resistors are intended for use only when there is less than 300V across them). This ageing effect can cause a dramatic increase in resistance over the years but will vary from component to component. So a string of *equalizing* resistors may no longer equalize the voltage across the diodes or electrolytic capacitors; if they have differing inverse leakage currents then there is a real risk that one component may fail (short circuit) bringing about further failures. Before replacing any diodes or smoothing capacitors it is advisable to check the values of the equalizing resistors - ageing will virtually always causes the values to increase rather than decrease. One or more of the 470k resistors may prove to be well over a megohm!

SECURE ATU COIL TAPS

THE HIGH COST of variable 'roller-coaster' inductors suitable for flexible, multiband ATUs encourages the use instead of multiple coil taps. It is not a simple matter to solder such taps securely. J D Bolton, G4XPP, recently

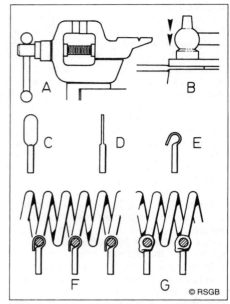

Fig 10: Making secure taps to an air-spaced coil as suggested by G4XPP.

decided to build an ATU suitable for end-fed antennas. In accordance with a published design, he obtained a suitable case, a substantial 12-way switch, 24 turn air spaced coil, 750pF high-voltage variable capacitor and the necessary sockets, wire, nuts and bolts etc.

All went well until the time came to attach securely the twelve taps from the switch to the coil. A few experiments showed that simply attempting to solder substantial wires of the same diameter as the plated copper-wire coil without affecting the adjacent turns etc would not be easy and unlikely to result in mechanically sound taps. The situation required a more thoughtful approach.

Fig 10 shows how G4XPP cracked the problem. His small hobby bench vice (A) has a small anvil on the back. With the vice screwed on the bench, the ends of the twelve wires were flattened (B,C,D) with a hammer. [Presumably any other suitable metal plate or 'anvil' could be used instead of a bench vice - *G3VA*].

Then, with a pair of snipe-nosed pliers he formed the flattened ends into open ended circles (E) and one by one these were slipped on to the coil (F) and clamped tight, at the tapping points, with the snipe nosed pliers. Finally, he snipped off the excess wire and securely soldered the wire circles to the coil (G). Result - no fear of the taps snapping loose the solder or short-circuiting to adjacent turns.

HERE AND THERE

CONTINUING THE SAGA of one bypass capacitor or two (*TT*, October, December 1992), Brian Bower, G3COJ, sends along BBC Technical Memorandum R.1027 (90) *Supply rail by-passing in video circuitry* with which he was involved before his retirement. This is introduced with the statement:

"In video circuitry (frequencies up to about 6MHz) one sometimes sees supply rails with an electrolytic capacitor used for by-passing together with a smaller capacitor, typically a 22nF ceramic, across it to improve HF performance. The drawback to this has long been known but is not always appreciated."

The report concludes: "Supply rail by-passing in video circuitry should be by a single capacitor, never by two in parallel. A tantalum capacitor is preferable and arrangements must be made to limit inrush current on switch-on. In more general applications a parallel combination can provide lower impedance decoupling at higher frequencies than a single electrolytic provided component values are chosen so that the parallel resonance frequency is placed where it will not be a problem - a series element is then optional."

Reg Moores, G3GZT, points out that if you received one of those Christmas cards that plays out musical notes, then you have one of the simplest and cheapest (about 50p) code oscillators ever. When connected to a Morse key, the musical notes do not have time to operate and just a single note is produced even at low speed. Ideal for anyone starting to learn the code. Perhaps we should send some to those who apparently want to write off Morse code as obsolete!

John Ridd, G8BQX, much interested in wartime radios, points out that the excellent American signals vehicles - SCR299/399/499 - fitted BC-312 and BC-342 receivers and not the Hammarlund Super Pros (BC-779, BC-794, BC-1004) suggested in September 1992. The BC-312, BC-342 and mains version BC-348 were all popular 'surplus' buys in the late 1940s despite their upper frequency limit of 18MHz.

ELECTROLYTIC CAPACITORS

THE RECENT *TT* items on the use of electrolytic (preferably tantalum rather than aluminium types) bypass capacitors at HF make it appropriate to recall that electrolytics have long had the unenviable reputation of being among the least reliable of components. Low impedance bipolar transistor circuitry has led to an enormous number of such components being used, although fortunately accompanied by improved reliability, though perhaps not as much as might be desirable.

An article 'All about Electrolytic Capacitors' by Ray Porter in the January 1993 issue of

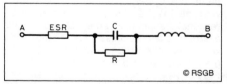

Fig 11: Simplified equivalent circuit of an electrolytic capacitor. A and B are the terminals, C is the effective capacitance, R is the shunt resistance (insulation resistance) through which DC leakage current flows. ESR is the equivalent series resistance and L the capacitor's self-inductance due to its terminals, electrodes and geometry, (*Television*, Jan 93).

Television has been followed in the April issue by the same author's description of a 'Simple ESR meter for Electrolytics' designed to measure the ESR values of PCB-mounted electrolytics.

In the January article, Ray Porter notes that manufacturers seem to regard the life of components used in consumer electronic products as being a minimum of three-to-five years. This is checked by testing at maximum temperature for up to 10,000 hours. But he adds that degradation limits with bottom-of-the-range electrolytics are specified for only 500 hours. This means that significant deterioration may occur after about a year if the capacitor is operated with a high internal temperature (in the UK ambient temperatures for consumer equipment are normally 20-30°C). Manufacturers consider the end of an electrolytic capacitor's useful life to be when 40% of the electrolyte has evaporated and escaped through the end seal, but catastrophic failures may occur before this point is reached. He writes: "The most common cause of failure when electrolytic capacitors are being tested for life expectancy is a short-circuit through the dielectric because of voltage stress. In field servicing the most common cause of failure is the absorption of hydrogenated hydrocarbon cleaners, which attack the aluminium foil, through the end seal. Current 'green' practices in industry are to use no wash or water washable fluxes while soldering, which should reduce this type of failure."

The equivalent circuit of an electrolytic capacitor is shown in **Fig 11**. The shunt resistance R represents the effect of DC leakage. A very small amount of power is dissipated in R although this is negligible compared to the power dissipated in the equivalent series resistance (ESR). Ripple current or AC passing through the capacitor produces a power loss in the ESR which results in heating. The ESR also affects the effective impedance of the capacitor with increasing frequency - making electrolytics unsuitable for by-passing at VHF etc. The demand for low impedance, high frequency capacitors with high ripple current ratings has greatly increased due to the popularity of switch-mode power supplies for which low ESR is necessary. Ray Porter writes: "A capacitor with a higher voltage rating tends to result in longer dielectric life because of the voltage derating factor, while the drying up process will be slower because the internal temperature will be lower. Internal temperature is reduced because high voltage capacitors have a larger case size and a lower ESR value. Because of the heat handling capability of higher voltage capacitors their ripple current rating increases with voltage rating for a given capacitance value."

It is worth noting that an increase in ESR can occur without affecting the capacitance of the unit, so that a check with a high value capacitance meter may not reveal that the capacitor has become 'lossy' and no longer represents a low impedance to RF.

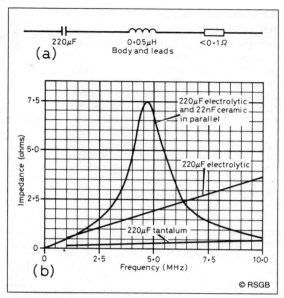

Fig 12: (a) Equivalent circuit of a 220μF electrolytic capacitor with (b) showing the impedance at frequencies 0-10MHz when used alone or in parallel with a 22nF ceramic capacitor showing the large increase in impedance of the pair around 5MHz. From *BBC Technical Memorandum R.1027 (90)*.

Ray Porter gives the following glossary of the terms used for electrolytic capacitors:

a) Dissipation factor (DF): The ratio of the effective series resistance (ESR) of a capacitor to its reactance at a specified frequency.

b) Effective series resistance (ESR): This is the 'lumped' element that's used for purposes of calculation to explain the power loss within a capacitor when it passes AC.

c) Etching: An electrochemical process that roughens the surface of the aluminium foil, thereby increasing its surface area in comparison with unetched foil.

d) Quality factor (QF): The ratio of capacitive reactance to ESR at a specified frequency and thus the inverse of DF.

e) Working voltage: The maximum DC voltage that can be applied to a capacitor for continuous duty at the maximum rated temperature.

He provides a table showing typical characteristics of electrolytic capacitors. This indicates that the ESR of a 220μF capacitor measured at 120Hz has an initial specification of 1.5Ω for a 10V 105° type and 0.5Ω for a low ESR type in a 16 x 31.5mm case, and would cope with a maximum ripple of 1.1A. In life tests the permitted dissipation factor for a 105°C type after 500 hours would be 1.5 x initial value; for a low-ESR type after 2000 hours twice the initial value.

It would seem that for critical applications, such as by-passing or filtering, there is much to be said for using tantalum electolytics with a generous voltage rating in a reasonably large can. **Fig 12** from the BBC report provided by G3COJ shows how resonance effects can impair the by-passing capabilities when an electrolytic capacitor is paralleled with a ceramic capacitor.

Advice that has been given before in *TT* is to mount electrolytics away from sources of heat such as power amplifier valves. They remain in better shape longer when running cool. *G3VA*

BEVERAGE AND HIS 'WAVE ANTENNA'

THE DEATH LAST JANUARY of Harold H Beverage, one-time W2BML, at the age of 99 years, has taken from us one more of those immortal pioneers of radio communications who were willing to admit that their interest in radio engineering stemmed from amateur radio. Harry Beverage began as an amateur-radio enthusiast, yet he rose to the highest ranks of the professionals. Honoured in 1957 by The American Institute of Electrical Engineers "for his pioneering and outstanding achievements in the conception and application of principles basic to progress in national and world-wide radio communications".

Beverage not only invented diversity reception – for long a key feature in point-to-point communications – but also the 'Wave Antenna' that for almost 70 years has generally been called the 'Beverage antenna'. It was so described in *QST* in 1922 by Paul Godley (W)2XE who met Beverage on the liner *Acquitania* en route to the UK. Godley came to Britain on behalf of ARRL for the transatlantic tests in the winter of 1922/23. Beverage in cooperation with Chester Rice and Edward Kellog (who were later responsible for the moving-coil loudspeaker) presented detailed information in a 50-plus page paper 'The Wave Antenna – A New Type of Highly Directive Antenna' in the *Journal of the AIEE* spread over six issues (March 1923, pp258-269, April pp372-381, May pp510-519, June pp636-644 and July pp728-738).

In *TT*, October 1970, pp686-7, I wrote: "Top-band DX enthusiasts will probably need no reminding of the Beverage antenna which has recently been used on both sides of the Atlantic for the reception of 1.8MHz signals .... The antenna was developed in the early 'twenties for the reception of commercial transocean stations operating on the very low frequencies [in the region of 15,000 metres]. In its simplest form it consists of a very long straight wire, extending up to several miles in length, mounted on quite low poles, and correctly terminated at the far end to earth so as to prevent reflections (**Fig 1(a)**) – not exactly an antenna for the amateur with only a short garden.

"But a check with the original description has brought to light several features which are seldom mentioned. For instance, the normal system on VLF was to use two wires with a reflecting transformer at the far end and the terminating impedance at the receiving end, making it possible accurately to null out [off-beam] interference [the same principle as the Jones, the W1ETC and the VK5LR noise-cancelling systems described in *TT*, March 1993].

"Then again, although one normally thinks of the Beverage as being many wavelengths long, this was always impossible at VLF, and the paper suggests that pronounced directional effects can be achieved with an electrical length of one-half to one-wave-length – putting a different order of magnitude on the real estate needed on HF! The Beverage is related to the vee-beam and rhombic antennas, and is not limited to low frequencies .... The 1923 paper showed how the electrical length of the antenna could be reduced by 'stretching' the wire by inserting a series of

Pat Hawker's
Technical Topics

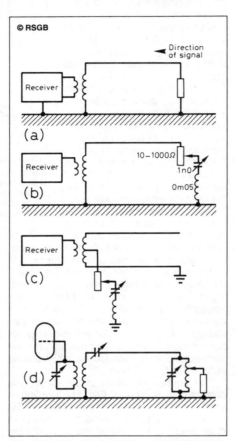

© RSGB

Fig 1: Some of the many possible variations of the Beverage or 'Wave Antenna'. (a) The basic arrangement as used by a number of amateurs on 1.8MHz for long-distance reception. (b) an arrangement suggested by Harold Beverage in 1923 for 'short waves' (ie wavelengths less than about 450 metres). (c) Is a variation of (b) enabling the termination to be at the receiving site. (d) This was an arrangement illustrated in the 1931 edition of the 'Admiralty Handbook of Wireless Telegraphy'.

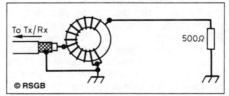

© RSGB

Fig 2: An all-band 'terminated long-wire' Beverage antenna used in the 1970s by Richard White, G3SRO, and suitable for transmission as well as reception. It was about 400ft long, 40ft high. At the far end terminated with a non-inductive high-wattage 500Ω resistor earthed to an 8ft aluminium stake via a vertical down-lead. The transmitter fed the antenna via a ferrite toroidal step-up transformer using a toroid of about 1.5in diameter, with 3 turns input and 7 turns to the antenna, bifilar wound and space. It should have a worst SWR on any band 3.5-28MHz of only about 1.8:1. Unlike a low antenna this has two main lobes and by directing it towards central America G3SRO got good coverage of North and South America.

capacitors at intervals along its length [the basis of G6CJ's 'Loaded wire dipoles' described in the *RSGB Bulletin*, July 1961 [and since then in *TT*, *ART* and other RSGB publications].

"One of the famous early Beverage antennas was that erected by Paul Godley at Ardrossan in Scotland during the vital amateur transatlantic tests of 1922 when his 400-metre long wire collected signals from a number of American amateurs between about 200 to 300 metres. I can recall using a wartime Beverage antenna [at Hanslope Park in late 1941] about 0.5-mile long, on frequencies of the order of 3.5 to 9MHz where it proved a very effective antenna [for receiving an Abwehr network of stations in Norway].

"So far as signal collecting properties are concerned, there is little point in stringing this type of antenna higher than is required for ordinary security and to pass over obstructions. One of the organisations [BBC Monitoring Service near Reading] currently using Beverage antennas for the reception of overseas MF broadcasting stations has recently [late 1960s] been carrying out theoretical studies on optimum lengths and heights to see if any improvement could be obtained by raising the present antennas (from 1000ft to 2500ft long and about 10ft high) to a height of about 30ft. Generally, these studies indicate that the first effect of raising height is to degrade sidelobe performance: the only real advantage in raising height would seem to be where extremely long antennas are possible, since additional height lowers the rate of attenuation. It is also shown that by connecting two Beverage antennas in parallel it is possible to slew the directivity over a useful angle. The [BBC Research] study suggests that these antennas are useful for the reception of signals arriving at angles of 5° to the horizon". I have added text within square brackets – *G3VA*.

As a result of Harold Beverage's work, RCA built six VLF transmitting stations on the Atlantic coast of the USA, some using high-frequency alternators, plus one receiving station at Riverhead, Long Island. Here a Beverage antenna some six miles long erected between Eastport and Riverhead was used to prove the system. Terminated, very long, wire antennas can also make excellent unidirectional transmitting antennas but in this case it is usually necessary to raise the height which reduces ground absorption but degrades the sharp directivity into two lobes. **Fig 2** shows a transmitting type 400ft all-band unidirectional terminated long-wire for HF operation reported some years ago in *TT* (*ART7* p305) by Richard White, G3SRO.

Further background information on the Beverage antenna is given by Peter Lankshear in a four-page article 'The Vintage Beverage' (*Electronics Australia*, April 1993, pp98-101). This shows that Beverage began development of his directional antenna in 1917 at the suggestion of Dr E F W Alexanderson, chief engineer of General Electric (USA) to safeguard wartime traffic across the Atlantic from the possibility of German jamming. Beverage always acknowledged that he drew on the earlier work on directional antennas by Marconi (1906) and the 'Ground Aerial' developed in Germany by F Kieblitz in 1911 who had found that he could obtain good directional signals at the centre of a length of wire supported about one metre above ground and earthed at its extremities. The first Wave Antenna was erected at New Brunswick (New Jersey) near the high-power US Navy station NFF equipped with an Alexanderson alternator.

COMPATIBILITY – BUT WITH HOW MUCH POWER?

MOST OF US HAVE from time to time echoed, or at least agreed, with the thoughts expressed by Gary Breed, K9AY, in his editorial 'An EMC wish list', *RF Design*, August 1992. He complained about there being too

many electronic gadgets in the home which are affected by radio-frequency interference at extremely low RF field strengths. He noted that although some products such as TV sets and video recorders (VCRs) have been getting better, consumers are buying more electronic devices than ever, and they have a right to expect them to work reliably. He added: "Those RF designers who understand EMC tell me that even a few simple concepts can help with both (unwanted) radiation and susceptibility. Strategically placed two-cent bypass capacitors, minor changes in PC board layout or careful routing of cables can contribute many decibels towards improved EMC performance."

I don't suppose that, when he wrote his editorial, K9AY expected many of his professional or amateur readers to disagree. However this proved not to be entirely the case. He duly published (February, 1993 issue, p13) a letter from Robert Orban of Belmont, California under the heading 'Turn down the power before turning up the price' that puts forward a view that, however unpopular it may be for most amateur radio enthusiasts, should at least make us think.

Robert Orban wrote: "While I support your idea that consumer equipment should be more resistant to EMI than most of it presently is, my jaw dropped when I read that the FCC had measured a 9 volt/metre field induced in a hapless neighbour's home by a ham running a 1kW HF transmitter. This is a huge, absurd amount of RF for a piece of consumer equipment to reject!

"EMI suppression is not free. If a $300 (retail) VCR can have no more than about $40 in actual component cost, the cost of adding sufficient EMI suppression to reject a 9V/m field can significantly affect the selling price of such equipment. I would ask you why tens of millions of consumers should be so taxed to permit a few amateurs to indulge their hobby. In the 1930s, it did not seem unreasonable to let people fire up 1kW rigs in residential neighbourhoods. In the 1990s, it seems absurd to permit this. Reducing power to 10W would reduce the electric field 20dB (to 0.9V/m). While this is still a lot of RF, the power level now becomes comparable with other services, like cellular phones and the like. It is time for the FCC to act to reduce the permissible RF fields that amateurs can blast into their neighbours' homes."

I can imagine the shudder that would follow an announcement by the Radiocommunications Agency that maximum output power of UK licences would shortly be reduced from 400W to 10W! It is true that, like all pre-WW2 newly licensed amateurs, my own licence (or more precisely the G3VA issued to my father on my behalf) specified a maximum of 10 Watts DC input on the, then, 1.7, 7 and 14MHz bands only. In practice this proved sufficient power for me to work enough CW DX on 14MHz and European AM phone on 1.7 and 7MHz that I did not bother to apply (through the RSGB) for a 25-Watt permit after six months. A few pre-war UK Old Timers held high-power permits of up to 1kW. With so many 'straight' receivers still in use, I found that even my 10W of 1.7MHz AM phone could be heard by broadcast listeners in the town. BCI was a problem long before TV arrived on the scene.

It is clear that we cannot really expect consumer-electronics receiver and appliance manufacturers to build into all their products sufficient RF immunity to cope with a high-power transmitter a few feet away. In the 1930s, power levels at most UK amateur stations were much lower than those at professional transmitting sites, such as broadcast, coast stations, fixed point-to-point services and these were seldom located in residential areas. Today, the situation is very different and there are many TV local relay stations, cordless telephone transmitters working at what amateurs would regard as QRP. And for mobile transmitters for cellular radio, PMR (private mobile radio) etc, only a

AUSTRALIAN AMATEURS ON LONG WAVES

THE JULY 1923 ISSUE of the Journal of the AIEE with the final instalment of 'The Wave Aerial' also contains an article 'The Electrical Plant of Transocean radio telegraph' by E F W Alexanderson and other RCA engineers which reflects the professional viewpoint in the days before amateurs showed the value of the short waves. Incidentally, 'short waves' in 1923 were wavelengths between 200 and 600 metres! This paper stated:

"The economical wavelength for communicating over a certain distance can be selected by the practical rule that the economic range of a station for reliable communication is about 500 to 1000 times the wavelength. If too short a wave is selected the signals will be weak in daytime and strong but variable at night . . . . generally speaking for distances over 3000 miles

the reliability of wavelengths of over 11,000 metres is so much greater than that of shorter waves. Long waves have therefore been universally adopted for long distance communication."

So strongly was this opinion held that the paper concluded: "Thus it can be stated that guess-work has been eliminated from the development of radio communication, and that sound foundations, both technically and financially, can be laid for all future expansions of our system."

A number of countries who do not use long-waves (LF) for broadcasting have in recent years issued experimental LF permits for amateurs. In *Amateur Radio* (April 1993) John Adcock, VK3ACA, (with LF experimental callsign AX3T35) describes "The day we crossed the Tasman on Long Wave". In the past he has used about 100 Watts to a 'back-yard' antenna. On 196kHz, however, efficiency is very low with only about 0.2W radiated. Nevertheless with this set-up at Oak Park, Victoria, his signals have been heard all over Victoria, Adelaide, Hobart and parts of New South Wales in daylight and as far away as Brisbane at night.

His latest exploit, using the rather more efficient 1.8MHz antenna of VK3BDJ at Gordon, Victoria, was heard in New Zealand across the Tasman Sea (roughly about 1200 miles) by ZL3PN, ZL4MD and ZL2CA although atmospheric noise was fairly bad. 3.5MHz was used for call-back. The antenna at VK3BDJ is built in typical broadcast antenna style comprising a triangular steel lattice galvanised mast 109ft high standing on a base insulator. It is guyed with three sets of guy wires radiating out in three directions at 120° around the mast, with eight levels of guys vertically. To improve the loading and capacitance of the antenna on 196kHz an extra 16ft vertical steel pole was added to the top, to which a top load of some 30 radial wires around 50ft long was also added. A counterpoise was constructed at the base consisting of a hexagon of wire with six radial spokes, with each span about 16m long suspended from eight poles about 3m high, and insulated with stick porcelain insulators: **Fig 3**. Even so it is probable that radiated power on 196kHz is less than 10 Watts.

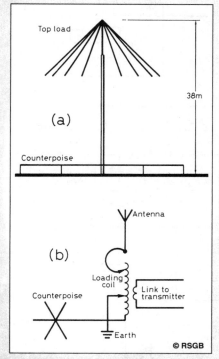

Fig 3: The antenna that put signals across the Tasman Sea from Australia to New Zealand on 196kHz with under 100 Watts (radiated power probably under 10 Watts) . . . . (a) Outline of antenna (guy wires not shown). (b) Antenna loading arrangement.

few military vehicles have comparable power to the maximum powers that can legally be used /M by amateurs.

David Sumner, K1ZZ, in his editorial (*QST* March 1993) introduces two articles that explore the question of using appropriate power for fixed rather than mobile operation. He writes: "There are occasions when the maximum legal power is necessary. There are also plenty of times when it isn't. Knowing the difference and acting accordingly has always been a part of responsible operating."

Carl D Gregory, K8CG, describes the use of automatic RF power control for AMTOR operation, drawing on power-adaptive systems developed in recent years for professional and military data transmission. At the receiving terminal, incoming signals are evaluated and the terminal automatically transmits back control signals that adjust the power of the distant station.

A long article 'Transmitter Power: What it is, What it does, and How to use it' by Diehl Martin, N5AQ, and David Newkirk, WJ1Z, stresses that excessive power is worse than wasted – it represents potential interference. As someone who usually runs an 813 power amplifier providing rather over 100W HF output on CW, I can recognise that at times, particularly on 3.5 and 7MHz, this is more than necessary – reflected in those S9 + 20dB reports. The answer for CW operation would seem to be a switch to cut power by an order of magnitude or so (I do in fact have a switch that turns off the screen voltage on the 813 and must remember to use it more often!). For SSB there is the problem that the linearity of an amplifier is optimum when correctly adjusted for its rated output.

An editorial in *Amateur Radio* (April 1993) by Ron Henderson, VK1RH, Federal President, 'Being a Good Neighbour' points out that while Australian licences, like those in the UK, have a power limit of 400W PEP, very few linears are available in Australia of that rating. He writes: "The most common is 1.2kW with some up to 2kW; three to five times the legal limit. It would be naive to think all of these are meticulously adjusted to 400W PEP. How natural the temptation must be to up the output as the sunspot number falls.

"In living with our neighbours we will all be faced at one time or another with the problem of RF interference . . . . if the neighbour's TV is a cheap import, fitted only with rabbit's ears (set-top antenna), the authorities will generally support us. But what if that TV has passed a stringent type standard? Now the laws of nuisance apply; the neighbour has as much right to receive clear TV as the amateur has to pursue his hobby . . . ."

A 14MHZ 50/120W VALVE AMPLIFIER

ONE DOES NOT TEND to associate the Japanese with valve equipment. But looking through *CQ ham radio* (Nr 2/93) my eye was caught by the diagrams for a grounded-grid triode amplifier by 7L10PH using one of the relatively ancient 809 directly heated triodes: **Fig 4**. If I have understood the article correctly (*CQ ham radio* has a curious mixture of Arabic figures and type numbers within masses of the impenetrable (to me) Japa-

nese kanji characters) the amplifier can provide some 120W output on SSB/CW and 50W on FSK/AM with 15W PEP drive. But, to my mind, the most interesting feature of this design is the use of a high-voltage-multiplication PSU in which some 800V HT is derived from a mains transformer with a secondary winding rated at 120V 0.8A and five power diodes plus some 350V electrolytics. With high-voltage transformers, even the 350-0-350V secondaries formerly widely used in audio-amplifiers, no longer readily available, and usually quite costly, voltage multipliers with silicon power diodes become increasingly attractive. For example, the late John Brown, G3EUR, showed *TT*, October 1989, p37) how a 15V + 15V transformer could be used to provide both heater and 150V HT supplies for a two-stage QRP transmitter based on the PCL84 triode-pentode valve still readily available: **Fig 5**.

The 7L10PH transmitter uses the tuned cathode approach in conjunction with heater chokes L1, L2 (100µH, 4A rating) which can involve some loss of filament voltage unless care is taken to check this carefully at the

valve socket. A two-part article on 'Grounded Grid Linears' by D Kooistra, PA0DKO, (*Electron*, February and March 1993) recalls an alternative approach which was described by Harold C Barber, W6GQK, and Robert I Sutherland, W6UOV, in 'High-Power Zero-Bias Grounded-Grid Linear' (*QST*, September 1961). This presented full constructional details of a 1kW (1500W PEP output) amplifier using the then new 3-400Z zero-bias triode: **Fig 6**.

The authors pointed out that the driving impedance of the 3-400Z is a nominal 122ohms: "Since this figure varies widely over the operating cycle, a high-C tuned cathode circuit, C1-L1, is employed to stabilize the load impedance as seen by the exciter. Filament voltage is applied to the tube via the coil of this circuit which is in the form of a coaxial winding having two sets of taps. One set of taps (S1B) is for establishing resonance in the various bands. Excitation is fed to the second set (S1A). The latter is set for minimum SWR on the coaxial line from the exciter (50ohms). The usual driving difficulties experienced with grounded-grid amplifi-

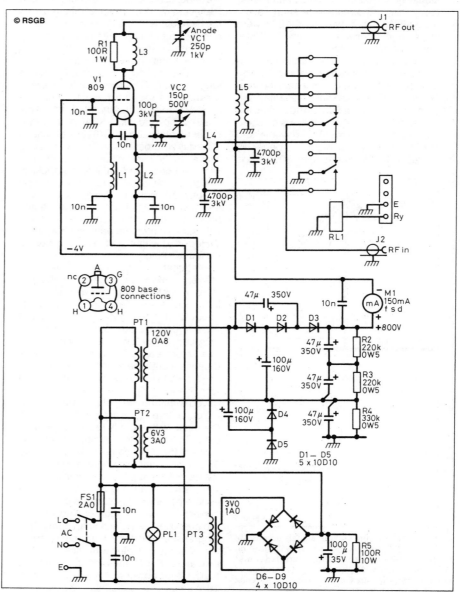

Fig 4: The 14MHz 50W grounded-grid 809 linear amplifier described by 7L10PH in 'CQ ham radio' No 2/93 showing the use of a voltage-multiplying PSU in conjunction with a 120V 0.8A transformer winding.

ers are entirely absent and no coupling problems have been found in switching from band to band. Increased power output, reduced intermodulation distortion, and ease of drive are gained when a tuned cathode circuit is used in preference to the old-fashioned untuned RF choke input circuit.

"The tuned cathode circuit is built as a discrete sub-assembly. The unit consists of the coaxial coil L, the tuning capacitor C1, the coupling capacitor C2, bypass capacitors C3 and C4, and band switch sections S1A and S1B. The coaxial coil is wound from a 61in length of standard $^3/_{16}$in soft copper tubing . . . . Before the coil is wound a length of No 12 Formvar, insulated copper wire is passed

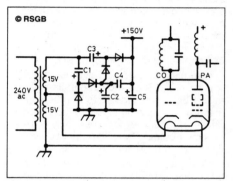

Fig 5: The late John Brown, G3EUR showed how a one-valve QRP transmitter could be powered from a 15V + 15V, 15-20W toroid or laminated core transformer. D1-D4 1N4003. C1-C4 50µF (100V). C5 25µF (200V).

through the tubing, leaving about three inches protruding from each end. Be sure you sand the ends of the tubing to a smooth, rounded edge to prevent marring or scraping the insulation of the wire during this operation. Wire with enamel insulation should not be used, since enamel is too soft and may be easily damaged. Next, the coil is wound around a 1⁵/₈th inch form (a section of water pipe may be used) making a coil of approximately 10.5 turns . . . ." The 1961 article provides detailed constructional information on what was clearly a high-performance linear, but my purpose here is primarily to give a reminder of the use of a coaxial-coil for the tuned cathode circuit.

FLAMMABLE ATMOSPHERES, EMC HAZARDS AND MOBILE RADIO

A RECENT IEE COLLOQUIUM "Operation of radio transmitters in proximity to flammable atmospheres" included a report by Brian Colwell (ERA Technology) on a study carried out on behalf of the DTI on 'The safe use of radio transmitters on road tankers and other vehicles'. This noted that "The benefits of use of mobile radio telephone systems, particularly by sales and distribution personnel, led to their proliferation. Similarly, the use of CB radios amongst lorry drivers proved a useful aid to the advance warning of traffic jams or other hazards so avoiding action could be taken."

It was foreseen that flammable atmospheres could occur at the tanker loading

depots and at petrol station forecourt areas, particularly if spillage occurred. Flammable gases and vapours which can be ignited by an electric spark include fire damp in mines, methane and petroleum spirit, ethylene and hydrogen.

Fortunately, there are few recorded explosions that can indisputably be ascribed to the operation of mobile or fixed transmitters, although much evidence of sparks induced across gaps in metal structures by high-power broadcast transmitters (see for example 'Sparks flying in Riyadh' TT, September 1984, p774).

Mr Colwell added: "For radio telephone equipment, the maximum effective radiated power that can be authorised [for professional or commercial applications] is 25 watts and their frequency bands range from 41MHz to 960MHz. In practice, each application is considered with due regard to range required, base transmitter antenna height etc, and to the possibility of interference to or from adjacent transmitters in terms of location and frequency. The net result . . . . is that transmitter powers, particularly for mobile or hand portable sets, are licensed generally for much lower effective radiated power than the maximum. The effective maximum is less than 10 watts ERP . . . . CB radio transmitters are currently authorised to operate on 27MHz (2W ERP) and 934MHz (25W) although early use on 27MHz was AM. Illegal use on 27MHz using a 100W power amplifier ('burner') was considered in the study . . . . Some concern had been expressed that an Army Land Rover

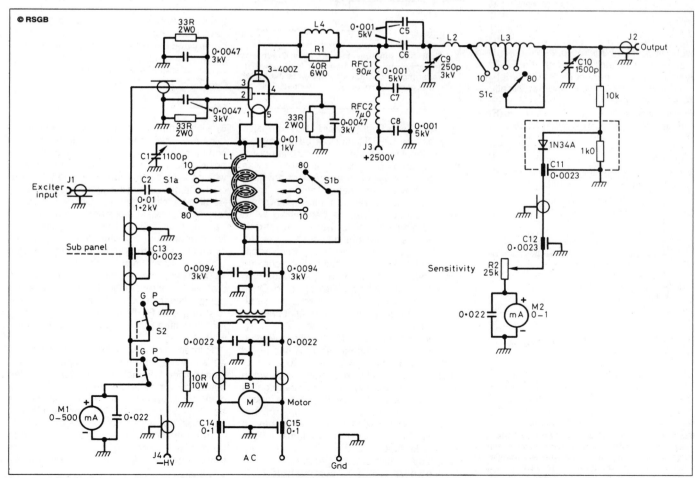

Fig 6: The 1kW zero-bias ground-grid linear described in 1961 by W6GQK and W6UOV showing the use of a coaxially-wound filament coil.

carrying operational radio equipment could transmit adjacent to a petrol station . . . . A range of amateur radio transmissions were considered up to 1240MHz at the authorised maximum transmission powers. This frequency was chosen as the highest at which a simple monopole/dipole antenna would be used . . . ."

While this particular study concentrated on transmitters likely to be used within tanker vehicles, it is clear that there are circumstances where even 25W transmitters could create a small but potentially hazardous spark. The ERA report found "The worst case situation observed was at a petroleum distribution terminal where an overhead gantry is used to top or bottom load a tanker lorry. These situations gave a URA (Unintended Radio Antenna) loop perimeter of 9.5m. For a transmitter onboard the same vehicle the antenna had a worst case separation distance of 1m from the nearest top loading tank inlet. Likewise, the separation distances from the URA were identified for the range of transmitter types and the fuel loading/unloading locations [not given at the IEE presentation]." **Fig 60** shows examples of how URAs with spark gaps can occur.

All this emphasises once again the advice given before in *TT* that mobile transmitters should never be used on petrol-station forecourts. Some instruction manuals provide such a warning but manuals may not be passed on to those buying equipment second-hand etc or such instructions may be disregarded as unimportant.

There is, however, another reason why one should be very careful when installing mobile transmitters of more than just a few watts output. Many modern cars are fitted with all sorts of microprocessor-controlled gizmos that cannot cope with the RF from typical amateur transceivers. Consider the sad story of W8JH as reported initially in *WorldRadio*, then *CQ Magazine* (May 1992) and most recently reprinted in *Break-in* (September 1992) by John Walker, ZL3IB:

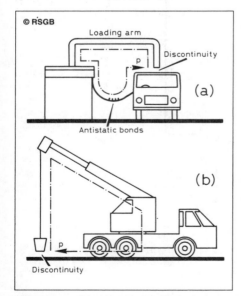

Fig 7: How a metal structure can form an 'unintended radio antenna (URA)' with a discontinuity forming a potential spark gap when a transmitter is located in the immediate neighbourhood. (a) Tanker loading facility. (b) Mobile crane. (ERA Technology).

MORE ON THE DIRECT-READING CAPACITANCE METERS

AN ERROR IN THE ORIGINAL *Break-in* circuit diagram for the direct-reading capacitance meter (Fig 2 of the April *TT*) although fairly self-evident by comparison with Fig 1, slipped through into *TT* and is corrected in the comments by John Wylde, ZL1ALS, published in the October 1992 *Break-in*: "Congratulations to ZL2AKW on his capacitance meter design – simple, practical and it works. With a little tweaking of the range resistors I had mine working quite accurately three days after receiving the September Break-in but with a few modifications due to my junk box not producing all the specified components: (1) I used a 7805 regulator with a couple of diodes in the E lead to produce the 6V. (2) 0-50µA meters cannot be bought in Whitianga on a Sunday and would be expensive anyway so I installed a modified crystal socket on the panel and plug in my multimeter switched to the 10mA scale. The socket is shunted with a 4k7 trimpot to adjust to 50µA FSD. (3) Instead of terminals for Cx I brought out short leads with small alligator (crocodile) clips. This ar-

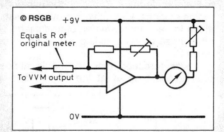

Fig 8: An arrangement used by Ken Green that not only permits the use of a less sensitive meter movement but also prevents the meter from being destroyed by an overload.

rangement works fine for all sizes and shapes of capacitors, even those with 0.25in leads.

"The circuit diagram contains a few minor errors – RA and RB for the 5µF scale should be 8.2M and 1M (not 8.2k and 1k). Also the text and circuit are at odds re the top range – 5µF or 10µF. I adjusted R4 to make S1 multiply by 20 giving me a 10µF range, others may choose to make it x10 and 5µF."

Ken H Green writes: "For the original direct-reading capacitance meter (Fig 1 of the April *TT*) you point out that it is necessary to avoid overloading the 50µA meter movement – how true! May I suggest a modification that would eliminate the problem while, at the same time, allowing the use of other less sensitive meters.

I was given an old AVO valve multimeter which uses a 30µA movement; its intermittent behaviour I traced to a burned out meter coil – puzzling since the balanced driver-amplifier was capable of only 40uA maximum output. One of the current shunts appeared to have been burnt too.

"A replacement meter was available as far as shape and size/type was concerned but had an FSD of 100µA. A local contact with younger fingers than mine swapped the meter scales and I turned it into a 30µA FSD meter with the aid of a bit of modern electronics magic – details submerged in the compost heap but something like **Fig 8**. I padded the meter out so that it gave FSD when connected across a 9V battery and then fed it from the main body via an op-amp current-to-voltage converter. Works like a dream and my previous meter is bomb-proof."

"W8JH found out the hard and expensive way that the 1992 Toyota Camry automobile will definitely not support any mobile operation with an output greater than 10W. It was confirmed via Toyota's hotline that anything over 10W would in a sense fry the car's onboard computer. In W8JH's case repairs came to $1,115 for which he was responsible. What is becoming evident is that our electronic marvels are sometimes a two-edged sword. What we like as features in a particular car and what makes us lean towards purchasing that model may also be at great odds with using that vehicle for mobile operation. Obviously, Toyota did not take into account in their design the [relatively few] potential sales to Amateurs.

"If you are interested in mobile operation (beyond the occasional use of a hand-held unit) scratch this model from your list of options. Use W8JH's experience to help when you select any new car. Specifically ask if there will be a problem if you operate a mobile rig. We can now add cars to computers and other home entertainment devices as having potential RF susceptibility problems. It does seem odd, though, that we, in a lawful manner, should represent the problem."

Five years ago, a *TT* item 'Vehicle EMC affects reliability and safety' (May 1988, pp347-

8) it was emphasised that the use of CMOS microprocessor-controlled systems in cars, combined with the increasing use of 'composites' such as fibreglass rather than metal, was causing car manufacturers to take seriously the question of immunity against strong RF fields, including those from nearby radio, television, radar stations and carphones. But I added that "it should not be forgotten that few manufacturers contemplate the possibility that a radio amateur may wish to install a high-power transmitter in the vehicle."

The Toyota incident would seem to confirm that while increasingly car electronics are being designed to make them less vulnerable to strong local RF fields, this holds good only for transmitter powers of less than about ten watts.

Remember this when installing one of those 40W models, or when contemplating really high power HF mobile operation. Sudden failure of, for example, electronic breaking could be extremely dangerous – as well as being costly to repair. Whether we like it or not, it is unrealistic to expect the vehicle manufacturers to provide immunity to transmitter powers significantly higher than those found in the cellular or PMR mobile services.

G3VA

FIGHTING ANTENNA CORROSION

IT IS SOME YEARS since *TT* tackled the very real problem of the corrosion of aluminium antenna elements including verticals, yet this remains a perennial source of poor performance as shown clearly in the three-page article 'Fighting Antenna Corrosion' (*QST*, April 1993) by Scott Roleson, KC7CJ. He describes how just six months after installing a trusty Butternut antenna in the dry climate of inland California it suddenly ceased to work – "one day it was fine; the next it wouldn't load properly."

Initially he suspected a broken connection but finding that substituting a dummy antenna gave correct loading, he realised that the problem was at the antenna: "As I dismantled the vertical I noticed a fine, white powder at each joint, corrosion had crept into every connection although on installation I had tightened each clamp and bolt securely."

KC7CJ describes the basic physics of corrosion, showing how metal tends to return to the natural corroded state of the original ore by such processes as bi-metallic corrosion where an electrolyte is present at a junction of dissimilar metals, particularly where these are well separated in the galvanic series: see **Table 1.**

He writes: "Tin and gold are metals that illustrate how troublesome bimetallic corrosion can be. Both metals are commonly used to coat electrical connectors yet are galvanically remote. Sometimes, connectors with pins coated with these metals are inadvertently attached to each other. If the contact pressure is insufficient to keep out moisture, or if the metals are used in an environment where electrolyte forms easily, the tin surface oxidizes. I've seen this happen in personal computers, where plug-in cards with gold-plated edge connectors are plugged into tin-plated motherboard connectors. The resulting problems are usually intermittent and difficult to localize. Simply removing a card and reinserting it may remove enough oxide that the problem disappears – temporarily at least. After a while the oxide reforms and the problem returns."

KC7CJ continues: "Making and keeping good electrical connections in antennas is really simple – as long as you pay attention to the basics. The best way is to start with galvanically compatible materials, then clean all connections well before assembly. To make sure these connections stay good, seal all contact points so moisture can't enter the joint to form an electrolyte and start corrosion. In my case, I had done the first, but not the second."

In respect of mating surfaces, electrical contacts occur between microscopic bumps and points where the metals meet. Joint impedance is proportional to the number of points in contact. KC7CJ writes: "A smooth, clean surface ensures that there will be lots of these points and little between them to get in the way. For antennas, I've found it's best to first buff all joining parts with steel wool, emery cloth or a wire brush, then with a nylon scouring pad . . . . For metal tubing, it's important not to forget to clean the inside surfaces of telescoping parts. I wrap steel wool around a pencil or form it into a pencil-

Pat Hawker's
Technical Topics

like shape so I can get to the tubing's inside surface. Finally, I use a clean rag to wipe off any powdered metal and oxide. I do my best to refrain from touching the mating surfaces and contaminating them with body oils. (Using cotton gloves during antenna assembly is a good idea).

"Pressure between mating surfaces is important. Oxides start to form immediately, so there must be enough pressure to break through the oxide layer. Furthermore, contact pressures must be high enough to ensure joints are stable and tight during normal flexing. A phenomenon called fretting corrosion occurs when a connection is repeatedly opened and closed. The closure breaks through a fresh surface oxide, so fresh metal is in contact with fresh metal. However, when the contact opens, this fresh metal is again subject to oxidation. With time, the oxidation builds up. Eventually, the contact pressure isn't enough to break through the oxide layer and the connection fails."

In a section on minimizing corrosion, KC7CJ advises the use of parts that are galvanically similar and assembled for minimum galvanic differences. Aluminium and copper are not very compatible but connection of copper wires to aluminium antenna elements is often necessary. This problem can be minimized by tinning or solder-plating the copper wire, forming a gas-tight seal between the copper and plating. Then use stainless-steel hardware to secure the connection since stainless steel is galvanically quite close to both tin and aluminium, and won't rust like other steel hardware. Use a stainless-steel washer between an aluminium surface and a tinned wire, or lug, connected to it. This should help the joint last longer if (or when) an electrolyte gets into the joint.

He adds that another way to form a gas-tight seal with hardware is to use star washers

```
"Anodic End"
Magnesium
Zinc
Aluminium
Mild steel
Iron
50-50 lead/tin solder
Stainless steel (US type 304 & 316)
Tin
Nickel (active)
Brass
Aluminium-bronze
Copper
Nickel (passive)
Silver
Gold
"Cathodic End"

Source: KC7CJ, QST (April 1993)
```

Table 1: Relative galvanic series in sea water

which break through oxides and cut into the mating surfaces under the pressure of the screw and nut used to hold them in place, so that fresh metal is in contact with fresh metal. This technique works best for hardware that is to go on once, or at most, only a few times since repeated assembly can damage a surface, possibly providing a path for moisture to enter the joint.

Special pastes, fluids, and other joint compounds help seal joints and inhibit electrolyte action (discussed in detail in 'Fluids vanquish intermittent contacts' by S Leibson in *EDN*, March 14, 1991, pp59-64). KC7CJ writes: "These compounds are squeezed away from the microscopic points of contact by mating pressure, but fill in around the points of contact to inhibit air and moisture passage. For aluminium antennas, I use pastes available for aluminium electrical wiring available [in the USA] at electrical-supply houses, hardware stores and building-supply outlets. A few antenna manufacturers provide an anti-oxidant compound with their antennas. The joint compound can be spread with a cotton-tipped applicator. Wire-brushing the surface after compound application helps ensure all quickly formed oxide is broken down and prevents a new layer from forming. Tooth-brush-size wire brushes are available from hardware stores.

"Joint compounds, unfortunately, don't last forever. they harden and crack, or with time and temperature, simply flow away from joints. For this reason, some sort of finishing barrier or overcoat is needed, such as plastic tape, paint, or silicon rubber sealant (bathtub caulking). Choose a material that is flexible and resistant to ultraviolet light. Many paints and plastic tapes eventually harden and become brittle from exposure to UV light. Normal antenna flexing in the wind cracks them, and moisture seeps in through these cracks. This argues for regular maintenance. Plastic tape is easy to remove and replace. If you use paint, use a bright colour, red or yellow. If you need to disassemble a joint for cleaning, the bright colour is easier to see so you can tell if you've removed it all."

SOLAR POWER AND RENEWABLE ENERGY

FOR MANY YEARS it has been easier to generate RF power than the AC or DC electric power needed to run a transceiver. Fortunately, most of us can draw upon the 240V AC mains supply power system, either directly or for keeping batteries charged. For mobile operation, the car electrics system normally provides all that is required. Handhelds are designed to be sufficiently low in power consumption to permit operation from batteries – preferably rechargeable nicads or compact lead-acid batteries. Disposable batteries have an energy cost some hundreds of times that of mains supplies. But for field events or for DXpeditions to remote areas, the question of suitable power generation looms large, as indeed it did for wartime clandestine and paramilitary radio links.

At that time many different forms of transportable electricity-generating and charging systems were pressed into use more or less successfully. They included conventional mains chargers, and both hand and pedal-chargers. Amongst these was the ingenious 'beach chair' devised by the late John Brown, G3EUR – a tubular-metal 'deck' chair in which the user pedalled a generator with the chair capable of being folded up to form a backpack.

Then there were small dynamos that could be attached to the back wheel of a jacked-up bicycle, thermo-electric (1A) chargers using arrays of about 350 chromium-constantan cells heated in a charcoal, wood or gas fire, wind generators on collapsible 10ft poles, and 6V or 12V DC petrol-electric generators (eg 'Tiny Tim'). There was even a steam generator with a boiler suspended over a brazier – this had a flexible steam tube to a small steam engine (total weight about 70lb) which could charge a 6V battery at about 4A, again using a wood or charcoal fire.

At least some of the power needed to be at HT, or preferably 220 or 110VAC, to permit the use of conventional mains-powered transmitters/receivers. Most vehicle batteries of that era were 6V rather than the now universal 12V (or 24V for heavy vehicles and aircraft). For low-power loads, mechanical vibrator units were available which could have efficiencies of up to 90%. For larger loads, rotary convertors such as the series of American Dynamotors were used. 110V or 220VAC could be generated directly with petrol-electric generators (eg American ONAN) of about 150W to 2kW rating and these were used for signals vehicles. Some 150W units, for example, were used in Norway during the war, at sites where the give-away noise was unlikely to draw unwanted attention.

All such approaches have continued to be developed and improved during the post-war period and a pedal/hand generator capable of providing some 40W at 110VAC was, for example, part of the Mark 123 kit. However, the arrival of the low-voltage solid-state era and, in particular, the development of silicon solar (photovoltaic) cells have had a major impact. Battery technology has also progressed, although there is still room for improvement. Many of the developments have so far made less impact than expected and the main motivation in this field remains the electric car. For DC-DC or DC-AC conversion, solid-state invertors have replaced mechanical systems such as vibrator units and rotary converters, although the AC output tends to be either square-wave or 'stepped AC', waveforms which can cause problems with some equipment. Near sine-wave invertors are available but are more complex and cost more.

Solar energy offers great promise for the two-billion or so people – 70% of the population of the developing world – who remain without mains electricity. An article 'Sunshine for light in the night' in *Nature* (22 April 1993) by authors associated with the Solar Electric Light Fund and United Nations Development Programmes emphasises that many rural regions remain hungry for electricity to meet even the most rudimentary of needs. For these, small solar-power systems (SSPS) are proving an appropriate technology.

To quote *Nature*'s explanation of photovoltaic-based small solar-power systems (SSPS): "Solar cells convert light to direct-current electricity. Light impinging on single crystal or polycrystalline silicon wafers gener-

SIMPLE 3.5MHZ DIRECT-CONVERSION RECEIVER

NIC HAMILTON, G4TXG, has underlined that considerable care needs to be taken in the design and construction of direct-conversion receivers to obtain a performance, on the higher frequency bands, truly rivalling that from a well-designed superhet ('Improving direct conversion receiver design' *RadCom*, April 1991, pp39-44). This is particularly true in connection with keeping the local oscillator under control and reducing the effects of LO leakage, AM breakthrough, hum pick-up and microphony. However, on the lower frequencies such as the 3.5MHz band, reasonably satisfactory performance can usually be achieved with simple, easily-constructed designs.

Jeffrey Harrison in the 'Circuit & Design Ideas' feature of *Electronics Australia*, May 1993, p60, presents a simple design based on the ubiquitous NE602 chip as balanced mixer (product detector) and oscillator. A 50Ω input is stepped up to match the IC input by a balun transformer (2 turns primary, 10 turns secondary wound on toroid balun core). As shown in **Fig 1**, the input circuit is untuned on the presumption that with a double balanced mixer, strong even-harmonic signals will be rejected. However (in the absence of an ATU to provide the 50Ω line and act as a band-pass filter) strong signals on odd harmonic frequencies could prove troublesome.

Jeffrey Harrison notes that in these circumstances a single or, preferably, dou-

ble tuned circuit should be connected across the input to the IC pins 1,2 (see for example the receiver input shown later, in the *TT* item on the 3.5MHz DSB transceiver).

The local oscillator uses the Colpitts arrangement tuning from about 3.3 to 3.8MHz. Pins 6 and 7 of the NE602 provide connections to the base and emitter of an internally biased transistor. For a stable fixed-channel stand-by receiver a crystal could be substituted for the tuned circuit.

The NE602 provides a gain of the order of 18dB with a balanced output across pins 4 and 5 which is amplified by a differential audio amplifier (741 op-amp) with a voltage gain of up to 500. This is followed by an emitter-follower to drive 32Ω headphones to ample volume. The 47nF capacitor across the NE602 output provides a crude low-pass filter (a sharper, narrower filter would be preferably for CW reception). With the high audio gain, the leads in the audio amplifier, including those to the gain control, should be kept as short as possible in order to prevent oscillation.

The 78L05 and red LED provide a regulated supply of about 7V, below the NE602's 8V maximum and ensures that pins 4 and 5 are biased to approximately half of the supply voltage. The power supply should be from 9 to 15V and must be well filtered because of the high audio gain.

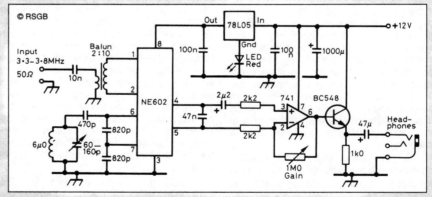

Fig 1: Simple 3.5MHz D-C receiver based on the NE602 chip as described by Jeffrey Harrison in 'Circuit & Design Ideas', *Electronics Australia*, May 1993.

ates hole-electron pairs which are separated at a p-n junction fabricated into the wafer. The separation of charge by the junction creates a potential difference that produces a current in an external circuit. The current is used to charge a battery which, on demand, provides power for lights and other appliances. Individual solar cells are encapsulated and fabricated into multicell units, the solar panels.

"A standard roof or pole-mounted solar module, with typically 36 10cm diameter solar cells, charging a car lead-acid battery can provide enough power for both household fluorescent lighting and a radio and television set. For example, in the tropics, the average daily insolation will often exceed 5kWh per square metre. With a 40Wp solar module (a

module producing 40 Watts at noon under direct sunlight), this insolation will produce enough electricity for three fluorescent lights each operating for three hours, as well as three hours of radio and three hours of television. The solar modules are generally mounted on roof tops or on poles which allow them to be turned to maximize daily charge near the Equator and to keep them cool. Car battery storage provides up to five days of power supply during overcast periods . . . . charge indicators and charge-discharge controllers are the key to long battery life . . . . High-efficiency fluorescent DC light fixtures using electro-polished aluminium reflectors and invertor ballasts minimize lighting power requirements with, for example, one 9-Watt

PROTRACTOR DIALS

ANOTHER OF THOSE USEFUL IDEAS that have turned up before in *TT*, but many years ago, re-emerges in a note from J D Bolton, G4XPP, who has been busy constructing an ATU with secure coil taps. He writes: "Once the ATU has been constructed with secure coil taps (see *TT*, May 1993, p57, Fig 10) there remains the problem of ensuring accurate settings of the variable capacitor(s) with band/frequency changes in order to reduce tune-up time to a minimum. Several ideas were tried without success. But then acting on a suggestion from G0PXQ the solution proved astonishingly simple.

"Buy a 360°, 100mm diameter, transparent plastic school protractor (available from W H Smith book shops). After removing the centre of the protractor, glue a piece of white card to its back. After giving time for the glue to set firmly, place the protractor over the centre spindle of the tuning capacitor. I placed it with the 0°

point on the left of the centre spindle which in my case is at the right-hand side of the ATU. After lining it up carefully with the marks I had made for drilling the spindle hole, I marked off the 0, 90, 180 and 270° points and then applied glue to the back.

"The result (**Fig 2**) is an attractive finished look and an extremely accurate means of precise setting before tune up. Either 180° or 360° protractors can be used. Apart from my home-brew ATU for long-wire antennas, G0PXQ and I have used this approach for TM1000 and SPC3000D ATUs. Provided that settings for the various frequencies are carefully noted the first time they are used, then next time I find that I do not need to tune up for more than a second or two just to check that the VSWR is near unity."

I must admit that I still have, and use, at least one of those large knobs calibrated 0-180° that were popular for broadcast receivers in the early 1920s. Even when worse for wear, such a knob can be touched-up using white Tipp-Ex fluid. Many will recall the Eddystone 0-180° dial plates used for many years with their early slow-motion drives.

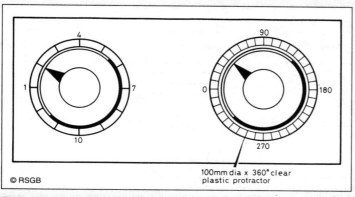

Fig 2: Accurate setting of G4XPP's ATU is made easy by the use of a plastic protractor as a dial plate.

fluorescent tube producing as much light as a 50-Watt AC incandescent bulb."

The *Nature* article reports that about 100,000 families, farms and businesses in the developing world are currently using solar-powered residential electric lighting and communications systems which currently cost from US\$350-750 including shipping, tariffs

and installations and have projected lifetimes of some 20 years.

"Typically, nearly 60% of the initial cost is in the solar module itself, another 25% or so in the battery and lights, 10% in wiring and circuitry and 5% in installation costs. (However, the recurrent cost of battery replacement can be higher than the original cost of

the module over its 20-year life span.)" This presupposes that locally made car batteries with thick plates should last more than five years. With an SSPS the sun supplies the resulting electric power for free.

One of the big challenges, the authors stress, is to develop better methods of energy storage that would make possible higher power systems: "New methods of regulating both charging and discharging promise to lengthen battery life. Imported, long-life, deep-discharge batteries would be more desirable, but at present they are too expensive for most rural households. More efficient capacitive storage batteries will also be useful if the cost can be kept low. Eventually, it may be that other power-storage methods such as fly-wheel energy accumulators, pumped storage or solar-hydrogen energy systems will provide alternatives to batteries. But – and it cannot be over-emphasized – cost is the crucial consideration. Unless the improvement can be manufactured cheaply and in high volume, the people most in need of them will not be able to afford them . . . . but the success of SSPSs in the field shows that this technology works as it is."

It is clear that the growing use of relatively low-cost SSPS systems offers a significant improvement in the quality of life in tropical developing countries, including Zimbabwe, Sri Lanka, Kenya and the Dominican Republic. It also opens the way for more amateur radio activity in such regions, although clearly the prime need is for providing thin-line telecommunications and lighting in the villages. Even in the UK, where solar energy is significantly lower than in more sunny climes, solar cells can still provide an effective method of keeping lead-acid batteries charged during portable or field operation, although power for permanent installations, particularly in coastal or hill sites, may need to be supplemented by a wind generator.

TT, January 1983 page 44, described an experimental IBA installation at Bossiney on the Cornish coast where for a few years a four-channel UHF television relay station was run from 36 large lead-acid batteries with a total storage capacity of about 28kWh kept charged by an array of 24 solar panels, plus a wind generator. The 864 photovoltaic silicon cells provided an output of about 780W in peak sunlight, supported by a wind generator having an output of some 150W at a wind-speed of 7m/s: **Fig 3**.

In practice, after a few years, this experimental installation was replaced by the conventional mains supply mainly because it was ·found that on-site maintenance – with battery and wind-generator problems – was rather heavy. Thus the saving on bringing a mains supply to remote sites (which can cost many thousands of pounds) would seldom be really justified.

Last January at an IEE colloquium, Peter Best of British Telecom presented a paper 'Renewable energy supplies for radio systems serving rural customers'. He defined 'renewable energy sources' as those which do not consume a fuel, and included wind, solar, tidal and certain natural thermal sources. He noted that there are many different small wind turbines available on the market but that it is necessary to consider not just the (claimed) power output for the generator (quoted as a

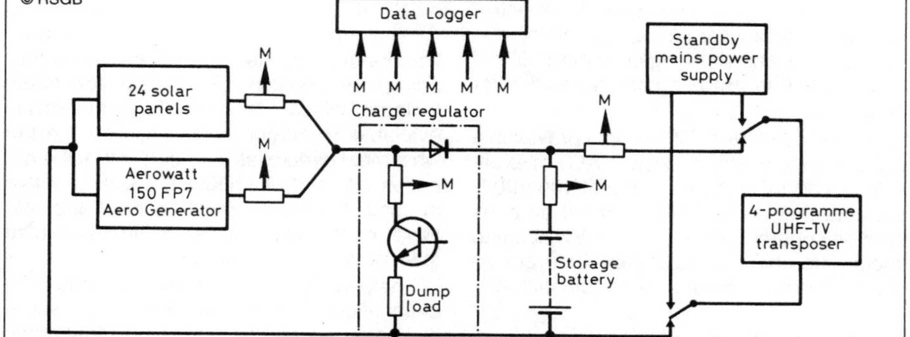

Fig 3: The experimental natural energy system used by the former IBA in the early 1980s to power a four-channel very low-power local television relay station at Bossiney on the north Cornish coast. The solar panels provided a maximum output of almost 800W in peak sunlight and were supported by the output from a 150W (7m/s) wind generator.

function of wind speed) but also its ability (ie mechanical strength) to withstand strong winds.

He pointed out that water power comes in many guises, including small-scale hydroelectric systems (such as the so-called 'Micro-hydro-turbine') which could be built in or around a stream or small river [but note there are strict regulations in the UK covering taking or diverting water from streams and rivers – *G3VA*]. Wave-powered or tidal-powered generators are also alternative sources of water power: "The biggest advantage of the micro-hydro-turbine is that it is the most predictable of renewable energy sources; most streams do not normally dry up . . . . however, water powered installations will inevitably require some degree of civil engineering, and each installation will be totally site specific, not only in terms of the power generated, but also in terms of the design of the installation."

Peter Best revealed that BT has used solar powered equipment for about 18 years, with three installations powering single-channel radio sets, but each representing an average power consumption of less than one Watt, requiring only a modest sized solar panel which float charges a small battery. However in 1992 a more ambitious hybrid wind-and-solar-system was installed in Norfolk for a 2GHz radio system which has a stand-by consumption of about 40 watts. During the planning of this project, it was found that a solar-only system would cost over 30% more than a hybrid system. As a further precaution, to ensure that the system would not go down during a protracted period of overcast weather with no wind such as can occur in coastal areas subject to sea mists, an aluminium-air fuel cell can be used to provide a high power output to recharge the batteries and then be switched off once they are fully charged.

In its regular 'Lab Notes' feature, *QST* (April 1993) concentrates on the provision of power for Field Day operation noting that the American Field Day rules include bonus points when a specific number of contacts have been powered from natural energy sources. It is noted that a typical 100W HF transceiver may represent a peak load on transmit of some 400 Watts and that power will also usually be required for a lamp (60W), a laptop computer (40W) and a hefty (outdoor) soldering iron say 100W, and possibly other appliances. These could well add up to a total peak load of some 600-800W, at an average Field Day station.

QST stresses that while conventional vehicle batteries are capable of providing the extremely high currents over short periods needed by starter motors, they are not intended for deep discharge applications, and will not tolerate many such cycles: "A deep-discharge lead-acid battery is better suited. It can be discharged repeatedly without damage, and will maintain full output voltage over much of its discharge cycle. They are not much more expensive than regular automobile batteries and are designed to deliver moderate current for long periods of time."

While it is possible to operate a 100W station from lead-acid batteries without continuous float-charging this represents a heavy drain. The battery is unlikely to last more than a few hours before it needs recharging – less if cold (cold batteries can lose up to 70% of

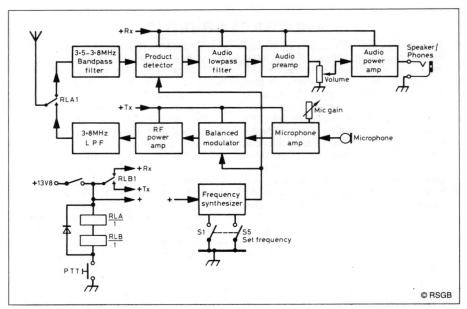

Fig 4: Block diagram of the low-cost 3.5MHz DSB channelised transceiver – a constructional project by VK2DOB in *Electronics Australia* (Part 1, May 1993).

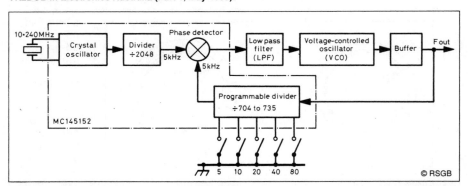

Fig 5: Block diagram of the frequency synthesizer in which five toggle switches are used as an economical way of setting the operating frequency in incremental steps of 5kHz. Based on the use of a Motorola MC145152 chip.

their normal capacity). A typical deep discharge battery may have 1000Wh capacity but equipment is unlikely to function when the voltage drops below about 12V.

It is noted that solar panels with polarity protection diode as marketed in the USA can deliver 15-18V at 600-1500mA in full sunlight and will not damage a deep-cycle lead acid battery. More care may be needed with nicads and medium-capacity gelled-electrolyte lead-acid (1Ah to 50Ah) batteries which need regulated charging. If a gel-cell is charged too rapidly, bubbles can develop in the electrolyte, permanently damaging the battery. It is advisable to limit charging current to 10% of output rating in Ah as common practice for nicad cells.

DC-AC converters ('invertors') providing a square-wave or stepped-wave AC are available or can be built for ratings of 100-400W but note that some motors cannot be powered by square-waves, and it is advisable to check beforehand whether the system generates RF noise or overheats on full output.

A CHANNELISED 3.5MHZ DSB TRANSCEIVER

THE MAY 1993 ISSUE of *Electronics Australia* also presents the first of a two-part construction project 'A low cost 80m DSB

transceiver' by Leon Williams, VK2DOB of which the introductory notes seem pertinent:

"One of the great advantages of an amateur radio licence is that it allows amateurs to build and operate their own transmitters and receivers. The last couple of decades, however, has seen the proliferation of 'black boxes' resulting in a rapid decline in homebrewing of station equipment. The satisfaction of finding all the bits and pieces and putting them together, and the thrill of that first contact is something that a lot of new amateurs unfortunately no longer experience.

"The arguments against home construction generally relate to the average amateur being unable to construct transceivers equal to those which are currently commercially available. This is generally true, of course, but what most people fail to realise is that it is not necessary to have a $3000 transceiver with a hundred knobs, computer control and 400 Watts output power to talk to friends across town or across the country."

The *EA* project covers the construction of a channelised, double-sideband, suppressed-carrier transceiver with 8W PEP output with a simple frequency synthesizer giving 5kHz steps between 3525kHz and 3675kHz (optionally with an extra switch above 3675kHz): see the block outline in **Fig 4**. No provision appears to be made for CW operation for

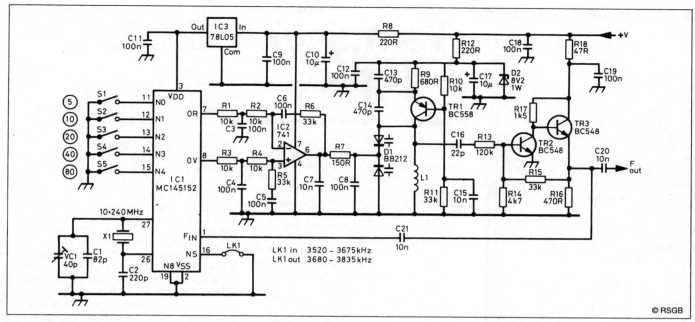

Fig 6: Circuit diagram of the frequency synthesizer. Link LK1 sets the tuning range.

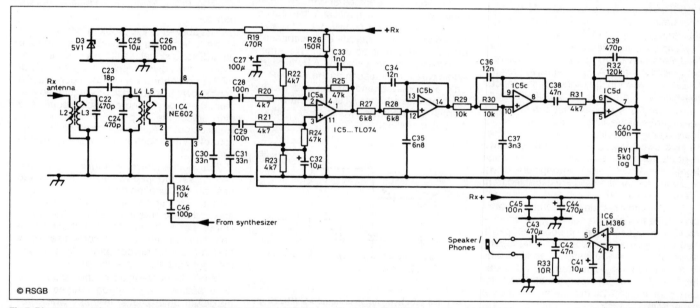

Fig 7: Direct-conversion receiver section of the 3.5MHz low-cost DSB transceiver uses three ICs, apart from the joint receiver/transmitter frequency synthesizer.

which the 5kHz steps would preclude netting.

A most unusual feature of the design is the use of a PLL (phase-locked loop) frequency synthesizer with 5kHz increments to eliminate the need to build a stable VFO suitable for suppressed carrier operation. It is pointed out that, over the years, there have been many designs for QRP transceivers published but with a few odd exceptions they have all been for CW operation: "This design fills the need for a simple voice transceiver that should provide a lot of satisfaction for those who build and operate it."

Figs 5 and 6 show the synthesizer which is set by panel switches marked 5, 10, 20, 40 and 80. With all switches off, the output is at 3525kHz but, for example, with the 5 switch off, the 10 on, the 20 and 40 off and the 80 on, the output would be 3610kHz. The direct-conversion receiver incorporates a bandpass input filter: **Fig 7**. The transmitter delivers about 7W PEP from a IRF511 power FET.

The 20mW output from the synthesizer is amplified with a BC548, the carrier suppressed in a balanced modulator (2 x IN4148 diodes), a further BC548 and then a BD139 power bipolar providing voltage drive to the IRF511.

Clearly this is not a rig with the flexibility or performance of the black-boxes but is presented by *EA* with the recommendation: "Discover the thrill of talking to other radio amateurs with a transceiver you built yourself. Using a PLL frequency synthesizer for drift-free operation, this simple transceiver for 80m is compact, inexpensive and easy to build. It also operates from 13.8V DC making it suitable for portable operation if desired."

HERE AND THERE

ROBERT HAWES (Tel: 081 808 2838), editor of the Bulletin of the British Vintage Wireless Society, is currently restoring one of the compact MCR1 wartime receivers designed by the late G3EUR, destined for the Vintage

Wireless Museum in West Dulwich, but it is minus four of its coil assemblies and lacks the mains unit. He would like to hear from anyone who might have these parts to spare. He is also seeking a Huntley & Palmer biscuit tin of the period since many of the sets were parachuted into occupied territory in these. The Vintage Wireless Museum is open by appointment (telephone first, 081 670 3667) and has gained world-wide recognition for its remarkable collection of broadcast receivers etc. It would be a fitting resting place for a fully restored MCR1.   *G3VA*

HF SINGLE COIL 'Z-MATCH' ATU

THE GI2FHN DUAL-LOOP indoor antenna (*TT*, February) made use of the dual-tuning technique long popularised by the Z-match ATU. This technique stemmed from its use in the early 1950s in transmitters and exciters as a means of avoiding the complications of band-switching. In its usual configuration it uses two coils and a ganged tuning capacitor. A useful feature of the Z-match ATU is that it simplifies the provision of a balanced output suitable for open-wire or 300Ω feeders, increasingly popular as a means of providing a multiband antenna covering WARC and traditional HF bands.

In the March 1992 issue of *Break-in*, T J Seed, ZL3QQ, showed that theoretically a single-coil Z-match tuner should be possible, but did not present a practical design. However, a number of prototype units were built by Ron Cook, VK3AFW, and Ron Fisher, VK3OM, who write the monthly 'Random Radiators' column in the Australian *Amateur Radio*. These have been examined and some further suggestions made by Lloyd Butler, VK5BR, who is soon to present in *AR* detailed information on this form of ATU, including a design covering 1.8 to 21MHz.

Meanwhile the February 1993 'Random Radiators' provides practical information on a single-coil Z-match ATU covering approx 3.5 to 30MHz although the range of impedances to which it will match is not specified: **Fig 1**.

The two Rons suggest that one of the big advantages of the single coil Z-match is that there is only one output link, and this does not require switching. There are now only two controls (tune and load) to cover the full range from 3.5 to 30MHz. The following component and constructional details are extracted from 'Random Radiators'.

For use with a standard 100 watt HF transceiver, the two-gang variable capacitor has a maximum capacitance of about 350pF "a 1950s style broadcast receiver tuning capacitor is ideal". For 400 watts a capacitor with wider plate spacing is needed. For 100 watts, the 20-350pF (or so) input variable capacitor can also be one of the old-style receiver capacitors.

An early version had the output coupling coil wound directly over the earthy end of the main coil. It was later discovered, however, that rather better results including a wider matching range could be achieved by winding the output link on a short section of plastic pipe slipped over the earthy end of the main coil.

The coil can be wound on a scrap piece of plastic water pipe with an inside diameter of 50mm and outside diameter of 53mm. If the coupling coil is wound separately use another piece of plastic water pipe with an inside diameter of about 60-65mm. Length of the main coil is about 100mm, and about 55mm for the coupling coil. Wind the coils with 14-18SWG tinned copper wire. The main coil requires 14 turns spaced over 80mm:

"Winding turns on to plastic water pipe is not as easy as it looks. First wind the coil on to a smaller former about 40mm in diameter. When you remove it, it will spring out to about the required diameter. Secure the top and bottom of the winding through holes drilled

through the former and run some Araldite down the winding in a couple of places to hold the wire in place. If you want to experiment with the tap positions, cut a slot in the former about 50mm long and 10mm wide but otherwise we suggest you leave this out."

Vernier drives are used on the capacitors three terminals and an SO-239 coax socket are the only other components. The Australian prototypes were built on a wooden baseboard and Masonite (fibre board) front panel, although a metal cabinet would avoid the slight 'hand capacity' effect of wooden construction.

"Layout is quite straightforward but keep connections between coil and the two-gang capacitor as short as practical. While the unit will be earthed via the coax to the transceiver, we recommend a separate earth connection to your usual station earth point. This is more important if you are using the ATU to feed a single wire antenna such as the W3EDP . . . . It's a good weekend project and you will finish up with a better ATU than many commercial units costing two or three hundred Australian dollars."

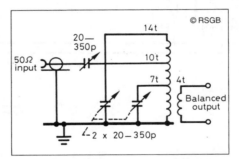

Fig 1: The prototype *Amateur Radio* **3-30MHz single-coil Z-match ATU.**

LINEAR AMPLIFIER TUNING AND SUPPLY REGULATION

MIKE HALL, G3USC, noted the brief reference in the June *TT* to tuning up valved SSB amplifiers in the general comment on reducing power when this is appropriate: "For SSB there is the problem that the linearity of an amplifier is optimum when correctly adjusted for its rated output."

G3USC writes: "Nothing wrong with this of course, but it does assume that the power supply feeding the amplifier has perfect regulation. In the real world, the supply regulation is usually far from perfect, and I believe that this oft-quoted statement is misleading in many practical situations. Making matters worse, the suggestion is often made that the loading should be increased beyond that which results in maximum output in order to improve the linearity. Contrary to this view, observations of my own G2DAF-type amplifier –

which I consider has a beefier power supply than many linear amplifiers are blessed with, indicate that this approach will result in excessive loading when the amplifier is driven with speech.

"The power supplies commonly used with linear power amplifiers have no regulation circuits as such and rely upon a bank of capacitors to provide good dynamic regulation. Under continuous carrier drive, however, as used for tuning up, the poor static regulation due to a scrimpy power transformer can cause the HT to drop by as much as 20% [or more if, for example, voltage-doubling circuits are used in the PSU – G3VA]. Adjusting the amplifier loading at its rated output, and then some more, will therefore result in heavier than optimum loading under syllabic conditions. This could be the reason why I hear so often on the air that 'my final amplifier valves went soft and I had to replace them'. Driven to the same peak voltage with SSB speech, the power supply capacitors had probably been happily crucifying these poor valves, which had been attempting to supply rather more signal current than they should. Maybe also this is one cause of so many diabolical signals that I hear on the HF bands.

"The answer to this problem is to abandon single-tone tuning in favour of a two-tone drive. Such a signal results in a much smaller drain on the power supply for a given output PEP. Beg or borrow a two-tone generator (I don't know if black boxes come equipped with them these days) and an oscilloscope, and then adjust the amplifier for its maximum linear output on each band, marking the positions of the load control to allow fast set-ability later.

"For routine tuning, it is then only necessary to set the load control to the marked position and tune the amplifier for maximum output. This can be carried out at low drive and will help to preserve the life of the valves. Unlike that of the tune control, there will be only a tiny difference in the correct setting of the load control between band edges, so one mark for each band is sufficient.

"While in possession of the 'scope, the drive settings can also be marked at the maximum drive points, ie those which just prevent flat-topping when driven with speech, or, if a powerful amplifier, the points which result in maximum legal output – 400V deflection between modulation crests in a 50Ω system. [High-power addicts may claim that the UK licence does not specify a maximum output power from the amplifier but only the RF power delivered to the radiating element, so that with a long feeder line or lossy ATU even a 1kW or more amplifier may be 'legal' – G3VA].

"My way of extracting a signal for the 'scope is simply a series 10k, 2W pick-off resistor mounted in my SWR meter at the feed end of a coax, the other end being terminated at the 'scope with 50Ω (a BNC T-piece and terminator plug). This results in a 46dB loss (x200) and provides a convenient level for the 'scope's input amplifier.

"Of course, the 'scope must have adequate bandwidth if the intention is to use it for power measurement, but if not, 10-20MHz bandwidth should be adequate for the HF bands. I do not advocate making a connection directly to the deflection plates of 'scopes as their HF compensation could be affected if the wiring is disturbed, and not least because there are some nasty voltages about.

"In place of a two-tone generator, it is sometimes suggested that either a further single audio tone be injected into the microphone socket, to be mixed with the transmitter's internal tone generator, or that a balanced modulator be temporarily unbalanced in order to allow some carrier leakthrough. With care, these approaches are feasible but, with either, it is all-too-easy for signal levels through the various stages to be higher than normal, and may cause distortion of the modulation envelope which no amount of final amplifier adjustment will remove. A two-tone generator having an output level comparable to a microphone is therefore by far the most convenient and best approach.

"A source for low-distortion two-tone generators, since I have not seen them advertised in *RadCom*, is Radio Data & Signalling Ltd, 5 Church Street, Crewkerne, Somerset TA18 7HR, priced at £30 plus VAT. They come in a small box and are powered internally by a PP3 battery. Adjustment of a trim pot supplies outputs of either one tone or the other, 1.0kHz and 1.6kHz approximately, or a mixture of the two. Normally, this pot would be used to compensate for the passband amplitude ripple in SSB filters, which otherwise has the effect of unbalancing the tones."

Details of two two-tone generators were given in *TT* in 1989. The first (*TT*, March 1989, pp35-36) was taken from the *Radio Handbook*, (22nd Edition, 1981, pp31-56) and is shown again in **Fig 2**. This generator provides a pair of linearly added sine waves with the second harmonic and intermodulation products at least 35dB below one tone. It is designed to operate from an internal 9V battery with no inductors or transformers that might induce mains hum.

Two Wien-bridge AF oscillators and associated buffer/mixer stages are based on a single LM324 quad IC. One generator is adjusted for 1000Hz, the other for 670Hz although the oscillators could be modified for other combinations. The original model was enclosed within an aluminium utility box (3.5 x 2 x 1.5in) with all components mounted on a perforated circuit board. The 9V battery was mounted below the board in a small clip. The unit provides either balanced or unbalanced output.

This prompted Jack Hollingworth, ZF1HJ, to offer (*TT*, September 1989, p39) an alternative 'quick and dirty' design using a readily available 'touch tone' generator IC (MC14410). He suggested that while the output waveforms may not be as clean as those from the *Radio Handbook* design, they should prove adequate for most purposes and the component count is much lower: **Fig 3**.

ZF1HJ wrote: "By temporarily jumpering the points indicated single tones of 697 or 1477Hz are generated, enabling the balance of the tone levels to be set using RV1. This is best done by observing the transceiver output power rather than by looking at the output level from the generator. Closing S1 produces simultaneous 697 and 1477Hz and also keys the transmitter. The output is adequate to drive most HF transceivers from the microphone input but a simple op-amp buffer

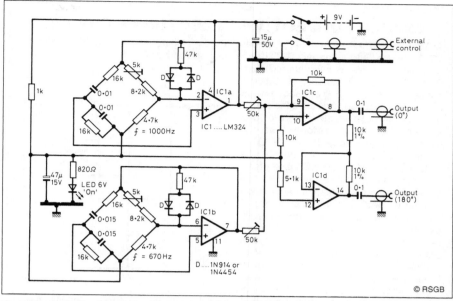

Fig 2: Circuit diagram of low distortion two-tone generator (source *Radio Handbook*).

amplifier could be added if desired. In some transceivers it is possible to replace the built-in tone generator by this two-tone unit, thus producing a two-tone drive whenever 'tune' is selected.

"The jumpers may be replaced by two sets of three diodes, with anodes to MC14410 pins 3, 4, 12 and 3, 13, 14 respectively, and with the cathodes of both sets commoned and grounded via single pole (normally-open) switches or push-buttons. This is more convenient if frequent adjustment of the balance control is required when using the unit with different transceivers."

"INVISIBLE" AND INDOOR ANTENNAS

A GROWING PROBLEM in many countries is the imposition by local authorities, landlords, estate managers, etc of restrictions on the erection of any type of outside antenna. Where such restrictions do not cover TV antennas, it is possible for amateurs to use these as, in effect, random length HF antennas with the outer-braid of the coaxial feeder cable connected to an ATU. Efficiency of such antennas is likely to be reduced by the proximity of the cable to the building but nevertheless they usually provide plenty of contacts.

A more efficient, and well-tested, technique is to use a fixed outdoor long-wire antenna using very thin enamelled wire (24 or 26 gauge) supported by nylon kite string. Such an antenna will be almost impossible to spot from a distance. Provided that it is between fixed supports that do not sway with the wind, such an antenna can last a reasonably long time, unless broken by an unwary bird for whom such antennas can be a hazard – and vice versa. Another echo from war-time clandestine radio is to use an aluminium-wire 'clothesline' or to conceal a wire in a cord clothesline or indeed in any rope that does not seem clearly out of place.

A more challenging situation arises when there are restrictions against any sort of antenna and no supports for an 'invisible' an-

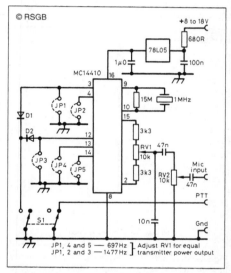

Fig 3: The simple 'quick and dirty' two-tone generator that ZF1HJ found adequate for checking SSB transceivers.

tenna. Albert Parker, N4AQ, in *QST*, May 1993, p65 tells how when he moved to a retirement community in Florida in 1991 he faced and overcame this difficulty. He writes: "I was eager to get on the air and began looking around for an inconspicuous antenna. It couldn't be just any antenna; I needed one with multiband capability.... but not one that would send the clear message (of traps) when displayed in public – "Ham Antenna Here!"

His solution was to purchase a Hustler 4-BTV four-band trap vertical antenna which he felt he could squeeze inside a 2-inch PVC pipe. At his first attempt he found the hose clamps on the traps were too large: "Knowing nothing about plumbing and even less about PVC pipes, I was very discouraged. I journeyed to another hardware store and found another 2-inch section of PVC and again tried to insert the trap. To my delight, it fitted perfectly!

"This was thin-wall PVC whereas the first one I had tried was heavy-duty PVC I

SIMPLE SUBJECTIVE SELECTIVITY FOR CW

ALMOST 20 YEARS AGO in *TT*, October 1973, the late 'Dud' Charman, G6CJ, first disclosed to amateurs his system (British Patent No 916,843, January 1958 taken out by EMI) of providing enhanced weak CW signal reception. This used the principle of slightly delaying the signal provided to one ear thus providing a form of pseudo-stereo. Later, with Richard Harris, G3OTK, he provided full construction details of a suitable 'stereocoder' (*RadCom*, September 1975). It was a fairly complex unit and since it provided a detectable advantage only on weak signals in the presence of QRM the original system never really caught on. However a number of simplified arrangements that can to some extent provide a stereo-like effect have appeared.

One such arrangement appears in 'Reflecties door PA0SE' (*Electron*, April 1993) ascribed to LA8AK, uses two standard AF pot cores tuned about 5Hz apart fed separately to the two earphones, and

thus providing a form of pseudo-stereo-like audio filter: **Fig 4**.

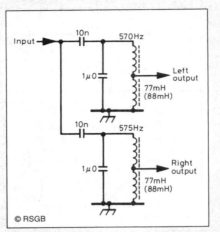

Fig 4. Simple form of CW 'stereo' audio filter described by LA8AK.

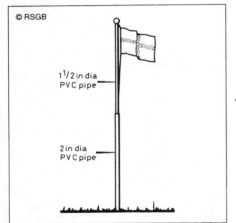

Fig 5: Sketch of N4AQ's disguised flagpole antenna in which a Hustler 4-BTV trap vertical is concealed in 2-inch PVC pipe as described in *QST* (May 1993).

purchased a 14ft section of thin-wall PVC along with a 12ft section of 1.5 inch PVC. I assembled the Hustler and cut the 2 inch PVC to fit over the lower part of the antenna, ending about two inches above the 20-metre trap. At that point I used a reducer to couple to the 1.5 inch PVC that I had slipped over the thinner top section that remained. When I finished, the entire antenna was enclosed in PVC! I had to leave off the 7MHz capacitance hat but later found no trouble operating on that band without it.

N4AQ drove a 1.5in thick wall pipe about 4ft into the ground to serve as base, trimming the length to keep the feed point about 4in above ground. A 5ft section of copper pipe was driven into the soil to serve as a ground connection (burying radial wires might have attracted attention). Buried 50Ω coax cable was used to feed the antenna with about 10 turns of coax cable near the base to act as an RF choke [probably not necessary with a buried cable – *G3VA*] and another 10 turns near the MFJ989C ATU. The antenna, **Fig 5**, loads his Collins KWM-380 transceiver well on the four bands from 7 to 28MHz providing

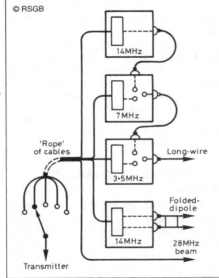

Fig 6: Layout of the feeder cables and switching relays used in 1950 by the late G2EC for his 'quick put up and take down antennas' on the roof of a seven-storey Mayfair building in 1950 after his earlier more visible antennas had been declared architecturally unsightly. Although he declared the antennas "fell far short of the ideal" they enabled him to obtain the leading G score of 130,442 points in the 1949 ARRL DX Contest.

good CW and SSB reports even if not really capable of competing with high-gain antennas.

N4AQ adds: "Finishing touches consisted of adding a used toilet-tank-float ball on top of the pole as an ornament, and a three-inch bolt near the top to mount a pulley. The base is hidden by flowers which I water often to enhance my ground conductivity! My neighbours see the Stars and Stripes flying proudly day after day, unaware that the flagpole is really a multiband antenna."

The use of aluminium flag-poles as vertical 'whip' antennas was a well-known arrangement for Diplomatic HF installations in embassies etc in the days when most countries

used HF for diplomatic traffic, but the idea of enclosing a multi-band trap vertical in a plastic pipe is new to me.

How one well-known amateur overcame similar problems while living in a sixth-floor flat in Mayfair was described over forty years ago by G2EC in 'Aerial Systems for the Flat Dweller!' (*RSGB Bulletin*, August 1950, pp55-56). G2EC was, of course, the unique call (the only British two-letter call with an 'E') of the late Major-General Eric Cole, CB, CBE, Director of Telecommunications at the War Office, 1956-61, and President of RSGB in 1961, who died last December at the age of 86 years. For reasons that will become obvious, no name was attached to his article.

In 1950 he wrote: "Some eighteen months ago, after much argument with higher authority, the aerial systems, erected with much painstaking effort on the roof of the building, were declared architecturally unsightly and 'were to be removed forthwith'. Courses open were thus: (a) Give up Amateur Radio; (b) Change location; (c) Use 'invisible' wires; or (d) Use systems which could be erected and dismantled at short notice for use during darkness hours or when censorious eyes were absent.

"The latter, course (d), was chosen and though it has been irritating to have to move out of a warm room and grope around a roof 80ft high in stygian blackness, sometimes in wind and snow, before being able to put the transmitter on the air, it has proved on the whole very well worth while."

The final system he adopted, based on a 'put up and take down quickly' principle included a long-wire (132ft) antenna for use on 3.5, 7 or 14MHz, end-fed by one of the three 72Ω coaxial cables through suitable impedance matches with matching unit remotely selectable from the operating position; a half-wave, three-wire folded dipole for 14MHz to cover the nulls of the long-wire; and a three-element rotary beam for 28MHz (the 21MHz band was not available until 1952). G2EC reported: "These were so arranged that after considerable practice, all three could be erected and put into operation from their normal completely prone positions lying flat on the roof of the building in a total time at night of eleven minutes away from the operating shack. Times were slightly quicker in daylight!"

The roof of the seven-storey building was some 150ft long and 50ft wide at its widest point and with lift and water outhouses on the top. To feed RF from the transmitter, **Fig 6**, a rope of 73Ω and relay switching cables, terminated at the operating position in a five-way coaxial switch, was led out through the shack window juxtaposed to a black, though otherwise friendly drain pipe, and thence to the roof; the resulting cable run was virtually invisible from the street below.

G2EC described in detail the construction of the antennas on 12ft poles and (for the beam) a 12ft steel mast all arranged so that they could be quickly heaved up and fitted into prepared bases. He wrote: "It looks so simple in print, but in complete darkness, single-handed, possibly in a half-gale with a 70ft unfenced drop to the street a few feet away, the writer recommends manipulating 28lb at the end of a 12ft pole to upset even the most well-behaved human circulating organs, at least until confidence is gained . . . . The aerials fall far short of the ideal, but nevertheless, observing the local strictures, they permitted G2EC to continue to enjoy the 'vice' of Amateur Radio without causing affront. After all 'What the eye never sees, the heart never grieves over'".

Another exploit of G2EC while SU1EC in the 'thirties is recalled in an obituary note in *The Journal of the Royal Signals Institution*: "In 1934, while serving in Egypt, he participated in a three-car expedition through the Western Desert and the Libyan Sand Sea, a round trip of some 1500 miles. Radio contact was maintained with Egypt Signals using a transmitter and receiver constructed by Eric Cole, proving that 'long distance' communications [from a vehicle] were possible, later becoming routine practice for units such as the Long Range Desert Group". The writer also notes that during WW2, while serving with Joint Combined Operations, G2EC designed the Wireless Hand Cart – nicknamed the 'Radio Pram' which was used during the Normandy landings.

Reverting to the topic of invisible antennas, there are unfortunately many flat dwellers who have no access to a large flat roof, or even a balcony, and must perforce make do with either an indoor antenna or a thin wire lowered out of a window or, for example, coupling their RF into a metal drainpipe or metal windows etc.

The effectiveness of an indoor antenna depends on many factors that cannot be readily predicted or measured. For example a wire antenna erected in a roof-space of a conventional building can often prove almost as good as one outside at a similar height; on the other hand an antenna in a room in a steel-framed building is unlikely to perform well. 144MHz VHF single-element quad antennas can be taped to a window and will radiate well in the direction faced by the window. A number of designs for simple indoor antennas were given in *TT*, July 1983 as shown in **Figs 8 to 10**. The three random-length Marconi antennas for HF are taken from the manual for the paramilitary/clandestine Mk 123 transmitter-receiver. Rather better results could be expected from a compact 'magnetic loop' antenna since there would be less absorption by nearby objects. I would not advise the use of any form of room antenna for high-power operation, but with say 20-40 watts CW there should be no difficulty in achieving plenty of contacts. This assumes you can overcome the potential problems of RFI, often due to leakage into the electricity wiring etc.

SWR BRIDGES & HARMONICS

PETER CHADWICK, G3RZP, with the aid of professional instruments, has been testing out the widely held belief that an SWR bridge should always be followed by a low pass filter to cope with harmonics generated by the diodes. The results are revealing and should prove of interest to those with transmitters that would not otherwise require an LPF. He writes:

"For many years, it has been assumed that the diode detectors in an SWR bridge will cause harmonics which will be radiated at a level high enough to cause interference to

EXPERIMENTAL C & R FILTER/ATTENUATOR

THE USUAL ATTENUATOR consists of a network of resistors (R) while the usual high-pass filter is a combination of inductors (L) and capacitors (C). Peter W Haylett, G3IPV, has been experimenting with a combination of C and R, originally as an attenuator to reduce intermodulation in receiver front ends but which appears to have other applications calling for a filter that passes VHF/UHF signals without undue losses but attenuates HF signals particularly those on the lower HF bands such as 3.5MHz. He writes:

"**Fig 7** shows the basic circuit of this filter which is of a high-frequency pass, low-frequency attenuation type. Experiments with this filter have been carried out by placing it in the antenna coaxial feeder cable of a TV receiver, a 3.5MHz receiver and a simple spectrum analyser. Although the filter does attenuate to some extent the incoming TV signal this does not appear to be a problem except in weak-signal areas. When the attenuation of the filter is observed using the 3.5MHz receiver and spectrum analyser, it appears, as might be expected, to be high in the HF/MF spectrum (1-30MHz) – suggesting that such a filter might have a number of applications. Although this filter has been initially tested at the UHF TV frequencies, it could probably be used in any part of the radio spectrum. Performance would depend on the separation between the higher wanted frequency and the lower unwanted frequency, the value of the series capaci-

tance and the relative intensities of wanted and unwanted signals. The capacitance should be adjusted by trial and error to the minimum practical value at the wanted signal frequency. If necessary attenuation can be reduced by omittng the output resistor.

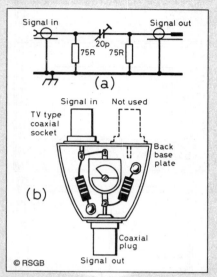

Fig 7: (a) Circuit diagram of the simple R-C high-pass, low frequency attenuation filter as developed by G3IPV. (b) As implemented by G3IPV in a Wolsey 'aerial combiner' unit but other layouts are possible provided that there is a minimum of coupling between input and output sockets except via the low-capacitance trimmer.

other services, notably TV. The UK amateur is most fortunate in that he has no VHF services to worry about, unlike amateurs in other parts of the world; nevertheless, it is taken as an article of faith that troublesome harmonics will be caused and most texts show an LPF following an SWR bridge.

"A degree of cynicism about technical shibboleths is no bad thing and it was decided to put this common assumption to the test. A number of SWR bridges in various instruments were tested: Bird 43 Thruline wattmeter with 50W and 1000W plug-ins; Asahi-Sangyo NEII (two meters, forward and reverse, rated for 100W); Labgear E5048; Daiwa CN620A (crossed needle, power and SWR, 20/200/1000W ranges); and a homebrew Bruene-type meter.

"Of these instruments, the Labgear E5048 and the Asahi-Sangyo MEII are based on the principle of pick-up lines, as in the original 'monimatch', and are frequency sensitive, with an in-

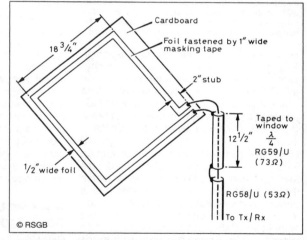

Fig 8: A 144MHz single-element quad antenna suitable for use on windows and made from household aluminium foil mounted on cardboard.

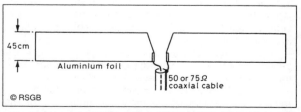

Fig 9: An indoor broadband 'fat dipole' antenna using aluminium ('kitchen') foil for use in lofts or for mounting on indoor walls. Suggested lengths for 3.5MHz are two by 12m; 7MHz two by 6.2m; 10.1MHz two by 4.4m; 14MHz two by 3.4m.

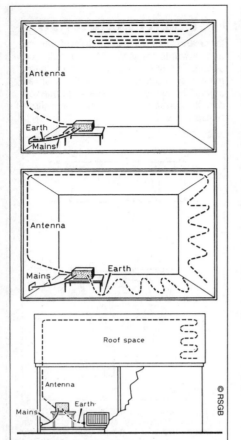

© RSGB

Fig 10: Random-length Marconi HF antennas as suggested in the manual for the Mark 123 paramilitary transmitter-receiver. (a) Preferably in a room high in the building and using a 'mains earth'. (b) Alternative arrangement using a wire counterpoise on the floor. (c) Antenna in roof space with central-heating radiator used as 'earth'. For transceivers intended for fixed 50Ω feed an ATU suitable for end-fed antennas would be required.

crease in coupling to the coaxial line at high frequencies. The Bird Thruline uses a coupling loop with frequency compensation, while the Daiwa CN620 is a Bruene-type with a wide-band current transformer (a typical example of a Bruene-type instrument is shown in the RSGB *Radio Communications Handbook*.)

"Initial measurements were made with an FT102 transceiver on 21.2MHz feeding a low-pass filter, the SWR meter under test, a 100W 30dB wide-band attenuator and a Hewlett-Packard 8562A spectrum analyser. A calibration run was made in each case without the SWR meter, and the meter then placed in line. Power was varied up to the limits of the power meter concerned or 100W, whichever was the lower.

"The results were interesting. With any of the SWR meters, no change in the harmonics could be detected down to –70dB, the limit of measurement.

"The possibility of the phenomenon being power related was considered; the next step therefore was to replace the attenuator with a Hewlett-Packard 778D 20dB wideband directional coupler feeding a dummy load, and to couple the forward signal with harmonics, via the 30dB attenuator to the spectrum analyser. The same answers were obtained at 100W, so the next step was to switch in a power amplifier. At 500W, results remained the same. It was not until the forward power was over 900W that any harmonics caused by the SWR meters could be seen. Even then, only the Labgear E5049 and the Asahi-Sangyo showed any signs of harmonic generation: at 1kW, the harmonic production was about –60dB relative to carrier.

"In a well-matched system, there is no reverse power, and so there should not be any current flowing in the diodes; therefore there should be no harmonics generated. The Asahi-Sangyo meter has two coupling lines – one for forward power and one for reverse power, so the problem in this case is probably produced in the forward detector. However, the instrument is rated for only 100W, and the resistors terminating the pick-up line object violently to 1kW through the device for more than a few seconds. The Labgear E5048 was designed for an 80Ω system, and so was indicating a 1.5:1 SWR. It too is not rated for 1kW and, fitted with Belling-Lee style TV connectors, is quite capable of producing harmonics in the connectors at this power level.

"A works colleague, G8WKS, told me that he once had problems at the –75dB level on a professional VHF transmitter, so the performance of the IC251 was examined. The third harmonic was –68dB relative to carrier, and no change was found when the built-in SWR bridge was disabled.

"The possibility that the effect occurs only when feeding an antenna, which will not offer a good match at the harmonic frequencies was investigated. Again, no harmonic generation observable!

"What conclusions can be drawn? The evidence does not support the original, widely-held premise insofar as the only SWR meters found to produce detectable harmonics were being run a long way outside their power ratings at levels which are illegal in the UK.

"So does an SWR meter need to be followed by a low-pass filter? It does not appear to be so, although the filter itself is probably useful as a precaution against causing interference with low-band private-mobile-radio (PMR) users. Sharp cut-off filters, such as elliptic function or Chebyshev types may well produce an in-band SWR of their own that is high enough to cause confusion when an antenna is being trimmed to resonance, so placing the SWR bridge prior to the filter can be misleading. So much for sacred cows!"

D-I-Y POLYSTYRENE SOLUTION

GRAHAM THORNTON, VK3IY, in *Amateur Radio*, April 1993, p20 shows how to 'Make your own polystyrene solution'. He writes:

"Those of us who can remember the good(?) old days of coil winding will recall the use of polystyrene coil dope. This was used to provide a low-loss sealant and to keep the turns secure. If you want to get a strange look from your component-store salesman, ask for some! However, all is not lost – it's quite easy to home-brew.

"There is an abundance of waste expanded-polystyrene in the environment, ie 'styrofoam'. This dissolves readily in ordinary turpentine. The fizz given off is the release of normal hexane used to expand the polystyrene (be-ware – inflammable). It takes quite a volume of this material to make a little solution. The polystyrene is not soluble in every component of the turps. The end result is a two-layered solution. The viscous lower solution is the desired result. Simply pour off the supernatant liquid. (No need to waste it – it's still useful turps.)

"It can be applied with a small brush. It seems to take overnight to dry. The same material can be used to make castings for insulators, if desired. Dowelling spreaders, dried in the oven, and painted with this solution, are excellent for transmission lines, eg 'open-wire' tuned feeders."

HERE & THERE

QST (MAY, 1993) REVIEWS a recently published 124-page paperback book 'Heath Nostalgia' by Terry Purdue, K8TP that brings together a number of recollections by former employees of the Heath Company whose decision last year to withdraw from the Amateur Radio kits market was noted nostalgically in 'Goodbye Heathkit – Farewell Leicester Square' (*TT*, November 1992, pp44-45). The review reveals that the original founder, Ed Heath, had no particular interest in electronics but was intensely interested in aviation, founding the 'Aerial Vehicle Company' in Chicago – later renamed the Heath Airplane Company which sold airplane kits, parts and ran a flying school.

Ed Heath was killed in a plane crash in 1931; the new owner moved into the electronics field after WW2 and the first kit was the OT-1 five-inch oscilloscope. Heath's second owner, however, was also killed in a plane crash, and his widow ran the firm until it was acquired by Daystrom Inc in 1955, a year after the entry into the ready-to-build Amateur Radio kit market, becoming for over 30 years the world leader in electronic kits.

Two letters from Holland – from Dick Rollema, PA0SE, and Jaap Dijkshoorn, PA0TO – express surprise that I had never come across transformer-type temperature fuses in practice (*TT* Sep '92). PA0SE recalls similar fuses being used by Van der Heen, an electronics firm in the Hague, for which he used to work until the firm was taken over by Philips in 1967.

PA0TO also recalls that many such transformers were fitted in broadcast receivers made by Philips. He writes: "In the late-1940s and 1950s, the purchase of new power transformers threatened to ruin my schoolboy's pocket-money. So on the days when people put out their rubbish for collection, a schoolfriend and I would ride through that part of The Hague where a refuse collection was due. We looked for thrown-out radios made by Philips at Eindhoven since this firm used temperature-fused power transformers in many of their sets.

"We looked for sets where the temperature-fuse had 'opened' and then set about removing the transformer and any other components that we felt might be useful. For we had discovered that often in the discarded sets it was the thermal fuse that had blown, not the transformer. We simply connected the AC mains to one end of this fuse and another power supply could be built – with much saving of pocket-money! **G3VA**

THE CLASSIC G2DAF LINEAR

IT IS NOW 30 YEARS since the late GRB Thornley, G2DAF, as part of his series of constructional designs for an HF receiver and HF SSB/CW transmitter, described a 400W linear amplifier (*RSGB Bulletin*, April 1963) based on the passive-grid technique and suitable for use with an SSB exciter/transmitter of around 50W PEP. The original model used two 4-125A (Mullard QY3-125) or two 813 tetrode valves, operated under zero bias conditions, and with the screen voltage derived by rectifying a small portion of the input signal in a voltage-doubler arrangement. This configuration avoided the complication of the carefully regulated screen supply required for many linear amplifiers.

The basic G2DAF design has proved its worth down the years, and in *TT*, September 1991, p33 and again in *TT*, February 1992, p37, some modifications, including the use of silicon diodes instead of diode valves to provide the screen voltage, were described, stemming from the work of ZS2PL, ZS6AOZ, F6IDC (G4ZU) etc.

Now Mike Hall, G3USC, writes: "Many of the modifications to the original G2DAF design that have been described over the years in *TT* I have incorporated with very beneficial results in my amplifier: **Fig 1.** Voltage quadrupling rather than voltage doubling and a grid leak resistor certainly improved both the efficiency and linearity. My amplifier dates back some 25 years and is still going strong with the original valves, although these were probably already some 25 years old when I acquired them!

"However, when modifying my amplifier, lack of space prevented me from using the specified 6U4 or EY81 screen rectifiers. Two small 6AL5/EB91 signal diodes with independent heater supplies have coped quite adequately. In a voltage quadrupler arrangement they supply 400V to the screens when fully driven. I did not use semiconductor diodes because at that time I was worried about their reliability for this application. The data sheet maximum PIV for the EB91 is 420V with the peak current rating 54mA, so I do not feel I have abused them unduly.

"Readers may be interested in a modification that did not prove successful. Wanting to drive the amplifier from an exciter that had only a single 6146 output valve, I spent much time investigating trifilar-wound input transformers to give a 50-Ω match to a 470-Ω grid resistor (actually ten 4k7 resistors in parallel). I tried many types and sizes of toroidal cores, even

Pat Hawker's Technical Topics

high permeability ferrite, in order to try to reduce the number of turns needed for 3.5MHz, but there was no way I could get the leakage inductance down to an acceptable figure for the 21 and 28MHz bands. The input capacitance of the valves was just too high. In the end, to my annoyance, I was forced to use a separate bandswitched L-network in the grid circuit.

"My amplifier has been quite stable with this relatively high grid resistor. Its disadvantage is that there is a lack of swamping which is apparent on a scope trace when driven with a two-tone generator; a definite kink in the waveform occurs, I believe, where the screen diodes begin to conduct to a significant degree. However, on-air reports have always been very complimentary.

G2DAF-type linear amplifier built by G3USC, one of many satisfied users.

"I also concur with an earlier contributor to *TT* that the anode stoppers are unnecessary; indeed, like his, mine disappeared in smoke on 28MHz.

"Another point. I wound the RF choke as suggested by G2DAF but found it very difficult to avoid a resonance in one of the bands. After several burnouts, the successful attempt used sections of winding spaced $^3/_{16}$in and consisted of 68 + 19 + 16 + 13 + 10 turns of 24SWG wire on a $^{13}/_{16}$in former. It does not appear to overheat and a GDO shows it to be free of in-band resonances, including the WARC bands, though there is one just above 24MHz which might mean that a little pruning would be necessary for an amplifier used on that band.

"Finally, I originally designed the amplifier pi-tank to provide a proper match when used with a lower than normal supply voltage (1.8kV). There were two reasons for this: I had a suitable transformer and I felt that the tank circuit Q could be controlled better on 21 and 28MHz. It worked with this voltage but the efficiency and power gain were low as might be expected. Matters improved significantly when I returned the bottom of the screen multiplier (only a doubler in those days) to +70V instead of zero volts. I now run the amplifier on 2.6kV (quiescent) with the bottom of the screen quadrupler at zero volts, accepting a high pi-tank Q on 21 and 28MHz.

"Partly as a result of the high tank Q, I find that the available linear output on 28MHz is quite a lot lower than on 14MHz and below, but I am still able to push a reasonably clean 250W up the feeder on this band. The other reason for this low output and lower linearity, I guess, is due to electron transit times in these big valves and the series inductance of their internal, and necessarily long external connections. [The original 813 valves were specified for full output power only up to 10MHz – *G3VA*]. A couple of 4CX250s would probably have done the job a lot better, though not without some plumbing.

"It would be fun to attempt a survey of how many of these amplifiers have actually been built and how many are still in use today. Better still, if it were possible, to run a Christmas draw and donate a prize of a couple of 813s to the lucky entrant, with a 10V, 10A, centre-tapped filament transformer to the runner-up. I shudder to think what the latter would cost today as a bespoke item. I have contacted quite a few owners of these G2DAF linears, and know of someone who is still collecting the bits together to join the existing satisfied users!"

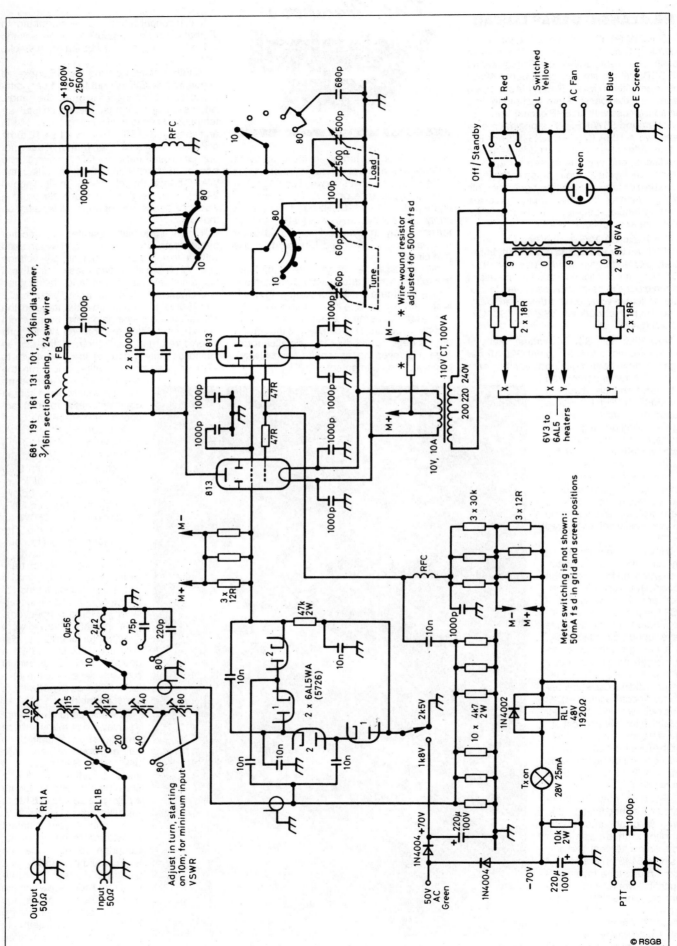

Fig 1: Circuit diagram of G3USC's HF linear amplifier based on the 1963 G2DAF design but incorporating some modifications.

© RSGB

SUPER-LINEAR HF RECEIVER FRONT ENDS

NOTES IN THE February *TT*, drawing on the long article 'Recent advances in shortwave receiver design' by Dr Ulrich L Rohde, KA2WEU/DL2JR (*QST*, November 1992) and the IEE's book 'Radio Receivers' edited by Dr W Gosling, drew attention to current thinking on advanced, high-performance, HF receiver front-ends. It referred, in particular, to mixers and associated circuitry capable of providing excellent dynamic range. This was followed in the April *TT* by information on 'An ultra low distortion HF switched FET mixer' designed by Eric Kushnik (*RF Design*) that required significantly less oscillator power than is generally needed for mixers having a very high third-order intercept point.

The subject also crops up in 'A high-dynamic-range MF/HF receiver front end' by Jacob Makhinson, N6NWP, (*QST*, February 1993, pp23-28 with correction note *QST*, June 1993, p73). In this article, N6NWP, shows that "By properly applying known design principles, radio amateurs can construct a high-performance front-end which combines a very high intercept point with excellent sensitivity. Used with a low-noise LO, the front-end described in this article achieves a wide dynamic range even with its pre-amplifier stage in-line. A receiver incorporating such a front-end can provide strong-signal performance that rivals or exceeds that of most commercial equipment available to the amateur."

Fig 3 shows the essentials of the N6NWP, 14MHz mixer (with 9MHz IF) based on a Siliconix Si8901/SD8901 DMOS FET quad device together with a 74HC74 dual flip-flop to provide square wave LO injection from a VFO operating at about 10.5MHz. The mixer is followed by a simple diplexer network; N6NWP, also provides details of suitable high-performance pre- and post-mixer amplifiers. The mixer can be used either with or without the input pre-amplifier which, like the post-mixer amplifier, uses two MRF586 transistors in push-pull.

Colin Horrabin, G3SBI, has been investigating in depth the N6NWP mixer (with some modifications) and finds that it is possible to achieve extremely high third-order intercept points. In fact other parts of the circuitry, such as the diplexer or crystal filter rather than the mixer itself, tend to be the limiting factor. The following is a short summary of G3SBI's interim report on the measured performance of his implementation of the N6NWP mixer:

"The excellent Siliconix Si8901 device (which has been replaced by the identical SD8901 available from Calogic Corporation) contains four DMOS FETs already configured for use as a commutation (switching) mixer. N6NWP utilises this device with square wave drive to the gates of the FETs from a high speed CMOS D-type bistable device operating somewhat unusually from a 9-volt supply. Although the intercept point as usually defined would be about 2dB less than the +41dBm claimed (this is acknowledged in the correction note), this is still an excellent performance.

"It was decided to construct a mixer (**Fig 4**) based on the ideas of N6NWP, but utilising the more widely available Siliconix SD5000

LOW-COST CALIBRATED DIALS

THE ITEM IN THE July *TT* (p53) stemming from G4XPP on using transparent plastic school protractors as calibrated dials has attracted some alternative suggestions.

John Levesley, G0HJL, finds that the type of self-adhesive clear compass rose (**Fig 2**) intended for use with aviation and marine maps makes a very good scale on equipment cases. Mounted on plastic or metal discs they make equally good calibrated dials. They have a useful advantage over most protractors in having a smaller diameter which is more appropriate for smaller equipment cases. He writes: "I purchase them from my local pilot-supplier shop for about 25p each, and I think chandlers probably also sell them. There are advertisers in magazines for pilots which offer such compass roses by mail order."

Dick Biddulph, G8DPS, suggests a cheaper version of G4XPP's idea is to use 'polar coordinate graph paper' (eg Chartwell Graph Sheet No 7506). However I notice that these are quite large sheets (8.5 x 11in) so that they would need to be cut down to size and then the calibration markings (printed at the edges of the sheet) would need to be added. I suspect that for most purposes the small compass roses would be more appropriate.

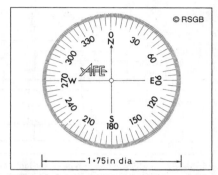

Fig 2: Example of the appearance of a self-adhesive clear compass rose as sold for use with aviation and marine maps. G0HJL finds they make excellent calibration scales on equipment cases and mounted on plastic or metal discs make very good calibrated dials.

---

quad DMOS FET array (batch 9042). Unfortunately, this array has gate-protection diodes, so the substrate must be negative biased to prevent gate conduction in certain conditions; however the array has the advantage of very close matching of drain-to-source on-resistance.

"A test board of the arrangement shown in Fig 4 was made using earth-plane construction, with all transformers and ICs fitted into turned-pin DIL construction, so that they could be changed easily. With the test set-up of **Fig 5** it was possible to achieve a true input intercept of +42dBm on 14MHz using a 5MHz local oscillator injection. An input intercept of +45dBm was obtained on 3.5MHz with a 5.5MHz local oscillator frequency. It was found that with a local oscillator running at 23MHz the 14MHz intercept was a few dBm down compared with the 5MHz LO.

"For this reason an advanced CMOS 74AC74 was used as the LO squarer, and

gave a near-perfect 50-50 square wave. To reduce ringing on this, only one D-type in the chip was used and stopper resistors were connected to the FET gates – a single ferrite bead in series with the Vcc pin also proved useful. It is important for the injection to be a clean square wave if the results indicated above are to be obtained . . . . The results were excellent with input intercepts of at least +42dBm on all HF bands and +46dBm on 1.8 and 3.5MHz.

"On 7MHz, no intermodulation distortion was visible on the spectrum analyser (**Fig 6(a)** with **(b)** showing the 7MHz input) even with a bandwidth of 10Hz, representing an input intercept of +50dBm. These figures were achieved with both 2kHz and 20kHz tone separations at an input level of +7dBm on the HF band under test. A substrate bias of −7.5V and a gate bias of about +4.5V were used. Conversion loss was 7dB. These are extremely good results.

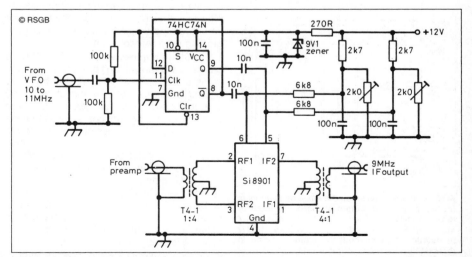

Fig 3: The basic high-dynamic-range MF/HF receiver front-end mixer circuitry as developed by N6NWP and described in the February 1993 *QST* using the Si8901 DMOS FET ring.

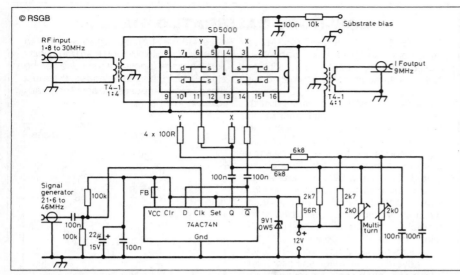

Fig 4: G3SBI's modified N6NWP-type mixer test assembly using the SD5000 FET array and 74AC74N to provide square-wave injection from a high-quality signal generator source with output at twice the required frequency.

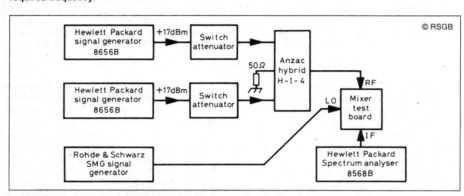

Fig 5: The test instrumentation set-up used by G3SBI for intermodulation tests on the mixer.

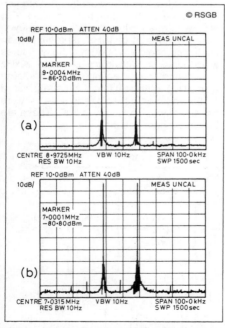

Fig 6: Spectrum analysis of the mixer performance. (a) Mixer spectrum output at 9MHz. (b) Input to mixer at 7MHz +7dBm/tone. Note that one of the signal generators had some low-level 10kHz modulation to cause the larger spurious signal in (b) and this appears after up-conversion to 9MHz in (a). The third-order distortion is on the baseline at the output of the mixer indicating a mixer input intercept point of +50dBm.

"However (now the bad news) the intercept point degrades sharply as soon as the input signal exceeds +7dBm (0.5V) which is still a big signal. It is thought that the reason for this is that the FETs that should be 'off' in the commutation ring see a negative drain-to-source signal voltage greater than −1.7V and start to conduct. The situation can be recovered by dropping the gate bias voltage, but it is then no longer possible to achieve the super intercepts of greater than +45dBm . . . An alternative arrangement is being assembled that should make it possible to handle very large input signal voltages without degrading the intercept points."

For the post-mixer amplifier, G3SBI uses basically the same circuit as N6NWP but with some subtle changes (**Fig 7**) that have improved performance in terms of gain and output intercept point, and has a noise figure of 0.5dB. "An important change was the use of the MRF580A transistor instead of the MRF586 since this should give a lower noise figure at a collector current of 60mA." Measured performance of the amplifier gave gain as 8.8dB, output intercept +56dBm, noise figure 0.5dB. G3SBI points out that with intercepts of this magnitude it is important to remember that the measuring equipment is being pushed to the limit, and transformers must be looked upon as possible sources of limitations in overall linearity. Also that, unfortunately, the measurements are for operation into a resistive load. In practice, the crystal

filter driven by the post-mixer amplifier would present a complex impedance to the amplifier. Particularly on the slope and near the stopband, this would seriously degrade the amplifier performance.

G3SBI has also investigated the performance of quadrature hybrid 9MHz crystal-filter combinations and finds that the performance of budget-priced crystal filters is a serious limitation. He found that this can be reduced by eliminating the post-mixer amplifier, with the mixer going immediately to a quadrature hybrid network 2.4kHz-bandwidth filter, followed by a low-noise amplifier. In this case, the 2.4kHz filter is, in effect, used as a roofing filter. With such an arrangement, assuming the effective noise figure to be 5dB due to the filter and amplifier, another 7dB from mixer loss, and a further 1.5dB loss due to the antenna input bandpass filter, this gives an overall noise figure of about 13.5dB [sufficient sensitivity up to at least 14MHz – *G3VA*]. The intercept point on 7MHz would then be about +51.5dBm. Nevertheless, G3SBI comments that "This is not the ideal solution since slightly better intercepts could have been obtained by the conventional (post-mixer amplifier) arrangement with a filter having an intercept figure of +55dBm."

In conclusion, G3SBI writes: "One might ask the question does one need input intercepts of +50dBm? For amateur purposes the answer has to be the higher the better. [But note that the April *TT* quotes G3RZP as believing that 'a +20dBm third order intercept appears adequate, even on 7MHz at night' – *G3VA*]. The name of the game is to be able to copy a sub-microvolt signal in the presence of a heavy hitter a few kHz away from the desired signal. In addition, on 7MHz the proximity of the broadcast band is a problem with antenna signals greater than −10dBm present at times. Extreme linearity is thus desirable if a sub-microvolt signal is to be copied in these circumstances.

"The fact that the intermodulation performance of the crystal filter can be a serious problem at these intercept levels was not completely unexpected. The effects of this can be minimised as described by omitting the post-mixer amplifier, but filters with +55dBm intercepts would enable the construction of a high-performance front end with a post-mixer amplifier. It may be worth considering the use of home-made crystal ladder filters as part of a quadrature hybrid arrangement since no transformers are used, suggesting that the intercept figure could be high, although this has not yet been checked. In addition the low insertion loss of some ladder filters (about −2dB) would permit higher IF-stage noise figures.

"The mixer remains the most critical device if input intercepts of +50dBm are to be obtained on 7MHz. This performance has been achieved with all SD5000 chips of batch 9042 that were available; one from batch 9024 did not meet this figure on 7MHz, achieving +44dBm.

"To summarise, Jacob Makhinson, N6NWP, has pointed the way ahead for home construction of very high-performance HF receivers using a 9MHz IF. Given that, at a price, high-intercept filters are obtainable, the linearity of the mixer itself is still the limiting factor."

G3SBI next draws attention to published information on quadrature hybrids, including an article 'Twisted-wire quadrature hybrid directional couplers' by Reed Fisher, W2CQH, that appeared in *QST*, January 1978, pp21-23 with the sub-heading: "That title scare you off? Well, don't let it. Just read this and we'll make believers out of you." In the article, W2CQH points out that 3dB directional couplers or quadrature hybrids for paralleling UHF amplifiers or for achieving circular polarization are commonly implemented in stripline but that "unfortunately, the UHF strip-line models cannot be scaled down to the HF bands since their dimensions become prohibitively large." His article shows how compact, low-cost, lumped-element, quadrature hybrids can be easily constructed for use in the HF amateur bands.

G3SBI then considers N6NWP's method of controlling the impedance seen by the post-mixer amplifier. A 6dB attenuator between amplifier and mixer has a significant effect on the system noise figure as seen at the input to the post-mixer amplifier. This is especially so with the 5dB or 10dB insertion loss of a narrow-band CW crystal filter. He believes that a better solution (if the additional expense is acceptable) is to use two identical filters, in addition to quadrature hybrids. His experimental work shows that satisfactory results can be obtained in this way with 9MHz narrow-band filters. But the use of two commercial crystal filters would represent a significant additional cost although this approach, using home-built ladder filters, might be feasible for someone determined to achieve +50dBm intercept points range on all bands. It must be stressed that performance of the standard being investigated by G3SBI calls for high-quality (although not necessarily high-cost) components and diode-ring mixers. Development work also involves measurements close to, or beyond the limits of, professional-standard test equipment.

Since the above was written, G3SBI has developed an alternative SD5000 mixer configuration capable of intercept points greater than +50dBm (limit of measurement) on all HF bands. More on this later.

MORE ON ANTENNA CORROSION

THE JULY *TT* ITEM 'Fighting antenna corrosion' based on the *QST* article (April) by Scott Toleson, KC7CJ, made a brief reference to

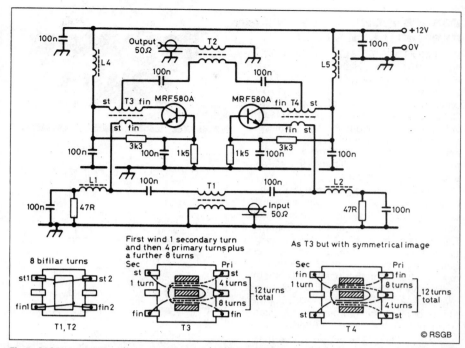

Fig 7: G3SBI's modified post-mixer test amplifier adapted from the N6NWP design but using MRF580A devices. All resistors 0.25W metal-film RS components. All 0.1μF capacitors monolithic ceramic RS components. L4, L5 4t of 0.315mm dia bicelflux wire on RS components ferrite bead. L1, L2, T1, T2, T3, T4 on balun core fair-rite 28-43002402 (Cirkit components). L1, L2 6t 0.315mm dia bicelflux wire RS components. T1 to T4, user 40SWG bicelflux wire. Take two glass fibre Cambion 14-pin DIP component headers, cut each in two parts and bend the tags 90° outwards. Stick a piece of double-sided tape onto the header and mount the balun cores on this. Wind the transformers as shown above. The amplifier is constructed with earth-plane layout.

'fretting corrosion' but did not expand on this phenomenon. A panel in *QST* explained it as follows: "Fretting corrosion occurs whenever there is a small repetitive or cyclical motion at a metal-to-metal joint or seam. This motion can be either a make-break or sliding action. Basically, joint flexing or sliding exposes clean, fresh metal to the air, and an oxide begins to form. This oxide is broken or scraped away with each reconnection or flex, but begins to reform when it is exposed again.

"Over time, the oxide builds up at the joint, and eventually the reconnection or scraping won't remove all the oxide at the point of contact. Joint resistance gradually increases, and the joint eventually becomes intermittent. How long a joint or contact lasts before it becomes a problem depends on joint pressure. It also depends on how oxidation-prone the metals at the joint are, and other conditions such as temperature, humidity and the existence of surface contaminants."

Dick Biddulph, G8DPS, stresses that "fretting corrosion needs only the slightest movement of one surface relative to the other. It is prevented, as implied by KC7CJ, by preventing either the movement or the ingress of water or, preferably, both."

On other aspects of antenna corrosion raised by KC7CJ, G8DPS, writes: "The use of 'star washers' is only OK if the metal can't flow or creep. Lead and solder both creep at room temperature. Another point is that RTV (room temperature vulcanising) silicone rubber has a very good resistance to sunlight and whatever the weather can throw at it. There are some which do not give off acetic acid fumes when used and are therefore less likely to cause corrosion. Dow Corning 'Silastic 744' is one and is available from; Industrial Silicones

and Lubricants, International Centre, Spindle Way, Crawley, West Sussex RH10 1TG."

HERE AND THERE

EMERSON M HOYT, WX7E, in *QST*, June 1993, p75 reports having found a simple way to install radials in a lawn or reasonably soft ground. He writes: "I use a square tip, flat-bladed spade and a Stanley No 10-T nail remover. I use No 8 bare copper wire, but other husky wires (such as No 10, 12 or 14 house wire) can also be used.

"I use the spade to make an approximately 2 to 3-inch-deep vertical cut along the radial location, and widen it into a V-shaped notch by rocking the spade back and forth. The wire can be laid into the groove, and then pushed down to the bottom of the groove with the Stanley tool. The large and very comfortable handle on this tool is very easy on the hands. The groove can be closed with some foot stamping, and in a few weeks all signs of the installation are gone."

Steve Ortmayer, G4RAW, reports that he has built and tried several QRM eliminators (see 'Phasing out interference – another look', *TT*, March 1993, pp34-35). He writes: "I have made the VK5BR and a friend has made both the VK5BR and W1ETC null steerers. All work, but with reservations! I have the VK5BR arrangement on 3.5MHz and it eliminates local electrical noise from vacuum cleaners and the like; it will also deal with computer noise from my boy's computer in the next room. The problem is where the QRM or QRN arises some way away so that the pick-up on the auxiliary antenna is not sufficient. My friend has tried using a 20dB pre-amplifier on the noise antenna, and also tried it just before the toroid. "   *G3VA*

G3SBI'S HIGH PERFORMANCE MIXER

LAST MONTH'S *TT* ITEM on G3SBI's investigation of N6NWP's 'High-dynamic-range MF/HF receiver front end' (*QST*, Feb 1993, pp23-28) revealed that he had subsequently developed an entirely new way of using an SD5000 DMOS quad-FET array that promised to provide even greater dynamic range, particularly on the higher HF bands. His new 'H-mode' configuration fulfils this promise and seems to open the way to a multiband HF receiver of superlative performance.

In presenting information on this new mixer configuration, it should be made clear that Colin Horrabin, G3SBI, is a professional scientist/electronic engineer at the Science and Engineering Research Council's Daresbury Laboratory which has supported his investigative work on the H-mode switched FET mixer and consequently holds intellectual title to the new mixer. This does not, of course, prevent readers from taking the development further or using the information presented in September or this current *TT* item.

G3SBI writes: "The previous information covered an investigation of all the component parts of a high-performance front-end including a note on the limitations of the crystal filter intercept point. Although the intercept point of the filters readily available on the UK amateur market appeared to limit the performance of a front end to some degree, this could be made compatible with high-performance mixers if no post-mixer amplifier was used in front of the filter and a quadrature hybrid network with two low-loss SSB filters immediately followed the mixer. The SD5000 DMOS FET mixer described in the September *TT*, followed basically accepted practice in commutation (switching) mixers and achieved a +50dBm input intercept point on 7MHz with the use of square-wave drive.

"However, as noted, it was not possible to achieve this performance on all amateur HF bands, including bands lower and higher in frequency than 7MHz. The results were improved on the lower frequency bands by altering the capacitive balance of the RF input transformer, but this had no significant effect on 14MHz and above. It was felt that a configuration for the mixer where the RF input signal was not in the gate source switch-on path would prevent modulation of the true gate-to-source local oscillator voltage by the RF input signal.

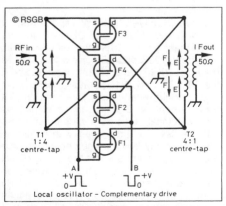

Fig 1: Conventional commutation mixer arrangement based on quad-FET array.

Pat Hawker's
Technical Topics

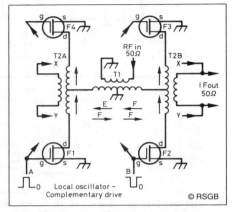

Fig 2: The new 'H-mode' commutation mixer.

"The performance of the new mixer is as follows: With an input RF test level of +11dBm (0.8V RMS two tones spaced at 2kHz or 20kHz); conversion loss 8dB; RF to IF isolation -68dB; LO to IF isolation -66dB. Input intercept points: 1.8 to 18MHz +53dBm; 21 to 28MHz +47dBm or better; 50MHz + 41dB. These results were achieved with a gate-to-source DC bias of +1.95V and -8V substrate bias, a square-wave local oscillator amplitude of 9V and an IF at 9MHz.

"**Fig 1** shows a conventional commutation ring mixer: if A is 'on', FETs F1 and F2 are 'on' and the direction of the RF signal across transformer T2 is given by the 'F' arrows. The main deficiency of this classic circuit is that as the RF input signal level increases, it has a significant effect on true gate-to-source voltage needed to switch the FET 'on' or keep it switched 'off'. Larger local oscillator amplitudes are then required, but linearity problems may still exist because of the difference in the FET 'on' resistance between negative and positive RF signal states.

"The alternative arrangement is shown in **Fig 2**. The shape of this diagram illustrates why the new mixer has been named 'H-mode'. Inputs A and B are complementary square wave inputs derived from the sine-wave local oscillator at twice the

required frequency. If A is 'on' then FETs F1 and F3 are 'on' and the direction of the RF signal across T1 is given by the 'E' arrows. When B is 'on', FETs F2 and F4 are 'on' and the direction of the RF signal across T1 reverses (arrows 'F'). This is still the action of a commutation mixer, but now the source of each FET switch is grounded, so that the RF signal switched by the FET cannot modulate the gate source voltage.

"In this configuration the transformers are important: T1 is a Mini-Circuits type T4-1; T2 is two Mini-Circuits T4-1 transformers with their primaries connected in parallel. It is possible that a special five-windings transformer might give even better results, but so far the intercept points achieved with a home-made transformer have been unsatisfactory; it is probably a question of having the right ferrite material. However, the parallel-connected transformers give good balance and perform well.

"The practical test circuit is shown in **Fig 3**. It is constructed on an earthplane board and all transformers and ICs are mounted in turned pin DIL sockets. The printed circuit tracks connecting T1 to T2 and from T2 to the SD5000 are kept short and of 0.015-inch width to minimise capacitance to ground. Operation is as follows: The local oscillator is divided by two in frequency and squared by a 74AC74 advanced CMOS bistable similar to the SD5000 mixer described in the September *TT*. However the bistable is run from +10V instead of +9V and a cut-down RS Components ferrite bead is inserted over the ground pin of the 74AC74 to clean up the square wave.

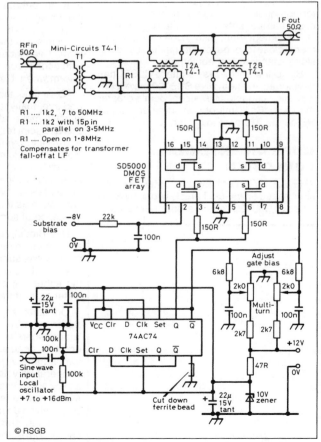

Fig 3: Test assembly for 'H-mode' mixer as investigated by G3SBI.

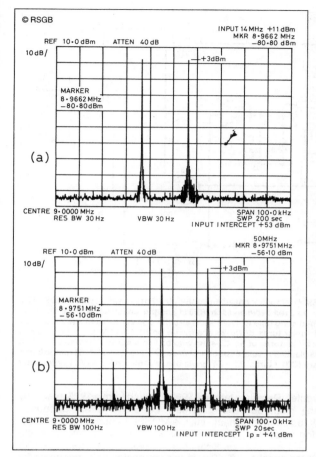

© RSGB

INPUT 14MHz +11dBm
MKR 8·9662 MHz
−80·80 dBm

REF 10·0 dBm   ATTEN 40 dB

10 dB/

+3dBm

MARKER
8·9662 MHz
−80·80dBm

(a)

CENTRE 9·0000 MHz   SPAN 100·0 kHz
RES BW 30 Hz   VBW 30 Hz   SWP 200 sec
INPUT INTERCEPT +53 dBm

50MHz
MKR 8·9751MHz
−56·10 dBm

REF 10·0 dBm   ATTEN 40 dB

10 dB/

+3dBm

MARKER
8·9751 MHz
−56·10 dBm

(b)

CENTRE 9·0000 MHz   SPAN 100·0 kHz
RES BW 100Hz   VBW 100 Hz   SWP 20sec
INPUT INTERCEPT Ip = +41 dBm

Fig 4: (a) 14MHz input intermodulation spectrum for output at 9MHz of the 'H-mode' mixer showing an input intercept of +53dBm. (b) 50MHz input spectrum showing an input intercept of +41dBm.

"The professional test equipment set up used to determine the H-mode mixer intercept points was the same as that noted in the September *TT* for the N6NWP-type mixers, including two Hewlett-Packard signal generators and spectrum analyser and a Rohde & Schwarz SMG signal generator to provide the LO sine wave input.

"The best method of setting the gate bias potentiometers proved to be as follows: One is set to the desired bias voltage for a specific test run, the other is then set by looking at the RF-to-IF path feed-through on the spectrum analyser at 14MHz, and adjusting the potentiometer for minimum IF feedthrough. The setting is quite sharp and ensures good mixer balance.

An RF test signal of 11dBm (0.8V RMS) was used for each test signal for the two-tone IMD tests. The results obtained were the same with 2kHz and 20kHz tone spacing [an indication of the purity of the LO source]. All the major HF amateur bands were used as RF sources in these tests and the spectrum analyser results recorded. The gate bias level chosen enabled an input level of +12dBm to be reached before the IMD increased sharply, breaking away from the normal 3:1 slope on a log plot.

"Spectrum plots for 14MHz and 50MHz are shown in **Fig 4**, indicating input intercept points on these bands of +53dBm and +41dBm respectively. These are excellent results but it is probable that even larger RF input signals might be handled with a lower gate voltage bias and a larger amplitude square wave

injection. The use of the 74AC74 bistable as a square-wave generator is convenient, but the characteristic curves of the SD5000 suggest that a higher gate-to-source 'on' voltage would give a superior FET 'on' resistance for positive and negative drain-to-source signal voltages, possibly giving even better linearity, particularly on 50MHz."

G3SBI also concludes that an H-mode mixer does not have to be driven from a square-wave drive and suggests that it is likely that good results could be obtained with transformer-driven sine waves provided the injection was via capacitors so that the bias pots could still be used. Similarly he believes there is no reason why such a mixer should not be used in an up-conversion arrangement (rather than the 9MHz IF used with both his N6NWP-type and H-mode test mixers) as employed today in most factory-built receivers. The same approach could probably be applied at VHF/UHF with resonant-lines and GaAs FETs as switches. He is convinced that his work proves that the H-mode FET switching mixer is capable of extremely good intermodulation performance at HF with a 9MHz IF and merits further investigation for other applications. Development of the H-mode mixer has been a sideline to his professional work at SERC and it is unlikely that he will take its development further. However, he feels he has enough information to design a complete high-performance HF receiver, after first building and testing the necessary antenna input bandpass filters to ensure that they have intercept points in the +60dBm region.

Some initial tests by G3SBI with a simple two-crystal 9MHz ladder filter suggests that, as forecast in the September *TT*, this approach is likely to overcome completely the intercept limitations of most available lattice-type crystal filters.

THOSE REFLECTOMETER DIODES, IPS & HARMONICS

SEVERAL READERS HAVE pointed out that G3RZP's investigation into 'SWR bridges and Harmonics' (*TT*, August) leaves some unanswered questions. For example, when the antenna is not ideally matched, so that there will be reverse current flowing through the bridge diodes, a by-no-means unusual situation. Then, as Dennis Lisney, G3MNO, points out, there is the possible effect of the SWR-bridge diodes on incoming signals. He writes: "A few years ago I switched on my FT301 on 3.5MHz to find the band apparently full of 'rubbish', seemingly broadcast-based. This turned out to be generated by a non-linear Belling-type coax connector. A gentle wipe

with wire wool provided a cure for another year or so. But some time later I changed the ATU for a pi-network to find the problem reappearing. The 'cure' this time was to remove the reflectometer after tuning up.

"Unfortunately, this does work with the FT290 and HX-240 transverter. The transverter seems to have a hard-wired protection reflector built-in. In my case, the problem seems to be connected with the very strong signals on 1.6MHz from the Capital Radio MF transmitter only a few miles away. This provides some 1V into 50Ω when my [low-pass pi-network] network is set to 3.5MHz. I have ducked the problem by using a link-coupled ATU of more 'classical form' (I have a preference for ATUs which isolate the antenna-earth from the mains-earth as experience suggests that this reduces interference from TV receivers etc). I have tried a number of reflectometers of several types. With a low-pass, pi-network ATU, I just cannot leave any in circuit and receive on 3.5MHz – on higher bands no problem – although I could not detect any meter deflection in either forward or reflected positions.

"There is a basic problem with reflectometers and ATUs in that one tends to think of them as working at the chosen frequencies, not the out-of-band frequencies!"

QUICKIE TRANSISTOR CHECKER

MANY YEARS AGO, *TT* described the ZL2AMJ Kwik-Sorta Mk 2 as a simple test set for bipolar transistors and diodes. It can sort out good from bad devices, identify lead connections and determine whether a transistor is a p-n-p or n-p-n device (details can still be found in *ART7* pp363-364).

A rather difference approach is described by Brian J Field, VK6BQN (*Amateur Radio*, August 1993, p26): **Fig 5**. He writes: "Almost all parts can be found in the junk-box and none is critical. The principle is that the transistor acts as an oscillator using the centre-tapped primary of a low-voltage [mains] transformer. The secondary (240V winding) drives a meter to indicate oscillation. If the transistor is a dud nothing happens and the meter doesn't move."

VK6BQN points out that some versions use a NE51 neon bulb instead of a meter, but the 1mA FSD meter is more sensitive since the NE51 requires about 60V to strike. He adds: "The transformer I used was 10-0-10V but 6V or 12V either side of centre tap should work. The only thing is to make sure there is something on the 240V winding that can be

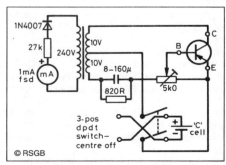

Fig 5: VK6BQN's 'Quickie Transistor Checker' (Amateur Radio).

measured. Use your scope initially to make sure the device oscillates by connecting the probe to the total of the low voltage side and if necessary adjust the value of the 8µF capacitor to whatever is a suitable value for reliable operation. Once you are sure it is oscillating there is the matter of getting the meter to indicate. This is best done experimentally depending on the meter sensitivity and voltage obtained. There are some hefty spikes but since the meter is only going to read average voltage it should be set to about 30V full scale (ie 27k resistor with 1mA FSD)."

In construction various transistor sockets (TO3, TO66 and TO220) or crocodile clips etc are mounted on a Bakelite panel: "Mount the sockets for TO3 and TO66 with round head screws so that they will touch the transistor case to make the collector connection. I also reamed out the holes for E and B on these two sockets to accommodate devices with solder traces on their pins. The switch should have a centre-off position to avoid draining the battery. In operation it is merely a matter of plugging in the transistor and twiddling the pot to get it to oscillate."

Although VK6BQN used a conventional 8µF electrolytic, he points out that more reliable operation with polarity reversals when switching from NPN to PNP would be obtained with a bipolar or a plastic dielectric capacitor. He warns that at one extreme of the pot travel, the base collector junction may be damaged if reverse polarity is applied. The current is limited only by the transformer winding and the internal resistance of the C cell. VK6BQN has not experienced trouble but warns that the possibility exists.

RAZOR COUNTER-MEASURES

THE STORY OF THE development of British radar (RDF/radiolocation) as a means of defending the country against the air attacks of the second world war has been told a number of times, both by those who were concerned and by historians. But there has been relatively little written about the equally impressive development of naval radar. William Hackmann writes, in reviewing in *Nature* (29 July, 1993) the book *Radar at Sea: The Royal Navy in World War 2* by Derek Howse (Macmillan, 1991, pp383, £25): "In March 1935, the only instrument available on Royal Navy ships for detecting aircraft was a pair of binoculars of magnification x7. Shortly after the Munich crisis [September/October 1938], the battleship Rodney and the cruiser Sheffield could detect aircraft 60 miles away with apparatus that had not even been on the drawing board four years before.

"This book chronicles the evolution and influence of naval radar during the nine momentous years from late 1936, when the first experimental set (type 79X) was fitted for trial in the elderly mine-sweeper *Saltburn*, to 1945, when the cruiser *Norfolk* was fitted with the latest radars (type 274 for gunnery and types 277, 293 and 181B as warning sets) and other electronic gear for action information and target indication, such as the plan position indicator, skiatron and automatic plotting table."

It has been said recently by Lord Jenkins of Hillhead, Chancellor of Oxford University, that "Meticulous historical research is almost

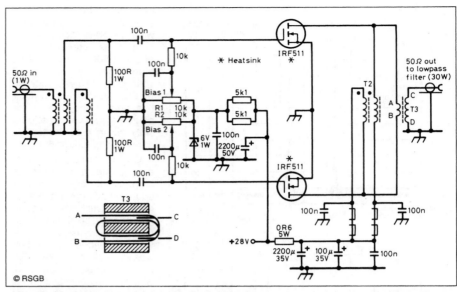

Fig 6: AA3X's '1W-in, 30W-out on 3.5MHz' amplifier based on push-pull IRF511 low-cost power MOSFETs. An NTE Nr TP0006 insulating wafer was used between each IRF511 and the 'chassis heat sink' and their mounting bolts were wrapped with insulating tape to avoid short circuits. It is essential to use a low-pass filter following this amplifier. T1 12 trifilar turns of No 26 enam wire on FT-50-43 (Amidon) or F-50-43 (Palomar) toroidal ferrite core. T2 12 bifilar turns of No 22 enam wire on two stacked FT-50-43 or F-50-43 cores. T3 as shown, wound with No 18 plastics-insulated hook-up wire on Amidon BN-43-7051 jumbo balun core. Primary (AB) 2 turns. Secondary (CD) 3 turns. Z1 – Z4 ferrite beads (Amidon FB-43-801 or Palomar FB-8-43).

always the enemy of good anecdote". Derek Howse, however, would probably disagree since his book is clearly carefully researched yet apparently finds room for the following anecdote:

"In late 1943 the Germans started attacks on the British fleet using aircraft-launched radio-controlled glider-bombs, assaults that caused consternation. A naval scientist happened to switch on his electric razor during one of these attacks in the Bay of Biscay, and to the amazement of the ship's crew the bomb began to gyrate about the sky and eventually gave chase to the very aircraft that had launched it. An order was issued by the Admiralty Signal Establishment that when ships came under these attacks, all able-bodied men who had electric razors should rush on deck, plug their instruments into the nearest power point and wave them wildly at the offending missile(s). The effectiveness of this counter-measure is not recorded, but it must have boosted morale until electronic jammers were developed." If not true, it surely deserves to be!

BOOSTING THE QRP RIG

ALTHOUGH THE QRP ENTHUSIASTS demonstrate the ability to make contacts with outputs of less than five watts of RF, I suspect that there must be times when most would willingly fit a broadband linear amplifier that can provide some 30 watts on 3.5MHz with 1W drive, reducing to about 10W on 14MHz or 5W on 18MHz using two inexpensive IRF511 MOSFETs in push-pull. To achieve these powers the supply voltage needs to be 28V rather than the 13V used for RF power bipolars. The high drain-to-earth capacitance of these devices is probably responsible for the relatively low output on the higher frequency bands, but the amplifier provides useful output powers on 3.5, 7 and 10MHz.

Such an amplifier is outlined by Jim Wyckoff, AA3X, in the 'Hints and Kinks' feature of *QST*,

January 1993, derived from a 1983 design by Doug DeMaw: Fig 6. He writes: "Because I heat sink the MOSFETs directly to the chassis enclosure with insulating wafers, no expensive heat sink need be purchased. An 8 x 8 x 2in aluminium enclosure is adequate for shielding and sinking purposes. I originally mounted and heatsinked this amplifier on an old frying pan . . . . Since the MOSFETs' turn-on voltages may differ slightly from device to device I bias each one separately by employing a scheme designed by Wes Hayward and Jeff Damm (*QST*, November 1989).

"To adjust this amplifier for Class B linear operation, remove drive and terminate the output with a 50Ω dummy antenna. Insert an ammeter in the drain supply line and adjust RV1, Bias 1, and RV2, Bias 2, to the threshold at which quiescent current just starts to flow. If you prefer class AB operation, tweak RV1 to show, say, 10mA, and then tweak RV2 to double this current – 20mA in this example. The quiescent current level is not critical if kept small, but the device-to-device balance is. I suggest that you do not exceed 3.5V bias on either gate; I prefer a value in the 2.5V region.

"The amplifier's stability is excellent. Proper power supply decoupling and keeping the input impedance low (200Ω or less) were the only steps necessary to achieve what I call unconditional stability."

POLYSTYRENE SOLUTIONS

THE AUGUST *TT* ITEM 'D-I-Y Polystyrene Solution' originating from Graham Thornton, VK3IY, in WIA's journal *Amateur Radio*, suggested that polystyrene coil dope was no longer readily available from component distributors but could be made by dissolving styrofoam in ordinary turpentine.

This item has attracted comments from several readers. Lorin Knight, G2DYK, points out that there is still no real need to make one's own coil dope. He writes: "I have found the polystyrene cement made by Humbrol, and sold in handy 12ml tubes by model shops, to be ideal for this purpose. It appears to be nothing more than polystyrene dissolved in trichloroethane and dries in about ten minutes at room temperature.

Similarly, Ray Loveland, G2ARU, writes: "For some time now I have been using the general-purpose polyurethane varnish available in all DIY stores for treating coils. This needs some hours to harden but only one coat is normally required and it really does lock the turns firmly in position. As far as I can tell it has only a negligible effect on the Q of the coil."

However, Don Symonds, G0PRZ, adds further information on making your own liquid styrene, although he warns that the apparatus involved would be regarded with deep suspicion by the Customs and Excise! He writes: "I was interested to read about VK3IY's use of turpentine as a solvent for polystyrene. This must be genuine oil of turpentine and not turpentine-substitute or white spirit which is not a solvent for polystyrene.

"With the almost complete non-availability of suitable solvents due to toxicity, ozone-layer-damage or their involvement in solvent abuse, there is a need for alternatives since solvents are useful in a variety of ways. However, I have used quite successfully styrene monomer (ie the raw material from which the polymer is made) as a solvent for polystyrene.

"Polystyrene can be readily depolymerised to styrene by heating in what I can describe only as a 'Heath Robinson' still. This consists of a lever lidded tin about 500ml capacity to which a copper tube (6mm diameter) is fixed by brazing, either through the lid or the side at the top. This joint must be gas-tight and must be brazed and not soft soldered. The tubing (about 1m in length) can be coiled and mounted vertically and immersed in a water container with the lower end of the tube projecting very much in the manner of a still.

"Pieces of clear polystyrene, not coloured or pigmented, are placed in the can and heated gently with a gas burner. A colourless liquid will drip from the end of the tubing but use only sufficient heat to produce a slow drip. The whole operation is best done outside the house or in a very well ventilated area. Styrene has a strong and penetrating odour as anyone who has used styrene-polyester resins for car repairs or boat building can testify.

"The liquid styrene will keep for some days but in time will thicken and solidify. It is a powerful solvent of the polymer and not much is needed. Expanded polystyrene can be used in the still but has to be squashed to get even a few grams into the can."

A BATTERY SAVER

MODERN TEST EQUIPMENT is often run from batteries which can soon be run down by forgetting to turn off the instrument after it has been used briefly. A good example is the portable digital multi-meter but there are many other instruments that can easily be left running.

In the January 1993 issue of *Electronics*

TT columnist Pat Hawker, G3VA, was a welcome guest at this year's HQ open day. He chatted to visitors and signed copies of his popular book *Amateur Radio Techniques*.

Australia (pages 111-113), Peter Murtagh in his 'Experimenting with Electronics' feature described an extremely simple 'battery saver' comprising little more than an RC timing circuit and a VN10K power MOSFET, **Fig 7(a)**, in which the charge stored in capacitor C1 keeps TR1 switched on until C1 is gradually discharged through a high resistor, R2. The time constant C1 x R2 determines how long will elapse after pressing PB1 before the MOSFET is turned off, remembering that the rate of discharge decreases exponentially. With the values shown, the switch off time is about 6.5 minutes (much longer switch off times are possible by increasing the value of C1).

In the July issue of *Electronics Australia*, p51, D S Chambers in the 'Circuit & Design Ideas' feature comes up with a more sophisticated design (**Fig 7(b)**) that gives a rapid switching action and a more definite turn-off threshold for the FET. These improvements are gained by using two of the Schmitt trigger

gates on a hex inverting 74C14 chip. He writes: "Integral to these gates is a well-defined and temperature-compensated switching threshold. This gives a high impedance RC timing, with t = 1.13 x R1 x C1. Diodes D1 for switching 'on', and D2 for 'off', are needed to ensure rapid switching of the gates. The values of R3 and R4, and transistors TR1 and TR2 allow TR2 to be either an FET or a bipolar transistor to handle any magnitude of load. The VN10K of the simple circuit was retained for its low on-resistance, resulting in only an 18mV voltage drop for my DMM. The extremely low 'off' battery drain was not measurable on my meter."

SIMPLE 50MHZ CONVERTER

ALTHOUGH THE Signetics/Philips NE602 mixer-oscillator IC is not suitable for use in cases where a wide dynamic range is essential, it has rightly become an extremely popular device for use in simple receivers (direct-conversion or superhet). Its main advantage is that its input and output are available in either balanced or single ended form. Also, the current consumption is very low (2 to 3mA) and it has a price tag much lower than that of devices intended to achieve the widest dynamic range. As SN Larsen, ZL4THO puts it in 'A simple 6-metre converter' (*Break-In*, Oct 1992, pp6-7): "I think the big plus with this device is the small number of external components required to form an operational circuit."

In view of the seasonal nature of DX on this band, ZL4THO often confines his 50MHz activity during the summer months to listening. For this reason he prefers an economical approach to equipment for this band. He has built a number of MOSFET converters which perform well but found that they can be rather difficult to get up and running. "A typical converter can have two or more stages and can be fairly complex. In order to reduce complexity to an absolute minimum, I decided to use the NE602 in the simple arrangement shown in **Fig 8**." It should be appreciated that ZL4THO's design is not for a high-performance converter of wide dynamic range but rather for listening on the band ahead of a fairly simple HF receiver.

ZL4THO writes "Signals in the 50MHz band are coupled to L1 via C1. The latter is included to provide DC isolation from any additional stages which might be added later. Signals

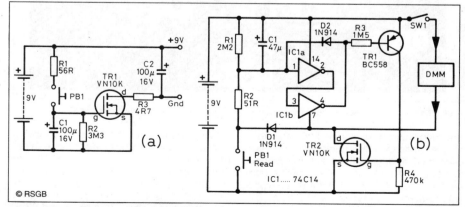

Fig 7: 'Battery Savers' that automatically switch off, for example, test instruments after a few minutes. (a) Simple circuit described by Peter Murtagh in *EA*, January 1993, p111. (b) Improved design outlined by D S Chambers in *EA*, July 1993, p51.

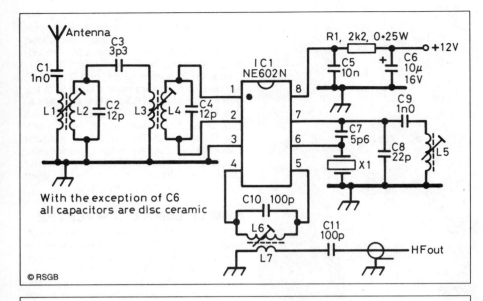

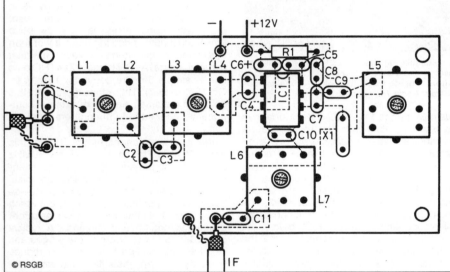

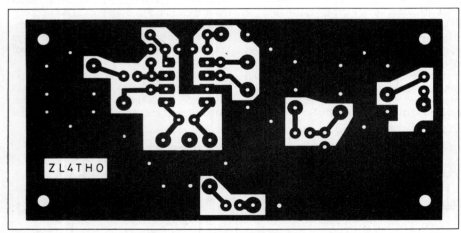

Fig 8: ZL4THO's simple 50MHz converter based on the Signetics NE602 mixer/oscillator IC.

are then inductively coupled to L2 with a simple bandpass filter formed from L2 through L4 and C2 through C4. A balanced connection to pins 1 and 2 is made available from each side of L4. The oscillator is a Colpitts type formed around pins 6 and 7 using C7, C8, C9, L5 and X1. The crystal is a third overtone type, with the correct overtone selected by adjusting the slug in L5.

"The output from the mixer is available from pins 4 and 5 and is tuned to the required resonant frequency (IF) by L6 and C10. Inductive coupling to a low impedance link winding completes the arrangement. C11 is used for DC isolation. Supply is through a current limiting resistor R1, with C5 and C6 as supply bypass capacitors.

"Alignment can be achieved using a GDO

or signal generator. Set the latter to the signal frequency of interest and adjust all inductances for best overall response. The crystal may be adjusted to frequency by light inductive coupling to L5 before the shield (can) is put in place. A frequency counter or scanner may also be used for this. Coil details for alternative IFs are provided. For the prototype, the IF was made 7MHz to allow the converter to be used with an existing 7MHz direct-conversion receiver. Although this project is offered as a novelty, its performance is most reasonable. Optimizing the circuit configuration or component values may even improve results further."

There is, of course, no reason why with suitable component changes such a simple NE602 converter could not be used for 28MHz or 21MHz in front of a simple 7 or 3.5MHz receiver. The crystal frequency will be F(xtal) = F(signal) - IF. A low IF, however, could result in excessive image response unless additional pre-mixer selectivity were added.

Coils are wound on standard slug-tuned formers with metal shielding cans. L1 and L3 1.5 turns of 26SWG enamel wire; L2, L4 and L5 11 turns of 26SWG. L6 and L7 depend on the tuneable IF output which in the ZL4THO was 7MHz with L6 75 turns of 42SWG, L7 10 turns of 42SWG, with a 43.000MHz (third overtone) crystal. Alternative values for outputs on 14, 21 and 28MHz are:

Band (MHz)	L6 (turns)	L7 (turns)	SWG	C10 (pF)	Crystal (MHz)
14	20	3	32	47	36.000
21	20	3	26	33	29.000
28	20	3	26	15	22.000

REVERSE – POLARITY PROTECTION

FOR MANY YEARS it has been desirable to provide polarity protection for solid-state equipment operated from batteries that could be connected the 'wrong way round'. As noted in *ART7* [see *BookCase* p94 to order your copy – *Ed*], the most common arrangement is simply to connect a diode to block the supply from the load when wrongly connected: **Fig 9(a)**. The inclusion of an extra diode and indicator bulb (**Fig 9(b)**) provides a reversal indicator, with the bulb lighting only when the supply is wrongly connected. A full bridge circuit (**Fig 9(c)**) makes it possible to forget about battery polarity but means that two diodes are always in circuit.

The addition of one silicon diode in circuit reduces the voltage delivered to the load by 0.6V and thus brings forward the 'end point' of the battery discharge. The voltage drop can be reduced significantly by using a germanium power diode but even this may not always be acceptable. With silicon diodes, the bridge circuit drops the voltage by more than a volt. Michael A Covington, N4TMI, in 'Reverse-Polarity Protection for Your Gear' (*QST*, July 1993, pp40-41) shows how the problem can be largely overcome.

The simplest method of eliminating the diode-voltage drop, although one that is not truly 'fail-safe', is to connect the diode in parallel with the load instead of in series (**Fig 10**). If the supply is reverse connected, the diode conducts heavily and blows the fuse or trips a circuit breaker. It is clearly essential that the fuse blows before the diode! N4TMI gives as a rule of thumb that the diode should be rated for three times that of the fuse (ie for a 1A fuse, use a 3A diode). But he does not mention that should for any reason the diode become disconnected or open-circuit the load will no longer be protected.

However N4TMI points out that another way to eliminate the mandatory diode-voltage drop is to use a power MOSFET instead of a diode as the switching element, **Fig 11**: "When power is applied correctly, the FET conducts and becomes the equivalent of a low-value resistor. [The voltage-drop then follows Ohm's Law and can be very low for moderate loads]. If the power supply is applied in reverse, the FET doesn't conduct and no current flows.

"**Fig 11(a)** shows how to use this approach with cheap, readily available N-channel MOSFETs; **Fig 11(b)** shows how to use similarly a P-channel MOSFET. Although P-channel MOSFETs are presently more expensive than N-channel MOSFETs, a P-channel device is often preferred because it interrupts the positive supply lead rather than the negative one; this lets you use the negative rail as ground in the more conventional way.

"The FET must be an enhancement-mode device, with a turn-on voltage ($V_{GS(th)}$) substantially lower than the power-supply voltage, and with an on-resistance ($R_{DS(ON)}$) low enough that the voltage drop is negligible. Because the FET operates as a switch, it dissipates little power and no heat sink is required. Suitable MOSFETs are listed in **Table 1** . . . . Notice that the current flows backward through the FET (from drain to source). That's okay; FETs are inherently bidirectional devices. Fig 11 shows a diode inside each FET. That's the parasitic diode formed by the source and substrate and is why we have to use the FETs backwards. Otherwise the diode would be incorrectly orientated and would allow reverse-polarity current to flow."

N4TMI also notes that some of the newer voltage-regulator ICs have built-in reverse-polarity protection: see **Table 2**. A practical circuit is given in **Fig 12**. N4TMI writes: "These regulators are often known as PNP voltage regulators, and the capacitors at the input and output are required for stability. The main selling point of PNP voltage regulators is that they have lower drop-out voltage than earlier types. For example the conventional 7812 has a 2V drop-out rating. That means that if you want 12V out, you have to supply at least 14V in. But the newer LM2940CT-12 has a drop-out voltage of only 0.5; you can get 12V out with just 12.5V in – a real convenience when using battery power."

HERE & THERE

THE APRIL 1992 *TT* carried a note that Tony Smith, G4FAI, was compiling information on the many varieties of the wartime British Army Morse key, known generally as type 'WT8 Amp' but manufactured by a number of different firms in different countries. Results of his mammoth efforts, though he admits that there are still gaps to be filled, occupy 17 of the 48 pages in the June 1993 issue (No 28) of *Morsum Magnificat* and form a major

source of reference for the increasing number of dedicated collectors of Morse keys. The earliest version so far identified is a 1935 Key WT8 Amp No 2 made by Willis & Co Ltd, installed with a wireless Set No 1 at the Royal Signals Museum in Dorset. Later, over 100 different versions were made in the UK, Canada, Australia, New Zealand, South Africa and the USA. G4FAI lists all versions reported under 16 basic group headings, using 8 different characteristics to assist in identification as well as providing information on the key and plug assemblies in which many of the keys are mounted; where identified the uses of the different types of key is shown. Single copies of *Morsum Magnificat* No 28 can be obtained from G C Arnold Partners, 9 Wetherby Close, Broadstone, Dorset BH18 8JB, price £2.20 (cheques payable to G C Arnold Partners). While personally not a fan of the WT8 design, I continue to be enthusiastic about the contents of the bi-monthly *MM*, proudly 'Flying the flag for Morse'. *G3VA*

Type	Polarity	Max V	Max A	$V_{GS(th)}$	$R_{DS(ON)}$	Max A for Fig 99	
IRF510	N-chan	100	4	2–4	0.54	1
IRF511	N-chan	80	4	2–4	0.54	1
IRF520	N-chan	100	8	2–4	0.27	2
IRF30 N-chan		100	14	2–4	0.16	3.4
IRF540	N-chan	100	27	2–4	0.09	6
IRF9Z10	P-chan	50	4.7	2–4	0.5	1
IRF9521	P-chan	80	6	2–4	0.6	1

Table 1: Power MOSFETs for Polarity Protection.

Type	Volts	Max A with heat sink	Input Voltage
LM2940CT–5	5	1	5.6 to 26
LM2940CT–12	12	1	12.6 to 26
LM2940CT–15	15	1	15.6 to 26
LM2941	5 to 20	1	(O/p + 0.5) to 26

Table 2: Voltage Regulator ICs with Reverse-Polarity Protect.

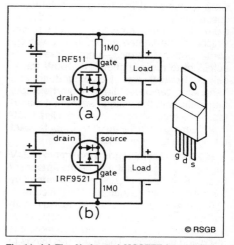

Fig 11: (a) The N-channel MOSFET input-voltage protection circuit turns power on only when the input-voltage polarity is correct. The voltage drop across the MOSFET is low. (b) Using a P-channel MOSFET puts the input-voltage interruption in the positive line which is preferable where the battery is directly connected to chassis as usual practice in mobile installations. The reason why the FETs appear to be connected 'backwards' is given in the text.

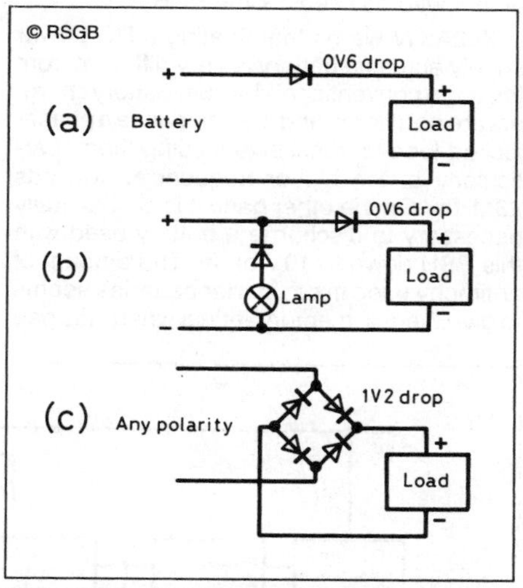

Fig 9: Reverse-polarity protection for battery-operated equipment – simple and effective diode protection for use where the forward voltage drop of 0.6V per silicon diode can be tolerated, but raising the battery discharge 'end-point'.

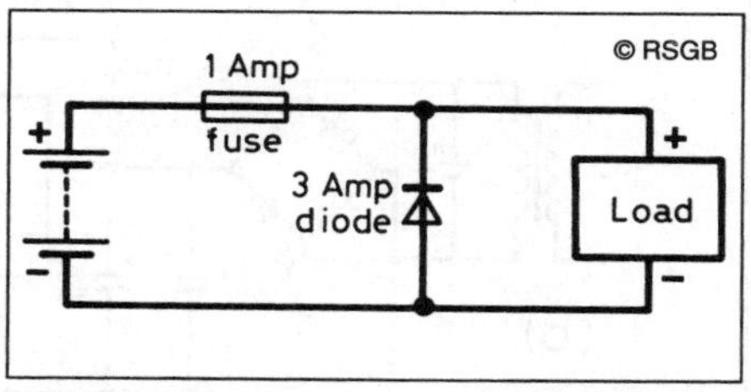

Fig 10: With this arrangement, there is no forward voltage drop across the diode but it is necessary to ensure that the fuse blows rapidly if the input-voltage polarity is reversed. The diode should be capable of handling significantly more current than the fuse. However if the diode becomes open-circuit or disconnected there is no protection for the equipment.

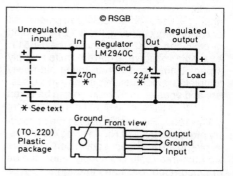

Fig 12: An LM2940 or similar low-voltage-drop PNP IC voltage regulator provides 'built-in' reverse-polarity protection. With these regulators, the capacitor shown at the input of the device is required if the distance between the regulator input and PSU filter capacitor is more than 6 inches. For stability, the capacitor connected to the output pin must have a value of at least 22µF, an equivalent series resistance (ESR) of less than one ohm, and be located as close as possible to the regulator output pin. It must also be rated over the same operating-temperature range as the regulator.

A 'DUZ EVERYTHING' PSU/CHARGER

TREVOR KING, ZL2AKW, in *Break-In*, July 1993 presents a voltage-variable and current-variable regulated power supply and charger based on the L200C IC regulator. This device, which has been around for quite a few years, provides user programming of the output voltage over a range of 2.85V to 36V and current limiting from a few milliamperes up to about 2.5A. It has on-board power limiting, thermal shutdown and input voltage protection (up to 60V). **Fig 1** shows the basic arrangement although the ZL2AKW prototype includes metering, fast blow fuses and an auxiliary output socket fed via a protective diode using an octal valve socket and plug made from a discarded valve base. This outlet provides isolated power which can be floated across a 12V vehicle starter battery to provide a ripple-free power sufficient to run a modern HF 100W transceiver. Smaller rigs, including dual-band handhelds, can be run directly from the output terminals, with the voltage set to suit manufacturer's recommended voltage. Nicad battery charging is via the auxiliary output socket taking care to check polarity.

ZL2AKW recommends a maximum of 24V DC input to the regulator since the amount of heat that has to be dissipated is governed by "unwanted" voltage multiplied by the current. On heat sinking he writes: "While it is practicable to bolt the L200C to the cabinet wall via a mica washer and insulated bushings, it is still going to get hot. There are two things to do: first, use a small finned heat sink on the PCB side of the cabinet wall (the PCB has the regulator right at one end to make this easy to do); second, it is advisable to use a mains transformer with a tapped secondary to limit 'unwanted' voltage differential."

In his prototype he uses a junk sale transformer with a 21V secondary winding tapped at 5V, thus providing 5VAC, 16VAC or 21VAC depending on how it is connected; ZL2AKW incorporates switching so that he can use the 5V tapping for lower voltage applications such as nicad charging at 25mA for the AAA size, 50mA for Penlite cells and 120mA for C or D cells with fully discharged cells given 150% of their labelled capacity over 15 hours; the 16V tapping is used for all 13.8V equipment and for car-battery charging; the full 21V winding for powering HEXFETs such as the IRF511. A variable voltage and current limited supply is particularly useful when trying out newly completed apparatus; this helps avoid disasters and enables measurements to be taken and circuits tweaked before final installation.

The 1000pF capacitor across the secondary prevents rectified RF entering the mains, helping to ensure direct-conversion receivers are hum-free (both DC supply leads can be wrapped about five turns through a 72-type toroidal core to increase the decoupling). The 1μF stabilizing capacitor should be connected very close to the L200C input pin 1. Keep the smoothing capacitor(s) isolated from chassis or cabinet to avoid earth loops. The 3k3 voltage sensing resistor can be 0.25W but the current limiting control (20 or 30Ω) should be wire-wound and it is essential to ensure the minimum setting is only a small fraction of an ohm or the output current will be less than the maximum 2.5A. If the supply goes into blocking oscillator mode when feeding a sharply varying load, increase the setting of the current limiting control.

Polyester capacitors are used for the decoupling capacitors to pins 5 and 2 of the regulator; the 10μF, pin 2 to 'earth' capacitor copes with transient current demands. There is also a 1000pF disc-ceramic capacitor with very short leads for RF decoupling. Component values were chosen after experimentation and may differ from those given elsewhere for the L200. A diode provides output clamping. Not shown in Fig 1 are off-the-board stabilization resistors to ensure a minimum load current, one across the output terminals and another to bleed the charge from the filter capacitor(s), these can be 4k7 resistors. Calibrated current and voltage meters make this a flexible unit; the output meter is in series with the positive output lead, with an Amidon jumbo ferrite bead over the output wire as it leaves the PCB.

ZL2AKW warns that floating a DC power supply across a battery is very different from floating a conventional charger. Battery chargers are not filtered and may modulate a phase-locked-loop in transceivers using them, particularly at the higher frequencies towards 28MHz: "On the other hand it is occasionally necessary to discharge a battery used with this PSU down to 10V or so. The amount of antimony used in car starter batteries seems to give them a 'memory'-effect when charged

with pure DC, akin to the so-called Nicad 'memory' effect. It is also a good idea to make a very accurate measurement of the open circuit voltage from the octal socket at 13.8V, this will avoid boiling all the electrolyte out of the battery when it is permanently connected to the power unit and used as a no-break transceiver power source." His original starter battery can still provide 25Ah of emergency shack lighting as well as run his current rig.

NZART Branch 50 Projects is supplying New Zealand amateurs with L200C regulators, pre-drilled boards (board layout is not shown in the *Break-In* article), 60V filter capacitors and the board-mounted components, but the information given above should at least draw attention to the way in which a flexible PSU/charger can be fashioned around a readily-available L200C.

RSI, KEYBOARD CRAMP & GLASS ARM

DAVID GOSLING, G0NEZ, noted the *TT* item 'RSI, Keyboard Cramp and Brass Arm' (May 1990, pp28-29) which in commenting on recent interest in the problem of 'Repetitive Strain Injury' suffered by keyboard operators, suggested that it was akin to the form of telegraphist's cramp (popularly called glass or brass arm), as discussed in a long unpublished monograph written in the late 1930s by Colonel Prynne, a retired Chief Medical Officer of the GPO, which I had unearthed in the Post Office Archives.

As noted then "Telegraphist's cramp was no joke – in severe cases experienced operators lost completely the ability to manipulate a morse key and, in its final stage, telegraph operation becomes a matter for dread and the emotional repercussion may be such that the touch, sight or even memory of a telegraph instrument and its working may induce intense apprehension, tachycardia, tremors, hyperidrosis or loss of emotional control . . . . [Hence the Class B license? – *Ed*]. Telegra-

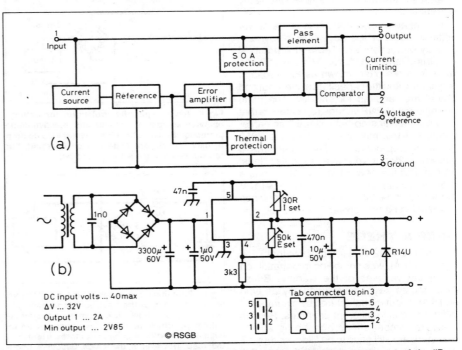

Fig 1: (a) Functional diagram of the L200C IC voltage regulator. (b)Basic arrangement of the "Duz-Everything" variable voltage, current-limited PSU/Charger described by ZL2AKW.

phist's Cramp is a disease of the central nervous system, and is the result of a weakening or breakdown of the cerebral controlling mechanism in consequence of strain upon a given set of muscles." *TT* also noted that the 1930s GPO management was anxious that, if Colonel Prynne found a publisher for his monograph, all reference be deleted to the fact that a few cases had also occurred among teleprinter keyboard operators.

RSI is currently being claimed in the Courts to be a real and not an imaginary problem affecting keyboard word-processor/VDU operators. It is usually associated with working long hours in an awkward posture. Recommendations have been given advising VDU operators to face forward with feet on the floor, with head and neck balanced and the bottom of the elbow in line with the keyboard: see **Fig 2** adapted from the *Hemel Hempstead Herald & Post*. But G0NEZ (and I fully

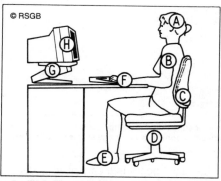

Fig 2: "The right way to work" to minimise RSI problems as suggested in G0NEZ's local newspaper. A, balanced head position. B, upper arm vertical. C, lower back support and adjustable back rest. D, adjustable chair height. E, feet flat on the floor. F, balanced wrists. G, swivel stand and adjustable screen height. H, tilting screen.

agree with him) feels that mental stress is an equally important factor; undue concentration on getting it right, working long hours under pressure to a very tight schedule, handling urgent and important material, etc, etc.

G0NEZ writes: "I think, myself, that the amount of concentration on 'Getting it Right' ie no errors via key/paddle/keyboard etc is the real cause of muscular 'tension' in all areas, ie eyes, fingers, arms, upper limbs and torso in general . . . . perhaps we should seek to become aware of our own correct 'time on the key/keyboard'." My own advice would be to sit comfortably and keep calm and relaxed even when that choice DX station never seems to answer your calls!

A three-page article 'RSI on trial' (*New Scientist*, 11 September 1934) links RSI with writer's cramp first described by Bernadino Ramazzini in 1713. It lists such symptoms as aching necks, shoulders and arms, tingling fingers, and loss of feeling. Research suggests that symptoms can be aggravated by psychological factors such as stress and anxiety associated with repetitive tasks carried out over long periods without breaks.

NORWEGIAN AND AUSTRALIAN MULTI-BAND HF BEACONS

BACK IN JANUARY 1991, *TT* described (p33) how in order to assist the work of the CCIR (ITU) Study Group 6, it was planned to set up a worldwide system of automatic radio beacons. These were to be time-shared in the same way as the useful amateur 14.1MHz beacon network and operated on five widely spaced frequencies: 5470, 7870, 10,407, 14,405 and 20,945kHz. Although it had originally been hoped that up to 15 beacon stations would be established, it was clear by

Time of transmission (minutes past hour)			Freq (kHz) (VK4IPS)	Freq (kHz) (LN2A)
00	20	40	5470	14,405
04	24	44	7870	20,945
08	28	48	10,407	5470
12	32	52	14,405	7870
16	36	56	20,945	10,407

(Four minutes per band, 20-minute cycle through five bands)

Table 1: Transmission schedule for the two ITU HF beacons

1990 that in practice far fewer were likely to come into operation.

However, a first station, then located near Melbourne, Australia began operating in Autumn 1990, initially using the callsign AUS1MLB. By May 1991, I was reporting that Neville Paul, G3AUB had been receiving this beacon quite regularly in the mornings and afternoons on all five frequencies.

An ITU statement of 22 April 1993 (passed to me by the Radiocommunications Agency) reveals that the Australian beacon transmitter has been relocated near Brisbane and now uses the call VK4IPS. It has been joined by a Norwegian beacon, LN2A. This is located at Sveio (59.5° N, 05.3° E) on the west coast of Norway, north of Stavanger and roughly west of Oslo. Both beacons operate continuously on a 24-hr basis (**Table 1**) with nominal power of 1kW to omnidirectional antennas (VK4IPS a wideband spiral antenna – LN2A a five-band trapped vertical monopole). Power of both is a nominal 1kW.

As described in January 1991, the transmission format is designed to permit a number of propagation measurements (including multipath) to be made automatically but includes Morse identification and three-seconds or so of steady tone, making the signals of use to anyone equipped with a general-coverage HF receiver. The 12-second signal format (repeated over four minutes) comprises one second of 100bit/s FSK (850Hz shift); CW identification (about three seconds); 1.2kbit/s sequences for about 0.75 second; four seconds of FSK reversals; and steady tone for at least three seconds. The final sequence may be cut short to permit change of frequency.

THE PROS OF SURFACE MOUNTED DEVICES

THE COMMENTS BY G4EIK and myself in the February *TT* on the difficulty of repairing equipment using surface mounted technology and excessive miniaturisation brought correspondence not only from those who agreed that SMD does call for 20/20 vision, but also those who felt that *TT* may have given the impression that surface mounted technology was not really suitable for home construction and failed to bring out the value of this remarkable technology.

In fact, in 1985-86, *TT* included several items on the then developing role of SMD and hybrid microminiature assemblies and forecast that it would not be long before such technologies were used in amateur radio equipment. **Figs 5-7** from *Electronics Australia* outline the basic SMD approach.

FEEDBACK ON THE G2DAF LINEAR

G8DPS SPOTTED AN unfortunate error in the published circuit diagram of the classic G2DAF linear as used by G3USC. In *TT*, September 1993, Fig 1, the screen metering of the 813s is short-circuited as in **Fig 3(a)** although this would not otherwise affect the amplifier. The correct circuit is shown in **Fig 3(b)**.

Leslie Toke, G3ETU, is another G2DAF enthusiast. He built one in the early 1960s which is still going strong. Bill Wheeler, G3BFC built his linear using two 813s in a Pye PMR cabinet in 1967 while 5A5TE in Libya (one of his many overseas postings with IAL) with a design taken from the *ARRL Handbook*. He similarly endorses the age-old 813 as compared with more modern (and more expensive) valves such as the 3-500, 4CX250B, 572B etc for those wishing to enjoy the pleasures of home construction of high-power linears.

Steve Cook, G4ANA, kindly sends along photocopies of American valve data (pp2410-2435) from a near 50-year-old copy of the 28th edition (1944) of the 2 inch thick *Handbook of Chemistry and Physics* which he feels comes near to being a 'book of all known knowledge'. From the types listed I suspect the valve

data may have been compiled a few years earlier as it does not include the 813 but does list some of the higher-number 800 types such as the water-cooled 862 which had a tungsten filament rated at 33V, 207A! With 20kV on the anode, it could pass 3A, representing a DC input of some 60kW! It lists the 807 and the small Acorn 944, 955 types introduced about 1937.

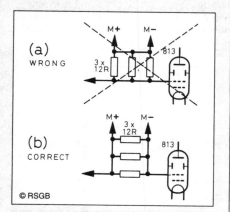

Fig 3: Correction to the screen-grid metering of the G2DAF linear amplifier. (a) As shown in *TT*, Sept 1993, Fig 1. (b) Correct connections.

Dr Gil Cleeton, G3LBS, at the Department of Communication and Neuroscience at Keele University, is involved with signal processing for cochlea ear implants. These enable totally deaf people to hear again. Their device passes RF at about 7MHz across the skin so that no wires pass through the body.

"We used the kits from Blue Rose Electronics (who are apparently not currently trading) and found them easy to build. They worked first time - a jig was supplied to hold each component down, but with practice we now find we no longer need it. I use a fluorescent lamp magnifier but younger colleagues manage without one.

"The advantages of SMT are that the entire circuit is on top of the board - there is no drilling for wire ends. My colleague, Dave Thomson, discovered that we could make the breadboard circuit twice final size and the components in 1206 size would still bridge the footprints so that normal size ICs could be used. Then for the final circuit we would go to half size and use the small outline integrated circuits. Admittedly, for my eyes, 1206 is as far as I can go, but some people can solder the smaller 0805 size by hand! These days, we find SMT so good we hate using wire-ended components!"

Similarly, Albert Heyes, G3ZHE, writes: "Your comments on surface mount construction raised a smile - I'm 58 years old and find that as I get older the electronic bits get smaller! But I have built a number of SMD items over the past year for QRP operation. They work first class and now I find pushing component wires through holes seems all wrong.

"To make SMD construction easier, I have made a jig (**Fig 8**) for holding the components

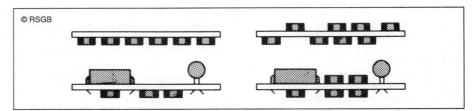

Fig 5: Surface-mounted components can be mounted on or below the printed circuit boards.

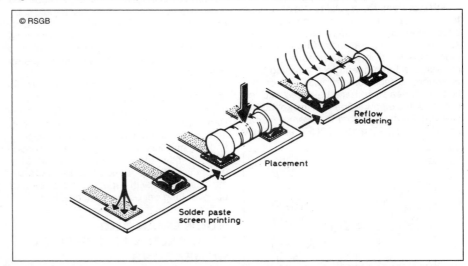

Fig 6: An alternative mounting procedure in which glue is used to hold the component to the board during flow soldering. This makes subsequent removal of faulty components rather tricky as it is easy to damage the board.

to the PCB. It resembles a small gibbet made of double-sided PCB and mounted on a small wooden base. I aligned two 2BA nuts and soldered them to the arm, then used an old knitting needle suitably weighted at the top.

The circuit board is then placed under the needle point, one end of the component can now be soldered using a small iron. The surface tension of melting solder will move small components if they are not pinned down.

'BATTERY-LOW' INDICATOR

WITH THE INCREASING amount of equipment powered from rechargeable and disposable batteries, there is a place for a simple monitor that provides an audible warning when the battery voltage falls below some chosen value. Such a device was described by J Ruffell in *Elekto Electronics*, March 1990, and reprinted in John Walker's, ZL3IB, 'Technical Forum' column in *Break-In*, January/February 1991.

The indicator (**Fig 4**) is small enough to fit inside most battery-operated equipment, drawing current of not more than 1mA at 9V with a TLC272 dual op-amp chip (or about

250µA with a type TLX27L2). It is suitable for use with battery voltages between 4.5V and 15V, and the 'low-voltage' point is accurately adjustable with RV1.

Op-amp IC1a, connected as a comparator, compares the battery voltage, applied to the inverting input via the input network, with a reference voltage of about 4.7V derived from the zener diode D1 (note that with the low zener current, the reference voltage may not be exactly 4.7V). As the battery voltage drops, the potential at the inverting input decreases much more rapidly than at the non-inverting one, so that the compara-

tor always toggles at the same battery voltage as set by RV1. When the zener voltage exceeds that across R3 + RV1, the level at point A rises to that of the battery voltage. C2 is then charged slowly via R5 causing IC1b to toggle, and the output of IC1b goes low. The Darlington device T1 and consequently the buzzer, BZ1, is switched on. BZ1 is a DC type with built-in oscillator and its operation causes the voltage across C2 to fall, switching off T1 and the buzzer. This process continues to repeat until the equipment is switched off and the battery replaced or recharged.

J Ruffell writes: "Since the whole circuit consists of only 15 components, it is easily constructed on a small piece of prototype or Veroboard. It is preset as follows: Assuming that the battery is 9V and the buzzer required to start operating at about 7V. Connect a regulated variable power supply to the circuit and set its output precisely to 7V. Turn RV1 to maximum resistance. With a multimeter, measure the voltage at test point A; this should be virtually zero. Slowly turn RV1 until the voltage at A suddenly rises to 7V. Within a few seconds the buzzer should sound. The indicator can then be fitted into the relevant equipment and its battery connections soldered to suitable take-off points behind the on-off switch."

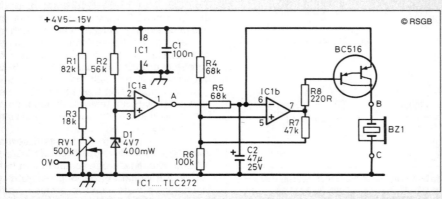

Fig 4: 'Battery Low' monitor that buzzes when the voltage falls to a pre-set value set by RV1.

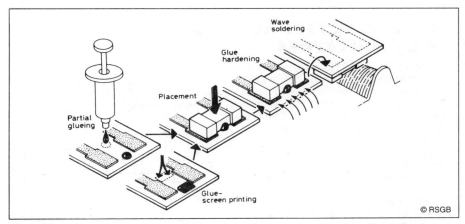

Fig 7: A standard procedure for fixing surface-mounted components on the upper side of a PCB, using solder paste screen printing as used professionally.

"I have used the Blue Rose Electronics small AF amplifier kit mentioned in the February *TT* including its construction as part of an electronics-badge course I run for the local Scouts. It makes a fine output for a crystal set! One of the Scouts built one as his second project despite little previous soldering practice. Sadly the supply of these kits has dried up."

COOKING UP HIGH POWER TRANSFORMERS

SALVAGING AND RECYCLING high-cost components from cast-off consumer-electronic appliances has long had a traditional role in amateur radio, but modern technology does not always make it a simple matter to remove parts from printed-circuit boards, etc. Perhaps it is time we began to look at the potential of some of the less obvious sources. For example, microwave ovens.

I recollect reading an article in an American magazine on how to build a simple TV transmitter in a scrap microwave oven but otherwise the subject seems to have cropped up only in connection with the interference that can be generated by these ovens. However, Dave Penny, G3PEN, shows that a discarded oven can be the source of some very useful components. He writes:

"Being ever reluctant to throw away any

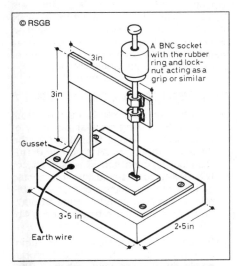

A BNC socket with the rubber ring and lock-nut acting as a grip or similar

3in

3in

Gusset

3·5 in

2·5 in

Earth wire

Fig 8: G3ZHE's home-made jig making it easy to hold the components to the PCB for soldering.

possible source of electrical or mechanical parts for amateur radio use, I recently stripped a (donated) microwave oven, a faulty Toshiba Model ER-672, which had been diagnosed (probably correctly) as having a dying power microwave valve. The oven worked at defrost levels but cut out on higher loadings, so it appeared there was a good chance that most of the other parts were in working order. Apart from a useful range of electro-mechanical parts including the 1-hour timer clock and several micro-switches, the obvious prize was the power transformer.

"The primary winding in this model was found to use 18SWG wire, allowing about 3.5-4.0A, depending on which data tables are consulted. This represents about 840-960VA which is reasonable for an oven rated at 650W output. The secondary delivers 1860VAC unloaded and 1800V loaded to about 200mA. My calculations suggest that the allowable RMS secondary current should be about 400mA. The core appears to be standard E/I laminations, of good size and proportions.

"The primary winding is untapped (presumably intended for 240V mains supplies) and the secondaries comprise a well-insulated heater winding, and a single untapped HT winding, which is connected to earth (transformer core) at the inner end. I would not advise 'lifting' this connection to permit bridge rectification, as the insulation between inner end of the winding and core may then be insufficient. The original oven power supply used the half-wave mode, with a single (unmarked) diode and a 1μF high-voltage capacitor as the only smoothing – not recommended for amateur radio applications!

"However with half-wave rectification, and using normal component values, a continuous rating approaching 300mA DC at up to 2000V DC should be achievable – nearly 600W. Enough for almost any power amplifier or linear amplifier within the UK legal limit – at very little cost! No doubt ovens of other makes and models would provide similarly rated transformers.

"Incidentally, the transformer, although fitted with bolt-holes for lamination clamping in the usual way, did not use them, but was arc-welded across the laminations in several 'stripes' around the core, possibly increasing iron losses but resulting in a transformer totally free of audible hum."

Finally, an oven can also provide useful

mechanical and screening materials, including magnetic strips from around the door, and fine metal mesh from the door itself. I still haven't found a use or market for tired microwave valves – possibly one exists. I haven't tried to look into them in case they echo solid-state power devices in containing beryllium."

FERRITE BEADS NOT STEEL WOOL FOR W2DU BALUNS!

WALTER MAXWELL, W2DU, the highly-respected antenna expert and originator of the ferrite-loaded 1:1 current balun (see for example *TT*, September 1992, Fig 7 and January, 1993, p43), has sent me, along with other topics I hope to report on in a future *TT*, a copy of an article of which a shortened version appears in the September 1993 issue of *QST*, p77. It shows conclusively that steel-wool, as used by W0KKQ (*TT*, March 1993, pp36-37 based on an item in *QST*, November 1992) is not, repeat *not*, suitable as a substitute for ferrite beads in this application. Extensive measurements by W2DU "prove that the high isolation impedance required to perform the balun function is simply not obtained using steel wool as the loading material."

He adds: "The steel-wool-on-unjacketed-coax device in the *ARRL Handbook* is useful in reducing RF radiation from coaxial lines due to conducted chassis radiation. But in this case, no isolation impedance is required between a load terminating the line and the line itself, as there is with a balun. Here the steel wool presents a highly absorptive, low-resistance path for the RF, dissipating it in the form of heat." My apologies to anybody who was misled by *TT*!

FESSENDEN – PIONEER OF RADIO TELEPHONY

RONALD MARTIN, VE3ORN, has drawn attention to a letter by John S Belrose, VE2CV, in *The Canadian Amateur Radio Magazine*, June 1993, under the heading "Fessenden – the inventor of radio as we know it today". VE3ORN, writes: "It seems to me that I have heard other versions of who invented radio and would appreciate another opinion".

VE2CV's letter is a paraphrase of the introductory remarks of the 15th Annual Alexander Graham Bell Lecture which he presented last November at McMaster University, and included the rhetorical question: "Do you know: (1) Who first used the word and the method of continuous waves? (2) Who was first to transmit voice over radio? (3) Who devised a detector for continuous waves? (4) Who first used the method, and the word heterodyne? (5) Who was the first to send two-way wireless telegraphy messages across the Atlantic Ocean? (6) Who was first to send wireless telephony (voice) across the Atlantic Ocean? and (7) Who made the world's first wireless broadcast (voice and music)?

VE2CV then gives the answer to all seven questions as "Reginald Aubrey Fessenden, a Canadian-born radio pioneer working in the United States. Fessendon must clearly be the pioneer of radio communications as we know it today. I wonder how many of you have heard of him?"

My feeling is that most of us who are interested in the history of radio recognise that it was Fessenden who made the first 'broadcast' of music and speech in 1906. In fact, none of the seven claims made by VE2CV, can be seriously disputed, although A F Collins had demonstrated a form of 'electrostatic' radio-telephony by 1900. Fessenden's major contributions stemmed from his work with radio-frequency alternators rather than with spark. His alternator was later vastly improved in power output by E F W Alexanderson and became a key factor in the formation of RCA. Canadians have every reason to be proud of his work. The 1934 Science Museum handbook *Radio Communication – History and Development*, in the chapter 'Early wireless telegraphy experiments', briefly reviews the contributions of Sir Oliver Lodge, Prof A Popoff, Sir Henry Jackson, Dr Ferdinand Braun, Prof Slaby and Count Arco, Nikola Tesla, R A Fessenden and then devotes several pages to Senator G Marconi. The contributions of Clerk-Maxwell, Hertz and Hughes are discussed earlier, and Americans point to the work of Loomis.

The note on Fessenden is as follows: "Fessenden was one of the earlier workers in the field of wireless communication and radio frequency measurements, and some of his researches are notable for the influence they bore after a lengthy period. Thus he proposed the beat reception of continuous wave signals as early as 1902, before adequate means had been devised to propagate them. He afterwards patented the separate heterodyne method of reception after the introduction of the valve, in 1913. He did valuable work on high frequency measurements and compressed gas condensers and was one of the pioneers of the high frequency alternator. He broadcast speech and music, by modulation of the output of a small alternator, in 1906, and also obtained musical spark transmission by means of a rotary discharger independently of Marconi, who also developed such a method."

A detailed, illustrated article 'The First Radio Broadcast – Christmas 1906' by W S Marcell (Reprinted in *Radio Bygones* No 20, Christmas 1992 from a 1969/70 issue of the training and information bulletin of the Canadian Forces Communication System), quotes Ormond Raby of Toronto: "Reginald Fessenden has been the victim of both the vast progress in science since his death, and the almost total neglect of his Canadian compatriots. As a result, his work instead of being recognised as perhaps the greatest contribution ever made to science by a Canadian, has been relegated to near oblivion."

HERE AND THERE

A RECENT EDITION of the BBC World Service programme *Waveguide* drew attention to the difficulty that seriously visually handicapped people have when using modern hi-tech radios and audio equipment where digital push-buttons have largely replaced a small number of analogue controls. It was reported that large international companies when approached about the possibility of producing special models for the blind and nearly blind were unwilling because of the relatively small numbers concerned. A member of the Wireless for the Blind organisation suggested that broadcast radios made by the UK firm of

CERAMIC FILTERS AS BFO OSCILLATORS

JOHN BEECH, G8SEQ, recalls some information on the use of ceramic resonators and ceramic filters to provide stable beat frequency oscillators that he published some time ago in *Sprat*. *TT* has in the past included information on the use of ceramic resonators rather than higher cost crystals in oscillators and also for variable-frequency 'VXO-type' oscillators (eg *TT*, February 1991, pp30-31 and December 1985, p937).

It has been shown for example that it is easier to *pull* the frequency of ceramic resonators rather than crystals without significantly degrading stability. Ceramics are lower Q than crystals and have a higher temperature coefficient but will function satisfactorily for a number of applications including their use in BFOs.

G8SEQ gives (**Fig 9**) a typical oscillator using a 455kHz ceramic resonator. He measured a change of frequency of only about 125Hz for supply voltage changes of from 5-10V while delivering between 4 and l5Vp-p output.

Finding himself without a ceramic resonator, he experimented with ceramic CMF filters types CMF 24550 (455kHz) and also a 10.7MHz ceramic filter type CFS as in **Fig 10(a)**. He found that provided he connected pin 2 (normally grounded when the device is used as a filter) as a 'centre tap' in a Hartley/Colpitts configuration. With the 455kHz filter, the output frequency tends towards the bottom edge of the filter bandpass (ie about 450kHz). With the 10.7MHz filter (type CFS), oscillation was at the top end of the bandwidth - ie about 10.87MHz.

G8SEQ adds: "Using the 4550 as an oscillator in conjunction with a 4550 IF filter, upper sideband can be effectively demodulated: **Fig 10(b)**."

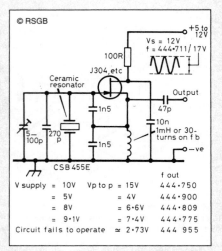

Fig 9: BFO oscillator using ceramic resonator.

V supply		Vp to p	f out
= 10V		= 15V	444·750
= 5V		= 4V	444·900
= 8V		= 6·6V	444·809
= 9·1V		= 7·4V	444·775
Circuit fails to operate		≃ 2·73V	444 955

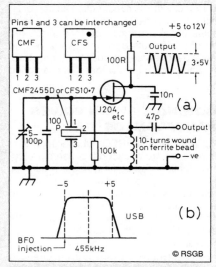

Fig 10: (a) BFO oscillator using a mechanical/ceramic filter (b) 455kHz filters can be used for the IF strip and carrier injection oscillator to demodulate VHF SSB.

Roberts Radio were reasonably user-friendly and that there are also substances that can put 'feelable' identification marks on the controls. While listening I could not help wondering how 'white stick' amateurs cope with modern transceivers some of which now have over 50 front-panel push-buttons and rotary controls, and with operation dependent on liquid crystal displays and multipurpose meters. By no means, I would guess, simple to get used to even with 20/20 vision, particularly if one cannot read the manual.

Wilf Boothman, G3SWP, sent a cutting from the *Electrical Review* "Dry cell recycling claims get battery makers charged up" which shows how the long-term controversy surrounding the recharging of dry-batteries using 'dirty-DC' still rambles on despite all the evidence that this can be economically worthwhile, provided that care is taken to avoid overheating of the cells leading to the possibility of explosion. A mail-order company, Innovations, has recently introduced two models claimed to recharge, a useful number of times, 90% of all primary batteries, including zinc chloride, alkaline manganese and

mercury-free types, as well as Nicad and alkaline rechargeables, but not lithium, mercury and other button cells. As might be expected, the British Battery Manufacturers Association (BBMA) casts doubt on the safety of these chargers. Since their widespread use would eat deeply into a £1-million per day market, in the classic phrase of Mandy Rice-Davies, "They would, wouldn't they".

CORRECTIONS - OCTOBER *TT*

(1) G3SBI's H-mode mixer. Three errors crept into Fig 3 showing the test assembly of this new mixer. The Q, Q outputs from the 74AC74 should pass through 0.1µF DC-blocking capacitors. The 6k8 resistor to the left-hand bias-adjustment pot should be joined to the junction of the two 150R resistors to pins 3 and 6 of the SD5000 and not as shown. (Compare with Fig 4 of September *TT*).

(2) Reflectometer diodes (p56), third column, second paragraph should read: "Unfortunately, this does not work with the FT290 and HX-240 . . . ." **G3VA**

MAINS ADAPTERS ARE NOT FUSED

GEORGE HOOK, G2CIL, recently reported that a teenaged visitor from the USA used an 'Austin House type 3-300' mains adapter to plug her hair drier into one of his 240V AC three-pin mains sockets. The drier was intended for 117V American mains supplies; the ring-mains had the usual 30A fuse. The inevitable result was that the drier burnt out!

G2CIL suggests that the Hong Kong mains adapter should have been fused (presumably at 2A), but to my mind that is not a valid suggestion since such adapters are intended for use with a variety of appliances etc. While mains plugs attached to an appliance can and ideally should be fused, I do not believe that any of these adapters, including those still used in the UK for converting the old three round-pin sockets into flat-pin sockets, are ever fused. The real problem, it seems to me, is that visitors from or to overseas countries are often unaware of the local mains supply voltage. While the UK is standardized at 240V, most countries in 'Continental Europe' have 220V supplies and North America 117V.

The package in which the Austin House adapter is sold in the USA and Canada carries a warning (although not prominently) "Does not convert electricity" and in French "Il ne s'agit pas d'un transformateur" as well as a note "Use with our converters and with Dual-Voltage Appliances" from which it would appear that the firm also market 'converters' (presumably transformers) to cope with 240/220/117 voltages. But, one can understand that visitors who have lived all their lives in North America come to Europe unaware of the difference in mains supplies. Similarly there are subtle differences in mains practice (including the third pin 'earthing') between UK and Continental-Europe that could in some circumstances be important when using such adapters with amateur radio gear.

The answer thus is not to be found in having fuses in such international adapters, which are useful devices, but in better customer education, ensuring that travellers are made more aware of the different mains voltages and mains practices in different countries. In the continued absence of 'universal' standards, and it is highly unlikely that mains voltages in Europe and America will ever be the same, this need will remain for the foreseeable future. I recall that at the IBA a frequent enquiry from the public was why television sets made for the European 625-line Standard G system would not provide 'sound' on the UK 625-line Standard I and vice versa.

With transatlantic tourism now big business, one hopes that American amateurs bringing over equipment, including battery chargers, should always be aware of the difference in mains voltages. *QST, 73* and *CQ* please note!

IMPROVING SPEECH PROCESSING ON THE FT901/902

GENERALLY, I DO not feel that *TT* is the right place for information on the modification of modern factory-built rigs since this is likely to be of interest to only a limited number of

readers and may invalidate guarantees etc. Nevertheless, modifications to equipment can illuminate ideas of general interest.

Jan-Martin Noeding, LA8AK bought a Yaesu FT-902 in 1988 but was disappointed when 'on-air' reports suggested that the RF speech processor had little or no effect. He writes: "I measured the IF after the processor ('Unit board'). With the processor switched in, the audio varied between 60mV (pure whistle, limiting operating) and 240mV (no limiting) whistling shhhhh. The IC is a typical 10.7MHz FM limiter (similar to the CA3028). It may work for a 'single-tone' but it clearly does not work for multiple-frequency bursts such as speech!

"There have been a number of items in the FT-Newsletter about modifications to the FT901 but I have been uncertain whether these are just proposals or are based on actual tests. The circuit boards for the FT-901 and FT-902 are nearly the same, and the circuit diagrams are the same except for a few component-value changes. An extra SSB filter is used for the processor so clearly it is intended to provide a significant facility.

"I connected two anti-parallel-connected diodes at the output from the limiter. The effect was excellent! The RF output from the board was now a steady 60mV independent of whether the input was speech or pure tones.

"There was another strange circuit (labelled 'Processor Level') for which the manual explanation seemed even stranger. This used a BC108-type transistor (Q207) with varying base current and no direct current in the collector circuit. I believe this was intended to vary the drive output from the board (not 'processor level' which should vary IF to the clipper circuit). In practice the circuit arrangement seemed to have no measurable effect. DL1BU has found a similar arrangement on another of the boards (AMGC) with less than 1dB variation."

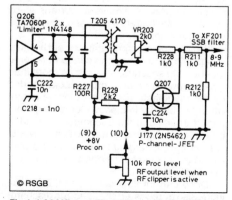

Fig 1: LA8AK's modified RF speech processor on his FT901/902 and possibly the FT101ZE (?). FT902: PB1994. FT901: PB1703c.

"I removed the NPN transistor and replaced it by a p-channel FET (a J177 proved to be the best). The result was that the IF level from the board could be varied, at least 25dB down, using the 'Proc Level' control. With a 2N5462 FET the control was only 15dB down.

"After making these modifications, the 'on-air' reports were very good, with operators on many bands reporting that they had never heard a better RF clipper! Several operators who are known to be quite critical of speech quality considered there was no significant distortion although speech levels were considerably increased. In fact it was found to be an advantage to leave the processor *on* even for local contacts. Of course, there are a few operators who seem to hate any clipping regardless of its quality but they are a small percentage.

"The modified RF processor (**Fig 1**) has been used successfully at LA8AK for almost four years."

HAND-HELDS AND SMALL LEAD-ACID BATTERIES

IT IS GENERALLY recognised that one of the perennial problems when using hand-held VHF/UHF transceivers for emergencies, or where operation in the field is required over an extended period, is the limited capacity of the usual rechargeable nicad batteries, and the relatively high cost of replacement packs if they are damaged by over-charging, etc. There is also the problem that the charge of an unused nicad battery leaks away quite quickly so that it may be found to be 'flat' when needed in a hurry.

This problem is tackled in an article 'A long-haul H-T battery system' by Thurman Smithey, N6QX (*QST*, Sept 1993, pp 23-26) which stresses that sometimes the utility of a hand-held transceiver (H-T) is limited by its standard-issue, (usually) short-duration battery: "If you're providing public-service communications for an all-day event, for example, you may find that your battery has died long before your stint is over. There are many other situations, including emergencies of all kinds, where a portable, heavy-duty H-T power source would prove advantageous."

N6QX's answer to this problem is to use two series-connected, compact, sealed 6V, 2.5Ah lead-acid batteries to provide the 12V needed for his transceiver, together with a charger that enables the batteries to be recharged from any 10-15V DC source. Batteries and charger are portable enough to be carried in a small shoulder-slung bag.

His system is based on the following requirements:

(a) The battery must be chargeable from any 10-15 volt DC source.

(b) The charger must be shut off automatically when the battery is completely charged. An indicator must be provided to signal when charging is complete.

(c) There must be an accurate means to indicate the discharge level of the battery as it is being used.

(d) The battery output voltage must be regulated to suit the requirements of any H-T that can't be operated directly from its 12-volt output.

N6QX stresses the importance of the choice

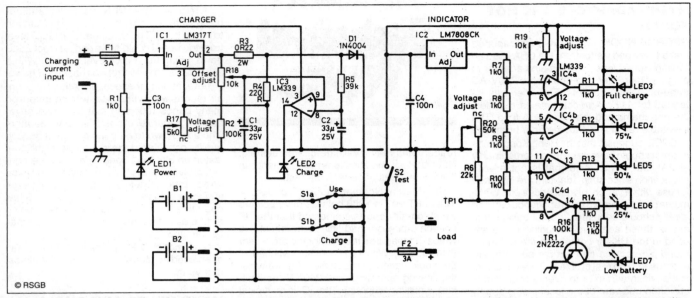

Fig 2: Circuit diagram of the charger/indicator unit for use with small lead-acid batteries providing 'long-haul' operation of hand-held transceivers. BT1, BT2, 6V batteries, eg Panasonic LCR6V2. DS1 T-1.75 LED, yellow. DS2, 3, 4, 5 and 6 green. DS7 red.

of battery: "I selected sealed, paste-electrolyte, lead-acid types. They hold their charge better than Nicads and they're readily available at reasonable prices. I chose two 6-volt batteries which are paralleled for charging, then connected in series to provide a 12V source for powering H-Ts. An added benefit of this switchable series/parallel approach is that it allows the use of either battery to supply 6V loads (video cameras, video lights, portable electric lanterns etc)".

His system, other than the batteries, includes the charger, the battery-condition indicator and the output regulator: "A sealed, 12V lead-acid battery of from 2 to 4Ah capacity is fully charged when its terminal voltage reaches about 15V and the charge current has dropped from its initial value to about 0.25A. This assumes that the charging source maintains a constant voltage at the end of the charge cycle. The charger shut-off circuitry uses this current drop to define the full-charge condition". **Fig 2** shows the system as used for 12V loads and suitable for many popular H-Ts. **Fig 3** shows the voltage regulator system needed for H-Ts designed for operation from lower voltages such as 9V.

The *QST* article provides a detailed description of the operation of the charger circuit (using an LM317T adjustable voltage regulator and LM339 quad comparator), the battery-condition indicator circuit (using an LM780CK voltage regulator and all four sections of another LM339 quad comparator), the output regulator as well as details of constructing and calibrating the charger and battery-condition indicator. N6QX notes that he has found that no single calibration of the indicator unit is truly accurate with several different battery types: **Fig 4** shows the discharge characteristics of four different batteries, all with the same 100Ω load, all having just been charged using the charger. He considers the variations to be great enough to affect significantly the accuracy of the indicator.

N6QX also provides hints on reconditioning small lead-acid batteries often offered cheaply in an 'as found' condition. He writes:

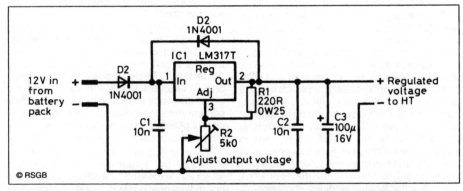

Fig 3: Voltage regulator used for hand-held transceivers requiring less than 12V. R2 .5W linear taper, 15 turns.

"Most of the used batteries appear completely dead, showing no open-circuit voltage at the terminals. A battery in this condition can still be returned to a portion of its original capacity, but it takes a bit of doing and may not be worth the effort.

"When you first place such a battery on charge, it appears for all intents and purpose to be an insulator. If checked with a milliammeter, however, there will be a small current flowing, which increases with time. If possible apply a higher voltage. I have put up to 50V on a 6V battery to get the current started, but be warned and include a suitable resistor to prevent excessive current which could melt the battery if it comes 'alive' when you are not around.

"If this is not enough to start current flowing, try applying the charging voltage in reverse for about 30 seconds, allowing no more than 0.5A to flow – a process often recommended by the manufacturers. The rationale is that when the battery is inactive for a long time, one of the electrodes becomes surrounded by a film of distilled water, which prevents current flow. Charging in reverse for a brief time has the effect of mixing some ions with the distilled water.

"Once current flow has started, it can be increased by repeated charging and discharging until it behaves much as a normal battery. However, the capacity is unlikely to be more

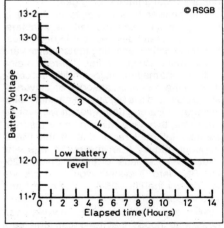

Fig 4: Battery discharge test results on various new and rejuvenated batteries. No 1 new Panasonic LCR6V2.4P. No 2 used Gates 2V. 2.5Ah, D-cell array. No 3 as No 2. No 4 used Yuasa 4Ah. All discharged through 100Ω load.

than about 60% of its original rating. When shopping for second-hand lead-acid batteries, take along a small load, eg a bulb. If the bulb lights there is a good chance that you have a winner. If the battery is completely flat, it will need a lot of work to bring it back to life and results may be mediocre.

"D-sized cells are popular on the surplus

'TWO-CLICK' PTT SWITCH

TREVOR DAY, G3ZYY, originally developed a double action switch to activate a digital voice recorder for contest use, but then realised that it could equally well function as a push-to-talk switch for repeater tone-burst operation. He writes: "All converted PMR rigs and a large number of factory-made amateur transceivers have their toneburst buttons/switches, if fitted at all, mounted on their front panel. When operating at home, this is not a problem, but it tends to be annoying, if not dangerous, particularly if the panel is not easily reached while operating mobile.

"The circuit shown in **Fig 6** will enable you to send a brief toneburst at the start of transmission simply by 'double clicking' the push-to-talk switch. A single click has no effect other than to switch the transmitter on; a double click switches on the transmitter but also adds the toneburst to the start of the transmission. The circuit comprises three NE555 timer chips operating in a standard configuration but with the interconnecting wiring determining whether or not the third 555 (IC3) will operate. The first closure of the PTT switch starts IC1 and would start IC3 if its supply line were powered. However, IC3 is powered by the output of IC2 which is still 'off'. Meanwhile, IC1 remains operating for about 100 milliseconds and on completion triggers IC2 which is set to operate for about 500 milliseconds during which it provides a supply for IC3. A second click of the PTT during this period will trigger IC3, which then provides an output of 12V for about 250 milliseconds; this output can be used to power a toneburst circuit directly or used to operate a small 12V relay which can activate an existing toneburst.

"In brief, activating the PTT once in the normal fashion will not produce an output from the circuit; but if operated twice within less than half-a-second will provide an output that can be used to activate a toneburst (or equally well used for some other application).

"The device can be built externally and added to any existing rig without modification. Most converted PMR rigs and some of the older 144MHz rigs will usually have enough space internally that will accommodate the small circuit board. The prototype was built on double-sided copperclad PCB using one side as ground, but it could equally well be built using Veroboard, etc, since the layout is not critical."

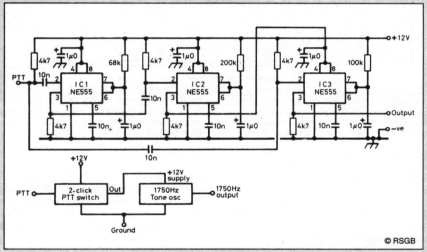

Fig 6: G3ZYY's 'two-click' push-to-talk switch giving toneburst with the second click.

© RSGB

---

market, either as individual cells or packaged assemblies. If the price is right it may be worthwhile to buy say 20 cells and then discard those found to be substandard. I recently purchased 20 individual D cells all of which showed 2V or more at the terminals but eventually discarded 12 as substandard. However, despite the time involved, I still wound up with one good battery set for very little cost."

Earlier items in *TT* have described a rather different method of rejuvenating sealed lead-acid (gel-electrolyte) batteries such as the 12V 1.1Ah and 6V 2.6Ah batteries marketed under the brand names 'Dryfit' or 'Sonnenschein'. For example *TT*, Feb 1988 showed how such batteries could often be rejuvenated by drilling a hole into each cell and injecting a little distilled water by means of a syringe; later sealing the holes with a suitable adhesive, **Fig 5**. It was noted that although these are 'sealed' units (eliminating acid spillage) and with a 'solid' electrolyte, for safety reasons they include pressure vents to deal with any excessive build-up of pressure due to over-loading or over-charging.

The procedure, based on an article in a German magazine, was given as follows: "First carefully drill into the top cover of the battery (just clear of the cell vents) with a 2-3mm diameter drill. Three cells in a 6V battery, six in a 12V one. Then, with the aid of a syringe, inject into each cell some distilled water, approximately 1.5ml/Ah of normal capacity. Leave the battery for some hours and then re-seal the holes with an adhesive such as Uhu-plus. After a couple of charge/discharge cycles, the capacity of the battery should then be restored to nearly its original value, although one cannot guarantee success."

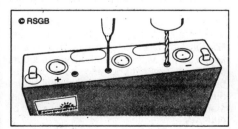

© RSGB

Fig 5: Rejuvenating the three cells of a 6V Dryfit rechargeable battery by drilling a hole into each cell and injecting a little distilled water by means of a syringe, and later sealing the holes with Uhu-plus or similar adhesive.

AN EARLIER SINGLE-COIL Z-MATCH ATU

INTEREST IN SINGLE-COIL Z-match ATUs – as initially described by Tom Seed, ZL3QQ, and then taken up by a number of Australian amateurs – continues to be widespread. For example Bill Orr, W6SAI, has featured this ATU in the August and September issues of *CQ*, including a report on his experience in constructing and trying out an ATU based on the circuit shown in the August *TT* (Fig 1). He gives ten practical suggestions to help those building or using this design, from which these brief notes have been extracted: "....

(2) The fibreglass coil form is mounted in the clear, in a vertical position. The coil is 'hot' so keep it clear of the capacitors ..

(3) The 4-turn pickup coil (L2) is a loose slip fit over the main coil. I used high-voltage hookup wire wound by hand into a coil with five plastic cable ties used to hold the coil in shape ....

(4) Tuning is sharp and interlocking. A dual-needle SWR meter that registers forward and reverse power, plus SWR, will simplify tuning. Tune for minimum reflected power at the same the maximum power output is obtained. One eye on the ATU dials and the other on the SWR meter does the trick! Once you have found the correct dial settings, log them for future use ....

(6) The 'tune' circuit is high-Q and plenty of circulating current flows in the coil and the leads to the capacitors. I first tried a commercial air-wound inductor of No 16 tinned wire. It ran quite hot. Substituting a coil of No 12 enamel-coated wire resulted in much less heat loss ....

(7) With the values given, the unit tunes from 3.5 to 11MHz and 13 to 30MHz with a gap between 11 and 13MHz ....

(10) There is an intense RF field around the coil. Leave plenty of air and don't cram it in a small metal box ...."

A useful technique for making secure taps to ATU coils was indicated by G4XPP, in *TT* May, 1993, p57, Fig 10. Although intended for air-spaced coils, it could be adapted for large diameter wires wound on formers.

Tom Seed, ZL3QQ, has kindly sent me a copy of his original three-page article 'A single coil Z-match antenna coupler' as published in *Break-In* (March 1992), including two corrections to the type-setting of the

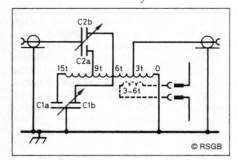

Fig 7: PA0FRI's 3.5/28MHz 'single-coil' Z-match-type line matching unit as described in *TT*, July 1989 and suitable for use with resonant antennas, some non-resonant antennas but should not be expected to cope with a very wide range of reactive impedances.

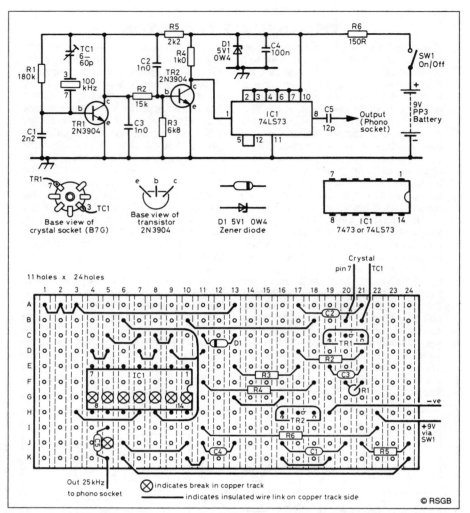

Fig 8: The 'Tuna Checker' providing 25kHz marker signals up to at least 30MHz and using easily obtainable components. Typically, it may be constructed on a piece of stripboard such as Veroboard. (*D-i-Y Radio*, September-October 1993). [Turn to page 59 for *D-i-Y Radio* Christmas offer price – Ed].

mathematical expressions. This recognises that the genesis of virtually all antenna matching circuits is the basic 'L-section' network of which there are four possible arrangements including one using a series capacitor and a shunt inductance. He provides the fascinating information that the combination used in the conventional two coil Z-match circuit, exhibiting parallel resonance at two different frequencies and a series resonance between them, was described as early as 23 March, 1918 (yes, 75 years ago!) in *Circular C74* of the Bureau of Standards, which includes reference to the use of the series resonance condition to suppress unwanted harmonics!

And although ZL3QQ appears to be the first to have published a detailed explanation of the theory of operation of a single-coil Z-match ATU together with practical designs, a basically similar approach was used by PA0FRI as a line matching unit and featured in *TT*, July 1989. Surprisingly, it seems to have attracted relatively little attention at the time. In view of the current interest in this approach it seems worth repeating this pioneering 1989 item:

"Frits Geerlings, PA0FRI, whose PL509 linear design appeared in the June [1989] *TT*, also contributes details of his 'Freematch' line matching unit (LMU) for reducing the SWR seen by a transmitter on the coaxial cable feeder to resonant antennas (see **Fig 7**). It is a modified version of the well-known Z-match and is designed as the results of experiments in flattening the SWR on the five HF bands between 3.5 and 28MHz (plus the WARC bands) without the necessity for switching coils and with a minimum of knobs. It is essentially a 'kiss' approach, cheaper and faster than an automatic ATU provided that the calibrated settings on each band for minimum SWR are known so that the capacitors can be quickly reset.

"PA0FRI writes: 'The Freematch has been devised as an unbalanced tuner for improving the SWR at the transmitter end of coaxial feeders to resonant antennas (eg verticals, dipoles, trapped dipoles, G5RVs, Yagis, loopquads, etc). In practice it has proved more flexible than expected and in some cases permits matching to non-resonant antennas. With an extra 3-6-turn bifiliar winding over the earthy end of the coil (as indicated) a 'balanced' output for 75Ω twin wire or 300Ω ribbon feeder is feasible. However, it should be noted that this design cannot satisfy all possible matching conditions (eg random

length wires), though it is possible that this can sometimes be overcome by increasing or decreasing the length of the coaxial feeder and/or reversing the input/output terminals of the Freematch. To meet all possible matching conditions a more complex arrangement would be necessary.

"Component information: Coil 15 turns of 2.5mm diameter enamelled copper wire on 5cm (2-in) inner diameter. For powers lower than 200 watts, a T200-2 toroid can be used with 15 turns on 0.75 of the body covered with plumbers' PTFE tape. Taps 3, 6 and 9 turns from earthy end. Variable capacitors can be receiver-type twin-gang (10-490pF per section) for powers up to about 100 watts or for higher powers if power is reduced during tuning. For QRP operation a T200 toroid and two air-dielectric variable capacitors discarded from transistor radios can be used. If random sized coils are used the taps should be ratio n, 2n, 3n for a coil having 5n turns."

25KHZ CRYSTAL CALIBRATOR

IT IS A LONG time since *TT* has included circuit details of one of the ever-useful crystal calibrators that provide marker signals up to or beyond 30MHz, and those given in *ART7* are based on dated components. It therefore seems well worthwhile to reproduce the cir-

cuit diagram (**Fig 8**) of the Tuna Checker fully described by Steve Ortmayer, G4RAW in a constructional feature of the RSGB's *D-i-Y Radio* (September-October, 1993, pp6-7). This provides marker signals spaced at 25kHz intervals derived from a 100kHz crystal (suitable crystals in glass envelope and B7G socket obtainable from J Birkett of Lincoln, price £2.55 including post & package) using a 74LS73 divide-by-four IC. The calibrator is powered from a 9V PP3 battery but note the requirement for the 5.1V Zener diode to reduce the voltage applied to the chip.

The name 'Tuna Checker' derives from the fact that G4RAW constructed his in a tuna tin on which the crystal is mounted externally with a stripboard such as Veroboard (11 holes by 24 holes) held inside by the stiff wires connecting the socket. The battery is held with a bracket bent from a strip of aluminium. For fuller details including a component list keyed to the Maplin Electronics catalogue, see *D-i-Y Radio*. If you tend to be forgetful, battery consumption would probably be reduced by using a push-button switch rather than the small toggle-type switch specified by G4RAW.

OUR DEBT TO ARTHUR, G2MI

The sad news of the death, after nearly 70 years as an active amateur, of that 'grand old

METAL FATIGUE & ANTENNA ELEMENTS

ON A NUMBER OF occasions, *TT* has noted that tubular antenna elements often fail after they have been fluttering, or vibrating, over a long period even in a relatively low wind speed, and has suggested that this is due to a combination of metal fatigue and vortex shedding. Medium speed winds, at well under 35MPH, when they strike an elongated cylindrical object create vortices or swirls of air; if these are shed from the object in a regular, orderly manner related to a natural resonance of the object, they constitute an exciting force. A commonly cited example is the pronounced low-frequency hum that comes from overhead telephone wires when the wind blows at a specific speed.

As explained in *TT*, November 1989, p30, when aluminium is flexed at levels below its yield-stress, while no permanent bend results, the damage accumulates and if the flexing is repeated sufficiently often there will be a fatigue failure. In effect metal fatigue is the weakened condition induced in metal parts of machines, vehicles or structures by repeated stresses or loadings, ultimately resulting in a fracture under a stress much weaker than that necessary to cause fracture in a single application,

It was suggested by K5IU that antenna-element fatigue failures can be minimised in a number of ways, including filling the inside of tubular elements with the type of foam intended for sealing and insulating cracks and holes in buildings, or by fitting energy absorbers at the ends of the antenna elements to reduce flutter-type oscillation.

Energy absorbers, of a type suggested many years ago, can be made from a sheet of flat rubber or pliable plastic material 1/8th to 1/4-in thick by 5-6in long, If this is made just wide enough to wrap once round the element, the damping will be matched to the size of the element. This material is cut lengthwise to make four taps and positioned so that the free end of the tabs are about 2in from the ends to prevent changes in the electrical length or impedance of the elements: **Fig 9**. Roger Bunney, for many years the DX-TV columnist in *Television*, noticed the earlier reference to fatigue failures in *ART7* and comments as follows: "Some years ago I was involved in a partnership with South West Aerials and made a number of aerials for Band I (41–68MHz) TV-DX enthusiasts. The problem of flutter metal fatigue was noticed and quickly rectified. At these frequencies, resonance tends to occur on very warm still days and can cause a loud buzzing/rasping noise. I found

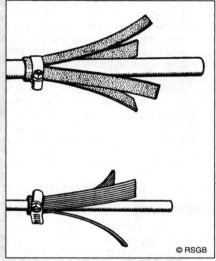

Fig 9: Energy absorbers fitted at the ends of antenna elements to reduce flutter-type oscillation brought about by vortex shedding at specific, low wind speeds.

that climbing a mast to examine a 50MHz element will show the points of resonance: on a reflector cut to Channel E2, there are usually two points of vibration in each element (ie the two elements comprising the one reflector) one very close to the boom and another near the extreme end. Touching the point of vibration can be very uncomfortable, almost painful.

"In all my aerials only the reflector would display this resonance. Elements made of seamed alloy generally do not display this problem which occurs primarily in seamless tubing. We always used hard-drawn seamless tubing for maximum strength so as to avoid bending or damaging the elements during erection. The solution was simply to insert about 12-in of sash cord into each element. this will damp the resonance and prevent vibration. If the elements are plugged then normal sash can be used; otherwise use waxed sash to prevent water soaking up and producing a heavy weight that will cause the ends of the element to sag. Elements should be plugged, in any case, as a precaution against wind whistle! Another TV-aerial firm of yester-year, Telerection of Weymouth used to make numerous Band 1 arrays, filled their elements with sawdust – this tends to soak up water but the general principle is the same."

On the topic of antenna metalwork, a rather different tip comes from Peter J Cott, G3BDV. He suggests that when the household needs a new rotating 'washing line', have a good look at the old one before it is thrown away. In his case he found that by turning it upside down, it became an instant antenna support for experimental purposes, as shown in the illustration. But don't be tempted to use one that has not been discarded or this could provoke domestic discord!

---

man' of Amateur Radio, Arthur Milne, G2MI, has been reported elsewhere, but it seems appropriate for *TT* to recall how much the original *T&R Bulletin* of the 1930s and then the *RSGB Bulletin* of the 1940s owed to him.

By 1931 he was a member of the Society's small editorial committee which in those 'non-professional' days was responsible for actually putting together the monthly journal – with Arthur acting as the draughtsman, redrawing most of the hundreds of circuit diagrams etc submitted by contributors. One of the first of his own contributions was 'The preparation of circuit diagrams for publication' (*T&R Bulletin*, October 1933) followed a few months later by a detailed description of an ingenious automatic Morse sender. This was based on a surplus uniselector as then used in Strowger automatic telephone exchanges (*T&R Bulletin*, March 1934) that he built long before the time when such auto-keyers could be based on electronic memory. By wiring suitably the eight arcs of 25 contacts, his mechanical device could key a transmitter to send at choice repeated sequences of 'TEST de G2MI', 'TEST BERU de G2MI', 'TEST 56 de G2MI' or a string of 'VVVs', noisy but effective!

In July, 1939 while Honorary Editor, Arthur

took over from HAM Whyte, G6WY (post-war for many years VE3BWY), 'The Month on the Air' which all too soon became 'The Month *off* the Air'.

As a Council Member in 1939, he was one of the first Voluntary Interceptors for the Radio Security Service (M15/M18). A few years ago he told me how in Spring, 1940 he received urgent 'broadcast transmissions' from the SIS/diplomatic transmitter in Norway helping this to regain contact with the Whaddon base station in time for arrangements to be made to bring King Haakon VII to the UK. As a result, he was invited to Wormwood Scrubs prison, temporary wartime HQ of MI5, to receive personal thanks from Colonel (later Brigadier [Sir]) Richard Gambier-Parry, ex-2DV, head of MI6 Section VIII and Special Communications.

He gave a lifetime of unstinting service to the Society and to amateur radio. We should honour his memory. [A full obituary of Arthur Milne can be found on page 89 – *Ed*].

HERE AND THERE

N D N Belham, G2BKO, writes: "I have been using the MSM6322 in connection with some

hearing-aid research and have found that the signal-to-noise problem can be almost eliminated by discarding the internal microphone amplifier. Using the Maplin board the output from an external microphone is fed into pin 9 and the link LK2 cut.

A common 8 volt supply was used with a 7805 IC regulator, mounted on pins 1 and 2 and connected to pins 3 & 4, to supply the Maplin board with 5 volts." [The OKI MSM6322 integrated circuit was featured in 'Simply Silicon', *RadCom*, Sept '93 – *Ed*].

The May *TT* item 'Radiating light bulbs' included a report on Tom Saxton's, G3LJR, experiences with the new ranges of compact bayonet-socketed fluorescent lamps in which he reported that while his Osram lamps did not result in any significant RFI problems, the lower cost Mazda range did.

Further confirmation comes from George Clarkson, G3RHM, who found that his long-life 60 watt equivalent (actual consumption 13 watts) Mazda "LOWenergy" lightbulb generated radio frequency noise that peaked around 2.2MHz, extending downwards but falling off around 3MHz: "It is a positive loud horror on 1.8MHz . . . . designed for places where lights are left on for long periods!" **G3VA**

"KEYBOARD INJURY DOES NOT EXIST"

KEYBOARD/MORSE KEY users must have raised their eyebrows when, within a few days of the publication of the November *TT* item "RSI, Keyboard cramp & glass arm", they were told by a High Court judge that the condition of repetitive strain injury does not exist and that keyboard users forced to give up their jobs because of aching muscles and joints were "eggshell personalities who needed to get a grip on themselves"!

That judgement may of course be overturned on appeal and in the meantime, it remains prudent for those using keyboards and keys over long periods under conditions of stress to minimise the risk of falling victim to "non-existent" [yet well documented in the 1930s by Colonel Prynne, a retired Chief Medical Officer of the GPO] telegraphist's cramp that does not appear to be confined to "eggshell personalities".

One *TT* reader who believes that sensible precautions should be taken to minimise the risk of RSI is Bob Mersh, G8JNZ, who has been a professional RTTY telegraphist for close on 30 years and in similar work as a police controller for the past four years; a job that can be extremely stressful – taking calls from distressed or irate members of the public or controlling a vehicle or foot chase or dealing with bomb incidents etc. He writes:

"In my control room there are three operators coping with seven telephone lines, a radio system and three computer systems – often calls come in on all of these at the same time. At certain times of the day the telephone lines never stop – a continuously stressful environment.

"Our Health & Safety people recommend a 'stress break' of ten minutes in every hour which I endeavour to practise although work circumstances often dictate otherwise. I think this practice is a good idea and should be followed by amateur computer buffs who sit straining over the beastly thing for hours at a time. Go for a wander, make a cup of tea/coffee and, importantly, have a good stretch of one's limbs and let the mind relax.

"A comment on Fig 2 of the November *TT* depicting 'The right way to work'. A simple rule of thumb to gauge a good operating position is that the forearm should be horizontal as this does not put too much strain on the wrist and fingers. I was taught this at the Post Office training school. However, I have not previously heard of the recommendation that the upper arm is kept vertical and would suggest that unless one is able to tailor-make the operating position this may not be possible. For those of us with beer bellies it will be an impossibility! Let your arm hang vertically and your forearm horizontally and see where your hands end up unless you have extraordinarily long forearms.

"Fig 2 has the screen at the correct height but does not stress this in the notation, merely saying 'tilting screen'. The point is that the screen should be positioned only slightly below eye height so that one does not have to lower or raise the chin making for an unnatural position of the head, giving rise to neck-ache.

"It is also felt that VDUs should be placed sideways-on to any windows to reduce glare. My control room has indirect fluorescent light which is bounced off the ceiling by a strange suspended structure, rather like plastic guttering with the tube laying in it. It works very well and gives a nicely diffused lighting on a dimmer control of course . . . . Indirect, and somewhat dimmed lighting is infinitely preferable to the 100W bulb in the ceiling lamp which illuminates many shacks.

"There are varying views on the usefulness of polarizing filters. The VDUs in our control rooms have special anti-glare glass on the CRTs and are reasonably non-reflective. For my own VDU, however, I have fitted a good quality American glass polarizing screen which is a definite improvement and makes the colour screen less harsh on the eyes.

"My personal theory as to why RSI seems to strike at VDU operators is that modern keyboards are harder on the fingertips than the old fashioned sprung keys of a typewriter or teleprinter with a long travel. On most teleprinters the keys never had to be depressed their full length before activating the print mechanism. Modern computer keyboards come to an abrupt halt at the bottom of a short travel and are somewhat akin to drumming ones fingers on a table top for ten minutes. [This could also explain the reason why Col Prynne found that glass arm was seldom experienced in the USA with their different design of manual Morse keys – *G3VA*]

"To sum up, my own experience has shown that the *TT* advice to keep calm in front of the machine is sound. Because I use a computer for my living *and* when I come home, I have a strict rule in the house: the minute I start to feel irritated or even minutely stressed by the beast it gets turned off and I go and do something else. It's not worth suffering mental stress over a hobby. I get paid for the stress of my job!"

CRYSTAL FILTERS FOR HIGH-PERFORMANCE MIXERS

THE *TT* ITEM ON 'G3SBI's high performance mixer' (October 1993, pp55-56 with correction to Fig 3 in the November *TT*, p48) referred briefly to the problem that as the intercept point of the mixer is raised, a limitation to overall performance of the receiver is likely to be set by the linearity of the crystal filters available on the amateur market.

This was also mentioned in the September *TT* in connection with the N6NWP mixer; as a result of which Peter Chadwick, G3RZP,

JUNK BOX CROWBAR

GEOFF SWITZER, VK2SR, in *Amateur Radio* (November 1993, p15) shows how an effective over-voltage crowbar can be added to a high-current 13.8V PSU without the use of an expensive heavy-duty silicon controlled rectifier (SCR) by anyone with a junk box stock of rugged transistors such as the 2N3055. The arrangement he adopts (**Fig 1**) is for an over-voltage to fire a light-duty SCR which then turns on as many power transistors as needed to blow the fuse quickly and reliably.

VK2SR suggests that a current of 3A per 2N3055 would be suitable (he uses eight 2N3055s for his highest current PSU). Since they conduct for only as long as it takes to blow the fuse no heat sinks are necessary. He writes:

"The sensing circuit is conventional and the 200Ω resistor could be a preset of, say, 500Ω to adjust the protection voltage. The values shown sense an over-voltage of 14.5V. The 180Ω base resistors are desirable and can be found in many junk boxes. Some care should be taken in selecting the 15kΩ and 250Ω resistors across the incoming supply. These values provide a standing bias to the 2N3055s which should draw only a few mA for the group and should therefore stay cool.

"When fired, the C196 SCR effectively short-circuits the 15kΩ resistor and the whole input voltage, say 25V, is applied to the bases of the power transistors. At the same time the 250Ω resistor is placed directly across the supply and will carry 100mA until the fuse blows. This should be only a few milliseconds but the power dissipated for this time is 2.5W. The 0.1μF capacitor on the C106 gate prevents false spikes. A smaller value will reduce the time constant.

"The idea is presented as a basis for experiment but could provide a valuable outboard attachment to commercial PSUs which do not include over-voltage protection."

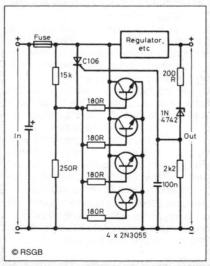

Fig 1: The 'junk box crowbar' as described by Geoff Switzer, VK2SR.

wrote: "IMD in filters should not come as a surprise. It was first mentioned in a paper by Malinowski and Smythe of Motorola in a paper at the 1973 Frequency Control Symposium: the next known mention was in *TT* in July 1977, p533 in a letter I wrote which appeared under the heading 'Receiver IMD and crystal filters' and which began "We all like to think that quartz crystal filters are passive, linear, reciprocal, two-port networks. In practice they are two-port and passive; but they are far from linear or reciprocal! Typically an HF SSB crystal filter will have an intercept point of +15 to +18dBm. Turning it round will often alter the intercept point. The IMD products in the passband are more of a problem than those removed by 10 or 20kHz . . . ."

"Since then, the problem has become 'recognised' professionally. Incidentally, SAW filters are very good because they don't stress the quartz, while transformers have no effect unless they are badly designed. The main cause of IMD appears to be the electric field stressing the crystals beyond the point where Hooke's Law holds, and this explains why higher frequency filters are worse than low-frequency filters; the crystal is thinner, so the volts/mm exceeds the point where Hooke's Law applies at a lower voltage.

"A more pertinent point in connection with the latest high-performance mixers is whether their good intermod performance can be used in practice. In a well-designed receiver, the IF selectivity, the phase noise and the IMD limited instantaneous dynamic ranges should be the same. Thus in a receiver with a 10dB noise figure, a 2kHz-wide IF has a noise floor of −131dBm. If the intercept figure is +40dBm, two signals at −17dBm will produce an IMD product at the noise floor. For the phase noise from a 17dBm signal to equal the noise floor, the phase noise must be 147dBc/Hz (this is derived from the intermod ratio (114dB) plus the bandwidth ratio − in this case 33dB. Getting −147dBc/Hz from an HF/VHF oscillator (especially a synthesizer) is not easy, particularly close in, such as at 20kHz spacing, even if you spend £10,000 on a good signal generator! So extremely good mixer performance is not in practice usable: the designer is up against the classic problem of improving one thing and then needing to improve another."

Colin Horrabin, G3SBI, accepts that if the performance of his H-mode mixer (October *TT*) is to be translated into a practical superlinear receiver then new thinking must be applied to both the IMD performance of crystal filters and to reducing the phase-noise of synthesized oscillators (with the more ready availability of direct-digital-synthesis (DDS) chips). As a start he has been investigating the performance of 9MHz post-mixer low-loss crystal ladder filters. The following notes are based on his report of this work carried out at the SERC Laboratory:

The H-mode FET switching-mode mixer has been shown to be capable of a +53dBm input intercept. However, experimental measurements have also shown that the input intercept of budget-priced half-lattice-type crystal filters available in the UK were not up to this performance but that the ladder-type filter might give better performance, although at that time no detailed measurements had been made. He writes:

"A number of stock 9MHz crystals (ref A164A) were purchased from IQD Ltd (Crewkerne, Somerset). This crystal is specified as 9MHz with 30pF parallel capacitance and is in an HC49 holder. Measurements have shown that series resonance is about 8.9975MHz so that ladder filter designs need a series capacitor for each crystal to move the passband centre frequency to exactly 9MHz. An important measurement showing the high quality of these crystals is that the series resistance is typically under 9Ω enabling very low-loss ladder filters to be constructed: less than 1dB insertion loss for 2.5kHz bandwidth, −60dB 15kHz, ultimate attenuation −80dB, Rt 450Ω.

"Measurements made on a number of ladder filters of different bandwidth using these crystals have enabled a typical input intercept for the filter of +40dBm to be achieved with input signals of 0 and +10dBm (still showing a 3:1 slope on a log plot). This is about the same as good commercial 9MHz SSB filters made for the amateur market by IQD Ltd. If

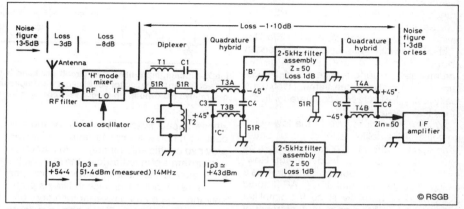

Fig 2: High-performance front-end based on the G3SBI, H-mode mixer and low-loss 9MHz crystal-filter system without a post-mixer amplifier. 13.5dB noise figure. Component details: C1, C2 330pF + 18pF Suflex. C3, C4, C5, C6 150pF + 15pF Suflex. T1, T2 (0.88μH) 16t of 0.5mm (Biceflux RS Components) wire on Fairite T50-10 toroid (Cirkit Components). T3A, T3B, T4A, T4B (0.88μH) 16 bifilar turns of 0.31mm Biceflux enamelled copper (RS Components) on T50-10 toroid (twist wires together using hand drill to a twist of about 1 turn on 0.1inch). The 2.5kHz filter assembly is shown in Fig 3.

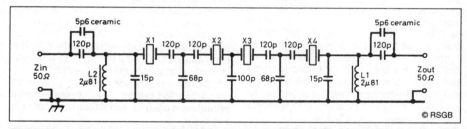

Fig 3: 2.5kHz crystal filter assembly (SSB). Components X1, X2, X3, X4 IQD (Crewkerne) stock No A164A 9MHz 30-pF parallel resonance HC49 holders. All capacitors except 5.6pF ceramic 2.5% Suflex. L1, L2 (2.81μH) 31 turns of 0.31mm dia Biceflux wire (RS Components) on Fairite T37-6 toroids (Cirkit Components).

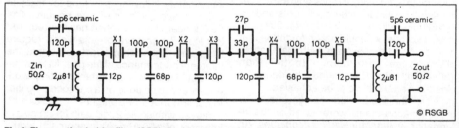

Fig 4: Five-section ladder filter (SSB). Performance −6dB at 2.2kHz, −60dB at 8.5kHz, insertion loss 1.4dB, ultimate stopband −95dB. Components X1-X5 IQD Stock No A164A (9.0MHz in parallel with 30pF). All capacitors 2.5% Suflex except those shown as ceramic. Inductors (2.81μH) 31 turns 0.31mm dia Biceflux enamelled copper (RS Components) on T37-6 toroids (Cirkit components).

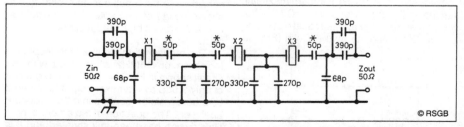

Fig 5: Three-section ladder filter (CW). Performance −6dB at 400Hz, −60dB at 4kHz, insertion loss 4.0dB, ultimate attenuation −90dB. All capacitors 22.5% suflex. Capacitors marked * adjust the pass band centre frequency, in this case 8.9993MHz which is the centre frequency of a lattice filter to be used further down the IF chain. A fixed capacitor plus ceramic variable could be used.

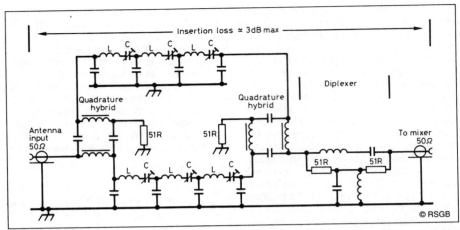

Fig 7: Antenna input filter. One circuit per band is required. Note that the bandpass filters are ladder networks with the capacitor coefficients with impedance the same as for the crystal ladder filters. L/C ratio determines bandwidth. Up to four sections of ladder could be used.

such a filter were used with the H-mode mixer plus a 10dB-gain post-mixer amplifier, the effective mixer input intercept would be reduced from 53dBm to about +38dBm. A better approach is to eliminate the post-mixer amplifier and instead go straight from the mixer into a home-made ladder-filter quadrature hybrid assembly as shown in **Fig 2**. The quadrature hybrid and diplexer system will always present a 50W termination to the mixer, masking the impedance changes of the crystal filter with frequency. Using the design approach shown in Fig 2 enables an antenna input intercept of about +54dBm for a noise figure of 13.5dB to be achieved, giving a two-tone dynamic range of 120dB for a 2kHz bandwidth. This could be increased to about +56dBm if crystals of better intermodulation performance could be obtained, but this slight improvement would not really justify the likely cost compared with the stock IQD crystals used.

"Ideally, the output load to the low-noise post-filter IF amplifier should be of better shape-factor SSB and CW filters than can be expected from low-loss ladder filters. However, if this amplifier could be configured as a cascode-connected dual JFET, AGC could be applied fairly easily since the amplifier itself is likely to have an output intercept of some +30dBm. If the gain were 20dB its input intercept would be +10dBm so that coming down the slope of the ladder filter by 30db (with a filter input intercept of +40dBm), the antenna intercept figure would be +54dBm for interfering signals more than 3kHz off the receiver tune frequency using a four-section SSB ladder filter. Performance would degrade closer to the tune frequency giving an in-band intercept of about +20dBm at the antenna. This approach could prove an acceptable compromise to avoid the complication of high-intercept amplifiers based, for example, on 7GHz transistors with feedback and PIN diodes for AGC control.

"Improvements to the close-in intercept figures for both SSB and CW could be obtained by having post-mixer ladder filters with selectable bandwidth. It is possible that a five-section SSB ladder filter could be standard (1.4dB loss) with a 600Hz ladder for CW (3dB loss). However it should not be forgotten that a local oscillator system with compatible phase-noise performance (better than 150dBc/Hz) would be needed if this degree of close-in signal path is to be achieved.

"All of the ladder-filter designs used for these measurements were based on the information in *Amateur Radio Techniques*, 7th edition, pp68-69 [*ART7* is £6.38 to members, plus postage, see *Book Case* pages – *Ed*] stemming from an article by J Pochet, F6BQP, in *Radio-REF* (May 1976) and are maximally flat designs. Jack Hardcastle, G3JIR has found that the original theoretical work used by F6BQP was done by J E Colin (France)

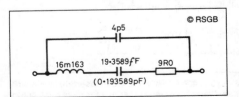

Fig 6: Typical parameters for an IQD A164A 9MHz crystal.

whose paper gives coefficients for the capacitors for up to six crystal ladders (F6BQP provided coefficients for only up to four crystals). In terms of insertion loss, the four crystal units proved the best in terms of loss per crystal used, but a five section filter is probably the best compromise for insertion loss versus shape factor. **Fig 3** shows a four-crystal 2.5kHz SSB 9MHz filter in which a parallel L network is used to obtain the 50Ω match. A five-section filter with 2.2kHz (-6dB) bandwidth is shown in **Fig 4**. A CW roofing filter is shown in **Fig 5**.

"All of these filter designs were first computer-simulated using a schematic entry package, Microcap 3. It was gratifying to find that the measured results were identical to the simulation. The crystal parameters were obtained by measurements on a Hewlett Packard 4195a network analyser with an equivalent circuit-function facility. The individual crystal parameters used for simulation are shown in **Fig 6**.

"From this work it is possible to conclude that a low-insertion-loss crystal filter is necessary (ideally less than 1.5dB) if it is to be used immediately following an H-mode mixer in order to avoid a noise-figure penalty. The SSB ladder filter described has the required low loss. To improve on this would require filters with better shape factors so that the intercept performance of the post-filter amplifier would be of less importance. Some work now needs to be done on a cascode amplifier to confirm that a noise figure of 1dB can be achieved with some 20dB gain for an output intercept of +30dBm. This approach would lead to a relatively simple and low-cost front-end of high performance. If a pre-mixer RF amplifier were to be used to provide increased sensitivity, a push-pull design similar to that shown in Fig 7 of the September *TT* would be needed to give a high output third-order intercept.

"The measured mixer input intercept performance on 14MHz when used with the circuit shown in Fig 3 is +51dBm, a reduction of only 1.5dB over a mixer output terminated by a 50Ω resistor (straight into the spectrum analyser). The question of the antenna input filter design has been investigated and it is likely that two identical LC filters coupled through quadrature hybrids and followed by a diplexer would be needed for each HF band

(Fig 7) to maintain a broadband 50Ω impedance match to the input of the H-mode mixer. Alternatively a single LC filter followed by a diplexer could be tried. However, there would be impedance variations at the edge of the filter passband, so that a 20kHz two-tone test may be satisfactory yet tones at 1MHz separation may show poor intermodulation performance. The question of implementing a low phase-noise local oscillator remains to be addressed if full advantage is to be taken of the excellent signal-path dynamic range shown to be possible.

RECYCLING COMPONENTS

I SUPPOSE THAT MOST of us who entered amateur radio in the era of valved equipment soon came to appreciate the pleasure that stems from having well-filled junk boxes of recycled components recovered from discarded radio and TV receivers. These could (and can) be used to build the tolerant circuits of CW and AM transmitters or simple HF receivers. War surplus gave us the opportunity to turn swords into ploughshares for many years! It comes as a surprise that so many of later generations seem to believe that faulty electronics is now a consumer disposable - admittedly, recovering parts from crowded printed circuit boards and especially those tiny surface mounted devices is not as easy as in the days of metal chassis construction.

However, Gordon Sweet in an article in *Vital Spark* (the monthly journal of the Hastings Electronics and Radio Club) June 1992 wrote enthusiastically on the continuing possibilities of 'Recycling Components' as the following extracts show:

"In this age of increasing environmental awareness I find it a great shame that more is not done to reclaim components from faulty and disused equipment, especially among the amateur experimenters. I have little sympathy for those buying equipment at our local junk sales for a pound or two, who complain that it does not work, when the value of the components is ten times what they paid for the lot in the first place.

"Most of my collection consists of such gear, some obtained as job lots. I consider it a tragedy to see someone present a shopkeeper with a long list of components required for some pet project, often to be told that many of them are not in stock, when a rummage through reclaimed bits and pieces would solve the problem. Many will point out the risk of damaging components during removal. The answer is to check them before use. In my experience there is often no real guarantee that brand new components will be any more reliable.

"A good multi-meter is essential to check resistors and it is worth building a simple C/R bridge to check capacitors etc, plus perhaps a simple gadget to check the leakage and approximate gain of transistors. A simple ohmmeter test for diodes, transistors and rectifiers should show polarity and whether the junctions have broken down. Remember that silicon components show higher resistances than germanium .... The main danger probably comes with higher voltage electrolytic capacitors since after a long period of disuse the voltages applied should be raised gradually over a period to allow the component to reform, preferably using a current-limited variable voltage supply. Once the working voltage has been reached the leakage current should be measured [for a high-voltage electrolytic capacitor the leakage current after reforming should not exceed about 1mA per microfarad, and preferably less - *G3VA*].

"I find it best to use the larger, hotter soldering irons and in view of the increased amount of wear involved it is not a bad idea to use one of the cheaper, imported irons. I have little patience with the various desoldering gadgets, unless the component is extremely valuable .... The big problem is the multipin chip. Surprising though it may seem, I employ a small methylated spirit blowlamp, though I must admit it gets too hot to handle after a while, and the jet is liable to clog. The little butane blowlamps should be ideal. Most of the chips that I have prized off using this method have been usable after cleaning.

"They are best stored by pushing them into large polystyrene panels for ease of identification, with a coat of silver foil first for the CMOS types to prevent static damage ...."

HERE & THERE

A PATENT BATTLE may be fought over the Innovations 'Battery Manager' charger for disposable batteries (noted in *TT*, November, p48) with *New Scientist* reporting that although Innovations filed a patent application for a 'dry cell recharger' on June 3, 1993, it may have been stymied by a patent application filed in January 1992 for a similar technique of carefully monitoring the state of the batteries under charge. The use of pulsed or dirty DC for charging dry batteries, with circuit diagram, was advocated by G3BY in *TT* many years ago, based on work in Holland in the 1950s. Attention was also drawn to advice on recharging carbon-zinc dry cells from the US National Bureau of Standards:

"From time to time attention has been turned to the problem of recharging dry cells. Although normally considered a primary battery it may be recharged for a limited number of cycles under certain conditions .... (1) The operating voltage on discharge should not be below 1.0 volt per cell when the battery is removed from service for charging. (2) The

DATA INTERFERENCE ON 144MHZ MOBILE

P R KEMBLE, G3UYK, draws attention to a problem that can affect 144MHz mobile reception in town centres caused by insufficient pre-mixer selectivity in many transceivers – and points the way to a solution. He writes: "The (Standard) transceiver in my car has always been prone to suffer from occasional bursts of interference, particularly in town centres. This takes the form of bursts of data lasting about five seconds and can swamp the reception of 144MHz signals. More recently I discovered that while a Yaesu FT-530 worked perfectly on its normal rubber duck antenna, it suffered similar interference when connected to a collinear antenna on the roof. FT23 and FT470 handhelds were also susceptible to this interference when connected to an antenna having some gain. It appears that the problem is caused by overload of the receiver due to the strong signals from the network of paging transmitters operating at 153 – 154MHz when close to these transmitters.

"A simple notch-filter using quarter-wave sections of RG213 coaxial cable proved unsuitable because of the closeness of 153MHz to 144MHz, but I am glad to report that a three-pole strip line filter as described in the *Radio Communication Handbook* (page 7.51) has cured the problem. Instead of using copper strip, however, I used some scrap double-sided, copper-clad board with the two sides bonded at each end. [**Fig 8** outlines this type of filter. Full constructional details are given in *RCH – G3VA*]

"The only snag for many amateurs is the problem of aligning the filter properly, which would be virtually impossible without adequate test equipment. Fortunately I have access to an RF sweeper. With its help, the filter achieved between 144-146MHz a 1.5dB insertion loss, 23dB return loss, and gave 18dB rejection at 153MHz. The only operational disadvantage is for those using dual-band transceivers with a single output connector. Such amateurs would need always to remember to remove the filter when transmitting on 70cm!

"Many others must have experienced this type of 144MHz interference. I hope this will at least identify the cause and suggest a simple-to-build cure. The long-term answer is for transceiver manufacturers to improve front-end selectivity."

American magazines are carrying advertisements for a new Orion three-stage helical filter claimed to reduce signals outside the American 144MHz band (144-148MHz) by at least 40dB with an automatic sensing circuit to switch filter out. Connection to a hand-held or mobile rig is stated to be fast and easy and the advertisement asks the question: "Is your 2m radio receiving signals that you do not want?"

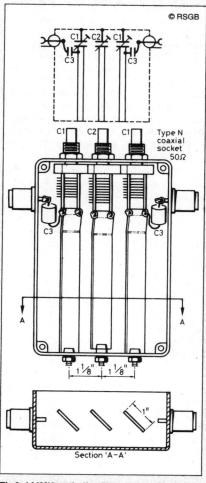

© RSGB

Fig 8: 144MHz strip-line filter as described in the *Radio Communication Handbook* **(p7.51). Line lengths for 144MHz 6 1/8th inch (centre line slightly shortened to allow for rib in the cast box and longer capacitor) 2.5in for 432MHz. Both in 1-in flat copper strip. Capacitor values for 144MHz C1 50pF, C2 60pF, C3 4.4pF.**

battery should be placed on charge very soon after removal from service. (3) The ampere-hours of recharge should be 120 – 180 per cent of the discharge. (4) Charging rate should be low enough to distribute recharge. (5) Cells must be put into service soon after charging as the recharged cells have poor shelf life. See *ART7*, p250.

A paper 'Effects on portable antennas of the presence of a person' by Jørn Toftgård et al of Aalborg University, Denmark in *IEEE Trans on Ant & Prop* (June 1993) discusses the influence the presence of a person has on the performance of antennas for hand-held

portable telephones at 900MHz and 1900MHz, although the results would seem generally applicable at VHF/UHF. As generally recognised the results show that a shadow effect in the far field pattern occurs in the direction of the user.

It is shown that: (a) the resonance frequency of a quarter-wave antenna drops when it is used by an operator; (b) the radiation pattern changes significantly, and considerable cross-polarization takes place. The main radiation mechanisms is diffraction around and scattering from the head; (c) 45% of the power is lost in the head at both 900 and 1900MHz. It is suggested that on average a system loss of 3 – 4dB should be included in a link budget, and there is considerable fading, even in a radio-anechoic chamber, when users move around in a natural manner.

MONOPOLE LOADED WITH FOLDED DIPOLE

ON A NUMBER OF OCCASIONS in the past, *TT* has discussed antennas loaded with resistances in order to widen the effective bandwidth. an interesting and novel derivative of this approach is described by Dr Edward E Altshuler (Hanscom AFB) in 'A monopole antenna loaded with a modified folded dipole' (*IEEE Trans Ant & Prop*, July 1993, pp 871-876). This notes that a travelling-wave distribution of current can be produced on a linear antenna by inserting a resistance of approximately 240Ω one-quarter wavelength from its end to form an antenna which is very broadband and has much weaker mutual coupling than a conventional linear antenna. A travelling-wave antenna or section of an antenna is where the current and voltage remains substantially the same along its length as in the terminated rhombic or terminated

long-wire antenna. Travelling-wave antennas may also have directional properties useful for special applications, such as Beverage-type antennas. Dr Altshuler points out that the main disadvantage of the resistance-loaded travelling-wave antenna is that it is only about 50 per cent efficient because part of the input power is absorbed by the resistor [unless the element(s) are very long so that most of the energy is radiated before it reaches the resistive termination – *G3VA*]. He points out that it is possible to replace the resistor with a resonant antenna having a radiation resistance approximately equal to the matching resistor, ie in this case about 240Ω. the input section still has a travelling-wave distribution of current up to the inserted element, but the power previously dissipated in the resistor will now be radiated, although since the impedance of the folded element is more frequency sensitive than that of the resistor, the antenna will not be so broadband as with purely resistive loading.

This new form of loaded antenna may be implemented either as a loaded dipole or a loaded monopole over a ground plane. The article describes a model monopole antenna (1.2GHz) in which the folded section is a modified folded dipole; by adjusting the length of this element, a radiation resistance of about 240Ω can be obtained.

The horizontally polarized patterns are similar to those of a horizontal dipole over a ground plane, and vertically polarized patterns in a plane orthogonal to the folded element are similar to those of a monopole over a ground plane. Dr Altshuler presents input impedance, current distribution and radiation patterns as computed using the Nu-

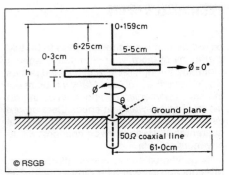

Fig 9: Monopole antenna loaded with a modified folded dipole resulting in the lower segment having a travelling-wave distribution of current so that it can be of virtually any length. A similar (even more broadband) effect can be achieved by inserting a non-inductive 240Ω resistor (of suitable wattage) in place of the folded dipole, but this will reduce radiated power by up to 50%. Dimensions are for the 1.2GHz antenna were measured in a model antenna range. Such antennas can be implemented as monopoles or dipoles etc.

merical Electromagnetics Code (NEC); input impedance and radiation patterns were also measured in a model antenna range. Results are obtained for half-lengths varying from 0.35 to 2.0 wavelengths at a frequency of 1.2GHz on a monopole antenna loaded with a modified folded dipole as shown in **Fig 9**.

CORRECTION

STEVE ORTMAYER, G4RAW, points out that the 'Tuna Checker' circuit (*TT*, Dec 98, Fig 8) should have the output pin of the 74LS73 as 9 (not pin 8 which is unconnected) and the 5.1V connected to pin 14.   *G3VA*

A 3KV 600MA OVEN PSU

JOHN HARPER-BILL, G3IZM, was interested in the salvaging and recycling of high-voltage transformers and components from scrap microwave ovens as noted by Dave Penny, G3PEN, in the November 1993 *TT*, p47. G3IZM is professionally connected with the domestic appliance industry and as such has access to many scrap items from microwave ovens. He writes:

"The power supply for my 4CX1000 linear amplifier is made from two identical oven transformers. As suggested by G3PEN it is dangerous to lift the earthy end of the secondary winding as the insulation to ground is insufficient. However if two identical transformers are used, both earthed ends can form the centre tap of a 2700-volts-plus transformer which will deliver well over 500mA. Obviously, correct phasing must be observed when paralleling the primaries, but the result can be full-wave rectification with consequent improvement of the ripple filter, working at 100Hz rather than 50Hz.

"If you have enough scrap microwave ovens, you can also recycle the high-voltage rectifiers. Some ovens use non-encapsulated diodes that can be used directly but other diodes are encapsulated in oil in the 'HV Unit'. This is a can containing both the capacitor and the diode. In this case you need four HV units as the diode dissipation is enhanced by being in oil. The cans may be cut open and the diodes removed. I series-connected two diodes in each leg of a full-wave rectifier as shown in **Fig 1**. The diodes as removed from the cans already had the 200k resistors across them."

G3IZM's PSU incorporates an AC Variac to provide an input to the transformers of 0 – 250V AC, providing an adjustable 0 – 3000V DC output. The smoothing capacitor consists of ten 400V electrolytic capacitors fixed to the aluminium plate. The diodes are mounted on a stand-off board parallel with disc ceramic and 330k resistors (he removed the original flat-film 200k resistors).

The 600W oven transformers used by G3IZM are made in Bristol by Jackson Appliances Ltd (Model 001) with nominal ratings as follows: primary 240V, 4.92A; secondary: 2765V, 0.58A, heater 3.35V, 14A; frequency 50Hz, Insulation class H.

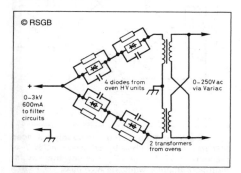

Fig 1: Basic details of G3IZM's high-voltage power supply unit based on two ex-microwave ovens and four ex-oven high-voltage rectifiers. Fed via a Variac this provides 0 – 3kV DC at up to 600mA to the ripple filter circuit including ten 400V electrolytic capacitors. Without the input Variac the unit would function as a 2.8kV high-voltage unit. The PSU includes soft-start circuits. At these voltages extreme care should be taken to avoid any risk of lethal shock from the PSU or associated amplifier.

These are used on Creda microwave ovens (and similar ones on Hitachi ovens). Class H insulation implies that they can run at extremely high temperature without damage. The usual voltage of filament winding on oven transformers is 3.37V at 14A; G3IZM does not use these windings in his PSU; since they have few turns they can be fairly easily removed if not required.

It goes without saying that with any high-voltage power supply unit and the associated linear amplifier, it is essential to recognise that the voltages concerned are lethal and *great care* should be taken to ensure complete safety!

G3IZM also adds to G3PEN's list of useful material that can be salvaged from ovens. He writes: "There is still more to be got from the scrap oven. G3PEN may like to know that dud magnetrons also yield useful parts. Most commercial magnetrons are held together with 'toymakers tabs' which can easily be prised open to liberate two extremely powerful ring magnets. One of these has been tested as a 'mag mount' at up to 100MPH carrying a 144MHz quarter-wave whip antenna!

LOW-NOISE UHF PRE-AMPLIFIERS

AT UHF, UNLIKE HF, there is still a requirement for high gain, low-noise signal-frequency pre-amplifiers, and at such frequencies the GaAs FET devices are now being joined by various HEMT (High Electron Mobility Transistor) and related devices (see *TT*, August 1992, p40 for the noise figures of various state-of-the-art modulation-doped field-effect devices).

In the ARRL's *QEX* (November 1993), Zack Lau, KH6CP/1 describes a 13cm (2.3-2.45GHz) preamplifier which uses an NEC NE32684A PHEMT device and 100pF ATC IOOA chip capacitors with a measured noise figure of approximately 0.4dB and a gain of around 14 to 17dB.

Two MGF1302 GaAs FETs are used by Davide Cardesi, I1DDS, (*Radio Rivista*, November 1993 p36) for a 900-1800MHz low-noise pre-amplifier: **Fig 2**. At 1296MHz this has a gain of some 27dB and a noise factor of 1.5dB, and is based on a design by Matjaz Vidmar, YT3MV, published in *VHF Communications,* February 1992.

THE COMUDIPOLE IS REVISITED

JOHN HEYS, G3BDQ, ADDS a suggestion concerning the PA0SE 'Comudipole' multiband antenna (*TT*, May): "The technique of having a 'pre-ATU' matcher is one I have found useful, especially on 1.8 and 3.5MHz when using end-fed wires presenting an unworkable impedance/reactance into a conventional ATU.

"I feel, however, that the PA0SE design as shown presents a practical problem: weight and sag. The balun as described will have appreciable weight (500cm of coax plus former and hardware) with the coax downlead, even when using RG58 or similar, will add to this. Were I to make a similar antenna, I would have a vertical section using open wire, 300Ω slotted line, or the new, excellent 450Ω slotted line which would descend down to a wood pole about 10ft (or less) high, at the top of which would be the balun. Onwards would be the coax (even heavy UR67) which could be run along the ground to the operating posi-

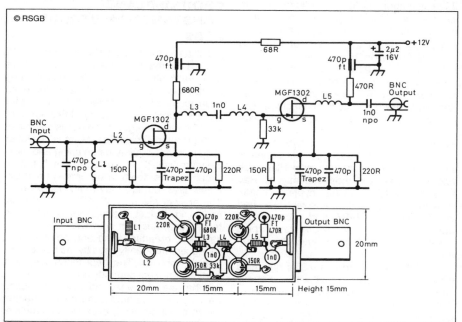

Fig 2: 1296MHz (900-1800MHz) low-noise UHF pre-amplifier as described by I1DDS providing some 27dB gain and a noise factor of 1.5dB based on an earlier design by YT3MV. L1 6cm of copper wire of diameter 0.15mm with diameter 1mm. L2 1 turn of silvered copper wire diameter 0.5mm to a diameter of 3mm. L3 and L4 represent the inductance of the 1nF (NPO) capacitor. L5 is the inductance of the GaAs drain lead.

tion. An added bonus to this scheme would be that the open-wire part of the download would in effect increase the total length of the antenna, making it effective on 3.5MHz even were the top (A-B) only 60 or 70% of the half-wave dipole length for the lowest frequency band." G3BDQ adds: "The high SWR on the coax (up to 20:1) means that for powers above about 100W it would be advisable to use good quality UR67 or similar to avoid the flash over that could occur with 'thin' cables." **Fig 3**.

I might also add that the weight problem with the balun situated as specified by PA0SE might also be overcome with the antenna erected as a symmetrical inverted-vee with central support.

SUPER-LINEAR FRONT ENDS

BY COINCIDENCE, TWO VERY similar comments have come to me in respect of the *TT* items on the double-balanced quad-FET mixers described originally in *QST* by Jacob Makhinson, N6NWP, (*TT*, September 1993) and the improved H-mode variation of Colin Horrabin, G3SBI, (*TT*, October). A letter from J Broutin, RS87251, of Biscarrosse, France and a telephone call from B J Mitchell, G3HJK, both felt that full acknowledgement for the early development of super-linear receiver mixers should be given to W K Squires, W2PUL, who in 'A new approach to receiver front-end design' (*QST*, September 1963) was the first to draw attention to the importance of balanced switching mixers based on beam-deflection valves such as the now virtually unobtainable 7360 in improving the strong signal performance of single and multiple conversion communication receivers. The 7360 had originally been developed by RCA as a high-level mixer for SSB transmitters and W2PUL appears to have been the first to investigate in depth its value as a receiver mixer: **Fig 4**. Some details of this article and W2PUL's mixer duly appeared in *TT* (December 1963) and subsequently in every edition of *Amateur Radio Techniques* including *ART – Edition 7* which is still in print.

W2PUL's radically new approach to receiver design (no RF amplifier was required in front of the 7360 mixer) was subsequently adopted for the Squires-Sanders SS-1R receiver but soon afterwards both Squires and Sanders were killed in an air crash. The merits of the balanced beam-deflection mixer lived on. In the UK such a mixer was used by Peter Martin, G3PDM, for a hybrid valve-solidstate receiver described in a series of articles in *RadCom* under the title 'Plagiarize and Hybridize' and most recently by Ray Howgego, G4DTC, in his 'hybrid ultimate' receiver of which the front-end was described in *TT*, December 1987, and subsequently appears in the new *Technical Topics Scrapbook, 1985-89* [see *Book Case* page 93 – Ed].

W2PUL showed that a 7360 balanced switching-mixer could cope with extremely strong signals without cross-modulation or desensitization (blocking) but in 1963 little attention was paid to the IMD products of receiver mixers and amplifiers. At that time valve-mixers were still superior to solid-state mixers. However in 1968, R P Rafuse presented a paper 'Symmetrical Mosfet mixers

of high dynamic range' including an arrangement with a dynamic range of 115dB. His experimental double-balanced broadband HF mixer used four Fairchild 2N4067 FRET devices with a local oscillator power of 2.5 watts (*TT*, March 1973, Fig 1).

Ed Oxley, KB6QJ, of Siliconix developed a basically similar double-balanced JFET mixer covering 50-250MHz using four U310 (*TT*, March 1973), **Fig 5**, as the forerunner to a series of high-performance switching (commutation) mixers based on integrated FET arrays such as the Si8901 used by N6NWP and the D5000 used by G3SBI. By the 1970s it was recognised that probably the most critical characteristic of a receiver was the hypothetical 'third-order intercept point' roughly some 15dBm higher than the compression point. Peter Chadwick, G3RZP, has pointed out that although the basic strong signal handling performance of the 7360 was extremely good, its intercept point was less impressive. The H-mode mixer is thus truly state-of-the-art for HF mixers.

Both RS87251 and G3HJK drew attention to an article by Ray Moore, 'Designing communications receivers for good strong signal performance' (*Ham Radio*, February 1973) in which he discussed the problem of intermodulation. However it was not until later than this characteristic began to be usually specified in terms of ±dBm.

A number of articles by Ulrich Rohde, DJ2LR, while working in the USA, have further described high-performance solid-state mixers, and the advantages of doubly balancing instead of singly-balancing as in the original W2PUL 7360 mixer are now well recognised. However, it seems appropriate to trace the lineage of high-performance mixers including the latest H-mode mixer which can be seen as a direct descendant of W2PUL's 7360 mixer and the radical approach he adopted for the SSR-1 receiver of 1963.

GROUND-PLANE CONSTRUCTION VERSUS PCBS

DURING 1992 A NUMBER of items in *TT* pointed out that for home construction there were valid alternatives to the use of d-i-y printed circuit boards, which seem too often to be accepted as the essential technique for modern electronic circuitry. Mike Graber, WA1SVF in the regular Lab Notes column of *QST* ('Printed-Circuit Board Circus', October 1993) provides guidance on using and making your own PCBs, but also asks: "Printed-circuit boards seem to be almost universal these days, but are they really necessary?" The answer given by WA1SVF is: "In most cases no. In fact, many other construction techniques, such as wire wrap, 'ugly' construction, breadboarding and point-to-point wiring, are frequently used by the home electronics hobbyist. The best technique for a particular project depends upon its complexity, the need for easy modifications during development, durability, the environment in which it will be used, ease of construction, components used, operating frequency and other circuit requirements."

But WA1SVF then concentrates solely on etched-PCB construction. It seems apposite

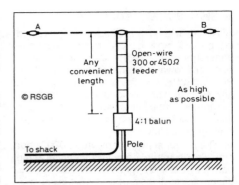

Fig 3: G3BDQ suggests that supporting the pre-match-unit (balun) of PA0SE's 'Comudipole' multiband HF antenna (*TT*, May) on a low pole with an open-wire section would minimize sag and weight problems and permit effective use of smaller A-B top spans.

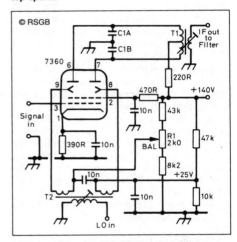

Fig 4: The 1963 recommendation of W2PUL using the RCA 7360 beam-deflection valve as a first or second receiver mixer as a means of reducing cross-modulation and blocking in HF communications receivers. This was incorporated into the radically new receiver configuration of his SS-1-R receiver marketed by Squires-Sanders Inc (associated with Clegg Laboratories) until both were lost in an aircraft accident. The mixer functioned as a balanced, switching (commutation) mixer. Oscillator voltage at deflection plates some 1-10V rms. T1 and T2 and general layout needed to be arranged to maintain balance.

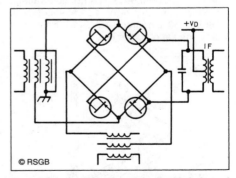

Fig 5: Basic configuration of the doubly-balanced FET mixer as described by Ed Oxley, KB6QJ, of Siliconix in *TT*, March 1973 opening the way for high-performance semiconductor mixers. This was developed as a broadband 50-250MHz mixer using four Siliconix U310 FETs.

to quote a 1992 letter from R C Arnold, G8ZDU, who also sent a number of photographs of equipment built without the use of conventional PCB techniques: "Like many others of the older generation of radio amateurs, I have encountered many problems with the manufacture of one-off PCBs and have seriously questioned many of the on-board wiring configurations needed to joint quite simple componentry together. Often there were serious problems when I tried to etch the unwanted copper-laminate off the board as it tended to take part of the wanted tracks so wasting the time-consuming labour spent in preparing the track layout on the board.

"I could not see the wisdom, at least for one-off projects, of firstly having to draw the circuit onto a board with all the problems of overlapping wiring or tracks which had to travel all round the board. I found myself questioning the wisdom of having long lengths of tracks that must be inductively or capacitively coupled to each other. I felt that point-to-point wiring must be simpler and present fewer problems. Many of my store of components were unsuitable for PCB construction, along with the need to predict accurately their fixing positions and pin-layout. In 1968, faced with the onslaught of ICs and semiconductors, I decided to abandon the PCB approach in favour of the to me more familiar ground-plane, point-to-point wiring which seemed to have more credibility for the projects I wanted to build.

"Although at first it was impossible to obtain double-sided fibreglass board (single sided formica type board tended to warp badly) I now use only double-sided boards. An early system I adopted was to have one face as the VCC+ rail, with the other face as ground plane. Although this presented no difficulties, it made later identification of the stuck-on ICs impossible due to their upside-down mounting, and tended to look scrappy and non-

professional. This technique has therefore been relegated to history.

"Then I found that pre-drilling holes for ICs presented a problem with the end of small-size drill tending to skate over the surface of the laminate. This was remedied by outlining the pinout on a spare piece of Vero (proto-type) board and then using this as a drill guide and drilling template. It became quite easy to counter-sink two holes each side of the board using a 3.5mm drill, where the Vcc+ and signal control legs required insulating from the board. The IC can then be located with a small amount of glue on the back to fix it to the board or, as I sometimes do, just solder the grounded legs of the IC to the ground plane. The remaining pins provide adequate fixing points for the necessary point-to-point wiring. Other insulated fixing points can similarly be provided by inserting a serrated pin into a drilled and countersunk hole.

"One of my favoured set-ups is to segregate the VCC+ supply wiring from the signal path wiring; this simplifies decoupling and inductive wiring runs which could inter-react with other circuit elements by having these on one side of the board and the signal path circuits on the other side of the separating ground planes. This has the additional effect of simplifying the circuitry on the signal-path side of the board.

"Transistors can be located by drilling out an appropriately-sized hole and countersinking each side to prevent the case from making contact with the ground plane; then pushing the transistor in dead-bug fashion, through a nylon washer and then into the tightly-fitting hole in the board. Hole size can be adjusted with a half-round needle file. I note that industry is now beginning to use similar techniques for test projects and UHF equipment."

HEAVY DUTY (15A) POWER SUPPLY UNIT

AL AKERS, ZS2U (*Radio ZS*, June 1993) claims no originality for the power supply unit shown in **Fig 6** but reports that it has given him eleven years of trouble-free service in providing a well-regulated supply for his FT7B transceiver. He writes: "The circuit diagram is

largely self-explanatory. The transformer secondary needs to be capable of supplying the required current. Diodes DI to D4 should be rated at 100PIV with a current rating of preferably twice the required maximum current, with the fuse rating capable of sustaining the in-rush switch-on current and again roughly twice the load current.

Examples of ground-plane plus point to point wiring used by R C Arnold, G8ZDU.

"Use one 2N3055 for each 5A of required current. With the three shown it becomes a 15A supply. Mount the 2N3055s, the MJ2955 and the LM317K on suitably-sized heatsinks. The 0.2Ω resistors in the 2N3055 emitters should be wirewound and capable of each carrying 5A. The ferrite bead winding must be capable of carrying the required output (ie 15A in this case). This bead and the associated capacitors form an RF filter to prevent RF feeding back into the power supply. The 5k (linear) potentiometer is adjusted to give the required output voltage."

HERE AND THERE

DR HARRY KLEIN, W2SQ, notes in *QST* (October 1993) that a 46-year-old microwave technician in Ohio with electronics experience in the military and in TV broadcasting was diagnosed as having a lead level in his blood that was ten times higher than other members of his family. A university-based pharmacology and toxicology clinic discovered that for 20 years the patient often stripped wires with his teeth [Don't do this! I used to and it ruined my teeth – *Ed*] and sometimes chewed on bits of wire insulation. Samples of coloured-plastic wire coatings were analysed and found to contain 10,000 to 39,000 micrograms of lead per gram. A note in *Nature* (August 19, 1993) emphasises that lead-free solders are highly desirable, given the toxicity of lead; it points out that alloys of silver and tin offer high resistance to [metal] fatigue – good news to those who torture their circuits by repeated bending or thermal cycling. It has been shown that by adding just a smattering of zinc to an alloy of silver-tin a solder has been developed in which the microstructure is much more uniform giving it a peak strength of 48% higher than the zinc-free equivalent and an order of magnitude better high-temperature creep resistance.

George Benbow, G3HB draws attention to an item in a recent *IEE News* which states that with effect from January 1995, the nominal UK 50Hz mains voltage will be 230V with a tolerance of –6%, +10%. Minimum voltage

Fig 6: Heavy duty power supply unit used by ZS2U with a FT7B transceiver over the past eleven years without problems.

© RSGB

will thus be 216V, maximum 254V. Since these tolerances cover the present 240V, I remain uncertain whether a voltage change will actually be introduced next January.

Roger Wheeler, G3MGW, takes me to task for drawing attention to N4AQ's disguised flagpole antenna (*TT*, August, Fig 5) as a means of flouting restrictions on outside antennas: "I shudder to think, in the event of interference or collapse, what a lawyer would make of it, let alone what a huge dent it would put in our public image." He blames this lapse on my interest in wartime clandestine radio but doesn't mention the 1950s deception by a highly respected RSGB President!

John Taylor, G0AKN, suggests that a good way of keeping the sections of a mobile HF whip from getting damaged or lost when not in use is to carry them in a plastic tube. He purchased some scrap lengths of 1.5in diameter plastic water pipe from the local builders' merchant together with collars and screw caps for the ends. The collars can be glued to the tubing, if they are not a tight fit. This enables the whip sections and loading coils to be transported without risk of bending or becoming mixed up with bits from other antennas.

Those hifi enthusiasts bemused by the rival claims of digital-CD versus analogue-LP vinyl recordings may be relieved to learn that a German test showed that only 4 out of 160 audiophiles could successfully distinguish between analogue and digital sound sources, as reported by the *New Scientist*. While laboratory tests show that CDs have noise levels 20 to 30dB lower than disc records, with better stereo channel separation, and a superior dynamic range of some 90dB, it remains questionable whether these advantages can really be heard in a home environment. Results remained similar with tests using play out equipment costing £400 and £4000. But presumably the LP records were new and not with the scratch noise of many playings with a heavy pick-up.

Sadly, Joe Cropper, G3BY, died in late November at the ripe old age of 92-93 years. Joe contributed the original *TT* item on 'Dirty DC' recharging of dry cells and was also responsible for my naming PA0KSB's ingenious system for drift-free oscillators as the "huff and puff VFO" stabilizer, He was active on the bands to the end, in contact with some of his former wartime Hanslope Park (SCU3) colleagues including G4DR (Pat), G8DX (Ron) and G2DTD (Wilf) the week he died.

G3IPV'S STABLE POWERFET AMPLIFIER

ONE HAS COME TO EXPECT from Peter Haylett, G3IPV, some novel ideas centred around the problem of using FET devices in RF amplifiers not prone to self-destructive oscillation. As his latest offering he writes: "While constructing powerfet amplifiers it is possible to experience a number of problems that can result in the destruction of expensive devices. The main problems appear to be caused by self-oscillation, parasitic oscillation, switch-on transients and inadequate heat sinks.

"Self-oscillation and parasitic oscillation are caused mainly by inadequate control of feedback and by the presence of unnecessary

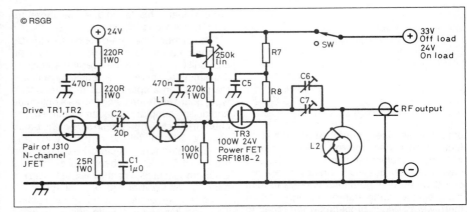

Fig 7: The G3IPV FET linear amplifier providing some 50 watts output on 3.5MHz and claimed to reduce the risk of self destructive unstable or parasitic oscillation. TR3 was an SRF1818-2 Powerfet (surplus from J Birkett with no data available). Bypass and capacitors are polyester layer types and C5, C6 and C7 are 1000pF mica compression high power capacitors (obtained surplus from J Birkett). L1 Ferrite toroid 47 turns 24SWG for 3.5MHz. L2 Ferrite toroid 3 turns 18SWG for 3.5MHz. R7, R8 each 1.5Ω, 50-watt metal cooled.

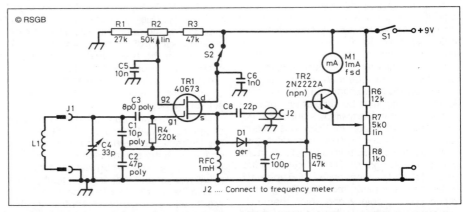

Fig 8: Circuit diagram of the dip-meter (GDO) built by I1FLC. Resistors ½W, capacitors ceramic unless otherwise specified.

inductance. I have found that ferrite beads can pick-up or radiate sufficient RF to cause trouble in amplifiers. The drain power-supply isolation and decoupling choke can act as a high-Q inductance with many resonant frequencies and so produce unwanted voltage feedback.

"In the amplifier shown in **Fig 7** all unnecessary inductances have been removed other than the stray inductances of the resistors which do not appear to cause difficulty. Feedback is controlled to a low value by the input series tuned circuit's tuning capacitor which must be less than about 10pF. This system was used in earlier amplifiers and worked well except that occasionally a powerfet was destroyed when the amplifier was switched on, apparently by transient voltages across drain-isolation and the decoupling RF choke. The problem has been overcome by using extremely high gate-bias resistors and, as an extra precaution, the drain choke has been replaced by high-wattage resistors.

"It would seem that N-channel JFETs are protected by using low-value gate resistors, whereas power FETs appear to be protected by high-value gate resistors, although this anomaly needs further research if all risk of self-destruction is to be achieved.

"The use of a low-value input series tuning and coupling capacitor does not reduce positive feedback to zero but rather to a reasonably safe value. Further investigation is needed into the linearity etc of the output from

an RF amplifier with and without feedback. Without any feedback or with negative feedback there would be much lower output than with some positive feedback as currently used with most FET RF amplifiers.

"The amplifier is currently used at G3IPV on 3.5MHz and delivers an output power of about 50 watts into a coax-fed pre-tuned commercial end-fed Zepp. Output power varies with changes of ground conditions under the antenna. On one occasion the amplifier was accidently left switched on without drive or antenna. No harm was done except the melting of the insulation of the output coax socket.

"No precautions seem necessary when the amplifier is in use such as switching on drive and antenna in a predetermined order; in practice the amplifier has often been used accidently without the antenna connected. It has been in use over a period of six months and come to no harm."

Reg Moores, G3GZT/VS6CD, warns that the power transistors in modern transceivers operating at low power can easily be destroyed, apparently by momentary parasitic oscillation. This occurs when the PTT switch is released and the drive stops and the antenna switches to 'receive' or, as in his case, the surge of power burns out a thermocouple ammeter in the ATU, resulting in the possibility of a form of solid-state 'TPTG' oscillation. He believes that this type of switching condition may be responsible for the by-no-means uncommon failure of PA transistors, particularly when using multi-band antennas. G3GZT suggests that when using a thermo-couple meter, for any purpose, it is advisable to fit a low-value non-inductive resistor in parallel with it. This is unlikely to significantly affect the meter reading but does insure that in the event of the meter burning out (which can happen with even moderate overloads) the antenna remains connected to the transceiver, although this may not prevent self-oscillation when the PTT switch is released.

Range (MHz)	Length (mm)	Diameter (mm)	Turns	L (µH)
3.0 - 4.5	30	21	75	59.60
4.0 - 5.5	25	21	62.5	47.85
5.0 - 7.5	19	17	47.5	23.50
7.5 - 11.0	10	17	25	10.25
10.5 - 16.0	11	11	27.5	5.55
15.0 - 22.0	6	11	15	2.50
20.0 - 31.0	6	9	15	1.80

Measurement of unknown capacitors or inductances is carried out by forming a parallel resonant circuit comprising one known value and one unknown value capacitor/inductance and then 'dipping' to find its resonant frequency (preferably using a counter rather than GDO calibration) in conjunction with the formula:

$$L = 25355/C \times F^2 \quad \text{or} \quad C = 25355/L \times F^2$$

where L is in µH, F in MHz and C in pF.

Table 1: Coil information for Luigi Falcone's, I1FLC, gate dip oscillator design.

THE UBIQUITOUS GDO

IT IS SOME TIME SINCE *TT* included details of a GDO (or dip-meter). This versatile instrument can be either a 'grid-dip oscillator' (still a valid approach) or more likely a 'gate-dip oscillator.' The value and flexibility of these devices can be further advanced when used in conjunction with a counter-type frequency meter to provide rather more accurate calibration than when used in isolation. A GDO is ideal for checking the resonance of antennas, antenna traps, measuring the value of unknown small capacitances or inductances, the velocity factor of transmission lines such as coaxial cables, etc, etc.

The GDO shown in **Figs 8 and 9** uses a standard handbook circuit and comes from an article by Luigi Falcone, I1FLC, in *Radio Rivista*, 10/92, pp23. He uses seven plug-in coils covering 3.0 to 30MHz in a Colpitts oscillator circuit. The coaxial socket J2 permits connection to a frequency meter when required. The coils are wound on Teflon formers with two 'female' sockets which plug-in to two 'male' plugs on the instrument. TR2 forms a DC amplifier permitting the use of a 1mA FSD meter with sensitivity controlled by R7. With TR1 switched off (via S2), the instrument forms a field strength meter/RF sniffer.

Such a GDO need not be constructed to duplicate exactly the I1FLC design, but care

should be taken that the oscillator components are mounted rigidly and not subject to 'hand-capacitance effects' in use. I1FLC built his GDO in a small metal box 16 x 10 x 6cm with the PCB mounted vertically but one could equally well use 'ugly' construction. If a somewhat larger value variable capacitor (C4) is used with a slow-motion drive the number of coils to tune 3 to 30MHz could be reduced. **Table 1** gives the coil information as published by I1FLC although the article does not give the gauge of the enamelled wire.

END OF AN ERA

OVER THE 21 YEARS THAT I have been using a Labgear/Pye LG300 transmitter manufactured over 35 years ago, I had come to believe that the Canadian Marconi 813 valve was virtually indestructible, unlike modern RF power semiconductor devices. Came the day, came the shock when I discovered the 50W filament had finally gone open-circuit. Fortunately new 813/CV26 valves are still available (although at a cost greater than I had originally paid for the LG300!). And a Mullard-manufactured CV26 has once again brought the old rig to life!

But rather sadly this trauma coincided with the last days of the old Mullard/Philips Mitcham factory which finally closed on 24 December, 1993 – a factory which in its heyday turned out more than a million valves a year – many destined to find their way into amateur rigs. Set up in 1928 as Mitcham Works Ltd (to conceal the link between Mullard and Philips of Eindhoven) for the production of radio sets, 1932 saw the beginning of valve production, with transmitting valves added in 1934 and CRTs in 1937. Production expanded during WW2 with the setting up of associated factories elsewhere. First production in the UK of the famous EF50 was at Mitcham.

Many British TV sets by various manufacturers owed much of their design to the work of the Mullard Central Applications Laboratory at Mitcham. Later the factory was responsible for many semiconductors when they began to reduce the demand for valves in the 1960s and 1970s.

According to *Philips Post*, (Winter 1993), while ordinary employees were allowed during wartime air-raids (the factory was hit several times) to seek safety under their benches, managers were expected to remain upright! Mitcham, it appears, was the site of ghostly phenomena, including 1937 appearances of a woman burned as a witch in the 17th century after predicting, inter alia, "strange instruments and devices from which would come forth musick and oft-times speaking or singing". Many people were afraid to walk past B building because of 'strange happenings'. An employee, George Wainford, it is claimed, "once saw a chain and padlock on the main gate unwind itself to allow the gate to open, then close and lock itself. No one else was around."

At its peak, Mitcham employed over 5000 people but in its final months there have been empty buildings and the ghosts of past commercial trials and triumphs. The factory, which made an impact when it was built in the 1920s by its size and modern European style of architecture, is being sold for redevelopment. *Sic transit gloria*!   **G3VA**

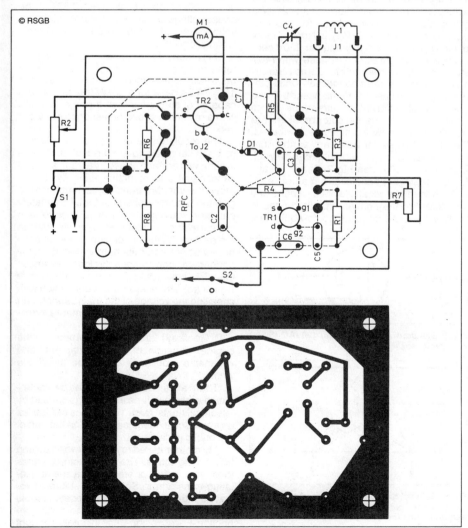

Fig 9: Printed-circuit-board layout as used by I1FLC for his GDO.

MAINS PRACTICES IN THE UK & OVERSEAS

THE DECEMBER 1993 *TT* item 'Mains adapters are not fused', pointed out the need for international travellers to be more aware of the differences in mains practice in different countries. This has resulted in a number of letters underlining the need for amateurs to be aware of the mains practices in all countries – including the UK. We need to be aware, for example, of the increasing use in the UK of "protective multiple earthing (PME)" – as described in *TT*, April 1987 (*Technical Topics Scrapbook, 1985-89, pp161-2*) and in more depth in *'Killing Ground, Earth Your Station Safely'* by Peter Chadwick, G3RZP, *RadCom*, June 1987. An additional problem is that mains practices are currently undergoing changes aimed at more standardization, at least in Europe. It is also clear that this whole question is rather more complex than suggested in the December notes.

George Benbow, G3HB, draws attention to the fact that, with effect from January 1995, the nominal UK 50Hz mains voltage will be 230V with a permitted tolerance of –6%, +10%. The change from 240V to 230V is apparently in line with European Community plans to standardize at 230V instead of the mixture of 240V and 220V.

Paul Coxwell (RS39369) writes: "I am sure that many UK amateurs are aware that US supplies are 120V, 60Hz, but other variations from the British practice are less widely known."

"In all but smaller, older homes in the USA, power is derived from a 240V centre-tapped transformer, and three conductors are brought into the service entrance panel. The centre-tap connects to the neutral bus bar, which is also connected to a ground rod and bonded to the panel's outer casing. Two 'hot' bus bars are provided, each being connected to one of the remaining incoming conductors. This arrangement allows most general circuits to run at 120V, the load being distributed evenly between 'hot' phases, while heavy loads such as electric ranges, clothes driers, air conditioners [and often linear amplifiers, etc – *G3VA*] are run on 240V, power being taken from the two hot bus bars.

"Colour coding on 120V circuits is black for 'hot', white for neutral, and green for ground. Receptacles are arranged as shown in **Fig 1**, although some older wiring may have ungrounded 2-pin outlets. Unlike British connectors, an American three-pin outlet will accept a two-pin plug. Note that the neutral slot is slightly larger than the 'hot' one; this is because some 2-pin plugs are polarized, having a widened end on the neutral pin. When line cords have only a single layer of insulation, the conductors themselves may be different colours: silver is the neutral and the bare-copper wire is the 'hot' wire. Circuits for 240V appliances each have their own special type of connectors, with pins set at various angles to avoid accidental connection to the wrong outlet, and two 'hot' wires are usually colour-coded black and red.

"Other differences that do not directly affect the connection and use of radio equipment, but which may be of interest are as follows. The peculiarly British 'ring' circuit is unknown; most outlets are on 15A branches

that feed several receptacles and lights. Indeed, it is common practice to have a wall-switch control one or more outlets in a bedroom or living room, allowing free-standing lamps to be controlled from the doorway. Most plugs are not fused, although a few types are designed to take a fuse, thereby obviating the need for one in the equipment itself. A minor point is the standard practice for switches to be 'up' for 'on' and 'down' for 'off', ie the opposite of current British practice.

"I hope these comments may provide background information for British amateurs who use American equipment or who visit America with their own equipment. In these days of international travel with amateur equipment, it might be useful to provide details on the arrangements used in other countries such as earthing systems, colour codes etc."

Jan-Martin Noeding, LA8AK comments similarly from a Norwegian viewpoint. He writes: "I am rather uncertain whether 220V is still a 'defined mains voltage' for Western Europe [see above – *G3VA*]. In Norway most of the supply network is triangular 230V connection, maximum 242V per phase, with 140V star connected transformers. Some rural circuits use centre earth connection while others do not (the case for Kristiansand). There are several different requirements as to whether earth-failure indicator breakers are necessary for new installations in houses. Because of the system used any earth failure for the Kristiansand urban/suburban network is limited to 140V, see **Fig 2**. There are two fuses per single-phase circuit in a house.

"I phoned the local electricity board and was told that the nominal standard used is 230V ±0%, but that since some equipment

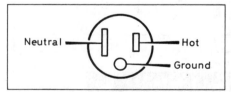

Fig 1: Standard American 3-pin, 120VAC (60Hz) receptacle (socket).

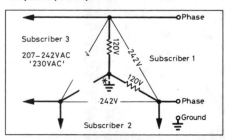

Fig 2: '230Vac' distribution system used in some parts of Norway, in which a failure of the supply earthing limits the voltage to a domestic earth to half the full supply voltage. Both 'phase' lines are fused.

could be damaged, mains voltage at the transformer is limited to 242V. This corresponds to 230V +6% –10% with lower than 212V to be avoided rather than the absolute minimum of 207V.

"A local electrician told me that the distribution system shown in Fig 2 is used only in Norway and Albania, although there is some use of the more normal three-phase 380V (418V) system in Stavanger with only one main fuse per phase.

"The term '220V mains' was used in Norway 30-40 years ago, but not more recently. Mains voltages measured in my shacks at several different QTHs have varied between 225 to 233V with little or no variation between summer and winter. However at some of the Norwegian telecommunication and broadcast stations with which I have been concerned, where the station is the only customer, the line voltage has been as high as 250V, resulting in problems until changed. At supply transformers (22kV or 9kV to 240V) it is possible to choose between different secondary taps on the transformer, but there is no automatic voltage regulation."

In the UK, high-power TV broadcast stations normally incorporate automatic voltage regulation since it is necessary to keep the power supplies to the transmitters within much closer limits of voltage variation than can be expected from the public mains supply. The usual voltage specification is ±0.5% of the phase voltage as compared with the statutory voltage limits of ±6% of the Electricity Supply Regulations 1937.

This means that automatic voltage regulators are installed in the feeds to each of the main transmitters, for example with a rating of 150kVA 3-phase for a 25kW transmitter and capable of correcting over a range of ±10% with a minimum speed of response of 1V per second.

The regulators tend to be of the electro-mechanical type and are air-cooled. Control is achieved on each phase by a transistorised sensor unit and reversing drive system to move the variable transformer brushgear to give the required voltage output. Fortunately amateur equipment can usually cope with normal mains variations although, as noted in the past in *TT*, the life of high-power directly or indirectly heater-filament valves is highly dependent upon reasonably close-tolerances (see *TT*, June 1982). The use of a Variac or similar adjustable system in conjunction with checking the voltage of the mains supply can contribute significantly to equipment longevity.

Dr Geoffrey Manning, G4GLM takes up the original question of mains adapters, and whether or not these should be fused. He writes:

"There are still too many deaths by electrocution and many fires in buildings caused by 'electrical faults' (*sic*). Yet there is still too lax an approach to electrical safety on the part of the public [including amateurs].

"My mother asked my advice when buying hair-curling tongs. The manufacturer states these may safely operate from a shaver isolating-transformer. So I fitted a suitable two-way round-pin plug for this purpose. Double insulation means that there is no earth connection. For occasional use in hotels, I bought her a Data adapter (marked '87' underneath,

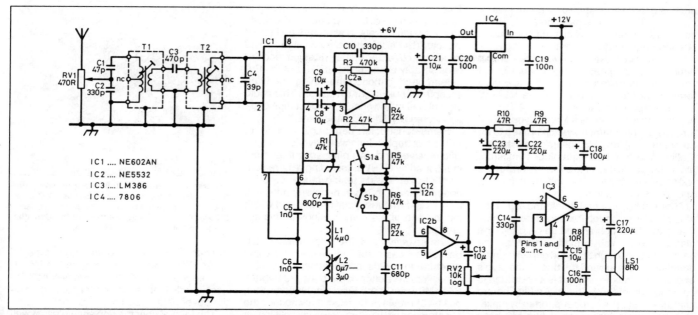

Fig 3: G4BWE's 3.5MHz 'Newbury' direct-conversion receiver featuring permeability tuning. L1 consists of 29 turns of 24SWG enamel copper wire wound onto a T68–6 dust-iron toroid (about 4μH). L2 consists of 13 turns of 22SWG enamel copper wire wound over a length of 25mm (1-inch) on a cylindrical plastic former (eg barrel of felt-tip pen) providing an inductance of about 0.7–3μH. T1 and T2 are Toko KANK3333R. S1 is open for CW, closed for SSB.

Permeability-tuning as implemented in the G4BWE 'Newbury' receiver.

possibly year of manufacture). This accepts shaver and continental two-way round-pins and enables them to connect to a standard 13A mains socket. But yes [unlike the adapter described in the December *TT*] it is fused! There is a miniature BS646 cartridge fuse, the type found in clock-point plugs. Low ratings (1A and 2A) are available. I would not let my mother use it without a fuse; if the fuse blows she would be unable to replace it on site – an effective form of 'fail-safe'.

"Next year, all Europe is due to change to nominal 230V RMS and, providing this actually happens as scheduled, it means that equipment made anywhere in the EC can also be sold and operated anywhere in Europe – although for many years there seem likely to remain a need for international adapters – preferably fused!"

THE 'NEWBURY' 3.5MHZ DC RECEIVER

DESPITE THE RECOGNIZED limited dynamic range of the popular NE602 chip (or the slightly better NE602A), the device continues to gain support as a means of building simple, but reasonably effective HF receivers, both superhet and direct-conversion.

Steve Price, G4BWE, noted the extremely simple direct-conversion receiver originally

described in 'Circuit & Design Ideas', *Electronics Australia* and given in *TT*, July 1993, page 52, but felt that some additional features would be desirable. He writes:

"Panic set in when I realised that I had no new projects to demonstrate at the annual 'home construction evening' of my local club, the Newbury and District Amateur Radio Society. As such events present a good opportunity to promote home-brewing to an audience not consisting entirely of 'converts' to this aspect of the hobby, I was eager to present a design which offered a range of features and yet was inexpensive and straightforward to construct.

"The NE602N and NE602AN mixer/oscillator chips have rightly proved popular with home-brewers, and I was inspired by the minimalist 3.5MHz receiver featured in *TT* – such simplicity is very difficult to resist! However I realised that it would be prudent to include pre-mixer selectivity in the form of a bandpass filter and this certainly helps reduce breakthrough of strong AM broadcast signals caused by envelope detection in less than perfect mixers. As this form of interference is level dependant and will normally disappear if the signal level is below a certain threshold, an RF gain control was added to provide variable input attenuation.

"In the arrangement shown in **Fig 3**, IC2a (one half of a low-noise dual op-amp type NE5532) provides some 55dB AF pre-amplification. IC2b is a low-pass filter which provides switch-selected cut-off frequencies of approximately 2.4kHz (SSB) and 800Hz. The 800Hz setting is used mainly for CW but can also be used to enhance SSB in the presence of fierce QRM. As a simple D-C receiver it lacks single-sideband selectivity and the 800Hz filter can help to compensate for this. Following the AF gain control is an LM386 audio power amplifier capable of delivering 250mW to an 8Ω loudspeaker.

"With some 100dB of voltage gain available, careful decoupling is mandatory – hence C22, C23 plus R9, R10 for IC2 and the use of

'active decoupling' courtesy of the 7806 voltage regulator IC4, which provides 6V for IC1.

"The provision of an effective tuning arrangement was the thorniest problem to overcome. Variable capacitors of reasonable quality are becoming rarer and increasingly expensive. But even when a capacitor can be obtained at a price which does not double the cost of a simple design, there is still a requirement for a smooth-acting reduction drive. Epicyclic types are popular, but the typical 6:1 reduction still leaves a decidedly coarse tuning rate of 100kHz per revolution; this assumes that the coverage is limited to the 300kHz of the European 3.5MHz band, with the shaft of a variable capacitor turning through only 180° between unmeshed and fulled meshed states. Another solution is to replace the traditional variable capacitor with a varicap diode and use a ten-turn potentiometer to develop the tuning voltage. This is fine for projects of intermediate complexity, but the cost of a suitable potentiometer (usually between £3 and £6) is still rather high for a no-frills DC receiver.

"For many years, high-class manufacturers such as Collins favoured permeability tuning in high-performance receivers and transmitters, and it has been used in up-market car-radios by Radiomobile and others. The American company, Ten-Tec still favours this approach (see the review of the Ten-Tec 'Scout 555 transceiver' in *RadCom*, November 1993, p66).

"A permeability-tuned VFO uses a fixed tank capacitor working in conjunction with a variable inductor. The most practical way of altering the inductance of a small, cylindrically wound coil is to vary the position of a suitable core (normally ferrite) within its former. As the core is pushed further into the windings, the inductance rises quite considerably. [With a brass core, inductance decreases – *G3VA*].

"Variable inductances are available in the form of 'slug-tuned' coils and RF transformers (eg the Toko types used in the bandpass filter of this design) but the variation in inductance is generally restricted to about plus or minus 20% and the small, threaded ferrite cores are too brittle to withstand continuous or even frequent adjustment.

"Luckily, a far more robust variable inductor offering a much greater range of adjustment can be made quite easily using a standard ferrite rod of the type used for the MW/LW antenna in portable radios: see **Fig 4**. For this design, the ferrite rod is a Maplin type 810 of 8mm (0.3-inch) diameter which is fixed to an 80mm (3-inch) long M6 bolt using a standard 'Belling & Lee' TV antenna plug. The centre pin of the plug is cut off to allow the end of the rod to be inserted into the bottom of the plug and glued with Araldite.

"The M6 bolt is inserted into the top of the plug exactly as though it were a coaxial cable (the end of the bolt should self-tap into the plastic insert which formerly supported the centre pin). Although the braid grip will tighten quite effectively around the bolt as the plug's end-cap is screwed home, it is a good idea to coat the end of the bolt with Araldite before final assembly. The bolt is supported by make-shift brackets which contain two M6 bolts (square-shaped 'roofing' types were used as these are easier to clamp). It will be evident from Fig 4 that each revolution of the make-shift tuning knob will move the ferrite rod over only a small distance, thus providing the equivalent of a reduction drive. In my project, the barrel from a Berol Notewriter felt-tip pen was used as the former for the tuning coil (L2).

"Calculations showed that in order to tune the VFO from 3.5 to 3.8MHz, the tank inductance needed to be decreased from 7 to 6µH.

This implied that the bulk of the inductance could remain fixed. In the interests of stability and a low tuning rate, a standard 4µH toroid inductor (L1) is wired in series with L2. The frequency coverage of the prototype receiver considerably exceeds the 300kHz of the European band, although the tuning rate is an acceptable 50kHz per revolution. This could be reduced by lowering the inductance of L2 and increasing L1 to compensate."

Home-constructed permeability tuning of VFOs has applications well beyond this specific receiver and can offer advantages not mentioned by G4BWE including a more constant-Q over a wide tuning range. G4BWE does not seem to have made any provision for a multi-turn tuning dial mechanism which can be one of the complications of this approach.

The scarcity of high-voltage variable capacitors at reasonable prices is encouraging a return to 1920s practice when variable capacitors were often home-brew. P J Behrtel, PA3AYP in the Dutch *Electron* (January 1994, pp11-13) provides detailed drawings for the construction of a 1-62pF low-loss split-stator capacitor suitable for the demanding application of a motor-driven capacitor for a 'mag-

Laboratory version of a Braun-type spark-gap transmitter as used by Dr John Belrose, VE2CV to make demonstration tapes of "the sound of spark". (Photo by Janice Lang, courtesy of the Canadian Communications Research Centre).

netic-loop' transmitting antenna. One of PA3AYP's drawings is reproduced as Fig 24. The appearance of the assembled component is sufficiently attractive for it to feature as the cover photograph of the journal!

The form of construction shown might well be adaptable to the construction of a differential capacitor in which the overall capacitance

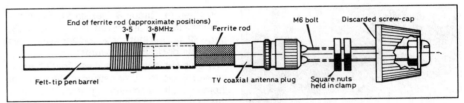

Fig 4: Constructional details of the permeability-tuned L2 inductance.

KISS MEASUREMENT OF INDUCTANCE

RON KAYE, G6RO, was prompted by the article by Laura Scott, G4HUV, on inductance measurement (*RadCom*, November 1993 p40) to write a short piece on his long-used method of measuring inductances by making the unknown inductance the basis of the tuned circuit of a simple two-terminal oscillator and then measuring the frequency using a calibrated general-coverage receiver. He used an AR88D for frequencies above about 550kHz and a B28 receiver for lower frequencies. He writes:

"The oscillator circuit must be of a type that requires no taps to the inductor and no capacitance network feedback to maintain oscillation, yet oscillates readily with sufficient output over a very wide frequency range. Originally I used a double-triode valve as a cathode-coupled oscillator but this was abandoned some years ago in favour of a source-coupled FET oscillator: **Fig 5**. This has proved ideal for the purpose with more than sufficient stability when built into a die-cast metal box, the base of which serves as the top panel carrying two terminals, one of which must be insulated from the box, and the on-off switch. A small 9V battery is inside the box. Output is taken to a co-ax socket on the back of the box. It oscillates well from at least 150kHz up to 30MHz, enabling inductance values from less than 1µH to a few mH to be determined. Toroids present no problem.

"In practice, the unknown inductor is connected to the terminals and the oscillator switched 'on'. The fundamental signal is then located on the receiver, using the BFO to tune to zero beat using a short pick-up wire on the receiver and about two inches of wire from the oscillator output socket will usually provide sufficient signal. The unknown inductance value can then be calculated from the formula:

$$L_x = 25330/(f^2 \times C)$$

with C the inbuilt capacitance across the

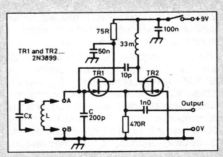

Fig 5: The source-coupled FET 'universal' oscillator used by G6RO for KISS inductance and capacitance measurement in conjunction with a calibrated, general-coverage receiver. L is the unknown inductance (without Cx for inductance measurement. Cx is unknown capacitance, in parallel with an L of about 0.75µH for capacitance measurement.

coil in pF (200pF in Fig 5). Lx is unknown inductance in µH f is fundamental frequency in MHz.

"This 'universal' oscillator can also be used to measure capacitors, especially those in the lower pF range. An inductor of about 0.75µH (exact value need not be known) is connected to the terminals, the oscillator switched on and the frequency determined. The unknown capacitor is then connected in parallel with the inductor and the new frequency measured. The value of the unknown capacitance can then be calculated (simply with the aid of a scientific calculator) from:

$$C_x = (C \times f^2/f_1^2) - C$$

where f is the frequency without the added capacitor (ie the higher of the two measurements), f_1 is the frequency with the added capacitor and Cx is the capacitor whose value is required.

"The technique is slower than with my capacitance bridge but is more accurate for very small capacitance values. A big advantage is that it requires no ancillary equipment such as signal generators or output meters. It could probably be used directly with a digital frequency meter in the absence of a general-coverage receiver. Finally, a 'universal' wide range oscillator is a useful device to have around."

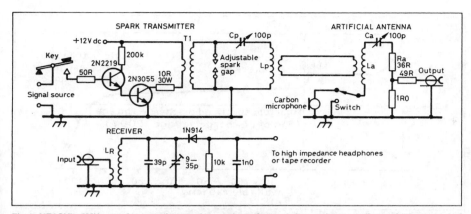

Fig 6: VE2CV's 5MHz spark transmitter and crystal receiver used to make recordings of "the sound of spark" including speech transmission as it must have sounded during Fessenden's historic 'first' speech transmissions in December 1900. Ca 100pF, Cp 100pF high-voltage vacuum capacitor. Lp, La, LR 22μH. T1 high performance automotive ignition coil. SW SPDT phone/CW switch. Signal source RC oscillator 60Hz, 120Hz, 800Hz and 10kHz. Power supply 12VDC Gel-Cell battery.

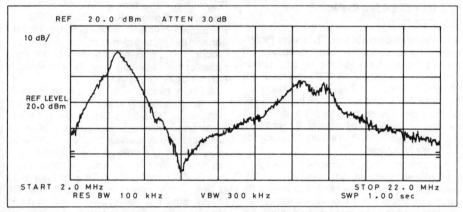

Fig 7: Output spectrum of the spark transmitter extending over many megahertz, and above the reference level of 20dBm for roughly 3MHz around 5MHz. Note significant third-harmonic output around 15MHz.

remains the same but shifts from one set of fixed vanes to the other, a type of variable capacitor that seems to have long disappeared from the market.

THE SOUND OF SPARK

I RECALL IN 1940 listening on 500kHz (600-metres) to distress messages being sent by an Egyptian ship that was still equipped with a spark transmitter.

Had it not been for the war, spark would have been completely phased out in the maritime service except for emergency (lifeboat) purposes by the end of 1939. The distinctive sound of spark is not easily forgotten, yet I suppose the vast majority of readers have no knowledge of how the spark transmitters used by experimental amateurs from about 1905 to about 1925 sounded when received on the simple crystal receivers of the day. Or what the first crude attempts of Fessenden to transmit voice on a spark transmitter must have sounded like.

Dr John S Belrose, VE2CV, was surprised to read my comments on his 1992 Alexander Graham Bell Lecture 'Fessenden and the Early History of Radio Science' in *TT*, November 1993. As a result Dr Belrose kindly sent along the full text of his interesting lecture as printed in the *Proceedings of the Radio Club of America* (November 1993, pp6-23). For this lecture, he devised and implemented a means of recording a demonstration tape of the sounds of spark transmis-

sion, including speech, as received on a crystal receiver.

He writes: "So far as I know, no one has recorded for posterity the sound of spark signals heard on a simple receiver. Because of the tremendous variety of gap speeds, for synchronous and non-synchronous rotary gaps, electrode shape and spacing, and operating high voltage, every spark station had its own characteristic sound. This was an advantage when there were a number of stations on the air. Spark signals were broad, and within the broad bandwidth of the simple receivers, there could be several stations operating . . . . communications would have been more difficult if all the signals had sounded the same.

"Some will have seen, heard and smelt (ozone) an operating spark transmitter in museums in Canada and the USA [there is or was a rather crude demonstration in the London Science Museum – G3VA] but few will have heard how the received signals sounded – and particularly the sound of speech over spark. Fessenden said of his first voice transmission: "Words were perfectly clear except accompanied by an extremely loud disagreeable noise.' Anyone who has thought about this experiment will agree on the comment about disagreeable noise, but could the words have been 'perfectly clear' – with a spark transmitter and a microphone connected in series with the antenna lead?

"So we constructed a 5MHz spark transmitter, using an automotive ignition coil for the

induction coil, and circuitry to simulate a Braun type transmitter with a 5MHz quarter-wave antenna. This was like the Braun transmitter, excepting that Ls (the secondary winding wound over primary Lp) was not directly connected to the antenna, but link coupled through a short length of transmission line (see **Fig 6**). The frequency and output spectrum is determined by the frequency response of the antenna system; a spectrum very broad, megahertz wide (**Fig 7**). Somewhat surprising is the magnitude of the third harmonic in spite of the fact that our simulated antenna, unlike a real monopole, was not resonant at the third harmonic.

"The output of the transmitter, attenuated by 120-140dB, was coupled directly to the receiver which comprised a simple tuned circuit, detector (admittedly a modern germanium diode), and tape recorder (high-impedance headphones are hard to come by nowadays). For speech, we used a carbon microphone from an old telephone hand set.

"To make recordings we had to relearn how to set up and 'tune' a spark transmitter. The primary and secondary circuits, the 'tank' and 'antenna' circuits, must not be overcoupled, since this results in a double peaked extremely broad amplitude-frequency response. The spark should take place between polished, hemisphere-shaped electrodes, not between pointed electrodes. And the widest gap possible consistent with regular sparking when the key is held down must be used, since otherwise the signal becomes all 'mushy' In effect, we 'optimized' our transmitter by gradually narrowing the gap for the best received sound before making a recording at a particular spark rate.

"Hence the sounds on our demonstration tape probably represent the best quality of sound that could have been achieved with Braun-type spark transmitters."

VE2CV sent along a copy of his demonstration tape (about 7 minutes of recording and commentary on a C60 audio cassette) containing brief examples of transmissions with about 60, 125 and 750 sparks per second and finally speech with about the 10kHz spark rate used by Fessenden on 23 December, 1900 to transmit over a distance of about one mile. Yes you can distinguish the words but "perfectly clearly" is perhaps "inventor's licence" of what one could call "spitch".

Readers who would like to hear this themselves can obtain a copy of the recording by writing to Dr John Belrose, VE2CV, 17 Tadoussac Drive, Aylmer QC J9J1G1, Canada enclosing $US10 to cover the cost of the tape, handling and mailing.

It was Fessenden who later invented the HF alternator and with difficulty persuaded General Electric to make one at his expense! Fessenden was later to comment: "No organization engaged in any specific field of work ever invents any important development in that field, or adopts any important development in that field until forced to do so by outside competition."

A profound statement (although one can think of exceptions such as the practical development of the transistor by Bell Laboratories) that underlines the importance of the independent inventor and the amateur experimenter!

A description of a 1914 rotary spark transmitter used in South Africa by the late W E Dixon-Bennett, A3V/ZS4W/ZS5EG, appeared in *Radio-ZS* (September, 1993): "My transmitter in 1914 employed a 1kW transformer, which stepped up the mains supply to about 10kV. The transformer embodied a magnetic shunt which was adjustable.... for controlling the primary input. The main condenser in the closed energy storage and oscillating circuit was of the glass dielectric type in a 1in by 10in by 6in container. The spark discharger was of the high speed rotary type, with twelve electrodes revolving between two stationary electrodes.... the rig put about 3A into a long Marconi antenna and could be loaded up to the then standard wavelength of 600m.... the operating range was normally 50-100 miles."

Even with the coming of valves, the practice of using MCW (modulated continuous wave) meant that coast stations and ship transmitters could often be immediately identified by their distinctive "note" and copied on crystal sets or broadcast sets without a beat frequency oscillator.

Dr Brian Austin, G0GSF, while not disputing Fessenden's role as the pioneer of radiotelephony, reminds us that 1994 is the centenary of the world's first public demonstrations of radio transmission by Sir Oliver Lodge. As a distinguished scientist, Lodge was President of the RSGB in 1925; in 1894 he was Professor of Physics at the University of Liverpool where he made his first radio experiments, based on the work of his friend Heinrich Hertz who had died on 1 January, 1894 at the tragically young age of 36 years. Professor Lodge accordingly delivered a memorial lecture on Hertz in London on 1 June, 1894 and in August, at Oxford, publicly demonstrated that Hertzian waves could be used for telegraphic signalling in the Morse code.

As noted in *Precinct*, the newsletter of Liverpool University, some of Lodge's first experimental transmissions were made in Liverpool between Lewis's department store to the clock tower of the University's Victoria Building. His original work was in pursuit of scientific knowledge rather than to develop a practical system of signalling without wires. Although he did not use an elevated antenna, the key to long distance communications, his demonstrations preceded those of Marconi. And he soon teamed up with Muirhead so that by 1898 he was able to demonstrate both manual Morse and machine transmission using a Muirhead punched tape automatic keyer with a siphon recorder as the receiving instrument.

Even earlier, in 1890, Lodge had evolved his resonance-jar experiment, the key to 'tuning'. In 1897 he took out a patent for selective tuning in advance of Marconi's more famous 7777 patent – the resulting patent struggle was settled in 1911 in favour of Lodge; his patent was extended for eight more years on the condition that he sold it to the Marconi Company.

An IEE History of Technology Weekend is being held at Liverpool University July 8-10 and there will be a conference organised by the Liverpool Physical Society on July 11, both marking the "development of radio" by Lodge.

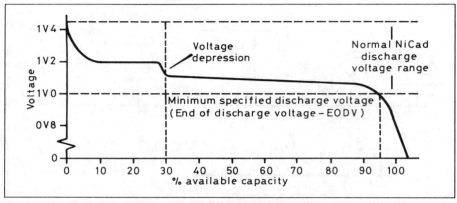

Fig 8: Discharge curve of a nicad cell showing a pronounced 'voltage depression' at about one-third discharge. Usual cause is overlong trickle charging although the effect is often attributed to the so-called 'memory' of nicad cells. Genuine cases of nicad 'memory' due to repeated partial discharges to exactly the same point are rarely met in practice.

MAINTENANCE-FREE BATTERIES

AT THE BRITISH LIBRARY (Science Reference and Information Service), I recently found among the recent additions by Dr Dietrich Berndt (Varta) published 1993 by Research Studies Press Ltd of Taunton and marketed by John Wiley & Sons. It runs to 362 + xxii pages, hard covers, but at a price of £65 it is clearly not targeted at amateurs. However there are some useful introductory statements that bear repetition.

For example: "Maintenance-free lead-acid and nickel/cadmium batteries are distinguished from their conventional counterparts mainly by the fact that topping-up with water at regular intervals is not required. Although this periodic direct work is no longer necessary, the generally applied term 'maintenance-free' should not mislead the user to abandon all kinds of supervision. To ensure its proper function, the maintenance-free battery has to be observed and checked regularly unless it is monitored automatically."

Dr Berndt makes it clear that although the term "sealed" can be applied to this category of nickel/cadmium and nickel/hydride batteries, it should not be applied to lead-acid batteries which are more correctly termed 'valve-regulated lead-acid batteries': "In the lead-acid battery, complete sealing can never be achieved because the generation of hydrogen can never be avoided completely. The valve has to open periodically to let small amounts of gas, mainly hydrogen, escape from the cell. Otherwise the internal pressure would exceed tolerable limits.

"Gradual water loss is connected with this gas evolution, and thus water loss causes slight changes in cell parameters during service life. But the rate of water loss can be kept so low that the initial amount of electrolyte is sufficient for a service life of ten years or more .... Besides these maintenance-free batteries, a wide spectrum of low-maintenance lead-acid batteries is on the market.

"The maintenance-free starter battery is beyond the scope of this book, when it is a flooded lead-acid battery, but with special constructional features, designed to outlast the usual service life in a car without refilling, although the principles are described briefly."

Dr Berndt notes that the history of the lead-acid battery stretches back to 1854 (Sinsteden) with practical implementation discovered independently in 1859 by Plante. Fundamental inventions in the field of nickeliron and nickel-cadmium batteries were made around 1900, with the principles of the seal nickel/cadmium battery described in German patents by G Neumann (1948).

An item 'Nicad memory – fact or fiction?' *TT*, June 1989, p34 (also *Technical Topics Scrapbook, 1985-89*, p308) showed that the common problem of loss of capacity of nicad cells, commonly ascribed to "memory" was more generally a voltage depression occurring at about one-third discharge due to overlong trickle charging: **Fig 8**. Genuine "memory" is only rarely encountered in practice. Dr Berndt puts this as follows: "The memory effect in nickel/cadmium batteries is a vague description of a temporary loss of capacity after:

● Subjecting the battery to a large number of unvarying partial discharge-charge cycles (the 'genuine' memory effect).

● Extended storage periods without recharge or periods with insufficient charge.

● Prolonged constant-current charging (float charging) eg in emergency-lighting applications.

As emphasised in the 1989 *TT* item, which was based on articles by Anton Wilson in *International Broadcast Engineer*: "The most prevalent cause of memory phenomena turns out to be long-term trickle charging .... in this case the continuous current can cause a metamorphosis to occur within a fully charged nicad cell ....

"Over a period of time the charged nicad compounds are transformed into a secondary alloy called Ni_5Cd_{21} which exhibits a lower voltage potential than a normal nicad cell."

It was pointed out that long-term trickle charging can also result in the even more serious problem of 'accelerated ageing' which can reduce the useful life of a battery, in terms of charge/discharge cycles, to only one-eighth of normal.

Roy Mander, GW4DYY found the battery for his hedge-trimmer did not charge overnight in his unheated garage. He found his charger had a thermostat that prevented charging below 5°C. A belated look at the instructions stated this was to prevent damage to nicad cells. As he has not seen this mentioned elsewhere he wonders how important is this precaution? **G3VA**

EASY TUNING ON VINTAGE RECEIVERS

MANY YEARS AGO, listening to the Presidential Address given by the late 'Dud' Charman, G6CJ, I was impressed by his recommendation that the CW operator needed to be able to tune his receiver carefully across the response curve of narrow-band morse signals and that this could be done only with a very slow tuning rate, much slower than usually provided on communication receivers of the pre-SSB era, even those fitted with good electrical or mechanical bandspread.

Ever since, I have tended to add an extra external slow-motion drive to both home-built and factory-built HF receivers. Currently I use this approach with a KW2000A receiver and for the VFO of the old Labgear LG300 transmitter, with resulting tuning rates of the order of 5-10kHz per knob revolution. I have always found it possible to fit outboard drives without drilling panels etc (not always a neat result but serviceable).

I was therefore interested to receive a letter from Frank Penton, G0RZK who was most complimentary about the new *Technical Topics Scrapbook,* 1985-89. He is much enjoying rediscovering items that he had previously read – and forgotten – and reading others for the first time.

But his prime purpose in writing was to report a simple modification recently made to his Racal RA17L which has greatly improved the tuning of this excellent receiver. Incidentally an excellent and very detailed, two-part article *Racal and the RA17 HF Communication Receiver* (including full circuit diagram of the RK17L Mk II) by Keith Thrower (Research Director of the Racal Radio Group Ltd) has been published in *Radio Bygones*, (Part 1, October/November 1993, issue No 25 pp4-9; Part 2, Christmas 1993 issue No 26 pp17-26).

G0RZK writes: "I acquired my RA17L at a rally and found it to be extremely deaf. I bought a manual, replaced a few valves and carefully realigned it. I was very impressed with its performance and in particular its ability to resolve SSB even in a totally unmodified state.

Generally speaking, anything I could copy on my FT990 I could copy on the RA17L, and on 7 and 3.5MHz at night, the RA17L was often better thanks to the high Q input circuits and lack of diode signal-path switching.

"The one real inadequacy lay in the high tuning rate which was too fast for easy SSB tuning or the use of the narrow bandwidths on CW. I considered adding electrical bandspread on the third IF oscillator using a small varicap diode but decided that the additional front panel control would not 'fit' conveniently and so turned to mechanical bandspread.

"I eventually hit on the solution illustrated in the sectional sketch shown in **Fig 1**. It requires the minimum of modification to the receiver and it can be restored to original appearance if required. A standard J-B ball drive mounted on the 'kilocycle' tuning shaft is secured to the front panel with a pair of internally-threaded pillars 24mm long.

"The front panel was drilled and tapped 6BA to take short lengths of 6BA studding to fasten the pillars to the panel. A plastic coffee jar lid was then prepared to serve as a tuning

knob to preserve the original tuning rate for rapid frequency changes. The cardboard insert from the lid formed a convenient template to mark out an aluminium disc that was cut from a scrap of aluminium sheet. This disc was then carefully marked out and drilled to match the dial mounting holes on the ball drive and to clear the central boss. The internal threads in the lid were removed with a pocket knife and the aluminium disc fitted inside the lid and fastened with small pop rivets (small pan-headed screws and nuts could serve as well).

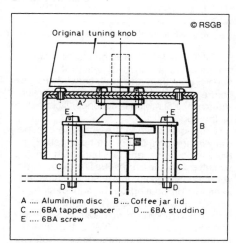

A .... Aluminium disc   B .... Coffee jar lid
C .... 6BA tapped spacer   D .... 6BA studding
E .... 6BA screw

Fig 1: Constructional details of a two-speed tuning arrangement used by G0RZK but applicable to other receivers having good drives free of backlash but with too high a tuning rate.

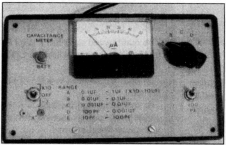

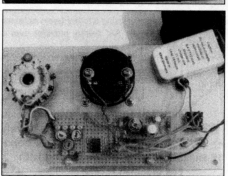

External and internal views of G3CW's direct reading capacitance meter.

"The lid was then drilled using the disc as a template and fastened to the ball drive using suitable short screws. The original tuning knob was then mounted on the ball drive shaft.

"The final result was a concentric-knob, two-speed drive with the bottom knob preserving the original tuning rate of approximately 108kHz per turn and the top knob approximately 15kHz per turn. The improvement in ease of tuning can be imagined. The same principle could probably be applied to other receivers having good drives free of backlash but too high a tuning rate for the easy resolution of SSB signals."

CONSTRUCTING THE CAPACITANCE METER

H F ('BERT') KNOTT, G3CU, was interested to see the recent notes on the direct-reading capacitance meter (*TT*, April and June 1993) originally described by Alan Willcox in *Television* (May 1976) and then briefly noted in *TT*, (January 1977 and January 1989). He had been preparing to write an article describing his construction of this simple but accurate bridge, but, in view of the recent *TT* items, he considers this would be largely redundant. However he has sent along photographs and layout drawings of his implementation of this device (using the original circuit diagram as Fig 2, April *TT*, p51). He writes:

"Following the publication of your notes some years ago and after making a careful study of the original circuit, I realised that the theoretical circuit lent itself to a simple physical layout and that the use of Vero PC Stripboard – 0.1in spacing – (33 holes x 14 holes) was feasible. With a little thought, the modifications suggested in the recent *TT* notes could, if needed, be easily included.

"**Fig 2** shows my layout of the original circuit, and the photographs show my approach to the finalised unit. With the information in *TT*, I had no trouble in constructing this useful piece of test gear.

"I retained the divide-by-two and the x10 functions, but instead of separate switches, I used a DPDT switch with a centre-OFF position.

"I have found the unit quite stable and it gives repeatable results, with no difficulty in measuring capacitance down to a few pF. I use a rechargeable PP3-size 9V battery and a push button switch for 'on' and 'off', ensuring that current is drawn only during test periods. The illustration shows that I have calibrated the unit for highest readings with the 'range' switch in an anti-clockwise position in order to help prevent overload damage to the meter. The whole unit is installed in a Maplin Desk Console style 1 (type M1005) plastics box 161 x 96 x 61/39mm – Catalogue No LH63T – which has an aluminium panel."

GRAY LINE DXING

AS MENTIONED A FEW months ago in *TT*, a number of additional comments have come in on the topic of gray (or grey) line propagation. But there has also been a good introduction to the subject by Tom Russell, N4KG (*QST*, November 1992) pp80-82). N4KG (formerly W8FAW and WA0SDC) has worked over 300 countries on 3.5MHz using dipole

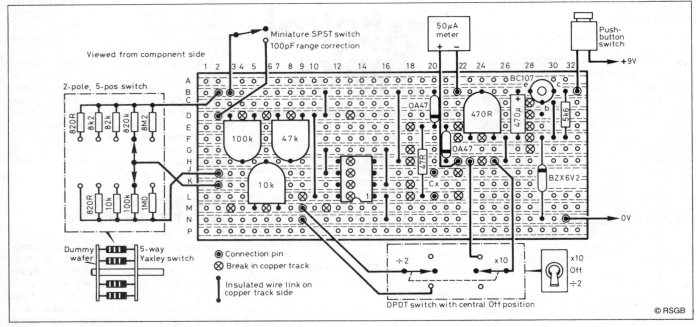

Fig 2: How G3CU lays-out his direct reading capacitance meter using the circuit shown in *TT*, February 1993, Fig 1, p51.

and vertical antennas and has clearly been aided by gray-line propagation.

So first some extracts from his introductory notes: "The transitions from darkness to daylight and daylight to darkness cause drastic changes in the ionosphere affecting all HF propagation. All-band DXers need to understand these changes to improve their chances of long-distance communication, especially over long or difficult paths.

"Several factors affect HF propagation: path, frequency, solar activity and time . . . . frequency and time are the only ones over which we have much control. Understanding the sun's effects helps to select the best frequency for a given time, or perhaps more importantly the best time for a given frequency, for each selected path and level of sunspot activity.

"Time is a complex factor in propagation, encompassing time in the 11-year sunspot cycle; time of year (season and tilt of the Earth); and time of day (daylight, darkness or twilight). From October through March, the North Pole is in partial to total darkness, permitting over-the-pole, northern hemisphere, low- and high-frequency propagation between opposite sides of the earth. This is also true for the south pole and the southern hemisphere from March through October. Summertime propagation is totally different from the rest of the year, with HF openings and closings occurring much later in the day. The polar paths are primarily restricted to 7 through 21MHz in the summer, while transequatorial paths predominate on the low bands and on 28MHz . . . . the ionosphere's behaviour at sunrise and sunset is highly dependent on frequency . . . .

"The sunrise/sunset line, also known as the terminator, gray line or twilight zone, is a circle about the Earth whose position depends on the time of year (season) and time of day. Maximum usable frequencies (MUFs) are highest on the illuminated face of the Earth. so is the absorption caused by the effects of the energized D region of the ionosphere. Propagation losses are lowest near

the MUF. the MUFs drop on the dark side of the earth, to a minimum value of approximately one third the day time MUF, just before sunrise. Absorption also quickly subsides as the D region is no longer illuminated by the sun.

"Propagation along the gray line is especially interesting. MUFs are rising rapidly on the sunrise side and are still high on the sunset side of the Earth. The D region has not yet been energized on the sunrise side, and is rapidly dissipating on the sunset side, resulting in low absorption. The net result is that for a period ranging from a few minutes at low and high frequencies (1.8MHz and 28MHz), to one or two hours at intermediate frequencies (14MHz), with suitable ionospheric conditions, stations in the twilight zone can communicate with stations at any other location within the twilight zone on any HF band!"

N4KG's article continues by examining these effects in greater detail but the important point to note is the period during which gray line contacts are possible varies greatly on the different bands. Since long-distance contacts are possible on 7MHz and above by other modes of propagation, amateur interest is centred primarily on 1.8MHz where the openings may last only a few minutes, 3.5MHz slightly longer, and to some extent on 7MHz where gray-line propagation opens paths that are very difficult at other times.

Nevertheless on 14MHz, 21MHz and the WARC bands it has long been recognized that dawn and dusk are the optimum times for long-distance contacts using 'chordal hop' paths without intermediate Earth reflection as utilised in the gray-line modes, and dependent largely on the ionospheric tilts as the F2 layer and the F1 layer merge or separate.

A point of considerable practical importance (as discussed in *TT* on several occasions during 1992) is that gray-line and chordal hop modes do not necessarily depend on low-elevation radiation antennas but on the position of the tilts in relation to the two locations. With the tilts nearly overhead, antennas such as relatively low dipoles can be

as effective as the best verticals, etc.

It should be emphasised, as N4KG does in his concluding remarks, that "Several problems combine to make low-band, long-path contacts difficult to rare. Low activity, brief openings, atmospheric noise, E-region MUF, absorption and station capabilities are other reasons. Yet with the right timing, persistence can be rewarded with rare and exotic DX! Although these openings do not always occur on a daily basis, they do always occur in the time periods indicated."

David Reynolds, G3ZPF, is one of those who has taken considerable interest in gray-line paths. His useful articles "Calculating grey line paths" appeared in the now-defunct British *Amateur Radio* magazine in March 1986 (pp34-38) and his earlier "Calculation of sunrise and sunset times using the Apple-2 microcomputer" in *Short Wave Magazine*, October 1982. In *Amateur Radio* he made the point that although the transition from day to night (and vice versa) varies in duration across the world, the width of the twilight zone is nearly constant. For a station at the equator to pass through the twilight zone requires a far smaller rotation of the earth than for one at a more northerly (or southerly) latitude. This is why it gets dark very quickly in the tropics.

G3ZPF adds some caveats: "First (and especially for the G/ZL path) find out how accurate the computer program (used to determine sunrise/sunset times) is. There is little point in using software which has ±15min accuracy to predict openings of just a minute or so. Do not be fooled by its accuracy at the home QTH. Errors in the software will vary with latitude.

"Secondly, I found that signals do not necessarily peak during the twilight zone. In sunspot minima years I found that signals could peak up to an hour after full sun-up, possibly, it seemed to me, because the less active sun was taking rather longer to 'cook' the ionospheric layers than in sunspot maxima years."

I presume that most of G3ZPF's gray-line operation was on 3.5MHz and he does not make N4KG's pertinent observation that the period over which gray-line propagation occurs depends on the band in use, with 1.8MHz being the most short-lived.

Old-timer Ted Cook, ZS6BT, follows up the earlier comments (*TT*, June 1992) on signal enhancement along antipodal paths: "It is not quite so simple as suggested. If we take the Poles as the two locations – and especially at an equinox – I would agree. But, taking the practical example I gave of Johannesburg and Hawaii with signals receivable simultaneously on different HF bands, at no time is there either common darkness or common daylight. It is however sunrise at one location and sunset at the other – the Great Circle twilight zone or gray-line path.

"Professional and most amateur HF communicators have traditionally thought of 'day' and 'night' frequencies with little mention of optimum 'median' frequencies for gray-line propagation over a reasonably extended period: I would suggest these as roughly 13 to 17MHz.

"Only the higher latitudes have twilight so it is misleading to talk of a twilight zone or belt. Rather there is a gray zone, about ±2 hours along with the sunrise-sunset great circle. Median frequencies prefer this zone and hence there is enhancement of (say) 14MHz signals in the gray zone between antipodal points. However, the higher and lower frequencies manage to sneak through the gray zone for a short time only.

"Secondly, signals on 'day' frequencies do not reach far across the gray zone into darkness and similarly signals on 'night' frequencies do not proceed very far into daylight areas. 'Median' frequency signals find it difficult to cross the gray zone at right angles but are happy to cross it at a more acute angle. this results in the 'go' and 'no-go' seasons for short path and long path contacts!"

Ted Cook emphasises that to take advantage of the gray zone on median frequency bands there is no need for accurate computer predictions of sunrise and sunset times but merely a rough idea of how the zone varies with the seasons which can be depicted on maps based on Mercator projection together with a great circle map on which to interpret the rule: "If a short path crosses a point, the long path will cross the antipodes of that point. We can now plot any great-circle path on the Mercator map usually in the form of a fancy curve."

Many years ago in *TT* and subsequently in *ART*, I attempted to provide a series of thumbnail sketches showing the sunset/sunrise boundaries at various seasons. The intention was to provide at least sufficient accuracy to show whether DX paths are likely to be 'go' or 'no-go' on, say, 14MHz. These were reproduced in *TT*, June 1992, as Fig 3, page 37. It has long been recognized that the G/VK and G/ZL paths (very roughly antipodal) are particularly reliable in the early mornings on 14MHz – a practical illustration of the importance of understanding the basics of propagation not only in terms of sunspot cycle, MUF, or 'conditions' but also, as ZS6BT puts it, in terms of seasonal illumination! Several writers have also emphasised that even on the lower-frequency bands, 'long-path' openings can be as important as 'short path' openings.

PSU LORE AND THE SWITCHING REGULATOR

EARL HORNBOSTEL, DU1AE, recalls that, some time ago, some comments of his concerning the use of SCRs (thyristors) as over-voltage protection in power supplies were published in *TT*. These emphasised that it is essential that the SCR (thyristor) itself should be protected against excessively high currents. Otherwise when turned on by an over-voltage it is likely to blow out virtually instantaneously, before the associated fuse has any chance of acting.

DU1AE notes, however, that this problem continues to be ignored in many published designs, including, for example, the lead technical article by Ben Spencer, G4YNM in *QST*, (November 1993, pp27-29) which is presented with the editorial comment: "This power supply's features, keep itself – and the equipment attached to it – safe!"

Earl writes: "You will note that the 25A SCR in G4YNM's article is placed before the regulator, after a 10A fuse which immediately follows the main 10,000µF reservoir capacitor. If the SCR is switched on, it will almost certainly burn out before the fuse, leaving the supply unprotected. What is needed is a suitable resistor in series with the anode of the SCR to limit the current to about 15A, enough to blow the fuse but not enough to harm the SCR. Yet this basic design fault continues to appear, time after time, in PSUs designed for or by amateurs."

DU1AE also draws attention to the new family of switching-type IC regulators which have become available during the past few years. He writes: "These can be used with very simple circuits with standard components and are available in several versions, both in current capability and fixed or adjustable voltage outputs. They have very low dropout voltages and since this form of power supply occupies a very small physical space, they can be mounted in the smallest battery-operated equipment.

"Their advantage, when used for battery equipment, is that they provide a regulated output at high efficiency and the equipment will have uniform performance over the life of the battery; in other words the output voltage can be kept constant while the input voltage to the switching regulator falls. A standard Leclanche cell will have a voltage drop from about 1.5V to about 1V as about 90% of its energy is used up.

"Using a switching regulator with a 9V battery, a constant 6-volt output over nearly the whole life of the battery is possible without

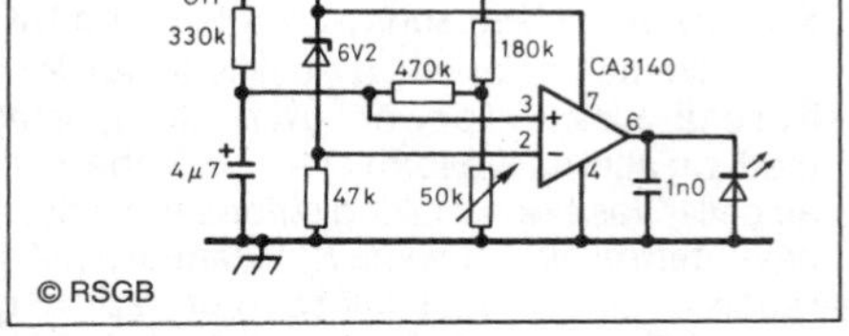

Fig 3: The blinking LED circuit which briefly shows when equipment is turned 'on' and which also blinks when the 9V battery is near its end-point voltage (6V). Used in conjunction with a switching-mode regulator as described by DU1AE.

wasting any appreciable energy. With this form of switching-mode regulator the higher voltage at the battery terminal is mostly converted to higher current at the output terminal. In converting from 9V to 6V the current into the regulator would be about 20% less than the output current; in other words voltage is converted into current resulting in high efficiency.

"I recently designed a small 50mW FM transmitter using 6V from 9V batteries; to give a proper usage indication, I arranged for the operator to know when the transmitter is turned on; also, when the battery voltage drops to an unacceptable level. **Fig 3** shows the circuit. It uses a 5-to-6V blinker type 5mm LED and a CA3140 high input impedance op-amp.

When the transmitter is switched on, the blinker will operate for a few seconds and then go off. On the other hand, the blinker will start operating when the battery voltage is down to 6V. The device takes up an extremely small space. The reason for having the LED operate for only a short time after turn on is to avoid wastage of battery, yet to show the operator to know it had been turned on. When on, but not blinking, the drain is only 1.66mA at 9V."

DU1AE enclosed information on the Micrel LM1576 and 2576HV "3A buck voltage regulator" one of a large family of switching regulators which uses 52kHz (±10%) switching in conjunction with an external standard 100µH inductance [perhaps one should note that with switching-mode devices there could conceivably be RFI problems in some circumstances – *G3VA*].

The device is described as follows: "The LM1576 series of monolithic integrated circuits (**Fig 4**) provide the active functions for a step-down (buck) switching regulator with a minimum of external components. Fixed versions are available with a 3.3V, 5V, 12V or 15V fixed output. Adjustable versions have a range from 1.23V to 37V (57V for the high voltage version).

Both versions are capable of driving a 3A load with excellent line and load regulation." It is pointed out that the fixed voltage version has an efficiency of 80% (better than 80% with the adjustable version) with thermal shutdown and current limit protection. This form of regulator substantially reduces the size of the heat sink used with conventional regulators and in many cases no heat sink is required: **Fig 5** shows typical applications of the LM2576.

AIR CELLS – LECLANCHÉ AND ZINC-AIR

MANY YEARS AGO (*TT*, December 1977 with a follow-up in May 1978) attention was drawn to the use at remote repeater sites in South Africa of large-capacity Leclanche air-cells. These were used in conjunction with 'reservoir' nicad cells which coped with occasional heavier (transmit) demands and were kept charged from the air-cells.

It was claimed by the South African writer, R T Hubbard, that the adoption of this system, rather than using thermo-generators, had reduced costs of providing power at remote sites by 80%, with the cost per station (in the 1970s) of a set of batteries about £80. Sev-

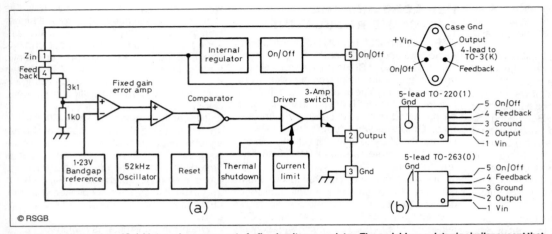

Fig 4: Switching regulator IC. (a) Internal arrangement of a fixed-voltage regulator. The variable regulator is similar except that the feedback (pin 4) goes directly to the error amplifier without the two resistors forming a potential divider. (b) Pin connections of the series for the TO-3, TO-220 and TO-263 packages.

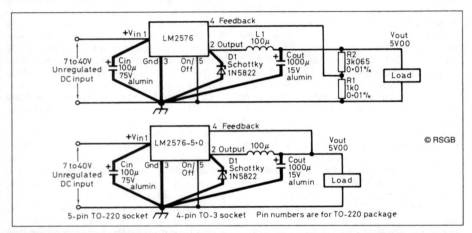

Fig 5: Test circuits for LM2576 and 2576-5.0 regulators. Note that as in any switching regulator, layout is very important. Rapidly switching currents associated with wiring inductance generate voltage transients which can cause problems. For minimal stray inductance and ground loops, the length of the leads indicated by heavy lines should be as short as possible. Single-point grounding (as indicated) or ground-plane construction should be used for optimum results.

eral readers subsequently pointed out that British-made air-cells of this type were used by British Rail.

To quote the 1977 *TT* item: "In effect, primary power is provided by a bank of 12 air-depolarized cells having an electrolyte of caustic soda and a capacity of 2000Ah. These cells (which are not a new invention) are air-depolarized, rather than using manganese as in the conventional Leclanché cell.

"The carbon element consists of a porous block of special construction which allows it to remain dry even when partially immersed in an electrolyte, yet permits gases generated by the action of the cell to mix freely within the pores and so cause hydrogen to combine with oxygen in the air, through the catalytic properties of the carbon.

"The cells have much greater capacity and far less weight for a given output compared with cells using chemical depolarizers, and have exceptional shelf-life [when not activated].

"The cell is in a black moulded case and is taken to the site before filling with water. Once the cell is connected and water added it is ready for immediate service . . . . They can supply a maximum of 1A in conditions of continuous discharge, enough for about 5W of transmitter power.

"To allow higher powers to be used, a nicad

battery is trickle charged via a current-dependent resistor from the air cells. With a 3A load on transmit the repeaters can operate for about three years from the bank of air cells which are then discarded and replaced." It should be noted that once water is added such air-cells are intended for continuous limited discharge.

It was stressed in the 1977 *TT* that such air-cell batteries are large and heavy and not suitable for portable operation but seemed a useful and reliable source of primary power at remote sites where mains supplies are not available.

Today, in sunny climates, the choice would more likely fall on solar generators in conjunction with large lead-acid rechargeable batteries although one suspects that the air-cell might still prove initially more economic, particularly in the less sunny climate of the UK.

While the Leclanché air-cell is an ancient, if useful, means of powering a relatively small load, an alternative form of air cell – the zinc-air cell – has been making strides recently. A news item in *New Scientist* (22 January 1944) reports: "Zinc and air will soon be replacing petrol and diesel as the driving force behind Germany's postal service. From next year, 40 electric postal vans will take to the streets, complete with novel zinc-air batteries that can store large amounts of energy, and be

recharged simply by replacing their electrodes . . . ."

These large-capacity vehicle batteries have been developed by the Jerusalem-based company, Electric Fuel Limited, and have an energy density of 207 watt-hours per kilogram, which is about four times better than a nicad battery and ten times better than a lead-acid battery. It is claimed that the EFL zinc-air battery can work at temperatures of −20°C, does not discharge itself, and cannot burn or explode. Zinc-air batteries work like a conventional alkaline dry cell; the oxidation that generates the electricity is achieved as the oxygen in the air turns the zinc electrodes to zinc oxide.

In tests by the German parcel post service, a 3.5-tonne electric Mercedes vehicle laden with a tonne of goods, fitted with a 350kg EFL zinc-air battery, gave a range of 350km and could be recharged in three minutes by changing the electrodes. Cost is put at DM1.40/km compared with 40 pfennigs/km for a diesel-fuelled van. Clearly the replacement electrodes do not come cheaply – but one could imagine such a power source having applications for Field Day and other events.

Small zinc-air batteries for portable and miniature equipment have been available for some years in the USA (and possibly in the UK). A survey *Choosing the best battery for portable equipment* in IEEE Spectrum (March 1988) listed zinc-air primary cells as providing highest energy density on continuous discharge; excellent shelf life (unactivated); limited rate capability and shelf life when activated; flat discharge characteristic with button cells available to 1150mAH; larger cells to 8.5AH. The nominal cell voltage is 1.4V.

This survey noted: "A zinc-air battery is unlike any other in that oxygen from the air is the active cathode material. Because the air cathode occupies only a tenth of a cell's internal volume and the anode can be correspondingly larger, a zinc-air battery can incorporate more anode material than any other primary battery of the same size.

In fact, zinc-air batteries have the highest energy density per volume or weight of any primary battery: **Fig 6**, from the 1988 IEEE Spectrum survey, shows the advantage of zinc-air cells in terms of energy-density per unit volume. To electronics designers, that means either a smaller battery compartment for the same operating life, or more capacity in a given space.

"The anode is an amalgam of powdered zinc mix with a gelling agent to keep it uniform during discharge. The electrolyte is a water-based solution containing potassium hydroxide and a small amount of zinc oxide. The air cathode assembly is a mixture of carbon, Teflon, and manganese dioxide impressed onto a nickel-plated screen.

Separating the electrodes is a semi-permeable membrane of Teflon, which prevents moisture from entering or leaving the battery and ensures the proper distribution of the air.

The air holes are sealed until use . . . . once activated the battery should be discharged within a few months for devices that are used frequently at low to medium drains, such as hearing aids, fetal-heart monitors, hand-held paging devices, and [small hand-held] transceivers."

It would appear that the Jerusalem-based EFL firm must have made significant developments in advancing the zinc-air battery from button cells for small portable equipments into a large capacity system, with rapid electrode replacement, for electric vehicles. Replacing the electrodes seems to be an easy and quick process but clearly for a large vehicle battery is a lot more costly than the conventional recharging of a large lead-acid battery. Nevertheless, these developments seem worth watching.

HERE & THERE

SYD FENWICK, G3AIO, noted my reference in the February *TT* to the failure of the 50-watt (5A at 10V) filament of the 813 in my ancient LG300 transmitter. He writes: "I acquired an LG300 in 1980 from the late G8ML and have used it almost daily since then. It came with the original 813 and imagine my chagrin when the filament went open-circuit a couple of years ago. Like you I had thought it would go on for ever! Fortunately G8ML had provided me with a spare 813. In my view the LG300 is still a good CW transmitter and in conjunction with an Eddystone EA12 (valve) receiver I can work plenty of DX. One drawback was VFO drift especially on the higher bands.

Perhaps it was good enough in the 1950s but not under present conditions – so I use an outboard VFO currently based on a BC221 mixer oscillator. All rather Heath Robinson but I no longer get reports of VFO drift." Like G3AIO, I used to get drift reports on 21 and 28MHz until I found that an easy answer is always to switch on the VFO for at least 15-20 minutes before operating – the drift could probably be cured by better thermal compensation of the oscillator but I have a suspicion that part of the drift arises from the influence of the buffer amplifier on the load on the oscillator. An external VFO or a 20-minute wait overcomes the problem on what remains an excellent 1950s CW transmitter.

Ray Loveland, G2ARU provides a practical tip: "The body of the pump-type toothpaste dispensers now on sale provides an excellent and robust coil former for larger coils such as those for ATUs. Made in tough polystyrene 400mm diameter and up to 120mm long. The small flange at one end is just about wide enough for mounting."

Hacker Radio by Geoffrey Dixon-Nuttall & Gordon Bussey (GDN Publications, Longmeadow, Miles Lane, Cobham, Surrey KT11 2EA, 1993, 28pp with 25 illustrations, £2.75 + 45p post & packing) traces the history of the Hacker brothers from 1927 to 1977 and the much misunderstood relationship between Dynatron, Hacker and Roberts Radio broadcast receivers.

During the 1939-45 war, the brothers offered Dynatron for service on a non-profit-making basis and were responsible for pre-

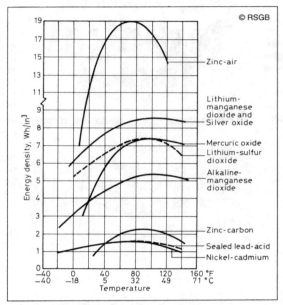

Fig 6: Energy density per unit volume of various primary and secondary cells. But note that energy density is sensitive to temperature and for all batteries is highest at room temperature. (Source IEEE Spectrum, 1988).

production models of Gee, Rebecca and Oboe. At the aborted 1939 Radiolympia, Keates-Hacker showed a 25-valve "Ether Emperor" receiver which provided choice between superhet or TRF reception and became a double superhet on short waves. It was priced at no less than 165 pre-war guineas, but presumably the outbreak of war meant that it never went into production. A well-produced and attractive booklet for those interested in the rise and fall of the British 'wireless' industry. It includes a list of Dynatron models introduced between 1927 and 1939, and Hacker Radio models between 1960 and 1976.

I wonder how many of those using 'Zener diodes' have realised that they are named after Clarence M Zener, who died in his home in Pittsburgh last July aged 87 years, and had their origin in a paper he wrote as long ago as 1934. A distinguished physicist, he was Director of Research at Westinghouse for 15 years from 1951 and in later years researched into the possibility of using differences of temperature at varying ocean depth to produce power at low cost without pollution – a possibility that some believe may come to fruition in the next few years.

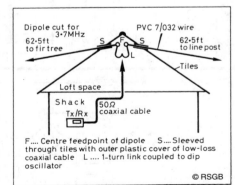

Fig 7: GWOGHF recommends using a GDO directly coupled to the feed-point of a dipole antenna rather than attempting to find resonance with a GDO at the transceiver end of a coax feeder.

The March 1993 blizzard along the eastern seaboard of the USA produced 59,000 cloud-to-ground lightning strikes, with a peak of 5,100 flashes an hour and a maximum density of strikes of 0.16 per square kilometre just south of Tampa, Florida. The blizzard also set new records for snowfall and low pressure. No information yet on how many solid-state equipments were put out of action!

In a letter to *Nature* (14 October, 1993, pp628-630) a team of scientists (N C Greenham et al) at the Cavendish and University Chemical Laboratories of the University of Cambridge report the development of more efficient light-emitting diodes based on polymers with high electron affinities. the first polymer LEDs (1990) were based on poly (p-phenylene vinylene – PPV) but they now report the fabrication of devices using a new family of processible poly(cyanoterephthaly-lidene)s. For hole injection indium tin oxide coated with a PPV layer is used and it has been shown that it is possible to achieve high internal efficiencies (photons emitted per electrons injected) of up to 4%. They write: "The demonstration of high efficiencies in polymer LEDs using metal electrodes which are not prone to oxidation represents an important step in the development of these devices. Long-term stability, both under storage and under drive, must be demonstrated before these devices can find applications, and there is much to be learned yet about the nature of the polymer-electrode interfaces. However, promising lifetime studies of the A1-PPV interface indicate the formation of a stable covalently bonded structure."

Brian Williams, GW0GHF, points out that the technique sometimes advocated for checking (with a GDO) the resonant frequency of coax fed antenna by terminating the end of the feeder in a one-turn loop produces misleading results. He finds that the method usually results in finding dips at many frequencies but none at or near the resonant frequency of the element [presumably because there will seldom be a perfect match between unbalanced co-ax and the element – G3VA]. His method is to disconnect the feeder from the antenna element and (in the case of HF dipoles) to insert a one-turn loop across the feed point; then couple the GDO to the loop. Unfortunately this may not be possible with the element at its full height although in his case the feedpoint of his 3.5MHz dipole is at the apex of his roof-space: **Fig 7**.

CORRECTIONS

JOHN BROWN, G3DVV, points out that the 1296MHz preamplifier, reproduced in the February *TT* (Fig 2) from *Radio-Rivista* but originally by YT3MV in *VHF Communications*, Summer (not February) 1992, should not have a 470pF capacitor across the input (not shown in layout diagram).

Another correspondent, C M Lindars suggests that the simple 3.5MHz direct conversion receiver (*TT*, July 1993, p52), reprinted from *Electronics Australia*, should have the 2.2µF capacitor in the lead from pin 5 of the NE602 to pin 2 of the 741 (via a 2k2 resistor) instead of between pin 4 of the NE602 to pin 3 of the 741. *G3VA*

VINTAGE RECEIVERS – AR88D, HRO ET AL

VALVES IN HF/VHF receivers are obsolete or at least obsolescent – how can one argue with this received wisdom! All one can say is that old soldiers never die they only fade away. There are still many classic receivers over 50 years old yet still providing their owners with excellent results on the amateur bands – and even a few constructors who find pleasure in putting together simple valve receivers.

Tony Tuite, GW0NSR (ZB2A 1950-54) has one of the classic AR88D receivers designed by RCA and now over 50 years old. He writes: "It still gives yeoman service, particularly on the lower bands. It cost me £6 10s plus a 1s 6d taxi trip to bring the heavy beast home! Recently, my XYL Joy is currently taking a Novice course at our local club so that alongside the AR88 sits a recently acquired Codar AT5 transmitter and PSU (£9.00 at the club junk sale). This can easily be modified to limit the power to the Novice 3W limit – and seems set on encouraging Joy later to progress from Novice to Class A. Meanwhile I have been using the set-up on 3.5MHz to work into Siberia, VE, LA, W5 etc on an 83ft antenna".

I recall that some years ago Ron Glaisher, G6LX, told me that the wartime RCA design was actually developed to meet a British inter-service specification. In the hectic days of 1940 no British company was available to meet this advanced receiver requirement and a delegation went to the States and persuaded RCA to undertake the project.

It emerges that there is also a firm British connection with the famous HRO receiver. In a *TT* item "HRODDITIES" (April 1992, p37) I wrote: "Although it is now some 45 years since I last used an HRO receiver built by the National Company of Malden, Mass, this set remains in my mind as the classic valve communications receiver designed for the amateur radio market. Perhaps this is just a nostalgic prejudice that stems from the five busy years (1941-46) spent spinning the unique PW dial of HROs (up to three at a time) for Special Communications, but the sound design of these sets is reflected in the number

Rotor-IV type receiver as constructed by C M Lindars.

that are still in good working order . . .". The item noted that the mechanical design of the early HROs was the responsibility of James Millen who had trained as a mechanical engineer, with the prototype electrical design undertaken by Herbert Hoover Jr, W6ZH, son of the former US President. As pointed out in Raymond S Moore's *Communications Receivers*: "The PW dial and gear drive, the ganged capacitors and the ganged coils and (plug-in) coil compartments are classics of mechanical design."

Recently Eric Sandys, GI2FHN, has drawn to my attention a fact that must be new to many who have used or admired the HRO dial which provides 500 clear calibration points in conjunction with the gear drive and four-gang tuning capacitor. He writes:

"Perhaps it has escaped my notice but in all

the articles on the HRO receiver I have never seen an acknowledgment that the 'PW' dial was a British invention. Patent Specification 419,002 "Improvements relating to Angular Motion Indicators" Application Date May 8, 1933. Complete Accepted November 5, 1934: "We, The Sperry Gyroscope Company Ltd, a British Company, of Great West Road, Brentford, Middlesex and William George Harding, a British Subject, of . . . . North Acton, London W3 do hereby declare the nature of this invention to be as follows:- This invention relates to angular motion indicators such as the dials of ships' compasses, radio tuning instruments, and the like, and has particular reference to a method of magnifying the motions of the dial or compass card of a repeater compass or other repeating device actuated by remote control from a master compass or master transmitter . . . ."

GI2FHN continues: "Presumably Mr Harding was an employee of the Sperry Gyroscope Co Ltd. I wonder whether he was responsible for any other inventions with a radio interest and whether he knew of the widespread use made of his invention during WW2 and subsequently. I notice on the reverse side of the National dial there is a small embossed logo which I take to be that of the Sperry company. The dial and drive unit was also made by Muirhead & Co Ltd during the 1940s and on the reverse side of their dial the Patent No 419002 is quoted and also 'Manufactured under Licence granted by the Sperry Gyroscope Co Ltd.' William Harding surely deserves a belated pat on the back should he still be with us."

For some home-brewers, the "classic" valve receiver remains the traditional two- or three-valve regenerative "blooper" and a number of magazines have been resurrecting such designs in recent months. For the uninitiated, the CW/SSB performance possible with such simple receivers continues to come as a great surprise. It was the relatively poor performance on AM that encouraged the general adoption of the superhet in the late 1930s.

Back in December 1976, *TT* published the circuit diagram (**Fig 1**) of the Dutch Radio Rotor Model IV, a commercially manufactured receiver based on two twin-triode ECC81

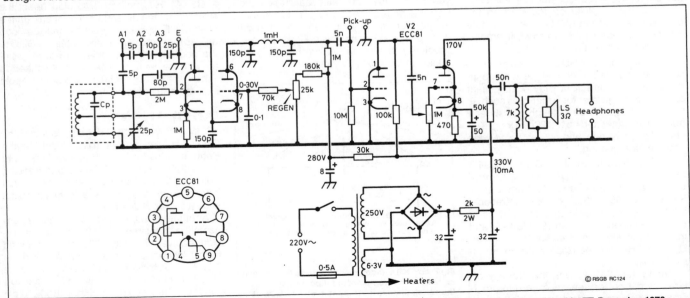

Fig 1: Circuit diagram of the Dutch Radio Rotor Model IV 0-v-2 receiver using a cascode-type regenerative detector as published in *TT*, December 1976.

Wartime advertisement photograph of the HRO receiver highlighting the famous PW tuning dial now known to have been a British invention.

valves with plug-in coils. Richard Kay, G3OQF/HB9ANW wrote: "Being completely fed up with all the commercial gear adverts, it was a real pleasure to see this circuit. I built it in a day, just a lash-up on the kitchen table and it worked first time (my coil was for the 3.5MHz band) . . . . After struggling with the Dutch text in the original "Electron" write-up I found the reason for the 1-megohm resistor in the cathode of V1 was to tame the reaction a bit."

C M Lindars also found the receiver brought back memories of the 'good old days' when similar receivers were the mainstay of short-wave reception. He found that a screen was essential over the grid leak and capacitor of V1 in order to minimize the pick-up of "ticky hum which would mar the excellent performance of this circuit where the audio gain is very high". He opted for Denco DP (valve type) plug-in coils. He added: "Sensitivity and selectivity are very good and the little receiver will provide much enjoyment to the SWL. The good performance on SSB makes it a useful standby when the main receiver is undergoing repair or modification. He offered readers layout details of his version."

Some 17 years later, Mr Lindars has sent along some photographs of his Rotor IV-type receiver. He writes: "Many readers sent for the suggested layout, and since then I have spent some time seeing if it could be improved in any way: I moved the transformers below deck and used a switched antenna input arrangement in lieu of the sockets on the front panel. I have wound a coil which covers 5.5 to 17MHz with a 160pF tuning capacitor. This coil has a B9A base and is so connected that an ordinary 'green' Denco coil may be used if desired."

WORKING WITH BALANCED LINE

OVER MANY YEARS, *TT* has pointed out the value of open-wire and ladder-type balanced feeders – and many suggestions for the construction of low-cost spreaders etc – not only in reducing feeder losses compared with co-axial cables but also, even more importantly,

---

EASY-TO-BUILD 25W MF/HF AMPLIFIER

MANY OF THE SOLID-STATE linear amplifiers that have been outlined in *TT* have tended to provide an output of around 10 watts and to take advantage of low-cost FET and HEXFET devices. A rather different approach is adopted by Gary Breed, K9AY in the February *QST* (pp31-34) in which the emphasis is the ease with which it can be built, low harmonic output etc rather than minimum possible cost. To quote K9AY's introduction: "Here's a 25W, 1.8-through-30MHz class-A linear power amplifier that's simplicity itself. What makes it simple is the use of a self-biased transistor module requiring few external components. To control harmonic output, a set of five-section low-pass filters is included. Power-supply requirements are +28V at 2.5A and −5V at 200mA. With a gain of about 13dB, a 1–1.4W driving signal is all that's needed to deliver 25W output. Gain is flat within ±0.75dB across the frequency range."K9AY shows that the amplifier (**Fig 2**) can be upgraded to 50W output by the use of an alternative transistor module. While packaged transistor amplifier modules have long been used at VHF, this has been much less common at HF where discrete devices with external biasing resistors etc have been usual. The modules used in this amplifier are made by one of the smaller, specialized US semiconductor companies, MicroWave Technology (4268 Solar Way, Fremont, CA94538) as the SLAM-0111 ultralinear 25W, class A self-biased power JFET module (50W version SLAM-0122) with SLAM an abbreviation for 'Solid-state-triode Linear Amplifier Module'. These devices include thick-film bias resistors which set the gate bias for class-A operation and establish a 50Ω input impedance. At the rated power and supply voltage, the push-pull output impedance is also 50Ω, requiring simply 1:1 balun transformers at the input and output.

The article provides full constructional details and also indicates that kits of components (including circuit boards, heat sink and rotary band switch but not the enclosure, connectors, TR relay or power supplies) are available from Crestone Engineering, PO Box 3702, Littleton, COL 80161 (25W kit $115 + $6 shipping). Clearly it is not the cheapest watts per dollar approach but K9AY summarises the case for the module approach: "This project shows how new RF products can make home construction of amateur equipment very easy. Home-brewers can benefit from a growing trend in RF product engineering: reducing development time by using 'super components' that require few external components and little engineering time to design them into a product.

"A secondary purpose is to show how even simple software tools can be used to speed up design. The programs used to design the amplifier's low-pass filters are inexpensive, and accurate at frequencies in the MF/HF bands. In this case, they made it possible to examine trade-offs among standard-value components for seven different filters, without having to build, measure and tweak each one.

"The result is a linear power amplifier with good gain and performance. Its uncomplicated design leaves little room for error, and no fancy test equipment is needed to build it successfully. Projects this easy can make an old-timer forget about the 'simpler' days of vacuum tubes!"

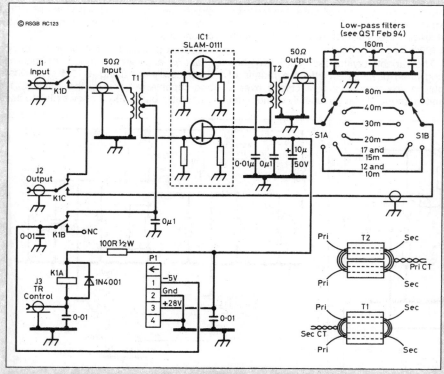

Fig 2: Circuit diagram of the K9AY 25W, 3.5-30MHz Class A amplifier based on an ultralinear self-biased FET module made by Microwave Technology. For further details see *QST*, February 1994.

in facilitating the use of multi-band antennas of which the 'tops' are not necessarily resonant on all (or any) bands. Admittedly, coax often seems easier to use and does not require an ATU with balanced output but there is much to be said for learning to make the best use of balanced line feeders.

A two-part article 'Working with balanced line' by Fred Bonavita, W5QJM (*CQ* January 1994, pp56, 58-59, Part 2 February pp26-27) provides useful information on using balanced feeders, drawing in part on RSGB publications by G6XN and G3BDQ. The USA makes considerable use of 300Ω balanced feeder for TV reception, and there is apparently available 450Ω 'windowed' (ladder) cable that does not seem to be advertised in the UK but would clearly simplify the use of balanced feeders.

Ribbon feeders do have the disadvantage that they change impedance when wet (at one time 300Ω feeder inside plastic tubing was manufactured in the UK to reduce this effect). There is still a lot to be said for home-constructed open-wire feeder with a spreader about every one or two feet. There are numerous sources of suitable plastic rods and strips to use to form spreaders, although it is advisable to check that the material is reasonably resistant to UV radiation.

For those more used to coax feeders, W5QJM provides a list of hints about installing balanced feeders:

"Keep them clear of metal. The rule-of-thumb holds that balanced line should be kept away from metal a distance equal at least to twice the width of the line. For 300Ω TV-type ribbon, for instance, that would be about an inch. For 600Ω line with a spacing between conductors of as much as 6in, the separation from metal should be at least a foot. Ladder-line and open-wire line cannot be taped to the leg of a metal tower but should be stood-off [W5QJM gives as an example the use of lengths of 3-foot long, 1-inch diameter schedule 40 PVC pipe to stand-off the line from the legs of the tower – *G3VA*].

"Don't bury the line.

"Changes in direction of balanced line should be gradual, not abrupt. An arc is preferred to a sharp angle.

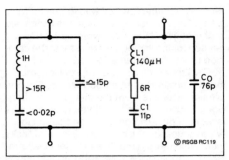

Fig 3: Equivalent circuit of (a) typical quartz resonator and (b) 4MHz ceramic resonator as described in 1985 by K2BLA.

"Avoid long, unsupported runs of twin-lead, especially in areas of high winds or where icing could occur. This applies also to coax feeder.

"When running balanced feed line, whether under the eaves of the house, up the side of a tower, or to the feedpoint, twist the line at least twice in every 3ft of length to minimise unwanted reaction and coupling to nearby objects."

VARIABLE-FREQUENCY CERAMIC OSCILLATORS

IT WAS NOTED IN *TT*, December 1985 (see also *Technical Topics Scrapbook* 1985-89, p69) that the long search for variable frequency oscillators of high stability and low phase noise 'jitter' had for long been dominated by the quartz crystal. In more recent years other control elements including cavities, ceramic dielectric resonators, yttrium indium garnet (YIG), surface acoustic wave (SAW) devices, steel and glass delay lines (eg PAL television delay-line components) etc have been used. Such control elements ranged from the lowest frequencies well up into the microwave region but all tended to be based on the principle of the control device stabilizing the oscillator frequency at or near a specified frequency.

The variable crystal oscillator (VXO) has long been used as an effective means of 'pulling' the frequency of a crystal over a limited frequency range (usually of the order

of about 0.1% of the nominal frequency) without undue degradation of the stability. However this is equivalent to only about 7kHz for a 7MHz crystal, even with inductance as well as capacitance loading, and although a useful means of providing a 'rubber crystal' to dodge interference, is not in itself an ideal range for a receiver or transmitter oscillator.

The *TT* item quoted briefly from a long article in the still-missed *Ham Radio* magazine of June 1985, pp18-26 by Al Helfrick, K2BLA (who a year or two later in *RF Design* introduced the concept of low-cost spectrum analysers; see many entries in *Technical Topics Scrapbook* pp85-89). K2BLA showed that low-cost ceramic filter resonators, as used to form the IF filters of broadcast receivers, when loaded by mechanically-variable or electronically-variable capacitors could be 'pulled' over much wider tuning ranges than higher-Q crystals. He quoted a range of some 2% compared with 0.1%, representing a stable tuning range of about 200kHz for a 10.7MHz ceramic resonator.

The main price to be paid for this extended tuning range is the greater temperature susceptibility of ceramic resonators compared with that of AT-cut crystals. For a fixed frequency oscillator using a ceramic resonator, the temperature drift could be minimized by using special –4400ppm/°C ceramic capacitors as the feedback elements.

K2BLA stressed that a ceramic-resonator VXO/VCO can be considered a useful compromise, offering much of the low phase-noise and short-term stability of a crystal oscillator, with a tuning range approaching that of a good LC oscillator. The Q of a crystal can be as high as 500,000. With a ceramic resonator the equivalent inductance is much lower and the Q typically 600, although the series resistance is lower; nevertheless this is significantly higher than that of an HF LC circuit with a typically Q of less than 60. **Fig 3** shows equivalent circuit parameters for 4MHz resonators.

K2BLA provided circuit diagrams of both capacitor and varactor tuned ceramic resonator oscillators using a 10MHz resonator and capable of covering the entire 10.1 to 10.15MHz band. **Fig 4** shows his mechani-

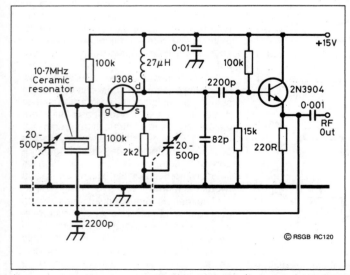

Fig 4: Mechanically-tuned variable-frequency 10MHz ceramic resonator oscillator (K2BLA).

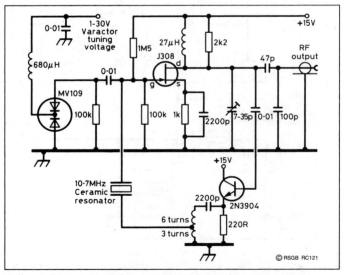

Fig 5: Varactor-tuned version of the K2BLA 10MHz ceramic resonator oscillator.

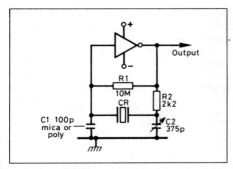

Fig 6: Arrangement used by G3BBD providing some 70kHz shift with a low-cost 3.58MHz ceramic resonator oscillator using a 375pF variable tuning capacitor and capable of good stability provided that the temperature of the resonator remains reasonably constant.

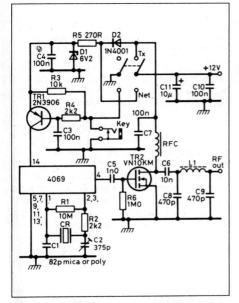

Fig 7: How G3BBD used his ceramic resonator oscillator to control a 1W QRP transmitter/driver covering about 3.52 to 3.59MHz with single 3.58MHz resonator.

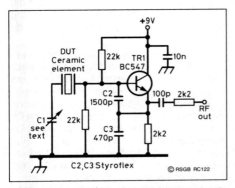

Fig 8: LA8AK's variable-frequency ceramic oscillator capable of covering the 3500 – 3600kHz CW section of the 3.5MHz band with a single 3.58MHz ceramic resonator.

1	15pF	40pF	80pF	115pF	150pF
1)	4023kHz	3965kHz	3935kHz	–	3916kHz
2)	4047kHz	3972kHz	3943kHz	–	–
3)	3620(0.25V)	3549(0.6V)	3517(0.8V)	3500(0.9V)	3490(0.95V)

The value shown in parenthesis is RF output (Vrms)

Table 1: Frequency versus tuning capacitance (C1).

cally tuned oscillator. Unfortunately it is not readily amenable to simple temperature compensation and has a temperature variation of approximately 230Hz per °C. Although it needs to be kept away from heat sources it is capable of forming an operationally useful variable oscillator. **Fig 5** shows a basically similar arrangement but electronically tuned.

Some five years later John Townend, G3BBD contributed an item to *TT* (February 1991, pp30-31) describing his experiences with ceramic resonator oscillators which had been sparked off by the *TT* summary of K2BLA's Ham Radio article, and noting the availability of 3.58MHz ceramic resonators costing only 54p each: "Experiments with this resonator in an oscillator circuit (**Fig 6**) using one hex-inverter section of a CMOS 4069 IC showed that it produced a frequency-stable output (provided that there was little change in the ambient temperature) over a range of some 70kHz with a 375pF variable capacitor. It was found that the oscillator could be keyed by breaking the supply to the device without significant chirp provided that the supply voltage did not exceed 7V.

G3BBD continued: "A simple QRP (1W) driver/amplifier transmitter was then constructed (**Fig 7**) using the oscillator. This provided a frequency coverage from 3.522MHz to 3.590MHz – a most useful section of the 3.5MHz CW band. Because the oscillator is keyed, full break-in operation is provided. A second section of the 4069 IC was used as a buffer stage driving a VN10K VMOS device providing an output of a little over 1W. This would be more than adequate to drive one of the VMOS or HEXFET amplifiers that have been described in TT to provide, say 10W output. John Beech, G8SEQ in TT, November 1993, p48 provided advice on using 455kHz ceramic filters as fixed-frequency beat-frequency oscillators".

More recently, Ian Braithwaite, G4COL, in 'Using Ceramic Resonators in Oscillators' (*RadCom*, February 1994, pp38-39) has provided further practical advice on the type of results that can be expected, together with a listing of the ceramic resonator frequencies (with part number codes) available from Electromail (RS Components) and Maplin.

The G4COL article encouraged Jan-Martin Noeding, LA8AK, to try the effect of using this approach, using an oscillator circuit that he has often used in the past for variable crystal oscillators. The values of the feedback capacitors were increased to a compromise between that required for a crystal-oscillator and Seiler-type VFO circuit: **Fig 8**.

This arrangement has been tested with a few available resonators: two Murata 4.00MHz (type 4.00G CMU (blue colour); and one 3.58MHz resonator of unknown manufacture (type KBR 3.58MS), see **Table 1**.

He finds that with this arrangement the elements will resonate above and below the

stated frequency, and that more than 100kHz tuning range is possible with 3.5 to 4MHz ceramic resonators. Oscillation ceases if the value of the tuning capacitor is too low. As with conventional Clapp oscillators, the output voltage varies over the tuning range, but within a 3.50 to 3.55MHz segment this is only about 3dB.

Since the main purpose of these experiments was to ascertain the useful tuning range, no attempt was made to optimise the oscillator for stability. But LA8AK stresses that as with other variable frequency oscillators, it is necessary to choose stable good-quality capacitors.

As an application for this VFCO approach, LA8AK has built a direct-conversion receiver using only low-cost, readily available components. This is based on the RA3AAE subharmonic anti-parallel diode mixer/detector (2 by 1N4148 diodes) as described in *ART7* (pp131-2) for 7 and 14MHz. With a BC547/BC557 cascode RF amplifier, 0.1µV CW signals on 7 and 14MHz can be read, providing a comparable performance to his Atlas 210-X. The receiver is to be described shortly in the Norwegian journal *Amatør Radio*.

MAINS PRACTICE & ADAPTERS

COMMENTS CONTINUE TO ARRIVE on the *TT* items (December 1993 and March 1994) on the question of differing mains practices in various countries and the general need for more 'consumer awareness' of travellers, including amateurs operating equipment overseas.

David Long, G3PTU – a former IBA colleague – writes: "You have stirred up a hornets nest over mains supplies . . . . I had heard about the harmonization of the mains supply in the European Union, yet when my local Yorkshire Electricity was contacted recently they seemed blissfully unaware of the impending arrival (January 1995) of the 230V AC specification!

"I have acquired some knowledge of the French practice of electricity supply. For very small consumers of, say 9kW peak, the supply is usually wired single-phase. For larger consumers in rural areas the supply is three-phase. A sliding household tariff is used which is higher for larger consumers.

In older properties socket wiring and lighting are often mixed on 10A or 15A fuses. Some sockets in a room may have some 380V between them. With modern French property there are usually three sockets wired back to a 16A fuse and a separate 10A circuit is used for the lights. The supply authority does not provide the earth, which has to be provided by the consumer but a RCCB (residual current contact breaker) always seems to be fitted. Voltage is still specified as 220V ± 10% but in practice the regulation in rural areas can be abysmal.

"In the UK, the days of the British BS1362A socket may be numbered since the European Union does not like 'ring mains', a system which does have some shortcomings.

"On the more general topic of 'Earths', I recently had the opportunity to use an old water pipe, which had been succeeded by a plastic pipe to form an Earth. Contact with the water pipe was extended to the shack using a length of 10mm Mains earth cable. To my surprise a DC resistance measurement to the Yorkshire Electricity cable outer (the house is not PME) showed a high value of 70W, despite the fact that the water pipe is about 0.7m below the surface and some 20m long. This illustrates that in some areas, a good low-resistance Earth is difficult to establish.

"Where no RCCB is fitted, the safety of an installation depends on the fault causing the fuse to blow by current flowing to earth and the protection offered by a 70ohm earth will be virtually non-existent.

It is my contention that every shack (and preferably every house) should have RCCB protection. There are still domestic fatalities occurring, for example, due to an open-circuit earth connection in the plug top of domestic appliances such as washing machines."

This topic of consumer safety is taken up by Philip Mansell, G3VKN, who writes:

"For some 14 years I have run a small shop selling electric equipment, electronic components, DIY materials etc and find that problems due to lack of electrical understanding are perennial . . . . Naturally, I make every effort to ensure that all the equipment I sell is more than 'fit for its intended purpose' and entirely safe. Yet, much as I would like to sell only items of 'Rolls Royce' quality, the economics of the marketplace dictate that the shop needs to carry a range of items, from a small basic plug-in PSU to stabilised units at twice the price. Both types have their legitimate applications but trying to explain to the uninitiated the pro's and con's of each is a nightmare. I tend to emphasise that when required to drive an expensive piece of equipment it is not worth attempting to penny-pinch with a low-cost PSU.

"More worrying, from a safety aspect, is the widespread misuse of mains plug-converters. My shop is near the local university so much of our trade is with students, both British and from overseas. While voltage harmonisation with mainland Europe is (supposedly) imminent, the day of the 'Europlug' is not – so plug-in converters are in great demand.

"'Shaver' adapter: this 3-pin 13A to 2-pin Continental/British/North American socket is fused at 1A (240W). While inevitably a compromise adapter but quite adequate for its intended use. Unfortunately, the majority of foreign students require it for their 600-1200W hairdryers so I have many requests for replacement 20mm ceramic 5A fuses. Trying to explain why I refuse to sell them such a fuse for that purpose, not to mention the considerations with Class 2 earthed appliances when applicable, tests both my patience and my limited linguistic abilities.

"Until last year the only safe solution was to cut off the continental plug and replace it with a British BS1363 type – much to the consternation of the customer. One local shop with unqualified staff were substituting 5A fuses in the adapters until the local Trading Standards Officer stopped the practice. I did an adiabatic test on some units and found that melting of the fuseholders occurred when passing some 5A.

"'Tourist' adapter: Fortunately there is now an approved adapter from British to most Continental/Australian 2-pin and 3-pin plugs

rated and fused at 13A. This is a fixed unit – not the type with suspect swivel selection pins which I have known occasionally to fall apart in use. Even with this adapter I have some reservations about the 13A current rating, though I am slightly reassured by the fact that continental appliances with such fitted plugs should not exceed 6A under normal circumstances. Nevertheless, the 13A fuse does not protect properly the flexible cable.

"American appliances: I never cease to be amazed by people who bring back appliances from the USA unaware of the supply difference (not to mention TV transmission standards). For an expensive, low-power piece of equipment, buying a suitable mains transformer may prove to be a good financial proposition (I won't sell the nasty cheap non-transformer adapters which can be hazardous). But for appliances incorporating even quite low power heaters, adequately VA-rated transformers may cost more than ten times the original cost of the appliance concerned!

"Finally, I agree that the ideal solution is consumer education provided that care is taken in deciding what information is given to the individual consumer. After spending some 15 years in teaching electrical engineering in further education and industry, it is always apparent that there is no point in trying to explain technicalities to someone with little-or-no technical ability: it is sufficient – and often safer – if they are just made aware that differences exist and are given a set of rules to work with, where necessary; for example guidance on correct fusing of mains plugs. Engineering will always be a compromise between perfection and cost. Most of us can't afford perfection, even if it were achievable. However I can live with this philosophy provided always that general health and safety are not compromised."

When the question of the proposed 230V −6% + 10% specification was originally raised by G3HB in TT, February 1994, pp53-54, I added the note "Since these tolerances cover the present 240V, I remain uncertain whether a voltage change will actually be introduced next January". Increasingly, this seems doubtful. As noted above, when G3PTU quizzed his local Yorkshire Electricity, they evidenced no awareness of any pending change.

Christopher Eley, GW4FTW, was concerned at the implications of a lower supply voltage on the efficiency of appliances and on the current consumption meters. He wrote to his supplier South Wales Electricity plc (SWALEC) who replied: "Basically, the nominal supply voltage will remain at 240 volts and

all meters will be tested using this standard output at varying inductive power factors to comply with the 1983 Energy Act. With regard to supply voltage as far as the company is concerned, there is no proposal to affect change. With reference to the system voltage tolerances, there is no proposal within this company to move away from the ± 6% tolerance presently in force." As GW4FTF puts it "It seems that, here in South Wales at least, it is a case of 'all change but no change' – whatever Europe says!"

HERE & THERE

HEINRICH KAIPERT, DJ6ZF, noted G4BWE's ingenious, simple-to-build form of permeability tuning for his Newbury 3.5MHz direct-conversion receiver (TT, March 1994, pp43-44) but adds a supplement: "Having been confronted with a similar mechanical 'problem' using two coils that had to be tuned simultaneously, I turned to the tuning assembly of an old car radio.

With this comes a gear drive 'for free' and three coils which, in my case, could easily be adjusted to the required inductance by merely partially unwinding them. Another 'goodie' is that you can preset the slugs, since this is provided by the factory for 'push-button' tuning of the car radio." Dr Tom Going (58 Cambridge Road, Southend, Essex SS1 1ES, home tel: 0702-334391), an ardent researcher into the history of valve technology, writes: "In the 1930s there were a number of small firms making valves in the UK but very little is known of their activities, how many employees they had, their key personnel etc. Two of the most interesting are Hivac (The High Vacuum Valve Company) and Lissen.

Hivac produced the well-known miniature and midget valves, as well as a range of Hivac-Harries critical-distance (beam) output power tetrodes (see 'The UK and the beam-tetrode' TT, July 1992, p38) and the Hivac-Harries all-purpose A15 valve. They also produced the mysterious J240, a double-tetrode RF pentode 'three-in-one' design dating from 1935, and said to have been produced for a specific home-construction design.

Their factory was in the Farringdon Road in London, a centre of the scientific instrument trade. Lissen of Isleworth, London produced a range of battery valves, a few 4V mains types and in 1934, the ACFC and FC2 triode-hexode valves, which, if issued, were the first such valves to be made in the UK. The company then faded out of the scene, either at the end of 1934 or early 1935. I would very much like to talk to anyone who was working for either company at the time, or who can shed any light on the technical, commercial or social life of either firm."

CORRECTIONS

In Fig 6 of the February TT, the MJ2955 transistor is shown incorrectly. It should be a pnp-type with the emitter connected to the 15R resistor and the collector to the 2N3055 pass transistors.

In Fig 5 of the February TT, the FETs should have been described as type 2N3819 not 2N3899.

Apologies for these errors.   **G3VA**

D/E Valves manufactured by Hivac and Lissen in the 1930s.

MULTIBAND OR ALL-BAND HF ANTENNAS?

THE AVAILABILITY OF THE 'WARC' bands not harmonically related to the 'traditional' amateur bands has led to increased interest in HF antennas that work well on all bands between 3.5 and 30MHz. However it has also apparently led to some confusion between such terms as 'broadband', 'all-band' and 'multiband' each of which refers to a particular class of antenna.

A broadband antenna is one that will present roughly the same feed impedance over a broad, continuous band of frequencies. Notable examples include the rhombic, terminated long-wire and other travelling-wave antennas. Directivity may be substantially unaffected by frequency.

An 'all-band' antenna as applied to amateur practice is one which can be made to operate (usually with the aid of a flexible antenna system tuning unit (ASTU)) on any of the amateur bands (efficiency will normally fall off on the lower bands unless the radiating element is some 30-40% of the lowest operating wavelength). Radiation pattern will normally differ on different bands unless, for example, this is determined by an additional element as with the W8JK centre-fed driven array.

A 'multiband' antenna implies an antenna that will work well on two or more of the amateur bands, but not necessarily on all

bands. A simple example is a 7MHz half-wave dipole which provides a near match on 21MHz but would normally not be used on the intervening 10 and 14MHz bands except possibly with the aid of a flexible ASTU and a reasonably short coax feeder capable of withstanding a high SWR.

These thoughts have been stimulated by an article 'On centre-fed multiband dipoles' by Dr John Belrose, VE2CV, and Peter Bouliane, VE3KLO, (*QST*, March 1994, pp34-36) with its provocative sub-title 'Is the G5RV really an all-band antenna?'. VE2CV notes the several references made in *TT* to the G5RV and to the modified version developed by Dr Brian Austin, ZS6BKW/G0GSF, using computer-aided design which can provide (without ASTU) an SWR of around 2:1 or less at five frequencies close to amateur bands, but which should always be considered a 'multiband' rather than an 'all-band' antenna.

The Canadian authors have long been

worried by some of the claims made (not by G5RV or G0GSF themselves) for this form of antenna. They point out: "Many amateurs regard this antenna with its so-called special feed-line arrangement as a panacea, particularly when it is used in a drooping dipole (inverted-vee) configuration. There is, however, nothing magical or superior about the antenna. It is merely a centre-fed dipole with a particular feed-line arrangement, which the newcomer to amateur radio may or may not want to duplicate. In fact, the performance of a multiband drooping dipole can be inferior to a dipole at the same apex height.

As pointed out many times in *TT*, the non-resonate centre-fed dipole (doublet) fed with open-wire (or ladder-line) feeder of any convenient length connected directly to a wide-range, flexible ASTU with balanced-output as in **Fig 2(a)** can provide an effective all-band antenna without the special feed arrangements of the G5RV, G0GSF antennas **Fig 2(b)** or PA0SE's 'Comudipole' etc. A variation of the Comudipole as praised by Jorge Dorvier, EA4EO, is shown in **Fig 3**. All three of these systems provide the attractiveness of a coax feeder into the shack and the ability of being able to use a G5RV/G0GSF antenna on at least one and possibly several bands without a wide-range ASTU. The justification for these variants is convenience rather than superior performance.

What seems to have got under the skin of the Canadian authors are the exaggerated

---

BROADBAND VALVE POWER AMPLIFIERS

THE CONCEPT OF THE broadband linear power amplifier which amplifies any, within limits, input drive frequency without the need for tuning/band-switching has become well established in these days of all-solid-state equipment. But it is less widely recognised that such amplifiers were used for professional applications in the thermionic era.

For example, a range of wide-band distributed amplifiers was developed in the early 1960s by the Marconi company and formed the basis of a series of advanced transmitters including the NT203 and NT204 broadband linear RF amplifiers for the maritime service. These were adopted by the Royal Navy (eg Transmitter type 640) for SSB/CW/FSK operation in the range 240kHz to 24MHz. The 640 was intended to run from 440V, three-phase AC supplies and required an external high-stability frequency standard (for the synthesizer), antenna tuning units (HF and/or MF) and a cooling air supply. The use of distributed amplifiers overcame the problem of retuning after a frequency change and also made possible simultaneous transmissions (at reduced power) on two or more frequencies. In order to avoid the generation of spurious signals, a high order of linearity was required and involved the use of an artificial transmission line with the shunt capacitances replaced by valve capacitances: **Fig 1**. The inductances, separating individual valves, effectively isolate the valve inter-electrode capacitances while the anode currents of the individual valves add up. The output line was designed as a compromise between a

uniform impedance (in which only the final valve would operate at optimum efficiency) and a tapered impedance (which would make valve voltages too low). The early stages thus constitute a uniform transmission line and, when correct operating conditions have been achieved, the characteristic changes so as to maintain a constant voltage swing on each succeeding valve.

The principles of this form of distributed amplifier and details of the NT204 broadband amplifier were described in a number of the papers presented at the 1963 IEE Convention on HF Communication (*IEE publication Ed4*). Since the 500W PEP output of the NT204 amplifier required the use of no less than six pairs of 4X250B tetrode valves, and its associated frequency synthesizer was of the high-cost 'mixer' type rather than a lower-cost PLL synthesizer, this approach was, as far as I am aware, never implement-

ed for amateur operation. It is possible that in the days when some amateur operation was permitted from Royal Navy vessels, before the security clamp-down of the late 1960s, some amateur contacts could have been made with maritime NT204s.

My interest in these distributed amplifiers has been revived by Malcolm Kirk, G4XMK, of Crowhurst, Surrey who for some years has had one of the heavy/bulky distributed power amplifiers (less the frequency synthesizer, PSU etc) in his garage. He now needs the space it occupies, and is looking for a 'good home' for it, possibly as a club station where there may be sufficient expertise to recover parts. I am not sure how much work it would require but the originally 'restricted' three-volume handbook of 1967 is indeed a formidable document, suggesting that this would not be a task to be undertaken lightly!

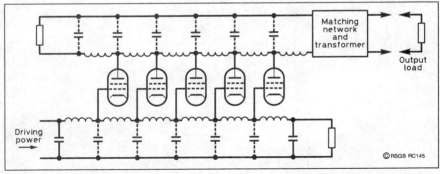

Fig 1: Simplified diagram of a distributed amplifier as used in the Marconi N204 transmitter.

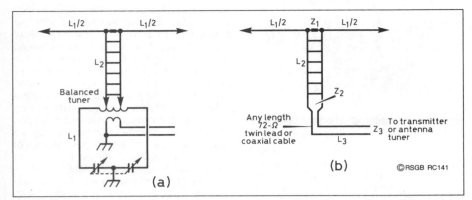

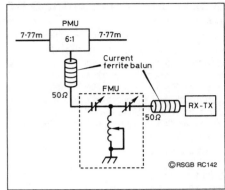

Fig 2: (a) Multiband or all-band dipole fed directly with open-wire line. The line is matched at the transmitter end with a balanced tuner. It is convenient (but not essential) if the length of the open-wire feeder is preferably an odd multiple of a quarter wavelength on the band in which the top element represents a resonant dipole in order to provide a low-impedance at the ASTU. (b) The basic arrangement of the G5RV or ZS6BKW variation, suitable for use (without an ASTU) on only some bands.

Fig 3: The EA4FO version of the Comudipole antenna. Note that the system works well without the toroidal ferrite current baluns. EA4FO uses 30m of RG-8 between the PMU and the FMU with no problems. Results have been excellent with an 8W transceiver. Between the FMU and the transceiver there is an SWR meter (not shown).

claims for the various variants of the doublet-antenna using special feed arrangements: "In our view, the correct feed-line length for a multiband dipole is that required to go from the output terminals of the antenna tuner to the antenna terminals, because – regardless of the length of the feed line – both the antenna and the feed line are made resonant by the tuner. Our recommendation, based on personal experience, is to use open-wire line for the total length of the required feeder. This will result in lower losses. An additional advantage in using a full-length feed-line is that any necessary balun can be inside the station, easing evaluation of its performance, or you can use a balanced tuner."

J H Gazard, VK5JG, in 'Tuned Feeders and Multiband Antennas' (*Amateur Radio*, April 1994, pp8-9) provides his experiences of both centre- and off-centre-fed antennas with tuned feeders. He concludes: "As a result of studying the operation of tuned feeders and making these and other tests my ideas of tuned feeder have changed and I have become aware of some facts that I have never seen in handbooks. These are that if the length of the antenna plus the length of each feeder wire is greater than a half-wavelength at the frequency concerned almost any combination of antenna length, feeder length, and feed point will function as a workable antenna . . .".

230V AC PETROL-ELECTRIC GENERATOR FROM SCRAP

RON MATHERS, ZL2AXO, in *Break-In* (September 1993) shows that it is possible to construct a 230V, 50Hz, 500W generator largely from discarded parts which should not prove too hard to find by a keen constructor. But while the generator is capable of powering relatively constant loads such as lighting, radio receivers, a TV set or, for example, a 20W transceiver, it is unlikely to prove suitable for supplying a 100W SSB/CW set since the rapid fluctuations of load represented by such a transceiver results in unacceptable swings in the generator terminal voltage.

The generator uses a discarded 3HP (petrol) lawn-mower motor as the prime mover and this is coupled by a belt drive to a 0.75HP single phase induction motor used as an induction generator. In practice the induction motor was an old 2850RPM pump motor salvaged from a local rubbish tip. [It is be-lieved that suitable induction motors can also be salvaged from a number of domestic appliances, etc]. Both bearings in the motor were renewed but no other modifications made to the motor. Capacitive excitation was used in the induction generator: **Fig 4**. ZL2AXO found that a capacitance of 36μF, made up from three 12μF, 400V AC capacitors, resulted in 230V, 50Hz at no-load. Changing the size of the capacitor changes the no-load frequency with the output voltage being kept at 230V by adjusting the throttle of the motor. ZL2AXO notes that induction generators with capacitive excitation rely on the residual magnetism of the rotor to initiate the build-up of magnetic field much as a DC shunt generator relies on the residual magnetism of its field poles. The magnetic field eventually rises to a value limited by the saturation curve of the machine. He found that with lower-power induction motors the residual magnetism could be lost if the generator was overloaded or short-circuited, but provides suggestions for restoring residual magnetism of such motors.

Induction generators offer a number of advantages: (1) Low maintenance – no brushes, commutator or slip rings to wear. (2) The output voltage is a sine wave. (3) The generator cannot be permanently damaged by a short circuit. He warns that lights powered by this generator tend to produce a noticeable flicker at a frequency equal to that of the power strokes of the petrol motor caused by the low flywheel mass of the motor. However this did not affect pictures on a TV screen or the operation of other appliances.

ULTRA-LINEAR VHF/UHF AMPLIFIERS

THE ENORMOUS EXPANSION of new forms of mobile, cellular and personal telecommu-

ZL2AXO's home-made 500 watt petrol-electric generator based on a lawn-mower engine and a domestic appliance type induction motor.

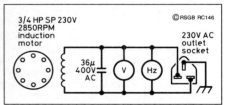

Fig 4: Induction generator as used for the 'scrap' 500W petrol-electric generator by ZL2AXO.

nications services, increasingly using digital speech and data modes, has brought about a major requirement for highly linear amplifiers. Such systems as the European digital cellular system (GSM), TETRA (European digital PMR), American and Japanese cellular and other emerging standards all require the use of linear (envelope varying) modulation formats to improve spectral efficiency. Unlike the traditional FM mobile services, a very high order of amplifier linearity is required in the transmitters to overcome the radiation of interference in the adjacent channels. In addition, both the UK and the USA are in the course of introducing 5kHz channelling for narrow-band modes such as SSB – in the USA such channelling is being located in part of the 220MHz band formerly used by radio amateurs.

The UK specification (MPT1376) for narrowband linear modulation PMR systems requires that the integrated power radiated in the adjacent channel should be 60dB below the in-channel PEP while the FCC transmitter mask requires any unwanted product (measured in a 100Hz bandwidth) more than 3.75kHz from the channel centre to be 61dB below the largest wanted signal.

To meet the requirements of these emerging or already operational systems, power amplifiers need to have two-tone third-order inter-modulation products specifications of some 55 – 60dB below peak level in circumstances where it is impractical to make use of Class A because of its overall low power efficiency.

A recent IEE colloquium 'Linear RF amplifiers and transmitters' (April 1994) provided some eight papers aimed at providing current experience on how such ultra-linear amplifiers might be implemented for mobile and also digital TV and sound broadcasting. Much of the present effort is based on the ideas originally put forward by V Petrovic a decade or so ago, initially for HF power amplifiers as a polar-loop amplifier (see *TT*, September 1979) and subsequently as cartesian feedback. With this approach (**Fig 5**), the inter-modulation performance of the amplifier can be of the order of 25dB with an additional 30 – 35dB provided by pre-correction based on demodulating a fraction of the output waveform and then comparing it with the input waveform to cancel out the waveform distortion (see **Fig 6**). The practical implementation of such feedback loops has been considerably facilitated by the use of digital signal processing.

From an amateur viewpoint, probably the most interesting of the colloquium presentations was 'A practical cartesian loop transmitter for narrowband linear modulation PMR systems' by Simon Whittle of Linear Modulation Technology Ltd (part of the Securicor Group). Securicor has been involved in 5kHz channelling systems since 1986, initially working with other firms on modified SSB equipment for DTI sponsored trials. LMT is currently manufacturing FCC-approved 220MHz trunked 25W mobile transceivers and base stations and has completed the design of a 100W base station.

The problems induced by Doppler shift etc with 5kHz-channelling mobile SSB are well-known but can be overcome by such techniques as Transparent Tone-in-Band (TTIB) modulation which provides a pilot carrier some

10dB below PEP, with Feed Forward Signal Regeneration (FFSR) originally developed at Bristol University (which now houses the Centre for Communications Research).

With TTIB, a reference pilot is placed in the centre of the RF channel and the band-limited baseband input signal is transposed symmetrically about the pilot typically 10dB below PEP. The pilot is normally the largest discrete signal and is, in effect, spaced as far as possible from the adjacent channels, minimising adjacent channel radiation. The FFSR technique allows a fading narrowband channel to be accurately equalised, improving voice performance and allowing 9600 bit/s 16QAM data to be transmitted reliably to a moving vehicle.

It is claimed that the cartesian loop transmitters now being marketed by LMT meet both FCC and MPT requirements for 5kHz channel-spacing PMR equipment, with image and carrier suppression of 35dB and two-tone IMD 60dB below each tone. The complete mobile transceiver requires 40W DC to produce a 25W PEP voice transmission, less than a third of the DC power required for an FM transmitter of comparable communications range. The LMT 100W amplifiers using FETs have two-tone IM products more than 70dB below each tone. Performance tends to be limited more by pick-up and supply modulation than by individual circuit blocks. The frequency synthesizers are particularly critical in this respect. The firm is currently developing equipment for other PMR mobile bands, and has started development of hand-portable equipment, using application-specific integrated circuits (ASICs) to reduce size, power consumption and cost.

Currently, it is admitted that compared with mass-produced FM mobile transceivers the

5kHz-channelling ultra-linear SSB units are 'premium-priced'. The improved performance and better spectrum utilisation of such systems seem to point the way that mobile radio will go – and clearly this is a portent also for amateur VHF/UHF operation, both fixed and mobile. From MF to UHF, ultra-linear power amplifiers and low-noise oscillators and synthesizers could 'clean up' the bands to a truly significant extent.

MAGIC OF MARGINAL ELECTRONICS – ANTENNAS & OSCILLATORS

FOR THOSE WHO BELIEVE that amateur radio has an important role to play in encouraging youngsters to take up the profession of radio communications engineering, it should not pass unnoticed that the current Chairman of the IEE's Electronics Division is Professor Mike Underhill, G3LHZ.

Over the years G3LHZ has made many contributions to both professional and amateur radio technology, including 'silent tuning' and 'quiet tuning' to avoid or minimise radiation during matching of antennas (Simple quiet tuning and matching of antennas' *RadCom*, May 1981, pp420-422) and also the concept of the two-stage approach to practical and versatile wide range antenna matching networks most recently exploited in the PA0SE Comudipole multiband antenna (*TT*, May 1993, pp54-55).

He has also been prominent in the development and better understanding of oscillators, including stabilisation by the use of delay lines and more recently in the investigation of improved frequency synthesizers.

In the written version of his Chairman's address ('The Magic of Marginal Electronics'

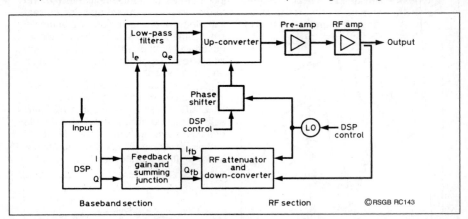

Fig 5: Basic configuration of a cartesian-loop ultra-linear amplifier, implemented using digital signal processing (DSP).

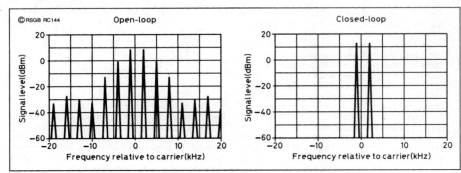

Fig 6: The open- and closed-loop performance of a cartesian-loop transmitter.

appears in the IEE's *Electronics & Communications Engineering Journal* (December 1993, pp359-368) he defines 'magic' as 'an extraordinary power or influence producing results which defy explanation', adding 'to many who have succumbed to the fascination of electronics this definition would seem very appropriate'.

He notes: "For scientific research it is the ultimate laws of science and nature that define the boundaries to be explored. For engineering it is the limiting trade-off between performance, safety, cost and timescale that becomes the challenge. Science is to a great degree curiosity driven, where the goal is better understanding of the laws of nature, whereas engineering has as a goal the modification or control of the environment (for the betterment of the human condition hopefully). Engineering needs science because not all engineering can be based on experience of what works in practice. It remains true that any engineering technology will ultimately only develop as far as the limits allowed by the laws of nature as discovered by scientific endeavour. Electronics has both its science and its engineering."

In the body of his address G3LHZ reviews the fundamentals of electrically small radio antennas, still often not understood by amateurs brought up on the idea that the only truly efficient radiator is a resonant half-wave dipole element. This concept is being slowly discarded in order to cope with the problem of HF antennas that need to cover both the traditional and the WARC non-harmonically related bands.

To quote G3LHZ: "The gain, or ability, of an antenna to radiate power (or receive power) in a given direction is almost the same for a very small antenna (no matter how small it is) as for its equivalent full-size antenna. (This is true for both monopoles and dipoles, where the full-size versions are, respectively, a quarter-wave and a half-wave in length). This is because the radiation patterns are almost identical for the small and full-size versions.

The gain is also proportional to the capture area of the antenna. The capture areas of a full-size and a small dipole, no matter how small the dipole is in length or wire thickness, are both a little over one tenth (0.12) of a square wavelength. If the antenna is made from a rod or wire of moderate thickness, the physical area of even a full-length antenna can be as little as one four-hundredth of the capture area.

"There is however a catch: the bandwidth of a very small antenna (that is the band of frequencies over which it works) is very small. There is a beautiful proof, originated by L J Chu but articulated in more practical terms by H A Wheeler, which shows that the bandwidth as a fraction of the frequency of interest cannot exceed a constant times the volume of the sphere (expressed in units of wavelength cubed) in which the antenna can be contained, no matter what shape the antenna is or what material it is made from. The fractional bandwidth is the reciprocal of the quality factor, Q, which is the ratio of the energy stored in the space around the antenna to the energy radiated or received during the time of one cycle of the waveform .... Q is very high for a small antenna [such as a transmitting magnetic loop] and we find that extremely strong electric and magnetic fields exist and store energy in the space immediately surrounding it when it is used for transmitting even quite low powers. A high value of Q is the price paid for having a capture area which is much bigger than the physical size of the antenna ....

"Fortunately H W Bode proved that it is possible to trade efficiency for bandwidth. For the case of a resonant (high Q) circuit a trade-off can be made between the bandwidth and the power loss .... for small transmitting antennas there is Foster's reaction theorem (based on an energy conservation argument) which is not very well known but which tells how to match a small antenna to a transmitter with a minimum of extra loss due to Q limitations. It also allows maximum bandwidth to be retained when matching an antenna for several frequencies of operation. (The secret is to minimise the stored energy by making all network reactances as far as possible of the opposite sign to the load reactances). This theorem was used in the design of the HF multicoupler in the beacon experiment in the first University of Surrey [UOSAT/AMSAT] satellite.

"Another nice theorem for radio antennas and radio transmission is the 'principle of reciprocity'. It means that if receiving and

TOROIDAL HELIX ANTENNAS

I GATHER THAT THE articles by Roger Jennison, G2AJV, on his compact single and twin toroidal antennas (*RadCom*, April and May, 1994) were mistakenly considered by some readers to be an elaborate April Fool joke rather than a practical approach to mobile and space-limited applications. It therefore seems worth pointing out that alternative forms of toroidal helix antennas (without the top and bottom plates) were outlined in *TT* in October 1983, pp889-890. This was the result of Alec Clelland, DJ0FL/G3UUQ drawing attention to the 70-page European Patent Application EP 0 043 591 AI made by James Corum of West Virginia, who, from the examples described, appeared to hold an amateur licence. [K1AON – *Ed*]

In his application, James Corum claimed that various implementations of the basic principle "possess greater radiation resistance and radiation efficiency than loop antennas of similar size". He also claimed that such elements "radiate controllable mixtures of vertically, horizontally and elliptically polarized electromagnetic waves, and possess radiation patterns different from those produced by small loop antennas, and can be used to form both driven and parasitic arrays." It was pointed out that although such elements are similar in form to a toroidal inductor, they are essentially not perfect toroidal inductors which would have zero radiation efficiency.

Examples given in the Patent Application (including those outlined in **Figs 7 and 8**) covered frequencies as low as 200kHz and as high as 450MHz. The inventor admitted that "one does not get something for nothing. The price one pays with the toroidal helix is that it is a narrowband (high-Q) structure and inherently not a broadband device .... [but] these antennas by virtue of their construction possess a greater radiation resistance than known antennas of similar electrical size not having the slow-wave winding features .... the helix permits the formation of a resonant antenna current standing-wave in a region of electrically small dimensions, and it permits the controlled variation of antenna currents, resonant frequency, impedance, polarization and antenna pattern."

I cannot recall the 1983 *TT* item attracting any great attention and we owe a debt to G2AJV for further developing this interesting antenna concept and showing its practical value for such applications as mobile operation. His articles clearly deserve to attract further work.

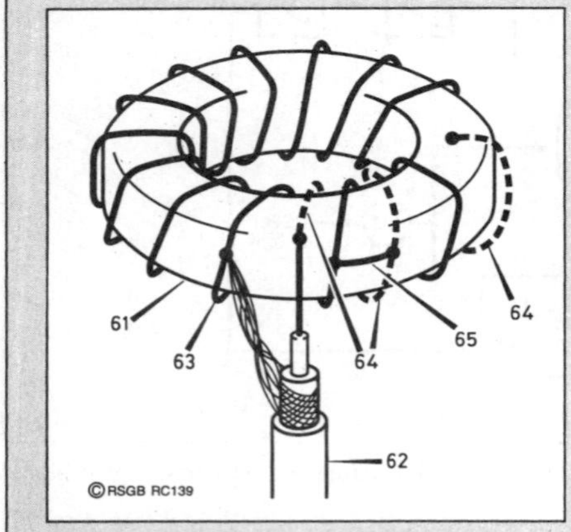

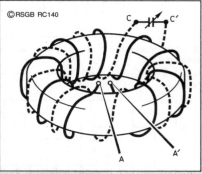

Fig 7: One of the several forms of toroidal helix antennas described by James F Corum in his patent application. Isometric representation of the antenna (61) and transmission line (62). The main conductor (63) is continuous. In addition there is a shorter inductor (64) helically wound around the toroidal support between some of the turns of the main conductor (63). A sliding tap (65) connects the two conductors 63, 64. One side of the transmission line is connected to one end of the shorter conductor (64) and the other side attached to the main winding 63. The sliding tap (65) is moved to provide proper impedance matching. This point is found empirically at the operating frequency by moving the sliding tap to the optimum position.

Fig 8: Use of a variable capacitor to vary the resonant frequency of a toroidal helix antenna without changing the number of turns. The antenna comprises two helices, one fed at points AA' and the other at CC'. The variable capacitor is connected across feedpoints CC'.

transmitting antennas are interchanged there will be no change in the received signal for a given transmitted power (the path loss is the same either way provided both antennas are power matched to their terminations)."

G3LHZ illustrates reciprocity by showing that this would apply even to the interchange of the Droitwich 198kHz 400kW antenna and a ferrite rod receiving antenna – at least for the few microseconds that 400kW could be fed into the ferrite rod antenna! But he emphasises that to obtain maximum radiated power an antenna [system] must be resonated to the transmit frequency and then matched in impedance to the transmitter. In practice of course much of inefficiency of electrically small antennas arises from the losses involved in the matching networks – all the power actually fed into the radiating element will be radiated apart from the usually small ohmic loss.

G3LHZ also underlines in his address the importance of oscillator phase noise: "If the oscillator used is itself noisy (having phase noise), then in the case of a transmitter the oscillator noise spills over into the adjacent channels and, in the case of a receiver, signals in the adjacent channels are allowed to corrupt the wanted signal by the process called 'reciprocal mixing'. In either case the adjacent channels become unusable.

"The phase noise of an oscillator, no matter how it is implemented, obeys a simple rule of thumb originally put forward by Leeson (*Proc IEEE*, 1966, Vol 54 (2) pp329-330), then extended by Underhill (Fundamentals of oscillator performance' *Electron & Comm Eng J*, August 1992, Vol 4 (4) pp185-193). The rule of thumb is that the timing jitter/noise which represents the phase noise in any oscillator is inversely proportional to the power P of an oscillator times the quality factor squared, Q^2. Thus for low phase noise in any oscillator, the figure of merit PQ^2 should always be as large as possible . . . . The phase noise of an oscillator can also be reduced if its temperature is lowered . . .".

ANALOGUE MULTI-METERS ARE VERSATILE

JOHN OSBORNE, G3HMO, believes there is still a place for old-style analogue multimeters which have a versatility not found in digital multimeters (DMM). He writes: "I find the DMM fine for accurate measurements of resistance for calibration purposes and very occasionally for some special facilities such as capacitance or frequency measurement. But it is not reliable for testing continuity as the applied voltage is often not enough to break down switch-contact resistance etc.

"On the other hand the analogue multimeter has a high enough applied voltage to break down switch-contact resistance [usually, but not always, low enough to avoid damaging semiconductors] when circuit testing. When testing capacitor insulation one notices the charging pulse for those over about 1μF. Then, if one gets a bigger pulse on reversing the leads, it indicates that leakage is small and it is a useful capacitor. There is no need to use sophisticated testgear for most work in the shack."

G3HMO illustrates the versatility of the analogue multimeter with two examples: (1)

Non-destructive test to find the breakdown voltage of semiconductors; and (2) wet-finger test for semiconductors.

(1) *Break-down voltage test:* Semiconductor devices have been described as the fastest fuses known to man. Exceeding the breakdown voltage can be very expensive and time consuming. The manufacturer's specification is likely to be conservative in order to cover variations in production. A particular specimen could be safely run above the specification if the real breakdown voltage is known. A typical plot of reverse voltage against current for a junction is shown in **Fig 9(a)**. When the voltage reaches the turn-over point, further increase in voltage produces an indefinite increase in current; the resulting wattage dissipation soon destroys the junction. Any test must limit the current to safe values.

The setup for a simple test is shown in **Fig 9(b)**. A variable voltage supply, moni-

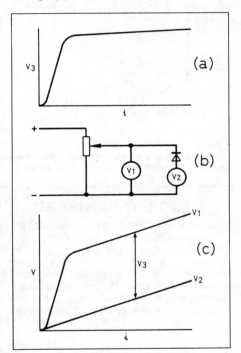

Fig 9: Use of analogue meters for non-destructive testing of the breakdown voltage of a semiconductor junction.

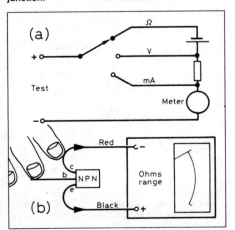

Fig 10: The 'wet-finger test' to check that a transistor is functioning and not a dud, using a high-sensitivity analogue multimeter such as the AVO Model 8.

tored by V1, is applied to the device. A second voltmeter connected in series should be a high-resistance moving-coil instrument which passes a small but measurable current. A 20kW/volt MM passes 50mA at full scale and 25mA at midpoint, whatever the voltage range. I find my AVO Model 8 ideal. This meter reads V2 the difference between the voltage across the device and the applied voltage. It also monitors the current through the device as already noted. Typical plots of V1 and V2 against the current in the device appear in **Fig 9(c)**. V2 is directly proportional to the current. V1 rises as the small current through the device rises. At the turnover point no further increase in voltage is required to increase the current and both voltages rise at the same rate. The difference is V3, the breakdown voltage of the device.

A little thought and practice reveal that the graph, Fig 9(c), is not needed. When winding up the voltage of the supply and watching the AVO the difference becomes a matter of mental arithmetic. Because the maximum current that can flow through the device with a high-sensitivity meter is so small the test is non-destructive.

(2) *The Wet Finger Test:* The requirement of an amateur is often simply to check that a component is viable and not a dud. With the common transistor, the requirement is usually not so much a precision measurement of gain as a confirmation that the device has some useful gain. The wet finger test, with an analogue multimeter on an ohms range, can indicate this. Digital meters are unsuitable. A transistor is effectively two back-to-back diodes (base-to-collector and base-to-emitter). First check each diode separately with the meter; in the forward direction a typical reading would be 200 to 600Ω; in the reverse direction (simply connecting the leads to the diode the other way round) the apparent resistance will usually be above 100kΩ, tending towards infinity.

In the simplest transistor amplifier circuit a transistor, has a supply voltage connected. With no current in the base, a negligible current will flow in the battery circuit. If a small current is caused to flow between base and emitter, a much larger current, perhaps one hundred times as much, will flow between collector and emitter. A multimeter on a high resistance range connected between collector and emitter will show a very high resistance. If a suitable resistance is connected between collector and base, the small current will be amplified and the meter will indicate a large drop in resistance. A suitable resistance can be readily provided by licking one's fingers and applying them between collector and base. Putting fingers in parallel with collector and base will indicate the order of magnitude of the wet finger resistance; the much bigger drop when connected between collector and base gives some indication of useful gain.

Note that the multimeter lead polarity is reversed on the ohms range. The basic circuit of a multimeter on the ohms ranges is shown in **Fig 10(a)**. The wet finger test is illustrated in **Fig 10(b)**. **G3VA**

TOWARDS THE SUPER-LINEAR RECEIVER: LOW NOISE OSCILLATORS

IT WAS EMPHASISED in the January TT (p39) that if full advantage is to be taken for high-dynamic range receivers of the latest super-linear mixers such as G3SBI's H-mode FET-array mixer there remains a need to produce free-running or preferably synthesised oscillators having an extremely low phase noise of the order of 150dBc/Hz or better, a few kHz off the tuned frequency.

Colin Horrabin, G3SBI has progressed significantly towards this target for a free-running oscillator although he recognises that to design and build a complete digitally synthesised local oscillator based on his preliminary results is still a major undertaking. However he feels that information at an early stage may encourage some readers to take these developments further and faster than his own other commitments permit.

He writes: "These present notes cover an oscillator suitable for use as a VCO (voltage-controlled oscillator) or as an overtone crystal oscillator that has low inherent phase noise. The initial measurements were made on an oscillator operating over 20 to 80MHz using conventionally wound inductors, but subsequently it has been found that a version using stripline inductors against a groundplane shows the most promise. This form of construction has been found to cut dramatically the sensitivity to stray capacitance fields.

"The prototype stripline version operates in the 36 to 150MHz region (capacitance

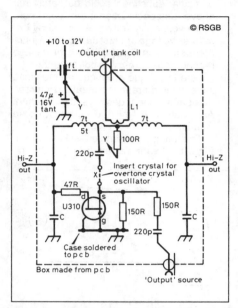

Fig 1. The initial prototype grounded-gate, low-phase-noise oscillator using lumped wound coils.

0 – 180pF) or 82 to 146MHz (0 – 27pF) but changes to the length of the line could give a 3.5:1 operating frequency range anywhere between 20 and 450MHz. The stripline artworks were produced by my SERC colleague, Alex Macdonald, on an Apple PC using MacDraw software with output onto a laser printer.

"**Fig 1** shows the original design using coils. It was constructed inside a box made from double-sided PCB material. Output at 50ohms impedance and 0dBm signal level for a spectrum analyser can be taken either from the FET source or via a two-turn link winding on the main tank coil L1. These are terminated in SMA connectors. The oscillator comprises a U310 junction FET in grounded-gate configuration.

The two capacitors marked C must be of the same value. Components: C Suflex or plate-ceramic capacitors between 15 and 220pF (Cirkit Components). L1 7 + 7 turns 6mm dia enam for about 20 to 80MHz. When used as a crystal oscillator, the oscillator is first used free running on the crystal frequency. One of the capacitors C is made variable the frequency can be tuned. The crystal is inserted after breaking line X and on the C adjusted for oscillation. Output from the source has slightly improved sidebands. For VXO use the 220pF capacitor can be varied to give about 5kHz variation at 53MHz. As a crystal or free running oscillator outputs of about 0dBm are available from source or tank. A high-impedance output of about 10V peak-to-peak can be taken as shown. The two Hi-Z outputs are 180° out of phase.

SIMPLE RF SNIFFER

THE ABILITY TO DETECT the presence of RF energy that has made its way to either desired or undesired hot spots is useful in the shack. Emmerson Hoyt, WX7E in the 'Hinks and Kinks' column of *QST* (April 1994, p82) provides information on a simple RF sniffer meter that has served him well for almost 50 years, proving nearly indispensable in the lab and radio shack for sniffing out the presence of RF (or even high audio) energy. It can show if RF is present on the outside of coax cable shields, or in regulated power supplies or audio amplifiers, as well as confirm its presence in those places where it should be, such as oscillators and RF or IF amplifiers, see **Fig 2**. Sensitivity depends on that of the meter, preferably a low-range microammeter with a full scale deflection of 100µA or less. WX7E writes:

"The circuit consists of a sensitive meter, two germanium diodes, a short piece of bus wire for a probe, and some suitable support hardware. The bus wire acts as antenna, and the diodes rectify the RF, feeding DC through the meter . . . . Germanium diodes (eg 1N34A) are better than silicon diodes because of the much lower turn-on voltage.

"With a microammeter, the device is quite sensitive. In many applications, the probe tip need not directly contact the circuit under investigation. In any case, circuit loading by direct contact is minimal for RF (in the HF region) or IFs. The diode leads can be soldered directly to meters with terminals

that allow this: solder lugs can be used for connections to threaded-stud meter terminals. In either case, be sure to provide adequate physical support for the junction between the diodes and probe wire . . . . Cover the probe wire with insulating sleeving, leaving only a very short length of the tip exposed. When working with valve-type

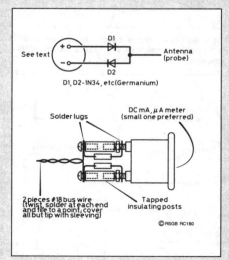

Fig 2: WX7E uses this simple RF sniffer arrangement to indicate the presence of RF energy in circuits etc. The germanium diodes rectify the RF, the meter displays the resulting DC. Sensitivity depends on the sensitivity of the meter.

circuits or other high-voltage devices, be careful if the probe is close to or in contact with the higher voltages."

An alternative, less sensitive, form of RF detector has been in use for several years at G3VA. An American reader kindly sent along a 'MicroChek' device marketed in the USA for checking possibly hazardous leakage of RF energy from microwave ovens. I found that it could also be used to indicate RF energy at HF or VHF. This handy device has no meter but two LEDs, one green and one red together with a button switch. When the button is depressed, the green light should come on to indicate that the two 1.5V cells forming the battery are in good condition. Then, to use as an oven checker, the microwave oven is turned on to high power, and with the button depressed, the device is run around all door openings etc. A 'blinking' red light indicates moderate 'impending' leakage whereas a constant red light indicates potentially dangerous leakage requiring the attention of a qualified technician.

Checked on my daughter's microwave oven, it proved possible to get some red light flashes with the device held close to the door hinges, but in the shack, HF energy showed up in both expected and unexpected places. Unlike WX7E's meter sniffer, there is no exposed probe and the sensitivity is insufficient to detect receiver oscillators etc. I imagine similar oven testers are marketed in the UK.

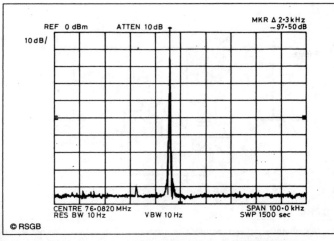

Fig 3. Typical free running spectra of the original oscillator at 76MHz.

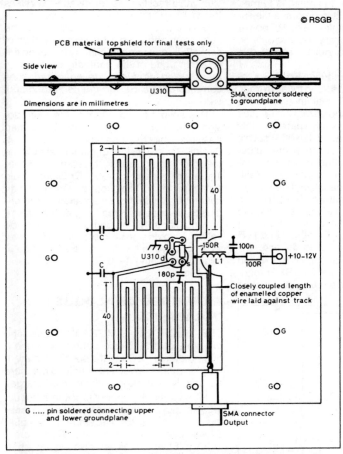

Fig 4: Prototype strip-line oscillator capable of providing an operating range of about 3.5:1 before oscillation ceases. length 'a' 40mm, width 'b' 2mm, width 'c' 1mm. To change the frequency range alter the length 'a' and the length of the output coupling wire. Typical frequencies with C 0pf about 145MHz, 27pF about 80MHz, 56pF about 60MHz and 150pF about 36MHz (plate-ceramic capacitors). 1/16in double-sided PCB note that the bottom ground plane covers the whole of the PCB. Output about 0dBm. The U310 FET is pushed through from the bottom side of the PCB until it touches the ground plane and soldered directly to the ground plane.

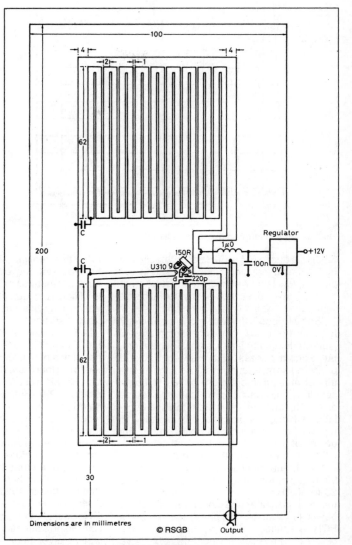

Fig 5: Later version of the stripline PCB artwork.

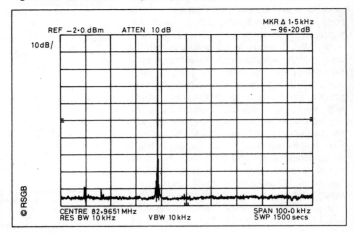

Fig 6: Spectra of stripline oscillator at 82.9MHz.

The grounded-gate happens to be the case of the FET so a hole is drilled in the groundplane and the FET pushed through with the case soldered to ground. A 47Ω resistor is necessary in series with the drain lead (but not in the stripline version) to control a 500MHz parasitic oscillation.

"L1 is a split coil; this is fundamental to the design in order to avoid the use of a by-passing capacitor to ground at its centre. The

other half of this coil acts as a series tuned circuit and therefore presents a low impedance at resonance to ground at the DC feedpoint. If necessary, push-pull signals at a high impedance can be taken between the ends of L1 to ground; C1 and C2 are identical values and must be changed together. Varicap diodes, if used, must be matched, since any significant difference in value of C1 and C2 will inhibit oscillation.

"Some tests were made using a 53MHz third-overtone crystal inserted between points. Noise sidebands were down 98dB at 200Hz from centre frequency.

"Typical free-running spectra of the original oscillator at 76MHz are shown in **Fig 3**, about 98dB down at 2kHz. Contrast this with the superior stripline circuit (**Figs 4 and 5**) at 82.9MHz (**Fig 6**) and 201MHz (**Fig 7**). Most of the close-in phase noise noted in a run at

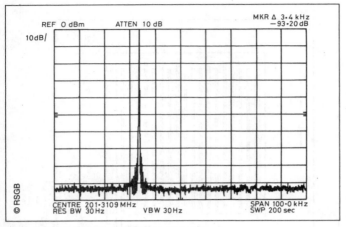

Fig 7: Spectra of stripline oscillator at 201MHz.

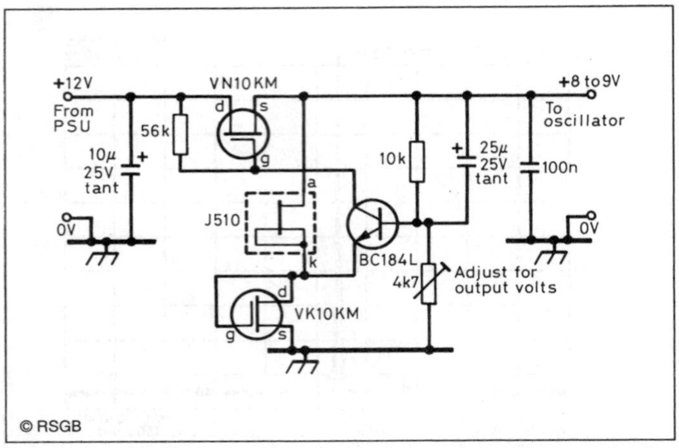

Fig 8: Low-noise voltage regulator as use for the G3SBI low-noise oscillator.

62MHz is due to FM at 50Hz presumably due to AC mains inducing fields in the tank coil causing low-level AM and FM modulation of the FET. In a closed loop of any useful bandwidth, these would be suppressed.

"So how good is the oscillator phase noise? It is visually superior to two of our professional high-grade synthesized signal generators, but without access to a Hewlett Packard phase-noise measuring system or other methods of measurement more suited to home construction, exact figures can not yet be given. Nevertheless, it is clear that the oscillator shows great promise. It is intended to use one or more stripline oscillators in the design of a low-phase-noise synthesized local oscillator system when time permits.

"Two further stripline oscillator layouts have been implemented for the frequency range 20 to 50MHz and are being tested. One of these uses thinner and closer tracks with the object of reducing the physical size of the PCB. A practical PCB layout for the local oscillator of a receiver would probably have the two striplines back-to-back on two separate PCBs so that a band-change wafer switch (perhaps driven by a stepper motor) would be simple to accommodate.

"Finally, it needs to be stressed that the design of the voltage regulator is important in order to obtain results as good as, or better than, a 9V battery as the oscillator power source. The best spectrum results have been achieved with a regulator output of 8 to 9V. Conventional IC regulators slightly degrade the oscillator noise floor, particularly close-in. The simple regulator circuit shown in **Fig 8** gives good results and was used during the measurements shown but could probably be improved with a little more loop gain. In this design the regulator voltage reference is a high gm FET type 10KM driven by a J510 JFET current source and has low-noise characteristics.

ORIGINS OF THE 'ULTRA-LINEAR' AUDIO AMPLIFIER

IN THE 1950s, MUCH USE was made in 'high-fidelity' audio systems of the so-called 'ultra-linear' amplifier circuit in which the screen-grid (G2) of the output pentode or beam-tetrode valve(s) is connected to a tapping (or tappings) on the primary of the audio output transformer as shown in **Fig 9**. Rather surprisingly I cannot recall any attempt to

utilise this configuration (sometimes termed the 'triode-tetrode' circuit) to improve the linearity of push-pull or single-ended RF power amplifiers although logically there seems no reason why this should not be effective in Class A designs.

Dr Tom Going (58 Cambridge Road, Southend, Essex SS1 1ES) has been trying to trace the origins of this 'ultra-linear' technique. He points out that it is well known that the famous Alan Blumlein of EMI took out a patent on this circuit in 1937 (British Patent 496 883) but his stated purpose was reduction of the output impedance of the valve and to prevent damage if the load became disconnected (Keith Thrower, 1993). An exhaustive study of the circuit by F Langford Smith and R R Chilton in 1955 reported that the earliest reference to the circuit they had traced was in student notes written in 1933 by R Lackey and R R Chilton of the Australian Radio College.

However, L Williams of Solihull has drawn Tom Going's attention to the Ekco RS3 broadcast receiver (four valve 'straight' receiver

plus valve rectifier) as reviewed in *Wireless World* (August 26, 1931) in which it was specifically stated "down the primary of the output transformer there is a potential drop of some 25V, and into this primary is tapped the screening grid of the pentode, *an arrangement which produces the necessary tone correction required with the pentode output valve.*"

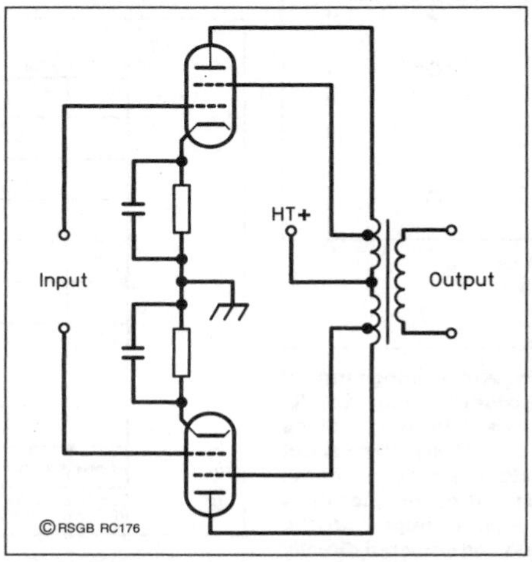

This seems to indicate that the Ekco design team (possibly Anthony W Martin, then Assistant Chief Engineer and/or Harold Hunt, Senior Radio Design Engineer) should be credited with originating the ultra-linear configuration as early as 1931. Dr Going would be interested to hear from anyone who can contribute any further information on the origins of this means of reducing distortion (improving linearity) of pentode and tetrode valves. It would also be interesting to discover whether anyone has investigated the use of this load-tapping technique for RF linear amplifiers.

EXPANDED ANALOGUE VOLTMETERS

THE TRADITIONAL METHOD of checking the state of a lead-acid battery is to use a hydrometer to measure the specific gravity. It may be more convenient simply to measure accurately its voltage under load or charge.

John Grebenkemper, KI6WX in introducing 'An inexpensive, expanded-range analogue voltmeter' (*QST*, December 1992, pp52-54 with correction to Fig 1 in *QST*, February 1993, p78) writes: "When discharging a battery, the potential across the battery terminals depends on the charge left in the battery and how fast you're discharging it. When charging a battery, the terminal voltage and the charging current can tell you how much the battery has been recharged. The charging voltage of a float charger must be set precisely, or the battery can be over- or under-charged. For a 12V, lead-acid battery, all of these voltages should be known to within 100mV to make a meaningful interpretation of a battery's condition.

"An inexpensive digital voltmeter can be used, but I prefer to use an analogue meter. Why? Because it gives me a better intrinsic feel for the actual state of the battery's charge. Unfortunately, conventional analogue voltmeters don't have sufficient precision for such measurements. However, by expanding the

Fig 9: A typical push-pull 'Ultra-Linear' Class A audio amplifier used in the 1950s and 1960s. The tetrode or pentode screen-grids are connected to tappings on the output transformer resulting in a mode of operation intermediate between tetrodes/pentodes and triodes. This form of distributed load offered the following advantages: less overall negative feedback required for a given result, thus giving a better margin of stability; reduction of harmonic distortion; greater efficiency, 36% against 27% for triodes or triode-connected tetrodes; much lower peak variations in current than inherent with triode output stages, placing less stringent requirements on the power supply.

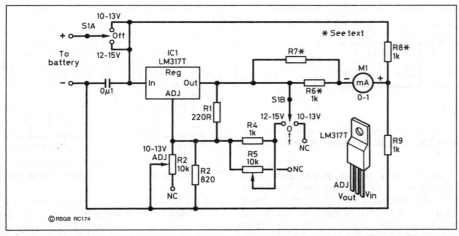

FIG 10: Expanded-range analogue voltmeter as described by KI6WX in the December 1992 issue of QST. Intended for checking the state of 12V lead-acid batteries it provides two expanded voltage ranges, 10 to 13 volts and 12 to 15 volts. Unless otherwise specified, resistors are 0.25W, 5% tolerance carbon-composition or film units. Use of 1% tolerance resistors for R6, R8 and R9 is desirable but not essential since variations are removed during calibration. Value of R7 depends on meter, KI6WX used 8.2K.

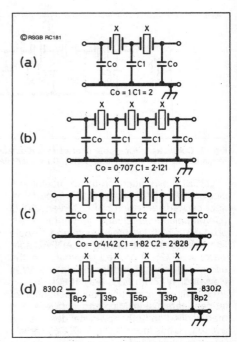

Fig 12: Crystal ladder filters as investigated by F6BQP in 1976 based on the earlier work by J E Colin. All crystals (X) are of the same resonant frequency. To calculate values for the capacitors multiply the coefficients by $1/2\pi fR$ where f is frequency of crystal in Hertz, R is input and output termination impedance, and 2π is roughly 6.28. Coefficients for 2, 3 and 4 crystal units are shown in (a), (b) and (c) respectively, while (d) shows a practical realization of a four-pole filter using 8314kHz crystals, 10% preferred-value capacitors and termination impedance of 820Ω. For crystals between 8 and 10MHz the termination impedance should be between about 800 and 1000Ω for SSB filters, lower frequency crystals require higher design impedances to obtain sufficient bandwidth. For CW filters use lower impedance and/or lower frequency crystals.

range of the voltmeter around the measurement range of interest, you'll significantly improve that accuracy."

KI6WX provided details of an arrangement whereby a 0-1mA meter could provide a voltmeter range of 10-13V for measuring the discharge voltage and 12-15V for the charging voltage. Expanded-range voltmeters are formed by connecting one end of the meter to a reference voltage instead of to ground. Most simple expanded voltmeters use a Zener diode to provide the reference voltage but this has the disadvantage of a reference voltage that varies between different Zener diodes, and temperatures. Instead, KI6WX uses a three-terminal adjustable voltage regulator such as the LM317T to provide the reference voltage since this varies only slightly over time and temperature variations.

Fig 10 shows the circuit diagram of the expanded-range voltmeter as described by KI6WX in his article. Subsequently, in the May 1993 issue, he presented a modified arrangement and also showed how the same principles could be applied to an expanded-range AC voltmeter (95-140V) using a voltage detector that approximately measures the average of the voltage. The average

value tracks the RMS value more accurately for complex (non-sinusoidal) waveforms than the more commonly used peak detector, making the meter's accuracy less dependent on the purity of the waveform.

P K S Rosenbeck, OZ5PZ (*OZ*, 3/94, pp140-142) draws on some but not all of KI6WX's ideas in presenting a single-range (10-15V) DC meter that can also be used with an adapter to provide a 200-250V expanded-range AC meter: **Fig 11(a)** and **(b)**.

LADDER FILTERS

THE JANUARY 1994 *TT* (pp37-39) described recent work by Colin Horrabin, G3SBI, on developing crystal ladder filters for use in high-performance receiver front-ends. The starting point was the information given in *ART7* (pp66-69) which drew on a 1976 article by J Pochet, F6BQP, who in turn had summarised a design published in 1968 by J E Colin, F6BQP. This provided the design co-efficients needed for ladder filters using up to four identical frequency crystals (**Fig 12**). G3SBI found that J E Colin had, in fact, provided co-efficients for up to six-pole filters. Jan *TT* included a five-section 9MHz filter by G3SBI.

While four and five-pole crystal ladder designs can produce effective SSB or CW filters, their shape factors tend to be inferior to the best half-lattice crystal filters, broadening out around the −50 to −60dB level. More sections can be expected to improve the shape of ladder filters provided that this can be done without unduly increasing the insertion loss.

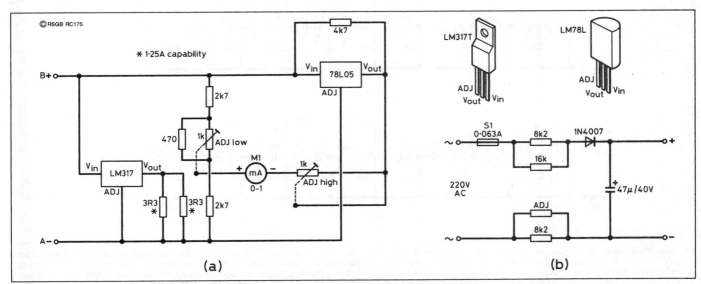

Fig 11: (a) OZ5PZ's battery tester with expanded range meter; (b) An adaptor for 220V AC mains voltages.

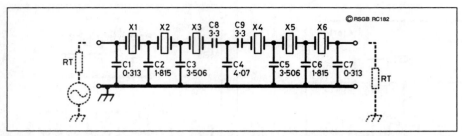

Fig 13: Coefficients for 6-pole filter as investigated by G3SBI. X1 to X6 are crystal of similar resonant frequency fr. Then F = 1(/2π x fr x RT). Cn = coefficient x F.

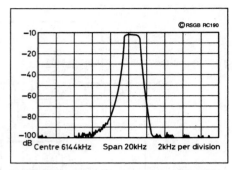

Fig 16: Measured performance of the 10-pole filter.

G3SBI draws attention to two useful articles on ladder filter design: (1) 'High-performance crystal filter design' by Bill Carver, K6OLG (*Communications Quarterly*, Winter 1993, pp11-18) which features 8-pole and 14-pole filters designed with the aid of LADPAC software; and (2) 'A unified approach to the design of crystal ladder filters' by Wes Hayward, W7ZOI (*QST*, May 1982).

G3SBI, has continued his investigation of ladder-filters using Microcap software and then verified on further practical designs. As a result, he has found that the J E Colin article appears to have an error in the centre coefficient given for the six-pole filter. G3SBI has also provided design coefficients for 8-pole and 10-pole filters together with practical capacitor values for 8-pole, and 10-pole (optionally 9-pole) filter designs, both using 6.144MHz crystal. He suggests that an optimum frequency for ladder filters for totally home-constructed receivers might well be around 6MHz.

His 6, 8 and 10-pole filters (see **Figs 13, 14** and **15**) have been constructed from IQD crystals (stock No A133A at 6.144MHz, HC49, 30pF). Nominal crystal parameters: Ls 36.3003mH, Cs 18.4952F-15, Rs 14Ω, Cp 4.5pF. going from 6 to 8 or more poles significantly improves the shape factor and symmetry: see **Fig 16** for the measured response of the 10-pole filter. The choice of 6.144MHz is the design impedance level for SSB bandwidths is then 1500Ω. For CW, a 225Ω design with 6-poles would give a –6dB bandwidth of 400Hz, a –60dB bandwidth of 1.2kHz and an insertion loss of 4dB. **G3VA**

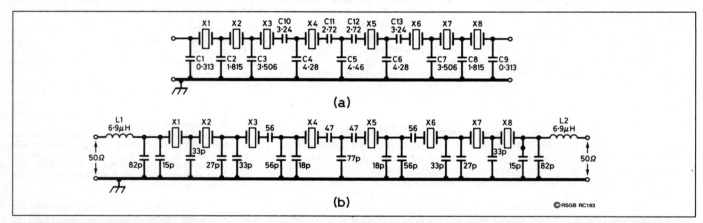

Fig 14(a): Coefficients for 8-pole filter. (b) Practical capacitor values for 8-pole 6.144MHz filter providing SSB bandwidth of 2kHz. All capacitors Suflex 2.50%, X1-X8 IQD Stock A133A, L2, L2 6.9μH comprising 39 turns of 0.314mm diameter bicezflux enamel on Micrometals T50-6 toroids (Cirkit). Measured performance: 2kHz at –6dB, 4.4kHz at –60dB, insertion loss 1.7dB. Stopband better than 100dB down. Note that the filter design impedance is 1500Ω. The 500Ω matching section capacitor includes 5.6pF capacitance due to C2.

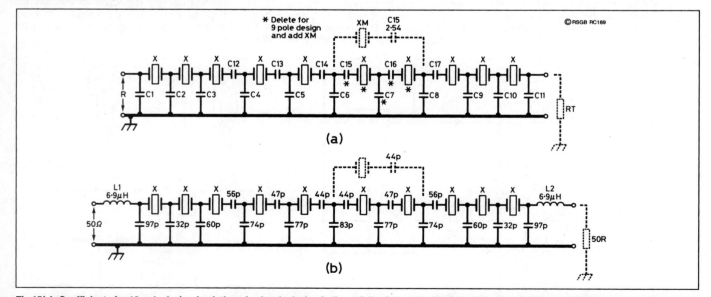

Fig 15(a): Coefficients for 10-pole design (variations for 9-pole design indicated) C1, C11 0.313. C2, C10 1.815. CV3, C9 3.47. C4, C8 4.28. C5, C7 4.46. C6 5.09. C12, C17 3.24. C13, C16 2.72. C14, C15 2.54. At 6.144MHz RT 2000Ω gives –6dB bandwidth of 2250Hz; with RT 1500Ω gives 1850Hz. –6 to –60dB shape factor 1.8:1. (b) Practical realisation of ten pole 6.144MHz filter with a design impedance of 1500Ω showing 50Ω matching networks. Insertion loss –2.1dB. –6dB bandwidth 1850Hz, –60dB bandwidth 3300Hz giving shape factor of 1.8:1. L1, L2 are 39 turns of Of 0.314 dia enamel on Micrometals T50-6 toroids (Cirkit). All capacitors made up from 2.50% Suflex.

MORE ON THE 1:1 BALUN

THE USE AND ABUSE of balanced-to-unbalanced (balun) devices inserted between a transceiver and the antenna system, can still provoke heated debate. 'Heated' is perhaps the appropriate word since it is all too easy to use up appreciable output power from the transmitter in heating up the wires or cores of matching networks and baluns. It can be very revealing to measure power output before and after an ATU or balun especially on the lowest or highest band for which it is intended, eg 1.8 or 28MHz.

It is not surprising that many of those using dipole-type wire antennas prefer not to use either an ATU or a balun, depending on careful adjustment of the dipole element to resonance. It is, however, widely recognized that in the case of Yagi beam antennas a balun is highly desirable; there is also the question of TVI/RFI that can result from the radiation of current flowing on the outer braid of a coaxial feeder.

A long, detailed and valuable contribution to this debate has been provided by Jerry Sevick, W2FMI in 'More on the 1:1 balun' (*CQ*, April 1994, pp26-46, less some pages carrying advertisements). W2FMI reviews the various types of broadband 1:1 baluns, reviews some of the more significant balun articles that have appeared in (mainly) American journals, and also presents the results of his own experiments from which he has developed several workable designs. He covers

the origins and practice of Ruthroff and Guanella ferrite toroid core baluns, the ferrite-rod balun, air-core baluns based on coaxial-line transformers, and the currently popular W2DU ferrite-bead 'choke' transformer.

In a section 'When to use a balun', he reports experiments with baluns used with a 14MHz half-wave dipole at a height of 0.17-wavelength, which gave a resonant impedance of 50**ohms**: "VSWR curves were compared under various conditions. When the coaxial cable was in the ground plane of the antenna (that is, perpendicular to the axis of the antenna), the VSWR curves were identical with or without a well-designed balun no matter where the outer braid was grounded. Only when the coaxial cable was out of the ground plane was a significant difference noted. When the cable dropped down at a 45-**degree** angle under the dipole, a large change in the VSWR took place."

From this one can deduce that with a dipole antenna, there is little or no need for a balun

provided that with a horizontal element (or an inverted-vee that is balanced about its support) the coaxial feeder drops down vertically from the element. W2FMI continues:

"Feeding a Yagi beam without a well-designed 1:1 balun, however, is a different matter. Since most Yagi designs use shunt-feeding (usually hair-pin matching networks) in order to raise the input impedance close to 50Ω, the effective spacing(s) of **Fig 1** is greatly increased. Furthermore the centre of the driven element is actually grounded. Thus, connecting the outer braid (which is grounded at some point) to one of the input terminals creates a large imbalance and a real need for a balun. an interesting solution, which would eliminate the matching network is to use a step-down balun designed to match 50ohm cable directly to the lower balanced-impedance of the driven element.

"In summary . . . . it appears that 1:1 baluns are really needed for (a) Yagi beam antennas where severe pattern distortion can take place without one, and (b) dipoles and inverted Vees that have the coaxial cable feed lines out of the ground plane that bisects the antennas or that are unbalanced by their proximity to man-made or natural structures. In general, the need for a balun is not so critical with dipoles and inverted Vees (especially on 40, 80 and 160 metres) because the diameter of the coaxial cable connector at the feed point is much smaller than the wavelength." Fig 1 shows the various currents at the feed point of

---

USING SCRAP MOTORS, SCRAP TOASTERS

THE JUNE *TT* ITEM describing briefly how Ron Mathers, ZL2AXO had built a 230V petrol-electric generator from a salvaged lawn mower as the prime mover in conjunction with a similarly salvaged single-phase induction motor used as an induction generator attracted interest. But there were some doubts expressed by those who had not previously come across the idea that with capacitive excitation such motors can be used as generators by making use of their residue magnetism.

ZL2AXO in his article gave as reference a near 60-year old paper in an Australian professional journal: Bassett, E D and Potter F M "Capacitive excitation for induction generators", (*Trans AIEE*, May 1935, Vol 54, p540) which is unlikely to be readily available to many *TT* readers. However, Bruce Carter, GW8AAG writes:

"I was intrigued by the reference to the ZL2AXO generator and soon afterwards came across the following book in a local library: 'Electric Motors' by Jim Cox (Cox, V J), workshop practice series No 16, published by Argus Books, 1988, (reprinted 1992) 134pp, £6.95, (621.462), ISBN 0 85242 914 2. On page 47, the author provides a table of capacitance needed for 50 and 60Hz motors ranging from 0.25HP (0.18kW) to 2HP (1.5kW). Apparently, the values are better 'understated' since higher values confer no advantage. Cox's chapter on stepper motors (including disc drives) is enlightening. The chapter on identifying and using scrap motors is required reading."

To quote further from ZL2AXO's *Break-in*

article: "In operation, as load is applied to the generator the terminal voltage needs to be kept constant by opening the throttle of the petrol motor. This increases the speed and results in an increase in the frequency.

The frequency is proportional to the rotor speed minus the slip speed which at full load is about 150rpm. With a load of 500W the frequency rises to 56Hz. This rise is unlikely

G3ERY finds that the high-impact plastics case of a discarded toaster (top) can be transformed into a housing for an antenna tuning unit, etc (bottom).

to be a problem in normal use apart from electric clocks running fast. To assist in the setting up of the generator a frequency meter was built up using an old Jonan automobile tachometer driven by a nine volt transformer. The speed of the generator at no-load is just over 3000rpm. This needs to increase with load until at 500W output an estimated 3500rpm is reached. On the petrol motor shaft a pulley of 095mm (3.75in) diameter drives a 0.50in vee belt to a 76mm (3.50in) diameter generator pulley."

The building of a 230V AC generator from scrap is in the proud tradition of amateur radio in the days when the idea of simply buying new purpose-made equipment (even if available on a limited market) would have broken the budgets of many enthusiasts, particularly the younger generation. It bred a generation that tended always to think twice before throwing away any discarded household items that could conceivably find an amateur-radio application.

Recent notes on salvaging components from old microwave ovens (*TT*, November 1993 and February 1994) encouraged John Wood, G3EAY to look carefully at his toaster when this proved to be beyond repair. He writes: "There were no electronic components to salvage, but the high impact plastics case looked interesting. With a little modification this has been transformed into an attractive housing for an antenna tuning unit. The case was lined internally with aluminium foil, stuck on with high-impact adhesive. The illustrations show the toaster case, before and after."

a dipole. I1 is the dipole current and I2 the unwanted inverted-L (imbalance) current on the outer surface of the braid.

W2FMI argues that "even though I consider some of the amateur articles [on 1:1 baluns] significant, their impact upon the use and understanding of these devices has not always been positive. In fact, in some cases just the opposite has been true." He points out that there are only two significant articles in the professional literature that provide the fundamental principles upon which the theory and design of this class of transformers are based, with later investigators only really extending the work of the two authors:

"The first presentation on broadband matching transformers using transmission lines was by G Guanella "Novel matching systems for high frequencies" (*Brown-Boveri Review*, Vol 31, September 1944, pp327-329). He coiled transmission lines forming a choke such that only transmission-line currents were allowed to flow no matter where a ground was connected to the load: **Fig 2(a)** . . . . The second article was by C L Ruthroff "Some broad-band transformers" (*Proc IRE*, Vol 47, August 1959, pp1337-1342). His 1:1 balun, **Fig 2(b)** used an extra winding to complete (as he said) the path for the magnetizing current with the third winding (5-6) on a separate part of the toroid forming a voltage divider with winding (3-4)." A modified form of the Ruthroff balun was introduced later by Turrin, W2IMU: **Fig 3**.

The two-conductor Guanella 1:1 balun came to be known as the basic building block for this whole class of broadband transformers. It not only presents a balanced power source to a balanced antenna system but can also prevent an imbalance current (an inverted-L antenna current) by its choking reactance when the load is unbalanced or mismatched or when the feedline is not perpendicular to the axis of the antenna.

After comparing the performance of the

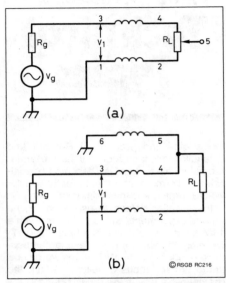

Fig 2: Two versions of the 1:1 balun as described by W2FMI. (a) The Guanella balun and basic building block; (b) the Ruthroff balun as originally drawn.

various forms of 1:1 transmission line baluns that have been described in the amateur literature, W2FMI provides details of low- and medium-power versions of his favoured bifilar toroidal (Guanella/current) 1:1 baluns. The low-power versions are capable of handling the output of most HF transceivers; the medium-power versions the full [American] amateur legal limit. **Fig 4** shows two versions of W2FMI's bifilar toroidal 1:1 baluns.

His baluns are capable of providing efficiencies of near 99% at 1.8MHz and 97% at 30MHz with type 250 ferrite material provided that the system is well matched. When a balun is exposed to a high impedance (VSWR of 2:1) voltage, the loss increases by about 40%; with a VSWR of 4:1 the loss doubles and with a VSWR of 10:1 the loss is more than three-fold.

W2FMI summarises his views on 1:1 baluns as follows: "In preparing this article I was quite surprised to see the ferrite- and powdered-iron-core 1:1 balun designs that have been available in the literature and elsewhere since 1964. They not only had poor low- and high-frequency responses, but they were also sus-

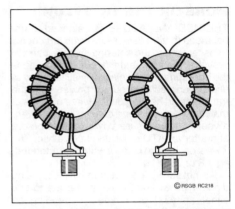

Fig 4: Illustration of two of the many versions of W2FMI's preferred bifilar toroidal (Guanella/current) 1:1 balun. The one on the right uses the cross-over technique of W1JR as used in his 1978 HF broadband balun.

ceptible to flux in the cores at their low-frequency ends. Furthermore, since they only used single-coiled wires, they were also prone to voltage breakdown. No doubt, these designs were responsible for the poor reputation that the balun has had for many years.

"It was not until 1978, when Joe Reisert, W1JR published his article "Simple and efficient broadband balun" (Ham Radio, September 1978, pp12-15 see also ART7, p334), see **Fig 5**, using thin coaxial cable wound on the toroidal core that a balun became available with all of the attributes of a good design, namely: (a) Is efficient because it uses a low-permeability core; (b) has sufficient choking reactance to meet its low-frequency requirement; (c) is not prone to flux in the core (and hence, saturation) since it has no third winding; (d) has a 50**ohm** characteristic impedance and thus maintains a 1:1 transformation ratio with a 50ohm load; (e) has a good

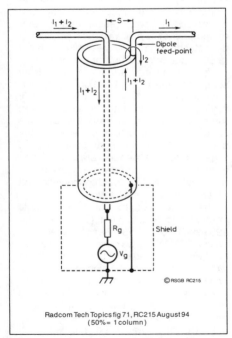

Radcom Tech Topics fig 71, RC215 August 94
(50%= 1 column)

Fig 1: The various currents at the feed point of a dipole element fed from an unbalanced coaxial cable feeder. I1 is the dipole current and I2 the unwanted inverted-L (imbalance) current on the outer surface of the cable braid.

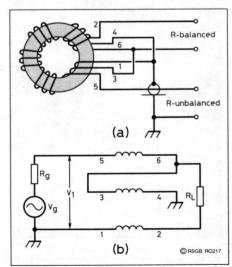

Fig 3: (a) Pictorial representation of Turrin's 1:1 balun, and (b) the schematic.

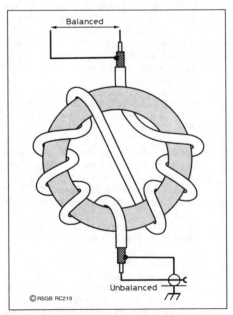

Fig 5: W1JR's 1978 broadband balun based on a thin coaxial cable winding. This used an Indiana General F368-1 Q1 core with some 12 turns (36-40-in of RG-141/U cable) and covering 3.5 to 30MHz with reduced efficiency on 1.8MHz. For use over 7-30MHz ten turns of cable should be sufficient and TC9 core might prove more suitable for lower frequencies. The basic design can be used at VHF if attention is paid to layout and lead lengths.

voltage breakdown capability (1.9kV); and (f) can handle a mismatched and/or unbalanced load.

"Succeeding investigators, however, failed to see the advantages of his design and proposed their own. Surprisingly, they belonged to two distinct groups. One favoured 'air-core' baluns and the other 'choke' (beaded-coax) baluns.

"The main argument given by the 'air-core' followers was that their balun would never experience the problems with saturation while the 'ferrite-core' balun would. The Reisert balun, however, is a current/choke type balun which could only have flux in the core by the imbalance (inverted L) current, which is much smaller than the transmission line currents. In fact, with any degree of choking reactance by the coiled transmission line, the imbalance current is essentially negligible. Therefore, saturation is not a concern with a Reisert type balun. But in all fairness, it would be pointed out that with the 4:1 current/choke and voltage baluns it is a different story. All three of these types of baluns have a 'magnetizing inductance' in their low-frequency models and hence a possibility of saturation with a poor design.

"The advocates of the 'choke' 1:1 balun claim that their beaded-coax balun can't saturate while the bifilar (current) toroidal balun can. This is entirely wrong, since they are basically the same kind of structure – neither has a third conductor which could allow a flux-causing current at the very low-frequency end. But of all the attributes listed above for the Reisert balun, the first one has the 'choke' balun at a disadvantage in the HF band. Since its transmission line is not coiled about a toroid, it does not have the multiplication factor of N-squared (due to mutual coupling) where N is the number of turns, while the toroidal balun does. Therefore, higher-permeability beads are required in order to obtain sufficient choking reactance. This results in lower efficiency."

In his final remarks, W2FMI admits to being quite sure that some readers will disagree with his views and/or think they have better designs than those of the Reisert baluns and the ones he presents: "If so, I encourage them to respond in print. In this way we will all benefit from the new information."

SOLID-STATE 'FIRSTS'?

THE NEWS ITEM in the February *RadCom* 'The Transistor Transmitter is Forty' continues to attract comment, although it must be stressed that the claim made for the February 1954 contact between Yeovil (G3CMH) and Haslemere (G3CAZ) was for the first 'skywave' contact using a transistor transmitter and not for a first contact using a solid-state device, for which there are records dating back at least 70 years, to the pre-transistor era of oscillating crystals.

For example, in an article in *Vintage Wireless* ('An invention that changed the world', Part 1 Vol 19 No 1) on the birth of the transistor, I noted that "although the transistor [born 1947] was clearly the first [practical] solid-state near equivalent to a triode valve, there was already a long history of crystal devices that could function, albeit unreliably, as amplifiers and oscillators . . . .

" . . . . there had been a flurry of interest in the 1920s, when peaking in 1924, articles in *Wireless World* described work by the Russian engineer O Lossev on oscillating and amplifying zincite crystal detectors . . . . Lossev had investigated many circuit possibilities for receivers and even low-power transmission: 'Using some of the circuits described, it has been possible to achieve transmission over a distance of one mile. On both sides the crystal served simultaneously as a generator and detector, so that even duplex transmission was possible.'. . ."

In 1953, the year before the Yeovil 3.5MHz skywave contact, Francis Ladd, W2IDZ made several 50MHz contacts using a point-contact transistor transmitter. He writes:

"I have some accomplishments using transistors that I would like to pass on. On March 7 and 8, 1953, I had CW contacts with W2WCM using a point contact transistor [input power 135mW]. I then modified the circuit for phone. The resulting signal was narrow-band FM. I had a phone contact with W2WCM on March 9. W2WCM then duplicated my transmitter and on March 10 we had two-way phone and CW contacts using transistor transmitters at both ends. All contacts were made in the 50MHz band and were prearranged. On March 10, I had a CW and phone contact with W2MEU which were not prearranged. I wonder if any of these contacts were records?"

W2IDZ sends along a photocopy of his log

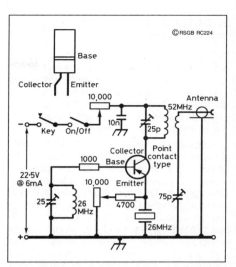

Fig 6: Circuit diagram of the CW transistor transmitter used by W2IDZ for his first 50MHz transistor contact at 1912 local time on March 7, 1953.

in which he recorded against the March 7, 1953 contact with W2WCM "My first QSO using a transistor transmitter . . . . I believe this is 1st 50Mc QSO using transistor." **Fig 6** shows the circuit diagram of W2IDZ's transistor transmitter as used for his first CW QSO at 1912 (local time) on March 7, 1953, as recorded in his log.

HOME-BREW BURGLAR ALARM

D S BROWN, G0LYX notes the increasing number of burglaries involving garden sheds, outhouses, garages etc, some of which form radio shacks with relatively costly equipment.

He provides details of a simple alarm circuit incorporates a switch-off delay circuit as now required by law.

He describes the functioning of the circuit diagram shown in **Fig 7** as follows:

(1) Mains on, press reset to activate TR1. This puts supply to on/off switch and lights the LED indicator.

2) On/off switch is placed to 'on' position. Power applied to TR2 which is in cutoff state when door/window micro- or magnetic-switch line is closed.

(3) Switch line broken. TR2 conducts activating Relay 2 which locks 'on' and simultaneously breaks circuit holding TR1 conducting. The time-constant of R1-C2 of approximately three to five minutes holds relay Rly 1 until discharged when supply to R2 is switched off (contacts 6-7 on Rly 1 also break, preventing circuit activating until reset button is pressed.

Note that the time that the alarm sounds can be varied by altering the values of R1-C2. In Fig 76 Rly 2 contacts are shown when reset button is pressed, those of Rly 2 when alarm is inactive.

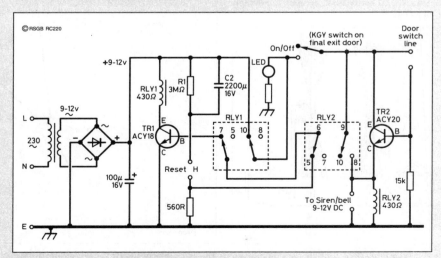

Fig 7: G0LYX's simple burglar alarm can be used to protect radio shacks, sheds, garages etc.

A CENTURY OF RADIO-TELEGRAPHY!

IN THE MARCH *TT* item 'The sound of spark', a brief reference was made to the fact that in August 1894, Professor Oliver Lodge of the University of Liverpool publicly demonstrated for the first time anywhere in the world that Hertzian waves could be used for telegraphic signalling in the Morse code.

A detailed appreciation of this historic event on August 14, 1894, together with an account of the many other – too often overlooked – pioneering achievements of Lodge has been described by Dr Brian Austin, G0GSF in a five-page article 'Oliver Lodge – The forgotten man of radio?' in *the Radioscientist*, Vol 5, No 1, March 1994, pp12-16: "When Lodge performed his demonstration he [like Hertz before him] made no claims for the eventual usefulness of his technique but it is the first recorded occasion on which intelligence was transmitted through space without wires. For a practical application of radio the world had to wait for the arrival in England of Marconi in 1896 . . . .

"At that demonstration in Oxford, which was at a joint meeting of physicists and physiologists on the subject of vision, Lodge transmitted Morse code letters from his induction coil and spark gap transmitter in the Clarendon Laboratory to a receiver some 60 metres away in the Oxford Museum. He described it as 'a very infantile form of radiotelegraphy', a statement reflecting his modesty but signifi-

cant because it established what he had actually done when the induction coil was actuated by a Morse key operated by his assistant EₗE Robinson.

The receiver (**Fig 8**) consisted of a coherer, a Lodge invention, which was connected to either a Morse recorder which printed onto tape or a Kelvin marine galvanometer, the deflected light spot of which made viewing by the audience easier. By about 1897, Lodge was using his 'definitive radiator' antenna system (**Fig 9**) which as G0GSF emphasises was an early form of biconical antenna.

G0GSF shows that Oliver Lodge made many other significant contributions including an attempt in 1894 to detect radio emissions from extra-terrestrial sources, most notably the sun. The experiment failed because his coherer detector of centrimetric waves was not sufficiently sensitive but is recognized as the first attempted experiment in radio astronomy and preceded the successful experiment by Jansky some 37 years later.

'KISS' VK2ABQ 14MHZ BEAM ANTENNA

VERSIONS OF THE 1973 VK2ABQ three-band two-element parasitic wire array (ART 7 etc) continue to attract interest: see for example 'Antenna Workshop' by Peter Dodd, G3LDO (*Practical Wireless*, June 1994, pp42-43) in which he traces an earlier but basically similarly shaped single-band version to W1QP/W8CPC in *QST*, October 1937. More recently, Fred Caton, VK2ABQ (formerly G3ONC) has described several even simpler and/or smaller single-band arrays, including a KISS array in *TT*, May 1992, p37. (But note that he has pointed out that the gaps between the elements given as 4-inches should have been 4-mm or about 0.25-in).

VK2ABQ has now sent along details of a simple array that does not use the 'square'

folding with crossed X-type bamboo spreaders, but retains the small gaps between driven and parasitic elements. This can be erected as shown in **Fig 10** as a single-mast, inverted-vee type structure or (for a fixed array) as a conventionally suspended array using a cantenery rope in lieu of the mast.

What VK2ABQ calls the phase adjustment gaps are adjusted for equal power in the two half-wave elements, as discussed in the earlier May 1992 item. He has, however, provided details of an improved 'current sampler' giving better position stability and greater sensitivity and, in his letter, provides some further hints on construction and adjustment but I find these a little confusing, and hope that the information given above and in the May 1992 *TT* will at least prove a starting point for investigating this simple directional antenna.

VK2ABQ acknowledges that modelling of this antenna was first done on 144MHz by VK3KZ in Melbourne who built a 7MHz version which proved very effective on long-haul DX to Europe etc. VK2ABQ claims that his antenna outperforms a much larger standard 2-element Yagi array and has a forward gain of the order of 5dB and a front/back ratio of over 30dB.

I suspect that other users may find the forward power gain of such an array to be rather less impressive when compared to the theoretically possible gain for a close-spaced two-element Yagi array of 5.2dB. Nevertheless, it should provide a useful power gain and a good front-to-back ratio.

In *TT*, October 1983, attention was drawn to the use by the IBA (now NTL) of a medium-wave vertical monopole antenna with a sloping twin-wire reflector. This approach gave a single-mast array with vertical polarization, providing roughly 3dB forward gain and an f/b ratio of from 5-15dB and better than 20dB in laboratory studies.

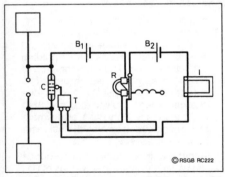

Fig 8: The receiving system used by [Sir] Oliver Lodge on August 14, 1894 at Oxford when Morse signals were received and demonstrated for the first time. B1, B2 batteries; C, coherer/T, trembler; R - relay; I inker.

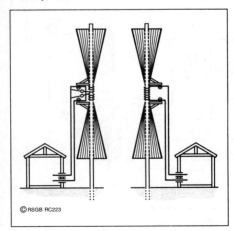

Fig 9: By about 1897, Lodge had developed transmitting and receiving antennas similar in form to the modern biconical antenna.

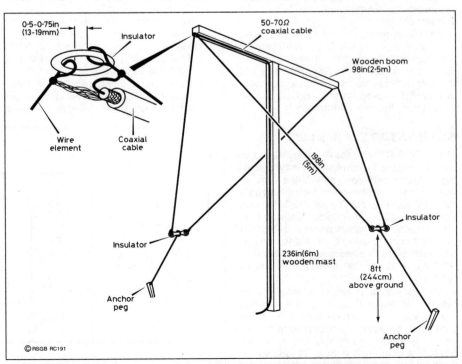

Fig 10: 2-element 14MHz 'KISS-type' beam antenna in inverted-vee form with the end 16-feet above ground level. It can be rotated at ground level by moving the ground pegs. Note that the two-dimensional representation shows the 90-deg angles as acute angles.

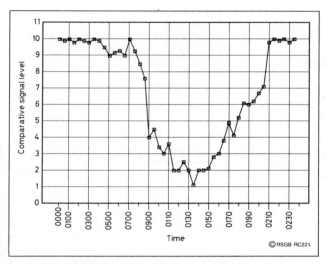

Fig 11: Plot of 1.8MHz signal levels over a 126-mile path during a September day made by G4HOJ showing that although 'daylight' existed for some 13 hours, only 4-5 hours show low levels of skywave enhancement with signals still peaking at regular intervals even through this period.

DAYLIGHT PROPAGATION ON 1.8MHZ

IN THE 1970s when I was involved with answering listeners' complaints about interference with the reception of the early Independent Local Radio medium-wave stations, it soon became obvious that the D-layer which absorbs MF sky-waves from distant high-power stations during 'daylight' does not re-form immediately at dawn and (particularly in the winter months) begins to lose its absorptive characteristics some time before dusk. This has the effect that interference from distant MF broadcast stations can be quite severe during much of a 'winter day'.

From an amateur viewpoint it is worth remembering that the 1.8MHz band is an MF band and not HF (MF spectrum 300 to 3000kHz). Contrary to simplified theory, sky-wave propagation is not limited to night-time.

This point is underlined by investigations made by P Hobson, G4HOJ in the course of developing a computer program which would model and predict the performance of short loaded whip antennas. In the course of this he built about 80 different whip antennas to explore all the different parameters. His work led to really accurate computer modelling.

He writes: "Most of the text books describe 1.8MHz as having a useful working range of around 50 miles in 'daylight – when no skywave is present'. Yet I found that I could frequently work up to 150 miles to good fixed stations, and sometimes more, even at lunchtime when much of the testing was done. This encouraged me to explore the belief that sky wave propagation was often present on 1.8MHz even at noon on a summer's day.

"After a few random checks I decided that the best appliance to take the tedium out of regular and frequent checking was the computer. I wrote a short program which made the computer check the voltage on a particular port every 2 seconds, and then to record the highest level reached during successive one minute periods .... The results obtained gave no specific measurement, but rather a comparison between the signal received at a specific time of day and the best night-time signal when high levels of skywave enhance-

ment were present. Information could be displayed on screen, or printed out.

"With a very stable, home-brew VXO receiver and a low active antenna, positioned to reduce response to ground-wave signals to a minimum, tests were made on a number of incoming signals, at different distances, repeated on a number of days. The equipment recorded signal level and time of day. The sampling method chosen did not record peaks and troughs since these were often so short in duration that they were missed.

"A plot made during one September day, (one of the poorest signal days) is shown in **Fig 11** with sunrise about 0525GMT, sunset about 1825GMT. Maximum temperature 22°C, minimum 10°C on a signal over a 126-mile path. Note that although 'daylight' lasted for 13 hours, only 4-5 hours show low levels of skywave enhancement. It would appear that at no time throughout the day was enhancement completely absent, although the signal levels, at their

lowest, might not be usable for communication purposes at noisy locations. But from a quiet site, the enhanced signals are useful on almost every day. Occasionally, the signal levels can be high even at noon.

"Winter days seem to produce wider differences although there is more enhancement right through the day."

G4HOJ sums up his results (which have been truncated in these extracts) as "proving to my satisfaction that 1.8MHz completely out-performs the alternative bands, particularly for mobile working, when short/medium distance is the objective. Perhaps more important is the reliability of the band, both from day-to-day and difficult terrain viewpoints. While this is appreciated by those who have used 1.8MHz in the past, there are many who remain unaware of the virtues of this band."

G4HOJ's home QTH is a village several miles from Swindon where the electrical noise level is presumably reasonably low. I recall making daytime contacts of over a hundred miles on 1.8MHz in the distant days when I operated from Minehead, Somerset. A very real problem in urban and suburban locations, at least in London, is the high level of electrical noise that can swamp weak daytime signals from more than a few miles away. Even without sky-wave enhancement, reliable 1.8MHz ground-wave signals between quiet sites having good ground conductivity can comfortably exceed 50 miles and proba-

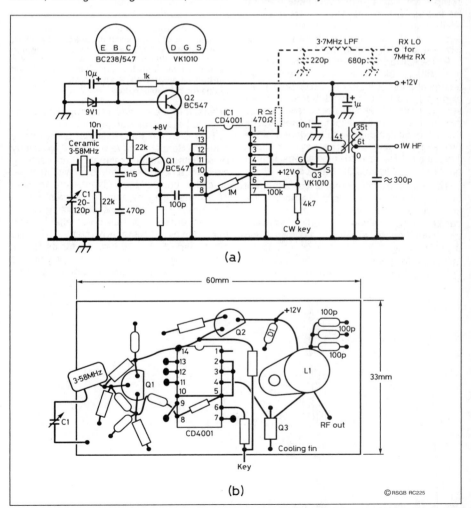

(a)

(b)

Fig 12: LA8AK's version of the QRP (1W) transmitter using a ceramic resonator in a variable frequency oscillator covering the 3.5MHz CW band.

bly well over 100 miles, particularly on oversea paths. The main snag is the low level of day-time amateur activity. However, perhaps G4HOJ's propagation experiments will encourage more use of this interesting and valuable MF allocation.

HERE & THERE

ADDING TO THE *TT* ITEM 'Variable-frequency ceramic oscillators' (May 1994, pp54-55), Jan-Martin Noeding, LA8AK has modified the G3BBD QRP transmitter circuit, using a few transistors and a CD4001 ic instead of the CD4069: **Fig 12**. He writes: "A 100 or 120pF tuning capacitor, covers the 3.5MHz CW band and RF output is about 1-watt.

"For simplicity, a parallel-tuned output circuit is used. Harmonic radiation may be reduced by using a good pi-network filter, provided that the input impedance is much higher than the load impedance. With 50Ω input/output with a single coil pi-filter, the harmonic attenuation is negligible below about 10MHz. The CMOS inverting amplifier (pins 8, 9, 10) solves the problem of the variable drive from the oscillator. If used for a receiver local oscillator, additional components may be required to establish constant RF voltage over the tuning range, in LA8AK's case for use with a 7MHz direct-conversion receiver using a RA3AAE-type harmonic mixer as mentioned in the May *TT*. **Fig 12(b)** shows how the main components for a QRP transmitter may be located using dead-bug mounting on the PCB earth side, with the IC and transistors installed upside down. L2 is 10mm diameter with iron core, dipped to 3.6MHz.

Bruce Carter, GW8AAG, provides a solution to the problem that is encountered when a coaxial cable (or other stiff conductor) has to be clipped tight to a wall, but at a corner such a method is likely to seriously damage the electrical and physical characteristics of the cable. His solution is to make use of the property of a tangent to an arc of a circle. Treat the cable run as forming a semicircle or quadrant as it approaches the corner.

The hard line of the corner is then a tangent over which the cable can 'slip' in an inch or so: see **Fig 13**. GW8AAG adds that the corner can be internal or external including two walls, a wall and floor, or a wall and a ceiling. Even a cable along one side of a sheet can be satisfactorily taken to the edge and back down the other side. Furthermore, the angle

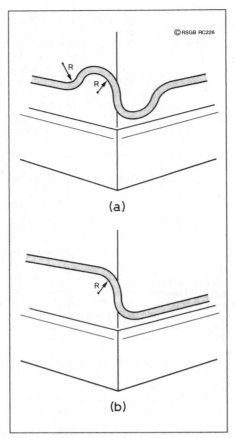

Fig 13: GW8AAG's method of overcoming the problem of taking a coaxial cable around a 90deg corner when the cable needs to be clipped tight to the walls. (a) Where it is necessary to retain the cable run at the same level; (b) where the cable run can be at different levels. R is the permitted minimum radius for the cable in use.

of attack to the corner does not necessarily have to be at a right angle.

Two German theoreticians, L Molgedey and H G Schuster, have produced what may be a mathematical explanation, and specification of a neural network to go with it, of the so-called 'cocktail party effect' ie the problem of disentangling meaningful signals from a background of otherwise distracting noise: see an article 'Cocktail party effect made tolerable' by John Maddox (*Nature*, 16 June 1994, page 517). They go so far as to mix together two library records of crying babies and show that the separate sounds can be

successfully disentangled from the mixed signal by a straightforward application of their technique. No doubt the next step will be to build the appropriate silicon chip to see whether it will function as intended." Ideal for a crowded band!

As we have noted before, the electronics industry has for many years used many chemicals and substances that are hazardous to the environment or in some cases directly to those involved in the assembly of equipments. For example, until the late 1980s, the industry used vast amounts of ozone-depleting substances including CFCs under many trade names and also 1.1.1. trichloroethane.

However the proof that man-made chemicals (particularly chlorofluorocarbons – CFCs) are seriously damaging the ozone layer, and the suggestion that they may also contribute to the global warming process have led to various international regulatory controls. As noted in an article 'The technical options for replacing CFCs for cleaning electronic assemblies' (*GEC Review*, Vol 9, No 1, 1993, pp3-20). There are now the Montreal Protocol and European Community regulatory controls. CFCs (Arklone, Freon, Frigen, Flugene, Forane, Kaltron, Fluorisol, Geneseolv, Delifrene, Isotron, Racon, Dional, Algofrene, Fronsolve, Daiflon, Flonshowa CG, Triflon, Isceon) were phased-out 85% by January 1994 and by 100% by next January. 1.1.1. trichloroethane (Genklene, Propaklone, Prelete, Sovethane, Dowclene) were cut by 50% last January and are due to be 100% phased-out by January 1996.

However, there is a range of technically-viable options. Choice for manufacturers, it is suggested, for cleaning PCBs will depend on factors other than a purely technical appraisal – cost, volume, market sector, customer requirements, health and safety, environment, etc must all be considered. GEC scientists have also been investigating 'Lead-free solders for electronic assembly' (*GEC Journal of Research*, Vol 11, No 2, 1994). The safe use and disposal of lead and lead-containing materials is an issue that is attracting considerable interest from both environmental and legislative bodies.

Correction: Although the callsign of Jorge Dorvier, EA4EO was given correctly in the text of the June *TT* item on page 53, it appeared incorrectly as EA4FO in the caption to Fig 3.   **G3VA**

QUARTZ RESONATORS – HISTORY AND PROGRESS

THE QUARTZ CRYSTAL seems such a simple component – little more than a two-pin plug that magically has the characteristics of an ultra-stable resonant circuit. It has existed seemingly throughout the valve and semiconductor eras. Just occasionally, someone – such as Mike Hall, G3USC, (*TT*, October 1991) – reminds us that there is more to the quartz resonator than we usually suppose. One result of this disregard or ignorance is that many amateurs when ordering or using crystals fail to specify their needs correctly and then blame the supplier when the performance does not come up to expectations.

In reality, the quartz crystal was not always available. Until the mid-1920s, valve transmitters were based on self-excited oscillators, either as power oscillators or less commonly as master oscillators driving power amplifiers. As amateurs opened the way to the short waves, initially '200 metres and down', subsequently around 110 metres, 80 metres, 40 metres and then the "daylight DX" band around 20 metres by the mid-1920s, notes became increasingly rough and unstable with drift a major problem. However, in the 1930s reasonably good VFOs could be made using Franklin or ECO circuits with their power supplies using voltage regulator tubes. But as so often has occurred in the history of radio, a solution came along at just the right time.

QST, in July 1924, published 'Oscillating Crystals' by H S Shaw (W)1XAU of the General Radio Company. He described how, drawing on the pioneering work of Dr W G Cady (Wesleyan University) and Dr G W Pierce (Harvard University) and with advice from Dr J M Miller, he had built an HF crystal controlled transmitter. This used two parallelled 5-watt valves working on about 3MHz (95 metres). He made several contacts with 1XAQ (S Kruse, then technical editor of *QST*) a distance of about 85 miles, almost certainly the first time crystal control had ever been used on HF (Dr Pierce with the Harvard transmitter 1XJ, had, on 25 January 1924 used a crystal-controlled oscillator to transmit over a short distance). Thus, by Spring 1924, Pierce and Miller crystal-oscillator circuits had been developed; both configurations (**Fig 1**) remain, some 70 years later, as the two basic single-active-device oscillator con-

figurations from which others have been developed. In his historic article, H S Shaw even proposed the use of crystals – with frequencies separated by about 1kHz – for transmitter and (straight) receiver oscillators.

The revolutionary nature of Shaw's article in an era of woefully unstable oscillators is underlined by Kruse's introductory editorial note: "Can you imagine a transmitter that never shifts its wave even a hundredth of a metre? Can you imagine making a schedule for 96.38 metres and knowing that you will be right on that wave and know that the other man will be tuned right to you? And can you imagine getting from the receiving operator a report that during hours of operation the beat note in his phones never changed even a particle? These things are possible with the oscillating crystal."

By 1920, the phenomena of pyro- (heat) and piezo- (stress) electricity in certain materials – including Rochelle salt, tourmaline, silicate of zinc, cane sugar, quartz and boracite – had been investigated by a number of scientists. For many centuries, it had been known in India and Sri Lanka, that when tourmaline was thrown into a fire it acquired the property of attracting the ashes, and the Dutch brought knowledge of this curious phenomenon, an effect of pyro-electricity, to Eu-

rope. In 1717, Lemery presented a tourmaline crystal to the French Academy of Science. Soon serious studies of the effect of heat and stress on a range of substances were being made. In 1881, Pierre and Jacques Curie formulated a number of rules showing clearly the link between pyro-electricity and piezo-electricity.

For radio applications, the breakthrough can be traced to Dr W G Cady and the publication of his paper 'The Piezo-Electric Resonator' in *Proc IRE* (April 1923, pp83-114). This opened with the note: "In the course of experiments with piezo-electric crystals, extending over a number of years, certain radio-frequency phenomena were brought to light, the practical application of which appeared worthy of development. The two applications that seem most promising at present are (1) as a frequency standard, and (2) as a frequency-stabilizer, or means of generating electric oscillations of very constant frequency."

Later, in his classic paper, he wrote: "There are several methods whereby the frequency of an electron tube generating circuit can be rendered practically free from disturbing capacity effects, variations in battery voltage, and so on. All make use of one or other of the properties of the piezo-electric resonator that have already been described."

Within a year, Dr G W Pierce and Dr J M Miller had developed simple crystal-controlled valve oscillators, including the Miller oscillator with a resonant tuned anode circuit adopted by Shaw in Spring 1924 for his HF transmitter: **Fig 3**. Shaw's firm, General Radio Co, later developed and marketed quartz crystals in holders of the form that became widely adopted for some 20 years, and a number of firms marketed unmounted crystal

---

TWO-COMPONENT EXPANDED-RANGE VOLTMETER

SOME IDEAS FOR expanded-range analogue voltmeters that overcome the disadvantages of using the customary zener diodes were included in July *TT*. This is achieved by using a three-terminal voltage regulator along with associated circuitry.

An expanded-scale voltmeter using just two components is described by D D Contrell in the 'Ideas for Design' feature of the American journal *EDN* (20 January 1994, p73). As shown in **Fig 2** this uses two complementary voltage regulators and a 0 – 5 voltmeter. It is claimed that this results in a linear scale of 10 – 15V and requires no calibration except possibly some mechanical adjustment of the zeroing of the meter.

To quote the *EDN* item: "By using a split-voltage reference system with floating output, the zero point of the voltage supplied to the meter equals the absolute sum of the two references. With the regulators shown in Fig 2, the 0 – 5V meter reads 10 – 15V inputs. If the voltage into the system falls below this level (ie 10V), the output to the meter changes polarity. This feature allows use of the mechanical zeroing of the meter, although this zeroing should never be necessary because most

regulators yield outputs more accurate than the meter can read.

"The pinouts of the TO-92 devices are perfect for this application. The small size allows installation of the circuit within most meter cases. Keep in mind that this circuit will present a load of 3 – 5mA and connectors should minimise any voltage drops . . . . For use with other voltages select regulators whose sum equals the lowest voltage to be displayed. As an example a 78L15 and a 79L05 will output a zero voltage at 20V; a 5V meter will then read 20 – 25V. You can make the circuit adjustable by substituting a 317L adjustable regulator and the necessary resistors in place of the 78L05."

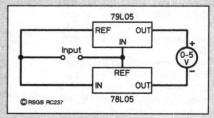

Fig 2: Simple expanded range voltmeter, providing a 10 – 15V range with a 0 – 5V meter. (source EDN 'Ideas for Design').

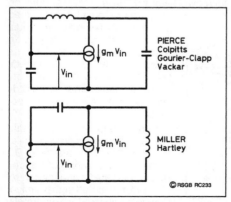

Fig 1: By Spring 1924, Dr G W Pierce and Dr J M Miller had proposed two basic configurations for single-active-device crystal oscillators that for 70 years have, with derivatives, remained standard arrangements.

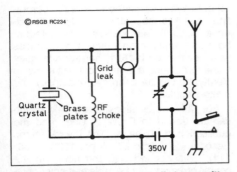

Fig 3: The original crystal-controlled transmitter built by H S Shaw (W)1XAQ in April 1924. It used two 5-watt triode valves with the crystal oscillator circuit suggested by Dr Miller. The resonant anode circuit (not used in the earlier Pierce oscillator) was tuned to approximately the 3MHz crystal frequency.

Fig 4: How the *QST* cartoonist saw amateurs tackling the problem of changing frequency upwards by grinding down the crystal. From the July 1924 article by H S Shaw (W)1XAQ.

plates for amateur bands. It was also found that 'quartz pebble' spectacle lenses could be made to oscillate. By 1926 a significant number of American amateurs were using crystal-controlled transmitters, with the practice spreading across the Atlantic in a matter of months. By the end of 1928, a number of British amateur transmitters were 'rock steady' with pure (T9X) notes.

Early quartz crystals were not cheap. In the *T&R Bulletin* of December 1928, one finds Quartz Oscillators Ltd of London NW2 asking £4.15s (more than the average weekly wage of that era) for a 7MHz crystal, with a 1.8MHz crystal priced at £2.15s. Quartz Crystal Company (QCC) founded by G2NH and G5MA at New Malden – destined to become a major supplier of crystals during WW2 – were supplying 7MHz crystals for £2.2s: "Every crystal guaranteed to oscillate with air-gap. We give the actual frequency accurate to 0.1%.... Really FB crystal holders four shillings." Throughout the 1930s, the Post Office demanded to inspect 'crystal certificates' before issuing amateur transmitting licences.

Initially, many British amateurs used 'pebble lenses', some even cut their own plates from natural crystals. Early crystal cuts (X and Y cuts) tended to be sensitive to temperature variations, much reduced with the coming in the 1930s of the 'AT zero-temperature-coefficient cut' which provided

virtually zero coefficient over a small range of temperature. An early cartoon demonstrates this process – **Fig 4**.

The idea of using quartz resonators to provide receiver IF selectivity (rather than for stability as foreseen by Shaw) can be traced to the British radio-engineer Dr Robinson (assisted by the late Ernest Gardiner, G6GR) and his 'stenode' broadcast receiver. He developed the basic single-crystal IF filter and lectured on his stenode system in the USA. Although the stenode broadcast receiver was based on the then common but wrong belief that sidebands existed only as mathematical concepts, James Lamb of ARRL realised that the Robinson crystal-gate filter was ideal for narrow-band CW reception and described its use in communications receivers in *QST* in 1932, one of the most important articles ever published in an amateur radio journal.

So much is history – a history in which amateur radio played a significant role. But what of the present? Piezo-electric quartz crystals remain a vital component in the continued search for ever more stable and selective transceivers. In digital electronics, the crystal 'clock' has become ubiquitous. Natural Brazilian quartz has been replaced by synthetic quartz and miniaturized, produced in countless millions at real costs a tiny fraction of what amateurs were prepared to pay in 1928!

Dr Dick Biddulph, G8DPS, has recently pointed out, in connection with the July *TT* item on 8- and 10-pole ladder filters, that Farnell supply 6.000MHz crystals at 65p (plus VAT and postage) each or 52p for ten-off, 43p for 24-off and 37p at 100-off. It should be noted however that these may not have quite the same characteristics for this application as the IQD crystals used by G3SBI with their relatively high-Q and low insertion loss.

Crystal technology and its application to oscillators have continued to progress. To overcome temperature problems there are now in addition to the simple uncompensated crystal oscillator (XO) the more stable temperature-compensated crystal oscillators (TCXO); digitally compensated crystal oscillators (DCXO); microcomputer-compensated crystal oscillators (MCXO); voltage-controlled oscillators (VCXO); temperature-compensated, voltage-controlled crystal oscillators (TCVCXO); and ever better oven-controlled crystal oscillators (OCXO).

State-of-the-art ultra stable crystal oscil-

lators have been developed for space satellites since 1958 at the Johns Hopkins Applied Physics Laboratory in the USA. A general survey of this work and the complex precautions needed to get the very best out of crystal oscillators in terms of frequency stability, environmental immunity, phase noise, ageing rate, size, mass and cost have been described by Jerry Norton and James Cloeren in 'Precision Quartz oscillators and their use aboard satellites' (*Johns Hopkins APL Technical Digest*, Vol 15, No 1, (1994) pp 30-37) from which the following notes have been abstracted: "The quartz resonator .... is the most important component in any quartz oscillator .... The size of the disc and the angle at which it is cut from the quartz crystal primarily determine the frequency of vibration .... Even with excellent oscillator circuits, performance cannot exceed the inherent quality or capability of the resonator. Less than optimum electronic circuits, however, can seriously degrade performance. The potential frequency stability has a wide variation from one part in 10^6 to 5 parts in 10^{14}, measured over 100 seconds. The resonator Q is the best measure of performance.

"Quartz resonators are produced in many shapes, sizes and operating frequencies and have many cost levels. For example, the resonator in a quartz watch is a relatively simple low-Q (about 30,000) device that is inexpensive (it costs less than $1). In contrast, a resonator for a high-precision oscillator is a complex, carefully processed, high-Q (over 3,000,000) device that is very expensive (more than $1000). A precision quartz resonator is capable of controlling frequency very precisely, but the operating environment must be very carefully controlled to realize the resonator's full potential.... A 5MHz resonator can have a Q exceeding 3-million and is the highest-Q resonator commercially available. If phase noise close to the carrier and low ageing rate are the most important oscillator parameters, a 5MHz resonator should be used .... The phase noise floor of an oscillator can be reduced at the expense of oscillator ageing rate.

"For a precision oscillator to generate an output signal that has a low ageing rate, high frequency stability, high spectral purity, and low phase noise, the following conditions must be met: (1) The quartz resonator must be kept excited (driven) at a very constant, low power level. (2) The resonator's operating temperature must be maintained precisely. (3) The resonator must be isolated from changes in external parameters such as power supply noise, magnetic fields, ionizing radiation, vibration, external loads, and parametric changes in the electronic components.

"**Fig 5** is a functional block diagram of a typical precision oscillator. A 5MHz, 3rd overtone, SC (stress compensated) cut quartz resonator is the frequency control element, fabricated from premium Q cultured quartz (hydrothermally laboratory grown). The oscillator is a modified Colpitts type with both alternating and direct current negative feedback to reduce

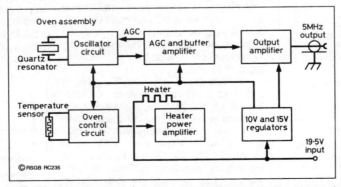

Fig 5: Functional block diagram of an ultra-stable quartz oscillator as used aboard small space satellites. The latest APL Johns Hopkins precision spacecraft oscillator has a frequency stability of 7 parts in 10^{14} over 100 seconds, consumes 0.9W, weighs 0.77kg and has a volume of 790.7 cubic centimetres.

flicker noise and stabilize gain. The AGC circuit . . . . maintains a constant resonator drive current and also provides a large degree of isolation from changes in circuit parameters, input voltage, and temperature. The low-level signal from the oscillator is amplified by a low-noise, high-impedance buffer amplifier to increase the signal level and further isolate the sensitive oscillator stage from the environment. The output amplifier provides power gain, impedance matching, and load isolation for the oscillator signal. A single proportional-controlled oven encloses the resonator, the oscillator circuit, and part of the oven control circuit. The temperature of the oven is adjusted to the turning point of the resonator (about 85°C) and is held within 0.001°C over the normal operating temperature environment."

Ageing rates of 2×10^{-12} per 24 hours have been measured during flight qualification tests and achieved in orbit. While ageing rates of caesium atomic standards are superior to this, they are comparable to those of rubidium atomic standards; moreover quartz oscillators are much less complex, more reliable and less expensive than atomic standards for small satellite applications.

While such extreme performance, which has to be maintained over the lifetime of a satellite, is vastly beyond any reasonable requirements for the Amateur Service – even the Amateur Satellite Service – the general principles remain valid and show the way towards higher performance for less rigorous applications. Remember that the calibration accuracy of modern synthesized transceivers depends upon the long-term performance of a crystal oscillator.

VALVE LINEAR SCREEN REGULATED SUPPLIES

IT WAS EMPHASISED IN *Technical Topics*, April 1986 (see also *TT Scrapbook, 1985-89*, p93) that the 4CX- family of RF power valves need to be treated with care if optimum performance is to be achieved. In respect of a number of suggestions from John Nelson, GW4FRX and others on the use of the 4CX250B, I wrote: "There is no doubt that the screen-grid power supply for this series of valves needs careful design, preferably with shunt regulators and capable of sourcing and sinking at least 40mA for negligible change in the screen voltage. High-voltage transistors and improved regulators with higher loop gain are proving an important advance on the older valve regulators." This assumed that modern high-voltage solid-state devices for the regulator would prove reliable without an undue degree of protection against voltage transients, etc. In practice this seems not always to have been achieved. Brian Horsfall, G3GKG, puts the case for a hybrid approach. He writes:

"As several previous correspondents have pointed out (eg *TT*, April 1986), when using valves of the 4X150/4CX250 family it is essential to provide a well regulated screen-grid supply voltage and to 'hold the screen down' with a hefty bleed resistor to allow for conditions where secondary emission and/or negative screen current can occur.

"At G3GKG, the power amplifier uses a pair of JAN 7609 (ruggedised 4X150D) valves in a classic 'tuned anode, tuned grid'

configuration, with a few watts of drive available from an ancient home-brewed exciter. Originally, a series stabilizer circuit was incorporated to provide the 325V screen supply and the bleed current was catered for with a parallel by-pass resistor providing most of that taken by the shunt resistor. Under normal loading and drive conditions, this meant that the bleed current was always greater than the actual screen current with the total current consumption of the regulated supply unnecessarily high; an offence to the frugal (half-Yorkshire) mind of G3GKG.

"Several unfortunate experiences with high-voltage (sic) solid-state devices in this application, led to the present, more elegant design (**Fig 6**) where a reliable, rugged (and to some old-fashioned) valve takes the strain and, with a 27V zener diode, ZD1, and medium-power transistor (TR1), provides the low-voltage supply for the solid-state op-amp feedback amplifier, IC1. The resistor, R1, is chosen to set the overall current to be drawn from a poorly regulated 360V supply (in some respects the poorer the regulation of this supply the better, see below).

"With this arrangement, current is taken by either the control valve, V1, or the PA screen-grids. There is no change in the current drawn from the supply and virtually no drop in voltage, unless or until the design current is exceeded by the demand of the screen-grids.

"A screen current meter is the best indicator of both tuning and loading conditions of this type of power amplifier. At G3GKG, the meter has its zero offset to allow for the possibility of negative current. When the amplifier is correctly loaded and fully driven by a two-tone generator (to 2mA grid current, more than 500mA anode current at 1500V EHT) the screen current peaks on 'tune' to only 20-25mA and the screen voltage remains steady within 1V. If the loading is too light, screen current can rise to alarming levels, so it helps to have a screen supply whose voltage drops rapidly in such conditions. In normal SSB operation, ALC feedback from PA to exciter is turned up so that the full 400-watts PEP RF output is obtained without driving into grid current and with only a few mA 'flicker' on the meter."

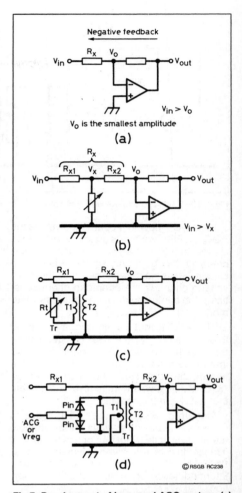

Fig 7: Development of improved AGC system. (a) Amplifier with negative feedback; (b) Attenuator placed at a point between V_{in} and V_{out}; (c) Transformer Tr reduces the voltage across Rt; and (d) Balanced PIN diodes provide linear attenuation. (source *RF Design*).

AGC ATTENUATOR

GIANCARLO MODA, I7SWX draws attention to an *RF Design* awards feature (March 1994, pp94, 96) submitted by Czech-born Carl Zatl who has been living in the USA since 1981. This is introduced as follows:

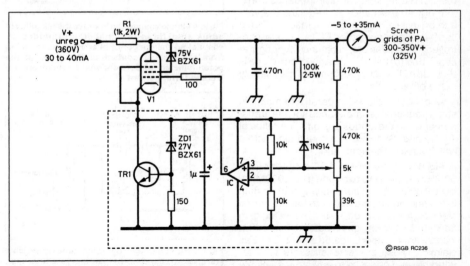

Fig 6: The hybrid valve/semiconductor screen-grid regulator developed by G3GKG for the 4X150/4CX250-series of high-power RF valves. Components within the dotted line are on a printed-circuit board. V1 can be 6BW6, 6AO5, EL84 etc. TR1 is a medium power transistor, eg TIP31. IC is LF355N (or 741). Resistor, R1, see text.

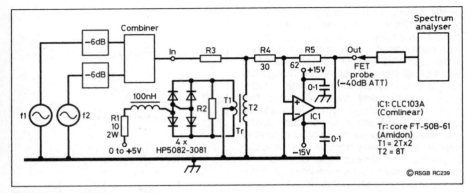

Fig 8: The final AGC system with test set-up.

"One weak spot in modern receivers is the AGC.... AGC voltage is used to vary the bias on the amplifier stages, increasing or decreasing the gain. As signal strength increases, less gain is needed and the AGC voltage changes the operating characteristics of the controlled device(s) to a less linear mode.

The result is that a strong signal is applied to an increasingly non-linear device, exactly the opposite of what is needed for good intermodulation performance. This problem has existed ever since the development of AGC. My goal was to minimise or eliminate that unfavourable condition."

Modern designs often use PIN diodes or FETs as variable resistances to form variable attenuators at the front end of a receiver. But if these devices are driven to higher attenuation, their non-linearity can produce intermodulation or cross-modulation distortion.

Carl Zati's approach is to reduce significantly the problem by placing the attenuating element into the negative feedback of an amplifier where signal amplitude is smaller: the principles on which this was developed are shown in **Fig 7**.

Fig 7(a) shows the point, V_o, where, in an amplifier with negative feedback, the smallest amplitude occurs; (b) shows an attenuator placed at a point between V_{in} and V_{out}; (c) further improvement is reached when the resistor R is replaced by an impedance transformer with resistance Rt, reducing the voltage on this resistance by the ratio T2:T1 (Rt can be voltage-controlled FETs, current-controlled PIN diodes etc, in balanced configurations); and (d) the non-linearity of one diode is reduced by the same but opposite nonlinearity of the other diode.

A resistor is placed in parallel to maintain some reasonable impedance for the transformer while the diodes are 'off'. The ratios of T1:T2 and Rx1:Rx2 are the main factors which specify the attenuator.

Fig 8 shows such an AGC amplifier for a 50MHz receiver in a two-tone (f1 50.000MHz, f2 50.100MHz) test set showing that as gain is decreased, the capability to handle strong signals grows; gain 0dB – IP3 = 38dBm; gain 6dB – IP3 = 42dBm; gain 12dB – IP3 = 45dBm with the input impedance 50 ± 10Ω. Carl Zatl claims: "These characteristics are very favourable and opposite to any other available AGC amplifier or attenuator; as gain is decreased, the circuit's capability to handle strong signals grows."

IMPROVING IC REGULATOR RELIABILITY

EDN 'DESIGN IDEAS' of 12 May 1994, p86 includes an idea from Peter Demchenko, in Lithuania pointing out that a small change to the standard circuit for adjustable three-terminal IC regulators (LM317, LM350 etc) improves reliability.

He considers that the standard circuit (**Fig 9(a)**) suffers from an inherent fault: if the wiper of the potentiometer, R2, loses contact the output goes high and may damage the load. Since the potentiometer is the most unreliable component in this standard circuit, it is worth considering the modified arrange-

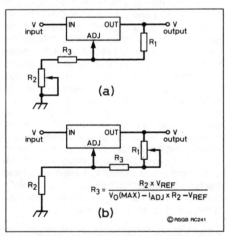

$$R_3 = \frac{R_2 \times V_{REF}}{V_{O(MAX)} - I_{ADJ} \times R_2 - V_{REF}}$$

Fig 9: A simple change can improve the reliability of adjustable three-terminal IC regulators by eliminating the danger of over-voltages resulting from the loss of contact of the wiper of the potentiometer. (a) Conventional arrangement. (b) Modified arrangement.

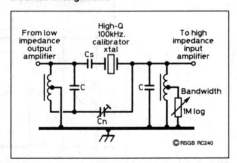

Fig 10: The super-selective, continuously-variable (10Hz to 2kHz bandwidth) 100kHz crystal filter used by SM5BSZ for EME (moonbounce) and similar narrow-band communications. Cn neutralizing capacitor. Cs crystal-equalizing capacitor required when two or more cascaded filter stages are used.

ment shown in **Fig 9(b)**. Now, if the wiper loses contact, the voltage output goes low, safeguarding the load. R3 limits the voltage excursion of the output even if the pot short-circuits.

SUPER-SELECTIVE CRYSTAL FILTER FOR EME ETC

THE CLASSIC ROBINSON/LAMB single crystal filter has, for many years, been largely superseded by multi-crystal bandpass filters. There are several reasons for this, including the higher intermediate frequency of modern designs, and the later development of effective bandpass half-lattice and ladder filters: the classic filter with its narrow 'nose' characteristics was primarily suited to 455kHz IFs and CW reception.

However, Jan-Martin Noeding, LA8AK has reported on how Leif Aasbrink, SM5BSZ has resurrected the Lamb-type filter in the form of a super-selective, continuously-variable filter for EME (moonbounce) reception. LA8AK writes:

"At a recent Scandinavian VHF meeting in Denmark, SM5BSZ described his approach to EME using a 500W power amplifier and 4 x 14-element yagi array but his main interest is the development of improved receiver performance. He has an extra receiver with digital signal processing (DSP) using Fourier transform to 'spectrum analyse' the received signals. He finds this also very useful when operating in the aurora-mode in order to investigate his own reflected signals using full QSK with 100W RF power and with BAY96 (some parallel connected) varactor diodes to form a transmit-receive (TR) antenna switch.

"To provide a high degree of (variable) selectivity, he uses a simple but effective form of the classic single-crystal filter. He found that MF/HF crystals tend to have too low a Q for this application whereas 100kHz calibrator crystals are entirely suitable. With the arrangement shown in **Fig 10**, he achieves a nose bandwidth variable between 10Hz and 2kHz depending on the setting of the output impedance which is governed by the setting of the 1M (log) 'bandwidth' potentiometer.

"SM5BSZ finds that even for EME, it is not practical to use the minimum 10Hz bandwidth achievable with this filter and 20Hz seems the lowest applicable limit. Unlike the filters used in the older communications receivers, such as the HRO, Super-Pro etc, this narrow-band filter must be fed from a low-impedance source (anode impedance of a valve is too high unless transformed down).

"The neutralizing capacitor (Cn) has much the same effect as the 'phasing control' of the classic filter in setting the rejection notch by balancing out the effect of the capacitance across the crystal. When cascading two or more such filters, it is important to tune both filters to precisely the same frequency, and an extra series capacitor (Cs) may be used to increase the resonant frequency for the crystal with the lower frequency.

"SM5BSZ uses two cascaded filters with transistor isolating amplifiers in his receiver. In order to adjust the selectivity over a wide bandwidth range a multi-turn potentiometer is highly desirable, tapped on to the tuned output circuit for impedance transformation."

PROJECT 6L6 – 1994 STYLE

1986 WAS THE 50th ANNIVERSARY of the introduction of the RCA Radiotron 6L6 beam tetrode followed a year later by an RF version, the classic 807. To mark the occasion, Dean Manley, KH6B, launched a 'Project 6L6 (*TT*, February, April, May and November 1986; see also *Technical Topics Scrapbook, 1985-89*). KH6B was seeking to encourage this project not only to mark the golden jubilee but also to revive interest in simple (KISS) rigs as club projects, home-construction etc. He then wrote: "It seems only natural for amateurs to build and experiment. A simple rig with a 6L6 would fill this bill. Building your own rig is half the fun. The other half is putting it on the air and convincing the disbelievers that you've really a metal 6L6 or glass 6L6G in the final, then taking the rig along to the local club and enticing others into the homebrew game."

I pointed out that such rigs are not necessarily confined to CW. Amplitude (Heising) modulation of a single stage crystal oscillator is not recommended practice, but in the past many did it. "A few brief contacts, just to prove it still works (and can be received as SSB), would hurt nobody. Indeed there is little reason why it should not be reintroduced more widely on 1.9MHz or 29MHz. A two-stage 6V6CO/6L6 or 807PA combination is better than a single-stage power oscillator."

Although we are now approaching the 60th anniversary of the beam tetrode, KH6B believes that the raison d'etre for such projects remains valid. In the February 1994 issue of the *BIARC Bulletin* of the Big Island Amateur Radio Club of Hilo, Hawaii, he returns to this topic reporting that this local club of over 100 members are this year pursuing 'Project 6L6' as a 'club kit' activity.

"Yes, homebrew, hot soldering irons, and valves!" he comments, adding: "Many years have past since the question of whether to build or buy was posed seriously. At one time, it was suggested that your first station should be 'home brew' even if you could afford to buy the best available station equipment. It was even assumed that if you built your own, you knew more than an operator who bought his station. Nothing replaces experience. You learn by building and if you build your own AM

transmitter, then put it on the air, you no longer qualify as an 'appliance operator'. Nothing can replace the fun, the educational value, and the pride of operating your own 'home brew' transmitter.

Fig 11 shows the two-stage 1.8MHz AM/CW transmitter that forms the basis of the current BIARC project for which KH6B has developed a kit. This has a Pierce-type crystal oscillator using a 6J5 triode valve plus a 6L6/6L6G power amplifier with pi-type matching network and using a 6.3V, 0.3A (US Nr 47) pilot bulb as tuning indicator. **Fig 12** shows the Heising anode modulator suitable for use with a microphone providing a fairly high output. A 350V, PSU is shown in **Fig 13**. In the UK a number of the components might pose problems for those without a good junk box salvaged from the valve era, but in many cases various substitutions could be made without impairing results.

HERE AND THERE

A NUMBER OF COMMENTS have been received on the May *TT* item about the invention by Sperry of the famous National *PW* dial as used in the HRO receiver, and we hope to return to this topic later. Meanwhile John Teague, G3GTJ, points out that this type of dial was used on a British-made S-band cavity wavemeter of wartime vintage to count the turns on the micrometer type plunger. The dial differed from the HRO dial in being thicker and possibly a little larger in diameter. On another topic, G3GTJ is currently researching one of the most significant wartime developments in radio communications technology: the No 10 microwave (4.4 Gigahertz) multiplexed radio relay system using pulse-width modulation. The first demonstration of pulse-TDM communications was made at SRDE in early July 1942 and was judged so successful that contracts were quickly placed for 600 equipments with GEC, Pye Ltd and the Telephone Manufacturing Company, with operational models available from January 1944, in time for their successful use during the liberation of France and Belgium (see my letter in *Radio Bygones*, No 4, February/March 1990). John

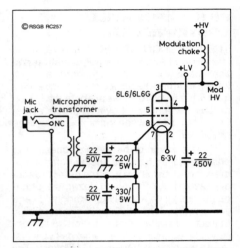

Fig 12: Anode modulator for Project 6L6 for use with carbon microphone.

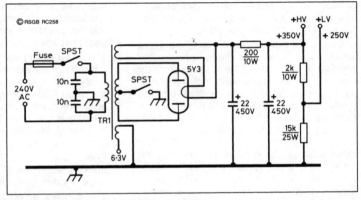

Fig 13: Suitable power supply for project 6L6.

Teague, (Perrotts, Lydford on Fosse, Somerton, Somerset TA11 7HA, Tel: 0963 240319) has plenty of technical data but is anxious to contact more of those who used this equipment which, he notes, was used by the RAF as well as the Army.

Many years ago, *TT* mentioned the possibility that one day a new form of tiny semiconductor microphone might be developed. This seems to have come much closer to practical implementation according to a paper presented by G Sessler of Darmstadt Technical University at the 127th Meeting of the Acoustical Society of America, MIT, June 1994. David Newland (*Nature*, 7 July, 1994, p21) reports that the German scientist described a two-chip silicon condenser microphone no larger than a pinhead. It is claimed that good sensitivity with a flat response up to 10kHz can be obtained with noise levels comparable to conventional condenser microphones. Micromachining methods can also be used to produce miniature piezoelectric microphones in which the membrane is of a piezoelectric material that generates an output voltage when it is deflected.

So far, silicon condenser microphones have the higher sensitivity and piezoelectric microphones the higher frequency response (first resonance frequencies up to 45kHz). Apart from their tiny size, silicon condenser microphones have other advantages, including the possibility of being manufactured in bulk using the techniques of the semiconductor industry, which means that they should be cheap and reliable. ***G3VA***

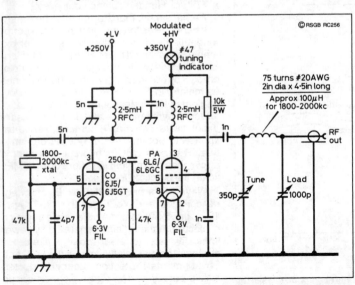

Fig 11: Two-stage 1.8MHz transmitter forming part of KH6B's current 'Project 6L6'.

RF HAZARDS STILL CONTROVERSIAL

THE QUESTION OF WHETHER relatively low-level non-ionized electromagnetic radiation – below the accepted standards at which known thermal effects occur – at frequencies from 50Hz to microwaves are potentially hazardous remains controversial, with something of a split between the biologists and the physicists.

TT last covered the general question of possible health hazards arising from the operation of transmitters in some detail in January 1990 pp 36-37 ('Health Hazards: tougher guidelines') with a follow-up 'Handhelds and your eyes' in June 1992, p40. The possibility that athermal effects of radiation could conceivably represent a leukaemia risk was first raised seriously by Dr Samuel Milham in *The Lancet* (April 6, 1985). Dr Milham's statistical study was noted in *TT* August 1985 and appears in *Technical Topics Scrapbook* , 1985-89, p46 with related material on pages 46, 66, 141, 234-235, 252, 258.

One might have thought that by now, the issue would have been settled one way or another. This is far from the case. As amateur transmitters we might wish that the public would give us the benefit of the doubt until the matter was settled beyond all doubt. But as Camelia Gabriel (King's College London/Microwave Consultants Ltd) puts it in 'The Radiation Risks – Are They Real?' (*The Radioscientist*, June 1994, pp70-71): "With an increasing public awareness of environmental issues comes a perception that exposure to EM fields may be detrimental to health. The public has the right to question the issue and to expect the scientists to consider matters, perform the necessary research and provide as many answers as possible."

She continues: "The main issue is that of biological effects resulting from the interaction of EM fields with living organisms including people. The extensive body of literature . . . . enables the following statements to be made for exposure to EM fields in the range 10MHz to 10GHz:

(a) When a person is exposed to EM radiation the incident external fields induce internal fields within the body. The internal fields interact with the body tissues at various levels of organisation and result in induced currents and energy absorption.

(b) The degree of energy coupling depends mainly on the field parameters and on the shape and size of the exposed person.

(c) Generally, when the rate of energy absorption during exposure exceeds the rate of energy dissipation, the body temperature rises. Most of the biological effects of EM fields are an indirect consequence of this thermal stimulation, and are therefore known as thermal effects.

(d) There is a strong correlation between the intensity of the internal fields and the severity of the biological effect. Internal fields are quantified in terms of the rate of energy they deliver per unit body mass, this quantity is known as the specific absorption rate (SAR) and is expressed in watts per kilogram (W/kg).

(e) There is a threshold whole body SAR above which there is an increasing likelihood of adverse health effects.

(f) The concept of whole body SAR is not sufficient to guard against adverse biological effect in exposure situations where acute localised heating is likely to occur. The partial body exposure to the non-uniform fields from hand-held transceivers results in complex field distribution within the body. The shape and layered structure of the tissues of the head make it particularly prone to non-uniform field distributions. In terms of SAR, the field patterns are further accentuated by difference in the electrical properties of the tissues.

(h) To safeguard against localised overheating, restrictions on SAR averaged over small masses of tissue must be postulated.

Fig 1 shows the reference levels at frequencies above 100kHz as advised by the UK National Radiological Protection Board published in 1989 in *NRPB-GS11* 'Guidance as to restrictions on exposures to time varying electromagnetic fields and the 1988 recommendations of the International Non-Ionizing Radiation Committee'.

Camelia Gabriel points out that the exposure standards developed by national and international bodies are almost exclusively based on threshold wholebody SAR and localised heating. They are formulated to guard against thermal effects and she concludes that on present knowledge, the concepts of threshold whole body SAR and SAR averaged over a small mass of tissue are adequate to protect users of hand-held transceivers.

She questions, however, the situation with low-level exposures which result in SAR below the level of thermal significance and which are implicitly assumed safe: "The debate over the potential health hazard of exposure to low levels of microwaves was recently reopened over allegations in the press of a relationship between the use of portable communication equipment and the development of brain cancer." She considers this view is not supported by the scientific evidence, but concludes that "it is generally agreed that there is a need for further research to improve and consolidate our understanding of athermal responses and their biological significance."

She accepts however that under certain conditions, exposures from hand-held transceivers with output powers of 7-watts (usually considered the safe upper limit) may give rise to exposure conditions that contravene the protection philosophy and that there is an obligation on manufacturers to ensure that, when used as intended, they do not give rise to exposure conditions that contravene the protection philosophy. A warning that the 7W exclusion clause of the ANSI standard needs to be revised downwards was given in a paper by Niels Kuser and Qurino Balzano which was referred to in *TT*, June 1992, page 40 in a *TT* item 'Handhelds and your eyes'.

Perhaps more than Europeans, the American public takes the unproven risks of electromagnetic radiation seriously – even, for example, questioning the effects of electric blankets in appearing to change the body's rate of production of such cancer-inhibiting hormones as melatonin. The ARRL advises the policy, originated by Professor Granger Morgan, of 'prudent avoidance', avoiding unnecessary exposure to EMFs as a common-sense response to potential – but not yet proven – health hazards. Not abandonment of electric appliances but minimizing exposure to EMFs when it's practical to do so.

Wayne Overbeck, N6NB in 'Electromagnetic Fields and Your Health' (*QST*, April 1994, pp56-59) considers the whole question of electromagnetic fields generated by power lines, TV sets, amateur radio gear etc. He emphasises that scientists from the FCC and Environmental Protection Agency conducted a field survey of EMFs at typical American amateur radio stations in 1990: They con-

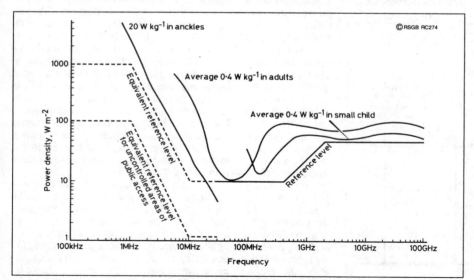

Fig 1: Advised reference levels above 100kHz and curves relating specific energy absorption rates in the body to incident power density (NRPB publication *GS-11*, May 1989).

cluded that most amateur operations do not produce EMFs strong enough to pose any health hazard.

However, based on guidelines developed by the Bio-Effects Committee of the ARRL, he puts forward a number of practical suggestions – some of which are considerably more rigorous than the official recommendations and not all of which I, in common with many amateurs, could claim to adhere to. (I must confess my antenna is less than 35ft high, partly in the roof space and end-fed in the shack with an RF power of the order of 100 watts, all transgressions of the ARRL code).

The following is a shortened and edited version of N6NB's suggestions:

● Transmitting antennas should be mounted well away from living areas. For power of 100W or more, if possible antennas should be at least 35 feet above populated areas. Transmission lines, open-wire or coax with high SWR should preferably be routed away from areas where people spend much time.

● With ground-mounted or mobile antennas, be careful not to transmit when anyone is near the antenna. A rule of thumb is to avoid transmitting when anyone is within three feet of a car-mounted 144MHz whip used with a typical 25W transceiver, or five or six feet with a 100W amplifier. With a beam antenna and 100W or more, don't transmit when anyone is within 35ft of the front of the antenna.

● Exercise particular care with indoor antennas, including attic antennas. In some situations these can generate substantial RF fields. Try to locate them as far from people as possible and use low power (10W output or less) and keep transmissions short when someone might be near the antenna.

● Never use a power amplifier that has its metal cover removed.

● UHF and microwave antennas and waveguides may produce hazardous levels of RF energy and must be installed carefully so that no person is in the line of fire. Never look into an activated waveguide or stand in front of a high-gain VHF-UHF antenna when the transmitter is on.

● When using hand-held transceivers use the lowest power possible and keep the antenna as far from your head as possible . . . . there is growing evidence that even 1W or 2W hand-held radios may produce significant EMFs within the user's head, with possible health effects that are not yet fully understood. Where possible use hand-helds in the 'low-power' position with only a fraction of a watt of output power.

● Be aware that low-frequency fields exist in your home. If possible avoid being within 24 inches of any electric motor or power transformer while it is turned on. Hair dryers, AC-operated hand drills and other appliances that are held close to the user's body often expose them to stronger EMFs than those produced by amateur-radio equipment. It is a good idea to stay about 24-in away from the fans and power transformers found in high-power amplifiers and 12V power supplies, for example.

The specific problem of possible RF interference to the safe operation of implemented cardiac pacemakers was discussed in *TT*, February 1989 (see the *TT Scrapbook 1985-*

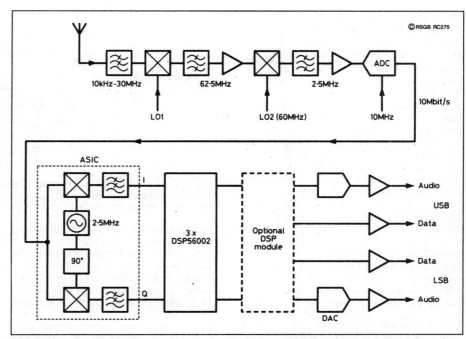

Fig 2: Simplified block diagram of the Marconi H2550 'digital' MF/HF communications receiver.

89, p287). This showed that while the immunity of such devices had been greatly increased since they were first introduced in the late 1950s, there remained considerable difference in immunity between various models and between pulsed and continuous wave RF. I then concluded "It seems reasonable to suggest that persons depending on implanted cardiac pacemakers should avoid areas subject to strong electromagnetic fields, either as operators or as visitors, or as members of the family, unless they are certain that their particular device is guaranteed not to be affected up to the range of levels involved.

A full-length article 'Pacemakers, Interference and Amateur Radio' by Fred Weber, MD, AA2KI (*QST*, July 1994, pp34-36) shows that while amateurs who have pacemakers can expect to safely use their stations, "these wonderful devices were [initially] not free of risk and reports of unwanted interactions between pacemakers and electrical devices began to appear."

AA2KI in discussing current risks to pacemaker users, singles out a number of sources of high EMFs, not usually met in practice; these include spot-weld machines, arc welding machines, submerged arc welders, neon sign test rooms; electrical sub-stations etc. Hostile environments may also be encountered in radiation therapy for breast cancer and within magnetic-resonance imaging (MRI) scanners.

He points out that when estimating potential dangers to pacemaker users, take steps not to generalize about particular models, configurations, lead systems etc: "Each patient is unique, and all variables must be carefully evaluated. Safe operation of a particular unit in a particular environment does not guarantee safe operation of that device in another."

For amateurs with pacemakers, he provides a number of tips for safe operation. He stresses that as long as accepted safety practices are maintained there is no increased danger. He does however note one final

precaution involving antennas: "Most hams use external antennas that limit their exposure to RF energy. Everyone is encouraged to do this – especially hams with pacemakers. The increasing use of indoor loops and attic wires, however, brings RF closer to the shack, sometimes even bathing it in RF. As a precaution, hams with pacemakers should avoid these types of antennas."

HF PROGRESS AT THE CONFERENCES

WITH THE RSGB 1994 International HF & IOTA Convention looming up (October 7-9, see *RadCom*, August p16) it seems apposite to consider some of the developments reported at recent professional conferences, in particular the IEE's 6th International Conference on 'HF Radio Systems & Techniques'. At one time it looked as though the coming of satellite communications, and long-distance satellite broadcasting, professional VHF meteor scatter etc might leave the HF spectrum virtually as a happy hunting ground for amateur radio.

Unfortunately, the already outdated idea that HF is no longer of importance to professional communications appears to have influenced the Director and management of the Science Museum in their highly regrettable decision to close down GB2SM, a decision that they will surely come to regret unless they can be persuaded at the last minute to reverse it. The full history of HF cannot yet be written. It is far from a dead technology!

It is clear from the IEE conference book of papers (*IEE Conference Publication No 392*) that despite all the problems of reliable HF systems, there remains a vast number of military and other systems still interested in HF with its unique potential for low-cost, long-distance communications in peace or war. Furthermore, quite a lot of the professional R&D is being carried out by those who, in their spare time, operate on the amateur bands. Dr Brian Austin, G0GSZ, who was on the IEE organizing committee (together with Les Barclay, G3HTF and Mike Underhill, G3LHZ) tells me that of the 211 delegates from 19 countries, 46 admitted to holding amateur calls: 16 of the 96 UK delegates, 13 of the large Swedish contingent of 29, five of the 21 from the USA.

J M Goodman (SRI International) in 'The last quarter-century of ionospheric study and prospects for the future' pointed out that "there are well-founded military imperatives which necessitate the continued use of HF (and other ionospherically-dependent) systems despite capacity restrictions. Moreover, within the military sector it is recognised that it is not prudent to put all one's eggs into a single basket . . . . effective management of a variety of communications media is needed . . . . It is well known that the HF spectral domain is limited and the number of users is vast, leading to a problem of spectral congestion . . . . There will be an obvious benefit if HF systems can be modernized to support data rates consistent with a seamless connection with ATM/SONET backbone. Primary use would be the support of long-haul connections of remote sites with base stations, corporate networks, and military headquarters. In addition, viable HF communication capability at high data rates could greatly leverage the well known advantages possessed by HF skywave at times of national emergency, including disaster relief following earthquakes, floods and hurricanes."

Reported hardware developments include a paper by R J Eassom (GEC-Marconi) de-

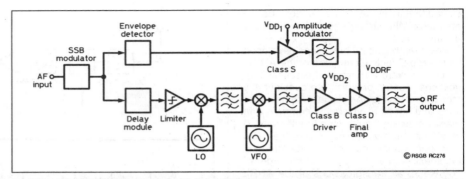

Fig 3: Simplified block diagram of high-efficiency SSB HF/VHF transmitter based upon Kahn-type envelope elimination and restoration with an average efficiency of about three-times that of a transmitter with a conventional Class B power amplifier. (Raab & Rupp, *IEE Conference Publication No 392*).

scribing the Marconi H2550 MF/HF analog/digital receiver covering 10kHz to 30MHz, together with an associated transmitter drive (H1550). Both of these new equipments have now reached the stage of being delivered to customers. It is pointed out that "the replacement of conventional analogue HF communications receivers by digitally-implemented equipments is becoming increasingly common. These offer the advantages of improved performance, increased flexibility and lower cost."

It is emphasised that naval communications presents one of the worst environments for HF radio equipment since high power local transmitters can result in unwanted signals as high as +20dBm at the receiver antenna input, with frequency offsets as low as 5%. At the same time, the wanted signals may be as

low as 1uVemf ie −113dBm. This results in a requirement for a receiver combining low noise figure, high signal level handling and excellent linearity – requirements equally desirable for amateur operation.

The H2550 (outlined in **Fig 2**) employs what is described as a novel bandpass sigma-delta analog-to-digital converter (ADC) on the second IF signal at 2.5MHz, with application-specific (ASIC) custom ICs in conjunction with digital signal processing (DSP). As with all 'digital communications receivers' so far described, the RF front-end uses analogue circuitry including 'a new mixer developed for high linearity coupled with minimum loss and low local oscillator (LO) drive level. A patent has been filed for this design as it achieves better than a +40dBm 3rd order intercept point for a +5dBm LO drive from the synthesizer. The same circuit is used for both mixers: RF to 1st IF (62.5MHz) and 1st IF to 2nd IF (2.5MHz). However, the mixers radiate high levels of LO harmonics, so screening, especially between the two mixers, was extremely important in the mechanical design." Unfortunately no further details of this mixer are given in the paper.

"The traditional crystal filter at the first IF, which can limit overall linearity, was replaced by a two-cavity helical resonator. Similarly, an LC design was used for the second IF filter rather than crystal type, although provision was made to fit a crystal filter as an option . . . . For naval applications, the receiver selectivity and reciprocal mixing performance is enhanced by a pre-selector filter. Organised as four couple-pair octave filters tuned by an arrangement of binary weighted capacitors, this provides 20dB rejection at 5% frequency offsets and 30dB at 10%."

F H Raab and D J Rupp (Green Mountain Radio Research Company, USA) describe a 'High-efficiency single-sideband HF/VHF transmitter based upon envelope elimination and restoration (EER)'. This multi-mode transmitter is based upon the EER technique (exploited also in polar-loop and cartesian-loop systems, see *TT*, June 1994, pp53-54) originally described by L R Kahn in *Proc IRE*, 1952, Vol 40, pp803-806, with sub-systems using a Class D RF power amplifier, a Class-S high-level amplitude modulator, an SSB modulator, a delay-compensated circuit and frequency translators:

"The experimental transmitter (**Fig 3**) is a prototype for both communication and jamming applications. It can produce a wide variety of signals, including SSB, AM and FM. Its efficiency is about 60% for all signal ampli-

CARE NEEDED WITH MOVS?

THE USE OF METAL-OXIDE varistors (MOVs) to remove spikes from mains supplies has been widely advocated and widely adopted for the protection of solid-state equipment including home computers and the like. In the UK, the usual specification for MOVs in this application is to use 275V AC working (350V DC) types with energy absorption ratings of from about 8 to 60 joules. I have always assumed that a clamping-value of 275V AC would safely handle mains-supply variations and MOV tolerances, while effectively removing the high-voltage transients that can damage solid-state equipment.

This would seem, however, to be disputed by Jim Sandoz, N2MPT in a long letter in the Technical Correspondence feature of *QST*, July 1994, pp82-83. In this he criticises the use of 130V AC MOVs with the American 120V mains, and argues that it is important to specify an MOV voltage rating of – at minimum – 1.5 times the nominal mains voltage. For 120V mains supplies this would mean 180V AC MOVs; for 240V mains 360V AC MOVs. N2MPT suggests that MOV tolerances can typically range from 5 to 20%: "The MOV clamping voltage is a function of many variables, including operating temperature, age, and transient event history. With this in mind, it's prudent to specify an MOV with a voltage rating of at least one and a half times the AC mains voltage."

N2MPT writes: "Should the MOV turn

on and stay on, there are a number of possible results. The least-hazardous outcome is that the fuse in the equipment opens due to the high current flow. Unfortunately, a large number of MOV applications depend on a circuit breaker or fuse located at the building's distribution panel. Taking into account the impedance of the mains circuit and the on impedance of the MOV, the current flow may not trip the overcurrent protection device and may attempt to continuously dissipate anywhere from 20 to 200 watts. As MOVs are designed for very short transients, anything but the lower end of this range is far above its thermal rating . . . . the overheated MOV package will either burst into flame and/or expel hot material, possibly igniting nearby components or materials. Unfortunately, this failure mode is fairly common."

He also draws attention to a different hazardous situation which occurs when MOVs are improperly applied in telecommunications applications, for example being connected directly across phone lines to remove transients. He warns against "do-it-yourself protection using MOVs is not a good idea unless all the risks are understood." I am not too sure how seriously we should take N2MPT's warning (although he seems to know what he is talking about) and wonder if any reader has experienced difficulties with 275V MOVs?

tudes, which makes its average efficiency for voice signals about three times that of a transmitter with a conventional class-B PA. For voice-bandwidth signals, the IMD products are 43dB or more below the peak carrier output (–43dBc)."

"A compact portable HF terminal" proposed by M Darnell et al (HW Communications Ltd) utilises a 100W amateur transceiver as the basis of a modern 'suitcase radio'. Their terminal provides a fully automatic HF radio system intended for digital transmission using MFSK (multiple frequency shift keying), based on the Piccolo concept, implemented via real-time DSP. Real-time channel evaluation (RTCE) provides automatic adaptive operation at data rates matched to channel conditions.

The authors point out that amateur radio enthusiasts make extensive use of the HF medium with modern amateur-grade transceivers. Although these are much lower in cost than professional/military systems, they are reliable and have good performance specification in some respects; but, in other respects, eg frequency stability, their performance is marginal for digital traffic.

The major elements of the proposed terminal (**Fig 4**) are: (a) amateur-grade transceiver with maximum of 100W RF output; (b) sloping-V or other simply deployable antenna for both transmission and reception; (c) 486-based laptop PC for overall system control and protocol generation; (d) a PC DSP expansion card to perform real-time signal generation and processing functions (–32C processor); and (e) flexible power supply facilities.

The MFSK modem would provide tone frequencies independently variable to an accuracy of 1Hz with tone positions adjusted to avoid sources of narrowband co-channel interference, with the number of tones adapted in response to path or equipment state would be from 2 to 32 tones. Error control based on Reed-Solomon codes. The system currently operates in low-speed data transmission modes but could be extended to transmit analogue speech, medium-rate data and digitised image information.

At the 11th National Radio Science Colloquium (University of Liverpool) July 1994, V Petrovic and M A Billsberry showed that the polar-loop technique can be applied to conventional radio transmitters without altering the transmitter other than by adding extra, external circuitry. While I have not seen their paper, the abstract (provided by Dr Brian Austin, G0GSF) states: "The polar-loop and cartesian-loop techniques are the most effective means currently available for improving the linearity of radio transmitters used in narrow-band modulation systems .... This [Polar-Loop] technique was implemented using a 20W amplifier operating at 220MHz. A reduction in third-order intermodulation products from –27dB to –53dB, on a two-tone test, was achieved. Further improvements are possible with more detailed circuit design."

MULTI-WIRE DIPOLE AND MONOPOLE ANTENNAS

AN INTERESTING LETTER from Dr David Pearson, GM3TLA, draws attention to various forms of multi-wire folded dipoles that are often overlooked, including the possibilities

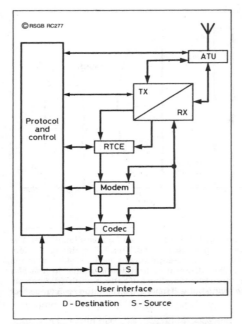

Fig 4: Professional low-cost 'suitcase' portable HF terminal using a 100-watt amateur transceiver and adaptive Piccolo-type MFSK digital transmission with real-time-channel-evaluation to control bit-rate (M Darnell, B Honary, R Enright & I Martin, *IEE Conference Publication No 392***).**

they present for dipoles with short-spans and their use as two- or multi-band antennas. This has arisen from his use as a receiving antenna of the four-wire, three-eights wave, folded dipole which was described originally by Dr John D Kraus, W8JK, in the late 1930s and which is briefly described in several editions of *Amateur Radio Techniques* (ART7, pp 296-7) and *TT, July 1987 (see also Technical Topics Scrapbook, 1985-89,* pp179-180).

GM3TLA notes that his antenna, with a three-eighths-wave span on 21MHz uses 20 metres of wire and also resonates on 7MHz, although the radiation resistance is probably too low to make this a really efficient 7MHz transmitting antenna – but it might be worth trying. Several other, too-often forgotten, types of folded dipoles and folded monopoles were described by W8JK. **Fig 5** shows some of these folded antennas and the approximate resistive feed impedance with wires of equal diameter when erected about a half-wave above ground.

It should not be forgotten, however, that a folded element used in a beam array will have a reduced input resistance which can, for example, provide a good match to 50 or 75Ω coax feeder. Similarly a wide variety of input resistances can be obtained by using wires of unequal diameter, a technique originally described by W Van Roberts, W3CHO in *RCA Review,* June 1947 and in the UK in an article by H A M Clark, G6OT (*RSGB Bulletin,* October 1947 with an abac for finding the input resistance for unequal wire/rod diameters etc). As for a single-wire half-wave dipole the height of a folded antenna above ground has an important effect on its terminal resistance and reactance, as does also mutual coupling to nearby objects or array elements.

While the three-eights-wave folded dipole means that a 14MHz antenna can be erected with the span normally required for 21MHz, GM3TLA raises the question that this type of

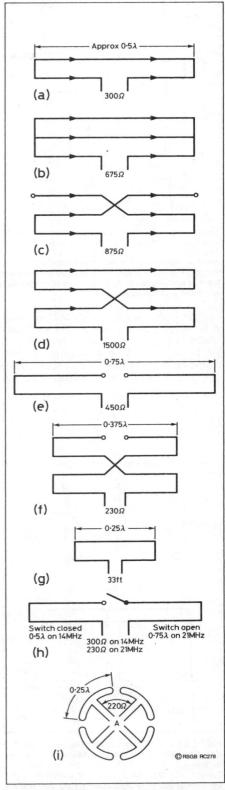

Fig 5: Various forms of folded dipole antennas. (a) and (b) physical span 0.49-wave. (c) 0.46 wave. (d) 0.47-wave. (e) 0.71-wave; (f) 0.38-wave. (g) basic quarter-wave, folded dipole, voltage-fed. (h) Practical two-band 14 and 21MHz antenna with switch closed on 14MHz. (I) The original Empire State Building TV-sound VHF ring antenna using four quarter-wave dipoles to form circular omni-directional ring. The mutual coupling reduces the feed impedance of each segment to about 220Ω, with four twin feeders parallelled at A and coupled to 55Ω coax cable via a balun. The folded parts are of equal length mounted one above the other but shown in two-dimension form in the diagram.

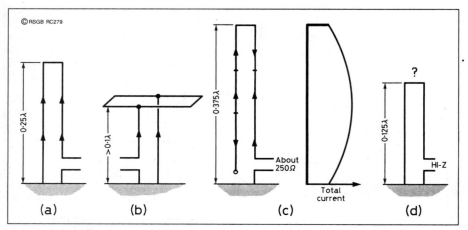

Fig 6: Various forms of the folded monopole antenna. (a) λ/4 folded vertical of conventional form. The feed impedance can be adjusted to required value by using wires/rods of different diameter. (b) Folded-Tee antenna developed by G3LNP (*TT*, August 1992). (c) Three-eights-wave vertical folded antenna working against earth with feed impedance about 250Ω. Current distribution is similar to that of a vertical top-loaded single-conductor antenna with maximum radiation a λ/4 above earth. (d) Possible form of a λ/8 wave monopole which might be worth trying but will have a low radiation resistance that will reduce efficiency.

multiple folding might possibly provide a way of building a dipole with one half wavelength of wire with an overall span of only one-eighth wave which could be erected in a highly restricted space. I suspect that such an antenna would require critical adjustment of the element to resonance. W8JK in his *Electronics* article (reproduced in the *Electronics Manual for Radio Engineers*) points out that the length of an antenna becomes more critical as the number of wires is increased beyond two, reducing rather than as might be expected increasing the effective bandwidth.

The original dipoles investigated by W8JK were for the pre-war 14MHz band (14.0 to 14.4MHz) and were constructed with No 12 (B&S gauge) with the overall spacing (d) of the order of 0.015 wavelength or less. Thus his two-wire 14MHz dipole was 34ft long and had a wire spacing of one foot.

In his article, W8JK referred to the work of N E Lindenblad for the original television (sound) transmitting antenna on the Empire State Building (*RCA Review,* April 1939). W8JK stressed that "The transmission line terminals of all the types described [in Electronics] are located at a current loop point. Lindenblad has recently described a folded antenna, which might be called a two-wire quarter-wave doublet, in which the terminals are located at a current node."

As I had never previously followed up this reference to a quarter-wave folded doublet, it seemed worth seeking out, in the IEE Library, the April 1939 issue of *RCA Review*. I found that the first VHF TV-sound antenna (modern TV antennas are broad-band and carry both vision and sound, usually on UHF for four channels) on the Empire State Building consisted of a loop antenna made up from four folded dipoles bent into circular segments.

To quote Lindenblad: "Among the dimensions of folded radiators which, at a given frequency, result in resistive input impedance, only the two smallest dimensions are of any interest in this case. At the larger of these

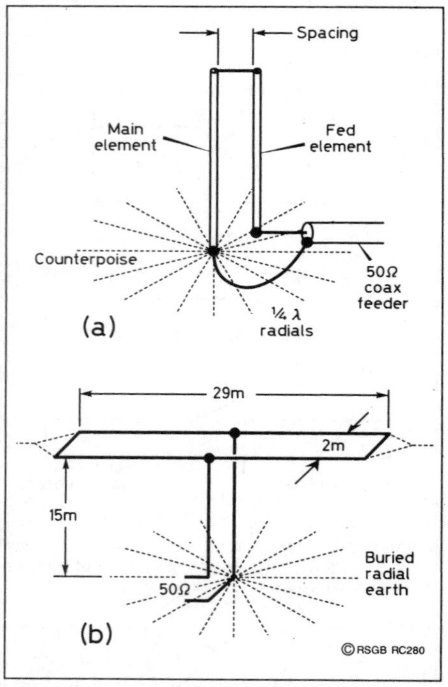

Fig 7: (a) Form of folded monopole investigated in detail by K8CFU in the mid 1980s. Provisional dimensions for 14.2MHz antenna are listed in Table 1. (b) Dimensions of a 1.85MHz folded-T antenna as described by G3LNP in 1992. Dimensions can be scaled for higher-frequency bands.

dimensions the distance between the folding points of the radiator is approximately a half wave: **Fig 5(a)**. The folding points coincide with maximum potential and the currents in the parallel conductors flow in the same direction.

"The distance between the folding points at the smaller dimension is only about a quarter of a wave: **Fig 5(g)**. The input terminals are at maximum potential and the currents in the parallel conductors flow in opposite directions. A ring antenna of this later type need only be about half the size of that required by the first type, reduces the possibility of undesirable mutual effects between the sound and the vision antennas and reduces the mechanical problems. For these reasons, the small-type folded dipole was chosen."

For a λ/4 folded dipole the terminal resistance would be very high, implying a voltage-fed system – possibly from a resonant open-wire feeder (preferably about one-quarter or three-quarters wave long to provide a current fed system from a balanced ATU output). In the case of the four λ/4 radiators in the RCA ring antenna, by properly spacing adjacent folding points, it was found possible to influence the characteristics of the radiator so that the input impedance of each radiator in the combination was reduced to 220Ω, permitting parallel connection of the four short open-wire balanced 220Ω lines via a balance converter [1:1 balun] to a 55Ω coaxial line without impedance transformation: **Fig 5(i)**.

For amateur operation with a quarter-wave dipole, it would presumably be possible to use 300Ω line as a resonant line on the fundamental frequency but as a flat line on the harmonic frequency at which it would be a conventional half-wave dipole.

There might also be a possibility of an effective one-eighth-wave high folded monopole. Dr Kraus pointed out the advantages of a three-eighths wave vertical antenna working against ground including the lower ground loss due to the higher feed resistance: **Fig 6(c)**. Whether a one-eighth wave vertical monopole without top loading (**Fig 6(d)**), would be effective is questionable but might form an interesting experimental project. The radiation resistance would be low. **Fig 7** shows two practical implementations of folded monopoles.

HERE AND THERE

JOHN GARDNER, GW4KVJ, was reminded of finding many old zinc-air primary cells in black moulded cases on the railway embankment he rents from British Rail . Cell No 518A, CAD on star (trade mark), described as an inert caustic soda cell with capacity of 850 to 1000 Ah. EMF 1.4V, discharge rates: continuous normal 100mA; continuous maximum 400mA; intermittent maximum 800mA. An 'important' note added "when in service the cell must be well ventilated". The makers, Le Carbone (GB) Ltd of Portslade, Sussex. GW4KVJ also recalls that in his youth he worked for an electrical contractor who had the task of maintaining the bell circuits of the composer Ralph Vaughan Williams. It was his job to check the bells, cleaning out the Leclanche cells, fitting new zinc rods and renewing the solution, mixing sal-ammoniac crystals with water to form ammonium chloride. **G3VA**

Base impedance	Height	Main el dia	Fed el di	Spacing
50Ω	15.1ft	0.25in	1.75in	3.0in
			2.75in	4.0in
			4.0in	6.0in
75Ω	15.1ft	0.25in	1.25in	14.25in
			1.75in	16.25in
			2.75in	22.5in

Table 1.

STABLE LC OSCILLATORS

DESPITE THE ATTRACTIONS of crystal resonators in conjunction with frequency synthesis as a means of obtaining stable frequency generation, there remains a real need for free-running LC-type VFOs with stabilities approaching those of low-cost crystal oscillators. The search for improved stability of LC oscillators began in the 1920s and continued in the 1930s and 1940s. By the mid-1950s, virtually all the basic requirements needed for reasonably stable LC oscillators were understood and suitable circuits developed for use with thermionic valves. Since then, there have been few major developments with most work focused simply on adapting the proven valve circuits for use with solid-state devices, although much more attention has been paid to oscillator noise since the publication in 1953 of the book *Vacuum Tube Oscillators* by W A Edson.

One of the earliest oscillators that provided good stability on HF was the Franklin oscillator developed in the 1920s: **Fig 1**. This used two active devices, providing sufficient gain in the amplifier/phase inversion section to permit very loose coupling to the frequency-determining high-Q LC resonant circuit. The Franklin has several other advantages including the connection of the tuned circuit directly to earth and the use of a two-terminal coil. Curiously, the Franklin oscillator, developed for the Marconi Short Wave Beam system, has never been widely used in the USA where engineers continued to investigate single-valve circuits based on variations of the Hartley and Colpitts oscillators.

The early 1930s, with the coming of higher-gain tetrode and pentode valves, saw the introduction by J R Dow (*Proc IRE*, Vol 19, (1931) pp 2095-2108) of electron coupling within the valve in conjunction with either Colpitts or Hartley oscillators to provide an oscillator much less affected by variations in the HT supplies. The ECO took advantage of the fact that a drop in screen voltage can compensate for a drop in anode voltage. The ECO, as adopted by amateurs, also had the advantage that the tuned anode circuit from which output is taken can be at double the frequency of the frequency-determining resonant circuit, making it easier to achieve good stability.

The introduction of neon-stabilised voltage regulator tubes by the end of the 1930s also made it possible to achieve better stability from basic Hartley and Colpitts oscillators without electron coupling, provided always that the components and circuit parameters were well chosen. It was soon recognised that a high-C tank circuit was particularly important, although this limited the frequency span of the oscillator; no problem for amateur bands but a disadvantage for general-coverage receiver oscillators.

A simple but important modification to the basic Hartley circuit was described by A F Lampkin (Lampkin's Laboratories, Florida and also a radio amateur of 1924 vintage who wrote frequent articles in *QST* in the 1930s) in 'An improvement in constant-frequency oscillators' (*Proc IRE*, March 1939). Surprisingly little advantage has ever been taken by amateurs of his discovery that by simply tapping the grid connection down the coil, the influence of the active device can be reduced

by a factor of ten or more: **Figs 2** and **3**.

Lampkin's idea was however recognised by Walter Van Roberts of the RCA Patents Division, but also, as W3CHO, the first person ever to describe a unidirectional close-spaced rotary Yagi beam antenna (*Radio*, January 1938, pp19-23 & 173). In 'The limits of inherent frequency stability' (*RCA Review*, April 1940) he concluded that to obtain optimum stability from an LC oscillator:

● Make the fundamental frequency as low as possible.

● Make the Q of the coil as large as possible at the fundamental frequency. This means that the coil should be as large physically as there is room for within the shield can, subject to clearance of at least half a diameter, as well as that the coil design should be good in other respects.

● Use the loosest couplings between the tuned circuit and the tube that will give the required output, and use a low enough bias resistor so that the effective transconductance in the oscillating condition is not seriously reduced.

● For the oscillator tube choose one which has a high ratio of transconductance to capacitance fluctuations when operating at the required level.

● Keeping the oscillation strength constant, vary the ratio between the grid and plate couplings. The best ratio depends on the ratio between the capacitance variations of the grid and plate.

These points remain as valid for solid-state devices as for valves. Walter Roberts also advocated as 'tricks of the trade': The use of temperature compensation; supporting the tuned circuit on a single rigid member to avoid bending and vibration of its parts; reducing the power taken from the oscillator as much

as possible and preferably taking output at a harmonic frequency; supplying screen voltage from a voltage divider whose two portions have resistances forming the combination that best compensated for variations in supply voltage, and stabilising the supply voltage.

About 1938, Geoffrey Gouriet of BBC Research developed a series-tuned form of oscillator (**Fig 4**) sufficiently stable to be used as a crystal-substitute for broadcast transmitters. Because of the war, full details of this was not published until after J K Clapp of the General Radio Company had independently developed a similar circuit in 1946, details of which were published in 'An inductance-capacitance oscillator of unusual frequency stability' (*Proc IRE*, March 1948). Clapp later recognised that his oscillator, quickly taken up and widely used by amateurs as the Clapp oscillator, should rightfully be called the Gouriet-Clapp oscillator. He also noted that the same form of oscillator had also been developed independently by O Landini in Italy and described in *Radio Rivista* in 1948. A detailed paper by Gouriet was published in *Wireless Engineer*, April 1950.

E O Seiler, W8PK (later W2EB) described in *QST* (November 1941) a 3.5MHz keyed VFO which he described as a 'low-C electron coupled oscillator' as an alternative to the popular high-C Colpitts oscillator and with a

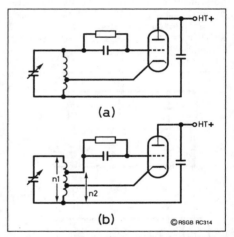

Fig 2: A F Lampkin in 1939 showed that a high-C Hartley oscillator (as typically (used in the once popular ECO VFO) could be improved by a factor of about ten times simply by tapping the grid [gate or base] connection down the coil.

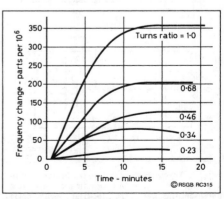

Fig 3: Showing how the long warm-up drift of a Hartley valve oscillator can be much reduced by tapping down the coil. Performance with various ratios of n1:n2 are shown.

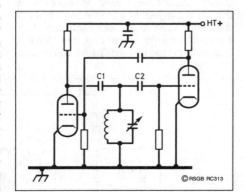

Fig 1: The basic Franklin Master Oscillator, first described in 1930, uses very low value capacitors C1, C2 (about 1 to 3pF) imposing a very light load on the high-Q tuned circuit. Further advantages include the two-terminal inductance, and the earthing of one end of the resonant circuit. This form of oscillator can be readily adapted for use with MOSFET devices.

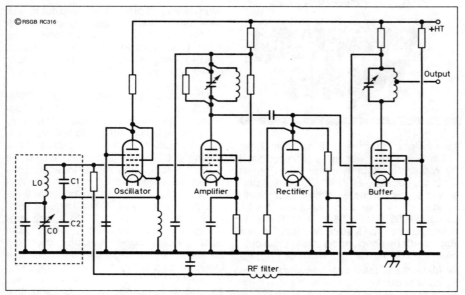

Fig 4: The BBC high-stability master oscillator developed by Geoffrey Gouriet about 1938 but not fully described by him until 1950. The stability obtained is, for all practical purposes, a function only of the parameters of the single tuned circuit at series resonance. The unit provided a one hour stability of the order of ± one part in a million, and ten parts in a million over 24 hours. The same basic oscillator circuit was later developed independently by J K Clapp and published in 1948.

circuit arrangement similar to but different in some respects from the later 'Vackar' or 'Tesla' oscillator develop by the Czech engineer Jiri Vackar who worked for the state-owned Tesla organisation. Vackar developed his oscillator circuit in 1945. It was described with English-text in *Tesla Technical Reports*, December 1949.

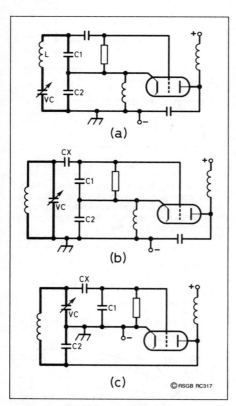

Fig 5: Three high-stability oscillator circuits showing the minor, but significant, differences between them: (a) Gouriet-Clapp with series resonance; (b) Seiler low-C Colpitt's oscillator with parallel resonance. (c) The Vackar oscillator in which the ratios C2:CV and C1:Cx should both be about 1:6.

The Gouriet-Clapp, the Vackar (Tesla) and W8PK's Seiler oscillators (**Fig 5**) were analysed by J K Clapp in *Proc IRE*, August 1954 ('Frequency Stable LC Oscillators') suggesting that the good frequency stability range of the Vackar extends over a tuning range of 2.5:1 compared with 1.8:1 for the Seiler and 1.2:1 for the Gouriet-Clapp, thus awarding the edge (at least for receiver applications) to the Vackar. In March 1955, Tesla submitted a report on the Vackar oscillator to the CCIR SG1, Document 57E, pointing out that the high frequency stability was accompanied by low harmonic content.

The first publication in an amateur journal was by David Deacon, G3BCM, *RSGB Bulletin*, March 1956, pp3471-2 ('The Tesla Oscillator') reproducing information on the precautions required to achieve high stability. Unfortunately, somewhere along the path from Czechoslovakia to Brussels to the UK there was an unfortunate mix-up with the result that G3BCM inadvertently transposed the suggested values for Cx and C1 of **Fig 5(c)**. These should have a ratio of about 1:6 to provide an impedance step-down from the resonant circuit to the active device. This quite serious error, which impaired stability, was reproduced in the *RSGB Amateur Radio*

Handbook (3rd edition, pp 169-70) and also in several designs published in the 'Bull'. It was not until 1965-66 that the error was spotted and corrected by W H ('Bert') Allen, G2UJ, and Lyell Herdman, G6HD, (see correspondence in the 'Bull', January and March 1965).

In September 1966 in a reply to E Chicken, G3BIK, I drew attention to the differences between the Seiler and Vackar designs. A Seiler-type oscillator using a bipolar transistor was designed by W3JHR in the early 1960s and became popular as the 'synthetic rock VFO': **Fig 6**.

By then bipolar transistor and FET devices were being used for Vackar type oscillators, although many designs continued (and still continue) to neglect another requirement of the Vackar for optimum stability and minimum harmonic content: the need to use a relatively high capacitance across the tuned circuit. Indeed one of the very few Vackar oscillators that meet all the original requirements for optimum performance was the FET design by Peter Martin, G3PDM, published originally in *TT*, (December 1969, pp846-847) and since reproduced in a number of other RSGB publications including *Amateur Radio Techniques* 7th Edition (pp166-167) and *Radio Communication Handbook* (4th Edition, pp 4.27 and also the new 5th Edition).

The G3PDM Vackar design (**Fig 7**), although now 25 years old, remains possibly the most stable LC oscillator ever described for home construction. His design intended as a tuneable local oscillator covering 5.88 to 6.38MHz in a double conversion hybrid valve/transistor receiver had a switch-on drift of 500Hz in the first 60 seconds (caused by the gate-source capacitance changing as the 2N3819 junction FET achieved thermal stability) and thereafter a drift of only about ± 2Hz per 30 minutes, that is about 3 parts in 10-million! As for all LC oscillators, the mechanical stability and correct choice of good-quality components is as important no matter which basic oscillator configuration is used.

To achieve the sort of stability quoted, G3PDM listed 15 points to watch. An updated version is given below:

● Strongly recommend the genuine Vackar circuit, ie with C1/(C4 + C6) = C3/C2 and both approximately 6:1 [C4 + C6 should have sufficient capacitance to form a high-C tuned circuit. In the original Vackar prototype covering frequencies around 1.7MHz, a 1000pF trimmer was used across the coil. The Seiler is a low-C

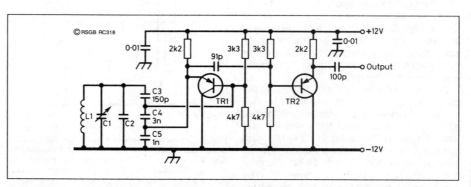

Fig 6: W3JHR's 'synthetic rock' popular transistor VFO of the early 1960s was an adaptation of the Seiler oscillator. In the original design, W3JHR used high-quality components from the American surplus ARC5 equipment. Transistors were 2N384 but similar later devices can be used.

configuration, the Vackar high-C - *G3VA*].

- Use a FET rather than a valve; they are more stable, last longer, use the same circuits, and are cheaper. [But note that solid-state devices are more affected by changes in the ambient temperature than valves once these have fully warmed up - *G3VA*].

- Use a strong box (die-cast or better).

- Use a high-quality variable capacitor. The so-called straight-line-frequency (SLF) laws are for a tuning range of 2:1 and not useful for normal amateur use. However Jackson Type U101 (or surplus RF-26 type) capacitors provide an almost perfect SLF law when tuning 500kHz in this circuit.

- To reduce the heating effect of the RF currents in C2, this should be an air-spaced trimmer; this allows adjustment of feedback so that the circuit just oscillates, reducing harmonic output and drift due to interaction of harmonic energy.

- All variable capacitors should be effectively cleaned, preferably in an ultrasonic bath, before using (G3PDM stressed this really makes a difference).

- Preferably use (continuously) adjustable temperature compensation. Originally G3PDM used an Oxley 'Tempatrimmer' or the lower cost Oxley 'Thermo Trimmer' with a more restricted range of compensation. [These appear to be no longer available. Suitable temperature coefficient capacitor(s) may have to be chosen by trial and error. Alternatively if a differential capacitor is available as shown in **Fig 8(a)** or with conventional trimmers as in **Fig 8(b)** - *G3VA*].

- C1, C3 and C6 should be silvered-mica types, Aralated to surrounding solid object (this reduces 'warbling' during a 'mallet test'.

- The gate resistor should be a 2-watt solid carbon type for minimum heating and low inductance.

- Use of a buffer/isolating amplifier is essential. With a feedback pair, the gain is readily adjusted while negative feedback maintains low harmonic content.

- Circuits using a diode from gate to earth for rectification outside the FET appear to increase drift.

- Power supplies must be very well stabilized, and disc ceramic by-pass capacitors should be liberally used to prevent unwanted feedback along the supply rails. [Note modern IC regulators would be an improvement on the use of Zener diodes - G3VA].

- Oscillator components around the tuned circuit (L, C1,2,3,4,6, R1 and FET source) should have a single common earthing point. (This usually means using one of the fixing screws of C4).

- Ceramic coil formers are preferred. An iron dust core facilitates VFO calibration, but ferrite cores must be avoided.

- Keep leads short, and use stiff wire (16 or 18SWG) for interconnections in the oscillator tank circuit.

G3PDM added that performance achieved

THE MULTEE QUARTER-WAVE FOLDED DIPOLE

RECENTLY IN DISCUSSING folded dipole antennas, I mentioned that I had not come across the concept of a quarter-wave folded dipole with high-impedance feed until following up a reference to the original American TV-sound antenna erected on the Empire State Building in the late 1930s. Memory is fallible - I now realise that the dual-band W6BCX Multee (**Fig 11**), described in *TT* over 30 years ago and reproduced in all editions of *Amateur Radio Techniques* (but in which an error has crept in giving the feed impedance of the λ/4 element as 600Ω instead of up to 6000Ω although this does not affect the dimensions or matching) has the top radiator (as used on the higher of the two bands) in the form of a λ/4 folded dipole, fed from 50Ω coaxial cable by means of the vertical section which forms a linear impedance transformer on the higher band while acting as a top-loaded vertical radiator on the lower band.

This antenna, described in various editions of *The Radio Handbook*, is claimed to form a compact antenna which can be used 'with excellent results on 1.8/3.5MHz (with 52ft vertical section and 70ft span) and 3.5/7MHz (with 28ft vertical section and 35ft span). The 'feedline' should be held as vertical as possible, since it radiates vertically polarized signals on the lower (fundamental) frequency. A good 'earth' system, preferably of buried or elevated radials, is desirable for the lower-frequency band but of little importance on the higher band with horizontally-polarized radiation from the λ/4 'top'.

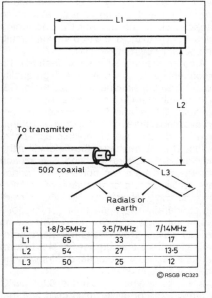

ft	1·8/3·5MHz	3·5/7MHz	7/14MHz
L1	65	33	17
L2	54	27	13·5
L3	50	25	12

© RSGB RC323

Fig 11: The Multee two-band antenna using L1 as a λ/4 0 folded dipole on the higher band, with the high feed-impedance (up to 6000Ω) provided by L2 acting as a linear transformer (λ/2 times velocity factor).

included: resetability - after switching off for 12 hours, returns to within 10Hz of previous frequency; voltage stability (without zener diode or other voltage regulation), 10% change in supply results in shift of 8Hz; G3PDM standard mallet test results in average shift of 6Hz; scale linearity - maximum error over 500kHz band, 12kHz 'without any codging'.

American amateurs have been relatively slow to adopt the European Vackar circuit. However, a number of articles have appeared in the American magazines since the 1970s, although few seem to have appreciated that the Vackar, unlike the Seiler, really requires a

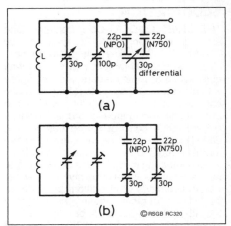

Fig 8: How adjustable temperature compensation can be achieved without the special Oxley devices. (a) With a differential capacitor; and (b) with two conventional trimmers.

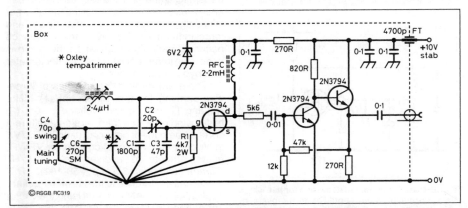

Fig 7: The high-stability FET Vackar oscillator covering 5.88 to 6.93MHz developed by G3PDM in the late 1960s but still a valid design for HF VFOs for receiver, transmitter and transceiver applications.

high-C tank circuit. This factor is still missing from an otherwise useful article 'The Vackar High-Stability L-C Oscillator' by Floyd E Carter, K6BSU (*CQ*, June 1994). He uses a dual-gate MOSFET (40673 or SK3050) and gives component values for tuning 4.0 to 4.3MHz: **Fig 9**. Although he gives impressive performance figures, it seems likely that these could be improved simply by reducing the inductance of L1 and adding considerably more capacitance to the trimmer C2 and tuning capacitor C3 to make it a true Vackar circuit, and possibly by removing D1.

Among the constructional features he recommends is the use of a high-quality double-bearing air variable capacitor for C3, with the trimmer C2 also a ceramic-base air variable. C1, 4 and 5 are made up from parallel capacitors adding up to the required value since the use of multiple capacitors reduces the RF heating of the dielectric in the individual capacitors. C1 and 5 are each implemented from two polystyrene capacitors, while C4 is a combination of an NPO ceramic and a silver mica capacitor, providing temperature compensation for the positive temperature coefficient of L1. This seems an odd way of providing temperature compensation since the purpose of C4 is to form part of a capacitive potential divider with the effect of tapping down G1.

In his prototype, he used a 62pF NPO ceramic with 8pF silver mica but I feel that G3PDM's use of a trimmer adjusted to just beyond oscillation together with temperature compensation directly across the tuned circuit should prove the better approach. For supply regulation, K6BSU uses an adjustable IC regulator type LM317 set to provide 12V, although he found that the circuit oscillated well with 7V supply. He recommended following the oscillator with a high input impedance Class A buffer amplifier. The use of a diode (D1) between gate and source of the MOSFET to provide a form of AGC is common practice but has been criticised by some designers. An effective AGC system (as used for example in the original Gouriet BBC VFO) is undoubtedly beneficial; a simpler arrangement has been proposed for use with a dual-gate MOSFET Vackar oscillator (**Fig 10**) although I have not heard of this being used in practice.

1:1 BALUNS - FURTHER ELUCIDATION

THE BRIEF QUOTATIONS from the long article in the April 1994 *CQ* magazine by W2FMI (*TT*, August 1994, pp44-46) concluded with the comment that W2FMI was quite sure that some readers would disagree with his views. Certainly his rather dogmatic criticisms of baluns other than his favoured bifilar toroidal designs based on the Guannella current balun concept stirred Les Moxon, G6XN to put a seemingly incontestable case for trifilar rod and toroidal types. He writes:

"In comparing my own considerable experience of baluns as set out in my *HF Antennas for All Locations* (2nd edition, pp56-60 includes considerable updating) published by the RSGB there appears to be little common ground with the views of W2FMI. I rest my case on the excellent performance of the 1970s KW balun, an early, low-cost design using a single-layer trifilar winding on ferrite

rod in full conformity with KISS principles. Far from observing any poor high or low frequency responses, I found the SWR was close to unity over the entire range from 3.5 to 30MHz; moreover it was remarkably tolerant of mismatch. See also the views of Ian White, G3SEK, as set out in his excellent article on baluns in the December 1989 *RadCom*.

"It is instructive to try to trace conflicting views on the reason for the failure of many early (and some later) balun designers to recognise the over riding importance of leakage inductance, an error *not*, repeat *not*, made by KW Electronics whose baluns first came to my notice in 1971. W2FMI's views on some 1:1 baluns are fully in line with my experience of one widely advertised balun kit (Amidon) which falls (or fell) into this error, although the fault is easily remedied as described in the 2nd edition (p58 col 2 and top of p59 col 1) of my book. A balun is not always needed but this is rarely a safe assumption (see my Fig 4.36 and related text), and the need for a tertiary winding is clearly demonstrated by J J Nagle, K4KJ (*Ham Radio*, February 1980).

"My view that SWR within the balun is usually not important appears to lack supporters but rests firmly on the assumption (admittedly not valid if one tries to cover four octaves with a single balun) that the line length is so short that it can be treated as a fragment of lumped circuit; as I have shown

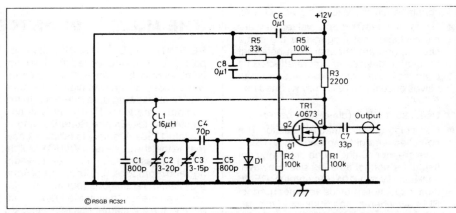

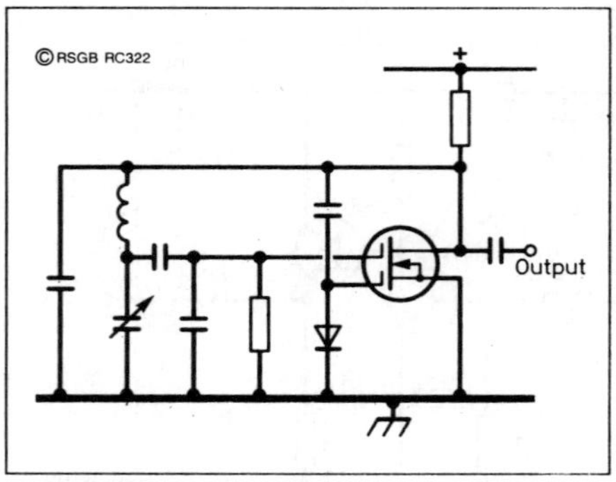

Fig 9: A recent 4.0 to 4.3MHz oscillator design by K6BSU. It seems likely that performance could be improved by increasing the value of C2 + C3 and decreasing that of L1 to make it a true Vackar oscillator. Component information recommended by K6BSU. C1, C5 800pF polystyrene (see text). C2 air trimmer for setting calibration. C3 air variable for main tuning. C4 70pF made up of NPO ceramic + silver mica to provide required temperature compensation. C7 33pF NPO ceramic. C6, C8 0.1µF 25V monolithic capacitor. TR1 40673 or SK3050 dual-gate MOSFET. D1 1N4153 or 1N914 silicon signal diode. L1 16µH 34 turns No 26 enam on 3/4in diameter ceramic form (no slug core) winding length 0.6in. All resistors 0.25W, 5%.

(2nd Edition, page 56) this and the transmission line approach used by G3SEK give the same answer as regards line imbalance, and both demand closest-possible spacings in the specially important case of low-impedance loads. I am not clear as to the reasons why W2FMI wants to cover 2-30MHz with the same balun."

Nic Hamilton, G4TXG, is also concerned that there is evidently still some confusion about 1:1 baluns and the third wire. He writes:

"There are two types of true balun as defined by W7EL in 'Baluns: What they do and how they do it' (*The ARRL Antenna Compendium Vol 1*): (1) the voltage balun, which forces the potential difference at its output terminals to be equal in magnitude and opposite in phase with respect to ground; and (2) the current balun, which forces currents through its output terminals to be equal in magnitude and opposite in phase.

"The two-wire 'balun' has been christened a 'sortabalun' by W6DEZ (see *Solid State Design for the Radio Amateur* by W7ZOI and W1FB, pp55-6). The two-wire 'balun' is a 'sorta current balun': when it is connected to a balanced load, the 'live' conductor carries a slightly greater current than the 'earth' conductor due to additional current through the magnetising inductance and resistance. This bias can be corrected by connecting a third wire between the 'live' output and ground.

"When the two-wire 'balun' is used on a transmitting antenna, the effects of this imbalance are very small, because the transformer is usually arranged to have small losses and large inductance. However, the imbalance becomes very important when the balun is used in an impedance bridge, a reflectometer or a hybrid transformer.

"There are three different types of three-wire winding for the 1:1 balun: (1) trifilar winding (Turrin): a true voltage balun; (2) bifilar winding with a third wire on a different core: a true current balun, as used by DJ7VY in 'Wideband directional coupler for VSWR-measurements on receiver systems' (*VHF Communications, 3/83*, pp158-162). [This article has a reference to the Hewlett Packard application note AN86, p11 'Using the vector impedance meters'. If anyone has one, G4TXG, 78 High Street, Henlow, Bedford-

Fig 10: Possible simple AGC system for use with a Vackar oscillator which should be an improvement over a diode connected directly between gate and source. D1 any good quality RF silicon diode.

shire, SG16 6AB would much appreciate a copy]. (3) Bifilar winding with a third wire on the same core (Ruthroff), a voltage balun at low frequency, a current balun at high frequency, and a 'sorta goodness knows what' in between."

CLEANING AND ADJUSTING SEMI-AUTOMATIC ('BUG') KEYS

'DOC' WESCOMBE-DOWN, VK5HY/ VK4CMY, believes that a straight hand keys and bug-keys are the only true Morse senders around - the electronic keyers and keyboard Morse generators have dehumanised the basic skill of Morse code, which is the making and spacing of characters, numbers and symbols correctly by hand".

While I guess that this is today a minority opinion it is true that "seasoned CW operators take pride in the upkeep and adjustment of both straight and bug keys, this never being seen as a chore but the key element in the formation of Morse." In *Amateur Radio*, July 1994, pp11-12, VK5HY provides detailed information on maintaining and adjusting semi-automatic keys, and the following information has been abstracted from his article:

He stresses that no two operators key exactly the same way and that the most important aspect is correct adjustment of the key for sending well-formed dots (dits). Again, just as a person's handwriting changes so does the 'feel' of the key change, so that you need to be able to adjust it to suit your current keying. Fig 12 shows the usual adjustment points of most makes of semi-automatic keys. Note that some experimenting with the following adjustments may be needed.

- Adjust both the left and right trunnion screws so that the vibrator arm (pendulum) lies perfectly straight and butts lightly against the damper wheel. This sets the initial 'hands off' key position.
- Slide the speed weight(s) on the vibrator arm to the end position giving the slowest dot speed. Tighten the weight(s) ensuring they do not contact the damper wheel.
- Hold the flat thumb paddle in the constant dot position and adjust the left trunnion screw so that the vibrator dot can move to the left about 0.4mm (1/64 inch). Use a small scale rule to check. Then tighten the left trunnion screw.
- Hold the paddle for steady dots and allow the vibrator arm to stop vibrating. Now adjust the dot contact screw (on the dot post) so that the contact just makes firm connection with the vibrator dot, giving steady tone from your monitor. Tighten contact screw and release paddle.
- To check dot adjustment, hold paddle to activate string of dots - there should be at least 40 dots for each paddle movement, if necessary repositioning dot contact screw to obtain this. When the vibrator arm stops oscillating, the vibrator dot should come to rest lightly touching contact screw.
- With two speed weights, to speed up dot rate, slide the innermost weight towards the paddle end. Always keep the outermost weight at end of vibrator arm, regulating dot speed with innermost weight.

- For dash adjustment, position dash contact for a lateral movement of 0.4 to 0.8mm (1/64 to 1/32 inch). Typically, thickness of a sheet of typing paper or a business card. Movement is a matter of personal preference, but the smaller the spacing the better the feel of the key.
- Adjustment of spring tensions is a matter of personal preference. Typical about one third of the tension available. The less tension, the easier the feel. It depends on whether you have a 'light' or 'heavy' arm action.
- Some users have been seen to use finger touch operation similar to that preferred by some users of electronic keyers. However, the bug key was developed to prevent 'glass arm' in protracted operation. VK5HY suggests "set the key side on to you (ie vibrator arm longways to the front of your body) located directly in front of the shoulder of your non-keying arm and rest the non-keying forearm parallel to the key. Also rest the keying forearm flat on desktop so your body weight is taken evenly by both forearms. The key is now operated by wrist rotation towards (dashes) and away (dots) from your body front. This posture immobilises whole arm action and encourages rolling of the wrist - just as with a straight key, wrist action produces rhythmical Morse, not 'nerve Morse'. Once this basic action is acquired, the bug can be repositioned to suit individual situations."

On the subject of key maintenance, VK5HY recommends periodic inspection of the condition of gold or silver contacts. They should be clean and bright. Place clean typing or copying (bond) paper between the contacts and pull it through several times to wipe the contacts. Use switch contact cleaner also but *no*, repeat *no*, matchbox striker paper, wet'n'dry paper, or any abrasive cleaner such as Brasso or Silvo. These should be used only when attempting to resurrect badly pitted and burned contacts although it is better to have new contacts or re-plate old ones. If you do wish to resurrect pitted contacts use (1) very fine emery paper; (2) very fine wet'n'dry paper; (3) crocus cloth or toothpaste on a polishing cloth; (4) bond paper.

To remove leftover polishing debris, use cotton buds and rubbing alcohol or petrol. Clean the areas thoroughly. Don't use CRC, or sewing machine oil, etc on a bug as these attract lint and dust. Use tiny dabs of silicone

lubricant at pivot points. When not in use keep the key in a dust cover.

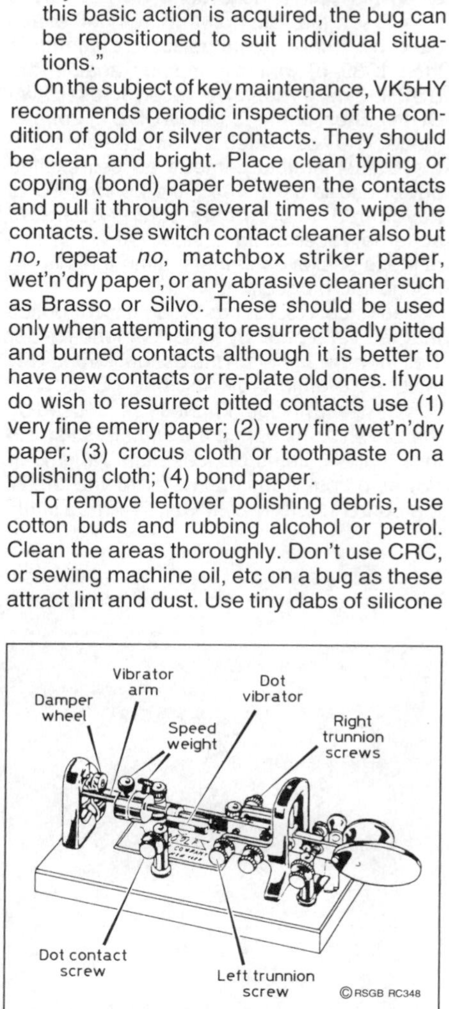

HERE & THERE

PERRY CRABILL, W3HQX (*QST*, August 1994, pp68-69) draws attention to RF interference caused by household electronics, including some TV sets, VCRs, cordless phones, fax machines and even the Kenwood R-5000 general-coverage receiver *when turned off*. The usual problem is that with remote-controlled equipment, the switching-mode type power-supplies remain on when the equipment is in a stand-by mode, radiating harmonics primarily at low frequencies (long- and medium-waves).

The June *CQ* magazine reports the deaths of two well-known amateurs: Captain Paul H Lee, USN (Rtd), N6PL "a veritable fount of antenna and communications information" whose articles and books on vertical antennas are read world-wide"; and also that of well-known DXer and author Katashi Nose, KH6IJ (one time K6CGK).

Drawing on information supplied by IOD (Station Road, Crewkerne, Somerset TA18 7AR), Martin Eccles in 'Applying Crystals' (*Electronics World + Wireless World*, August 1994, pp659-663) provides a useful round-up of general-purpose crystal oscillator designs and practice - both discrete component and logic-gate based - covering oscillators from VLF to VHF.

In the May *TT*, in the item 'Working with balanced line' I mentioned the increasing use in the USA of 450Ω 'windowed' (ladder) cable but added that such cable "does not seem to be advertised in the UK but would clearly simplify the use of balanced feeders." Les Hawkyard, G5HD, points out that 450Ω ribbon feeder has been available for some time from W H Westlake of Holsworthy, Devon (see *RadCom*, May 1994, p17).

G5HD adds: "As an enthusiastic user of open-wire feeders I have tried various matching units and note that some care is needed to avoid power loss in some of the ATUs often advocated for balanced lines. Using the ferrite or iron-dust-cored transformer; split or not, in each feed line produces enlightening results. In particular those using a balun followed by an 'L' match as suggested in *QST* and *G-QRP* seem to result in the RF in the feeder being about 60% down on the usual parallel-tuned unit."

Pat Painting, G3OUC, draws attention to the press and broadcast publicity given to the development by Trevor Baylis of a radio receiver powered from a clockwork motor, giving some 20 minutes operation from a single winding of the motor. Such a receiver could be of value in countries where the cost of batteries tends to limit the use of radios. G3OUC assumes that the clockwork motor drives a small alternator of the rotating permanent magnet type, the output passing through diodes and then a regulator to provide about half-watt DC at about 9V. He feels it could provide a unique challenge to QRP operators to make the first 'clockwork-driven' transceiver contact! I recall in my youth having a toy steam-engine which could drive a small electric generator giving sufficient output to light a small pilot-bulb so that it could well be possible to make either clockwork- or steam-radio QSOs.   *G3VA*

Fig 12: Adjustment points as found on most semi-automatic ('bug' or 'speed') keys.

MILITARY AND CLANDESTINE RADIOS OF WW2

RECENTLY, ALONG WITH Graham Phillips, G3XTZ, (who kindly provided transport), Geoff Voller, G3JUL and Jimmy Bolton, G3HBN, I paid my first visit to the Royal Signals Museum at Blandford, Dorset. Over the years, this collection of equipment and memorabilia has grown into a truly impressive display. Not only does this museum contain most of the transmitters used by Signals in WW1 and WW2, but many items of special clandestine equipment and those of the Special Air Service (SAS) in the post-war period. There are also a few of the German Abwehr 'agentfunken' that were used to send messages back to Germany under Allied control.

I was especially interested to see such transmitters as the Whaddon Mk 10 which used an 813PA to deliver an output of some 150 watts, and the Mk 33, the later version of the ubiquitous Whaddon Mk 3 (6V6-807) 30-watt transmitter. SOE and the London Polish equipment are also well represented, although, as for Whaddon, there still seem to be some gaps. This could be filled by donations from those wondering what they should do with ageing equipment while perhaps not anxious to see them all departing to private collectors on the other side of the Atlantic. Someone must surely be able to dig out an example of the simple Mk VII (Paraset) transmitter-receiver (**Fig 1**), one of the mainstays of Intelligence and de Gaulle's BCRA Resistance networks in France and the Low Countries - or the pocket Sweetheart (Type 31/1) receiver designed in 1942 by the Norwegian engineer, Willy Simonsen, at the Polish Radio Centre. Around 50,000 of these sets where built by Hale Electric. Sweetheart was a straight three-valve receiver using the then new 1T4 1.4V battery valves.

The 'Sweetheart' was not the first clandestine equipment built in the pocket type metal containers, later used by SOE for the Type 51/1 mains-operated transmitters and by the London Poles for their OP-3 superhet receivers (Photo on page 61). This form of container seems to have originated with the Abwehr super-regenerative ground-to-air radio-telephone of 1939/40 using British Hivac midget valves, a concept that was soon copied in a

Pat Hawker's

Technical Topics

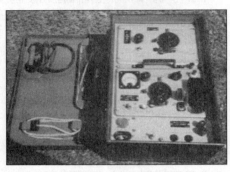

Can any reader identify the Service for which this equipment was built and when? Its purpose? The receiver appears similar to that used in the 68P Airborne/Paratroops man-pack. The transmitter is marked 'Sender SST Mk II' made by MICO Company Ltd of London.

different form in the UK for the widely-used 350MHz S-phone. The first HF equipment using this type of pocket container appears to have been the 'Stumpf' and 'Kynnel' series used by Finnish reconnaissance agents in their 1939/40 winter campaign against the USSR. The three-valve receiver used two DF11 battery pentodes and a DDD11 double-triode. The associated transmitter had a single DLL21 double-pentode as self-excited power oscillator. In 1945, the London Poles developed a prototype mains-operated superhet-receiver/transmitter (AP-7) in two of these pocket containers, although this did not go into production.

Ted Price, G3JPP has brought to my notice that the 1953 book by Major General Nalder *British Army Signals in the Second World War* includes a table providing brief "Data concerning the Principal Wireless Sets" used by the British Army during the war. This lists no less than 46 items of equipment ranging in power output from 0.2 watts to the 10kW Marconi S 11E (3 - 22.2MHz), used as a static

long-range station for high speed keying. The better known SWB 8E ('Swab 8') with an output of 3.5kW, (an example of which is in the Royal Signals museum), was used in the Golden Arrow mobile station.

The table includes four long-range items of equipment; nine medium-range sets (including the No 12HP, No 33, No 52, No 53 and the No 63 (1kW for teleprinter traffic); eight short range vehicle sets; 11 short-range man-pack sets; five armoured fighting vehicle sets; two armoured fighting vehicle intercommunication sets (including the No 19B set on about 235MHz); three radio link sets (including the 4.4GHz No 10 multiplexed set providing 8 duplex speech channels); three anti-aircraft sets; and two ground-to-air sets including the TR1143 normally associated with the RAF. Thus anybody attempting to build up a complete collection of WW2 Army sets would have a long way to go - and the Nalder list does not include any of the special sets for clandestine links etc.

The mention in the September *TT* of the No 10 set with its pulse-width-modulation has reminded Ian Waters, G3KKD, (who joined Pye in 1948) that the company used the experience gained with the No 10 set to develop a 'Videosonic' TV sound system. This used a single 10,125kHz (line frequency of the 405-line system) audio pulse placed in each line blanking interval. The idea was to remove the need for a separate sound transmitter. The system was proposed to the BBC in time for the restart of the 405-line TV service.

While the system was turned down on the grounds that the pulse rate would limit the audio bandwidth to about 5kHz, it seems likely that the BBC/GPO were primarily concerned not to make obsolete surviving pre-war sets (probably a few thousand of the 20,000 sets sold between 1936-39). The fate of the system was sealed when, during a demonstration to industry chiefs, one receiver went out of line-hold. This caused the audio gate to sweep across the video information and produce a long loud 'raspberry'.

It may also be worth recalling that EMI offered a 605-line system which, if it had been adopted, would have almost certainly become the European standard. This would have eliminated the trauma of the much later change over from 405 to 625 at a time when

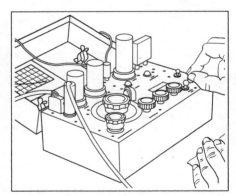

Fig 1: The Whaddon Mk VII/2 'Paraset' clandestine transmitter-receiver widely used between 1941-44. Drawing reproduced by courtesy of Pierre Lorain, F2WL from his book *Secret Warfare* (Orbis Publishing, 1983). Circuit diagram and panel layout diagrams were given in *TT*, November 1982, p961). The transmitter was a 6V6 crystal oscillator. The receiver used two 6SK7 valves in a straight (regenerative) circuit covering about 3 to 8MHz.

The HRO Senior receiver with bandspread coils and glass valves now in the possession of PA0SE.

Polish OP-3 MW/2.5/5-12MHz superhet receiver in the type of pocket containers used in a number of war-time clandestine equipments (about 7x5x1 inches).

there were millions rather than a few thousand sets; 605 lines would also have significantly increased the audio bandwidth if combined with the Pye Videosonic proposal.

G3KKZ points out that if the system had been further developed and adopted it would

have greatly simplified the design of TV transmitters and reduced their cost. It would have been particularly beneficial for transposers for local relays where the linear amplification of a combined vision and sound signal, without undue intermodulation, has always presented difficulties. The Videosonic system was resurrected in the 1960s by TV amateurs in the Cambridge area and used successfully to provide a sound channel for the 405-line AM 70cm TV transmissions then in use.

One curiosity was that if video was faded to black, leaving only sync and audio-modulated pulse, anyone tuning a communications receiver would find an audio signal every 10kHz across several MHz of the band! The sound-in-sync system used by the BBC for many years to convey mono and now stereo along programme links (and the basis of the present Nicam system) can be seen as a direct descendant of the Videosonics system but using high bit-rate digital pulse-code-modulation (PCM) rather than analogue pulse-width-modulation.

I took along to the Royal Signals Museum a photograph (on page 60) sent me by Staf Keustgers, ON5RE, of a boxed equipment that is proving difficult to identify. It may date from the immediate post-war period since it uses the American FT-type crystals that were not widely used in British equipment before 1945 (an exception was the SOE Type 51/1 pocket transmitter mentioned earlier). The receiver closely resembles that in the No 68P parachute man-pack used by airborne forces in 1944, developed from the earlier No 18 set. However the transmitter labelled 'Sender Set SST MK II' and made by 'MICO Ltd of London' is not the one used in the No 68P equipment.

The PSU is suitable for mains or car-battery operation.

The SST-1 was the main OSS (American) suitcase transmitter but the SST Mk II equipment is clearly British. The suggestion has been made (based on the panel colour and what appears to be a waterproof container) that it could be Naval or Royal Marine equipment rather than clandestine equipment. I wonder if anyone can identify the equipment, its application, date of manufacture or supply information on 'MICO Ltd'?

The discovery by GI2FHN that the classic HRO dial was based on the 1934 patent issued to W G Harding and the Sperry Gyroscope Company - a British subject and firm - was of particular interest to Dick Rollema, PA0SE, who recently inherited from the late PA0ID a vintage HRO receiver. He has cured some instability in the IF amplifier by replacing the 300Ω cathode resistor for the 2nd IF valve shown in the circuit diagram with the original 2.5kΩ resistor, making the amplifier perfectly stable with plenty of receiver gain.

PA0SE is so charmed by the ingenious HRO tuning dial and gear drive that he plans to use such a unit for a new 1.8-28MHz transceiver that he is planning. He has obtained one from a wartime German copy of the HRO made by the firm Koerting who in 1939-41 were able to import the gear drive with associated capacitors from the USA via Portugal and Spain. The photographs (on pages 60 and 62) taken by PA0SE show the clean lines of the early HRO receivers with glass valves, and a close-up of the dial and drive unit from the German receiver.

Stewart Revell, G3PMJ, was similarly interested in the *TT* note that the RCA AR88

THE SODA PRIMARY CELL

THE APRIL 1994 *TT* drew attention to the large Leclanche air cells used widely in the past for British railway signalling but also used in the 1970s in South Africa as a means of trickle charging smaller nicad cells able to supply intermittently the heavier currents required for operating remote repeater transmitters. These disposable Leclanche zinc-air cells delivered a small continuous current over many months.

Dr Alan Parkes, G7AXW, has sent me photocopies of some pages from the book *Railway Signalling and Communications* published in 1935 which not only covers these AD Wet Cells (220 and 222 types) but also the 'soda cell' form which would seem to have advantages over the AD Wet Cells in being capable of supplying relatively large currents at near-constant voltage over a long period, with a very low internal resistance.

To quote the 1935 text: "The caustic-soda cell is a comparatively modern type of primary cell, employed where a constant voltage is necessary and comparatively large current discharges are required, as in colour-light signalling. Its internal resistance is very low. The capacity of soda cells may be made high whilst keeping the size within such limits that the cells are convenient to handle. The essential

parts of the soda cell are elements of carbon and zinc, immersed in a solution of caustic soda (sodium hydroxide) in water, the carbon being attached to the positive terminal and the zinc to the negative."

After describing the chemical reactions etc, the author continued: "The containers for soda cells are usually of heat-resisting glass; the state of the elements can be seen without removing them from the electrolytic. This has led to the introduction of certain refinements, such as the moulding of a small indicating panel in the zinc which perforates when approximately 90% of the rated capacity of the cell has been expended, thus enabling the maintainer to see at a glance that the zinc needs attention.

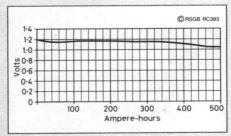

Fig 2: Voltage discharge curve of the large 'Soda' (zinc-air) cells used on the railways from about the mid-1930s.

As a result, the renewal may be carried out before the voltage of the battery is affected, and failures of apparatus are avoided. The open-circuit voltage of the AD 218 cell, of the type just described, is 1.4 to 1.5 volts. Currents up to 3A may be obtained: at 3A approximately 1.08V, at 1A 1.2V; and at 0.5A 1.24V. It is usual to attach the carbon and zinc to the porcelain lid of the cell so that the electrodes may be removed from the cell with a minimum of trouble." **Fig 2** shows the voltage obtainable from a 1935 AD caustic-soda cell on a constant load of 1A. It will be noted that the voltage is practically constant throughout the discharge.

I would imagine that it is this form of zinc-air cell that has been developed in Israel and is now being tried out for electric vehicles by the German Post Office as mentioned in the April *TT* and which one reader appeared to consider an April Fool joke.

[Readers may be assured that having over 30 years ago reproduced a filter in *TT* without realising it was a joke-circuit from an April issue of Radio-REF, and then seen it reproduced from *TT* in several overseas journals, I have a jaundiced view of realistic-looking April-fool technical articles, particularly those with a foreign-language text].

was developed in 1940-1 to meet a British Inter-Services specification (far more AR88s were acquired for amateur use after the war in the UK than in the USA where it has always been quite rare). He bought one of these in 1964 for £45 and it still provides an excellent general-purpose performance, following some careful maintenance. He writes: "About 15 years ago the performance became pretty bad with distortion and poor sensitivity. To cut a long story short, the problems were caused by most of the waxed paper capacitors in the AGC and noise limiter circuits becoming extremely leaky, showing insulation resistance of around 50K to 100K ohms. New polyester 400V capacitors were fitted inside the little metal boxes to replace the original ones. Also, C118 and C132, the audio-coupling capacitors, were changed (each 4700pF). Other waxed paper capacitors in the HT decoupling circuits were replaced (and fitted into their metal boxes). The result was that reception and sensitivity restored to normal and the AR88 fit for another 30 years or so. He also mentions that other owners should check that there is a small voltage across the cathode resistor of the 6SJ7 AF amplifier (V10) as he found this was short-circuited by internal connection of the valve's suppressor grid going to earth.

G3PMJ is puzzled by the style of circuit diagram used by the Americans for the AR88 and many other designs in the 1930-40s in which band-change switches are shown in pictorial rather than theoretical form. It can prove a time-consuming job figuring out where each contact of each wafer goes on each band.

Some years ago I asked the RCA London representative to try and trace some of the background to the design and production of the AR88. He did his best but the firm came up with little information except some leaflets on the post-war CR88 version the high cost of which ruled out amateur use. G3PMJ poses a number of questions and wonders if anyone knows the answers: How many AR88D and AR88LF receivers were built and when [1941-45], and where [not all at Camden NJ I believe - G3VA], cost to British Government, and how many lost in bringing them across the Atlantic due to U-Boats etc, and how many are still giving useful service after 50 years? Ray Moore in 'Communications Receivers' points out that "Most of production sold to England during World War II" and identifies Lester T Fowler as responsible for the electrical design, and George Baker the mechanical design.

A wartime British communications receiver that came near to the performance of the AR88 and HRO was the Marconi CR100 series, of which some 20,000 were produced between 1941 and 1946, with a production rate of 100 per week. One of the design team was Dr G L Grisdale, G5GZ, and he provides a detailed description including background information, full circuit diagram and notes on the associated CR100/2, CR150/3, CR200 (Navy B29) and CR300 models, together with suggestions on how to restore them to full performance, in *Radio Bygones*, No 31, October/November 1994. A feature was the inclusion of both a crystal-filter and a narrowband CW audio filter.

The clean chassis layout and the four-gang tuning capacitor with its PW drive.

144MHZ J-POLE & SLIM JIM ANTENNAS

BACK IN 1978 the late Fred Judd, G2BCX, described in *Practical Wireless*, a low-cost 144MHz vertical antenna based on the classic J-Pole antenna (**Fig 3(a)**) but with a folded element structure along with the integrated matching stub (**Fig 3(b)**). He named this antenna the 'Slim Jim'.

Later, in *TT*, September 1986 (see also *Technical Topics Scrapbook 1985-89*, pp124-5) I noted that a Modified Slim Jim (MSJ) antenna had been described and analysed in *IEEE Transactions on Broadcasting* (March, 1986) by Greek university authors as a suitable antenna for 101.8MHz VHF/FM local sound radio. Computer analysis of the G2BCX design (**Fig 3(b)**) had shown that this provided a 50Ω resistive match at 155MHz rather than the intended 145Mhz, with maximum radiation at about 22° above horizontal. VHF broadcast antennas (and amateur repeaters etc) should ideally radiate most energy at 0° or even slightly tilted downwards since the transmitters are normally located at a high site, serving adjacent lower areas. The Greek MSJ dimensions for 101.8MHz were thus not an exact scaling of those shown in **Fig 3(b)**. The dimensions used were: height 2.21m; leg distance 0.06m; height of gap (beginning) 1.10m; height of gap (ending) 1.25m; height of the feedpoints 0.37m; radius of wire 0.004m. These dimensions could be scaled for 145MHz.

The principle, if not the origination, of the Slim Jim has crossed the Atlantic. In 'More Bang for the Buck - How to build a really cheap but good antenna for 2 metres', Lew Mccoy, W1ICP (*CQ*, July 1994, pp50-51) recounts how, while attending a meeting of the Quarter Century Wireless Association in Palm Springs, he came across a group of local amateurs building Slim-Jim type antennas using ordinary 300Ω twin-wire feeder: "They had had very good luck with the antenna". W1ICP took a note of the dimensions they were using (**Fig 4(a)**) but found it difficult to get a good match for 50Ω; Their suggestion was to wrap a small piece of aluminium foil around the twin lead and then slide it up and down to achieve a match." In the outcome, W1ICP reverted to a design closer to the classic J-pole antenna but retaining the use of twin-wire line for the element, although using 450Ω ladder line rather than the solid 300ohm type: **Fig 4(b)**. He used an ELNEC program for the wire lengths, and then found that he could reproduce similar results (less than 1.5:1 SWR across the American band of 144-148MHz). In the USA the cost of such ladder line is less than 20 cents a foot and, since only 5ft is required, the cost is less than the dollar (buck) of his title.

He writes: "The antenna undoubtedly has good gain as compared to a quarter-wave ground plane and immeasurably more gain than a rubber duck. It is simple to hang one end of the antenna up on a support as high as possible. Also, it would be a good traveller's antenna because it can be coiled up and easily stored in luggage. The antenna connections could be coated with waterproofing material and installed outside. Still another method would be to slip the antenna inside a length of 1 inch PVC and mount the PVC up in the air. There are scores of possibilities . . I think it's pretty hard to beat one dollar or less for a fine-performing antenna."

VHF/HF FOX HUNTING

GLEN RICKARD, KC6TNF, in *QST*, January 1994, described a technique for obtaining accurate directional headings when using a

Close-up of the tuning capacitors and drive as recovered from a German-built copy of the HRO produced by the firm Koerting.

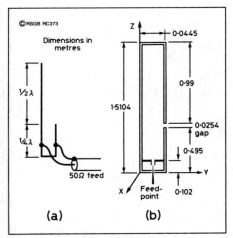

Fig 3: (a) The classic J-Pole antenna provides a vertical half-wave radiating element with quarter-wave matching stub: It rather resembles an inverted form of the original Zepp antenna as patented by Dr Hans Beggerow in 1909 as an antenna for balloons or airships. (b) Dimensions of the original 'Slim Jim' 145MHz antennas described by G2BCX in *Practical Wireless* in 1978, although later computed as resonating about 155MHz.

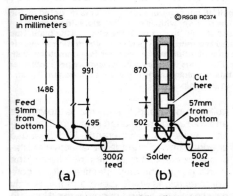

Fig 4: (a) The 300Ω twin-lead Slim Jim antenna as used by a group of Californian amateurs, although W1ICP found it difficult to obtain a good match. (b) The easily reproduced J-pole antenna made from 450Ω ladder line by W1ICP: Flat across 144-148MHz (SWR less than 1.5:1). Found to work very well with hand-held transceivers etc as a fixed or traveller's antenna.

hand-held VHF transmitter using body absorption. An additional simple device is used when near the hidden transmitter to attenuate the very strong signals that can defeat the body fade.

The method of using body fade for direction finding with a 144MHz hand-held transceiver (H-T) is simple. KC6INF writes: "You stand, holding the H-T to your chest, and slowly turn around, looking for a fade in signal strength as your body intervenes between the 'fox' transmitter and the H-T. Your body provides a shield that gives the H-T a cardioid sensitivity pattern, with a sharp decrease in sensitivity ('null') to the rear that indicates the direction of the transmitter: **Fig 5**.

"Unfortunately, it is not always quite that simple. As KC6INF puts it: "Anything that affects signal strength - including transmitter power, distance, receiver sensitivity, or the size and shape of your body - can work to smear or obliterate the null. The body fade null, which is rather shallow to begin with, can be obscured by reflections.

"The solution, according to KC6TNF, is to

use a foil-covered mailing pasteboard (cardboard) tube that acts as a 'waveguide beyond cutoff'. The tube should have sufficient inside diameter to accommodate the H-T. "Cover the tube completely with aluminium (kitchen) foil. If the tube is long enough there may be no need to cover the bottom end of the tube. Since the foil tends to be fragile, it is advisable to protect that by wrapping the foil in packing tape. Also needed is a short stout cord attached to the H-T like a wrist strap."

When an H-T is lowered into the tube, the signal will be attenuated at a logarithmic rate depending on how far the H-T is inside the tube, which forms an 'air attenuator'. In practice, the tube is used to reduce the received signal level until the required cardioid sensitivity pattern is re-established. The procedure recommended by KC6INF is as follows:

"Hold the tube to your chest (vertically), and lower your H-T into it until the signal begins to weaken. Holding the H-T in place, turn around slowly and listen for a sudden decrease in signal strength. If you don't get a good null, vary the depth of the H-T in the tube and try again. Repeat until you get the null that you need to determine the direction. You do not need to watch the S-meter; in fact it will likely be out of sight in the tube. Keep adjusting the depth until you get a sharp null.

"This method of direction finding is highly dependent on your body's particular shielding characteristics. The depth of suspension that works for another person will not necessarily work for you. Experiment until you get a feel for what works best . . . A word of warning about reflections: they can and will obscure or shift the null in unpredictable ways. If you are hunting in a car, step well away from the vehicle before trying to get a bearing. Avoid large buildings, metal fences, metal signposts and the like. Hunting in a crowd of people is nearly useless because many will be tall enough to form good reflectors at 146MHz. Make sure that anyone standing nearby is at least 10 to 15 feet away when you are taking a bearing.

"Precautions against reflections apply, of course, to other more complex VHF D/F techniques. KC6INF points out that a foil covered tube can supply an impressive amount of attenuation; he has obtained a good null while standing less than five feet away from a 30-watt transmitter, by extending the wrist strap with a shoelace to get sufficient depth in the tube.

A letter from O G ('Mike') Villard, W6QYT draws attention to an article 'Simple Equipment for HF Fox Hunting' (*QST*, August 1994, pp33-5) which, in connection with colleagues at SRI International (G H Hagn and J M Lomasney, WA6NIL), he wrote to show how the basic approach used by KC6TNF can be adopted for HF. This offers a simple technique not only for fox hunting on frequencies between about 3 and 30MHz but also for tracing local sources of RFI.

In essence, the principle is to use a compact battery-operated HF (broadcast or communications receiver (eg Sony ICF-7600 or similar, preferably with a BFO) with telescopic whip antenna, mounted on a conductive plate considerably larger than the receiver, using rubber bands to hold the receiver in place, and with a home-made Faraday shield placed around the antenna for close-in work.

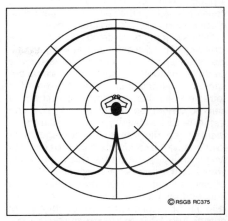

Fig 5: Idealised receive-sensitivity of a VHF hand-held transceiver when using body fade for direction finding. It is important to stand clear of reflective sources and nearby people who can distort the sensitivity pattern.

Such a device works best on ground-wave or local signals but, under some conditions, is capable of nulling sky wave signals, with a performance roughly equal to the long-established technique of using a shielded, single loop. **Fig 6(a)** shows how the receiver is mounted on a conductive plate (aluminium, brass, copper or copper-clad PC-board material, or even a foil covered wooden board) with the whip antenna extended along the diagonal of the square plate, in the plane of the plate.

To quote the *QST* article: "**Fig 6(b)** shows how the receiver's whip is pointed on end with respect to a radio wave. The wave has parallel fronts, so that the whip is aligned so as to be perpendicular to the electric field. No RF current is induced in the whip, except as a result of field distortion caused by the radio itself. If the reradiated energy is electrically symmetrical with respect to the whip, however, the antenna will still null the signal. Fortunately, the radio can be combined with a conductive plate in such a way that the reflected energy is symmetrical. In the null direction (the direction of whip, radio and plate), neither the incident wave nor the backward-directed symmetrical receiver scatter induce signal energy into the whip and the radio. The result is a clean null if there are no additional signal sources present.

"Modern portable SW receivers are thin enough to mount face up on the metal plate. When grounded to the plate, the radio effectively becomes part of the plate. (For best results the receiver ground (earth) should be connected directly to the plate, although receiver-to-plate capacitance will - at least partially - provide a connection in any event.). . ."

"When D/Fing, the plate, receiver and whip must always maintain the same mechanical position with respect to one another. The whip should always lie along a line formed by an extension of a line drawn diagonally across the plate and in the plane of the plate. . . .Arranging for the radio and plate to form a symmetrical structure is complicated by the unsymmetrical mounting of whips on most portable receivers. A plate area 20 to 50% larger than that of the radio usually permits a symmetrical layout. The strings supporting the plate and radio must be nonconducting. The device can be rotated back and forth like a puppet, while being held a foot or so from your body. Attach the radio to the plate with rubber bands attached to cup hooks. . . .

"The swinging plate device works particularly well when the signal is weak. By adjusting whip length, you can to some degree control sensitivity. Sometimes the signal becomes so strong that, even with the whip retracted to the last section, the gain changes can no longer be distinguished. You can further reduce sensitivity by holding the equipment close to the ground. A more elegant way to attenuate the received signal is to cover the whip with a partial Faraday shield. Make the shield in the form of a concentric cage of equally spaced parallel wires grounded at one end to the plate or receiver chassis (**Fig 7**). Cage diameter and length are not critical. About 0.50 to 1 inch diameter is about right. The shield reduces the amount of RF reaching the whip, but doesn't significantly alter directionality, because the whip and the shield are essentially parallel and concentric. The shield can be made from hookup wire taped to a paper cylinder that slips over the whip without electrical contact. A shield of eight wires introduces an attenuation of about 15dB. With more wires, the attenuation is proportionally increased.

"As with a loop, the null occurs when the whip is pointed directly towards or directly away from the transmitter or source of interference. Body absorption, as used by KC6TNF, may help determine the 'sense' of direction or be useful in checking results obtained with the device. If the received signal is so strong that it leaks directly into the receiver circuits, the radio may need to be placed inside a metal cylinder for further attenuation.

SCRAP INDUCTION MOTORS

IN *TT,* JUNE 1994, ZL2AXO described a method of making a 230V AC petrol-electric generator from scrap. Sid Newton, G7RDE was one of the readers who felt uneasy about using a single-phase induction motor as an induction AC generator. In the follow-up notes in the August *TT,* Bruce Carter, GW8AAG, referred to *Electric Motors* by Jim Cox (published by Argus Books). G7RDE wrote to Jim Cox seeking an expert opinion on this unorthodox use of induction motors.

Jim Cox has kindly replied to G7RDE as follows: "You are quite right in assuming that induction motors used as generators normally need to be driven over synchronous speed while connected to a main supply which controls the generated frequency. This is a stable operating condition, small changes in the driven speed control the current delivered to the main supply and it is the main supply that primarily determines the output voltage and frequency.

"If the driven motor is not connected to a main supply but driving a capacitive load, it can still generate output but the output voltage and frequency is unstable and very dependent on the type of iron used in the rotor and the load that the generator is driving.

"The basic characteristic is rather similar to a shunt wound DC generator but with the important difference that there is no independent control of field excitation and the field magnetic path (in this case the rotor) uses a thoroughly unsuitable grade of iron.

"The field path of a DC generator is chosen to be sufficiently magnetically 'hard' (ie the coercive force is high enough) to retain enough residual magnetism to initiate the necessary build up of field strength when the generator is first run up to speed. A magnetically 'hard' material has a large area hysteresis loop and therefore exhibits large hysteresis losses when operated with AC excitation. This is an undesirable characteristic in an induction motor rotor so rotor stampings are normally manufactured from the same material as the stator. This is an electrical grade of silicon iron processed to give the lowest possible hysteresis and eddy current loss. Because of this, there may well be insufficient residual magnetism to allow the induction generator to 'build up' when driving a load.

"In most cases (not all) there is sufficient residual to initiate build up if feeding a purely capacitive load (ie no resistive load) but the output voltage is not controllable and simply rises until the iron circuit saturates. Because of the very high iron losses this is not a practicable generating mode but can be used for regenerative braking (see *Electric Motors*, p96).

"If you are lucky enough to find a machine that retains enough residual magnetism to

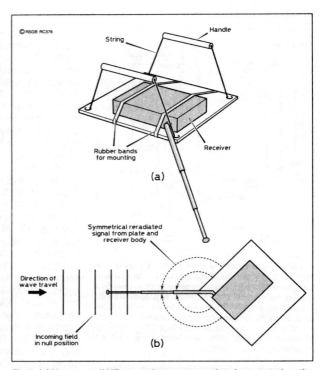

Fig 6: (a) How a small HF general-purpose receiver is mounted on the conductive plate. The receiver whip is extended along the diagonal of the square plate, and should always be in the plane of the plate. Use rubber bands to hold the receiver in place. (b) When the receiver is mounted on the conductive plate, the receiver is symmetrical with respect to the whip. Field lines of the incoming wave are perpendicular to the whip when this is pointed at or away from the transmitter and induce no voltage in the whip.

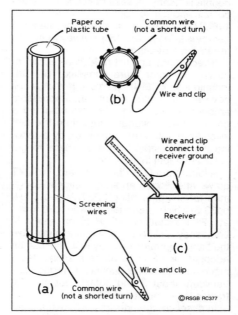

Fig 7: A home-brew Faraday shield over the whip reduces signal pickup and makes directional nulls more apparent on strong or local signals. Wires in the shield are insulated from the antenna by the hollow paper or plastic tube (about 1-in diameter) but connected to the receiver ground through a crocodile clip connected to one side of an external power or antenna connector or headphone jack. (a) Side view of shield. (b) End view. (c) Shield in place.

build up under load, there remains the voltage and frequency regulation problem. The voltage regulation is inherently bad because changes of load change the effective excitation level and this magnifies the effect of the load change. The only effective voltage control available is shaft speed and this is only practicable on a fixed or nearly fixed load. In principle, an external triac voltage regulator could be fitted but this is liable to run into severe stability problems arising from the interaction between output voltage and excitation level.

"Summing up, this type of generator is an interesting curiosity but of extremely limited practical use. If you need a home-brew alternator a better route is to machine away most of the rotor conductors of a motor and replace them as appropriate with a two or four pole field winding plus slip rings. Alternatively it is relatively easy to rewind a car alternator to operate as a low-power, high-voltage alternator." It is only fair to ZL1AXO to mention that he did in fact stress that there could be problems of insufficient residual magnetism and that the poor voltage regulation etc did not permit the use of such a generator to power SSB transceivers which present a widely fluctuating load. It is also now clear that the better the design of an induction motor, the more likely it is that the rotor material may not retain sufficient residual magnetism's to permit it to be run up as a generator under load. However, it is also clear that ZL1AXO's lawn-mower/scrap induction-motor generator is capable of providing a source of AC power for some limited applications without involving modifications.

G3VA

Notes on corrections

1. Simple Superhet diagram, p28. A correction appears on p66.
2. Ceramic resonator oscillator, Fig 7, p68. A correction appears on p82.
3. 28V heavy current PSU, p70. A correction appears on p82.
4. Electronic smog in 'Here and there', p66. A correction appears on p82.
5. DL9WU-type Yagi, Fig 9, p75. A correction appears on p82.
6. Doppler D/F, p 80. A correction appears on p99.
7. 'Sweet spot' 1.8MHz propagation, pp142-144. A correction appears on p154.
8. Toroidal cores defended, p153. A correction appears on p163.
9. GW0GHF MOSFET amplifier, p164. A correction appears on p167.
10. Balanced ATU, p185. A correction appears on p204.
11. Noise cancelling unit, Fig4, p196. A correction appears on p204.
12. Coaxial offcuts and mobile antennas, p208. A correction appears on p219.
13. G3SBI H-mode mixer, p230. A correction appears on p240.
14. Reflectometer diodes, p231. A correction appears on p240.
15. Crystal calibrator, p244. A correction appears on p250.
16. 1296MHz preamplifier, p251. A correction appears on p265.
17. Simple 3.5MHz DC receiver, p216. A correction appears on p265.
18. Heavy Duty (15A) PSU, p253. A correction appears on p270.

Index

The suffix 'n' denotes that the item will be found under the 'Pot Pourri', Here and there', 'feedback', etc headings. 'Corr' denotes that a correction to the item will be found at the page indicated.

A

Amplifiers, power, general
AGC on SSB transmitters 159n
back-EMF diode on relays 33n
big mouth, linearity and splatter 120-121, 135
linears and distorters 6
polar loop technique 295
two-tone testing with old oscilloscopes 102, 134
Amplifiers, audio 278
Amplifiers, power, solid state
20W push-pull FET linear for 50MHz 31-32
200W FM/CW amplifier for 70MHz 207
25W (1.8 - 7MHz) push-pull MOSFET linear 74
boosting the QRP rig 19, 232
KISS 70W power amplifier using VHF bipolar
    transistors 103
MF/HF 25W amplifier, easy to build 267
powerfet amplifier, stable, G3IPV 254-255
switching-FET RF amplifiers 7-8, 24, 28
ultra-linear VHF/UHF amplifiers 272-273
when multiple bypass capacitors may be needed 183
Amplifiers, power, valve
14MHz 50/120W amplifier 212-213
50MHz, using TV line output valves 59n
6146B substitution by 6146 187
beware of costly dust 19
broadband 271
G2DAF linear amplifier 109, 131-132, 225-226, 237
heater voltage regulation 48, 62
high-power 'frinear' linear (3 x PL519) 7-8, 21n, 162
KN5SS's low-drive, high power linear 47-48
linear operating conditions 36
loose pins and over-hot 3-500Z valves 100-101
matched pairs of valves 162-163
project 6L6, 1940 style 291
protecting power tetrodes 11
screen regulated supplies 289
tuning and supply regulation 220-221
vive la lampe de radio 155-156
VHF parasitics 58-59, 95-96
Amplifiers, small signal (see receivers)
Antenna measuring
measuring gain 41
resonant frequency, measured with GDO 265n
Antenna modelling
care and understanding 174n
horizontal loop antennas (real and with Mininec) 42
with ELNEC and MN-PRO 161
Antennas and earths (general)
analysing ground-plane and sleeve antennas 77
antenna lore 35-36
army low-profile loop 33-34
balanced line, working with 267-268
balun 1:1 .... 281-283, 300
balun, choke, 1:1, low cost 197-199
capacitive bottom loading 101
Chireix-Mesny array 10, 17, 28, 36

computer simulated 32-33
corrosion 164n, 215, 229
counterpoise 34, 101-102
dipole centre, simple 180n
earthing braids from scrap coax 198
earthing, low resistance 78
earth losses and vertical antennas . 172-174, 183-184, 201-202
earths, counterpoises
and radials 101-102, 115-116, 131
elevation drive 5
environmental effects on support
    ropes and coaxial cables 119
feeder spreaders 164n
ferrite-bead choke baluns 107
gain and efficiency 145, 161
insulators, temporary 129n
'invisible' and indoor antennas 221-223, 254n
ladder ribbon feeder 301n
made from superconductor 40n
magic of marginal electronics -
    antennas and oscillators 273-275
Mesny - a French pioneer 10
metal fatigue and antenna elements 245
mobile, container for 254n
modelling, Mininec 103-104
monopole loaded with folded dipole 250
prevention of corrosion 82, 90-91
radials, broadband 142
radials, laying 229
resonant meander antennas 130
sleeve baluns 187
static discharge for balloon supported 180n
SWR myths, persistent 182-183, 200
toroidal cores, baluns .... 131, 153-154, corr 163
toroidal helix antennas 274
waterproofing 129n
Yagi arrays, gain optimisation 123
Antennas, direction finding
VHF D/F loop with integral sensing 88
Antennas and earths (HF)
1.8MHz helical vertical dipole 62-63
7MHz dipole on 21MHz 135, 158-159, 167
bi-square array 49
bobtail curtain 156n
commudipole multi-band antenna, PA0SE .. 205-206, 251-252
compact loop, transmitting 111-113
dipoles, multi-band and all-band 202-203
end feeding a windom and related topics 83-84
extended double zepp 150
feeding an 80m delta loop on 1.8MHz 40
folded tee 160
ground-plane close to earth 177
horizontal loop antennas 42, 67-68, 121, 146-147
magnetic loop, dual-band, in the roof space 190-191
mobile, from coax offcuts .... 208, corr 219
multee quarter-wave folded dipole 299
multiband dipole,
    ZS6BKW / G0GSF .... 187-189, 191, corr 204
multibander, the lazy man's 63
multiband or all-band HF antennas? 271-272
multi-wire dipoles and monopoles 295-196

off-centre-fed multi-band dipoles 56-57, 84-85
'quad-loop' antenna, 50-ohm 131, 137
quad-loop, two band 155
square and delta-loop 53-54
steerable 7MHz DX antenna 17
VK2ABQ-type beam 125, 145, 284
W2DU-type current balun 169, 239
W8JK and the new BRD-zapper 43, 96
wire arrays, weather resistant 73

Antennas (mobile)
siting vehicle antennas 126-127

Antennas (receiving)
balanced active receiving loops 116-117
Beverage and his 'wave antenna' 210
phasing out interference .... 195-196, corr 204

Antennas (VHF)
144MHz unipole antenna 125-126
50.1MHz Yagi dimensions .... 74-75, corr 82
Chireix-Mesny array 10, 17, 28, 36
coaxial sleeves, sperrtopf 97
collinear, for VHF/UHF mobile operation 100
effects of the presence of a person 249
end-fed, for handhelds 43, 61

Antenna supports
blow (pipe) up your antenna 157
fishing for antennas with monofilament line 166
keeping antenna supports healthy 2
removing guy rope stakes 148, 163
tree-branch 118, 134n

Antenna tuner (ATU, ASTU, AMU)
3-in-1 antenna tuner and AF meter 15-16
balanced ATU feeds open wire lines 23-24
coil taps, secure 208
let the buyer beware 25n
remote 31n
toroidal cores, baluns and ATUs 131
Z-match, single coil 220, 243-244

Automatic gain control (AGC)
IF-derived, with Plessey ICs 77-78
still a difficult technique 89-90
attenuator 289-290

B

Batteries
air cells - Leclanche and zinc-air 263-265, 296n
alkaline manganese, reusable (RAM) 141-142
care and feeding 16
developments 12-13
electrically stirring electrolyte 144n
gell cells 29-31
lithium, wafer thin 157-158
maintenance-free 260
microminiature fuel cells 31-32
renewable energy 215-218
safety 38, 48-49, 62, 73, 99, 184
secondary, pointers and progress 4-5
small lead-acid, hand helds and 241-243
soda primary cell 303
using aluminium drinks cans 168

Batteries, charging
6 volt 158
555 window detector controls battery charger 58
constant current nicad charging 1
dirty DC charging of
disposable batteries 30, 184, 240n, 249n
'duz everything' PSU / charger 236
KISS constant-current nicad charger 14
secondary batteries: pointers and progress 4-5, 24n
solar power 143

Battery low indicator 238
Battery saver 233
Burglar alarm, home-brew 283

C

Cable, coaxial
coil formers from scraps of half-inch 180-181

elbow connectors - a word of warning 29-30, 87n, 128n
running round a sharp corner 286n
scraps, using 198, 208
storage and handling 187

Capacitors
decoupling, why use two
when one will do? 171, 183, 208-209
electrolytic 209
increasing capacitance of air-spaced 168n
vacuum-variable 25n

Cartesian loop feedback, linear UHF transceiver with 17-19

Clandestine transmitters and receivers
Anglo-Polish 172
B2, the passing of John Brown, G3EUR 203
coils wanted 219
D/F 20-21, 26, 46
homing pigeons 60n
in prison camps 51
military and clandestine radios of WW2 302-304
NEI 29
Polish 35
Sonya's Report 137-139
transmitting Morse key 147

Clarricoats, Peter 66n
Compact disks versus vinyl 254n
Cocktail party effect 286n

Connectors
coaxial plugs, fitting 15
low voltage, making non-reversible 167

Converters
144/28MHz, easy-to-build 45
50MHz, simple 233-234

Cropper, Joe, G3BY, silent key 254

CW (see Morse)

D

Digital techniques
digital communications receivers 132-134
HF receiver, Marconi H2550 294
KISSless future with VLSI / DSP? 189u
practical spread spectrum system 138
speaking in digits 14

Direction finding
Clandestine radio 20-21, 26, 46
144MHz hand doppler DF .... 79-80, 98, corr 99, 123-124
144MHz sniffer DF receiver /
field strength meter 75
fox hunting, VHF / HF 304-305
VHF D/F loop with integral sensing 88, 168n

E

Earth loop feedback 106-107
Earths (see Antennas)
Eddystone Users Group 132

Electromagnetic compatibility (EMC)
capacitive filtering and the EMC Directive 56
compatibility - but with how much power? 211-212
data interference on 144MHz mobile 249
electronic smog .... 66, corr 82
eliminating woodpecker interference? 41
experimental C & R filter / attenuator 223
flammable atmospheres,
EMC hazards and mobile radio 213-214
going mobile - safely 149
induction light bulbs and their
RFI potential 104, 206, 245n
interference from switch mode
PSUs when equipment turned off 301n
phasing out interference 195-196
RF affects test meters,
electronic regulators etc 82, 128n, 135-136
RFI from computers 22, 39-40
satellite TV - a source of reverse TVI 190
VHF noise from rear window heaters 76n

Electronic counter measures 232
Electronics as a hobby, demise of 83, 177-178

Ergonomics
    for visually handicapped people 240n
    small may be beautiful but bigger can be better 91, 194n

F

Filters
    capacitive, and the EMC Directive 56
    crystal, for high performance mixers 246-248, 279-281
    crystal, super-selective for EME etc 290-291
    flexible audio CW 27
    low pass, simple, 14MHz 154n
    shunt-type crystal ladder 108
    strip line, 144MHz to combat data interference 249
Fire and flood damage 180
Front panels
    brushed finish 128
    lettering 128, 158
    Letraset on metalwork 166-167
    matt finish, silver hairline 73-74
    dials, low cost 217, 227

G

Good old days? 115

H

Halligan, William, W9AC, founder of Hallicrafters 185
Hanslope Park 80-82
Health hazards (see Safety)
HF not outdated 293

I

Icom IC-2A owners, a tip for 11
Inductors
    coil formers from scraps of half-inch coaxial cable 180-181
    coil formers from pump-type toothpaste dispensers 265n
    knobbly RF choke 1
    polystyrene solution, d-i-y 224, 224, 232, 233
    stable 63-64
    winding coils on PVC 57-58
Integrated circuit devices
    application specific integrated circuits (ASICs) 37
    KISSless future with VLSI / DSP? 189
    MC3362, a simple HF superhet using 72
    MSM6322, improved signal to noise 245n
    NE602, getting the best from 42
    TBA820M, a useful audio amplifier 50
Interference (see Electromagnetic compatibility)
Intermodulation
    rusty bolt / passive intermodulation products 54-55
Inventors
    Bardeen, John 129
    Brown, John, G3EUR 203
    Eisler, Dr Paul - 'Mr PCB' 25-26
    Fessenden, Reginald Aubrey 239-240
    Kraus, Dr John D, W8JK 40n
    Lodge, Oliver 284
    Mesny - a French pioneer 10
    Zener, Clarence M 265n

K

Keys and keyers
    EPLD iambic 37-38
    semi-automatic ('bug'), cleaning and adjusting 301
    vintage 144, 235n
Keying arrangements
    QRP transmitter keying 78
    RSI, 'keyboard cramp' and
    'brass arm' 22-23, 60n, 236-237
    simple RS-232C to keying-line interface 23

L

Lee, Captain Paul H, N6PL, silent key 301
Lightning strikes 265n
Linear amplifiers (see Amplifiers)
Linear UHF transceiver with cartesian -loop feedback 17-19

M

Microphone, semiconductor 291n
Microwaves
    exploiting the millimetre-wave bands 20, 36n
    No 10 microwave multiplexed radio using PWM 291n
    state of the art SHF transistors 163
Milne, Arthur, G2MI, our debt to 244-245
Mobile / personal radio, new technology and 35-36
Mixers
    high performance, G3SBI .... 230-231, corr 240
    image rejection 204
    need less oscillator power 203-204
Modulation
    is it really ancient modulation? 49-50
    simplified frequency modulation 12
Morse
    copying weak CW signals 34-35
    'parfick' 144
    passive CW filter 59n
    practice oscillator 174n, 184n
    preferred CW-copying tones 20
    Russian 60n
    radio telegraph, a century of 284
    subjective selectivity, simple, for CW 222
Museums 129n

N

New technology and the spectrum 75-76

O

Oscillators
    audio (tone-burst), reproducible 152
    basics, crystals and the VXO 110-111
    crystal 301n
    crystal oven 117-118
    direct digital synthesis, lower cost 178
    Franklin and Butler two-device oscillators 9-10
    Harris cathode-follower (source follower) 71
    Hartley, valve and Q-gate FET 2-4, 13-14
    low noise, towards the super linear receiver 276-278
    magic of marginal electronics - antennas
      and oscillators 273-275
    Morse practice, simple 174n, 209
    overtone oscillator spurii 148
    Q-gate VFO stable to 39MHz 118-119
    quartz resonators - history and progress 287-289
    stability with valves and FETs 122
    stable oscillators 27-28, 53, 297-300
    synthesiser, as part of DSB transceiver 218-219
    universal VFO 107-109
    variable frequency
      ceramic oscillators .... 68-70, corr 82, 240, 268-269, 286n
    VFO, external for LG300 .... 265n
    VFOs, source of components 40n
    VFO, temperature compensation with thermistors 81, 106
    wide tuning range VXCO 85

P

Power supplies
    240V power relay 136
    blinking mains supplies 8-9
    clockwork, Trevor Bayliss 301n
    generator, 230V AC,
      petrol-electric from scrap 272, 281, 306
    mains practices in the UK and overseas 256-257, 269-270
    poor man's variac 68, 98
    power supply surges, suppressing 178-179, 294
    reverse polarity protection 234-235
    solar and renewable energy 128, 218, 265n
    trip switch (ELCB) troubles 150
    voltage of UK mains 253-254
Power supply units (PSU)
    10A PSU with three-terminal regulator 114, 139
    15A heavy duty PSU .... 253, corr 270
    25-amp powermate PSU (25-amp peak) 32
    battery power system 12

crowbar, junkbox 246
DC/AC inverters 128n
'duz everything' PSU / charger 236
heavy current 28V .... 70-71, corr 82
high power, from microwave oven transformers 239, 251
low power 12V-to-30V DC/DC converter 25
mains adaptors are not fused 241
mains transformers - are they hazardous? 165, 189
non-equalising resistors 208
regulator, IC, improving reliability 290
regulators, voltage limiting, efficient 201
soft start for high voltage PSU 144
solar charger, low cost 143
switching regulator 263
using low-voltage-drop IC regulators 11
voltage doublers 26, 38-39
Printed circuits (PCB) and alternatives
cheap supporting pillars 128-129n
cutting 'islands' in PCB material 136
Eisler, Dr Paul - 'Mr PCB' 25-26
ground-plane construction 167-168n, 252-253
home construction and the PCB 96-97
marking printed circuit boards 114
RF prototyping 1125
Veroboard techniques 27, 114
Propagation
1.8MHz in daylight 285
1.8MHz to the South Atlantic 150-151
auroral and polar cap disturbances 184n
beacons 86-87n, 237
beacons, the first 197
forecasting band conditions 144
gray-line DXing 261-263
gray-line globes, d-i-y 29
HF, the science of 176-177
HF/VHF scatter communications 61-62
ionospheric, on VHF 185-186
NVIS, skybeams and new HF beacons 64-65
solar cycles and propagation 44-46
solar flare damage 6n, 50-51, 148-149
'sweet-spot', Bryant-Clark,
   1.8MHz .... 136, 142-144, corr 154
Publications
magazines on wireless before transistors 21n
Hacker Radio 265n
Ham Radio magazine 47

Q
Quartz resonators - history and progress 287-289

R
Radio science
an ageing technology 199
bouncing beautiful RF sine waves 25
Receivers
144MHz sniffer DF receiver / field strength meter 75
clockwork by Trevor Bayliss 301n
crystal filters for high performance mixers .. 246-248, 279-281
digital communications receivers 132-134, 294
direct conversion, 3.5MHz, 'Newbury' 257-259, 270n
direct conversion, as part of
   3.5MHz DSB transceiver 218-219
direct conversion CW receiver with phasing-type
   demodulator 105
direct conversion, simple .... 216, corr 265
Eddystone Users Group 132
effective super-gainer 69
FETs as RF amplifiers 98-99, 151-152
full-wave envelope detector 171, 184
Hallicrafters, founder of 185
HF, advances in 191-194
HRO 141, 165-166
improving image rejection - a 1940 technique 65-66
low-level detectors 140-141
MOSFET pre-amplifier, GW0GHF .... 164, corr 167
permeability tuned 257-259, 270n

simple 3.5MHz SSB/CW superhet .... 52-53, corr 66, 87
simple HF superhet using the MC3362 chip 72
subjective selectivity, simple, for CW 222
super-linear HF front ends 227-229, 252
super linear receiver: low noise oscillator 276-278
UHF pre-amplifiers, low noise .... 251, corr 265
ultimate KISS rig 175-176
variable selectivity and sidebands 91-92
vintage 261, 266-267
Recycling components 248-249
Relay contact troubles 164n
Resistors
Kelvin-Varley heli-pot substitute 8, 21n
RF activated switch 126
RF voltmeters for transmitter tuning 4
Ryle, Sir Martin, G3CY 66

S
Safety and health hazards
batteries 38, 48-49, 62, 73, 99
CFCs and the ozone layer 286n
danger high voltages 85-86
earthing 51n, 87n
flammable atmospheres,
   EMC hazards and mobile radio 213-214
going mobile - safely 149, 163n
health hazards, tougher guidelines 5-6
lead, ingested by stripping wire with teeth 253n
mains transformers - are they hazardous? 165, 224
ozone from printers, copiers 31, 57
RF radiation 51n, 66n, 105-106, 154, 292-293
RSI, 'keyboard cramp'
   and 'brass arm' 22-23, 60n, 236-237, 246
soldering 88-89, 102-103, 127-128
sunspot flu? 21
trip switch (ELCB) troubles 150
understanding those radiation hazards 15
VDUs 246
Semiconductors
100W UHF power FET 82
FETs as RF amplifiers 98-99
integrated circuits .... (see Integrated circuit devices)
light emitting diodes, more efficient 265n
microphone, condenser, using semiconductors 291n
solid state 'firsts'? 283
state of the art SHF transistors 163
Zener, Clarence M 265n
Solar flares (see Propagation)
Soldering
aid, potato 207-208
safety 88-89, 102-103, 127-128
silver soldering to iron and steel 17
Speech processing
add-on speech processor 115
on the FT901 / 902 241
Spread spectrum .... (see Digital techniques)
Surface mount technology
G8VXB's surface mount tips 181-182
pros of surface mount devices 237-239
removing components 194n
Switch trick 28

T
Test equipment
144MHz sniffer DF receiver / field strength meter 75
3-in-1 antenna tuner and AF meter 15-16
analogue, expanded range 278-279, 287
analogue multi-meters are versatile 275
aural PCB track tracer 70
band-switched dip meter 55
capacitance meter, direct reading 200, 214, 261
crystal calibrator, 25kHz .... 244, corr 250
crystal tester, versatile 197
current sensing LED 26
GDO, ubiquitous 255
GDO, using to measure antenna resonances 265n

impedance / power meter 185, 55n
inductance measurement, KISS 258
logic probe, simple 68
low-level detectors for field strength meters 140-141
measuring current on the outside of coax 157n
RF affects test meters, electronic regulators etc 82
RF current probe, pliers type 170-171
RF sniffer, simple 276
small-signal diode-bridge detector 43
SWR bridges and harmonics 223-224, 231
transistor checker, quickie 231-232
two-tone testing with old oscilloscopes 102, 134

Transceivers
channelised 3.5MHz DSB 218-219
linear UHF, with cartesian -loop feedback 17-19
ultimate KISS rig 175-176

Transmitters
3.5MHz 45W CW transmitter for less than $20 9
one valve, 1920s 199
phasing-type SSB generators / demodulators 33-35
solar or lemon powered 153
spark, the sound of 259-260
SSB, military using envelope elimination
and restoration (EER) 294-295
transmitting Morse key 147

two-click PTT switch 243
ultimate KISS rig 175-176

V
Valves
beam tetrode, the UK and the 156
Hivac 270n
in-rush current 97-98
matched pairs of 162-163
Mullard / Phillips Mitcham factory,
end of an era 255
mystery of the DAH50 .... 86, 104, 113
quick heating 179n, 194n
space-charge 'tetrodes' 113-114
valve technology now respectable 179n
vive la lampe de radio 155-156
Veroboard (see Printed circuits)
VFO (see Oscillators)
VLF radiation from rubber bands 158

W
Weights and measures 60n
Workshop practice
movable bench spotlight, ... 176, 184n
stopping screws falling to the floor 180

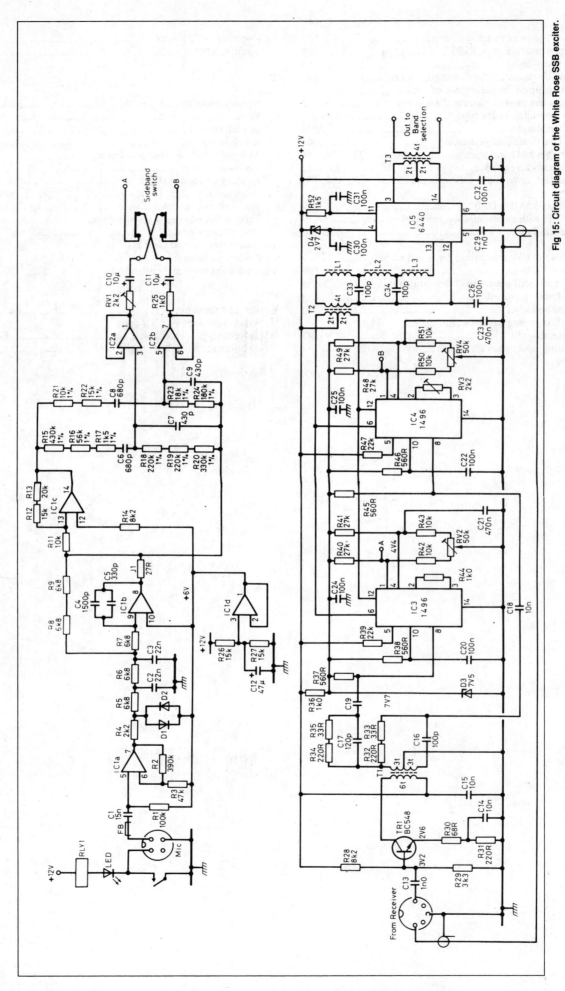

Fig 15: Circuit diagram of the White Rose SSB exciter.

The text for this diagram can be found on pages 92-94.